BOTANY

FOR DEGREE STUDENTS

PART – III

BRYOPHYTA

MULTICOLOUR ILLUSTRATIVE EDITION

BOTANY

FOR DEGREE STUDENTS

PART – III

BRYOPHYTA

B.R. VASHISHTA
Formerly Reader, Biology Study Group
Department of Botany
Punjab University, Chandigarh
Head of the Department of Botany
Multanimal Modi College, Modi Nagar
and
Punjab University College, Hoshiarpur

Revised by

Dr. A.K. SINHA
M.Sc., Ph.D., FPSI, FSB
Reader & Head (Retd.), Department of Botany

Dr. ADARSH KUMAR
M.Sc., Ph.D., FSB
Rader in Botany

Feroze Gandhi Postgraduate College
(Kanpur University), RAE BARELI (U.P.)

S. CHAND
PUBLISHING
empowering minds

S. CHAND & COMPANY PVT. LTD.
(AN ISO 9001 : 2008 COMPANY)
RAM NAGAR, NEW DELHI - 110 055

S. CHAND & COMPANY PVT. LTD.
(An ISO 9001:2008 Company)
Head Office: 7361, RAM NAGAR, NEW DELHI - 110 055
Phone: 23672080-81-82, 9899107446, 9911310888 Fax: 91-11-23677446
www.schandpublishing.com; e-mail: helpdesk@schandpublishing.com

Branches

Ahmedabad : Ph: 27541965, 27542369, ahmedabad@schandpublishing.com
Bengaluru : Ph: 22268048, 22354008, bangalore@schandpublishing.com
Bhopal : Ph: 4274723, 4209587, bhopal@schandpublishing.com
Chandigarh : Ph: 2625356, 2625546, chandigarh@schandpublishing.com
Chennai : Ph: 28410027, 28410058, chennai@schandpublishing.com
Coimbatore : Ph: 2323620, 4217136, coimbatore@schandpublishing.com (Marketing Office)
Cuttack : Ph: 2332580, 2332581, cuttack@schandpublishing.com
Dehradun : Ph: 2711101, 2710861, dehradun@schandpublishing.com
Guwahati : Ph: 2738811, 2735640, guwahati@schandpublishing.com
Hyderabad : Ph: 27550194, 27550195, hyderabad@schandpublishing.com
Jaipur : Ph: 2219175, 2219176, jaipur@schandpublishing.com
Jalandhar : Ph: 2401630, 5000630, jalandhar@schandpublishing.com
Kochi : Ph: 2378740, 2378207-08, cochin@schandpublishing.com
Kolkata : Ph: 22367459, 22373914, kolkata@schandpublishing.com
Lucknow : Ph: 4026791, 4065646, lucknow@schandpublishing.com
Mumbai : Ph: 22690881, 22610885, mumbai@schandpublishing.com
Nagpur : Ph: 6451311, 2720523, 2777666, nagpur@schandpublishing.com
Patna : Ph: 2300489, 2302100, patna@schandpublishing.com
Pune : Ph: 64017298, pune@schandpublishing.com
Raipur : Ph: 2443142, raipur@schandpublishing.com (Marketing Office)
Ranchi : Ph: 2361178, ranchi@schandpublishing.com
Siliguri : Ph: 2520750, siliguri@schandpublishing.com (Marketing Office)
Visakhapatnam : Ph: 2782609, visakhapatnam@schandpublishing.com (Marketing Office)

First Edition 1963
Subsequent Editions and Reprints 1966, 68, 70, 73, 75, 78, 79, 82, 83, 85, 86, 87, 88, 90, 91, 92, 93, 94, 96, 97, 99, 2001 (Twice), 2003, 2004, 2005, 2007, 2008 (Twice), 2010
First Multicolour Illustrative Revised Edition 2011; Reprint 2012, 2014
Reprint 2016 (Twice)

ISBN: 978-81-219-3569-2 **Code: 1003A 393**

This book is for sale in India & other SAARC countries only.

PRINTED IN INDIA

By Vikas Publishing House Pvt. Ltd., Plot 20/4, Site-IV, Industrial Area Sahibabad, Ghaziabad-201010 and published by S. Chand & Company Pvt. Ltd., 7361, Ram Nagar, New Delhi -110 055..

PREFACE TO THE REVISED EDITION

We take pleasure to present this thoroughly revised, updated, improved and multi-coloured edition of the popular book ***Botany For Degree Students – Bryophyta*** by ***Dr.B.R.Vashishta*** for the benefit of both undergraduate and postgraduate students. While the original format of the book remains unchanged, efforts have been made to make the book more useful by adding the topics and genera generally asked in the university examinations.

All the diagrams have been made of several colours making these more attractive. As per the new format of question papers, three types of questions-Essay type, Short answer type and Objective type questions have been added.

During the course of revision of this book we have been guided and assisted by the suggestions of a large number of students and professors of colleges and universities to whom we express our sincere thanks.

We also wish to express our deep sense of gratitude to Mrs. Nirmala Gupta, CMD, Mr. Navin Joshi, Vice-President (Publishing), Mr. R.S. Saxena, Advisor, Mr. Shishir Bhatnagar, Manager (Pre-press), Mr. Ashutosh Mani Tripathi, Asstt. Editor and Mr. Ajendra Negi, Sr. DTP. Operator of S.Chand & Company Ltd., New Delhi for their help and cooperation in bringing out this book in the present form. We hope that the present multicoloured edition of the book will prove to be of much more use to all its users.

Suggestions and criticisms for the improvement of the book will be gratefully accepted and acknowledged.

Dr. A.K. Sinha
Dr. Adarsh Kumar

PREFACE TO THE FIRST EDITION

Part III of the series deals with a small group of primitive, thalloid plants, amphibious in habit. They are placed in the division Bryophyta. The bryophytes are peculiar in having the game tophyte as green and independent and sporophyte wholly or partially dependent upon it. The subject matter has been presented in a simple lucid style. The obscure literary style has been avoided. The scheme followed is the same as in Parts I and II. An attempt has been made to include the latest and the significant results of botanical research on the subject. The type system is still considered the best for the undergraduate.

A simple and a clear account of structure, reproduction, function and relationships of the important members of each class is a notable feature of the book. A diagrammatic representation of the life cycle of each type gives a clear picture of the pattern of Alternation of Generations. Salient features of the division and its classes down to the orders and the type plants whose life histories have been discussed appear at the end of each respective chapter.

The byrophytes have been discussed as amphibious of the Kingdom Plantae in the first chapter which also deals briefly with the various life phenomena of this peculiar assemblage of plants whose origin is obscure even up to this age of scientific development. Chapter III deals with structure and the various theories which attempt to explain the origin of the *Marchantiaceous thallus*. In the concluding chapter some general topics relating to the subject have been dealt with. It also includes exhaustive comparisons between the type plants of the various classes of the bryophytes.

All the available standard text books on the subject and research journals have been consulted. Grateful thanks are due to the authors, editors and the publishers of these books and journals. The most eminent among the authors deserving special mention are Campbell, Bower, Cavers, Mehra and Proskauer. I am also grateful to Dr. Mehra for making available all his publications on the subject.

My sincerest thanks go to my colleague in the Department, Dr. V.P. Dube for critically reading a portion of the manuscript and for making most of the figures of *Funaria.* Without his enthusiastic support it would not have been possible to bring out the book this year. The author alone, however, is responsible for the factual mistakes. I also owe a deep debt of gratitude to Dr. P.C. Joshi (Principal and Head of the Botany Department, Government College, Rupar), Dr. A.B. Gupta (Head of the Botany Department, Christ Church College, Kanpur), Prof. D.N. Srivastava (Head of the Botany Department, Bareilly College, Bareilly), Prof. N.S. Madan (Head of the Botany Department, Government College, Rohtak) and Prof. S.P. Aggrawal (Head of the Botany Department, B.S.A. Degree College, Mathura) for the encouragement and inspiration received from them. Finally I express my thanks to my publishers particularly Sri Shyam Lal Gupta and Sri Prem Nath Kapur, the Production Manager, for providing me all the facilities in publication of the volume.

B.R. Vashishta

CONTENTS

Image of Sporophyte of *Takakia*

CHAPTER 1

THE BRYOPHYTA
Introduction to Bryophytes and their Primay Classification

- Bryophytes as Amphibians of the Kingdom Plantae
- Life cycle
- Salient Features of Bryophytes
- A Brief Account of the Development of Bryology in India

BRYOPHYTES AS AMPHIBIANS OF THE KINGDOM PLANTAE

Plants grow in two well-defined habitats. These are the water and the land. The plants which grow in water are called the **aquatics**, and the others **terrestrial**. The best examples of aquatic plants are the **algae** and of land dwellers the **seed plants** (spermatophytes). Between these two extremes of habitats is a transitional zone. It is represented by the swamps and the areas where water and land meet. It may well be called the **amphibious zone**. Inhabiting the amphibious zone are the mosses, liverworts and hornworts which collectively constitute a group of non-vascular land plants called the **bryophytes**. The latter are simple, thallus-like plants which suggest the stages through which the green algae may have evolved to become terrestrial. Most of the bryophytes are land dwellers which inhabit damp, shaded and humid localities. A few of them, however, live in or float on water. The aquatic habit, of course, has been acquired by these plants secondarily. When the water dries up they grow equally well on the drying mud. Some, of course, can withstand long periods of drought. During the dry period they become almost brittle in texture. With the onset of rainy season the apparently dried, brittle thalli turn green and become active to carry out the normal life functions. Even these apparently Xerophytic species grow actively only during the wet weather.

Bryophytes thus, include archegoniate, atracheate simple cryptogams in which zygote divides by mitosis and forms embryo. Embryo–the sporophytic phase depends upon gametophyte for nutrition and support. These are **amphibians of the Plant Kingdom.**

Evidence supports the view that these early land plants descended from alga-like ancestors which were probably green. Adaptation to land environment or sub-aerial life involved the development of certain features that were not possessed by their aquatic ancestors. These are :

1. Development of organs for attachment and absorption of water. Unlike algae the bryophytes which grow on land are not bathed in water. They must absorb it from the soil and be attached to it for support. For this purpose the bryophytes develop special, hair-like structures called the **rhizoids**. Like root hairs the rhizoids function as absorbing and attaching organs.

2. Protection against desiccation. The thick, compact multicellular, thallus-like plant body covered with an epidermis is protected to a certain extent against the drying effects of air. Of the numerous cells constituting it only the epidermal cells, which form only a small percentage of its total surface, are directly exposed to the dry air. Further even the free surface of the epidermal cells, in some species of liverworts, is coated with a waxy substance like *cutin* which is water proof and thus reduces the rate of water loss. Moreover, total surface area of a compact body is reduced in proportion to its volume.

3. Absorption of carbon dioxide from the atmosphere for photosynthesis. In many liverworts there are numerous pores on the upper surface of the thallus. These are called the **air pores**. They facilitate gaseous exchange between the atmospheric air and the interior of the thallus.

4. Protection of reproductive cells from drying and mechanical injury. The sex organs in the bryophytes are multicellular and jacketed. The jacket of sterile cells around the sperms and eggs is an adaptation to a life on land. It protects the sex cells against the drying effects of air.

5. The fertilized egg is retained within the archegonium. Here it obtains food and water from the parent plant and is protected from drying as it develops into an **embryo**. This adaptation is essential for the survival of the land plants. It ensures nursing of the young embryo and its protection against mechanical injury.

6. The thick-walled, wind-disseminated spores and the primitive vascular system in the form of a conducting strand are the other adaptations to land habit.

The bryophytes, however, cannot carry on their reproductive activities without sufficient moisture. Presence of water is necessary. Without it the sex organs do not reach maturity and do not dehisce. Water is essential for the transfer of sperms to the archegonium. The retention of swimming sperms is an algal characteristic. The bryophytes thus rely on water for the act of fertilization. Besides, they have inefficient absorbing organs in the form of rhizoids. Consequently they are unable to grow during dry periods. They require sufficient moisture both for reproduction and successful vegetative growth. This explains why the bryophytes usually inhabit moist, shaded situations (amphibious habitat) or grow in places where water is abundant at least at some season. Since the bryophytes usually grow in amphibious situations and cannot complete their life cycle without external water they can very appropriately be called the **amphibians** of the plant world.

LIFE CYCLE

The bryophytes have evolved a life cycle which comprises two phases—**gametophyte** and **sporophyte**. The former is the most conspicuous of the two. It is green, long-lived, freely branching and independent. We start our discussion of the bryophytes with this phase of the life cycle.

1. GAMETOPHYTE (Fig.1.1)

(a) Plant body (Fig.1.1). The bryophytes are a small group of most primitive land dwellers (Fig. 1.1). A few of them, however, are strictly aquatic. Examples of aquatic species are *Riella* and *Ricciocarpus*. The bryophytes number about 24,000 species which are grouped under nearly 960 genera. All of them are small and inconspicuous plants ranging in size from about a millimetre in length to 30 centimetres or more. The plant body (gametophyte) is undoubtedly more differentiated than that of a complex alga. It is compact and better protected against desiccation. However, it is relatively simple in the lower forms and still reminds one of the *thallus* of an alga. It grows prostrate on the ground and is thallus-like (A). It is attached to the substratum by delicate, unicellular, hair-like organs called the **rhizoids**.

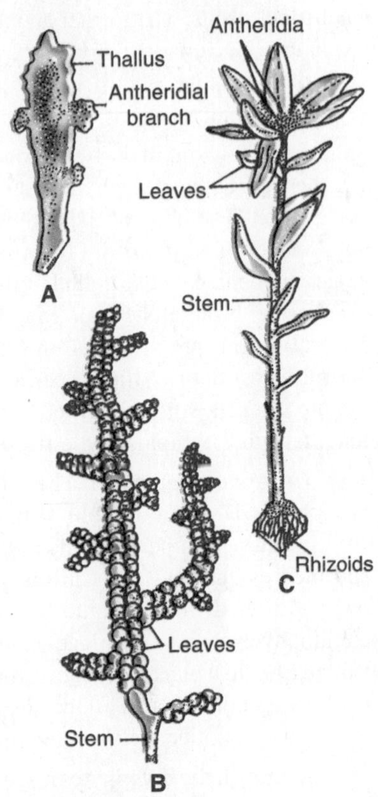

Fig. 1.1. (A—C). Bryophytes. A, thalloid male gametophyte of *Aneura pinguis;* B, prostrate, dorsiventral gametophyte of a leafy liverwort *Porella*; C, moss male gametophyte (A after Velenovsky).

The majority of the bryophytes, however, have the plant body differentiated into stem and leaves. The leafy gametophyte of the liverworts is dorsiventral (B) but in the mosses it is erect (C). The erect, leafy moss gametophyte has a stem-like central axis which bears leaf-like appendages. It is fixed to the substratum by means of branched, multicellular **rhizoids** apparently resembling the **roots** (C). The rhizoids arise from the older, basal part of the stem. These organs of the bryophytes are, however, not **homologous** with those of the higher plants. They lack the vascular tissue characteristic of the stems, leaves and roots of the higher plants. Besides, they belong to the haploid generation whereas those of the higher plants represent the diploid generation. The organs which are similar in function but different in origin are said to be **analogous**. The stem, leaves and rhizoids of the bryophytes are thus analogous to the stems, leaves and roots rather root hairs of the vascular plants. The root hairs like the rhizoids of liverworts are unicellular structures. In contrast the rhizoids are borne upon the gametophyte and root hairs on the sporophyte. The two are thus analogous to each other. Some botanists look upon even the moss type of plant body of the bryophytes as a highly differentiated thallus.

The thallus-like plant body of bryophytes bears the gametes. For this reason it is called the **gametophyte** plant. It is concerned with sexual reproduction and constitutes the most conspicuous, nutritionally independent phase in the life cycle.

(b) Reproduction (Fig. 1.2). Bryophytes show a marked advance over the thallophytes in the method of sexual reproduction. Without exception it is highly **oogamous** in the whole group. The gametes are produced in complex sex organs. They have attained a degree of complexity far above that of the thallophytes. In the thallophytes the sex organs are generally simple and unicellular. They are devoid of any wall of sterile cells. The gametes are formed directly out of the protoplasts of these sex cells. The bryophytes, on the other hand, have multicellular, jacketed sex organs. Each sex organ consists of an outer, protective wall of sterile cells surrounding the cell or groups of cells which produce the gametes. The male sex organ is still called the **antheridium**. The female, however, is known as the **archegonium**. Both kinds of sex organs may be developed on the same individual or on distinct plants. The former are called **monoecious** and the latter **dioecious**.

(i) Antheridium (A). The antheridium is a multicellular object ellipsoidal or club-shaped sometimes spherical in form. It is borne on a short stalk which attaches it to the gametophyte tissue. Often it is embedded in the latter. The body of the antheridium has a wall of a single layer of sterile cells. It surrounds a mass of small squarish or cubical cells called the **androcytes**. The latter produce the biflagellate male gametes called the **sperms**. Several sperms are produced in each antheridium. They are motile structure. Each sperm usually consists of a minute, slender, spirally curved body furnished with two long, terminal, whiplash type flagella (B).

(ii) Archegonium (C). The female sex organ of the bryophytes is a remarkable structure. It is called the **archegonium**. It appears for the first time in the liverworts and mosses and continues in the pteridophytes. In this respect the liverworts and mosses seem to be akin to the pteridophytes than to the algae to which they resemble in their thallus-like plant body. This common feature tempted the earlier botanists to place the bryophytes and the pteridophytes collectively in the division **Archegoniatae**.

Although the bryophytes resemble the pteridophytes in some feature but they are unlike in other features. The resemblances and differences between bryophytes and pteridophytes have been described elsewhere in this chapter. Hence, it is thought best to separate the liverworts and the mosses from the pteridophytes on one hand and the thallus bearing plants (Thallophytes) on the other. They are included in a distinct group **Bryophyta**.

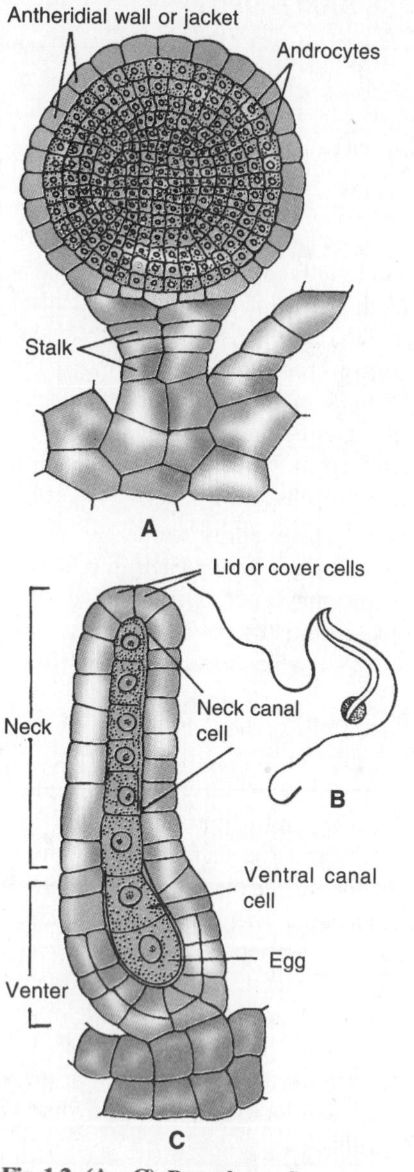

Fig. 1.2. (A—C). Bryophytes. Sex organs. Antheridium (A) and archegonium (C) of *Fossombronia;* B, biflagellates sperm of *Sphaerocarpus* (A, after Smith, B—C after Campbell).

The archegonium (Fig. 1.2 C) is a flask-shaped organ. The slender, elongated upper portion is called the **neck** and the lower sac-like, swollen portion, the **venter**. The venter is attached to and often deeply embedded in the parent plant tissue. The neck has a wall of a single layer of sterile cells which surrounds a central row of elongated, naked cells called the **neck canal cells.** The neck is usually projecting or freely exposed so as to be accessible to sperms. The venter also has a wall of sterile cells one or more cell layers in thickness. The venter wall encloses two cells. They are the larger **egg** cell or the **ovum** and the smaller **ventral canal cell** just above it.

(iii) Fertilization (Fig. 1.3). It occurs when the sex organs are mature. Moisture is essential for the maturing of the sex organs and also for the movements of the sperms to the archegonia. The mature antheridium ruptures at its apex liberating the sperms (A). At the same time the axial row of neck canal cells including the ventral canal cell in the mature archegonium disorganise (F). The tip of the archegonium also opens. A narrow canal opening to the exterior is formed. It acts as a passage

way to the ovum in the venter. The liberated sperms swimming in a thin film of water reach the archegonia (E). They enter through the open necks and swim down the canals of the archegonia (Fig. 1.3). Reaching the venter one of them, probably the first one to reach there, penetrates the ovum (F). It fuses with the nucleus of the ovum to accomplish fertilization. With the act of fertilization the gametophyte generation ends and the sporophyte generation starts. The gametes (sperms and eggs) are the last structures of the gametophyte generation.

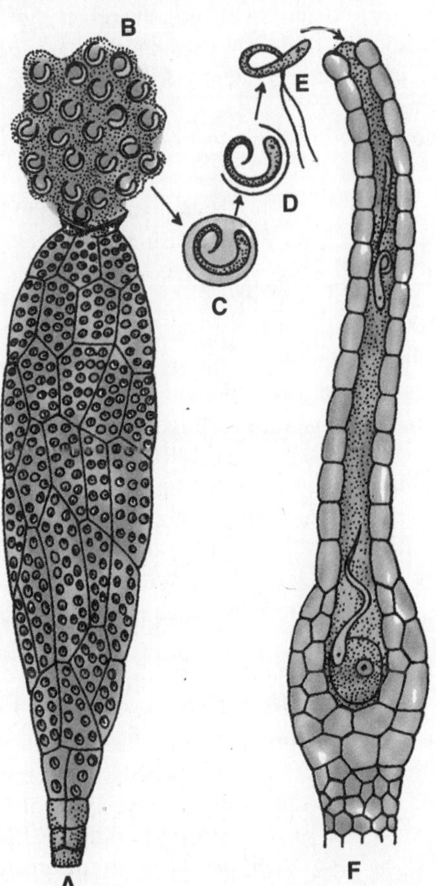

Fig. 1.3 (A—F). Bryophytes. Dehiscence of sex organs and fertilisation in a Moss plant. A, dehisced antheridium; B, androcyte mass; C, sperm within the androcyte membrane; D, androcyte wall dissolving; E. liberated sperm; F, dehisced archegonium showing fertilisation (Diagrammatic).

2. SPOROPHYTE (Fig.1.4)

With fertilisation starts the second phase in the life cycle of the bryophytes. It is called the **sporophyte**. The pioneer structure of this phase is the zygote.

(*a*) **Zygote.** The fertilised egg or ovum secretes a cellulose wall around it and is called the **zygote**. The latter has a fusion or diploid nucleus which contains chromatin material of both the male and the female gametes. The zygote marks the beginning of the sporophyte generation in the life cycle. It is neither independent of the parent gametophyte plant nor passes into the resting condition. In both respects it differs from the zygote of the green algae. The further development of the zygote into the embryo (embryogenesis) occurs within the venter of the archegonium which protects the egg, the zygote and the embryo against the vagaries of external environment such as desiccation.

(*b*) **Embryo** (Fig. 1.4). Within venter of the archegonium the zygote undergoes segmentation (A—D) and develops without a resting period into a multicellular, undifferentiated structure called an **embryo** (D). It obtains its nourishment directly from the thallus or the parent gametophyte to which it is organically attached. The zygote of the bryophytes has thus a better chance for growth as compared with the zygote of the thallophytes which is always independent. The latter accounts for the absence of embryo stage in the thallophytes. The embryo stage in the bryophytes is of short duration.

(*c*) **Sporogonium.** The embryo by further segmentation and differentiation finally develops into a full fledged sporophyte individual. It is called the **sporogonium** (F). The sporogonium in bryophyte is leafless and rootless. Throughout its life it remains attached to the gametophyte plant. It is thus spatially separated from the soil by the gametophyte (haploid) tissues. Generally, it has a limited life span. In some bryophytes it remains embedded in the gametophyte tissue (*Riccia*). Generally, it is projecting and consists of three parts, the **foot,** the **seta** and the **capsule** (F). The foot is embedded in the tissue of the parent gametophyte. It absorbs nutrition for the sporogonium. In some marsupial bryophytes (*Jackiella*) the foot is very reduced and its function is performed by haustorial collar which develops from the junction of reduced foot and seta (Fig. 21.10). The rest of the sporogonium is free and projecting to promote easy dispersal of spores.

The seta conducts the food absorbed by the foot to the capsule. The terminal capsule which is considered equivalent to a fern sporangium is mainly concerned in the production of spores which are non-motile and wind-disseminated.

The spores of bryophytes are highly specialised cells. They are differentiated from the diploid spore mother cells by *meiosis*. They are thus haploid structures and are known as the meiospores or gonospores. Morphologically, the spores produced in the capsule in all the bryophytes are **homosporous** They are alike in size and form in a given species. With meiosis the sporophyte generation in the life cycle ends. The meiospores thus mark the beginning of the new gametophyte generation. Each spore germinates under suitable conditions to give rise either to the main gametophyte plant directly or first to a juvenile, filamentous stage called the **protonema** from which sooner or later arises the main gametophyte.

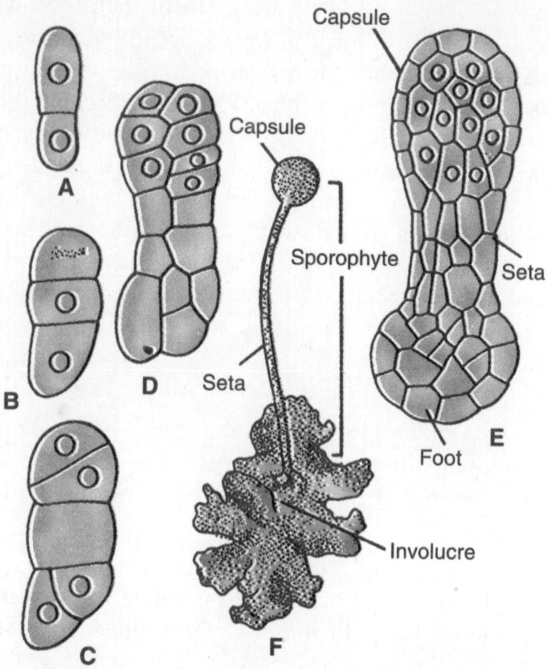

Fig. 1.4. (A—F).Bryophytes. Stages in the development of sporophyte of *Fossombronia*. A—D, early stages in the development of embryo; E, L.S. young sporogonium; F, portion of the gametophyte bearing a nearly mature sporophyte (A—E after Chalaud).

Sporogonium is the whole product of the sexual act. It remains attached to the parent plant bearing sexual organs (oophyte). It is considered a **second individual** in the life cycle and not simply a part or an **outgrowth** of the parent plant (thallus or gametophyte). *The reasons are obvious*. The sporogonium is an individual with a different inheritance as it is developed from the diploid zygote. It is made up of cells containing a diploid number of chromosomes as contrasted with the haploid number characteristic of the gametophyte. Besides, it differs from the parent gametophyte in its function. It produces haploid spores. For this reason the sporogonium of the bryophytes is often called the **sporophyte** The spores are non-motile and thus dispersed by air. In its nutrition of course, the sporophyte is dependent partly or wholly on the gametophyte plant.

Another remarkable feature of the bryophytes in which they differ from the thallophytes, is the complete absence of asexual spores called the **mitospores** (motile as well as non-motile) in the life cycle. Asexual reproduction takes place only by the vegetative methods of fragmentation and gemmae. No true asexual spores are formed.

ALTERNATION OF GENERATIONS (Fig. 1.5)

The life cycle of bryophytes is very interesting. It is split up into two phases, each represented by a separate adult. Thus in a single life cycle there occur two distinct multicellular, vegetative individuals. One of these is the green **thalloid** (liverworts) or **leafy** (mosses) plant. The other is the **sporogonium** The green individual is the most conspicuous of the two. It is an independent plant. It is haploid and bears the sex organs (antheridia and archegonia) which produce the gametes (sperms and eggs). As it bears the gametes the green, independent individual is called the **gametophyte** It is concerned with sexual reproduction. The gametophyte plant along with the structures produced by it constitutes the **gametophyte generation** In the life cycle it starts with the formation of **meiospores** and consists of the **green individual** and the **sex organs** The last structures formed during this phase are the **gametes** The gametes fuse to form the zygote.

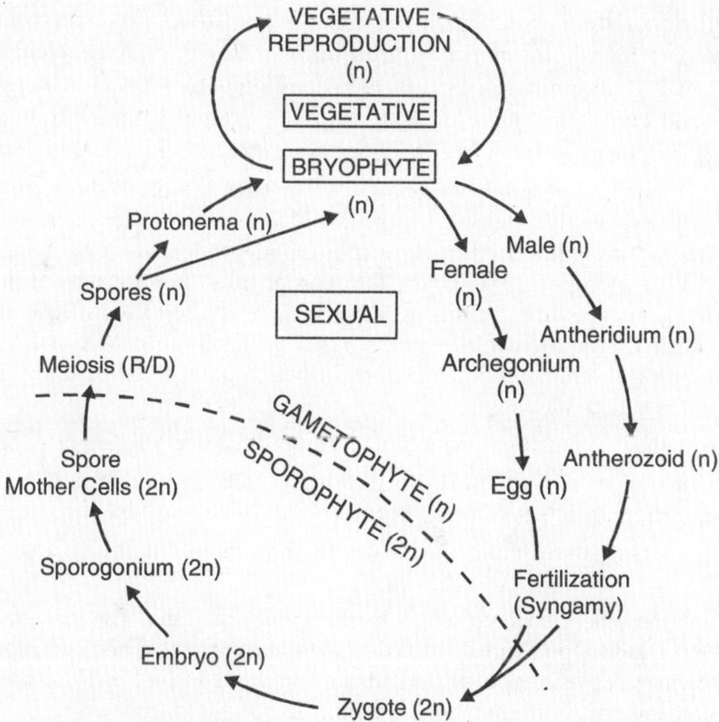

Fig. 1.5. Bryophytes. Graphic representation of the sexual life cycle.

The zygote, on germination, does not produce the gametophyte plant. It undergoes segmentation to form an **embryo**. The embryo by further segmentation and differentiation gives rise to the second adult called the **sporogonium**. It remains diploid and is usually differentiated into **foot, seta** and **capsule**. In due course of time, the diploid **spore mother cells** produced in the capsule give rise to haploid spores (meiospores) by meiosis. As the sporogonium is concerned with the production of spores it is called the **sporophyte**. The **zygote**, the **embryo** and the **sporogonium** together constitute the **sporophyte generation**. It is less conspicuous. Moreover, it is dependent for its nutrition wholly or partially on the gametophyte plant to which it is attached organically throughout its life. It starts with the zygote and ends with the formation of spore mother cells in the capsule. The meiospores are the pioneer structures of the next gametophyte generation. On germination each spore produces a gametophyte and not a sporophyte plant.

From the account given above it is evident that on germination the reproductive cells of one generation give rise to the alternate generation in the life cycle. The two generations thus regularly alternate with each other in a single life cycle. This biological phenomenon is called **alternation of generations**. It is defined as the alternation in the life cycle of two distinct vegetative individuals with different functions. Cycles of this type characterized by **alternation of generations** and **sporogenic meiosis** are termed **diplohaplontic** life cycles.

In the bryophytes alternation of generations becomes as integral part of the life cycle. It is a constant feature of all the species because the zygote invariably develops into a distinct sporophyte. This may be due to the fact that the egg is retained in the tissue of the gametophyte. Fertilisation takes place *in situ* . As a result the zygote has a better chance for growth. Moreover, the alternating individuals in the life cycle of the bryophytes are morphologically dissimilar. They differ not only in their structure but also in their physiology (nutrition). This kind of alternation of generations in which the alternating individuals are dissimilar is called **heterologous** or **heteromorphic**. The structural and nutritional difference in the two generations may be an evolutionary sequence due to the different modes of life. The gametophyte is independent. The sporophyte is not. It is attached and generally dependent wholly or partially on the gametophyte. The attached condition of sporophyte can lead to dissimilarity. This viewpoint is supported by an analogy from the red algae. The attached carposporophyte of *Polysiphonia* is quite different from its free living gametophyte. On the other hand, the free living tetrasporophyte is identical to the gametophyte.

In algae alternation of generations is not a constant feature of all the species. It occurs in isolated instances. The vegetative sporophyte is generally absent. It is represented only by the single-called zygote. The zygote is liberated in algae. Being independent it lacks enough resources to develop into a distinct sporophyte. Moreover, the sporophyte in algae when developed is always independent of the gametophyte plant. In cases where there is alternation of generations, the two alternating individuals in the life cycle generally resemble each other. Morphologically, they are identical. This type of alternation of generations in which both the alternating generations are structurally similar is called **homologous** or **isomorphic**.

Besides food, the two most important biological needs of every living plant species are :-

I. Production of new individuals. Really new individuals are produced by the fusion of male and female gametes from different plants. It is called **cross-fertilization**.

II. Their dispersal to suitable places where they can find their food without much competition.

In algae both these problems are solved by the agency of water. The gametes swim through water to fuse. The resultant zygotes are dispersed by the water currents. This accounts for the absence of structural differences between the two alternating plants in the life cycle. There is thus no division of labour. Hence, the alternating generations are similar.

Among the land dwellers such as the bryophytes the two probelms of cross-fertilization and dispersal are solved on the basis of division of labour. Each generation caters to and is suitably adapted to solve one of the these problems. The gametophyte is concerned with sexual reproduction. It thus caters to the need of cross fertilization. The sporophyte functions in the multiplication of beneficial effects of a single sexual union. It produces minute spores which are distributed by the wind. The division of labour among the two generations thus accounts for the structural difference between them in the byrophytes.

Alternation of chromosome number in the life cycle. Each cell of the gametophyte generation has a certain number of chromosomes in its nucleus. It is represented by the symbol n. The numerical value of n differs in the different species. Each gamete thus has n chromosomes in its nucleus. It is the basic number. At the time of fertilization the nuclei of the sperm and egg fuse. The *paternal* and the *maternal* chromosomes however, do not fuse. They simply become closely associated in pairs in the fusion nucleus. The fusion nucleus in the zygote now has $n + n$ or $2\ n$ chromosomes. The single number n is called *haploid* or *monoploid* number. All structures with n chromosomes are thus *haploid*. On this basis the gametophyte generation may be called the *haploid generation* in the life cycle. The $2n$ number is called *diploid*. The zygote with $2n$ number of chromosomes thus is a diploid structure. The sporogonium which is developed from the zygote by repeated mitosis is a diploid individual in the life cycle. All the cells of the sporophyte generation (sporogonium) up to and including the spore mother cells are diploid. At the time of *fertilization* the haploid generation switches on to the diploid. With *meiosis* the diploid generation switches back to haploid. The *alternation of generations* is thus accompanied by the alternation of chromosome numbers from the haploid to the diploid and back to the haploid condition.

Origin of alternation of generations. It is still a live question. Two theories, namely, **antithetic** and **homologous** have been proposed to explain how alternation of generations originated.

Antithetic theory. It was the first to be proposed. On the basis of this theory the gametophyte or sexual plant represents the original generation. The sporophyte or the non-sexual organism is a new and different phase evolved by progressive elaboration of the diploid zygote of some algal ancestor like *Coleochaete*. It is interpolated in the life cycle of the gametophyte of primitive land plants between the two crucial points, **fertilization** and **meiosis** in response to a life in a drier environment. The factors which caused its origin are prompt germination of the zygote accompanied by delayed meiosis.

The result is the production of a small sporophyte of *Riccia* consisting simply of a spore case. With further elaboration and increased sterilisation of the spore producing tissue a larger sporophyte with differentiation into a foot, a seta and a capsule is finally evolved.

Homologous theory. On the basis of this theory the sporophyte is simply a modification of the gametophyte and not a new generation evolved in response to a life in a drier environment. The advocates of this theory point to the fact that among the green algae the gametophyte plant reproduces by both the methods of reproduction. It bears spores and also the gametes. In the course of evolutionary sequence these two functions became separated in two distinct individuals. One of these produced the spores and the other produced gametes. The former came to be known as the **sporophyte** and the latter **gametophyte**. These two individuals occur regularly one after the other in the life cycle. The occurrence of two similar generations in most of the algae furnishes a strong argument in favour of this theory. The phenomenon of apospory and apogamy is another. Both the individuals in primitive land plants were photosynthetic and free living. Gradually, the sporophyte became attached to and partly parasitic on the gametophyte. Consequently, it became reduced.

SALIENT FEATURES OF BRYOPHYTES

1. The bryophytes are a small group of primitive **land dwellers**. They have a **leafy** or **thalloid**, green plant body which is small in structure rarely more than 5 inches.

2. In their vegetative structure they have become completely adapted to the land habit. However, they still rely upon water for sexual reproduction because the swimming habit is retained by their sperms.

3. The plant body lacks the true roots, stem or leaves. It is relatively simple in the lower forms and still reminds of the **thallus** of an alga. It grows prostrate on the ground and is attached to the substratum by delicate, unbranched, unicellular hair-like organs called the **rhizoids**. In the higher bryophytes (mosses) the plant body is erect. It consists of a central axis which bears leaf-like expansions. It is attached to the substratum by branched, multicellular rhizoids.

4. Like the thallophytes the most conspicuous phase in the life cycle is the **gametophyte**. It is independent and concerned with sexual reproduction.

5. The bryophytes like the **thallophytes** lack the vascular tissue (xylem and phloem) characteristic of the **higher plants**.

6. In sexual **reproduction** they show a marked advance over the thallophytes. It is invariably highly **oogamous**. The sex organs are **jacketed** and **multicellular**. In algae they are **non-jacketed** and **unicellular**.

7. Female sex organ in the form of an **archegonium** appears for the first time in the bryophytes in the plant world.

8. The sperms are **biflagellate**. Both the flagella are of **whiplash** type.

9. Fertilization takes place in the presence of water.

10. The fertilized egg is retained within the venter of the archegonium. It neither becomes independent of the parent gametophyte nor passes into the resting period. In both these respects the bryophytes differ from the algae.

11. The zygote undergoes repeated division to form an undifferentiated, multicellular structure called the **embryo**. The first division of the zygote is transverse and the apex of the embryo develops from the outer cell. Such an embryogeny is called **exoscopic**. It is characteristic of the bryophytes. *No embryo stage exists in the thallophytes.*

12. The venter wall enlarges with the developing embryo to form a protective, multicellular envelope, the **calyptra**.

13. The embryo by further division and differentiation produces a relatively small spore producing structure which is not independent. It is called the **sporogonium (sporophyte)**. In all bryophytes, the sporophyte is without differentiation into stem and leaves. It is rootless and consists of a foot, a seta and a capsule. In some the seta is absent (*Corsinia*) and rarely both, the foot and the seta (*Riccia*).

14. The sporophyte is thus simpler than the gametophyte and is organically attached to the parent gametophyte throughout its life. It is dependent upon it partially or wholly for its nutrition. In algae the sporophyte generation when present is always independent of the parent gametophyte.

15. The sporogonium is concerned with the production of wind-disseminated, non-motile, cutinized spores which belong to the category of **gonospores** or **meiospores**.

16. Morphologically the meiospores in a given species are of one kind. Thus the bryophytes, in general, are described as **homosporous**.

17. Each spore on falling on a suitable soil germinates to give rise to the gametophyte plant either directly or indirectly as a lateral bud from the **protonema**.

18. The occurrence of **heterologous** type of **alternation of generations** is a constant feature of the life cycle of bryophytes. In algae, when present, it is of **homologous** type.

Differences between the thallophytes and bryophytes

Thallophyta	Bryophyta
1. Mainly aquatic	1. Chiefly terrestrial.
2. The thallus generally consists either of a single cell or a filament of cells or of intertwining filaments. Layers of parenchyma occur in a few.	2. The thallus, excepting in the protonema stage, is never filamentous. It is made up of sheets of parenchyma cells.
3. Asexual reproduction by the formation of mitospores common in the growing season.	3. Complete absence of mitospores in the life cycle. Asexual reproduction takes place by vegetative methods only.
4. Reproduce by meiospores in addition to mitospores.	4. Reproduce entirely by meiospores.
5. The sex organs are usually single celled, sometimes of groups of single cells but always without a jacket of sterile vegetative cells.	5. The sex organs are always multicellular protected by a jacket of sterile vegetative cells.
6. Sexual reproduction ranges from **isogamy**, through **anisogamy** to **oogamy**.	6. Sexual reproduction is invariably **oogamous**.
7. The female sex organ is the **oogonium** or **ascogonium**.	7. The female sex organ is the flask-shaped **archegonium** which is characteristic of land plants only.
8. The zygote is usually liberated and frequently passes into the resting stage.	8. The zygote is neither liberated nor passes into the resting stage.
9. No embryo formation after gametic union.	9. All bryophytes develop embryo after gametic union.
10. Many exhibit alternation of generations but it is of **homologous type**.	10. All exihibit alternation of generations but it is always of **heterologous type**.
11. Both the gametophytes and sporophytes are independent.	11. The sporophyte is organically attached to and is nutritionally dependent upon the gametophyte.

Resemblances between the bryophytes and the Algae

1. Thallus-like plant body.
2. Lack of vascular tissue.
3. Absence of roots
4. Conspicuous plant in the life cycle being the gametophyte.
5. Autotrophic mode of nutrition.
6. Retention of the swimming habit by the sperms which indicates the algal ancestry of the bryophytes.
7. The early stages of development in the gametophyte of many bryophytes are green filaments which strikingly resemble the filamentous thallus of green algae.
8. The chloroplast pigments in the vegetative cells of bryophytes are identical with those of green algae.
9. The carbohydrate food reserve in both the bryophytes and green algae is **true starch** which contains a mixture of two kinds of glucose macromolecules, amylase and amylopectin.
10. The structure and composition of the cell walls is identical in both the bryophytes and the green algae. It consists of a wall layer containing cellulose surrounded by a pectic wall layer containing galacturonic acid.

To sum up, the bryophytes and the green algae have much in common at the level of cell structure and metabolic pathways. However, differences do exist between bryophytes and algae and these are as follows :

Differences between bryophytes and algae

Bryophytes	Algae
1. Amphibians i.e. grow in moist shady places as well as in water.	1. Usually aquatic.
2. Plant body thalloid or leafy.	2. Plant body unicellular to multicellular, filamentous, thalloid or leafy.
3. Tissue differentiation well developed.	3. Tissue differentiation only in higher forms.
4. Sexual reproduction oogamous only.	4. Sexual reproduction isogamous, anisoganous or oogamous.
5. Sex organs covered by a sterile jacket.	5. Sex organs not covered by sterile jacket.
6. Female sex organ is Archegonium.	6. Female sex organ is oogonium.
7. Zygote remain enclosed in the archegonium.	7. Zygote liberated from the plant.
8. Embryo produced from Zygote.	8. Embryo is never produced.
9. Sporophyte dependent upon gametophyte.	9. Sporophyte independent of gametophyte.
10. Sporophyte developed and differentiated into foot, seta and capsule.	10. No such differentiation of the sporophyte.
11. Mitospores absent.	11. Mitospores usually present.
12. Alternation of generation is Heteromorphic.	12. It will defined homologous alternation of generation.

The similarities between the bryophytes and the green algae at the level of cell structure and metabolic pathways give support to the view that Bryophytes have evolved from the algal ancestors particularly the green algae.

Affinities with Pteridophytes

(a) Resemblances between bryophytes and pteridophytes. The features in which the bryophytes resemble the pteridophytes are :

(*i*) Terrestrial habit.
(*ii*) Development of embryo after gametic union.
(*iii*) Development of embryo within the archegonium protected by multicellular maternal tissue.
(*iv*) Similar type of life cycle characterised by heterologous alternation of generations.
(*v*) Presence of cuticle.
(*vi*) Presence of stomata except the liverworts.
(*vii*) Multicellular sex organs with a jacket of sterile cells.
(*viii*) Presence of a unique type of female sex organ, the archegonium with a remarkable structure.
(*ix*) Multicellular sporangia.
(*x*) Complete absence of mitospores.
(*xi*) Oogamous sexual reproduction.
(*xii*) Flagellated male gametes.
(*xiii*) Presence of water essential for fertilization.

Differences between bryophytes and pteridophytes. Bryophytes differ from Pteridophytes and the points of differences between the two are as follows :

Bryophytes	Pteridophytes
1. In life cycle the gametophyte is dominant.	1. In life cycle the sporophyte is dominant.
2. Plant body is either leafy or thalloid.	2. Plant body is differentiated into root, stem and leaves.
3. The cells in plant body are haploid.	3. The cells in plant body are diploid
4. Vascular tissues like xylem and phloem absent	4. Vascular tissues like xylem and phloem present.
5. Sporophytic phase completely depends upon gametophyte.	5. Sporophytic phase is independent and autotrophic.

PRIMARY CLASSIFICATION

The word **Bryophyta** was coined and used for the first time by Braun (1864) who included algae, fungi, lichens and mosses in this group. In a later system of classification, algae, fungi and lichens were placed in a separate division **Thallophyta** and liverworts and mosses to **Bryophyta**. The rank of a division Bryophyta to this well-defined group of plants was first given by Schimper in 1879. Later Eichler in 1883 recognised two subgroups, **Hepaticae** and the **Musci** in the Bryophyta. Since then these two classes remained as separate, major entities within the division. Engler (1892) subdivided each of the two classes into three orders as follows :

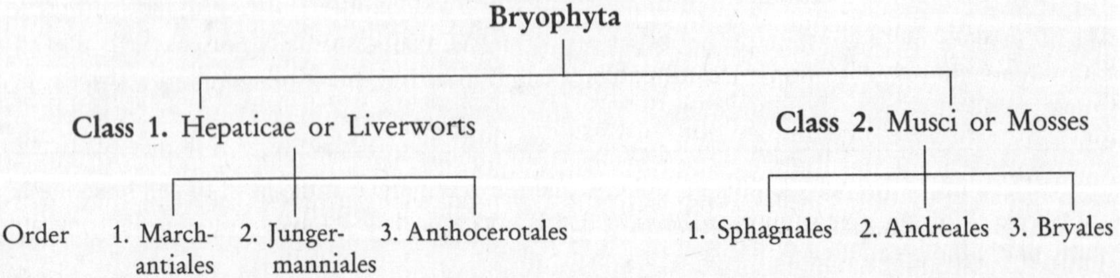

This system of classification with slight modification is still followed by many eminent bryologists. Chopra (1981) considered the Bryophyta to be triphyletic. The three sub-divisions proposed by him are Takakiophytina, Hepatophytina, and Muscophytina. The anomalous position of Anthocerotales as an order of the class Hepaticae was pointed out by many investigators very early. The important among them were de Bary, ex Janczewski (1872), Leitgeb (1879) and Underwood (1894). However, it was Howe who in 1899 gave the class status to the order Anthocerotales. He named it **Anthocerotae** and divided the **Bryophyta** into three classes : **Hepaticae, Anthocerotae** and **Musci**. Many eminent hepaticologists like Campbell (1918, 1940), Smith (1938, 1955), Takhtajan (1953) followed him and supported his move to divide the Bryophyta into three classes but Smith, Takhtajan and later Wardlaw (1955) and Schuster (1958) called the Anthocerotes as **Anthocerotae**. The consensus of opinion at present favours this view and the Bryophyta is classified into three classes, namely, Hepaticae, Anthocerotae and Musci.

Rothmaler in 1951 suggested the following class taxons for the old ones : **Hepaticopsida** for Hepaticae, **Anthocerotopsida** for Anthocerotae and **Bryopsida** for Musci. The new names suggested by Rothmaler have been recognised by the International Code of Botanical Nomenclature. Proskauer in 1957 suggested the name **Anthocerotopsida** for Anthoceropsida. The modern bryologists thus classify Bryophyta into the following three classes, namely, Hepaticopsida, Anthocerotopsida and Bryopsida.

Bryophyta

Hepaticopsida
(Hepaticae)
Liverworts
Orders :
1. Takakiales
2. Calobryales
3. Jungermanniales
4. Metzgeriales
5. Marchantiales
6. Sphaerocarpales
7. Monocleales

Anthocerotopsida
(Anthocerotae)
Hornworts
Order : Anthocerotales

Bryopsida
(Musci)
Mosses
Subclasses:
1. Sphagnidae
   Order : Sphagnales
2. Andreaeidae
   Order : Andreaeales
3. Buxbaumidae
   Order :
   Buxbaumiales
4. Bryidae
   Orders :
   (*i*) Fissidentales
   (*ii*) Dicranales
   (*iii*) Pottiales
   (*iv*) Grimmiales
   (*v*) Funariales
   (*vi*) Schistostegales
   (*vii*) Tetraphidales
   (*viii*) Eubryales
   (*ix*) Isobryales
   (*x*) Hookeriales
   (*xi*) Hypnobryales.
5. Polytrichadae
   Orders:
   (*i*) Polytrichales
   (*ii*) Dawsoniales

The above mentioned system of classification has been adopted by Takhtajan (1953), Schuster (1953), Parihar (1965) and Udar (1976). However, Tippo (1942) used the term **Atrachaeta** for **Bryophyta** while Takhtajan (1943) and Lam (1948) preferred the use of word **Bryopsida** for **Bryophyta**.

The division includes roughly 1800 species grouped in approximately 960 gerase. The science of study of bryophytes is called *Bryology* and the scientist as *Bryologist*.

Salient features of classes Hepaticopsida, Anthocerotopsida and Bryopsida

(a) Hepaticopsida

(*i*) The plant body thalloid or foliose.

(*ii*) Rhizoids are present and without septa; usually simple and tuberculate; ventral scales present.

(*iii*) Cells have chloroplast without pyrenoids.

(*iv*) Green cells contain simple or compound oil bodies.

(*v*) Sex organs develop from superficial cells on the dorsal side of the thallus except when they are terminal in position.

(*vi*) Sporophyte simple or differentiated into foot, seta and capsule.

(*vii*) Sporogenous cells develop from endothecium.

(*viii*) Columella is absent, elaters mostly present.

(*ix*) Sporophyte completely dependent upon the sporophyte for nutrition.

(*x*) Dehiscence of sporogonium is irregular or regular.

(b) Anthocerotopsida

(*i*) The plant body is thalloid and dorsiventrally flattened.

(*ii*) Rhizoids only simple without septa, ventral scales absent.

(*iii*) No tissue differentiation in thallus;cells bear a large chloroplast with a conspicuous pyrenoid.

(*iv*) Sex organs embedded in the thallus tissue.

(*v*) Antheridia develop from the hypodermal cells of the thallus on the dorsal side; located in the antheridial chambers singly or in groups.

(*vi*) Archegonia sunken on the dorsal side of the thallus, develop from superficial cells.

(*vii*) Sporogonium elongated and cylindrical, arise from the dorsal side of the thallus.

(*viii*) Sporogonium has foot, a meristematic region and capsule, meistem is intercalary in position and due to this sporogonium continues its growth throughout the growing season.

(*ix*) Capsule wall has chlorophyll and stomata

(*x*) Columella and pseudo-elaters are present.

(*xi*) Sporogenous tissue develops from amphithecium.

(c) Bryopsida

(*i*) The primary gametophyte consists of prostrate, filamentous or thalloid protonema and erect gametophore.

(*ii*) The adult gametophyte consists of 'stem', spirally arranged 'leaves' and the sex organs at its apical portion.

(*iii*) Rhizoids multicellular branched with oblique septa.

(*iv*) Sex organs develop from superficial cells with two cutting faces.

(*v*) Sporophyte differentiated into foot, seta and capsule.

(*vi*) Capsule wall has stomata.

(*vii*) Sporogenous mass develops mostly from outer layer of endothecium which in addition forms columella.

(*viii*) Elaters are absent.

(*ix*) Peristome is present in majority of mosses.

RECENT CLASSIFICATION OF BRYOPHYTE

All the known bryophytes, which number about 18,000, are grouped under three divisions (Phyla) which are as follows:

1. Marchantiophyta (liverworts)
2. Bryophyta (Mosses)
3. Anthocerotophyta (Hornworts)

1. **Marchantiophyta:** According to Stotler *et.al.* (2008) this phyla (division) has been classified into three classes:

   Class A Haplomitriopsida

   Class B Marchantiopsida

   Class C Jungermanniopsida

2. **Broyphyta:** Buck and Goffinet (2000) has classified this phyla (division) into five classes:

   Class A Takakiopsida

   Class B Sphagnopsida

   Class C Andreaeopsida

   Class D Andreaeobryopsida

   Class E Polytrychopsida

3. **Anthocerotophyta:** This phyla (division has beenclassified into two classess by stoler and Stoler (2005)

   Class A. Leiosporocerotopsida

   Class B. Anthocerotopsida

Regarding the phylogenetic analysis, as proposed by Mishler *et.al.* (1994) and Oui *et.al.* (2006), the aforesaid three divisions of bryophytes do not from a monophyletic group, but rather show a grade in embryophyte evolution.In most recent analysis liverworts are reduced as the first divergence of land plants i.e. embryophytes. More over, Schuster (1997), during the discussion of phylogeny of **Takakia**, stated that the Bryophyta form a single division and are not divisible into three divisions because the phylogeny of **Takakia** acts as 'glu' which binds the bryophytes together.

A BRIEF ACCOUNT OF THE DEVELOPMENT OF BRYOLOGY IN INDIA

Studies on Bryophytes of India were initiated by the noted taxonomist J.D. Hooker (1818, 1820) who published an account of mosses. About a decade later, Lindenberg and Lehman (1832) collected and described liverworts of India and Nepal. Griffith (1842, 1849, 1849a), who came to India as an Assistant Surgeon in 1832, recorded a number of mosses and liverworts collected by him largely from the Khasi Hills in Assam "under his private study and not his profession". The posthumous publication of his valuable notes "Notulae and Plantae Asiaticae" is regarded as the first notable contribution to Indian Bryology. In fact, Indian Bryoflora was so rich and unexplored that it attracted several Bryologists from abroad. Notable amongst them were Mitten (1859), Miiler (1853-1878) and Stephani (1906-1912).

The year 1914 may be regarded as the memorable year in the history of Indian Bryology when S.R. Kashyap published an article on theWest Himalayan Hepatics — this being the first on Bryology by an Indian botanist. Incidentally, Kashyap is the person who laid a solid foundation of the school of Indian Bryology. He also published a monographic book titled "Liverworts of Western Himalayas and the Punjab Plains." in 1929 and 1932. Due to his material contribution to this little known branch of Botany, he is rightly called the *Father of Indian Bryology.*

Encouraged and assisted by the contributions of Kashyap, his students initiated further research on morphology, cytology and physiology of bryophytes. These studies have been reviewed from time to time by Pande (1936), Pande and Bhardwaj (1952), Pande and Srivastava (1957), Maheshwari and Kapil (1963) and Udar (1970, 1973).

Another school of bryophyte was established by Prof. S.K. Pande under the headship of stalwart palaeobotanist Prof. Birbal Sahni at the Department of Botany, University of Lucknow. He published about 40 research papers on morpho-taxonomy, cytology and physiology. Prof. Ram Udar one of the ablest students of S.K. Pande continued Bryological studies in the Department. His main contribution was to explore the leafy liverworts of India. In 1976 he published a book, "Bryology in India" in which he reviewed the whole work done on Indian bryophytes.

Prof. P.N. Mehra established another school of bryophyta at Punjab University, Chandigarh. He started palynological, cytological and embryological studies of bryophytes. He put forward a new hypothesis on the origin of thallus in the Marchantiales and phyletic evolution in the Hepaticae.

In eastern India at Calcutta the work on bryophytes especially on mosses was carried out by Prof. H.C. Gangulee. He described the mosses of eastern India and adjacent regions.

Prof. T.S. Mahabale in Maharastra has been a pioneer on researches on bryophytes. He described the taxonomy of liverworts and mosses as well as the bearing of cytological studies on the phylogeny of Marchantiales.

Prof. P. Kachroo at Kashmir devoted his time mainly on liverworts. In 1969 he published, "Hepaticae of India – A Taxonomic survey and census I.Floristic and Taxonomic considerations". Prof. R.N. Chopra at University of Delhi carried out physiological and cultural studies on bryophytes. He published a book with S.C. Bhatla "Bryophyte development : Physiology and Biochemistry", in 1990. Prof. D.N. Rao at Banaras Hindu University, Varanasi started studies on affect of air pollution on Bryophytes, N.S. Parihar at University of Allahabad published an annotated revised census of Indian bryophytes. He also published a very popular book "An introduction to Embryophyta. Vol I Bryophyta".

Prof. S.C. Srivastava at University of Lucknow published a monographic account on Indian Metzgeriaceae. His main contribution includes comprehensive study on bio-diversity of bryophytes in India. He has published a list of endangered genera and species of bryophytes in India and in world.

The contributions of three eminent Indian bryologists have been briefly described below :

Prof. Shiv Ram Kashyap (1882-1934).

Born in 1882 in Jhelum of the former undivided Punjab of British India, Shiv Ram Kashyap obtained his B.Sc. and M.Sc. degrees from Punjab University. He then went to Cambridge, London for higher studies. On his return, he joined as Assistant Professor at Govt. College, Lahore and later he took over as Professor of Botany, Punjab University.

Although he did some work on Pteridophyta, he is mainly known for his studies on 'Bryophyta'. As a result of his frequent tours to Himalayas, he collected and described a large number of liverworts for which he is considered an authority. The result of his collections is the publication of the most valuable book "Liverworts of the Western himalayas and the Punjab plains" in two volumes. Besides describing fifty new species, he also created four new genera *Aitchisoniella, Stephansoniella, Sauchia* and *Sewardiella*.

He was a supporter of the theory of reduction in Marchantiales and to give further support he gave more evidences on the basis of his studies on himalayan liverworts. He was of the view that bryophytes originated from pteridophytes by reduction, and not from green algae by modification. Because of his memorable contributions he is regarded as the *Father of Indian Bryology*.

Prof. Kashyap has also the distinction of starting Post-graduate courses in Botany. He is also known with reverence for shaping the future of his students like Birbal Sahni, P.N. Mehra,

R.S. Chopra, S.K. Pande, K.C. Mehta etc. who themselves became internationally renowned botanists in course of time.

Prof. Kashyap was one of the key figures in the establishment of Indian Botanical Society and he was the first secretary of the society. He also chaired the Indian Science Congress session of 1932. The world of Botany especially that of Bryology lost its leader in 1934.

Prof. S.K. Pande

Professor S.K. Pande was born in village Aihar in district Rae Bareli (U.P.) on 17 February 1899. After securing his graduate degree from Canning College, Lucknow, he joined Punjab University for Master's degree in Botany. There he worked with Prof. S.R. Kashyap and came back to University of Lucknow in 1921 as demonstrator in Botany. He submitted his D.Sc. thesis in 1936.

He published 39 research papers in standard Journals from 1922 to 1960. His main contribution is on the members of Anthocerotales, Marchantiales and Jungermanniales and can be categorised as:

1. *Taxonomical studies* : He published a series on Indian Hepaticae from 1936 to 1952. He reported a new species of aquatic liverwort. *Riella* as *R. Vishwanathai* (synonym as *R. affinis*) from Varanasi and another new species *Nowellia indica* from western himalyas. He made some important contribution of leafy liverworts as *Jamesoniella microphylla, Chiloscyphus, Heteroscyphus, Cephalozia herzogiana* and of thalloid liverworts are *Riccia, Riccardia, Calycularia Sewardiella, Pallavicinia* and *Asterella*.

2. *Morphological studies*: He described the morphology of *Riccia sanguinea* (synonym-as *R. frostii*), *Notothylas indica, Riccia robusta* and *Notothylas levieri*.

3. *Cytological studies* : Pande in late fifties started cytological studies on Indian mosses. In 1957 he published the cytological studies on *Pogonatum microstomium, P. steveasil, Bryum nitens, Physcomitrium pyriforme, P. indica, Anomodon minor* and *Bartramia subpellucida.*

He was president of Indian Botanical society. He was elected as President of Botany section of Indian Science Congress. After his retirement from the Department of Botany, University of Lucknow, he joined National Botanical Garden (now National Botanical Research Institute, NBRI) Lucknow. Soon he left this place and became Professor and Head. Department of Botany at the University of Saugar (M.P.). He died on 25th November 1960 through an accidental fall at his Lucknow residence.

Prof. Ram Udar

Ram Udar was born in Basti and after passing Intermediate he joined Lucknow University where he came in contact with botanists like Birbal Sahni, S.K. Pande, S.N. Das Gupta *etc.* He developed keen interest in Botany and after passing M.Sc. examination with distinction he joined research under Prof. S.K. Pande and started his studies on the little known group of plants — the liverworts - both thalloid and leafy.

His contributions can be described in the following heads :

1. *Taxonomical studies* : Prof. Udar and his associates have completed monographic studies of several orders, families & genera. Some important monographs are on
   (*a*) Metzgeriales
   (*b*) Jungermanniaceae
   (*c*) Frullaniaceae
   (*d*) Lejeuneaceae
   (*e*) Notothylaceae
   (*f*) *Cyathodium*
   (*g*) *Chandonanthus*
   (*h*) *Notoscyphus*

He discovered and reported several genera from India for the first time. These are

(1) *Calobryum,* 1961

(2) *Buxbaumia,* 1970

(3) *Chonecolea* 1982

(4) *Cylindrocolea* 1982

The new species are *Riccia pandei, R. reticulata, Plagiochasma pauriana, Mannia foreani, M. persomii, Cyathodium denticulatum, Riccardia santapaui, Buxbaumia himalayensis, Calobryum indicum.*

2. *Morphological studies :* In 1960 he described the morphology of *Athalamia pinguis* - a member of family Sauteriaceae of order Marchantiales. Udar and Chandra (1965) published the morphology and life history of *Plagiochasma intermedium.*

3. *Palynological studies :* In 1964 he described the palynology of Bryophytes. He has reported the sporeling developed in *Athalamia pusilla* in 1972, *Exormotheca ceylonensis*, *Preissia quadrata, Fossombronia cristula* etc.

4. *Cultural studies :* The cultural studies were made by Udar in the genus *Riccia* in 1957 a and 1957 b, 1958.

5. *Physiological studies :* In 1960 a and 1960 b, 1961 he reported several enzymes of Hepaticae (liverworts).

6. *Oil-bodies :* He reported the oil-bodies in several species of leafy liverworts and emphasised their importance in solution of several taxonomical problems. In 1970 he reported the oil-bodies in north Indian liverworts and in 1971 in south Indian liverworts.

7. *Publications :* He published two books

(*i*) An introduction to bryophyta

(*ii*) Bryology in India

He was honoured when he was elected Fellow of National Academy (F.N.A.). He died in 1985 when he was serving as Professor of Botany at the University of Lucknow, Lucknow.

QUESTIONS

Essay Type

1. Give an account of differentiating features of *Anthocerotae* and *Hepaticae.* *(Lucknow, M.Sc.; 2006)*

2. Name one Bryophyta found in Kanpur and discuss its structure *(Kanpur, M.Sc;. 2006)*

3. Give an account of recent classification of Broyphytes.

4. (a) Describe the distinguishing features of Bryophytes. In what respects do they differ from Algae and the Pteridophytes ? *(Lucknow, 1992; Rohilkhand, 1993)*

(b) Write three important characters of Phylum Bryophyta. *(Poorvanchal, 2005)*

5. Give a general account of Bryophyta with special reference to its classification *(Gauhati, 2000)*

6. In what respects do bryophytes (*a*) differ from algae and (*b*) resemble algae *(Poorvanchal M.Sc;. 2003)*

7. Define alternation of generations. Point out the differences between the alternation of generations met within the algae and bryophytes *(Kumaon, 1995)*

8. List the salient features found in the life-cycle of bryophytes.

9. Give a brief account of the history of development of bryology in India.

10. What is ICBN classification of Bryophytes? Discuss its merits. *(Gharwal, 2000; U.P. College, 1996)*

11. Describe general characters of classes of Bryophyta. *(Rohilkhand, 1994)*

12. Write in detail the general features of Bryophytes with suitable examples. *(Kumaon, 1995)*

13. Give the classification of Bryophytes upto the order level and indicate special features of each class. *(Kumaon, 1999)*
14. Write on essay on general characters and classification of Bryophytes. *(Meerut, 1997)*
15. Write a brief outline of clasification of Bryophytes with examples and their characteristics *(Poorvanchal, 2002; Awadh, 1991, 1998, 1999)*
16. Describe important characteristics of Bryopsida. *(MDS Univ.; 1998)*
17. Describe general characters and classification of Bryophytes. *(Punjab, 1999)*
18. Describe briefly the chief characteristic features of Bryophytes. How do they resemble algae ? *(Himachal Pradesh, 1996)*
19. Give a brief outline classification of bryophytes and write atleast four characters of each class. *(Bundelkhand, 1995)*
20. Describe the salient features of the classes of Bryophytes with examples.
21. (*a*) Classify the Bryophytes upto order level. Describe their characters as well.
(*b*) Give a general account of Bryophyta with special reference to its classication. *(Gauhati, 2000)*
22. Give a brief account of the development of Bryology in India. Also mention the contributions of atleast *two* Indian Bryologists in India.
23. Describe the position, structure and function of the following in bryophytes studied by you.
(*a*) Rhizoids (*b*) Scales (*c*) Elaters *(Kanpur, 2004)*
24. Why bryophytes are called the amphibians of plant kingdom ? Give an outline of classification of Bryophytes according to Rothmaler. *(Rohilkhand, 2004)*
25. Give detailed account of general classification of Divison Bryophyta *(Awadh M.Sc.; 2001)*
26. Describe classification of Bryophytes in brief *(Kanpur, M.Sc.; 2006)*

SHORT ANSWER TYPE

27. Compare
(*a*) Thallophyta and Bryophyta
(*b*) Algae and Bryophyta
(*c*) Bryophytes and Pteridophytes.
28. Explain classification of Bryophyta *(Kanpur, 2008)*
29. Write a note on contributions of *two* Indian Bryologists *(Kanpur, M.Sc.; 2009)*
30. Write in brief
(*a*) S.R Kashyap (*b*) Ram Udar *(Kanpur, M.Sc.; 2007)*
31. In what respects do the Bryophytes
(*a*) Differ from algae
(*b*) Resemble with algae.
32. Write short notes on :
(*a*) S.R. Kashyap (*b*) Ram Udar
(*c*) General characters of Bryophytes. *(Meerut, 1998)*
(*d*) Classification of Bryophytes as proposed by N.S. Parihar. *(Rohilkhand, 1999)*
(*e*) Habit and Habitat of Bryophytes. *(Rohilkhand, 1996)*
(*f*) Amphibious nature of bryophytes *(Poorvanchal 2001)*
(*g*) Classification of bryophytes *(Poorvanchal, 2001, Andhra Pradesh, 2002)*
33. (*a*) Mention two important similarities between algae and Bryophytes. *(Purvanchal, 1997, 2000)*
(*b*) Describe the affinities of Bryotphes with Algae. *(Kanpur 2005)*
34. List general characters of Bryophytes. *(Purvanchal, 1997, 2000)*
35. Plant body of Bryophyte is Sporophyte. Write True or False. *(Purvanchal, 1998)*

36. Bryophytes are also called amphibians of Plant Kingdom. Why? *(Lucknow 2007, U.P. College, 1996)*

37. The plant body of Bryophyte is a gametophyte or sporophyte. Explain. *(U.P. College, 1996)*

38. Write three characters of Bryophytes. *(Nagpur, 1996)*

39. List the modes of perennation in Bryophytes. *(Himachal Pradesh, 1990)*

40. Write explanatory notes on :

(*i*) Classification of Bryophytes. *(Awadh 1992, 1994; M.S. Univ. 1995; Trichy, 1995; Calicut, 1995; Bundelkhand, 1993)*

(*ii*) Bryophytes are amphibians of Plant Kingdom. *(Awadh, 1992, 1995)*

(*iii*) Alternation of generation in Bryophytes. *(Poorvanchal, 2004) (Bundelkand, 1998)*

(*iv*) Classification proposed by Parihar *(Rohilkhand, 2002)*

(*v*) Amphibious nature of Bryophytes *(Poorvanchal, 2007)*

41. (*a*) Name the father of Indian Bryology.

(*b*) Briefly mention the contributions of Prof. Ram Udar. *(Bundelkhand, 1998)*

42. Write a note on Affinites of Bryophytes with Pteridophytes.

43. Write the salient features of

(*a*) Hepaticopsida

(*b*) Anthocerotopsida

(*c*) Bryopsida.

44. (*a*) Write a brief biodata of Prof. S.R. Kashyap *(Kanpur M.Sc.; 2003)*

(*b*) Give contribution of Shiv Ram Kashyap *(Kanpur M.Sc.; 2007)*

45. Who is the father of Indian Bryology ? In what respects do bryophytes resemble algae ? *(Poorvanchal, 2002; 2003)*

46. Why does sporogonium remain small in bryophytes ? *(Poorvanchal, 2003)*

47. What is the dominant phase in the life cycle of Bryophytes ? *(Meerut, 2002)*

48. Why liverworts, hornworts and mosses are classified in a single division bryophyta ? *(Poorvanchal, M.Sc., 1998)*

49. Give a short note on the affinites of bryophytes with algae. *(Kanpur , 2003)*

50. Why are bryophytes known as the amphibious group of plant kingdom *(Kanpur, 2005)*

OBJECTIVE TYPE

51. **(A) Select the correct answer :**

(*i*) The Indian bryologist who earned international fame was

(*a*) B. Sahni

(*b*) P. Maheshwari

(*c*) K.S. Mehta

(*d*) S.R. Kashyap.

(*ii*) The spore producing organ in bryophytes is

(*a*) Foot

(*b*) Seta

(*c*) Capsule

(*d*) Archegonium.

(*iii*) The production of sporophyte directly from a gametophyte without syngamy or sexual fusion is called.

(*a*) Apogamy (*b*) Apospory

(*c*) Fertilisation (*d*) Apomixis.

(*iv*) The haploid or gamete producing generation is commonly known as

(*a*) Sporophyte

(*b*) Gametophyte

(*c*) Adult

(*d*) All of the above.

(*v*) Father of Indian Bryology is

(*a*) S.K. Pande (*b*) R.S. Chopra

(*c*) S.R. Kashyap (*d*) Ram Udar.

(*vi*) The condition of producing only one kind of spores is called.

(*a*) Heterospory (*b*) Apospory

(*c*) Homospory (*d*) Autospory.

(*vii*) Alternation of morphologically different generation is called

(*a*) Homologous

(*b*) Heterologous

(*c*) Both of the above

(*d*) None of the above.

(*viii*) Which of the following is not a character of Bryophytc?
(*a*) Presence of archegonium
(*b*) Independent sporophyte
(*c*) Motile sperm
(*d*) Water is essential for fertilization.

(*ix*) Gametophytic generation is dominant in
(*a*) Bryophytes
(*b*) Pteridophytes
(*c*) Gymnosperms
(*d*) Angiosperms.

(*x*) Spore mother cells in Bryophytes are
(*a*) Haploid (*b*) Diploid
(*c*) Triploid (*d*) Tetraploid.

(*xi*) Which of the following statements is not true of Bryophytes ?
(*a*) They are photosynthetic
(*b*) They lack tracheids and sieve tubes
(*c*) Their zygote and the sporophyte are haploid
(*d*) The spores germinate and produce gametophytes.

(*xii*) The positive evidence of aquatic ancestory of Bryophytes is indicated by
(*a*) Some forms are still aquatic
(*b*) Thread like protonema
(*c*) Ciliated sperms
(*d*) Presence of middle vein on dorsal side of thallus.

(*xiii*) A bryophyte differs from a pteridophyte in
(*a*) Archegonia
(*b*) Lack of vascular tissues
(*c*) Swimming antherozoids
(*d*) Independent gametophyte

(*xiv*) Which one of the following statements is not correct for bryophytes ?
(*a*) They lack tracheids and Vessels.
(*b*) They are photosynthetic.
(*c*) Their zygote undergoes meiosis and then produces the sporophytes.
(*d*) Their spore germinates to produce gamnetophyte.

(*xv*) A female gametangium of a bryophyte differs from that of a fungus in possessing
(*a*) Large neck
(*b*) A venter
(*c*) Jacket layer of sterile cells
(*d*) A single egg cell.

(*xvi*) The gametophytes of most of the bryophytes possess
(*a*) Vascular bundles
(*b*) only phloem
(*c*) Nonvascular bundles
(*d*) Tracheids

(B) Fill in the blanks :

(*i*) The number of venter canal cells in Bryophytes is always__________.

(*ii*) The bryophyte having incubous arrangement of leaves is__________.

(*iii*) Spore mother cells of Bryophytes are__________.

(iv) Bryophytes are called__________plants.

Image of Porella *cordaeana*

CHAPTER 2

HEPATICOPSIDA (Hepaticae) Liverworts

- Liverworts as Land Dwellers
- Gametophyte
- Chief Means of Perennation in Liverworts
- Distinctive Features of Liverworts
- Classification of Liverworts

LIVERWORTS AS LAND DWELLERS

The liverworts are bryophytes in which the plant is a green, dorsiventral thallus. It frequently grows close to the ground to which it is secured by delicate, simple hair-like processes called the **rhizoids**. The rhizoids supply water and minerals needed for the plant's growth. The liverworts have thus completed migration to land. The aerial habit in plants, in general, seems to have been established through them. The fossil record indicates that about 350 million years ago there were found plants resembling the liverworts. Very little, however, is known about their structure and reproduction. For a life on land the first requirement is the presence of efficient absorbing organs. The second requirement is a compact plant body protected against desiccation. The third is a change from motile to non-motile aerial reproductive cells. The rhizoids which function as absorbing organs in the liverworts are short, delicate unicellular, hair-like structures. They are not as efficient absorbing organs as the roots because they have none of the complex features exhibited by the latter.

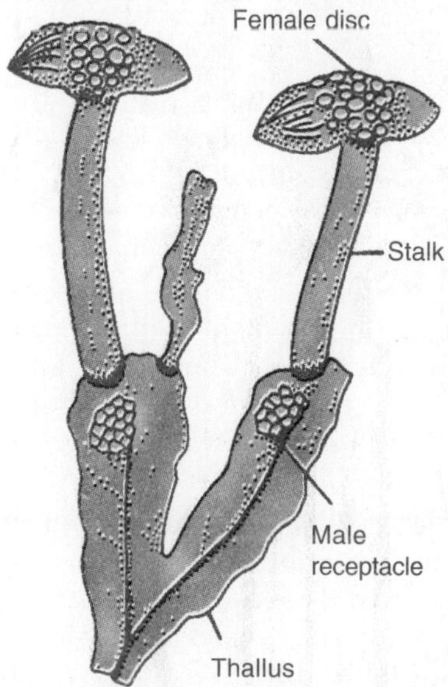

Fig. 2.1. Hepaticopsida. Thalloid gametophyte of *Asterella blumeana*. Note the sessile male receptacle behind the stalk of the female disc. (After Kashyap).

The plant body, no doubt, is more compact and better protected. The surface area is reduced as much as possible as compared with the filamentous, colonial or huge bodies of aquatic algae. The bulk of the cells constituting the thallus are protected by the epidermis. Fewer cells are directly exposed to water loss by transpiration. The prostrate habit is another advantage. However, the thallus is not completely protected against desiccation. The epidermal cells lack special, waterproof thickening. Besides, the epidermal layer is not continuous. It has unguarded pores. The latter allow aeration of thallus with miniature dehydration. The thallus is, therefore, not completely protected against desiccation. Consequently the liverworts must live in very moist habitats. They are unable to withstand the drying effect of the direct rays of the sun for any length of time. This accounts for their preference to grow in moist, shaded places on the ground, on the banks of rivers, on moist rocks, on tree trunks or floating on the surface of water or even submerged. In fact, the factors which favour their growth, are the combination of high humidity, shade and abundant moisture in the soil.

From the foregoing account it is evident that the liverworts have not become completely adapted to the land life. They are still in a transitional stage and in the process of becoming adapted to land environments. Although the sex organs are jacketed and thus protected against the drying influence of air yet the dependence of liverworts on water is even more pronounced in the case of sexual reproduction. Their sperms have retained swimming habit. The presence of external water is a necessary condition for the sperms to swim to the egg. In fact the male gemetes (sperms) produced by the liverworts are characteristic of water plants and not land plants. The quality of water which is affected by several factors such as temperature, pH and dissolved substances affects the ability of survival of sperms in liverworts. They furnish a clear sign of their aquatic ancestry. The spores, however, are non-motile and wind disseminated which is an adaptation to a land habitat.

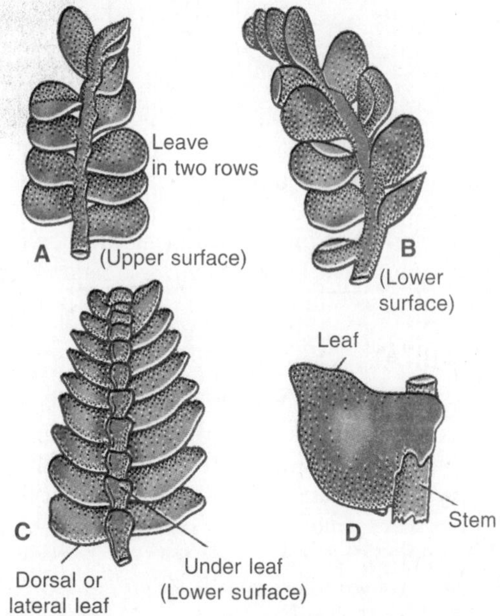

Fig. 2.2. (A—D). **Hepaticopsida**. Leafy gametophytes of Jungermanniales. A, dorsal view of leafy gametophyte *Plagiochila asplenioides* with two rows of leaves; B, Ventral view of A. Note the absence of under leaves; C, Ventral view of *Calypogeia neesiana* with three rows of leaves. (After Steare); D. Dorsal lobe of lateral leaf.

Gametophyte (Fig. 2.1)

The dominant plant in the liverworts is the gametophyte. It is a dorsiventral thallus-like structure which remains small in size. Why does it remain small ? The study of the thallus structure reveals that the tissues required for massive growth are lacking. It lacks the vascular tissue which is essential for conduction of water and minerals. It has no supporting or mechanical tissue in the form of long, thick-walled fibres. Besides, the absorbing organs in the form of rhizoids are not as efficient as the roots. Secondary meristems which provide increase in girth and additional cortical cells are absent. Consequently, a vegetative plant body remains a thin-walled, porous, flat, thallus-like structure which grows prostrate and close to the surface of the substratum. In land plants in which the corticating-tissues, which conserve water are lacking, the prostrate habit is useful. It reduces the exposed surface and the major portion of the plant body remains in direct contact with soil moisture. Besides, it furnishes maximum surface for fixation and absorption of water.

The gametophyte of liverworts is green and independent. Some liverworts like advanced Metzgeriales, Marchantiales, Sphaerocarpales and Monoceleales have a thalloid plant body (Fig. 2.1). It is flat and conspicuously lobed or branched. The branching is dichotomous. It very much resembles the thallus of a foliaceous lichen. However, the rich green colour of the liverwort thallus distinguishes it form the gray or grayish green colour of the lichen thallus. The different types of fruiting bodies in the two is another distinctive feature.

There are other liverworts like Calobryales, Jungermanniales and primitive Metzgeriales in which the gametophyte plant is leafy (Fig. 2.2). It consists of a central branched axis (stem) bearing leaf-like green expansions (leaves, A). The leaves are arranged in three rows: two rows in lateral sides and the third row on ventral side of axis. The leaves of third row in prostrate form of leafy liverwort are called amphigastria or underleaves. The underleaves gradually reduce in size and ultimately disappear. In *Fossombronia* only two rows of lateral leaves are present. It is believed that the thalloid form might have evolved from leafy form of liverworts.

Schiffneria, a member of order Metzgeriales represents a transitional stage in between thalloid and leafy forms. In this genus the vegetative plant body is thalloid but at reproductive stage the short abbreviated leafy shoots bearing sex organs are produced from the ventral surface of thallus. Both the so-called leaves and the stem lack vascular tissues. The leafy or foliose liverworts are more numerous. Both the thalloid and the leafy gametophytes are anchored to the substratum by unicellular unbranched rhizoids.

What factors induce rhizoid formation in liverworts ? The generally held view is that contact with the substratum (soil or decaying vegetation) stimulates rhizoid formation in the liverworts. The presence of an exogenous auxin in the normal environment of liverworts is mentioned as another factor which induces rhizoid formation. Soils particularly those rich in decaying organic matter are known to contain the auxin (Whitehouse, 1963). The auxin and humus are formed by micro-organisms (soil bacteria and fungi) associated with the decay of organic matter (Shadrake, 1971). La Rue (1942) reported that rhizoids are also induced in liverworts by wounding. Without exception, the gametophyte plant in all the liverworts is prostrate and dorsiventrally differentiated.

1. HABITAT

The liverworts do not grow in dry habitats as the plant body is not completely protected against serious desiccation. They prefer to grow in situations where there is high humidity, shade and abundant moisture in the soil. Thus they thrive in moist shady habitats such as banks of streams, marshy ground, damp soil and rocks, deep shaded ravines, deep in the woods, on the bark of trees in diffuse light as epiphytes and on the surface of leaf as epiphyllous. There the dense shade protects them from the intense rays of the sun. A few live submerged (*Riella*) or floating on water (*Riccia fluitans*). They often form soft, bright, green mats, over the substratum.

Based on habitat the liverworts may be :

(*i*) Terrestrial
(*ii*) Aquatic
(*iii*) Lithophytes
(*iv*) Epiphytes
(*v*) Epiphyllous

2. DISTRIBUTION

The liverworts are widely distributed over the earth's surface but are far more numerous in the tropics than in other parts of the world. Some of them are cosmopolitan in their distribution. They extend in their distribution form the arctic, through the temperate zones to the tropical forests. In India they abound in the outer Himalayas where rainfall is the heaviest. It is the home of the liverworts particularly within a range between 5,000 ft. and 8,000 ft. above sea level. The thallose forms are met with on the exposed slopes. The foliose liverworts are confined to the shady, moist situations. They occur on rocks or as epiphytes on tree trunks. Simla, Dalhousie, Mussoorie, Garhwal, and Almora are some of the hilly places rich in them. The liverworts are not found in Western Tibet. They show active growth during summer and rainy season from May to September. Winter is the resting period. August to September is the fruiting season. The Hepaticae number about 9,500 species. They are grouped under 280 genera.

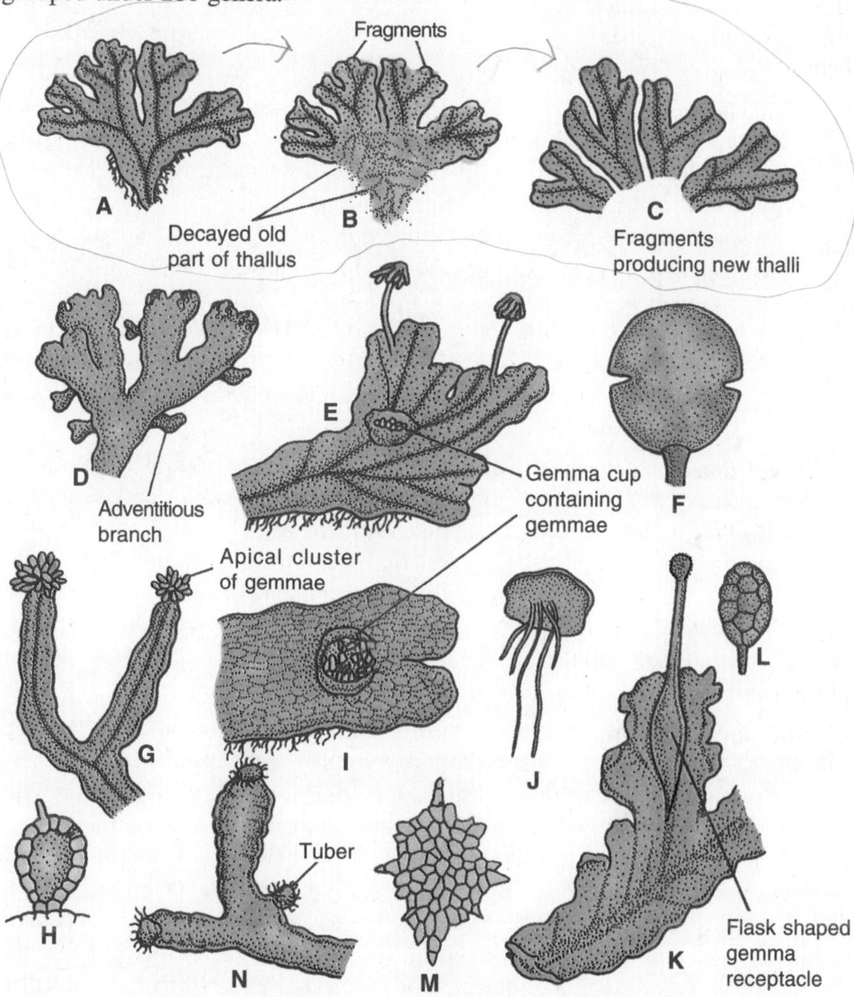

Fig. 2.3. (A—N). **Liverworts**. Chief methods of asexual reproduction. A—C, fragmentation in *Riccia;* D, adventitious branches in *Targionia;* E, *Marchantia* thallus bearing a gemma cup containing gemmae; F, single gemma of *Marchantia;* G, cluster of gemmae at the tip of a thallus lobe in *Metzgeria fruiticulosa*; H, a single gemma of *Metzgeria*; I, *Lunularia* thallus bearing a crescent-shaped gemma receptacle containing gemmae; J. single gemma of *Lunularia;* K, Flask-shaped gemma receptacle of *Blasia pusilla*; L, single gemma of K; M, stellate gemma of *Blasia*; N, thallus of *Riccia discolor* bearing tubers (K—M after Kashyap and N after Srivastava).

3. ASEXUAL REPRODUCTION IN LIVERWORTS (Fig. 2.3)

In liverworts asexual reproduction takes place by vegetative methods only. Like other land plants true asexual spores (mitospores) are lacking. Vegetative reproduction takes place during the growing season. The vegetatively produced descendants of a single plant are referred to as a **clone**. Asexual reproduction in the liverworts is brought about in a variety of ways. The most important among these are :-

1. Fragmentation (A—C). The cells in the posterior portions of the branched thalli die of old age and eventually disorganise. This results in the separtion of young thallus lobes. These are called the fragments. Each detached lobe or fragment by apical growth and dichotomy gives rise to a new plant. In this way the number of plants increases from time to time. The common example of plants which progagate by this method are *Riccia, Marchantia, Pellia* and the like. Fragmentation is a very efficient method of propagation when the environmental conditions are favourable for growth. It leads to increase in the number of plants in a locality but it does not permit spread of the plant to an entirely new locality.

2. Gemma formation (E—K). Many species of liverworts both thalloid and few leafy produce green multicellular asexual buds called the **gemmae**. They are produced in large numbers. Being small and sufficiently buoyant, they are easily carried, when detached, by water and wind currents to new habitats where each grows into a new individual immediately. The gemmae thus serve to disseminate the species to new localities. In *Marchantia* and *Lunularia* the gemmae are developed in small receptacles called the **gemmae cups**. The gemmae cups are circular in *Marchantia* (E) and crescent-shaped in *Lunularia* (I). They are developed on the dorsal surface of the thallus. In *Blasia* (K) the gemmae are produced in flask-shaped receptacles. Two celled gemmae may be produced within any cell of the thallus in *Riccardia* (Fig. 6.3 B). In leafy liverworts such as *Jackiella* & *Lethocolea* (Udar and Kumar 1981, 1986) two celled or multicellular gemmae are produced on leaf margins and on axis respectively.

3. Adventitious branches (D). Vegetative propagation also takes place by the formation of adventitious branches. They arise from the ventral surface of the thallus and become separated by death and decay of the tissue connecting the branch with the parent plant. The detached adventitious branch grows into a new plant. Examples are *Ricca fluitans*, *Targionia* and *Reboulia*. Kashyap reported the formation of adventitious branches on the ventral surface of the male disc between the lobes in *Marchantia palmata* (Fig. 5.6 D). Pande and Udar (1956) reported the origin of adventitious ventral branched from the midrib in *Calycularia crispula* (Fig. 6.4). Pande and Srivastava (1953) reported the same in *Pallavacinia canarana*.

4. Tuber formation (N). In some liverworts, especially those exposed to desiccation, special subterranean branches are formed towards the end of the growing season. These branches get swollen at their tips to form *tubers*. The tubers are usually buried underground. The plant dies at the onset of the period unfavourable for growth, the tubers remain dormant. Being buried they are not affected by drought. With the return of favourable season the tubers resume growth. In *Cyathodium tuberosum, Petalophyllum, Sewardiella* and *Fossombronia*, the tuber is formed at the tip of the plant at the end of the growing season (Fig. 6.31L). Tuber formation has also been reported in *Riccia billardierii, R. discolor* and *R. vesicata*. Tubers are portions of the thallus modified for food storage and dormancy. Primarily, the tubers serve as units of perennation. Secondarily, they serve as units of propagation when the plant bears more than one tuber.

5. Persistent apices. In certain species the growing apical portions of the thallus lobes with a certain amount of thallus tissue become thickened or otherwise modified. These thickened apices persist. The rest of the plant dies away. At the beginning of the rainy season the dormant apices resume growth resulting in a rosette of new plants. Examples are *Cyathodium, Athalamia, Cryptamitrium,* etc.

6. Regeneration. The liverworts possess an amazing power of regeneration. Some hepaticologists state that every part of the plant—rather every living cell of a liverwort thallus—is capable of regenerating the entire plant. Isolated scales and rhizoids of Marchantiaceae could be induced to grow into new plants under suitable conditions. The implications of the exceptional regenerative powers in the vegetative spread of the liverworts are thus obvious.

The student must bear in mind that asexual reproduction by vegetative methods is entirely a secondary phenomenon in the life cycle. It simply serves to propagate the gametophyte phase in the life cycle and plays no role in the phenomenon of alternation of generations.

Chief Means of Perennation in Liverworts

1. Tuber Formation. Some liverworts form tubers. Tubers being buried underground are unaffected by drought and extremes of temperature. Moreover, the outer two to three layers of cells of the tubers possess corky, hyaline walls which are waterproof. The inner or central cells are packed with food reserves such as starch grains and oil globules. The tubers, therefore, serve as a means of perennation.

2. The thallus of some liverworts such as *Reboulia, Grimaldia* etc., dries up in winter or extreme dry season. The margins of the thallus roll upwards. As a result, the upper surface is protected and the ventral surface with the scales is exposed. With the onset of the rainy season these thalli resume growth.

3. Persistent apices. In a few of the liverworts the whole of the thallus dries up with the approach of unfavourable period. Only the apices of the thalli remain alive. They become dormant as they get thickened or otherwise modified. The surviving persistent thickened apices resume growth with the advent of rainy season.

4. In most of the leafy liverworts the whole plant dries up. With the approach of the favourable season it becomes green and resumes growth. Such plants have evolved physiological adaptations which allow suspension of metabolism during periods of drought and its resumption when water is once more available. Buch (1947) called these plants *pollacauophytes.* In pollacauophytes water is lost rapidly to dry air. The cytoplasm, itself is highly resistant to desiccation.

4. SEXUAL REPRODUCTION (Fig. 2.4)

It consists in the union of gametes and subsequent production of meiospores. It is the usual method of reproduction in the bryophytes. The male and the female sex organs in some species of liverworts are borne on different plants. The examples of this kind are *Riccardia indica* (A, B), *Pellia calycina* and *Marchantia*. Such species are called *dioecious*. There are others in which two kinds of sex organs are developed on the same plant. They are called *monoecious*. *Riccardia multifitida*(C), *Asterella blumeana* (Fig. 2.1) and *Pellia epiphylla* are monoecious. The sex organs may be borne dorsally or at the anterior end. They are either embedded in the tissue of the thallus (*Riccia*) or raised on special upright branches (*Marchantia*) called the **gametophores.** In leafy liverworts, the sex organs are never borne upon stalked receptacles. In Jungermanniales, which is the major order of leafy liverworts, the antheridia are enclosed within sac like male bracts and archegonia within perianth. The perianth is innermost covering arround the archegonia. It is formed by fusion of either only female bracts (modified two lateral rows of leaves) as in *Jungermannia* or in addition with female bracteole (modified underleaf) as in *Frullania*.

Sporophyte. Following fertilization the zygote develops into the second individual in the life cycle called the **sporophyte**. It receives a special name **sporogonium** in the bryophytes. The sporogonium is without differentiation. Consequently, it suffers from certain disabilities. It lacks direct contact with the soil as it has no roots or other basal appendages of any kind. It remains (Fig. 2.4 C) attached by the foot to the parent gametophyte (thallus) which provides for its nutrition from its own resources. Owing to the limited ability of the parent gametophyte plant for absorption and conduction, the possibilities of the development of the parasitic sporogonium in the liverworts are limited. Moreover, it has no stem to bear leaves or to elevate and support photosynthetic appendages. Naturally it is doomed to remain small. The other disabilities it suffers from are :

(*i*) Absence of meristematic tissue.

(*ii*) Absence of any kind of lateral appendages and of branching habit.

(*iii*) Continuity of the archesporium leading to simultaneous ripening of spores.

All these factors collectively account for the liverwort sporogonium not progressing beyond a limited size. It remains dwarfed.

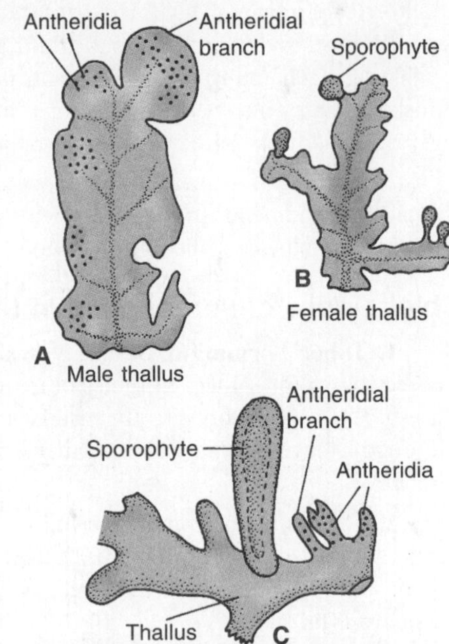

Fig. 2.4. (A—C) **Hepaticopsida.** Distribution of sex organs in *Riccardia*. A, male thallus of *Riccardia indica* with antheridia on the side branches; B, female thallus of *R. indica* with sporophytes; C, monoecious thallus of *R. multifitida* with separate male and female branches. (A—B after Kashyap, C, after Velenovsky).

In some species the sporogonium is differentiated into three parts, a **foot,** a **seta** and a **capsule** (Fig. 3.3B). In a few others (*Riccia*) both the foot and seta are absent (Fig. 4.16). The sporogonium of *Corsinia* consists of the foot and the capsule (Fig. 3.3A). The seta is lacking. The Jungermanniales have the ovoid or spherical capsule elevated on a long, fragile seta (Fig. 1.4 F). The sporogonium is a specialised body which is solely devoted to the production of meiospores and their dispersal. A large proportion of the cells of the endothecium are devoted to spore formation as compared with the other two classes of the bryophytes. The endothecium cells which do not form spores remain sterile and develop into **elaters**. In some genera of the Metzgeriales, a tuft of fixed elaters occurs at the base of the capsule (*Pellia*, Fig. 7.10) or at the apex (*Riccardia*), in addition, to the free elaters occurring intermixed with the spores. This elateral cluster is usually called the *elaterophore*. Recent investigations have shown that the elateral cluster is often attached to a small structure which represents an extension or thickening of the capsule wall. Thus strictly speaking; this elater-bearing structure is the *elaterophore*.

Protection of sporophyte

The nature has developed several means to overcome the disabilities of young developing sporophyte of liverworts both in subclasses Jungermanniae and Marchantiae separately.

1. Protection given to sporophyte in subclass - Jungermanniae

(*a*) Young sporophyte is enclosed within calyptra, perianth, female bracts and bracteole (if present) as in *Frullania*.

(*b*) Perianth fuses with bracts and bracteole and provides more thick and massive covering around calyptra as in *Eucalyx*.

(*c*) Both foot and seta are embedded in shoot apex where only capsule is enclosed by calyptra and other additional coverings like perianth and bracts and bracteole as in *Cephalozia bicuspidata*.

(*d*) The sporophyte is completely embedded in stem tissue. The foliage appendages are present up to the apex of the axis as in *Trichocolea*.

(*e*) An additional erect covering, other than calyptra, called erect marsupium is produced from stem apex where foliage appendages are left behind as in *Isotachys*.

(*f*) Incipient, rather small bulbous marsupium is produced from shoot apex as in *Notoscyphus*.

(*g*) Fully developed, cylindrical or tubular underground marsupium is produced from shoot apex as in *Lethocolea, Jackiella*.

Cavers (1911) has recognised three catagories of marsupium. These are :

(*i*) *Isotachis* type : This is erect type of marsupium as explained above in 1 : (e).

(*ii*) *Tylimanthus* type : Solid marsupium which grows at right angle to main axis and only young sporophyte (embryo) is found embedded within it.

(*iii*) *Acrobolus* type : Hollow marsupium which grows at right angle to main axis.

2. Protection given to sporophyte in subclass - Marchantiae

(*a*)Young sporophyte is enclosed within calyptra and involucre as in *Targionia* and *Cyathodium*

(*b*) In majority of the genera of the order Marchantiales the young sporophyte develops on underside of female receptacle (archegoniophore) in inverted form. It helps the sporophyte from direct sun-rays and from other external injuries from insects. In addition the sporophyte is covered by calyptra, perigynium and perichaetium as in *Marchantia*.

(*c*) In *Riccia*, where foot and seta are absent, the capsule is found embedded within thallus tissue which provides the proper protection to the sporophyte.

Sporogenesis (Fig. 2.5). It is a process whereby the diploid protoplast of the spore mother cell (sporocyte) is transformed into haploid dispersal units with resistant walls termed the *spores* or more appropriately the *meiospores*. The process is complex and comprises an integrated series of events involving a special kind of nuclear division termed **meiosis**.

In meiosis, the diploid nucleus of the spore mother cell divides before there is any division of the cytoplasm. The first nuclear division is reduction (C). It reduces the number of chromosomes to one half (haploid number). The second nuclear division is mitotic (D). Both constitute **meiosis**. Thus in meiosis, the nucleus divides twice but the chromosomes are replicated only once.

At the onset of sporogenesis, the spore mother cells increase in size and their walls thicken (B). The diploid nucleus of the spore mother cell (sporocyte) undergoes two successive divisions (C—D). The cell walls between the resultant 4 haploid nuclei are laid simultaneously after the second division dividing the spherical spore mother cell into four equal cells arranged in a tetrahedral manner (E). These cells thicken their walls and ripen into spores. The four spores of each sporocyte remain together until they are fully grown. It is called a **spore tetrad** (H). In a ripe spore, two sometimes three distinct layers can be differentiated in the spore wall. The outer layer is called the **exosporium** (exine or exospore) the inner one **endosporium** (intine) and the median one **mesosporium**. They develop in a centripetal succession as follows :— Each haploid cell of the sporocyte secretes a thick, gelatinous layer of callose around it unevenly (F). Immediately after, an outer layer of the spore wall known as the **exosporium** is deposited between the callose and the cell protoplast in the form of a series of lamellae (G). The lamellae of the exosporium next to the callose layer project into and follow the contour of the callose layer. The latter thus acts as a mold against which the markings of the exosporium are cast. The hepatic spores have tripartite lamellae in various arrangements throughout the entire exine. There is striking sculpturing of the exospore in the subclass Marchantiae. The median layer **mesosporium**, if present, is deposited on the inner side of the exosporium. The **endosporium** is deposited next to the spore protoplast during the concluding stages of spore development (H). When the spores in the tetrad are quite ripe, the callose layer and the common spore mother cell wall disappear (I). The spores separate and lie free in the capsule cavity.

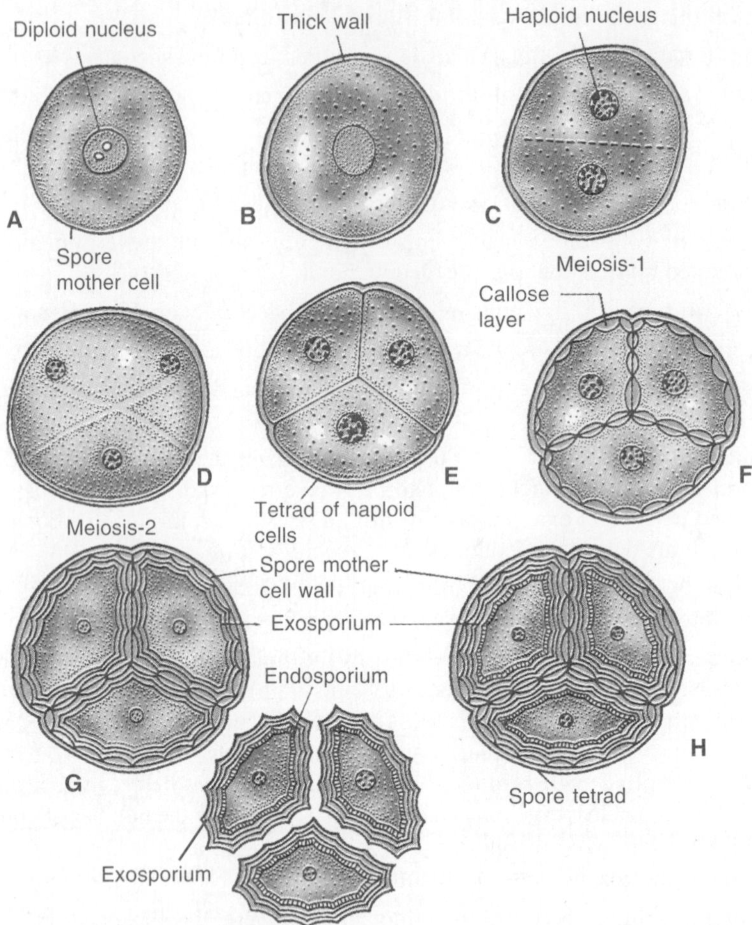

Fig. 2.5. (A—I) **Hepaticopsida**. Stages in sporogenesis. Explanation in the text.

The mature capsule dehisces in a different manner in the different orders of the liverworts. In the Marchantiales it dehisces irregularly. In *Asterella* it dehisces by the separation of a lid at the capsule. Most of the Jungermanniales have the capsule wall split into four valves.

Mature spore. The liberated meiospore consists of a tiny mass of protoplasm surrounded by a protective, stratified spore wall or coat technically known as the *sporoderm* which is differentiated into two or three layers, namely, exospore, the mesospore, and the endospore. The reserve food is stored in the form of starch and fatty oil droplets. Besides, there are granules mostly albuminous in nature. The small haploid nucleus is usually located in the centre. In some species (*Pellia*) chloroplasts are also present. The exospore is well developed in species exposed to dryness or excessive heat. It has a patterned and often elaborately sculptured exterior in the form of folds, ridges, or spines executed in the highly resistant material termed *sporopollenin* (Taylor, *et al* 1974). There is an additional layer external to the exosporium in some liverworts. It is called the **perinium** or **epispore**. It represents a part of the callose layer that has undergone modification.

The spores of Marchantiales and Metzgeriales are comparatively larger and highly ornate whereas those of Jungermanniales are small, spherical and with relatively simple ornamentation. Furthermore the spores of Jungermanniales are apolar — one with no triradiate mark whereas those of Marchantiales are strongly polar with a triradiate ridge.

Schuster (1979, 1984) emphasized that sporogenesis provides a character which helps to separate the two subclasses of the hepatics. The spore mother cells (sporocytes) of the subclass Marchantiae are spherical whereas those of the Jungermannie become deeply 4-lobed in the meiotic prophase.

On germination each spore produces the alternate plant in the cycle. It is the thallus (gametophyte) and not the sporogonium (sporophyte). Meiospore thus is the initial cell of the free living gametophyte in the sexual life cycle of the liverworts.

Distinctive Features of Liverworts

1. All the hepatics, with of course a very few exceptions, are dorsiventral in structure.
2. They are comparatively small in size never more than a few inches in length.
3. The plant body, which is always a **gametophyte**, is an independent plant. It is either thallose in form or leafy in nature. In the latter case it is differentiated into a branched central axis. Both the axis and the branches bear leaf-like expansions. The leaf has no midrib.
4. The gametophyte is secured to the ground by simple, one-celled, absorptive processes called the **rhizoids**.
5. Internally the gametophyte always has a photosynthetic tissue. The cells constituting it have simple or compound oil-bodies and numerous, small chloroplasts. The chloroplasts lack pyrenoids.
6. The sex organs exogenous in origin and are either dorsal in position, or terminal. Each develops from a single **initial cell.**
7. The sporogonium is small and generally without chlorophyll. It is attached to and lives almost entirely as a **parasite** on the parent gametophyte. The sporogonium lacks stomata.
8. The sporogonium is either differentiated into *foot, seta* and *capsule* or foot and capsule. In *Riccia* it is very simple with both the foot and seta lacking.
9. The sporogonium has no meristematic tissue.
10. The sporogenous tissue is endothecial in origin. A major portion of the sporogenous tissue forms the spores as compared with the other two classes of Bryophyta. The sterile cells elongate to form elaters with spirally thickened walls.
11. The columella is absent.
12. The spores, on germination, generally directly and in some indirectly develop into the gametophyte plants.

CLASSIFICATION OF LIVERWORTS

Engler (1892) subdivided the class Hepaticae (Hepaticopsida) into three orders, namely, *Marchantiales, Anthocerotales* and *Jungermanniales.* Many early hepaticologists considered that the Anthocerotales stand apart from the other two orders. Howe (1894) thus suggested class status to the order Anthocerotales. Many eminent bryologists such as Campbell, Smith and Takhtajan supported Howe's suggestion to elevate order Anthocerotales to the rank of a class, Anthocerotae. Cavers, Leitgeb and Jones recognized the anomalous position of the Anthocerotales but were opposed to the idea of giving it the status of a class. Many bryologists, however, followed in line with the new move. With the raising of the order Anthocerotales to the rank as a class, only two orders *Marchantiales* and *Jungermanniales* were left in the class Hepaticae. Cavers (1910) added a third to the list. He separated family *Sphaerocarpaceae* from the order Jungermanniales and gave it the status of an order naming it *Sphaerocarpales*. Later in 1936 Campbell suggested another change. He proposed to establish another order *Calobryales* comprising two genera *Calobryum* and *Haplomitrium*. The consensus of opinion favoured this view. Later, many workers proposed to split the order *Jungermanniales* into two orders, namely, the *Metzgeriales* and the *Jungermanniales* proper. The former included mainly the thalloid forms of the Jungermanniales and the later exclusively leafy forms. In this way the number of orders in the class Hepaticae rose to five. These were the *Marchantiales, Sphaerocarpales, Metzgeriales, Jungermanniales* and the *Calobryales*.

In 1958, Hattori and Inoue (1958) and Hattori and Mizutani (1958) suggested the establishment of a new order *Takakiales* with a single family Takakiaceae in the class Hepaticae (Liverworts). Their suggestion was based on the discovery of a curious new liverwort *Takakia lepidoziodes* from Japanese Alps in 1951 and later in Canada (Persson 1958). Very recently Grolle (1963) collected another species *T. ceratophylla* from Sikkim (Eastern Himalayas). The inclusion of Takakiales raised the number of orders in the class Hepaticae or Hepaticopsida to six.

In 1966, Schuster presented a scheme of classification of the Hepaticae (Hepaticopsida) which according to Watson (1974) appears reasonably natural and clearly workable. He divides the class Hepaticae (Hepaticopsida) into the subsclasses namely *Jungermanniae* and *Marchantiae*. The former includes 4 orders. Takakiales, Calobryales, Jungermanniales and Metzgeriales. The subclass Marchantiae comprises 3 orders, Sphaerocarpales Monocleales and Marchantiales.

Class Hepaticopsida or Hepaticae (Liverworts). Gametophyte practically always dorsiventrally differentiated; may be thalloid but more commonly leafy; leaves without a midrib; oil-bodies simple or compound; thallus attached to the substratum by simple, unicellular rhizoids; develops directly from the spores; sporophyte without any meristematic tissue; sporogenous tissue endothecial in origin, columella absent.

The class Hepaticopsida has been divided into following seven well recognised orders :

Order 1. *Takakiales*. Thallus radially symmetrical, differentiated into a basal creeping, leafless rhizome-like structure from which arise the erect leafy branches (termed gametophores), leaves isophyllous, spirally arranged in 3 rows on the axes with an ill-defined central strand; leaves formed of 1 or 2—4 fleshy, terete segments almost free to the base; polyseriate; total absence of rhizoids on the thallus; archegonia isolated, with the neck made up of 6 rows of neck cells; lowest chromosome number n=4.

Order 2. *Calobryales*. Like the Takakiales the thallus rhizomatous; leafy gametophores erect, bear simple, dorsiventrally flattened entire leaves in three vertical rows (2 lateral and one dorsal); leaves uniseriate but multiseriate towards the base only; rhizoids absent; archegonia aggregated into inflorescence; archegonial neck with 4 rows of neck cells.

Order 3. *Jungermanniales*. Thuallus dorsiventral but distinctly foliose in form and without any differentiation of tissues; leaf without a midrib; archegonial neck made up of 5 vertical rows of neck cells; apical cell used up in the formation of the archegonium (*arcogynous*); archegonia and sporophytes thus always terminal in position; capsule wall consists of more than one cell in thickness.

Order 4. *Metzgeriales*. Thuallus simple, flat in the lower forms but shows rudimentary, foliar development in the higher forms; dorsiventral; no internal differentiation of tissues, apical cell never used up in the formation of archegonia (*anacrogynous*); archegonia and sporogonia thus always dorsal in position; archegonial neck made up of five vertical row of cells, capsule wall more than one layer of cells in thickness.

Order 5. *Marchantiales*. Thallus flat, dichotomously branched; internally differentiated into dorsal region of air chambers and ventral parenchymatous storage region; archegonial neck composed of 6 vertical rows of cells; capsule with a jacket of sterile cells one cell thick.

Order 6. *Sphaerocarpales*. Thallus without any internal differentiation of tissues; each sex organ surrounded by an involucre; archegonial neck composed of 6 vertical rows of cells; capsule wall one cell in thickness.

Order 7. *Monocleales*. Thallus simple, upper surfaces smooth, ventral scales and air chambers absent, involucre present, numerous mucilage- hairs present around sex organs; archegonial neck composed of 6 vertical rows of cells; capsule cylindrical, one cell layer thick having two sets of thickening bands crossing each other on its cell wall.

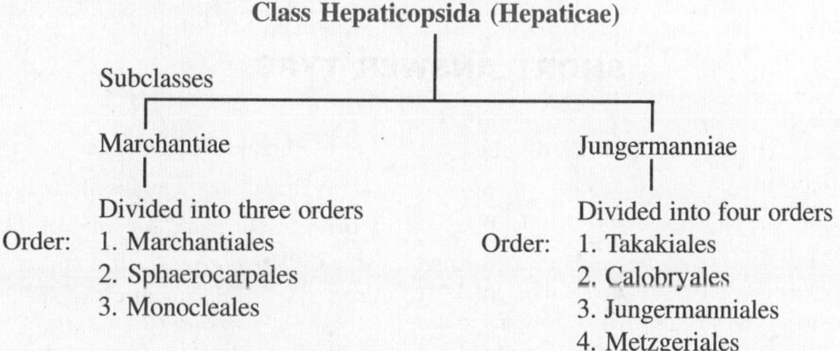

Crandall-Stotler, B., R.E. Stotler and D.G. Long (2008, 2009) are of the openion to construct three (phyla) divisions among bryophytes viz. (1) Marchantiophyta, (2) Anthocerotophyta, (3) Bryophyta. Under divison Marchantiophyta, which includes all the liverworts, they have proposed three classes viz. (A) Haplomitriopsida, (B) Marchantiopsida, (C) Jungermanniopsida.

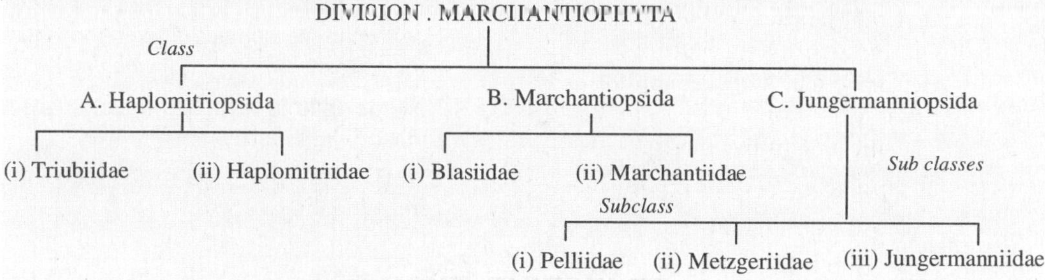

The class Haplomitriopsida has been divided in two sub classess; (i) Treubiidae, (ii) Haplomitriidae and similarly the class Marchantiopsida in, (i) Blasiiade, (ii) Marchantiidae whereas the class Jungermanniopsida has been divided in three subclasses; (i) Pelliidae, (ii) Matzgeriidae, (ii) Jungermanniidae.

Takakia, after the discovery of antheridia and sporophyte, has been shifted from Marchantiophyta (livevworts) to Bryophyta (mossess).

QUESTIONS

Essay Type

1. Describe giving examples the vegetative reproduction and perennation found in the Himalayan liverworts.
2. Give a brief account of classification of the class Hepaticae into orders and state the diagnostic characters of each order.
3. Describe the various methods of vegetative reproduction in Hepaticae.
(Lucknow, 1999, 1997, 1996)
4. Describe the characteristic features and classification of Liveworts.
(Kanpur, 1997; Bundelkhand, 1999; Himachal Pradesh, 1999)
5. Briefly describe the salient features and classification of Liverworts giving suitable examples.
(Awadh, 1996)

6. With the help of illustrations describe the structure and position of sex organs in Hepaticae studied by you. *(Allahabad, 2004)*

7. Discuss the origin of Hepaticae in the light of recent researches. *(Allahabad MSc., 2003)*

8. Give an illustrated and comparative account of vegetative thalli of Hepaticae studied by you. *(Lucknow 2005)*

SHORT ANSWER TYPE

9. List the distinctive features of class Hepaticopsida.

10. Why does the sporogonium remain small in the liverworts?

11. By means of labelled sketches only, depict the position and structure of sex organs in the genera of Hepaticae studied by you. *(Lucknow, 2000)*

12. Write short explanatory notes on :
    (*a*) Vegetative reproduction in Hepaticae.
    (*b*) Sexual reproduction in Hepaticae.
    (*c*) General characters of Hepaticae.
    (*d*) Distinguishing features of Hepaticopsida, Anthoceratopsida and Bryopsida. *(Awadh, 1997)*
    (*e*) Classification of liverworts. *(Rohilkhand M.Sc. 2000, 2002)*
    (*f*) Rhizoids in Hepaticae.
    (*g*) Branching of thallus in Hepaticopsida.
    (*h*) Structure and function of tuberculate rhizoids.
    (*i*) Types and functions of scales. *(Lucknow, 2005)*
    (*j*) Protective devices in the developing *sporophyte* of *Hepaticae*. *(Lucknow M.Sc., 2006)*

13. The plant body of some Bryophytes are Hepatic. Why ?

14. How do the sporophytes of liverworts take their nourishment ? *(Purvanchal, 1998)*

15. List the factors which induce rhizoid formation in Liverworts.

16. Briefly describe the chief means of perennation in liverworts.

OBJECTIVE TYPE

17. **Select the correct answer :**

    (*i*) The dominant plant in the Hepaticopsida is
    (*a*) Haploid (*b*) Diploid
    (*c*) Triploid (*d*) Tetraploid.

    (*ii*) Liverworts are usually
    (*a*) Green and thalloid
    (*b*) Colourless and thalloid
    (*b*) Red and thalloid
    (*d*) Blue and thalloid.

    (*iii*) Which one of the following factors induces rhizoid formation in liverworts?
    (*a*) Presence of photosynthetic pigments
    (*b*) Presence of carbohydrates.
    (*c*) Contact with the soil or decaying vegetation.
    (*d*) All of the above.

    (*iv*) The most common method of vegetative reproduction in liverworts is
    (*a*) Tuber formation
    (*b*) Gemma formation
    (*c*) Fragmentation
    (*d*) None of the above.

    (*v*) Sporophyte in liverworts is
    (*a*) Fully independent
    (*b*) Partially independent
    (*c*) Partially dependent on the gametophyte
    (*d*) Fully dependent on the gametophyte.

    (*vi*) The meiosis takes place
    (*a*) At the time of germination of zygote

(*b*) At the time of formation of spores
(*c*) During the development of sporophyte
(*d*) During the differentiation of foot, seta and capsule.

(*vii*) Chief means of perennation in liverworts are
(*a*) Persistent apices
(*b*) Tubers
(*c*) Spores
(*d*) Gemmae.

(*viii*) In Liverworts the capsule is formed of tissues which are
(*a*) Haploid (*b*) Diploid
(*c*) Triploid (*d*) Tetraploid.

(*ix*) In liverworts, the gametophytic generation starts with
(*a*) Zygospore
(*b*) Sporogonium
(*c*) Spore
(*d*) Rhizoids.

(*x*) The capsule in liverworts is devoid of
(*a*) Columella (*b*) Elaters
(*c*) Capsule wall (*d*) Spores.

(*xi*) The sporogonium in liverworts lacks
(*a*) Foot (*b*) Seta
(*c*) Capsule (*d*) Stomata.

(*xii*) S.R. Kashyap was famous Indian
(*a*) Bryologist (*b*) Pteridologist
(*c*) Mycologist (*d*) Phycologist

(*xiii*) In which of the following the sporophyte is attached with the gametophytes ?
(*a*) Algae
(*b*) Fungi
(*c*) Bryophytes
(*d*) Pteridophytes.

Image of *Marchantia polymorpha*

CHAPTER 3

HEPATICOPSIDA (Hepaticae) Marchantiales

- Distribution
- Gametophyte
- Origin of Marchantiaceous Thallus
- Sexual Reproduction
- Classification of Marchantiales

DISTRIBUTION

It is a well-defined, widely distributed group comprising more than 420 species placed under 35 genera. Among the latter, the well known Indian members are *Marchantia, Preissia, Dumortiera, Conocephalum, Exormotheca, Stephensoniella, Aitchisoniella, Cyathodium, Targionia, Cryptomitrium, Asterella* (*Fimbraria*) *Grimaldia, Reboulia, Plagiochasma, Athalamia and Riccia*. Nearly all of them are terrestrial. Generally, they inhabit moist situations and are strictly hygrophilous growing on damp soil or rocks. Few occur actually in floating water or submerged. Some with larger thalli are capable of growing in exposed situations that are relatively dry at certain seasons of the year although they are moist at others. In their distribution the representatives of this order range from the arctic to the tropical regions with a fair representation in the temperate zones. In India Kashyap made a fair collection of liverworts in the Himalayas west of Nepal and the Punjab plain. Eastern Himalayas, Gangetic plain and Southern India have also a fair representation.

GAMETOPHYTE

(a) External Characters (Fig. 3.1)

Generally, all the members agree very closely in their fundamental structure. The gametophyte plant is strictly thallose. The thallus is green, flat, thick and fleshy. It is dichotomously branched, dorsiventral, often with conspicuously prominent lobes. Generally, each lobe has an apical notch

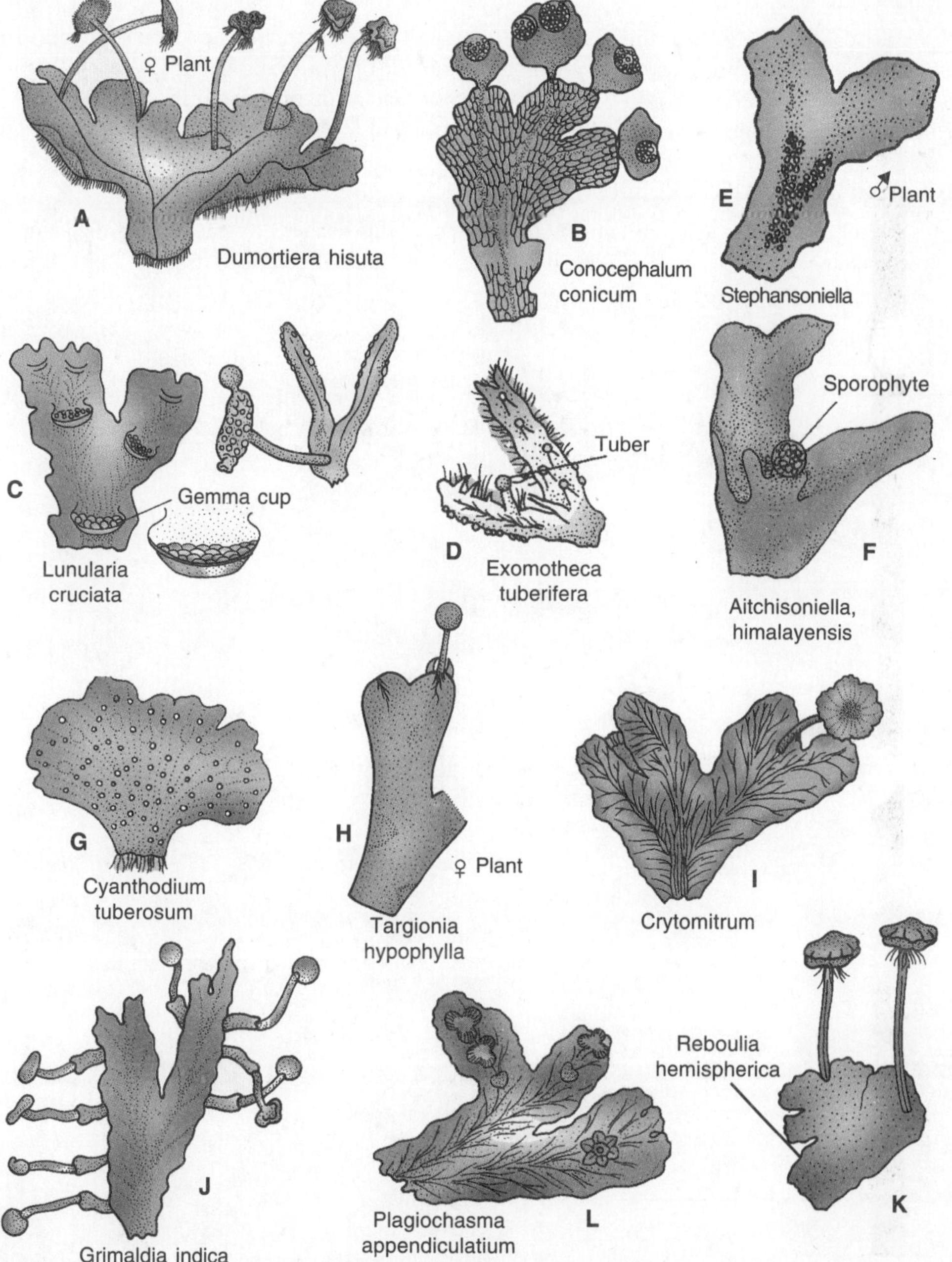

Fig. 3.1. (A—L). **Marchantiales**. Some of the important representatives of the order. (H, after Smith and the rest after Kashyap).

in which lies the growing point. The dorsal surface of the thallus in many forms is marked by polygonal areas called the **areolae**. Each such area has an air pore in the centre. The air pores are simple in some forms and compound in others. They lead into the air chambers within, the limits of which are marked by the areolae on dorsal surface of the thallus in some forms. From the lower surface of the thallus of all the members arise two kinds of appendages, namely, the **rhizoids** and the **scales**. The rhizoids are unicellular, unbranched, delicate, hair-like structures. They are of two kinds **smooth** or **plain-walled** and **tuberculate**. The latter have peg-like thickenings that project into the lumen.

The scales are purplish, thin, plate-like multicellular structures one cell in thickness. They may be arranged in one row as in the young thallus of *Riccia*, in two rows one on each side of the midrib (*Targionia, Reboulia*) or in two to four rows on each side of the midrib (*Marchantia*). They are irregularly distributed over the entire ventral surface in *Corsinia, Athalamia* and a few others.

(B) INTERNAL STRUCTURE OF THALLUS (Fig. 3.2).

Though the general plan of construction of the thallus in the Marchantiales is the same yet it presents a wide range of variation in details. It is differentiated into various tissues. These tissues are arranged in two distinct regions, dorsal and ventral.

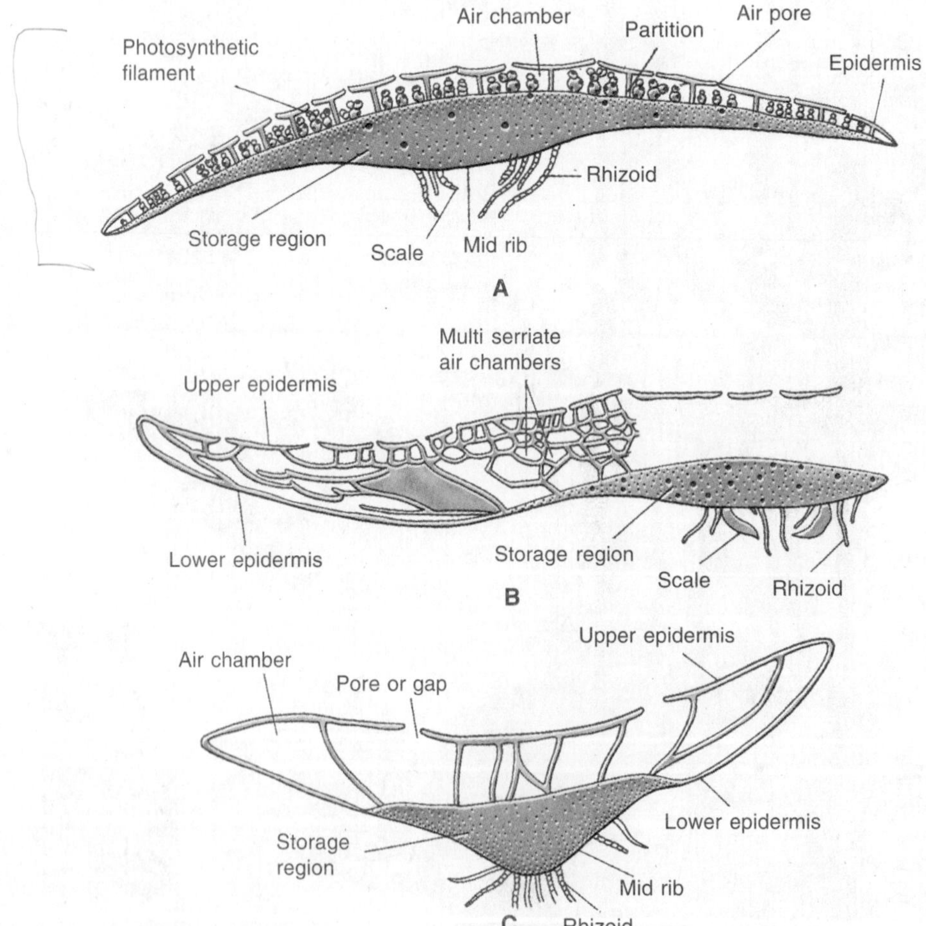

Fig. 3.2. (A—C). Marchantiales. Tranvserse sections of thalli. Thick dots represent oil cells. A, *Marchantia nepalensis* (outline sketch); B, *Plagiochasma appendiculatun* (outline sketch of a portion of the thallus showing the disposition of chambers); C, *Stephensoniella brevipedunculata* (outline sketch). (After Mehra)

The deep, green dorsal assimilatory region encloses air chambers. The chambers are roofed by a single layered epidermis. In the family Ricciaceae the chambers are reduced and are in the form of deep canals or channels. The chambered condition is represented in a relic condition in *Dumortiera* and is absent in *Monoselenium*. In species in which the chambers are present they may be in one or more than one layer. Each chamber is separated from its neighbours by partitions which are generally one cell thick. It may be empty or contains assimilatory filaments. When multi-layered the chambers are invariably empty. Each chamber opens to the outside by a pore. These pores vary widely in structure in different genera. In *Stephensoniella* the pores are simple and wide. They are large and barrel-shaped in *Marchantia* and *Preissia*. In *Targionia* they are semi-barrel-shaped.

The ventral zone of the thallus functions as the storage region. It lies below the air chambers and consists of colourless parenchyama. The parenchyma cells are compactly arranged. They lack chloroplasts but contain starch. Here and there are present the **oil cells**. The lowermost layer of this region bears two kinds of rhizoids and scales.

On the basis of anatomy Mehra divided the thalli of the Marchantiales into the following three categories :

1. *Marchantia type* (Fig. 3.2A). The midrib region is expanded. The ventral storage zone is several cell layers thick. It gradually thins on either side towards the margins where it is 3 or 4 layers thick. The parenchyma cells constituting it are colourless. They contain starch grains. There are oil cells here and there. The lowermost layer bears two kinds of rhizoids and scales. The upper assimilatory zone contains air chambers arranged in a single layer. The chambers are separated from each other by single layered partitions. From the floor of the chambers arise chlorophyllose filaments. Each chamber communicates with the outside either by a barrel-shaped pore (*Marchantia*) or by a semi-barrel-shaped pore (*Targionia*). To this category belong the species of *Marchantia* and *Targionia hypophylla*.

2. *Plagiochasma type* (Fig. 3.2 B). The midrib is not much fiattened. Consequently, the storage region is thickest in the centre. In the wings it consists of a single layer of cells which respresents the lower epidermis. The assimilatory zone consists of air chambers arranged in several layers one above the other. The chambers are empty and are separated by single layered partitions. The air pores are either star-shaped or semi-barrel-shaped. Examples are *Plagiochasma appendiculatum. P. articulatum, Reboulia hemispherica, Asterella mussouriensis, Grimaldia indica* and *Athalamia pinguis*.

3. *Stephensoniella type* (3.2 C). The midrib is least expanded and the ventral storage region consists of colourless cells which contain starch or protein granules. The wing on either side consists of the lower epidermis and a layer of air chambers above it. The chambers are spacious and mepty. They communicate with the exterior through large gaps or pores of extremely primitive type. To this type belong *Stephenosoniella brevipedunculate, Sauchia spongiosa, Asterella blumeana, A. reticulata, Riccia crystallina* and *Cryptomitrium himalayensis*.

ORIGIN OF MARCHANTIACEOUS THALLUS

Two widely divergent views have been put forth to explain the origin of the Marchantiaceous thallus. Some bryologists consider that simple gametophyte of the Marchantiales is the result of **retrogressive evolution**. Other hold that it is the result of **Progreesive evolution** or **elaboration**.

1. Mechanism of retrogressive evolution. The supporter of this hypothesis are divided into two camps. Majority of them, particularly the older bryologists, hold that retrogressive evolution has been brought about by progreesive simplification also called **reduction**. The view put forth by Mehra and Vasisht (1950) is that it has been brought about by **condensation**.

(*a*) *Reduction theory.* The reduction theory to explain retrogressive evolution (regression) was first proposed by Von Wettstein in 1908. He held that the primitive gametophyte of the Hepaticae was nearest the erect, leafy Acrogynous Jungermanniaceous forms. His theory with slight modifications received support from many eminent bryologist. The chief among them were Church (1919) and Evans (1939). Von Wettstein placed the Acrogynous Jungermanniales of the *Calobryum* type first. It is an erect, leafy gametophyte radial in symmetry and with leaves in three rows. The first step towards reduction was the adoption of the prostrate habit. With the appearance of dorsiventrality the leaves on the ventral side gradually diminished in size and finally disappeared in some cases. The changes in habit and diminishing size of the ventral leaves were accompanied by the flattening of the central axis. Associated with these changes was the gradual and complete elimination of the lateral leaves. These changes resulted in the formation of a leafless, flat, dorsiventral Anacrogynous Jungermanniaceous gametophyte of *Pellia* type. The latter by gradual progressive internal differentiation of tissues finally led to the formation of externally simple but internally highly differentiated thallus of the Marchantiales. The scales on the ventral surface of the thallus of the Marchantiales are considered as modifications of the leaves of the ventral row of the prostrate, foliose ancestor. Goebel (1930) and Kashyap (1919) were the other champions of retrogressive evolution by reduction in the Liverworts.

Kashyap, however, postulated the theory of the *Pteridophytean origin* of the Marchantiales by reduction. He was greatly struck by the resemblance in external form and structure between the radial prothallus of *Equisetum debile* and *Lycopodium cernuum* with the liverwort thallus in general and Marchantiaceous thallus in particular. The upright, chlorophyllose branched lobes of the dorsal photosynthetic region of these genera of the Equisetales and Lycopodiales respectively agree with the upright chlorophyllose filaments and walls of the air chambers in the Marchantiales. This resemblance tempted Kashyap to guess that the Marchantiales probably arose by reduction from these pteridophytean ancestors. Mehra has developed the following arguments against this hypothesis :

(*i*) It is difficult to reconcile the highly differentiated sporophyte of *Equisetum* or *Lycopodium* with the simple liverwort sporophyte.

(*ii*) Absence in the entire class of liverworts including the Marchantiales of any relic of the lost vascular system.

(*iii*) Absence of any strucutre on the undersurface of the prothallus of these Pteridophytes which could be interpreted as having been reduced to scales so characteristic of the thallus of the Marchantiales.

(*iv*) It is difficult to explain the origin of the upright, specialised, sexual branches of *Marchantia* from the ancestral prothalli particularly when Kashyap considers forms-like *Marchantia* to be primitive or ancestral in the Marchantiales.

(*b*) *Condensation theory.* Mehra and Vasisht (1950) suggested the derivation of the thalloid structure in the liverworts form the foliose forms by **condensation**. Later in 1957 Mehra adduced evidence in support of a real phylogenetic connection between the Jugermanniales and the Marchantiales. He propounded a theory explaining the origin of the Marchantiaceous thallus from the foliose Jungermanniales by "compaction, condensation and fusion of leaves". The outlines of this theory are :-

1. The overlapping of the lateral leaves succubously or incubously in the foliose ancestor.

2. Fusion of the lower portions of these leaves at the points of contact resulting in the formation of single layered wings on either side of the central axis and lamellae on the upper surface of each wing.

3. The one-cell thick lamellae were directed obliquely outward and as a whole formed open chambers of linear type.

4. The next step was the roofing of the air chambers by inward growth of the margins of the cavities of the chambers.

5. The roofed chambers, at first, communicated with the outside by large gaps. The gaps were later replaced by definite pores—a protection against loss of water by transpiration.

6. All these changes were accompanied by gradual flattening of the central axis till it reached the margin of the wings.

7. Formation of secondary partitions occurred across the chambers as the flattening of the thallus occurred.

8. In some genera adapted to Xerophytic conditions like *Plagiochasma* horizontal partitions were also formed between the lamellae forming multi-layered chambers.

9. Subsequent changes were the development of the assimilatory filaments from the floors of the chambers in members like *Marchantia* and the formation of barrel-shaped pores characteristic of some of the Marchantiales.

Progressive evolution. The adherents of this hypothesis hold that the Hepaticopsida originated from a simple, thallose gametophyte. The ancestral thallus was simple, prostrate and showed no external or internal differentiation. The theory of progression was originally suggested by Schiffner. The chief supporters are Cavers, Campbell, Fritsch, Bower, Smith etc. Cavers suggested *Sphaerocarpus* and Campbell thought forms like *Metzgeria* as the present-day Hepaticae which show a nearest approach to the primitive hepaticean gametophyte. From these primitive types progressive evolutionary sequence followed two diametrical opposed directions. This resulted in the evolution of the following two types of gametophytes :

(*a*) *Marchantiaceous gametophyte*. It is suggested to have evolved from the primitive thallose gametophyte by the following changes :

(*i*) Retention of external, simple, prostrate, thallus-like form.

(*ii*) Gradual but progressive internal differentiation of tissues. It finaly resulted in the formation of a thallus internally composed of a definite epidermis, pores leading into the air chambers containing chlorophyllose filaments and a parenchymatous, compact storage tissue.

(*iii*) Aggregation of sex organs into localized areas called the **receptacles**.

(*b*)*Jungermanniaceous gametophyte*. It involved the following changes :

(*i*) Retention of simple internal structure.

(*ii*) Gradual but progressive elaboration of the external form resulting in the formation of a leafy, prostrate thallus characteristic of the Jugermanniales.

ASEXUAL REPRODUCTION

In the Marchantiales it takes place by the vegetative methods of (*i*) **fragmentation** (*Riccia, Marchantia* and others), (*ii*) **production of adventitious branches** often from the underside of the midrib and separation of these to form new thalli (*Targionia* and *Riccia fluitans*), (*iii*) **gemmae formation** (*Marchantia and Lunularia*), and (*iv*) **tuber formation** (*Riccia bilardieri, R. discolor, R. vesicata, Exormothica tuberifera* and *Cyathodium tuberosum*).

SEXUAL REPRODUCTION

The appearance of sex organs is a significant event in the life of the gametophyte. The sex organs are of two kinds, the male (**antheridia**) and the female (**archegonia**). The two kinds of sex organs may be borne on the same thallus. Such species are called **homothallic** or **monoecious**. There are other species in which the two kinds of sex organs are produced on different thalli so that the male and female plants of these species are distinct. Such species are called **heterothallic** or **dioecious** (*Marchantia, Preissia quadrata*).

Sex organs. The sex organs in the Marchantiales are invariably dorsal in origin and develop in acroptetal order from the segments of the apical cell. In the simplest forms they occur singly and scattered, each in a separate cavity on the dorsal side of the thallus (*Riccia*, Fig. 4.7 A). Sometimes they tend to be aggregate into groups. There is a tendency in some of the members of the order to produce their sex organs regularly in median groups directly on the dorsal side of the thallus itself. Commonly, however, the sex organs are restricted to special circumscribed or localized usually cushion-like areas on the thallus. These are the **receptacles**. The receptacles may be sessile but in the advanced members of the order they are stalked *Marchantia* (Fig. 5.9). In some species the male receptacle may be sessile and the female stalked (*Asterella blumeana*, Fig. 2.1). The stalked receptacles are called the **gametophores**. The antheridia bearing stalked receptacle is called **antheridiophore** and the archegonia bearing is called **archegoniophore**. In fact, a well-defined evolutionary series of forms can be arranged from species which have the sex organs merely grouped on thallus to those with stalked receptacles.

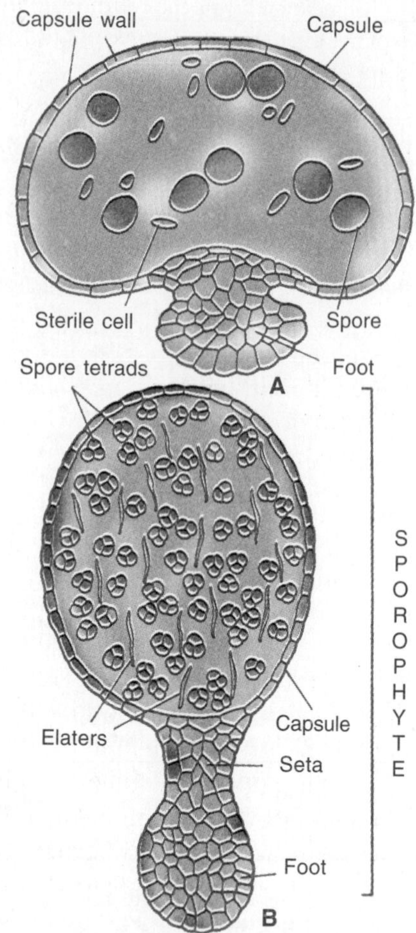

Fig. 3.3. (A—B). **Marchantiales**. A, L.S. of mature sporogonium of *Corsinia coriandrina;* B, L.S. of nearly mature sporophyte of *Targionia hypophylla* (A, after Meyer; B, after Smith).

Sporogonium (Sporophyte, Fig. 3.3). Following fertilisation the zygote by segmentation and differentiation develop into the second individual in the life cycle called the **sporogonium**. It represents the **sporophytic** or **diplophase**. It is very simple in structure and radial in symmetry. It bears no appendages. All its life it remains organically attached to the parent gametophyte (thallus), and is nourished by it. The sporogonium is concerned with the production of and dispersal of haploid spores (meiospores). Thus it receives the special name **sporophyte**. The sporogonium in all the Marchantiales (in fact Liverworts) remains covered and thus protected by the enlarged venter known as the **calyptra** until the spores within it are ripe. All the cells of sporogenous tissue may produce **spores** or a part of them produce **sterile cells** or **elaters**. Among the lower Marchantiales, the simplest type of sporogonium is found in *Riccia* (Ricciaceae). It is simply a spore fruit representing the capsule region only. Both the foot and the seta are absent. The sporogonium thus never projects above the surface of the thallus and remains covered by the calyptra. It consists of a peripheral layer of cells constituting the **capsule wall** and a central mass of spore mother cells practically all of which produce spores. Even the capsule wall disappears before the spores mature (Fig. 4.16).

The next stage in the evolution of the sporophyte in the Marchantiales is illustrated by forms like *Corsinia*. The sporogonium in *Corsinia* is differentiated into a basal portion, the **foot** which is an absorbing organ and the **capsule region** concerned with spore production (Fig. 3.3A). There is no seta. The capsule has a jacket layer one cell in thickness. The cell walls of the jacket layer do not develop secondary thickening. The sporogenous tissue within the capsule wall becomes differentiated into two types of cells, the **spore mother cells** and **sterile cells**. The spore mother cells differentiate into spore tetrads. The sterile cells persist until the spores are mature (Fig. 3.3 A).

The sporogonium in the higher Marchantiales (*Targionia, Marchantia*) has, in addition, a slender stalk-like structure the seta in between the foot and the capsule. The seta remains short until the spors are mature. With the ripening of spores within the capsule, the seta elongates due to the rapid enlargement in the vertical direction of its pre-existing cells. Consequently the capsule is forced through the calyptra and placed in a position favourable for the dispersal of spores by wind. The jacket layer of the capsule wall is one cell in thickness. The jacket cells in the most advanced members of the order may develop ring-like thickenings on their walls (*Marchantia*). Some of the sporogenous cells in these forms remain sterile and are distinguished by their elongated shape from the spore mother cells. These sterile cells develop into **elaters**. The spore mother cells by a process known as sporogenesis form the spores.

DISTINCTIVE FEATURE OF MARCHANTIALES

1. The plant body, which is a gametophyte, is a green, thick flat, dichotomously branched, dorsiventral thallus with a more or less marked midrib.

2. Internally it is differentiated into two distinct portions, the **dorsal** and the **ventral** regions.

3. The dorsal, green region generally encloses air spaces also called the **air chambers**.

4. The air chambers communicate with the exterior generally through **pores**.

5. The ventral region is composed of compact, colourless, parenchymatous **storage** tissue.

6. Scales are usually present on the ventral surface of the thallus.

7. The thallus is secured to the substratum generally by means of two kinds of unbranched, unicellular rhizoids, **smooth walled** and **tuberculate**.

8. The sex organs in a few species are scattered on the dorsal surface of the thallus (*Riccia*) but more usually assembled in **receptacles**, which may be sessile or stalked called gametophores.

9. The receptacles are generally elevated on slender stalks but are sometimes sessile.

10. The sporogonium is simple in structure and small, either with or without seta. It has a capsule wall one cell in thickness. In some genera like *Targionia* and *Cyathodium*, the capsule has a lid or operculum at its apex. Columella is absent.

CLASSIFICATION OF MARCHANTIALES

The order includes about 420 species. They are placed under above 35 genera. Campbell (1918) recognized only three families, namely, Ricciaceae, Corsiniaceae and Marchantiaceae in this order. He included the genus *Moroclea* and *Targionia* in the family Marchantiaceae. He, as early as 1898, was the first hepaticologist to point out *Monoclea's* relationship with the Marchantiales. This viewpoint was later challenged by Schiffner (1913). Verdorn, Evans and some others supported him.

Verdorn (1932) and Evans (1939) each recognised six families in the order Marchantiales. The former made out Marchantiaceae, Operculatae, Astroporae, Targionaceae, Corsiniaceae and Ricciaceae. Evans recognized Marchantiaceae, Sauteriaceae, Rebouliaceae, Targionaceae, Corsiniaceae and Ricciaceae. Both of them excluded *Monoclea* from this order and placed it in the suborder Anacrogynous Jungermanniales.

Later Campbell (1940) revised the classification of Marchantiales basing it on the following features :-

1. Nature of the receptacle.
2. Manner in which it is borne.
3. Structure of the sporophyte.

On the basis of the above-mentioned features he divided the order into the following five families :

1. Ricciaceae.
2. Corsiniaceae.
3. Targionaceae.
4. Monocleaceae.
5. Marchantiaceae.

It is evident that the families Ricciaceae, Corsiniaceae and Targionaceae are common in Verdoorn, Evans and Campbell's systems of classification. The families Marchantiaceae, Operculatae and Astroporae of Verdoorn and Marchantiaceae, Sauteriaceae and Rebouliaceae of Evans are equivalent to family Marchantiaceae of Campbell.

As stated above, Verdoorn and Evans excluded Monocleaceae from Marchantiales and placed it in the suborder Anacrogynous Jugermanniales whereas Campbell included it in the Marchantiales. To clear this tangel Proskauer (1951) made a critical study of the taxonomic position of *Monoclea* and suggested that the inclusion of the Monocleaceae in the Jungermanniales is unwarranted. According to him, *Monoclea* shows affinities with the Dumortieroid line of the Marchantiales.

Professor Kashyap reduced the number of families in the Marchantiales to three. In his extensive collections of the Himalayan liverworts he found many intermediate forms which connect the families Targionaceae and Corsiniaceae with the Marchantiaceae. Consequently he recognised only the following families in this order :

1. Ricciaceae.
2. Monocleaceae.
3. Marchantiaceae.

Carr (1956) added another family Monocarpaceae (=Carpaceae) to the list. This family includes a single thallose hepatic *Monocarpus sphaerocarpus*. It was discovered by Carr in 1956 and renamed as *Carrpos sphaerocarpos* (Carr) Prosk by Proskauer in 1961. This hepatic has an odd combination of characters. Like the genus *Sphaerocarpos* it has small simple thallus and relatively a large involucre. The presence of reduced photosynthetic air chambers opening by wide air pores on the dorsal surface; shortly stalked female receptacle with roofed air chambers opening by barrel-shaped pores, each consisting of two tiers of cells, sporogonium with a short seta, bulbous foot and lack of functional elaters suggest a close relationship with the Marchantiales. These features led Carr to assign *Monocarpus* (=Carrpos) to a new family Monocarpaceae (=Carrpaceae) within the order Marchantiales. Proskauer (1961) and Schuster (1963) endorsed his viewpoint.

The consensus of opinion, at present, is in favour of dividing Marchantiales into six families, namely, Ricciaceae, Corsiniaceae, Targionaceae, Monocleaceae, Monocarpaceae (=Carrpaceae) and Marchantiaceae. Schuster (1966), however, makes eleven.

However, Udar (1976) has recognised five families viz (*i*) Marchantiaceae (*ii*) Rebouliaceae (*iii*) Sauteriaceae (*iv*) Targioniaceae and (*v*) Ricciaceae to accomodate the genera ascribed to this order. The families Ricciaceae, Targioniaceae, Rebouliaceae and Marchantiaceae have been discussed in detail.

QUESTIONS

ESSAY TYPE

1. Describe the external features and anatomy of the gametophyte of the Marchantiales.
2. Discuss the structure and origin of Marchantiaceous thallus.
3. Give an account of the anatomy and reproduction in Marchantiales.
4. Describe the various types of thalli of Marchantiales. Add a note on the origin of the thallus in Marchantiales.

5. Describe the sex organs and sporogonia of the Marchantiales.

6. Describe the salient features of the order Marchantiales. Mention the names of families with examples.

7. Give an account of classification of Marchantiales.

8. Write a general account of thallus structure of Marchantiales. What do you know about the genera of Marchantiales endemic to India ?

(Allahabad M.Sc., 1999)

9. Give an account of Thallus structure in Marchantiales *(Lucknow M.Sc., 1999)*

SHORT ANSWER TYPE

10. Name the smallest liverwort.

11. Enumerate the distinctive features of the order Marchantiales.

12. Give a brief account of the classification of the order Marchantiales.

13. Comment on

(*i*) Origin and structure of thallus in Marchantiales.

(Rohilkhand, M.Sc., 1991)

(*ii*) General characters of Marchantiales

(*iii*) Alternation of Generation in Marchantiales.

(*iv*) Important features of Marchantiales.

(Kumaon, 1998)

(*v*) Asexual reproduction in Marchantiales.

(*vi*) Types of thallii in Marchantiales.

(*vii*) Spore dispersal in Marchantiales.

(Rohilkhand M.Sc., 2003)

OBJECTIVE TYPE

14. Select the correct answer :

(*i*) The presence of smooth walled and tuberculate rhizoids is the characteristic features of

(*a*) Anthocerotales (*b*) Sphagnales

(*c*) Bryales (*d*) Marchantiales.

(*ii*) The thallus of the genera of Marchantiales generally have

(*a*) Mucilage cavities

(*b*) Blue green algae

(*c*) Air pores

(*d*) Undifferentiated compact cellular structure.

(*iii*) Reduction division in Marchantiales takes place during the

(*a*) Germination of zygote

(*b*) Formation of capsule

(*c*) Formation of spore from spore mother cell

(*d*) Germination of spore.

(*iv*) Which of the following is haploid?

(*a*) Spore (*b*) Foot

(*c*) Seta (*d*) Capsule.

(*v*) Elaters are present in the capsules of

(*a*) Marchantiales (*b*) Bryales

(*c*) Sphagnales (*d*) Anthocerotales.

(*vi*) *Targionia* belongs to

(*a*) Ricciaceae

(*b*) Marchantiaceae

(*c*) Monocleaceae

(*d*) Targioniaceae

(*vii*) The dorsal green region generally enclosing air spaces are called

(*a*) Mucilage cavities

(*b*) Air chambers

(*c*) Algal cells

(*d*) Nothing.

(*viii*) Which of the following is present in the capsules of the Marchantiales?

(*a*) Spores

(*b*) Seta

(*c*) Columella

(*d*) Multicellular capsule wall.

(*ix*) Scales on the ventral surface of the thallus are usually present in the order

(*a*) Marchantiales

(*b*) Anthocerotales

(*c*) Sphagnales

(*d*) Bryales.

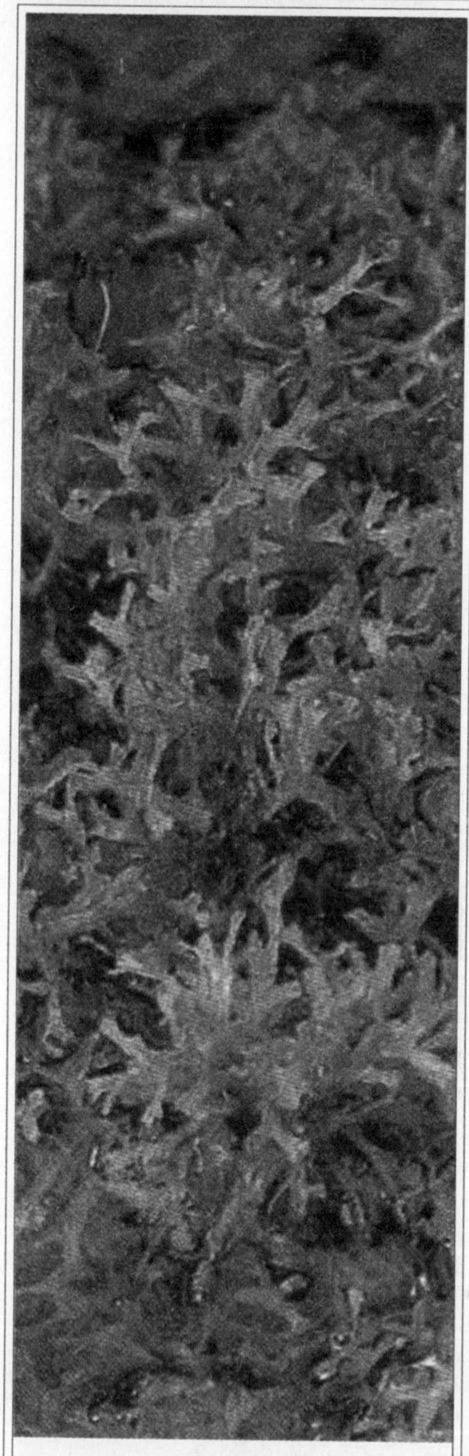

Image of Riccia Fluitans

CHAPTER 4

MARCHANTIALES
Ricciaceae
Riccia

- Ricciaceae
- Riccia (Mich.) L.
- Reproduction
- Sporophytic Phase
- Summary of the Life Cyucle of Riccia
- Discussion

RICCIACEAE

GENERAL CHARACTERS

The family Ricciaceae includes the simplest members of the order Marchantiales. They are characterised by—

1. The gametophyte is a flat, ribbon-shaped, somewhat fleshy, green thallus.

2. The upper or dorsal photosynthetic region of the thallus consists of close-set columns of green cells usually with fine air channels between them.

3. The air channels or canals lack special assimilatory filaments and thus are empty.

4. Each column of green cells commonly terminates in a colourless, pear-shaped cell. These hyaline cells together constitute the upper superficial layer, the so-called upper epidermis.

5. The thallus of *Riccia* thus lacks chambers containing assimilatory filaments and definite pores. The pores are either absent or when present they are rudimentary or unspecialised structures.

6. The **sex organs** occur scattered in or near the **median line** on the upper surface of the thallus in longitudinal rows.

7. They occur singly in open cavities embedded on the dorsal surface of the thallus.

8. The sporophyte or sporogonium is the simplest among the liverworts. It lacks both the **foot** and **seta** and thus consists of a spherical **capsule** immersed in the thallus tissue.

9. The capsule remains permanently locked in the calyptra.

10. The spores are set free by the decay of the surrounding sterile tissue.

11. Practically all the cells of the archesporium are devoted to spore formation.

12. The sterile cells or elaters are wanting.

The family includes about 140 species. They are placed under three genera. These are *Tesselina* (*Oxymitra*), *Ricciocarpus* and *Riccia*. The first two are represented by a single species each. All the rest are included in the genus *Riccia*. Practically all the Ricciaceae grow on the damp soil. The only exceptions are *Riccia fluitans* (Fig. 4.4 A) and *Ricciocarpus natans* (*Riccia natans*). They are aquatic. *Riccocarpus natans* has been reported from Kashmir Dal lake and Peshawar (Pakistan). *Riccia fluitans* occurs in Garhwal, Kashmir, Peshawar, Madras and Kapurthala (Punjab). The structure and life history of the type genus *Riccia* is considered here. The genus is named after an Italian botanist F.F. Ricci.

RICCIA (Mich.) L.

Distribution and Habitat

It is is the most widely distributed genus of the family Ricciaceae. It comprises about 138 species. They are found practically over all parts of the earth. About 29 species have been recorded from different parts of India both from the hills and plains (Srivastava, 1964). Later Udar added one more (*R. reticulata*) to the list raising the number to 30.Most important among these are *R. discolor* (Fig. 4.1 E), *R. pathankotensis* (Fig. 4.1 C), *R. frostii* (Fig. 4.7 A), *R. melanospora* (Fig. 4.1 D), *R. fluitans* (Fig. 4.4 A), *R. crystallina* and *R. gangetica* (Fig. 4.1 B). With the exception of *R.fluitans* which is aquatic all others are terrestrial. The terrestrial species generally grow for short seasons on clayey damp soil forming rosettes. *R. fluitans* occurs floating or partly submerged in still water in pools, ponds or lakes. It continues to live and grow but fruits only (Fig. 4.1 B) when it comes in contact with the mud at the bottom.

Gametophyte Phase

It has its origin in the life cycle with the maturation of spores. Each germinates to give rise to the gametophyte plant which is thallose in form.

Adult gametophyte (Fig. 4.1) (*a*) *External features* (A). The plant body is a thallus. It is small, green flat and rather fleshy. It grows prostrate on the ground and branches freely by dichotomy. Consequently it generally takes up a rosette form (Fig. 4.8 A). The branches of the thallus are called the **thallus lobes**. According to the species the thallus lobes are linear to wedgeshaped or obcordate. Each lobe is thickest in the middle and gradually thins towards the margins. The thick middle portion constitutes the **midrib** region. On the upper surface of each lobe there is generally a median **groove** or **furrow** usually called the **dorsal groove**. It is prominent and extends throughout the length of thallus in *R. gangetica* (B). The dorsal groove is in the form of a broad median channel in *R. pathankotensis*. It is narrow and deep at the anterior, becoming broad and shallow in the middle and disappearing in the posterior part (C). In *R. discolor* it is a narrow, median sulcus present only anteriorly in the male plants (E) and throughout the length of the thallus in the female plants.

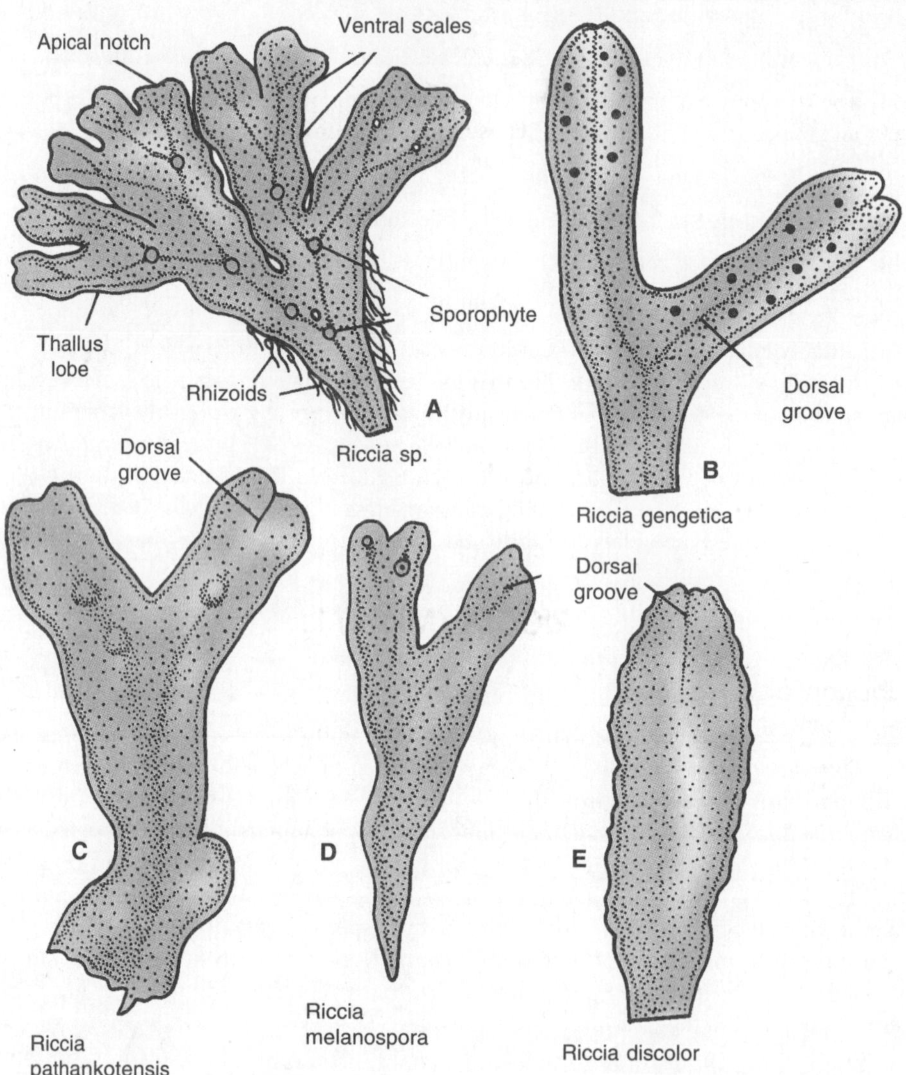

Fig. 4.1. (A–E). *Riccia* sp. A, *Riccia* thallus showing external features; (B—E), different species of *Riccia* showing the nature and extent of the dorsal groove. (C—E after Kashyap and B after Srivastava).

R. melanospora has a dorsal groove in the form of a deep, narrow sulcus near the apex (D). In *R. frostii* the upper surface is flat or slightly convex. The dorsal groove is absent. Each thallus lobe usually ends in a terminal notch in which lies the growing point. The terminal notch is absent in *R. frostii*.

The thallus is attached to the substratum by slender, simple unicellular processes called the **rhizoids** (A). The latter arise from the lower surface of the thallus. They are of two kinds, **smooth-walled** (Fig. 4.2 C) and **tuberculate**. The tuberculate rhizoids (Fig. 4.2 D) are narrower and lack protoplasm at maturity. They have peg-like outgrowths projecting inwards into the lumen from the wall. The rhizoids in form and function somewhat resemble the root hairs. The two, however, are analogous to each other and not homologous. They function as organs of attachment and also absorb water and soil solutes. The tuberculate rhizoids in *R. frostii* are either absent or they possess very faint tubercles. In the submerged species of *Riccia* the rhizoids are generally abhsent. Arising from the lower surface of the thallus, in addition to the rhizoids are the violet, *membranous* **scales** (Fig. 4.2 B). They are multicellular and one cell in thickness. The scales are not appendaged and are usually arranged in one transverse median row near the apex. They are situated closely and project forward to protect the growing point. In the older portion of the thallus lobes the scales split in the median line. Consequently they become arranged in two lateral rows, one near each margin of the thallus lobe. The scales are rudimentary in *R. crystalline* and *R. frostii*.

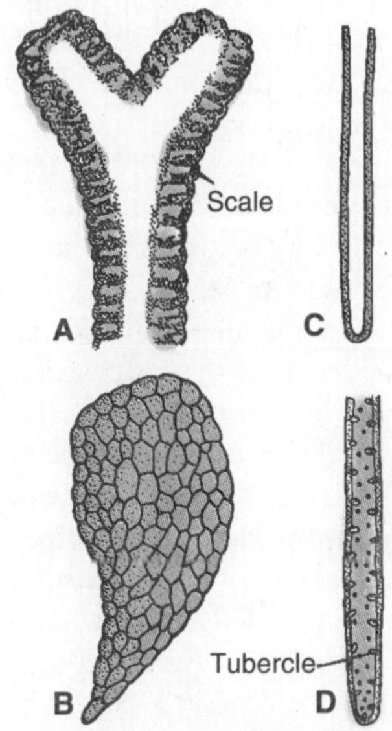

Fig. 4.2. (A—D). ***Riccia* sp**. A, part of the thallus seen from the lower surface showing ventral marginal scales; B, single scale; C, smooth walled rhizoid; D, tuberculate rhizoid (A and B after Srivastava).

(*b*)*Internal structure* (Fig. 4.3). The externally simple thallus of *Riccia* shows a more elaborate internal structure. It is many cells deep. A vertical section through the thallus reveals that these cells are arranged in the following two distinct regions (A) :-

(*i*) An upper or dorsal **assimilatory** or **photosynthetic region**.

(*ii*) A lower or ventral **storage region**.

(*i*) *Photosynthetic region*. The photoshynthetic region consists of loose, green tissue. It is composed of parenchymatous cells rich in chloroplasts (Fig. 4.3). These green or chlorenchymatous cells are arranged in vertical rows or columns and function as **pseudomesophyll**. Between the columns of green cells are very narrow, deep, vertical slits. These slits are called the **air canals** or **air channels**. They are wide and larger in the form of air chambers in *R. craciata* and *R. crystallina*. In *R. discolor* and *R. frostii* they are narrow, slit-like. The air canals or chambers in *Riccia* lack **assimilatory filaments** characteristic of *Marchantia*. The walls separating the air canals or channels consist of four vertical rows of green cells in some species (*R. glauca*). (Fig. 4.3 B). In others they are bounded by six to eight vertical rows of cells (*R. vesiculosa*). The uppermost cell of each row is somewhat distended, pear-shaped and hyaline. Together these colourless, terminal cells of the neighbouring rows from an ill defined, discontinuous layer, the functional

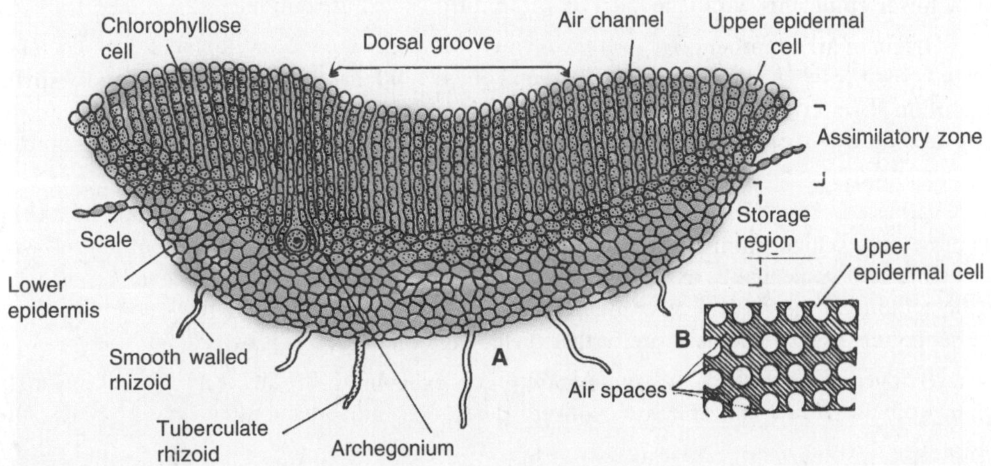

Fig. 4.3. (A—B). ***Riccia* sp**. A, transverse vertical section of the thallus lobe; B, air spaces bounded by epidermal cells as seen in surface view.

equivalent of the upper epidermis. It may be termed the upper pseudoepidermis. It is one cell in thickness and encloses the pseudomesophyll. The air canals or channels communicate with the exterior through gaps in the upper pseudoepidermis. These gaps are called the **air pores**. The air pores in *Riccia* are thus very unspecialized and rudimentary structures. They are simple, intercellular spaces bounded by 4 (Fig. 4.3 B) to 8 pseudoepidermal cells. No true or well-defined air pores characteristic of *Marchantia* are developed in *Riccia*. The wide air canals in *R. crystallina* communicate with the outside by their whole width. This upper region of air channels functions in photosynthesis. In the sterile thallus of *R. fluitans* floating under the water surface the upper epidermis is continous. The air chambers are large but closed (Fig. 4.4 C).

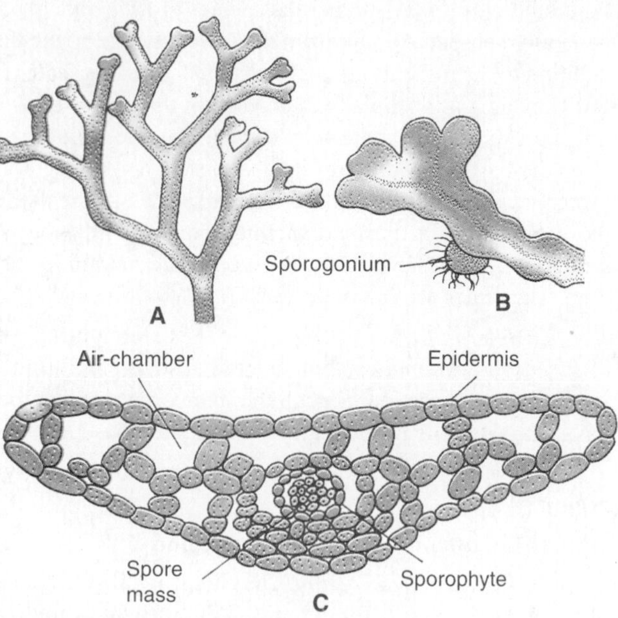

Fig. 4.4. (A—C). *R. fluitans*. A, floating form; B, land form; C, transverse vertical section of the thallus of a land form (A—C after Kashyap).

The assimilatory region in *Ricciocarpus natans* consists of large, irregular air chambers. They are arranged in several layers one above the other. The chambers of the upper layer communicate with the exterior through air pores.

(*ii*) *Storage region* (Fig. 4.3). The lower or the ventral portion of the thallus is colourless. It consists of closely packed, undifferentiated parenchymatous cells without intercellular spaces. The cells are colourless and may contain starch but no chloroplasts. They serve for water and food storage. The lowermost cells of this region are small in size and regularly arranged to form the so-called **lower epidermis**. From the latter arise the rhizoids and the thin scales.

Origin of air chambers. There are two views with regard to the development of air chambers. Lietgeb (1879), Hirsch (1910), Black (1913) and others hold that the air chambers arise by **surface involution**. They originate as depressions of the surface. These depressions are fomed by cessation of upward growth in certain portions of the thallus and vigorous upgrwoth in the adjoining portions. In this way depressions are formed in between.

Barnes and Land (1907), Evans (1918), Campbell (1918), Bower and others hold that the air chambers arise **schizogenously**. They originate as depressions formed by splitting of the cell walls. The young embryonic thallus tissue just back of the thallus apex is compact. Air chambers airse later by the splitting of the vertical cell walls. The consensus of opinion favours the second hypothesis. The supporters of the hypothesis are further divided into the followingf two camps :

(*i*) Some hold that the schizogenous splitting is **exogenous**. It starts from without inwards. It begins from the surface and extends downward. The ardent supporters of this view are Black, Orth, etc.

(*ii*) Many hold the opposite view. The chief among them are Barnes, Land and Pietsch. They contend that the splitting is **endogenous**. It starts within the tiisue of the thallus below the surface. It begins from below and gradually extends upward right up to the epidermal layer.

Apical growth (Fig. 4.2A). The growth in length of the thallus lobes takes place by means of a group **apical initials.** They are arranged in a horizontal row and vary in number usually from 3 to 5, sometimes more. The growing point containing the apical initials is located at the bottom of a notch at the tip of each lobe. Once the apical initials are established in the young thallus all further growth is brought about by their activity and growth of the daughter cells. The growing region comes to lie in a depression because the embryonic cells on the sides of the apical cells divide and grow more vigorously than the embryonic cells posterior to the apical initials. Each apical initial is wedge-shaped. It has four cutting faces but segments are usually cut off from the dorsal and ventral faces. A major portion of the thallus is however formed from the segments produced at the dorsal face. Each dorsal segment divides by a wall parallel to the surface of the thallus. The outer and the inner daughter cells divide and redivide. The segments derived from the outer daughter cell differentiate into the upper photosynthetic region of the thallus and the sex organs. The derivatives of the inner cell give rise to the ventral, colourless storage region. According to Pietsch, the segments cut off parallel to the ventral face of the apical initials give rise only to the **lower epidermis**, the **rhizoids** and the **scales**.

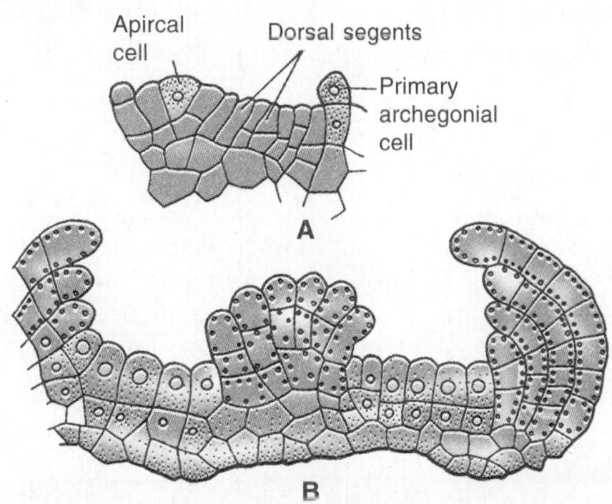

Fig. 4.5. (A—B). ***Riccia* sp**. A, vertical section through the growing point. B, section through the growing point showing dichotomy. (Diagrammatic).

Dichotomy (Fig. 4.5 B). Now and then some of the median cells of the row of apical initials divide vertically to form a tissue which separates the growing point into sets of apical initials. Each set functions as the growing point of a new thallus lobe. It is the beginning of dichotomy. It becomes more marked by the addition of more and more tissue between the two sets of apical initials.

Reproduction

Riccia starts reproducing when it has reached a certain stage of maturity. It reproduces vegetatively and by meiospores formed following a sexual process. The thallus reproduces by vegetative methods and is also concerned with the sexual process.

A. Vegetative reproduction (Fig. 4.6). *Riccia* thallus multiplies vegetatively during the growing season by the following first two methods :-

1. *Fragmentation* (A—D). It depends upon the ageing of the **vegetative cells**. The cells in the older portions die of old age and eventually

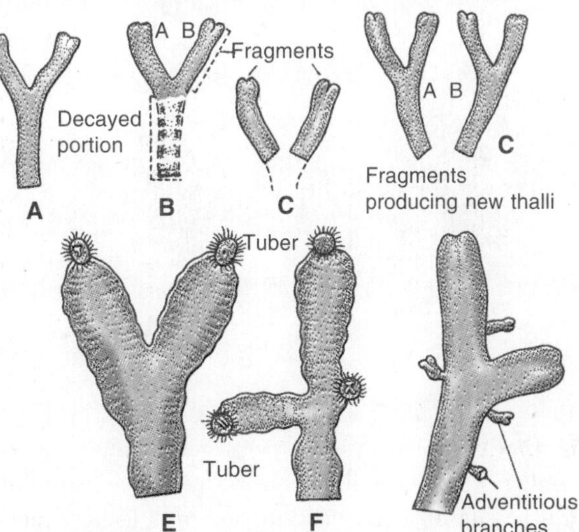

Fig. 4.6. (A—G). ***Riccia* sp**. Different modes of vegetative reproduction A—D, fragmentation in *R. fluitans*; E, formation of terminal tubers in *R. billardieri*; F, thallus with tubers (ventral view) of *R. discolor*; G, *Riccia* thallus with adventitious branches (E and F after Srivastava).

disorganise (B). When the death and decay of the older portions of the thallus reaches dichotomy the young lobes become separated (C). Each of these by apical growth grows into a new thallus (D).

2. *Adventitious branches* (G). In *R. fluitans* special adventitious branches arise from the ventral surface of the thallus in the midrib region. They become detached from the parent thallus by the decay of the connecting tissue and form new plants.

3. *Persistent apices*. In many species of *Riccia* which grow in regions with a prolonged dry season, as in the Punjab, the whole plant except the growing apices of the thallus lobes is killed. The surviving persistent apices resume growth in the succeeding rainy season. Kashyap reported that in *R. himalayensis* (*R. discolor*) at the end of the growing season the apices of the thallus lobes grow down into the soil and become thickened. The rest of the plant dies. During the next growing season the apices resume growth and form new plants.

4. *Tuber formation*. It has been reported in *R. perennis*, *R. discolor* (F), *R. vescata* and *R. billardieri* (E). The apices of the thallus lobes become thickened to form tubers at the end of the growing season. With the advent of unfavourable conditions the plant perishes. The tubers remain dormant and resume growth under suitable conditions.

B. Sexual reproduction. 1. *Distribution of sex organs.* The sex organs are developed on the thallus lobes which are not in any way specialised for the purpose. They are developed in lines extending back from the growing points. Generally they lie in the dorsal furrow or groove sunk deeply, each in a separate cavity. They are developed in an acropetal order. The younger ones are thus near the tip or near the growing point and the older are away from it. The antheridia and archegonia, in some species, are developed on the same thallus. Such species are known as **monoecious**. In others the two kinds of sex organs are developed on different thalli. They are referred to as **dioecious**. *R. crystallina, R. billardieri, R. melanospora, R. gangetica* and *R. pathekotensis* are monoecious while *R. discolor* and *R. frostii,* are dioecious. In the monoecious forms the antheridia are formed first and archegonia later. In a few cases they are formed successively, a few antheridia and then a few archegonia. The sex orgns arise singly and each lies in a separate

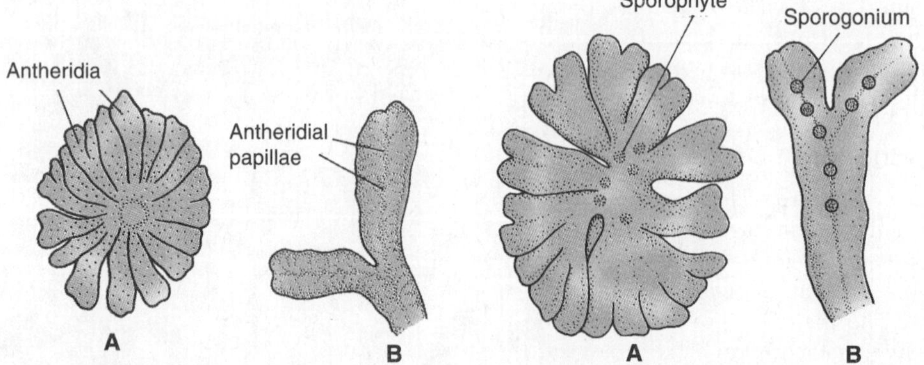

Fig. 4.7. (A—B). ***Riccia* sp.** A, male thallus of *R. frostii*; B, male thallus of *R. discolor*.

Fig. 4.8. (A—C). ***Riccia* sp.** A, female thallus of *R. frostii,* B, female thallus of *R. discolor.*

pit. The site of a sunken antheridium is usually marked by a tiny tower-like projection of the surrounding, thallus tissue. The thallus of *Riccia,* as it bears the sex organs, is known as the **gametophyte** plant. The sperms and the eggs are the last structures developed during the gametophyte phase.

2. *Factors influencing initiation of sex organs*. Benson Evans (1964) reported that *R. glauca* is a short day species. It produces gametangia with 6-8 hours of light diurnally only at 10°C. She

found little thermal effect on gametangial development and no critical photoperiod for the short day *Riccia* species. Chopra and Sood (1973) from their observations on *R. crystallina* stated that the presence of light and exposure to low temperature are the important prerequisites for gametangial initiation. Temperature is the critical factor for the initiation of gametes. Length of the light period is not limiting so long as a certain minimum period of illumination is provided.

3. *Structure and development of sex organs.*

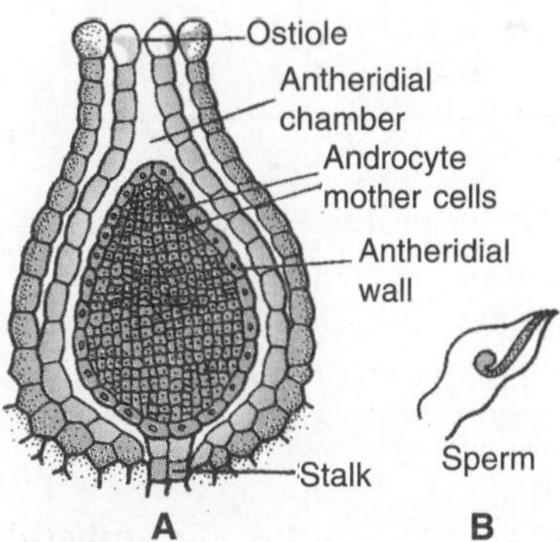

Fig. 4.9. (A—B). ***Riccia*** sp. antheridium in section showing structure. B, liberated sperm.

(*a*) Antheridium (Fig. 4.9)

(*i*) *Structure* (A). The mature antheridium is an elongated structure. It consists of an ovoid or a pear-shaped body seated on a short, few-celled stalk. It stands in a deep pit (**antheridial chamber**) and is attached to its bottom by means of its multicellular stalk. Each antheridial chamber opens at the upper surface of the thallus by a narrow pore called an **ostiole**. The body of the antheridium has an outer, jacket layer of sterile cells. It is called the **antheridial wall**. The antheridial wall is protective in function and one cell in thickness. It encloses a mass of small, fertile cubical cells called the **androcyte mother cells**. Each androcyte mother cell has a denser cytoplasm and a relatively larger nucleus. It divides diagonally to form two sperm cells known as the **spermatids** or **androcytes** (Fig. 4.11 A). The protoplast of each androcyte gets metamorphosed into a single sperm. In this way several hundred biflagellate sperms are produced in each antheridium.

Each sperm (Fig. 4.9 B) is a minute, slender, curved structure. It is furnished with a pair of whiplash flagella at its anterior end. The body consists of an elongated nucleus. The portion of the cytoplasm not utilized in the formation of flagella remains attached to the posterior end of the body of the sperm as a tiny vesicle. The sperms do not leave the antheridium unitl enough moisture is present to permit them to swim about.

(*ii*) *Dehiscence.* Presence of moisture is essential for the dehiscence of a mature antheridium in which the walls of the androcytes or spermatids have dissolved and the sperms lie free in the viscous fluid in the cavity of the antheridium surrounded by the jacket layer or antheridial wall. Water enters the ostiole and finds its way into the antheridial chamber. The cells at the apex of the antheridium absorb this water by

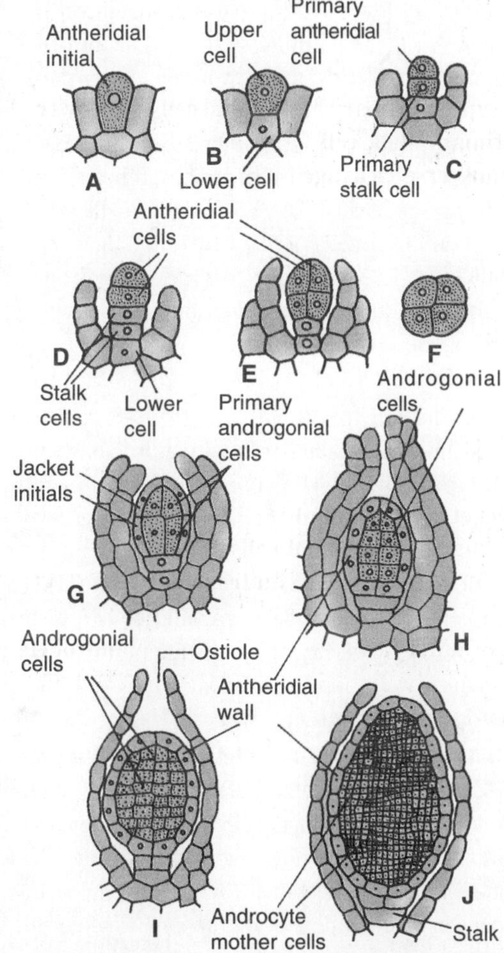

Fig. 4.10. (A—J). ***Riccia* sp**. Stages in the development of the antheridium. Explanation in the text (Based on Lewis).

imbibition. They get softened and eventually disintegrate to form a distal pore. The sperms may be short with considerable force or extruded slowly in a viscous mass through the pore. Eventually they escape through the narrow canal of the antheridial chamber to the upper surface of the thallus. Here they swim freely in a thin film of water in the dorsal furrow.

(iii) Development of antheridium (Fig. 4.10). Each antheridum develops from a single superficial cell called the **antheridial initial** (A). It lies on the dorsal surface of the thallus immediately behind the growing apex. The atheridial initial increases in size and becomes papillate. It then divides transversely into an **upper cell** and a **lower cell** (B). The lower cell undergoes a few divisions to form the embedded portion of the antheridial stalk. The upper cell enlarges and divides by a transverse wall into an **upper primary antheridial cell** and a **lower primary stalk cell** (C). Both these undergo a **transverse cleavage**. The young antheridium at this stage consists of a row of four cells (D). The two lower cells of this row function as the **stalk cells**. They undergo a few further divisions to form the stalk of the antheridium. The two upper cells of the row function as **antheridial cells**. Each antheridial cell divides by two successive vertical divisions at right angles to each other forming four cells (E-F).

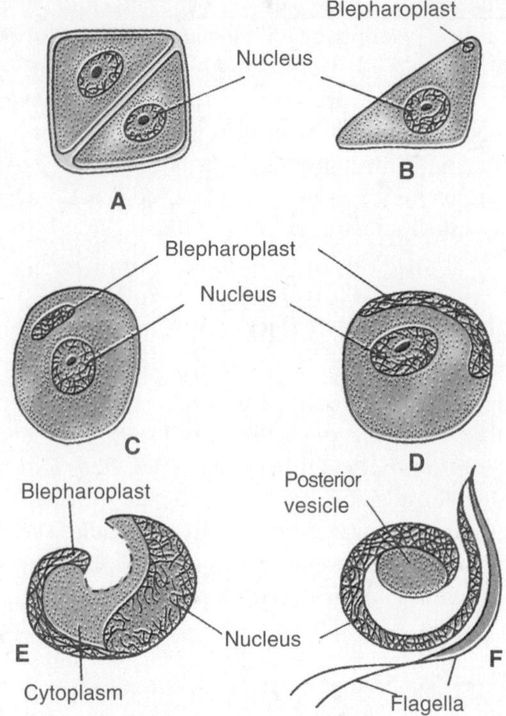

Fig. 4.11. (A—F). ***Riccia*** **sp**. Stages in the development of sperm. Explanation in the text (After Black).

The body of the antheridium at this stage consists of two tiers of four cells each (E). Only two cells are seen in each tier in a longitudinal section. Periclinal divisions now appear in all the cells of both the tiers (G). The young antheridium is now differentiated into an outer layer of eight sterile **jacket** or **wall initials** enclosing the eight fertile inner cells. The inner fertile cells are called the **primary androgonial cells**. The latter divide further. Eventually a mass of small cubical cells is formed. These are the **androgonial cells** (H). The latter undergo further division. The cells of the last cell generation of androgonial cells are sometimes referred to as the **sperm mother cells** or **spermatocytes** (J). Smith calls them **androcyte mother cells**. As the androgonial tissue increases anticlinal walls appear in the jacket or wall initials. This results in the formation of a jacket layer of sterile cells one cell in thickness. It constitutes the wall of the antheridium. Each androcyte mother cell divides diagonally without the formation of a wall into two triangular **sperm cells** or **androcytes** (Fig. 4.11). Each of these gives rise to a minute, biflagellate **sperm**.

Coincident with the early development of the antheridium, the neighbouring cells of the thallus tissue exhibit rapid upgrowth (C-E). They divide and grow upward around the antheridium. The latter at maturity becomes completely enclosed in a cavity or pit called the **antheridial chamber**. It opens by a small pore at the upper surface of the thallus.

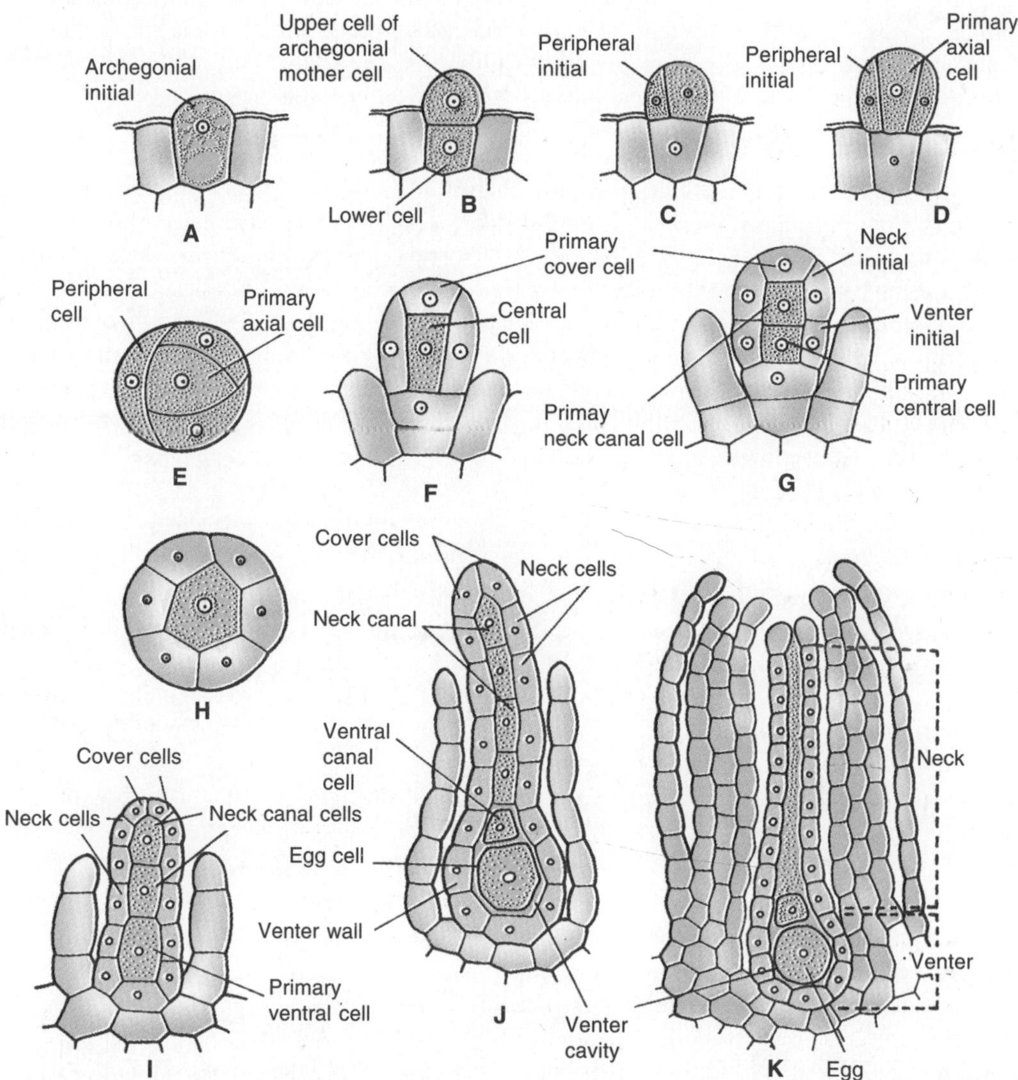

Fig. 4.12. (A—K). ***Riccia* sp.** Stages in the development of the archegonium. Explanation in the text. E and H are transverse sections. (B—D, F, G, I—K after Lewis).

Spermatogenesis in Riccia (Fig. 4.11). It is the process of transformation of androcytes into sperms. Black (1913) investigated spermatogenesis in *R. frostii*. According to him the protoplast of each androcyte mother cell divides diagonally without the formation of a cell wall into two triangular units called the **androcytes** (A). Each androcyte has a dense protoplast containing a distinct relatively large nucleus (B). There appears near the periphery of the androcyte protoplast a small granule-like extra nuclear body, called the **blepharoplast**. Thereafter the androcyte changes shape. It becomes somewhat rounded (C). Along with this change in the form of the androcyte is the elongation of the blepharoplast and the nucleus (D). The blepharoplast forms a thin cord-like structure with thickened head. The androcyte at this stage becomes coma-shaped (E). The cord-like blepharoplast extends and encircles the coma-shaped protoplast up to about 3/4 of the periphery. Meanwhile the nucleus which has become sickle-shaped and homogeneous also moves to the periphery of the coma-shaped androcyte protoplast and establishes contact with the cord-like blepharoplast (E). From the thickened end of the blepharoplast emerge the two **flagella**. The electron microscopy reveals the standard 9+2 fibrillar organisation of the flagellum. The curved nucleus forms the body of the sperm with the blepharoplast forming the apex furnished with two flagella. The unused portion of the androycte forms a small **vesicle**. The latter remains attached to the posterior end of the sperm (F).

(*b*) Archegonium (Fig. 4.12 J)

(*i*) *Structure*. The archegonium is a flask-shaped organ. It consists of two parts, the basal swollen portion called the **venter** and a long, slender **neck**. The venter is directly attached to the tissue of the thallus. There is usually no visible stalk. The next consists of a vertical row of four cells, the **neck canal cells** surrounded by a layer of sterile cells forming a protective jacket. The jacket or neck cells are arranged in six longitudinal rows. Each row is 6—9 cells in height. The tip of the neck is made up of four specialised large **cap**, **cover** or **lid cells** with greater diameter than the neck cells. The venter also has a jacket of sterile cells continuous above with the jacket of the neck. It is **venter wall**. The venter wall is also one cell in thickness. It encloses the venter cavity which is filled with two cells. They are the lower, larger **egg cell** and the upper smaller **ventral canal cell**. The latter functions like a plug holding the fomer in place in the venter. The egg cell is the largest of the axial row. Each archegonium lies within a cavity. The distal portion of the archegonial neck, however, projects above the surface of the thallus into the dorsal furrow. *R. frostii* is an exception in which the neck almost reaches the surface of the thallus.

(*ii*) *Dehiscence*. (Fig.4.12 K). When the archegonium reaches maturity the neck canal cells and the ventral canal cell degenerate. Their products, when hydrated, form mucilage. The mucilage imbibes water and swells. The pressure thus set up forces the cover cells to separate from one another. In this way a narrow passage, the neck canal is formed. It connects the cavity of the venter containing the egg with the outer world. The neck canal is now filled party with water and partly with the mucilage formed by the disintegration of the axial row of cells except the egg cell.

(*iii*) *Development of archegonium* (Fig. 4.12). The archegonium springs from a single cell called the **archegonium initial** (A). It is the superficial cell derived from the younger dorsal segment of the apical cell. The archegonial initial grows and projects above the surface of the thallus. It then divides by a transverse wall separating a lower cell from an upper cell (B). The lower cell takes no further part in the development of the archegonium. The upper cell functions as an **archegonial mother cell** (C). It enlarges and divides by three eccentric vertical walls (D). They separate three sterile, **peripheral initials** or **cells** surrounding a middle fertile cell. The latter functions as the **primary axial cell** (D). It slightly overtops the peripheral initials. Each of the three peripheral initials divides longitudinally to form six **jacket initials** or **envelope cells**. The primary axial cell now undergoes a **transverse cleavage**. This separates an upper primary **cover cell** from an inner **central cell** (F).

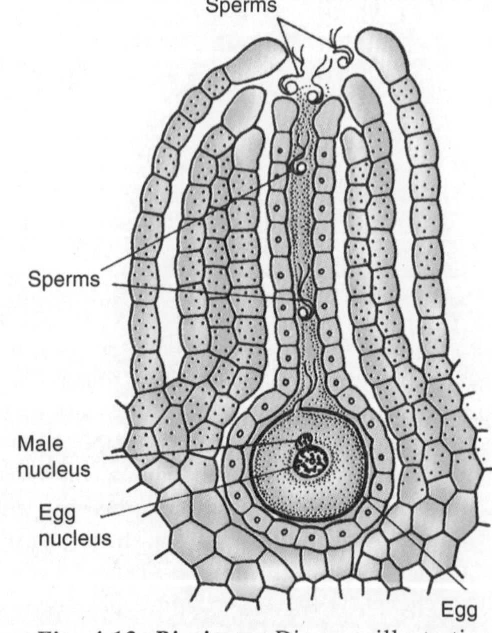

Fig. 4.13. ***Riccia*** **sp**. Diagram illustrating fertilization (Diagrammatic).

At this state a transverse division appears in the six jacket initials and the single central cell. This division differentiates the archegonium into two halves or two tiers of cells (G). The six jacket cells of the upper tier function as **neck initials**. The outer cell separated from the central cell functions as the **primary neck canal cell** and the inner as **primary ventral cell** (G). Further transverse divisions of the six neck initials and their daughter cells produce a slender, tubular neck one cell thick (I). The cells of the neck are arranged in six vertical rows. They enclose a row of four neck canal cells formed by two successive transverse divisions of the primary neck canal cell. The tip of the archegonial neck has a rosette of four **lid** or **cover cells**. They are formed from the primary cover cell by two successive vertical divisions at right angles to each other.

The six jacket cells of the lower tier which function as **venter initials** divide and redivide by transverse division forming the venter wall one cell thick (J). It encloses a cavity, the **venter cavity**. The latter contains a small, upper **ventral canal cell** and a large **egg cell**. They are formed by an unequal transverse division of the primary ventral cell. The archegonia have no protective sheaths around them. Each archegonium lies in a pit.

(*c*) Fertilization (Fig. 4.13)

It takes place in the presence of water. The dorsal furrow serves as a capillary tube. It takes in water in the forms of a thin film. The heavy dew provides sufficient water to permit movements of the sperms. The antheridium bursts and the sperms escape. At the same time the neck canal cell in the mature archegonia degenerate to form a mass of mucilage. The latter absorbs water and swells. The cover cells closing the neck canal are forced apart. A passage way to the eggs is thus formed. A bit of this mucilage oozes out of the open necks. The exuded mucilage contains certain chemical substances such as soluble proteins and inorganic salts of potassium. At the same time the liberated sperms swim about in all directions and in great numbers in the water film that covers the thallus in the region of the dorsal furrow. Some will chance to come near the open necks of the archegonia. Of these some gain entrance into the open necks. This is perhaps in response to certain chemical substances (proteins and inorganic salts) present in the mucilage which diffuses from the neck canal. They enter the venter. Usually one, probably the first to arrive, penetrates the egg. The nucleus of the sperm travels to that of the egg and unites with it to accomplish fertilization. The act of fertilization ends the gametophyte phase.

Sporophytic Phase (Fig. 4.14)

This phase in the life cycle is the direct result of the sexual process. It comprises the **zygote, embryo** and the **sporogonium**.

(a) Zygote (B). It is the fusion cell formed by the union of the sperm with the egg and the pioneer structure of the sporophyte phase. It secretes a wall around it and enlarges in size. The zygote is retained within the venter where it begins to grow immediately. It enters upon no resting period. The zygote differs from the unfertilized egg in the following two respects :

1. It has a diploid nucleus.

2. It has a cellulose cell wall around it. The egg before syngamy has a haploid nucleus and is naked.

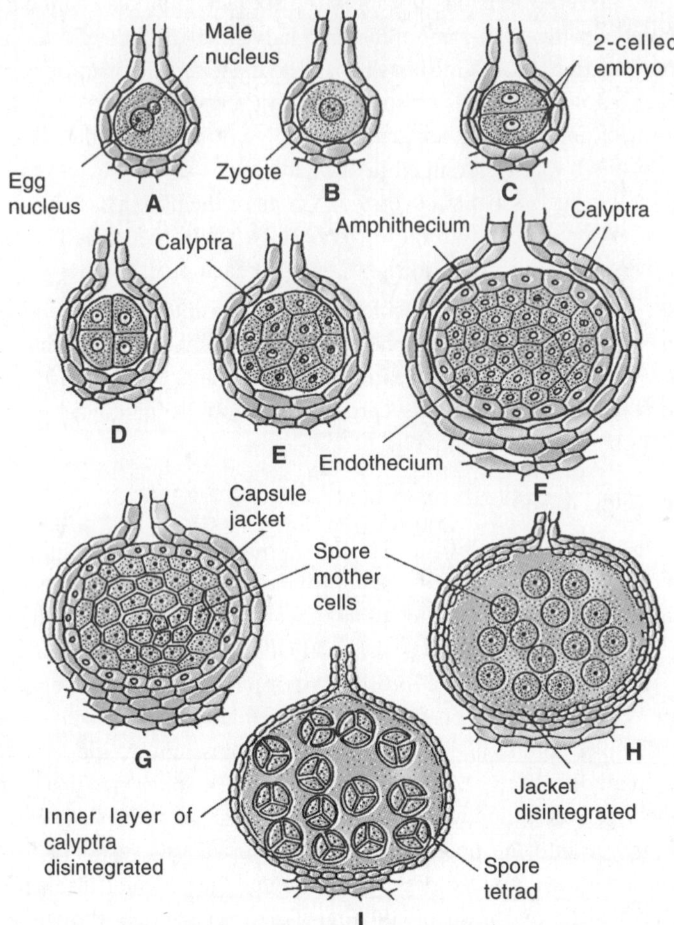

Fig. 4.14. (A—I). ***Riccia* sp**. Development of sporogonium or sporophyte. Explanation in the text. (A, after Pande and the rest after Pagan).

(*b*) **Development of embryo** (C—F). The zygote lying in the venter undergoes repeated cell division and cell enlargement (C—E). A spherical mass of undifferentiated cells called an embryo is formed (E). It fills the venter cavity. The archegonium is persistent. The venter expands as a close envelope over the developing **embryo**. It becomes two cell layers thick and is known as the **calyptra** (E). The neck of the archegonium later withers.

The first division of the zygote is by a nearly horizontal wall (C). It is in a plane at right angles to the long axis of the archegonium. The next division is at right angles to the first. The young embryo now consists of four cells. It is the **quadrant stage** (D) of the embryo. All the four quadrants are nearly equal. Each quadrant, as a rule, divides by a vertical wall at right angles to the preceeding ones. The embryo at this stage consists of eight nearly equal cells. Only four are seen in a longitudinal section. It is the octant stage (D). Garber and Lewis reported the formation of a four-celled filamentous instead of a quadratic type of embryo in some species of *Riccia*. Succeeding divisions in the eight-celled embryo are in an irregular sequence. A more or less spherical mass of 20 to 40 undifferentiated, colourless cells is produced (E).

(*c*) **Young sporogonium** (F). Each of the outer cells of he undifferentiated spherical embryo divides by a periclinal wall (F). A single layer of outer cells is separated from an inner, central mass of cells. The former is called **amphithecium** and the latter **endothecium**. The cells of the amphithecium are large and flat. They divide only by anticlinal walls to form the protective, sterile **jacket layer** which remains one cell thick and constitutes the wall of the young sporogonium (G). The cells of the endothecium are all alike. They constitute the first cell generation of the sporogenous tissue. It is called the **archesporium.** As the sporogonium advances towards maturity the archesporial cells divide and redivide to form a mass of sporogenous cells. The cells of the last cell generation of the sporogenous mass function as potential **spore mother cells** or **sporocytes** (G). The spore mother cells are the last structures of the sporophyte phase. During further development of the sporogonium the sporocytes begin to separate and become more or less rounded (H). Their walls become mucilaginous and contents densely granular. Practically all the sporocytes divide meiotically to form spores. A few, however, are said to disintegrate to form a nutritive fluid. They are called the **nurse cells**. Some bryologists consider the nurse-cells as the **forerunners** of the **elaters** of the more advanced members of the Marchantiales.

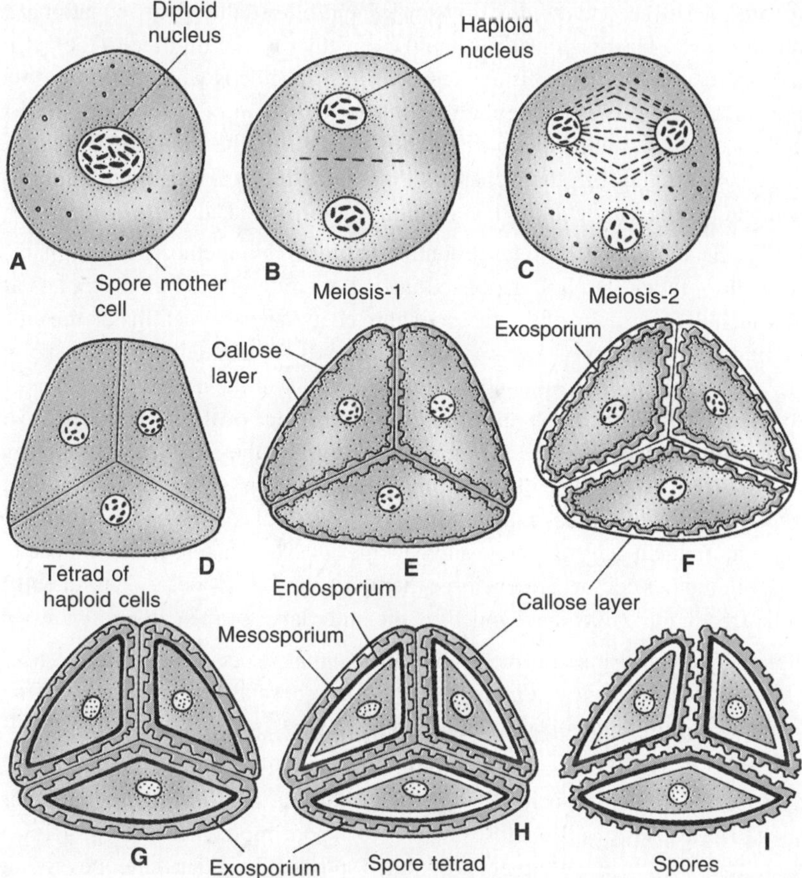

Fig. 4.15. (A—I). ***Riccia* sp**. Stages in sporogenesis. Explanation in the text.

As the spore mother cells enter upon meiotic division their walls disintegrate. The wall of the sporogonium and the cells of the inner layer of the calyptra also disintegrate (I). The rounded spore mother cells lie free in the cavity of the sporogonium surrounded by the outer layer of calyptra. The developing spores are bathed and nourished by the nutritive fluid formed by the disintegration of :-

(*i*) walls of spore mother cells.

(*ii*) non-functional spore mother cells.

(*iii*) jacket layer of the sporogonium.

(*iv*) inner layer of the two cells thick calyptra.

(*d*) **Sporogenesis** (Fig. 4.15). It is the process leading to the transformation of the diploid protoplast of the sporocyte (spore mother cell) into haploid dispersal units, the *spores* with resistant walls. The process consists of a complex integrated series of **events** involving a special kind of nuclear division called *meiosis*. In meiosis the diploid nucleus of the spore mother cell undergoes two successive nuclear divisions but the chromosomes are replicated only once. In *Riccia* almost all cells of the sporogenous tissue differentiate into **spore mother cells** or **sporocytes**. As the sporocytes begin to separate from one another they become more or less rounded. Their walls become mucilaginous and contents densely granular. Each sporocyte has a diploid nucleus (A). With the disintegration of their walls, spore mother cells increase in size and the diploid nucleus undergoes meiosis. The first meiotic division is *reductional*. It reduces the chromosome number to half of the somatic number (B). The second meiotic division which follows the first is equational mitosis (C). Both constitute **meiosis**. The resultant four haploid daughter nuclei migrate to the periphery of the sporocyte and lie at equal distances from each other (C). The cells walls delimiting the 4 haploid spores are laid simultaneously between the four nuclei at the end of the second division (D). This group of 4 cells is called an immature **spore tetrad**. The cells in the tetrad are typically arranged in a tetrahelral manner and the wall that separates them is in the form of a thin membrane. The four cells of the immature tetrad are enclosed, at first, in a common sheath (D).

Each cell of the tetrad now secretes around it within its thin membrane a comparatively thick, homogeneous **callose layer** (E). It is deposited unevenly around the spore protoplast and acts as a mold against which the markings of the mature spore coat (call) are cast. Inside the callose layer is deposited the first or outer layer of the spore coat known as the **exosporium** in the form of a series of lamellae (F). The latter project into and follow the contour of the callose layer. The second layer of the spore coat which is known as the **mesosporium** is deposited on the inner side of the exosporium. During the concluding stages of spore development is formed the third and the innermost layer of the spore coat. It is termed the the **endosporium**. The three layers of the spore coat thus develop in centripetal succession. As the spores mature, the spore coat thickness considerably. The exosporium which is yellow, at first, changes to orange and becomes black at maturity. The callose layer and the sheath of the spore mother cell, which encloses the four spores, disappear. Consequently, the spores separate and lie free in the cavity surrounded by the outer layer of the calyptra.

The diploid or somatic number of chromosomes in many species of *Riccia* (*R. trichocarpa, R. arvensis, R. sorocarpa* and *R. crystallina*) is 16 (n=8). According to Kachroo (1950), the haploid chromosome number in *R. melanospora* and *R. cruciata* is 16.

Sporophyte (Fig. 4.16). The sporogonium of *Riccia* is the simplest among the liverworts. It lacks both the **foot** and the **seta**. It is just a spore sac or capsule spherical in outline. It has a wall one cell layer thick. The capsule wall encloses a mass of spore mother cells (Fig. 4.15 G). The two layered calyptra forms as close investment around the sporogonium. The latter never emerges out of it. Before the spore mother cells divide to form spores the single layered wall of the sporogonium disintegrates (Fig. 4.15 H). Later the inner layer of the calyptra also breaks down (Fig. 4.15 I). The mature spores lie free in a cavity or sac surrounded by the outer layer of calyptra. There are no elaters (Fig. 4.16). The mature sporogonium of *Riccia,* in this cavity, thus has no diploid or sporophytic structures at this stage. The meiospores which represent the future gametophyte are housed in a sac provided by the parent gametophyte.

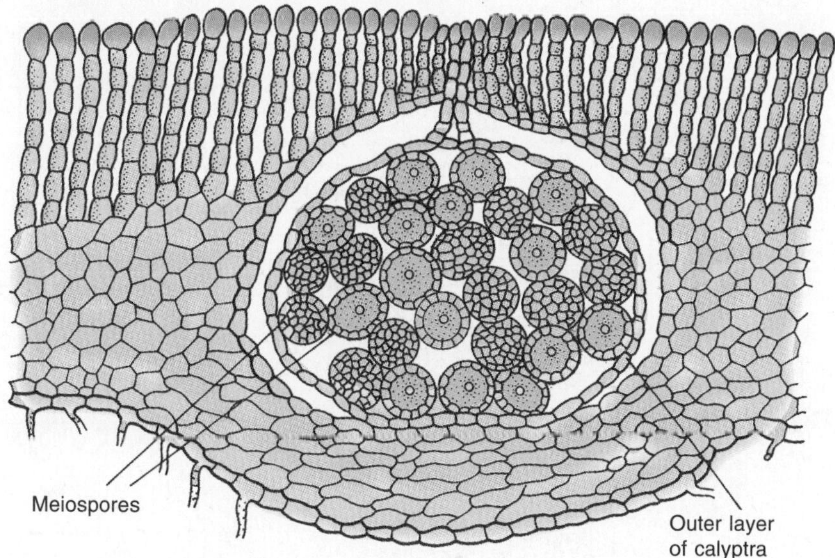

Fig. 4.16. ***Riccia* sp.** Mature sporogonium or sporophyte.

Nutrition. Unlike other liverworts the embryo, sporogonium and spore mother cells in *Riccia* develop no chloroplasts. Thus no starch is formed. The sporophyte remains totally dependent upon the thallus (gametophyte) for food materials, water and minerals in solution.

Comparison between the two generations. The sporogonium which is the sporophyte individual differs from the thallus (gametophyte plant) in structure, function and genetic constitution as well. It is radially constructed whereas the thallus is dorsiventral. It bears no appendages and is unbranched. The thallus bears appendages in the form of rhizoids and scales and is dichotomously branched. The thallus is green in colour and thus **autotrophic**. The sporogonium has no green colour and is **heterotrophic** in its nutrition. Because of the presence of air spaces the thallus is amply ventilated whereas the sporogonium, at first, is more or less a solid object. The sporogonium is the non-sexual individual which produces the **meiospores**. The thallus is responsible for **sexual reproduction**. The thallus represents the **haplophase** whereas the sporogonium represents the **diplophase.** These differences justify our stand to look upon the sporogonium of *Riccia* as a new individual in the life cycle. It is not an outgrowth of the parent gametophyte (thallus).

Dehiscence of sporogonium. The sporogonium of *Riccia* never dehisces. The spores are liberated by the decay or shrivelling of the surrounding outer layer of the calyptra and thallus tissue. The thallus perishes in the dry season. The spores remain behind on the soil. In this condition they may be dispersed by the wind. The remain alive for some time. Finally they germinate with the onset of conditions favourable for growth.

Morphology of the spore (Fig. 4.15 A-I). The liberated meiospore is pyramidal in shape. It consists of a tiny mass of cytoplasm containing a small haploid nucleus. The food is largely stored in the form of oil globules. The protective spore wall which is known as the **sporoderm**, is thick, black and sculptured. The surface sculpturing varies from species to species. It is, however, specific and helps to identify the species. The internal structure of the sporoderm is largely similar. The sporoderm (spore coat) is usually differentiated into two layers, outer **exine** and inner **intine.**

Intine. The intine is thin about 0.3 *um* in thickness. It is homogenous and composed of pectose and cellulose. According to Steinkamp and Doyle (1976), who studied the ultrastructure of the spore wall of some species of *Riccia*, the narrow intine is translucent and closely appressed to the innermost region of the exine.

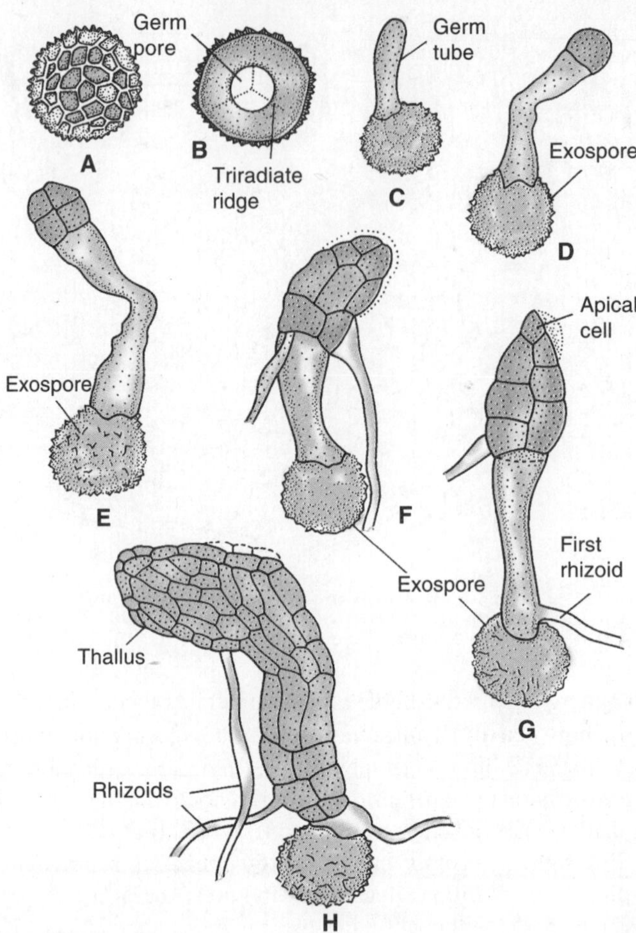

Fig. 4.17. (A—H). ***Riccia billardieri***. Stages in spore germination. Explanation in the text (After Udar).

Exine. The exine contains material resistant to acetolysis. It known as the **sporollenin**. The major surface sculpturing of the spore comprises ridges and depressions in areolate or irregular configurations. Finer surface features such as tubercles or papillae ornament the ridges or depressions. The exine is thick and differentiated into three concentric morphologically distinct lamellate regions. Denizot (1974) recognized four. The innermost region or layer of the exine which is in direct contact with the intine is composed of thin, closely spaced lamellae. It has a fibrillar appearance. The middle region of the exine consists of thick lamellae with electrolucent cores and thick electro-dense coating. The outermost region of exine is composed of distinct lamellae of intermediate thickness with a distinct electron dense coating. The lamellae of this region contribute to the ornamental surface features of the spore. The spore surface is usually marked by a triradiate ridge and equatorial rim. In some species of *Riccia* a pore usually occurs at the junction of the equatorial arm with the arm of the triradiate ridge. The pores are superficial and do not penetrate the exine. The two layers of the sporoderm develop in **centripetal** succession. The spore is the first structure of the future gametophyte.

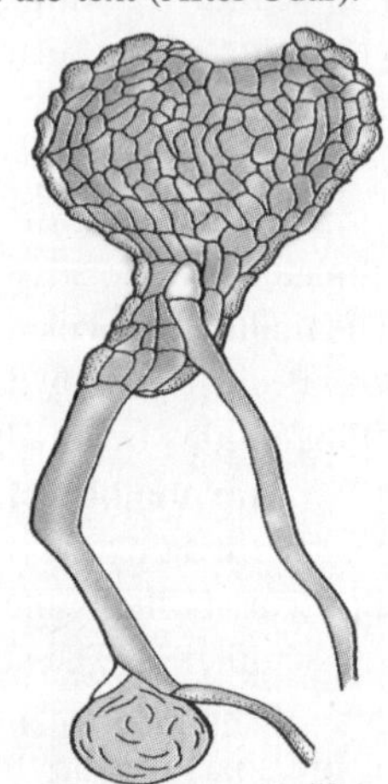

Fig. 4.18. ***Riccia trichocarpa***. A later stage in the germination of a spore. (After Campbell).

Spore germination. (*a*) *Factors affecting germination*. Inoue (1960) reported that the spores of *Riccia* like those of other liverworts do not germiante in darkness. Udar (1975) who studied spore germination in different species of *Riccia* incidentally remarked that the spores of *R. crystallina* enter upon no resting period and germinate in about 6-10 days after their release from the sporogonia. Chopra and Sood (1973) remarked that possibly there is natural dormancy in the spores of *R. crystallina*. Cold treatment (exposure to low temperature) before sowing shortens the dormancy period and increases the percentage of spore germination. Cold treatment is however, ineffective in darkness. It shows that presence of light also plays an equally important role in germination of spores of Riccia besides low temperature. Presence of moisture is another equally important and essential factor for spore germination in *Riccia*.

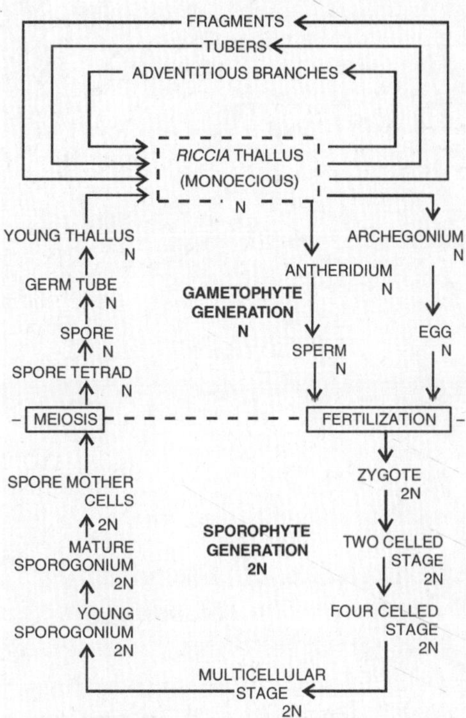

Fig. 4.19. ***Riccia*** **sp.** Graphic representation of the life cycle.

(*b*) *Stages in germination* (Fig. 4.17). Prior to germination the spore (A) absorbs moisture and swells (B). According to Campbell (1918), the black exosporium and the mesosporium rupture at the triradiate ridge. According to Pande (1924), Srinivasan (1940) and Udar (1957-58) the swollen spores may become more or less transparent. A prominent pore called the **germ pore** appears on the outer face opposite the triradiate mark (B). Thin colourless endosporium enclosing the contents grows out through the rupture (Campbell) or germ pore (Pande, Srinivasan and Udar) in the form of a small outgrowth. It is called the **germ tube** (C). It is not clear whether pore formation is the result of enzymatic activity or mechaical rupture. Probably it is due to enzyme action. The germ tube may grow rapidly into a long club-shaped structure but often it remains short and broad. Most of the spore contents migrate to its distal end where chloroplasts reappear. A transverse wall appears separating a large, terminal cell at the distal end of the tube (D). Meanwhile the first rhizoid appears at its base near the point of its emergence from the spore. It is plain-walled (G). Udar (1957) reported that the first rhizoid makes its appearance from the base of the germ tube when it is one celled. It is not separated from the germ tube by a septum. Chopra and Sood (1973) confirmed Udar's observations but added that the formation of the first rhizoid is affected by light intensity. Under low light intensity (50-500 lux) no germ rhizoid is produced. It invariably develops in the light of medium intensity (2000 lux). A second spetrum in the germ tube parallel to the first establishes another cell at the distal end. Each of these two cells next divides by a vertical wall followed by another wall at right angles to the first (E). In this way eight cells are formed at the distal end of the germ tube. They are arranged in two ties of four cells each (E). The four cells of the proximal ties divide by transverse walls. The daughter cells elongate to form the posterior portion of the young thallus (F). Meanwhile one of the four cells in the distal tier begins to function as an **apical cell** with two cutting faces (G). It cuts off segments alternately right and left parallel to its flat cutting faces. From the segments thus cut off are derived the tissues of the new thallus (H). The single apical cell of the young thallus is soon replaced by a row of apical cells (Fig. 4.18).

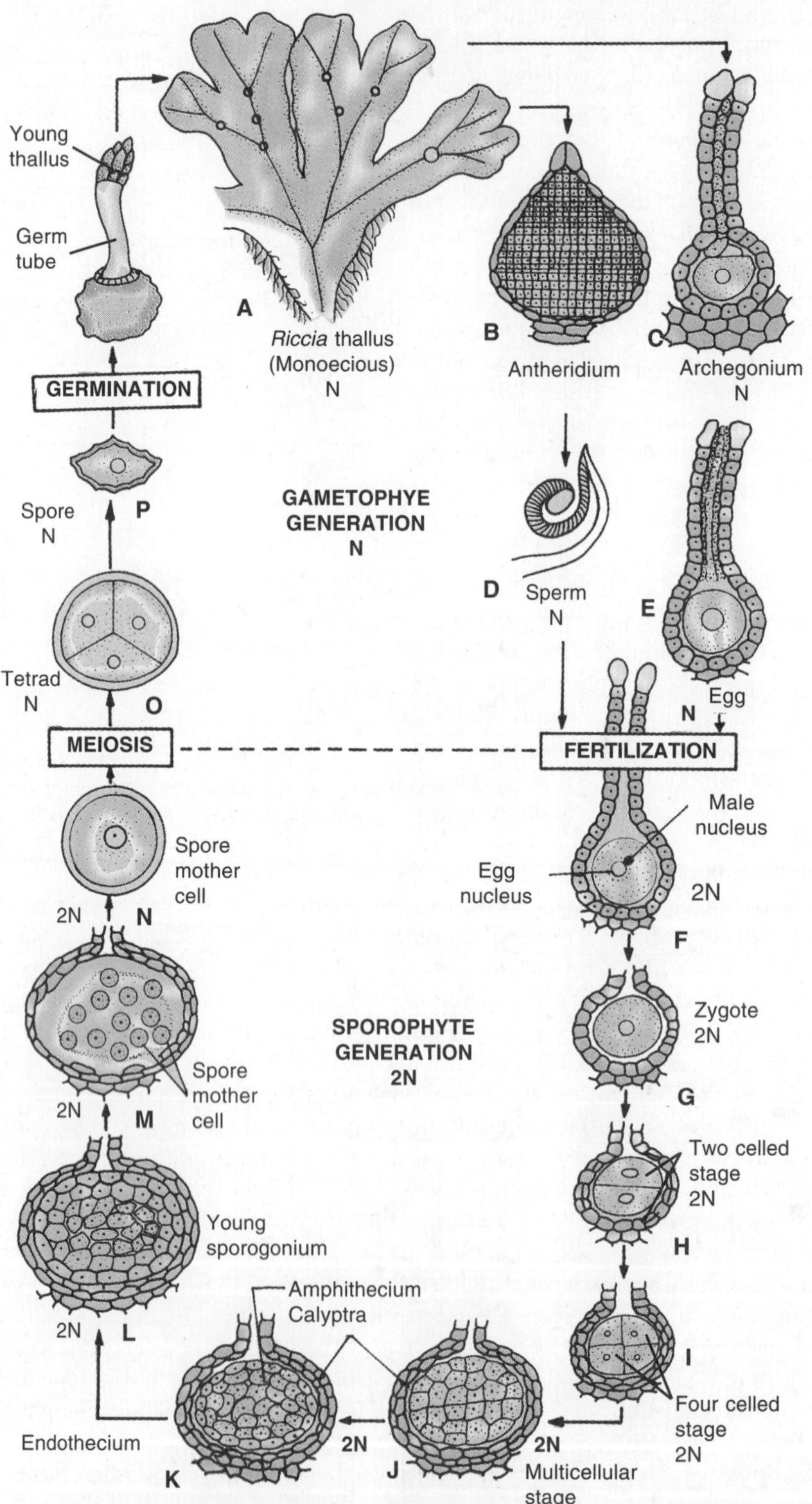

Fig. 4.20. ***Riccia*** **sp.** Diagrammatic representation of the sexual life cycle.

SUMMARY OF THE LIFE CYCLE OF *RICCIA* (FIG. 4.20)

The life cycle of *Riccia* consists of two vegetative individuals. One of these is the parent of the other. The most conspicuous and dominant of the two individuals is the green **thallus** (A). It is a small, flat, green object dorsiventral in construction. The thallus often branches repeatedly by dichotomy. It thus consists of a number of lobes. Each thallus lobe is linear to obcordate. It has a **dorsal furrow** and a depression at its apex. In the terminal depression is lodged the growing point. The thallus is fixed to the substratum by unicellular unbranched **rhizoids**. They are of two kinds, **smooth walled** and **tuberculated**. The rhizoids absorb water and minerals from the damp soil on which *Riccia* generally grows. The dorsal green region of the thallus is spongy. It is amply ventilated as it possesses simple pores and intercellular spaces in the form of deep narrow canals. The latter in some species broaden into air chambers. As the upper portion of the thallus bears chlorophyll and these green cells are bathed with air the thallus plant is capable of self-nutrition. It manufactures a large amount of food.

The thalloid green individual is concerned with sexual reproduction. It produces the gametes and is called the **gametophyte plant**. The gametes are produced in multicellular sex organs. The male sex organ is called the **antheridium**(B) and the female **archegonium** (C). They lie in the dorsal furrow at its bottom each in a separate cavity. They are developed in rows in acropetal order back from the growing apex. Some species of *Riccia* are **monoecious** and others **dioecious**. The antheridium has a globular or pear-shaped body elevated on a short, multicellular stalk. The body has an outer jacket of sterile cells enclosing a mass of androcytes. The latter produce several hundred biflagellate **sperms** (D). The archegonium is a flask-shaped structure. It consists of a long, narrow **neck** and an enlarged basal portion called the **venter**. Both the neck and the venter have one cell layer thick jacket wall. The venter cavity contains a single non-motile egg and a **ventral canal cell** above the latter. The neck has a row of **axial cells**. These are **neck canal cells**. The axial row of cells excepting the egg cell disintegrates when the archegonium is mature. In this way a canal leading to the egg (E) is formed.

All the structures produced by the gametophyte plant constitute the **gametophyte generation** or **phase**. The later therefore consists of the **green thallus plant**, the **sex organs** (antheridia and archegonia) and the **gametes** (sperms and eggs). This generation starts with the spores and ends with **fertilization**. The gametes are the last structures produced during the phase. All the structures constituting the gametophyte generation have *n* number of chromosomes in their nuclei. This number is also called **haploid**. The gametophyte generation is therefore, the **haplophase** in the life cycle. The sex cells (sperms and eggs) of this generation are incapable of giving rise to new individuals alone. They must fuse before they do so. This act of fusion between the sperm and the egg is called **fertilization** (F). The structure formed by the fusion of the two gametes is called the zygote (G).

The zygote has a diploid number of chromosomes. On germination it does not give rise to the gametophyte plant (thallus). It undergoes repeated segmentation and differentiation (H.K.). Finally it develops into a simply spherical object the **sporogonium** (M). The diploid number of chromosomes characteristic of the zygote is carried over by mitosis to all the cells of the sporogonium. The latter therefore, is a **diploid** vegetative plant. It is the second individual in the life cycle of *Riccia*. It is radially constructed and is solid before reaching maturity. It is very simple in structure. It is incapable of self-nutrition. It is nourished by the parent thallus in which is remains embedded throughout its life. Being diploid it represents the **diplophase** of the life cycle. The sporogonium has a wall of sterile cells one cell layer thick. It encloses a mass of spore mother cells (M). The spore mother cells are the last diploid structures produced by the sporogonium. Each spore mother cell (N) by meiosis produces four spores (O). The sporogonium, therefore, is the asexual individual which produces the meiospores. It is as well called the **sporophyte**. The structures produced by it constitute the **sporophyte generation** or **phase**. It starts with the zygote and ends with the spore mother cells. The structures produced during this phase are **zygote**, the **embryo,** the **sporogonium** and the **spore mother cells** (G-M.). The haploid spores produced from the spore mother cells are the first structures of the next gametophyte generation (O). Each spore (P), on germination, produces the green thallus plant (Gametophyte, A) and not the sporogonium (sporophyte).

From the account given above it is evident that in the life cycle of the single *Riccia* plant there occur two distinct vegetative individuals. They are the green independent, thalloid **gametophyte** and the colourless spherical, radially constructed **sporophyte** (sporogonium). These two individuals occur one after the other generation after generation. One plant regularly succeeds the other. The reproductive cells of one generation produce the alternate generation. This phenomenon is expressed by the phrase **"Alternation of Generations"**. It is a constant feature of *Riccia* and all other bryophytes. The two alternating individuals in the life cycle of *Riccia* are dissimilar morphologically. This kind of "alternation of generations" is called **heterologous** or **heteromorphic.** The life cycle of *Riccia* which is characterized by alternation of generations and sporogenic meiosis is called **diplohaplontic**.

IMPORTANT FEATURES IN THE LIFE CYCLE OF *RICCIA*

1. Externally simple, green, ribbon-shaped, dichotomously branched, dorsiventral **thallus** is internally differentiated into several tissues.
2. The thallus bears unicellular, unbranched, smooth-walled and tuberculate **rhizoids** and also minute **scales** on its ventral surface.
3. The dorsal green region of the thallus is chambered. The chambers occur as deep, narrow **air canals** or channels separated by vertical rows of green cells. They are empty and communicate with the exterior through simple, rudimentary and unspecialized pores which are simply air spaces bounded by 4 to 8 epidermal cells.
4. The ventral portion of the thallus consists of colourless, compactly arranged parenchyma cells.
5. Some species of *Riccia* are **monoecious** and others **dioecious**. The sex organs lie in the median dorsal furrow each in a separate pit.
6. The pear-shaped or ovoid body of the ripe **antheridium** has a jacket layer of sterile cells surrounding a mass of minute, somewhat coiled, biflagellate sperms.
7. The antheridial wall disintegrates at its distal end. A mucilaginous fluid containing sperms oozes through the pore of the antheridial pit at the upper surface of the thallus.
8. The typically flask-shaped **archegonium** has an outer layer of sterile jacket cells surrounding an **axial row** of cells. The basal cell of the row is called an **egg**. It lies in the venter. Above it is the **ventral canal cell**. The remainder cells of the axial row lie in the neck region and are called the **neck canal cells**.
9. Moisture is essential for the maturing of sex organs and fertilization.
10. The sperms swim to the archegonia in a thin film of water in the dorsal median furrow. They enter the open necks of the archegonia and swim down their neck canals to reach the venter where only one of them unites with the egg to accomplish fertilization.
11. The diploid zygote secretes a wall around it. It then undergoes cleavage to form a spherical, multicellular **sporophyte**.
12. The sporophyte of *Riccia* is the simplest among the liverworts. It is nothing but a **spore-case**. There is neither any **seta** nor a **foot**. It is nourished by the parent thallus. The two-layered venter now called the **calyptra** forms a close investment around it. The neck of the archegonium may wither by this time. By the time the spores mature the single layered

sporogonium wall and the inner layer of the calyptra disintegrate. The spores lie free in the space surrounded by the outer layer of the calyptra. At this stage there is no trace of the diploid sporophyte tissue. The spores are the first cells of the next gametophyte generation and the outer layer of the calyptra represents the parent gametophyte tissue.

13. The dispersal of spores takes place by the decay of surrounding thallus tissue.

Systematic Position of Riccia

Division	:	Bryophyta
Class	:	Hepaticopsida
Order	:	Marchantiales
Family	:	Ricciaceae
Genus	:	*Riccia*
Species	:	*discolor*

DISCUSSION : AS PRIMITIVE OR ADVANCED

Riccia is a very interesting genus of the Liverworts. It is rather an evolutionary riddle. The gametophyte is quite a complex structure. The sporophyte, however, is the simplest known among the liverworts. It is simply a spore case incapable of self-nutrition. It lacks both the foot and the seta. The capsule wall is one cell layer in thickness. Within the wall are the spore mother cells or spores. Some of the spore mother cells are said to degenerate. They are looked upon as the forerunners of the sterile cells or elaters of the more advanced members of the order Marchantiales. Are we then to regard Riccia sporophyte as a primitive or a reduced structure?

Bower, Campbell and Cavers hold that the simplest sporophyte of *Riccia* is **primitive**. The more complex sporophytes of the Liverworts when seriated illustrate a natural advance. They appear to have evolved from such a simple sporophyte. as that of *Riccia* by the gradual and progressive sterilisation of its potentially fertile cells (spore mother cells). Instead of forming spores they remain sterile and are devoted to somatic functions such as nutrition, spore dispersal, etc. This resulted in the differentiation of the sporophyte into foot, seta and capsule as in *Marahantia*. Some of the potential spore mother cells become sterile to form elaters which help in spore dispersal. This hypothesis of the three eminent botanists is called the **Theory of sterilisation**. It attempts to explain the evolution or the history of the sporophyte of the bryophytes forms an ascending series. The series begins with *Riccia* sporophyte.

The theory though appealing fails to account for the complex nature of the *Riccia* gametophyte (thallus). It is far from being the simplest among the liverworts. The primitive liverwort on the basis of this theory must be a simpler type. It should have the simplest gametophyte as well as the simplest sporophyte in its life cycle. This is not the case in *Riccia*. As a matter of fact such a combination is not known among the Liverworts.

Von Goebel, on the other hand, believes the other way. He holds that the simplest sporophyte of *Riccia* is **reduced** rather than **primitive**. He maintains that the simpler types like *Riccia* have resulted by reduction (also called **progressive simplification**) in both the alternative phases (gametophyte and sporophyte). His contention has been supported by Kashyap, Church and Evans. Kashyap suggested that the **genus** *Riccia* might have emerged from a genus like *Targionia*. This view is supported by the widespread evidence of reduction in the vegetative characters of the gametophyte of the Marchantiales. The reduction and simplification of the parts which bear and protect the sex organs runs side by side with reduction in the structure of the sporogonia which they produce. The outlines of this reduction series are :

(*i*) Loss of assimilatory filaments in the air chambers.

(*ii*) Simplification of the barrel-shaped pores of the advanced Marchantiales.

(*iii*) Shifting of the terminal gametophores (antheridiophores and archegoniophores) to the dorsal position. This is accompanied by the gradual elimination of the stalk of the gametophore. The receptacles become sessile. The antheridia and archegonia actually come to lie on the upper surface of the thallus.

(*iv*) Associated with these changes is the elimination of perigynium and involucre.

All these changes are accompnied by reduction in structure of the sporophyte. The first step in reduction is the elimination of seta. This is followed by the disappearance of foot. Consequently the sporophyte becomes a mere spore case. Later in ring-like thickenings disappear from the cells of sporogonial wall. Subsequently all the endothecium cells become fertile. This step eliminates the elaters.

QUESTIONS

ESSAY TYPE

1. Draw the external morphology of aquantic species of *Riccia*. In what respects it differes from that of terrestrial species. *(Kanpur, M.Sc., 2007)*
2. (*a*) Draw only labelled diagrams of transverse section of thallus of *Riccia, Marchantia, Pellia* and *Anthoceros*. *(Kanpur, 1995)*

   (*b*) Compare gametophytic and sporophytic generations of *Riccia*. *(Kerala, 1999)*
3. Give identifying characters of *Riccia, Marchantia* and *Anthoceros* thallus growing in nature. *(Kanpur, 1996)*
4. Make only labelled diagrams showing the life-cycle of *Riccia*. Demark the haploid and diploid phases.
   (Kanpur, 1996, Mahatma Gandhi Univ., 1998)
5. Give a comparative account of the gametophytes of *Riccia* and *Marchantia*. *(Kanpur, 1998, Bundelkhand, 1998)*
6. Write a comparative account of the structure of gametophytes in *Riccia, Marchantia, Anthoceros* and *Pellia*. *(Rohilkand, 1992, 1996, 2000; Awadh, 1999)*
7. (*a*) Compare sporogonium of *Riccia, Marchantia* and *Anthoceros*. *(Rohilkhand, 1995)*

   (*b*) Describe the sex organs in *Riccia* and *Marchantia*. *(Kerala, 1997)*
8. (*a*) With the help of suitable diagrams compare the external and internal features of the gametophytes of *Riccia, Marchantia, Pellia* and *Anthoceros*. *(Rohilkhand, 1998; 2003; Gorakhpur, 1994)*

   (*b*) Describe the internal structure of the thallus of *Riccia* with the help of a diagram. *(Mahatma Gandhi Univ., 1996)*
9. Explain the identifying characters of *Riccia, Marchantia, Pellia* and *Anthoceros* by comparing the external and internal structures of gametophytes. *(Rohilkhand 1999).*
10. Describe sexual reproductive organs in *Riccia/Pellia* *(Awadh, 1995)*
11. (*a*) Write comparative accounts of the gametophytes of *Riccia* and *Marchantia*. *(Awadh, 1995)*

    (*b*) Describe the structure of thallus in *Riccia*. *(Kerala 1998, 2001)*
12. Describe the life cycle of *Riccia* or *Pellia* with the help of labelled diagrams only. *(Awadh, 1997; Purvanchal, 1996; Bundelkhand, 1995)*
13. Give a comparative account of the structure of sporophytes of *Riccia,*

Marchantia, Pellia and *Anthoceros* with the help of labelled diagrams.

(Awadh, 1998; Gorakhpur, 1992, Kanpur, 2005 Mahatma Gandhi, 1998; Kerala, 1996, Raipur, 1993, Ajmer, 1998)

14. With the help of suitable sketches compare the thallus structure of *Riccia* and *Pellia.* *(U.P. College, 1998)*

15. Give an illustrated account of the gametophytic structures in *Riccia, Pellia/ Marchantia* and *Anthoceros.*

(Kanpur 2004; Gorakhpur, 1991, 1997)

16. Give a comparative account of the thallus structure in *Riccia*, *Marchantia* and *Anthoceros,* or *Porella.*

(Gorakhpur, 1995; Punjab 1998, 1999)

17. Give a comparative account of the gametophytes of *Riccia* and *Anthoceros* with respect to the following :

(*a*) External appearance

(*b*) Internal structure

(*c*) Sex organs with their structure and arrangement.

(Agra, 1991; Punjab 1992)

18. Write comparative account of sex bearing organs in *Riccia, Marchantia* and *Anthoceros.* *(Agra, 1992)*

19. If the thallii of *Riccia, Marchantia, Pellia* and *Anthoceros* are mixed and placed in a bottle, how would you identify them on the basis of external features ?

(Agra, 1995; Bundelkhand, 1999, 2004)

20. Write a comparative illustrated account of the gametophytes of *Riccia*, *Marchantia* and *Anthoceros*

(Agra, 1996)

21. By the help of labelled sketches, differentiate between the sporophytes of *Riccia, Marchantia* and *Anthoceros.*

(Agra, 1996)

22. Describe the development of sex organs in *Riccia* or *Pellia.* *(Allahabad, 1991)*

23. List the characteristic features of the family Riciaceae and give the systematic position of *Riccia.*

24. With the help of a series of diagrams give an account of the life cycle of *Riccia.*

25. Describe the process of spore formation and mechanism of spore discharge in sporophyte of *Riccia.*

26. Describe the various views with regard to the evolutionary position of *Riccia* sporophyte. How far is Goebel justified in assuming that forms like *Riccia* are reduced and not primitive?

27. Analyse the mature spore case in *Riccia.* Is it a sporophyte or gametophyte? Justify your answer giving cogent reasons in support

28. Justify the truth or falsity of the following statement : The sporogonium of *Riccia* is a new individual in the life cycle and not an outgrowth of the thallus.

28. With labelled sketches compare the gametophytes of *Riccia* with *Anthoceros.*

(Punjab, 1996; Kerala, 1995)

30. (*a*) Describe the development of antheridium and archegonium of *Riccia.* *(Punjab, 1996)*

(*b*) Describe the archegonium of *Riccia.*

(Kerala, 2000)

(*c*) Female reproductive organs of *Reccia* *(Kanpur, 2006)*

31. Compare sporophytes of *Riccia*, *Anthoceros* and *Funaria.*

(Punjab, 1999; Kottoyan, 2004)

32. Explain the gametophyte of *Riccia.*

(Trichurapally, 1995)

33. Describe the mechanism of spore dispersal in *Riccia/Anthoceros.*

(Punjab, 1993)

34. (*a*) Compare the structure and position of archegonia in *Riccia, Marchantia* and *Funaria.*

(Himachal Pradesh, 1993)

(*b*) Compare the structure and position of antheridia in *Riccia, Marchantia* and *Funaria.*

(Himachal Pradesh, 1994)

35. Give an illustrated account of the sporophyte of *Riccia* and compare it with that of *Marchantia*. Bring out their resemblances and differences.

(Bundelkhand, 1996; Kerala, 1997)

36. Compare the gametophyte and sporophyte of *Riccia* and *Anthoceros.* *(Bundelkhand, 1997)*

37. With the help of suitable sketches give an account of progressive sterilisation of sporophytic tissues in *Riccia, Marchantia* and *Anthoceros.* *(Mahatma Gandhi, 1997)*

38. Give a comparative account of sexual reproduction in *Riccia* and *Anthoceros* *(Rohilkhand, 2001)*

39. Describe the development of sporophyte in *Riccia.* *(Meerut, 2002)*

40. Discuss the sporangia of *Riccia, Marchantia, Anthoceros* and *Funaria.* *(Gharwal, 2000)*

41. Discuss the sexual reproduction in *Riccia.* *(Punjab, 2000)*

SHORT ANSWER TYPE

42. Describe the internal structure of dorsal surface of *Riccia* thallus only. *(Kanpur, 2002)*

43. Who proposed the simplest sporophyte of *Riccia* is reduced rather than primitive ? *(Poorvanchal, 2003)*

44. Give the name of free floating aquatic species of *Riccia.* *(Poorvanchal, 2003; Kerala, 2001)*

45. (*a*) Name the species of *Riccia* in which the spore tetrads are isobilateral. *(Kanpur M.Sc., 2002; 2003)*

(*b*) Which type of branching is found in *Riccia* gametophyte. *(Kanpur, M.Sc., 2002)*

46. Is the sporophyte of *Riccia* wholly dependent on the gametophyte for nutrition ? Justify your statement. *(Kanpur, M.Sc. 2003)*

47. Draw neat and labelled diagrams of the following :

(*i*) T.S./V.S. thallus of *Riccia.* *(Kanpur, 1999, Awadh, 1993; U.P. College, 1999; Kumaon, 1997; Mahatma Gandhi Univ., 1998; Kerala, 2001)*

(*ii*) L.S. /V.T.S. of *Riccia* thallus passing through sporophyte with developed archesporium. *(Rohilkhand ,1996; Awadh, 1997; Allahabad, 1993)*

(*iii*) Sporophyte of *Riccia.* *(Awadh, 1992, 1994)*

(*iv*) V.S. gametophyte of *Riccia* (Cellular). *(U.P. College, 2000)*

(*v*) T.S. *Riccia* thallus showing mature archegonium. *(Kumaon, 2000)*

(*vi*) V.T.S. thallus of *Riccia* passing through antheridial chamber. *(Allahabad, 1994)*

(*vii*) Sex organs of *Riccia.* *(Kanpur M.Sc., 2002)*

(viii) Life Cycle of Riccia *(Kanpur, 2009)*

48. Draw only labelled figures of transverse sections of thallus of *Riccia, Marchantia, Pellia* and *Anthoceros.* *(Awadh, 1991)*

49. Explain the identifying features of *Riccia.* *(Rohilkhand, 1997)*

50. List the important features in the life cycle of *Riccia.*

51. (*a*) List in tabulated form the differences between the gametophyte and sporophyte of *Riccia.*

(*b*) Differentiate between simple and tuberculate rhizoids. *(Lucknow, 2001)*

52. Answer the following :

(*i*) Give the names of spore wall layers found in *Riccia* spores.

(*ii*) In which species of *Riccia* the midrib is absent?

(*iii*) Which is the aquatic species of *Riccia* ? *or* Name an aquatic species of *Riccia.* *(Poorvanchal, 2001; Kerala, 2004)*

(*iv*) Name a bryophyte which has simplest sporophyte.

(*v*) Name a bryophyte in which rhizoids are dimorphic.

(*vi*) Give the structure of sperms of *Riccia.*

(*vii*) Mention two important features of sporophytes of *Riccia*.

(*viii*) What is the difference in photosynthetic filaments of *Riccia* and *Marchantia* ?

(*ix*) Enumerate the differences between thallii of *Riccia* and *Marchantia*.

(*x*) Name the types of rhizoids in *Riccia*.

(*xi*) Name the parts of sporophyte of *Riccia*. *(MG Univ., 2004)*

(*xii*) Why *Riccia* is called highly advanced bryophyte ? *(Poorvanchal MSc.,1998)*

53. Write short notes on the following :

(*a*) Differences between external and internal structures of thallus of *Riccia* and *Marchantia* *(Awadh, 1997)*

(*b*) Systematic position of *Riccia*. *(Awadh, 1997)*

(*c*) Sporophyte of *Riccia*. *(Kumaon, 1996, 1997, 1998, 1999; Gorakhpur, 1997; Kerala, 1995; Allahabad, 2005)*

(*d*) Spore dispersal in *Riccia*. *(Purvanchal, 1998)*

(*e*) Vegetative propagation in *Riccia*. *(Kanpur, 2008; Poorvanchal, 2001; Gorakhpur, 1991, 1998)*

(*f*) Name a species of *Riccia* which is hydrophytic and compare its structure with that of land species. *(Gorakhpur, 1994)*

(*g*) Thallus structure in *Riccia*. *(Mahatma Gandhi 1998; Kerala, 1999, 1997, 1997)*

(*h*) Rhizoids of *Riccia*. *(Mahatma Gandhi, 1997; Kerala, 2000)*

(*i*) Nutrition of *Riccia* sporophyte. *(Mahatma Gandhi 1996)*

(*j*) Sexual reproduction in Riccia. *(Poorvanchal, 2002)*

(*k*) Male gametophyte of Riccia *(Kapur, 2005)*

(*l*) Female Differentiate between Rhizoids & Scales *(Lucknow, 2008)*

OBJECTIVE TYPE

54. Select the correct answer :

(*i*) Which of the following species of *Riccia* is aquatic?
- (*a*) *Riccia fluitans*
- (*b*) *Riccia gangetica*
- (*c*) *Riccia discolor*
- (*d*) *Riccia crystallina.*

(*ii*) The simplest sporophyte is found in
- (*a*) *Riccia* (*b*) *Marchantia*
- (*c*) *Anthoceros* (*d*) *Funaria.*

(*iii*) Which of the following has only capsule in its sporophyte?
- (*a*) *Marchantia* (*b*) *Riccia*
- (*c*) *Anthoceros* (*d*) *Funaria.*

(*iv*) The scales in *Riccia* are
- (*a*) Multicelled and appendiculate
- (*b*) Multicelled and ligulate
- (*c*) Unicelled and ligulate
- (*d*) Unicelled and appendiculate

(*v*) In *Riccia* the growth of thallus takes place by the activity of
- (*a*) A group of intercalary initials,
- (*b*) Group of apical cells
- (*c*) Single apical cell
- (*d*) Basal meristem.

(*vi*) Spores are liberated from the sporogonium only by the decay of gametophyte in
- (*a*) *Marchantia* (*b*) *Riccia*
- (*c*) *Funaria* (*d*) *Anthoceros.*

(*vii*) *Riccia* is a bryophyte because it
- (*a*) Occurs mostly on land and has motile sperms
- (*b*) Has heteromorphic alternation of generations
- (*c*) Has multicellular sex organs with a sterile jacket and lacks vascular tissues
- (*d*) Has nothing.

(*viii*) In *Riccia crystallina* the ventral scales are
(*a*) Multicelled
(*b*) Bicelled
(*c*) Unicelled
(*d*) Rudimentary or absent.

(*ix*) In which of the following plants, sporophyte is completely dependent on the gametophyte?
(*a*) *Riccia* (*b*) *Marchantia*
(*c*) *Pteris* (*d*) *Brassica.*

(*x*) In *Riccia*
(*a*) Only smooth rhizoids are present
(*b*) Pegged rhizoids are present
(*c*) Both smooth and pegged rhizoids are present
(*d*) Rhizoids are absent.

(*xi*) In which of the following species, dorsal groove is absent?
(*a*) *Riccia discolor*
(*b*) *R. frostii*
(*c*) *R. gangetica*
(*d*) *R. melanospora.*

(*xii*) Elaters are not found in
(*a*) *Marchantia* (*b*) *Riccia*
(*c*) *Pellia* (*d*) Anthoceros

(*xiii*) In which of the following bryophyte the sporophyte is embedded in the thallus ?
(*a*) *Marchantia* (*b*) *Pogonatum*
(*c*) *Riccia* (*d*) Pellia

(*xiv*) The antherozoids of *Riccia* are
(*a*) Monoflagellate
(*b*) Biflagellate
(*c*) Quadriflagellate
(*d*) Multi flagellate

(*xv*) In *Riccia* the antheridium is
(*a*) Oval (*b*) Spherical
(*c*) Pear shaped (*d*) Fask shaped

(*xvi*) In *Riccia* the sporophyte
(*a*) Is divisible into foot, seta, and capsule
(*b*) Is divisible into foot and capsule
(*c*) Does not contain foot and seta
(*d*) The capsule is absent

(*xvii*) The neck cells in the archegonium of *Riccia* are found in how many rows ?
(*a*) 3 (*b*) 4
(*c*) 5 (*d*) 6

(*xviii*) In *Riccia* how many rows of vertical cells form the wall of the neck of archegonia ?
(*a*) 2 (*b*) 4
(*c*) 6 (*d*) 8

Image of *Dumortiera hirsuta*

CHAPTER 5(I)

MARCHANTIALES
Marchantiaceae
Marchantia

- Marchantiaceae
- Marchantia (Mich.) L.
- Gametophyte Phase
- Reproduction
- Fertilization
- Important Features
- Discussion

MARCHANTIACEAE

General Characters

This family is represented by over 250 species. They are grouped under about 23 genera. The deep green, dorsal surface of the thallus, in most genera, is marked by rhomboidal areas (**areolae**), each with a central pore. Internally the thallus is chambered. The chambers are usually well developed with or without photosynthetic filaments. Exceptions are *Dumortiera* in which the chambers are represented only in a relic condition and *Monoselenium* in which they are lacking. The **airpores** are well developed. The sex organs occur on the dorsal surface and are always united into groups which are confined to a special region of the thallus called the **receptacle**. The female receptacle is always stalked. The male receptacle is commonly sessile but in the more advanced members of the family it is also stalked. The sporogonium is usually differentiated into the **foot**, **seta** and **capsule**. The latter produces both spores and elaters. The capsule dehisces either by the separation of a lid or by valves. The family includes a number of genera. The chief among them are *Dumortiera, and Marchantia.* The most common and highly differentiated of these is *Marchantia*. We shall therefore study *Marchantia* as a type of this family.

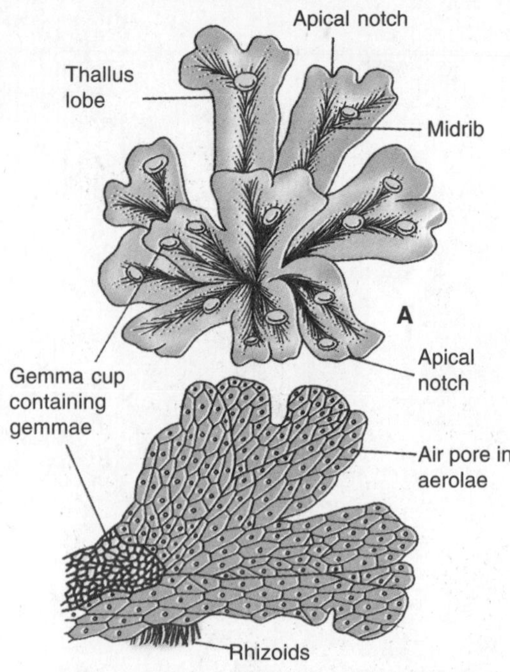

Fig. 5.1. (A—B). ***Marchantia* sp**. A, small patch of plants showing habit; B, part of the thallus showing airpores, areolae and gemma cups on the upper surface.

MARCHANTIA (March.) L.

Habit and distribution. *Marchantia* is the most common, highly differentiated and in many ways the most interesting genus. It is commonly found in moist, cool, shady situations and areas of burnt ground. The surface of dampsoil, the sides of streams, springs, water courses, walls of wells, swamps, damp ravines and wet rocks are the places suited for the growth of this Liverwort. It grows in large mats (Fig. 5.1). It has about 65 species. They are found all over the world . There are about 11 Indian species as reported by Chopra (1943). They are mostly confined to the Himalayas. The following three species of *Marchantia* have been reported by Kashyap from various parts of India, plains as well as the hills :

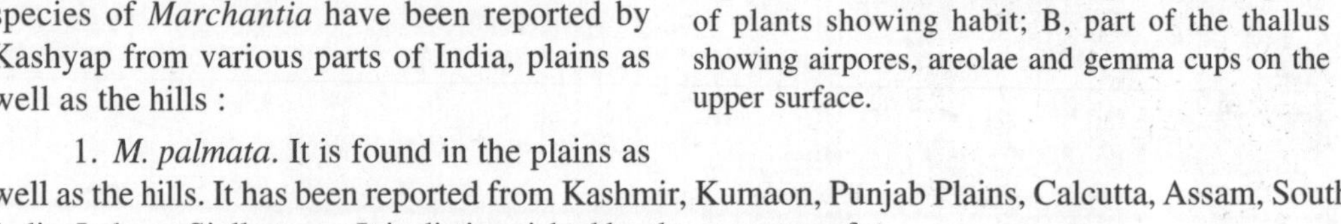

1. *M. palmata*. It is found in the plains as well as the hills. It has been reported from Kashmir, Kumaon, Punjab Plains, Calcutta, Assam, South India, Lahore, Sialkot, etc. It is distinguished by the presence of a median, dark streak on the dorsal surface of each lobe of the thallus. The lobes are long, narrow, margin entire and apex emarginate.

2. *M. nepalensis*. The median dark streak is lacking. Lobes are short and broad and margin generally crisped. The apex is emarginate. It has been reported form the Outer Himalayas, Punjab Plains, Kashmir, Garhwal, Kumaon, etc.

3. *M. polymorpha* (Fig. 5.2). It has been reported from the hills such as the Outer Himalayas up to 8000 ft., Pangi, Ladakh, Leh, etc. The thallus is relatively large, broad, slightly concave or flat. The margin of the thallus lobes sinuate to lobed.

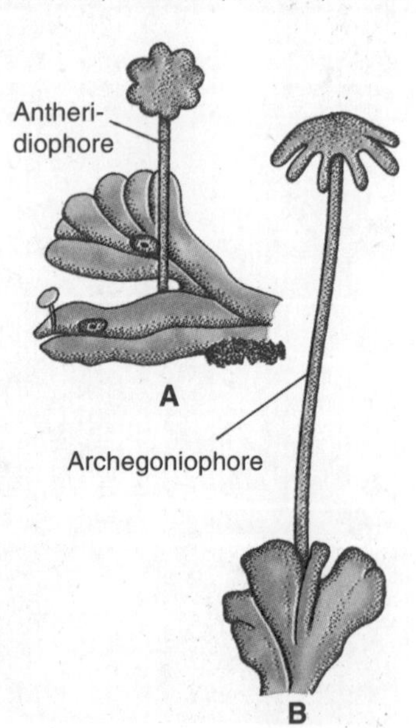

Fig. 5.2. (A—B). ***Marchantia.*** Male (A) and Female (B) thalli of *M. polymorpha*.

GAMETOPHYTE PHASE

It begins, as in *Riccia*, with the maturation of spores. Each spore on germination, produces a green thallus. Externally it has the same general appearance as that of *Riccia*. However, it differs in its large size, coarse nature and more prominent and pronounced elongated lobes. It is somewhat better adapted to grow on land than *Riccia*. The green thallus is the gametophyte plant.

1. External morphology of the thallus (Fig. 5.1). It is a dark, green, somewhat fleshy, flat, once or a few times dichotomously branched structure with a dorsiventral symmertry (B). Each thallus branch or lobe is traversed by a broad, thick, central **midrib**. It also has a **notch** at its apex. At the bottom of notch is located the growing point. The upper surface of the thallus is marked by rhomboidal to polygonal areas called the **areolae** (B). The boundaries between these areas mark the limit of the underlying **air chambers**. Each area has a tiny conspicuous hole or an **air pore** in the centre. The pore is visible on the surface as light dot. The air pores permit aeration of the thallus with minimum dehydration. At times little cup-like structures, the **gemma cups**, are seen on the surface of the thallus. They arise in the **midrib** region. The margin of the cup is toothed and membranous. From the bottom of the cup arise numerous, green, flat, multicellular bodies called the **gemmae**. The mature gemmae get detached. The detached gemmae are washed on to the soil where each gives rise to two new gametophyte plants.

When the thallus attains sexual maturity it bears gametangia bearing upright, stalked umbrella-shaped structures at the apices of certain lobes of the thallus (Fig. 5.2). These are called the **gametophores** or **gametangiophores**. They are of two kinds, **antheridiophores** (A) and **archegoniophores** (B). The former bear antheridia and the latter archegonia. The two kinds of gametophores are borne on different thalli so that *Marchantia* has male plants distinct from female plants.

From the lower or the ventral surface of the thallus arise numerous elongated, single celled, hair-like outgrowths, the **rhizoids** (Fig. 5.3 A). The latter anchor the plant to the substratum. In addition they absorb water and minerals in solution. The rhizoids are of two kinds **smooth walled** (Fig. 5.3 B) and **tuberculate** (Fig. 5.3 C). The tubercles are pronounced, peg-like invaginations of the wall. They extend across the cavity but do not form complete partitions. The tuberculate or peg rhizoids are thick walled, narrow and appressed to the surface of the thallus. They arise from beneath the scales and function as a capillary conducting system which serves to carry water to all the absorptive parts of the thallus. The smooth-walled rhizoids stand out from the thallus and penetrate the substratum to absorb water and to fix the thallus to it. They are broad, thin-walled with colourless contents. They are the first to be formed on germination. Besides the rhizoids the ventral surface bears purplish, flattered **scales** (Fig. 5.3 D). They are usually arranged in two to four rows on either side of the midrib (A). They are never in a single row as in *Riccia*. Each scale is a plate of cells one cell layer thick. It is attached obliquely and is divided by a narrow constriction into two parts, the **body** and the **appendage** (Fig. 5.3 D). In some species the appendage is absent. The scales are separate from the beginning. They are not formed by the splitting of a single lamella as in the case in *Riccia*. Galatis

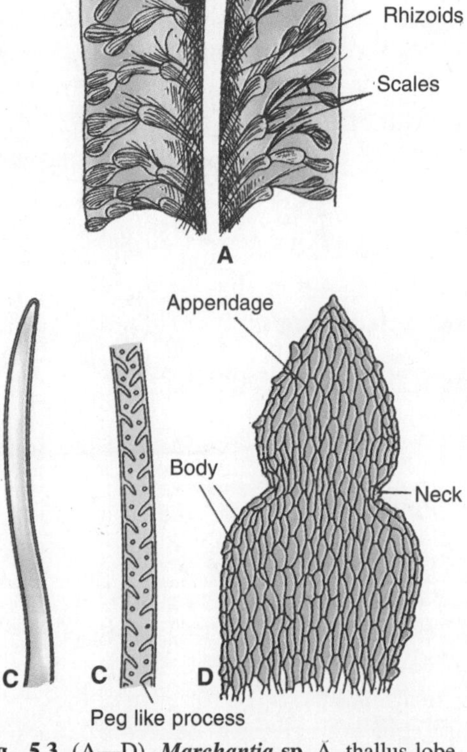

Fig. 5.3. (A—D). ***Marchantia* sp**. A, thallus lobe bearing scales on the lower surface; B, smooth-walled rhizoid: C, tuberculate rhizoid; D, appendaged scale.

and Apostolakos (1977) reported the development of mucilage papillae from the periphery of the scales in *Marchantia*. These arise as idioblast cells, elongate and appear club-shaped. The mucilage papillae secrete mucilage which surrounds and thus protects the growing region of the thallus from desiccation.

2. Internal structure (Fig. 5.4). There is greater internal elaboration of the thallus in *Marchantia* as compared with *Riccia*. In a vertical section the thallus is many cells deep. The cells are arranged in three distinct regions (A) instead of two as in *Riccia*. These are : (*i*) the **epidermal** region, (*ii*) the **photosynthetic** region and (*iii*) the **storage** region.

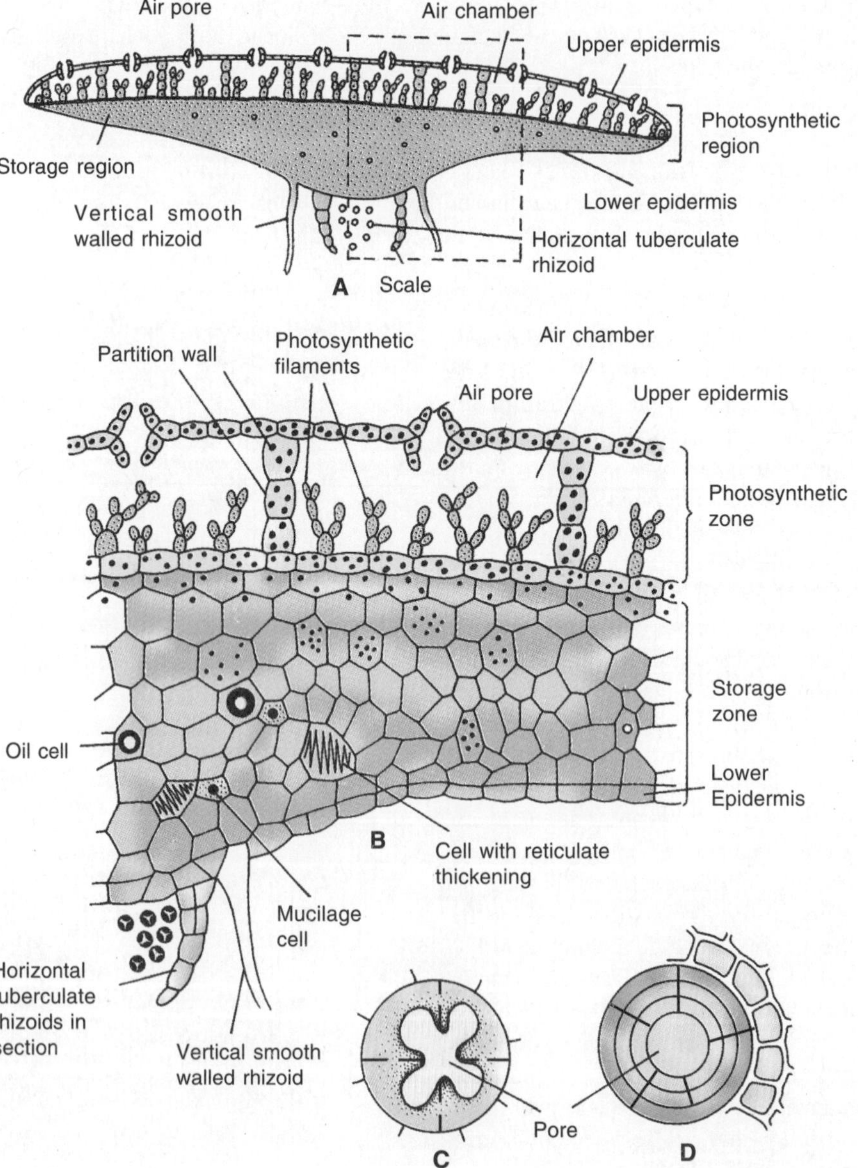

Fig. 5.4. (A—D). ***Marchantia* sp.** A, outline sketch of a vertical transverse section through the thallus lobe; B, detailed structure of a part of the thallus marked a in A above; C, air pore as seen from below surrounded by the papillose cells of the lowermost tier; D, air pore as seen from above.

(*a*) *Epidermal region* (B). It consists of a well-defined **upper epidermis** and **lower epidermis**. The upper epidermis forms a surface layer over the photosynthetic region. It consists of a single layer of thin-walled cells with slightly thickened outer walls. The epidermal cell contain few chloroplasts. The outer walls of the epidermal cells are practically water-proof. The epidermis is thus protective in function. It tends to check transpiration from the underlying tissues. Embedded in the epidermis are special, chimney-like or barrel-shaped **air pores**. Each pore is surrounded usually by four tiers of four or five cells each. The number of tiers, however, may go up to eight. These tiers form rings of cells one above the other. They are arranged in the form of a small chimney which encloses a wide passage. The passage is broad in the middle and narrow above and below. The pore wall lies half below the epidermis. The opening of the pore is thus slightly raised above the surface of the thallus. The cells of the lowermost tier in some species are papillose (C). They project into the passage. However, they do not close it. A star-shaped channel remains open. Each pore leads into an underlying chamber. The presence of air pores in the epidermis facilitates gaseous exchange necessary for photosynthesis and respiration. The raised epicuticularized waxy pore margins play a primary role in preventing water entering the underlying air chambers (Schonherr and Zeigler, 1975). Apparently the pores bear resemblance to the stomata of the higher plants. To them they are only **analogous**. The stomata are always absent on the gametophyte plant. The cells around the air pore do not regulate the opening as the guard cells do in the stomata. Walker and Pennington (1939) have reported that the surrounding cells by imbibitional changes in their cell walls bring about opening and closing of the air pore.

(*b*) *Photosynthetic region* (Fig. 5.4 B). Beneath the upper epidermis are the **air chambers**. They are of fairly regular size, simple and distinct from one another. They are arranged in a single horizontal layer. The chambers are bounded by one cell layer thick partitions. The partitions are three or four cells in height. Each chamber communicates with the exterior through a barrel-shaped or chimney-like **pore**. From the floor of each chamber arise short, simple or branched filaments of green cells, known as the **assimilatory** or **photosynthetic filaments**. They nearly fill the cavity of the chamber. All the cells of the floor, side walls and the photosynthetic filaments contain numerous ovoid chloroplasts. Even the cells of the overlying epidermis may contain a few chloroplasts. The chambered region constitutes the ventilated photosynthetic tissue. It is the principal centre of **photosynthesis** in the thallus. Photosynthesis is at its maximum rate in dim light. The arrangement of the cells in the photosynthetic region of the thallus of *Marchantia* is thus quite different from that of *Riccia*.

According to Barnes and Land (1907), the chambers in *Marchantia* originate as intercellular spaces. They are formed by the splitting of the cell wall (**Schizogenously**) and not by surface **involution**. The splitting starts usually below the epidermis. It progresses gradually inwards. For a detailed discussion of the **origin** of the **air chambers** in the Marchantiales refer to page 50 (Chapter IV).

(*c*) *Storage region.* Just below the photosynthetic region lies the ventral **Storage region** of the thallus. It is thickest in the centre. Towards the margins it is reduced to 3-4 layers of cells in thickness. It consists of a uniform tissue made up of relatively large, colourless, thin-walled polygonal, parenchymatous cells which usually lack chloroplasts and are compactly arranged. Most of them contain starch and protein grains. Isolated cells may contain a single large oil body or may be filled with mucilage. The former are called the **oil body cells** and latter **mucilage cells**. Galatis and Apostolakos (1976) reported that the central vacuole in which the oil body appears is progressively formed in the cell. In addition they observed microbodies and a system of cytoplasmic tubules in the oil body cells. The tubules transverse the cytoplasm close to the vacuole and run parallel to the tonoplast and also show relationship to the elongated microbodies. The function of this association between the microbodies and the cytoplasmic tubules in the oil body cells of **Marchantia** is obscure.

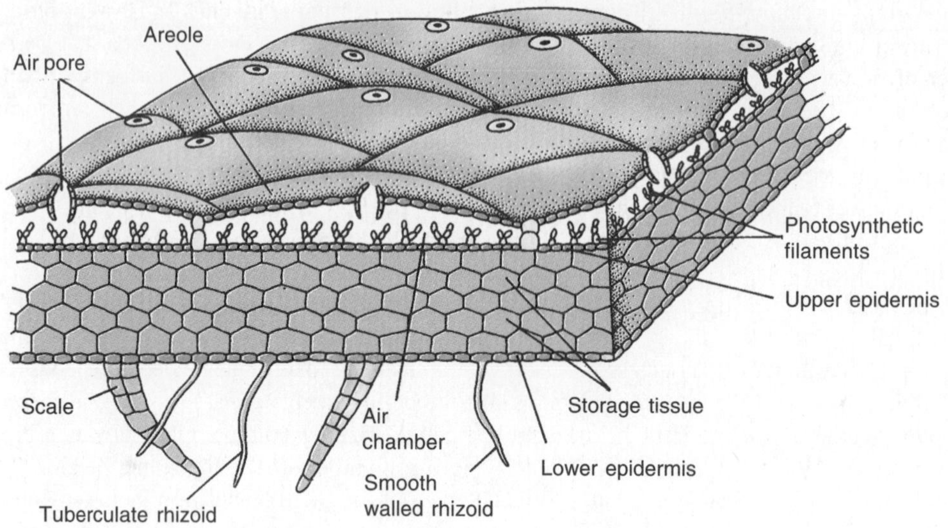

Fig. 5.5. *Marchantia* sp. Three dimensional view of a part of the thallus lobe.

The colourless cells of the midrib region in *M. polymorpha* are elongated in the sagittal axis and have walls with reticulate thickenings.

The lowermost layer of the storage region is composed of cells similar to those of the upper epidermis. It is the **lower epidermis**. From it project the **rhizoids** and the **scales**. The scales help to retain the moisture below the thallus. This enables *Marchantia* to grow in much drier places as compared with *Riccia*.

The presence of an endogenous **auxin** in *M.polymorpha* has been demonstrated by Schneider, Troxler and Voth (1967). The role of this hormone in rhizoidal initiation, orthogeotropism, gemmae cup formation, regeneration and apical dominance has been investigated by various workers. Maravolo (1976) reported that the auxin transport is basipetal and mainly occurs in the midrib region. Dorothy *et al* (1982) carried on tracer experiments using exogenous 14C indoleacetic acid and found that its transport occurs in the cells of the midrib region of the thallus. The transport is both basipetal and acropetal. Basipetal transport is, however, significantly greater in intensity.

3. Comparison with Riccia. In general form, structure and development of the thallus *Marchantia* resembles *Riccia*. Both resemble each other in the following features :

(*a*) In both the green thallus is dichotomously branched, dorsiventral in construction and as a rule fleshy in texture.

(*b*) From its lower surface in both arise the unicellular, unbranched, smooth and tuberculate rhizoids and the multicellular scales.

(*c*) Internally it is differentiated in both into the upper, well ventilated, photosynthetic region and the lower compact, storage region.

(*d*) In both the growing point is lodged in a notch at the tip of each thallus lobe.

(*e*) The apical growth in both takes place by means of a group of apical cells arranged in a transverse row.

The *Marchantia* thallus, however, is more advanced and thus differs from the *Riccia* thallus in the following respects :

(*i*) Its definitely larger size, broader, thicker and coarser lobes.

(*ii*) Better adapted to grow on land than *Riccia*.

(*iii*) Prominent expanded midrib.

(*iv*) Upper surface of the thallus marked with rhomboidal areas each with a distinct central pore.

(*v*) Internal differentiation of thallus into three distinct regions (epidermal, photosynthetic and storage) instead of two (photosynthetic and storage) as in *Riccia*.

(*vi*) A definite layer of air chambers with photosynthetic filaments arising from the floors.

(*vii*) A continuous water proof epidermis with definite barrel-shaped air pores.

(*viii*) Presence of scales in two to four rows on either side of the midrib. They help to retain moisture below the thallus. In *Riccia* they are arranged in two rows one near each lateral margin.

(*ix*) The scales in *Marchantia* commonly appendaged whereas in *Riccia* the appendage is absent.

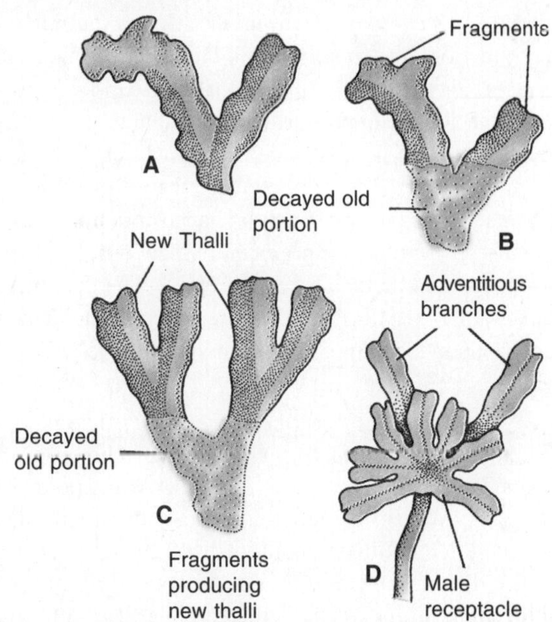

Fig. 5.6. (A—D). ***Marchantia* sp**. A—C, showing fragmentation of the thallus and the fragments producing new thalli; D, adventitious branches arising from the lower surface of the male disc between the lobes.

(*x*) Presence of gemma cups containing gemmae.

These features indicate that *Marchantia* thallus (gametophyte) is more advanced than that of *Riccia*. The presence of scales on the ventral side and not the margins as in *Riccia*, and a continuous well defined epidermal layer enable *Marchantia* to grow in drier habitats as compared with *Riccia*. The ventral scales help to retain moisture below the thallus which can be absorbed by the rhizoids. The epidermis helps to check transpiration from the underlying photosynthetic tissue. Inspite of the foregoing features which make *Marchantia* better adapted to a life on land than *Riccia*, abundant moisture is still required for its active growth and fertilization.

Apical growth. The growing point lies at the bottom of a notch at the apex of each lobe. It consists of a horizontal row of meristematic cells. By the activity of these the thallus grows in length.

REPRODUCTION

Marchantia thallus reproduces **vegetatively** and also by a sexual process.

Vegetative reproduction (Fig. 5.6). The thallus plant reproduces vegetatively in the growing season by the following three methods :-

(*a*) *Fragmentation* (A—C). It is brought about by the ageing of the vegetative cells. The aged cells in the rear or basal part of the thallus rot and disintegrate (B). When this decay of cells reaches dichotomy the lobes become separated (B). Each of the detached lobes by apical growth and dichotomy develops into an independent plant (C). In this way there is rapid increase in the number of plants in a particular area and constant invasion of the new territories.

(*b*) *Formation of adventitious branches* (D). These may develop from any part of the thallus particularly its ventral surface. In *Marchantia palmata* development of adventitious branches from the stalk and disc of the female gametophore was reported by Kashyap. These branches when detached by the decay of the connecting tissue develop into new individuals.

(*c*) *Gemmae formation* (Fig. 5.7). Another interesting and elegant method of vegetative reproduction in *Marchantia* is by the formation of mutlicellular bodies called the **gemmae** (B). The gemmae develop inside little, shallow, cup-like growths with fringed margins (A). The cups are developed on the upper surface of the thallus, generally in the midrib region. The gemmae are small, green, disc-like, slightly bi-convex structures. Each gemma stands on edge on a short, delicate single-celled stalk (B). The stalk attaches it to the bottom of the gemma cup (D). Intermingled with the gemmae in the cup are the club-shaped **mucilage hairs** which secrete mucilage copiously (D). With the absorption of water provided by dew or rain the mucilage swells and causes the gemmae to get detached from their stalks rather easily. The gemmae are then washed on to the soil or carried by a current of water far from the parent plant. The detached gemmae grow into new thalli on suitable soil. Voth and Hammer (1940) and Lockwood (1975) demonstrated that for gemma formation short days were required.

(*i*) *Structure of gemma* (Fig. 5.7 B). The gemma at maturity is a lens-shaped, multicellular structure. It is several cells thick in the median portion and deeply notched on the two opposite edges. In each marginal notch lies the growing point. The latter consists of meristematic cells located along the margin of the notch: These are small and full of cytoplasm. There is another shallow indentation marking the point of attachment to the stalk. Majority of the cells constituting the body of the gemma are green. They contain abundant chloroplasts and are called the **green** or **chlorenchymatous cells**. Isolated cells just within the margin may contain oil bodies instead of chloroplasts. They are called the **oil cells**. The two flattened surfaces are alike and have no innate dorsiventral symmetry. Both the surfaces possess isolated, superficial colourless cells known as the **rhizoidal cells**. The dorsiventral symmetry becomes fixed at the time of germination and is controlled by the gradients of light, temperature and other environmental factors.

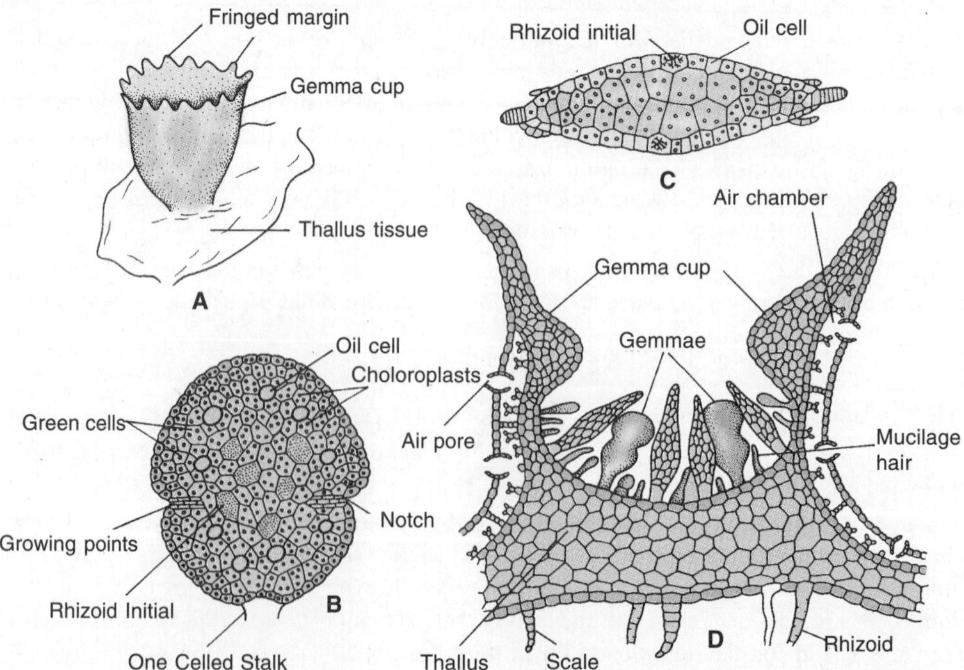

Fig. 5.7. (A—D). ***Marchantia* sp.** A, gemma cup with a part of the thallus tissue; B, single gemma showing structure; C, transverse section of gemma; D, vertical transverse section of the thallus lobe passing through the gemma cup.

(*ii*) *Germination of gemma* (Fig. 5.7C). When the gemmae fall on a suitable soil the colourless rhizoidal cells of the face next to the soil develop rhizoids. The meristems or growing points in both the marginal notches begin to grow simultaneously in opposite directions. Rotting away of the central protion of the parent gemma results in the production of two separate plants. Gemmae formation is usually common during the growing season. It provides a very rapid device for multiplication and a successful means of dispersal. It has been experimentally determined by De La Rue and Narayanaswami (1957) that the germination of the gemmae *in situ* (gemma cup) is inhibited by the secretion of auxins from the growing tips of the parent thallus lobes. The auxins diffuse basipetally.

(*iii*) *Development of gemmae* (Fig. 5.8). The cupules are formed a short distance back from the growing point. They arise in the form of circular ridges of cells. The gemmae originate from single superficial cells lining the floor of the cupules. Each such cell grows into a papillate outgrowth. It is the **gemmae initial** (A). The gemmae initial divides by a transverse wall into a **lower** and an **upper cell** (A). The lower cell divides no further. It forms the one-celled **stalk**. The upper cell again divides by a transverse wall (B). Each of the two resultant cells undergoes a similar division (C). A row of four cells is formed (C). These four cells undergo division both in the vertical (D) and horizontal planes (E). As a result a thin plate-like structure with a notch on the opposite sides is formed (F).

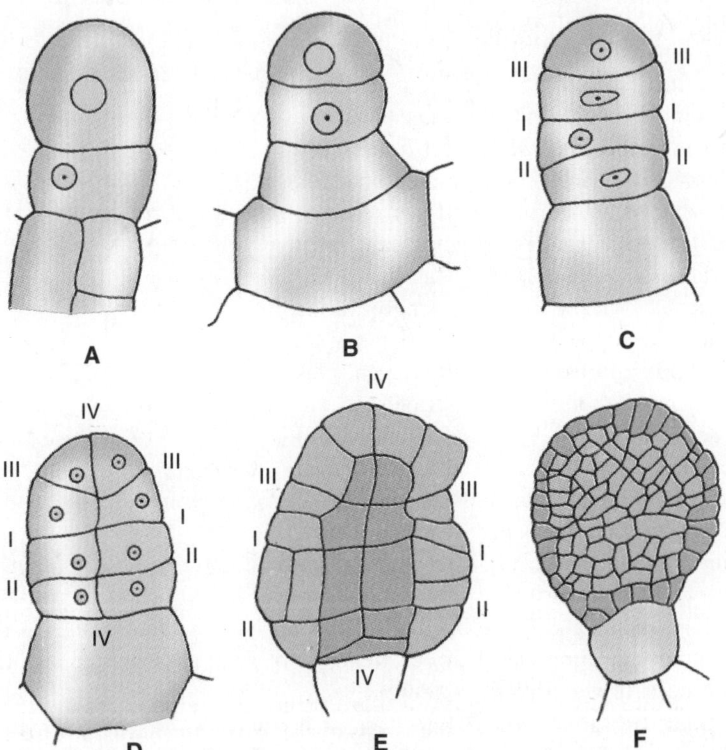

Fig. 5.8. (A—F). ***Marchantia polymorpha***. Stages in the development of a gemma. (After Campbell).

Sexual reproduction. It is the concern of the thallus plant and is of **oogamous** type. It takes place only once during the growing season in high **humidity** when the days are long (Wann 1925) and nitrogen content in the environment is low.

(a) Position and distribution of sex organs (Fig. 5.9). The sex organs in *Marchantia* are borne on the vertical branches of the thallus, highly specialised for this purpose. The sexual branches are **apical** or **terminal** in position (A and B) as each develops from one half of a dichotomy of the apical cell. The growth in length of the thallus lobes ceases after their development. Each upright sexual branch thus is a direct continuation of the prostrate thallus lobe from which it arises. It is called the **gametophore** or **gametangiophore**. The thallus-like nature of the gametophore is shown by the presence of rhizoids in the grooves on the anterior side of the stalk and photosynthetic chambers on the posterior side (Fig. 5.11).

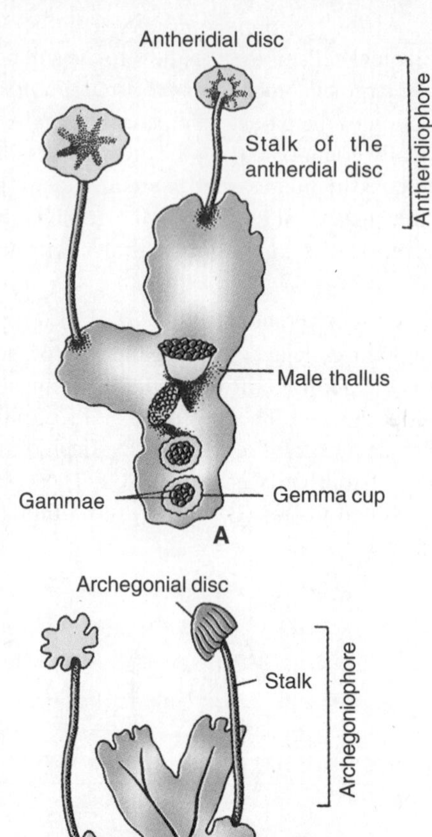

Fig. 5.9. (A—B). ***Marchantia***. A, male thallus of *M. polymorpha;* B, female thallus of *M. palmata*.

The gametophores in *Marchantia* are *unisexual*. The one bearing the male sex organs (antheridia) is called **antheridiophore** (A) and one bearing archegonia is called **archegoniophore** (B). Both the antheridiophores and the archegoniophores constitute accessory apparatus of sexual reproduction. The essential organs are the **antheridia** and the **archegonia**. The antheridiophores and the archegoniophores are borne on different thalli usually in late April or May (Maravolo et al 1976). Sexual reproduction thus involves two kinds of plants—male which bear the antheridiophores (A) and female which bear the archegoniophores (B). Marchantia.is, therefore, sexually *dimorphic* and *heterothallic* (*dioecious*). Abnormal receptacles bearing both archegonia and antheridia in the same receptacle have also been reported in *Marchantia*. These bisexual receptacles have been termed *androgynous receptacles*. In addition the androgynous receptacle bears antheridia singly in pits opening outwards on the upper surface. Haberlain (1929) and Srinivasan (1930) reported androgynous receptacles in *M. palmata* whereas Naidu (1973) described them in *M. polymorpha*. Kashyap (1929) and Khanna (1930) observed gametophores with branched stalks each branch ending in a disc in *M. palmata*. Udar and Chandra (1964) found receptacles with branched stalks in another species *M. grisea*. Parihar and Jagdish Lal (1972) described abnormal carpocephala in *M. palmata* in which the disc itself was divided into two parts by a shallow groove. The two-parts disc was borne terminally on a common short thick stalk. Some bryologists look upon these abnormalities as freaks of nature. Majority of them, however, consider their occurrence as of great phylogenetic significance denoting reversion to the ancestral *monoecious* condition.

(b) Antheridiophore (Fig. 5.9 A). It consists of a stalk bearing terminally a disc or **receptacle** with a margin bearing rounded teeth. The stalk is more or less cylindrical. It is one to three centimetres long. A cross-section through the stalk reveals that there are chambers and pores on its posterior side and two rhizoidal grooves on its anterior side (Fig. 5.11). The grooves or furrows run longitudinally the entire length of the stalk. They contain rhizoids and scales. These tissues of stalk correspond to those on the dorsal and ventral surfaces of the thallus lobe and prove its dorsiventral nature.

The terminal **male receptacle** is a flattened, lobed disc. Typically it has eight lobes occasionally four. Each lobe has its growing point lodged at its tip. The receptacle thus is a branch system. It is the result of repeated, localized dichotomy in quick succession. A vertical section of the male receptacle (Fig. 5.10 A) shows that it has the same tissues as are found in the thallus. There is the upper epidermis with air pores. The latter open into the underlying chambers containing the photosynthetic filaments. Beneath the chambers is the compact region of colourless parenchyma cells. The lower epidermis bears scales and rhizoids. Deeply sunk in the upper surface of each lobe are the **antheridia**. They arise in the acropetal order and are arranged in a radial row. Each antheridium lies in a flask-shaped pit (**antheridial chamber**). The latter opens by a narrow channel on the upper slightly concave surface of the disc. The opening is called an **ostiole**. The antheridial cavities or chambers alternate in position with the air chambers.

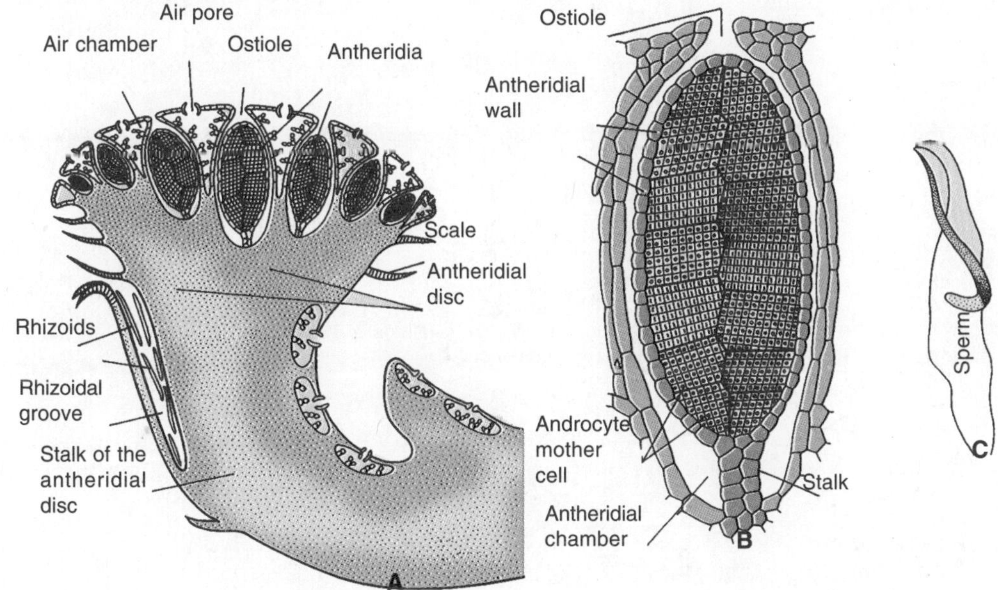

Fig. 5.10. (A—C). ***Marchantia* sp**. A, longitudial section through the young antheridiophore; B, V.S. through the antheridial chamber containing a nearly mature antheridium; C, biflagellate antherozoid.

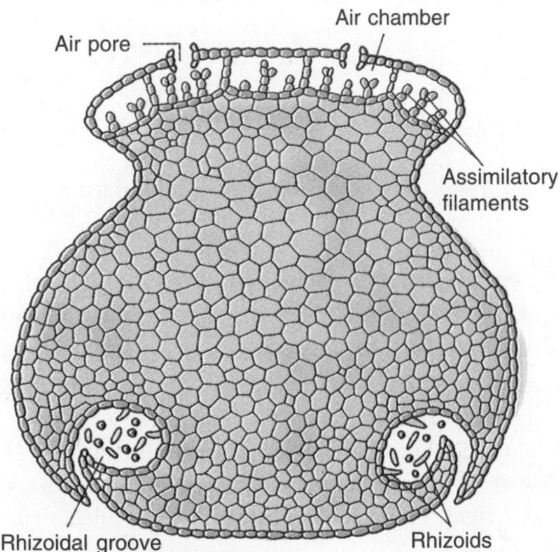

Fig. 5.11. ***Marchantia* sp**. A, cross-section through stalk of antheridiophore.

(*i*) *Structure of antheridium* (Fig. 5.10 B). The mature antheridium is an ovoid object raised on a short, multicellular stalk. The stalk attaches the antheridium to the floor of the antheridial chamber. The body of the antheridium has a jacket layer of sterile cells constituting its **wall**. The latter encloses a mass of **androcyte mother cells**. Each androcyte mother cell divides to form two **androcytes** or **sperm cells**. The protoplast of the androcyte metamorphoses into a biflagellate **sperm**.

Dehiscence. The ripe antheridium dehisces on the access of water. It is provided by rain or dew. From the concave upper surface of the male receptacle the water finds its way through the ostiole into the antheridial pit. There it comes in contact with the cells in the upper portion of the **antheridial wall** which eventually disintegrate. The antheridium thus ruptures at its distal end. A slimy mass of androcytes oozes out of the chamber at the upper surface of the receptacle into the water. Reaching the surface of water the androcytes spread out thinly as a delicate film. The sperms are now set free by the dissolution of the walls of the androcytes.

A liberated sperm (Fig. 5.10 C) is usually described as a small, narrowly curved structure. It is an elongated nucleus with the cytoplasm forming an extremely thin investment. From its one end project the two flagella which always point backwards. Sato (1954) reported that the liberated sperm is rod-like in *M. polymorpha*. While swimming it takes the form of a crawl of a snake with one flagellum lashing forward and the other backward.

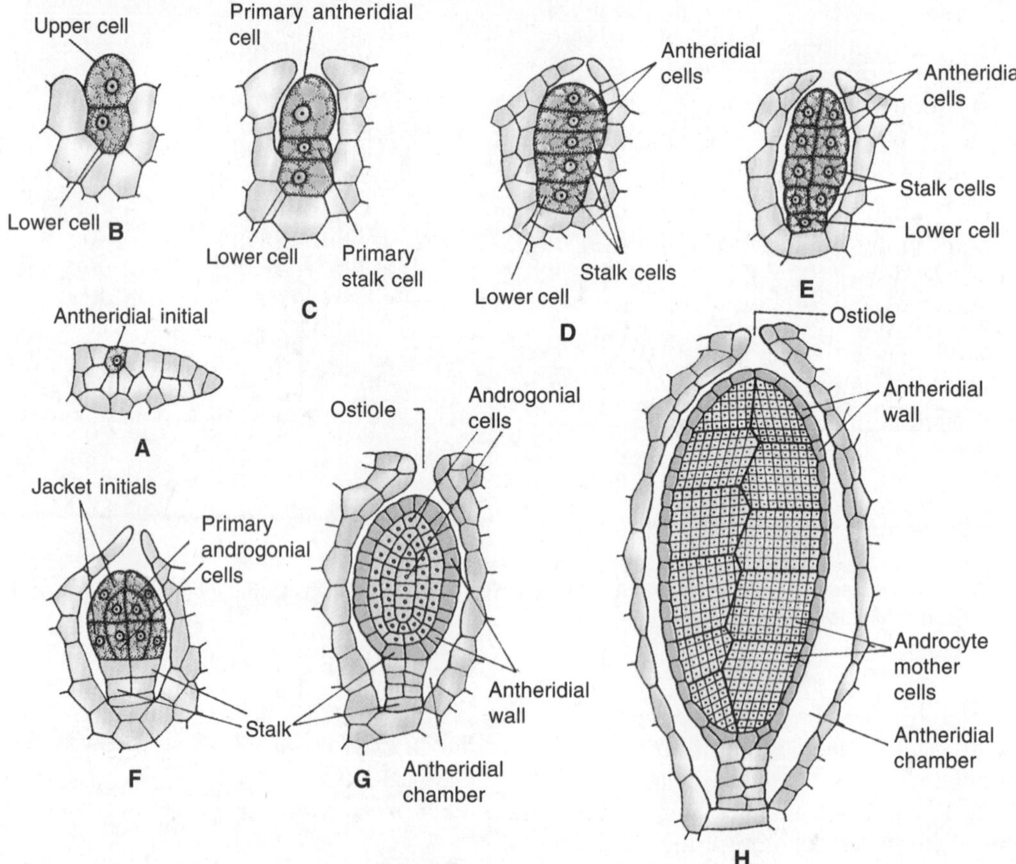

Fig. 5.12. (A—H). ***Marchantia* sp.** A—G, early stages in the development of antheridium; H, nearly mature antheridium. Explanation in the text.

(*ii*) *Development of antheridium* (Fig. 5.12). The growth of the thallus ceases with the development of the antheridiophore. The growing apex of the very young unelongated antheridiophore divides by dichotomy. The division is repeated a number of times. The result is the formation of a disc with a wavy margin. Each lobe of the disc has a growing point situated at its apex. The antheridia arise in acropetal order behind the growing point of each lobe of the disc. The young disc or receptacle is covered by conspicuous papillae. The paillae denote the position of antheridial chambers.

Each antheridium, as in *Riccia*, arises from a single superficial cell, the **antheridial initial**. It lies 2 or 3 cells behind the growing point of the lobe of the male receptable (A). The initial increases in size and divides by a transverse divison into two cells (B). The lower cell undergoes no further development. The upper, however, divides again transversely to separate a basal **primary stalk cell** and a terminal **primary antheridial cell** (C). The former undergoes a few divisions to form the stalk of the antheridium. The primary antheridial cell divides by parallel cleavage to form a row of usually two or three cells (D) sometimes more. Each of these cells now divides by two successive vertical walls at right angles to each other (E). The body of the antheridium at this stage consists of 2, 3 or 4 tiers of four cells each (E). Periclinal divisions appear in all the cells of the tiers. These divisions separate an outer layer of cells enclosing a mass of inner or central cells (F). The outer cells are called **jacket initials** and the inner ones **primary androgonial cells**. During further development the jacket initials divide only by anticlinal walls to give rise to the **wall** of the antheridium (G). The primary androgonial cells undergo a considerable number of divisions. The cells of the last cell generation are called the **androcyte mother cells** (H). They are small, cubical and numerous in number and are easily distinguishable from the preceding spermatogenous cells (androgones) by the presence of two small dotlike darkly staining structures; the **centrosomes** which arise *de novo* in the cytoplasm (Moser, 1970). Each centrosome takes its position to be occupied by the pole of the spindle. At this stage the protoplast of the androcyte mother cell undergoes the final mitotic division which is diagonal (A—B). The two resulting daughter protoplasts are not separated by a division wall. They are called the **androcytes** or **spermatids** (C). The androcytes eventually metamorphose into biflagellate sperms.

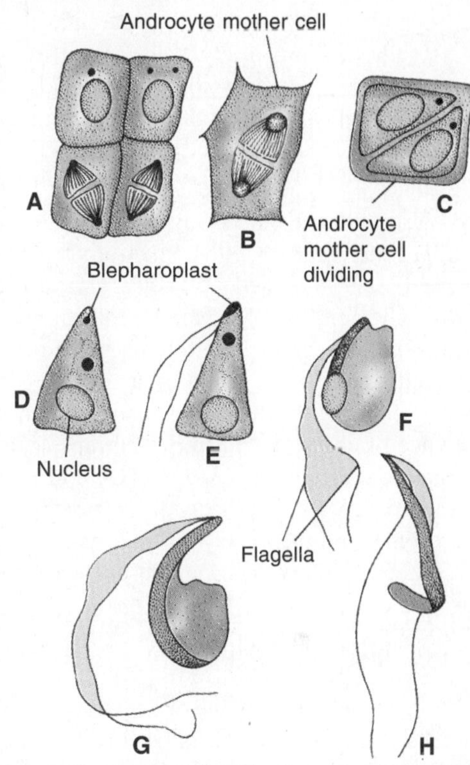

Fig. 5.13. (A—H). ***Marchantia* sp**. A—C, showing androcyte mother cell dividing diagonally into two androcytes; D—G, stages in spermatogenesis; H, a single sperm. (After Ikeno).

Spermatogenesis (Fig. 5.13). It is a complex process consisting of an integrated series of events leading to the transformation of the androcyte into sperm. It involves two stages or phases namely, (*i*) the development of **blepharoplast** and (*ii*) the elongation of androcyte nucleus.

(*i*) *Development of blepharoplast*. The young androcyte is triangular in section (D). It has a dense granule situated in the acute angle. This granule which behaved like a centrosome in the androcyte mother cell is now termed the *blepharoplast* (Ikeno, 1903) in view of the function it performs in the androcyte. It behaves like an organ different from the centrosome. The blepharoplast elongates to some extent and puts its whole body in close contact with the inner contour of the androcyte thus giving the impression that it has arisen as a local thickening of the plasma membrane (E). From the elongated blepharoplast emerge the **flagella**. Prior to emergence of the flagella and any change in the nucleus, a strongly staining extra-nuclear round body of unknown origin appears in the androcyte cytoplasm (D). Ikeno (1903) termed it chromatid "*Nebenkorper*". He believed that the Nebenkorper directly takes no part in the development of the sperm. Eventually it disappears. As the flagella emerged from the blepharoplast, a special bank-like structure differentiates from the cytoplasm and grows in the direction of the anterior end of the future sperm. It finally connects the nucleus with the blepharoplast (F). Ikeno thus believed that the blepharoplast produced flagella only and the specially differentiated cytoplasmic band is of a different origin. Motteir (1904) held that this specialized band connecting the nucleus with the flagella bearing structure is derived from the flagella bearer itself and is not a separate formation. Campbell (1905) stated that the portion of the sperm between the blepharoplast and the nucleus is derived from the "Nebenkorper" and not form the cytoplasm.

The ultrastructural study of spermatogenesis in *M. polymorpha* by Kreitner and Carothers (1976) revealed astonishing details. They reported that the centrosome consists of a pair of coaxial rod-like structures, the **centrioles** with their proximal ends opposed to the mid point of a common hub. Associated with the centrioles at their proximal ends is a zone of dense cytoplasm which represents the *microtubule organising centre* (MTOC). In a young spermatid (androcyte) the two centrioles (2-part centrosome) and the MTOC migrate as an integral unit to the periphery and come in contact with the plasma membrane.

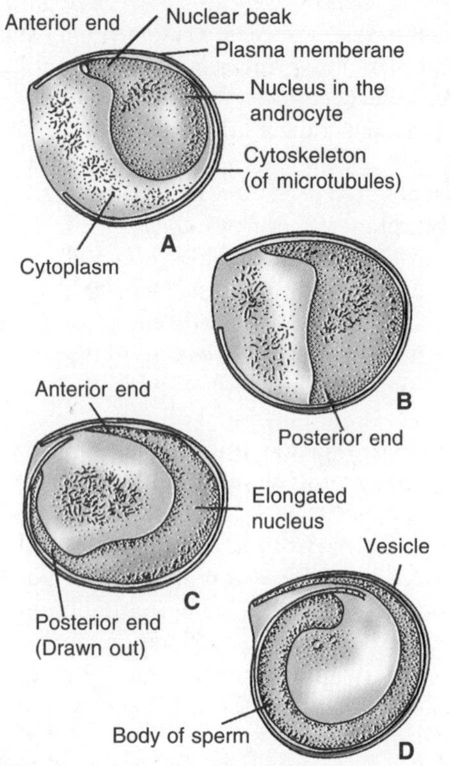

Positioned as such begins the development of blepharoplast. Following structural and functional transformation the two centrioles become the basal bodies for flagella production. A multilayered structure (MLS), the *spline apparatus* forms in the dense zone (MTOC) beneath the proximal ends of the incipient basal bodies. It has a four-layered organisation. Each layer comprises a number of microtubules. The spline apparatus is flat and strap-shaped in *Marchantia*. The basal bodies together with the closely substanding multilayered structure or spline apparatus that develops beneath them constitute the **blepharoplast**. It is an elaborate structure, elongated and somewhat widened in form.

Fig. 5.14. (A—D). ***Marchantia* sp.** Diagrammatic representation of the stages showing elongation of the nucleus along the cytoskeleton of microtubules as seen in side view of the androcyte. Based on Kreitner and Carothers.

From their distal ends both the basal bodies produce flagella. The flagella lengthen until they encircle the cell through a full turn or more. The strapshaped spline apparatus has a broadened anterior end for a short distance which tapers distally to form a long thin band consisting of about 6 microtubules. The narrow band encircles the androcyte beneath the plasma membrane. The cross linked microtubules of the MLS or spline apparatus function as a cytoskeleton or supporting framework for the elongation of the androcyte nucleus.

(*ii*) *Elongation of the androcyte nucleus* (Fig. 5.14). With the development of locomotory apparatus (blepharoplast) which takes palce in the early development of the androcyte, the spherical nucleus moves from the posterior half of the cell and comes in contact with the spline apparatus. It presses against it and the plasma membrane of the androcyte. In this position it develops a beaklike porojection (A) which lies beneath and aperture (spline aperture) in the bluntly leading end of the spline apparatus. The nuclear beak extends anteriorly and is inserted in the pre-existing diverticulum on one side of the spline apparatus. It thus joins the nucleus to the blepharoplast. Concurrent with the formation of the beak-like projection, the body of the nucleus elongates and curves. It is drawn out posteriorly (B) along the cytoskeleton till it becomes crescent tapering at both ends (C). Further elongation converts it into a long, tapered rod-like coiled structure completing a little more than one gyre (D).

Morphology of the sperm. The sperm consists of 3 parts namely, (*i*) the so-called *head piece*, (*ii*) the *nuclear portion* and (*iii*) the *cytoplasmic portion*. The head piece comprises the basal bodies with the emerging flagella, the rounded proximal part of spline and the anterior mitochondrion. The nuclear portion consists of the long narrow rod-like coiled nucleus, and the long, narrow portion of the spline appressed to it. The cytoplasmic part of the sperm includes the plastid filled with starch and the associated mitochondrion. A thin film of cytoplasm may sometimes be discernible beneath the plasma membrane.

(c) **Archegoniophore** (Fig. 5.15). It is also a sexual branch that turns upwards and grows vertically (A). It becomes specially modified like the antheridiophore. It consists of a stalk bearing a lobed disc at its distal end. In its external and internal structure the stalk resembles that of the antheridiophore. It is however slightly longer. It may be 2 to 3 inches long. Typically the female disc is an inconspicuously eight lobed object. The growing apices of these lobes bend downwards and inwards towards the stalk. From the margin of the disc between the growing points grow out long cylindrical processes. These are called the **rays** (D). They are usually nine in number. The rays give the mature female receptacle a **stellate form**.

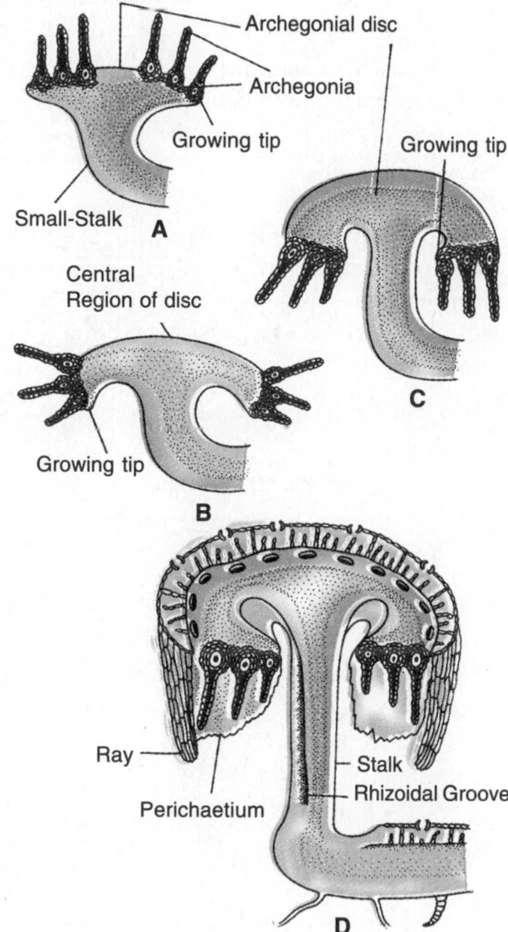

Fig. 5.15. (A—D). ***Marchantia* sp.** L.S. through the archegoniophore at various stages of development showing inversion. Explanation in the text.

(*i*) *Position of archegonia* (Fig. 5.15). The archegonia in very young receptacles are borne on the upper surface of the receptacle with their necks directed upwards (A). They are developed in acropetal order and stand free from each other in eight radial rows. The youngest is near the growing point. There is one row to each lobe and 12-14 archegonia in each row. At this stage the stalk of archegoniophore is practically absent or very small so that the receptacle appears sub-sessile. The first formed archegonia in the rows reach maturity. Fertilisation takes place at this stage. After fertilisation the stalk of the archegoniophore begins to elongate. Associated with this is a rapid growth in the central sterile region of the upper surface of the receptacle. With more growth above than below the cap, the growing points become gradually pushed downwards and inwards towards the stalk (B and C). Consequently the archegonia become transferred to the lower surface. In a mature female receptacle they are pendulous and thus hang downwards from the under surface of the disc with the youngest near the stalk (D). The inversion of the archegonia is accompanied by the development of a plate-like tissue on either side of each row of archegonia. It is the **perichaetium** or the **involucre** (D). The perichaetium is a two lipped, curtain-like structure. It is a single layer of cells in thickness. It grows and hangs down vertically from the under surface of the lobe and is fringed at the lower edge. Each row of archegonia is thus separated from its neighbour by the perichaetium. In the meanwhile from the upper surface of the disc develop long, stout, green cylindrical processes called the **rays**. The rays emerge radially between the rows of archegonia and are generally nine in number. They extend out and in a young receptacle hang downwards like the ribs of a tiny umbrella. At maturity they spread widely apart giving the female receptacle a stellate (star-shaped) appearance.

The mature female receptacle (Fig.5.16 A) has the same internal structure as the male. There is the upper epidermis with air pores embedded in it. Beneath it are the air chambers arranged in a single layer. From the floor of the air chambers arise the assimilatory filaments. There are no pits alternating with the air chambers as are found in the male receptacle.

(*ii*) *Structure of archegonium* (Fig. 5.16 B). The archegonium of *Marchantia* is supported on a short but distinct multicellular **stalk**. The stalk attaches the archegonium to the under surface of the receptacle. The body of the archegonium consists of two parts, the **venter** and the **neck**. The venter forms the swollen, basal portion of the archegonium. It is continued into the long, slender, tubular neck. The venter consists of a **wall** of a single layer of sterile cells enclosing the **venter cavity**. The latter contains two cells. The larger **egg cell** lies at the base and when mature is surrounded by a fluid. Above it is the smaller **ventral canal cell**. The jacket or wall of the venter is continued

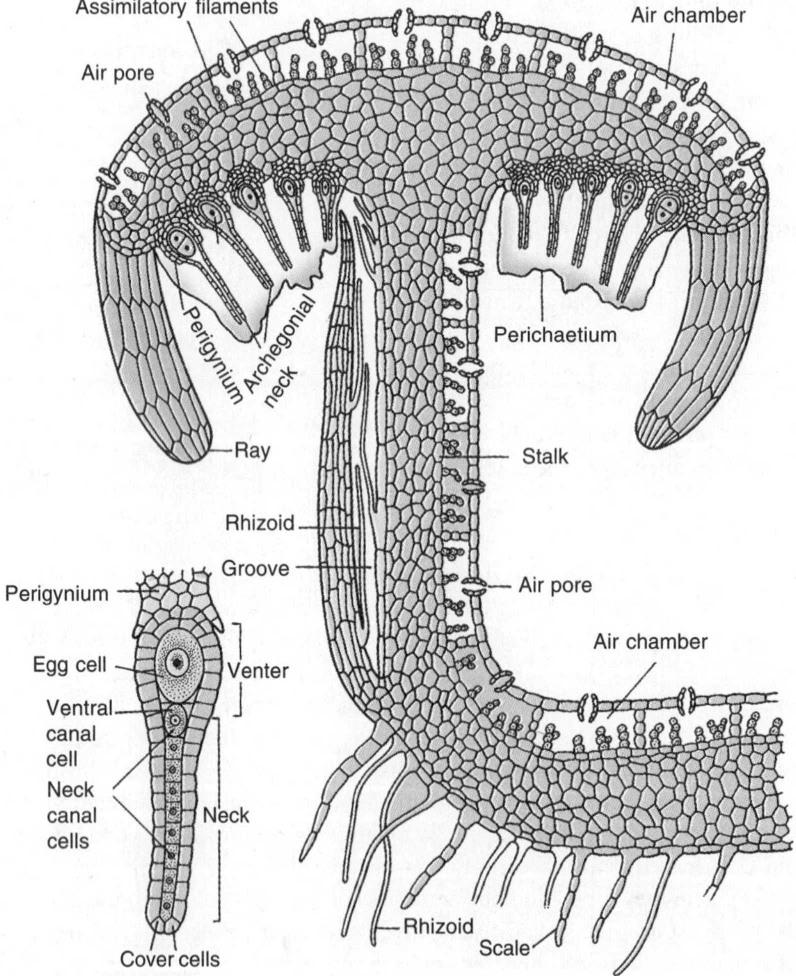

Fig. 5.16. (A—B). ***Marchantia* sp.** A, a longitudinal section through the archegoniophore showing structure; B, a nearly mature archegonium in section showing structure.

into the jacket of the neck which consists of six longitudinal rows of **neck cells** characteristic of the Marchantiales. The neck cells enclose a central canal called the **neck canal** which contains an axial row of about 8 **neck canal cells**. The mouth of the neck is closed by a rosette of 4 **lid** or **cover cells**. Around the base of the venter of each archegonium is developed a collar-like structure. It consists of a ring of cells and surmounts the archegonial base. It is called the **perigynium** or **pseudoperianth**. The formation of the perigynium is stimulated after fertilization. The ventral canal cell and the neck canal cells degenerate at maturity. Their products, on absorption of moisture, give rise to mucilage which swells and forces apart the lid cells.

(iii) Development of archegonium (Fig. 5.17). The archegonium arises from a single superficial dorsal cell. It lies just close to the apical cell of each lobe of the female receptacle. It is called the **archegonial initial** (A). The archegonial initial enlarges. It then divides into an inner **primary stalk cell** and an outer **primary archegonial cell** (B). The primary stalk cell undergoes a few irregular divisions to form the short but distinct stalk of the archegonium.

The primary archegonial cell is hemispherical in outline (B). It has a centrally located nucleus with a prominent nucleolus and usual cell organelles. The cytoplasm contains quite numerous mitochondria. Less abundant are the plastids, each with few parallel lamellae. The primary archegonial cell divides by three successive vertical intersecting walls which separate three **peripheral initials** surrounding the fertile cell in the middle (C—D). The latter is called the **primary axial cell**. By a transverse cleavage in the axial cell an upper, smaller **primary cover cell** is separated from an inner large primary **central cell** (F) which functions as the mother cell of the axial row. At this stage the three peripheral initials divide longitudinally to form six **jacket initials**. Following small increase in size, the six jacket initials and the central cell divide transversely (G). The archegonium now consists of two tiers of seven cells each. The outer six cells of the upper tier function as **neck initials** and its

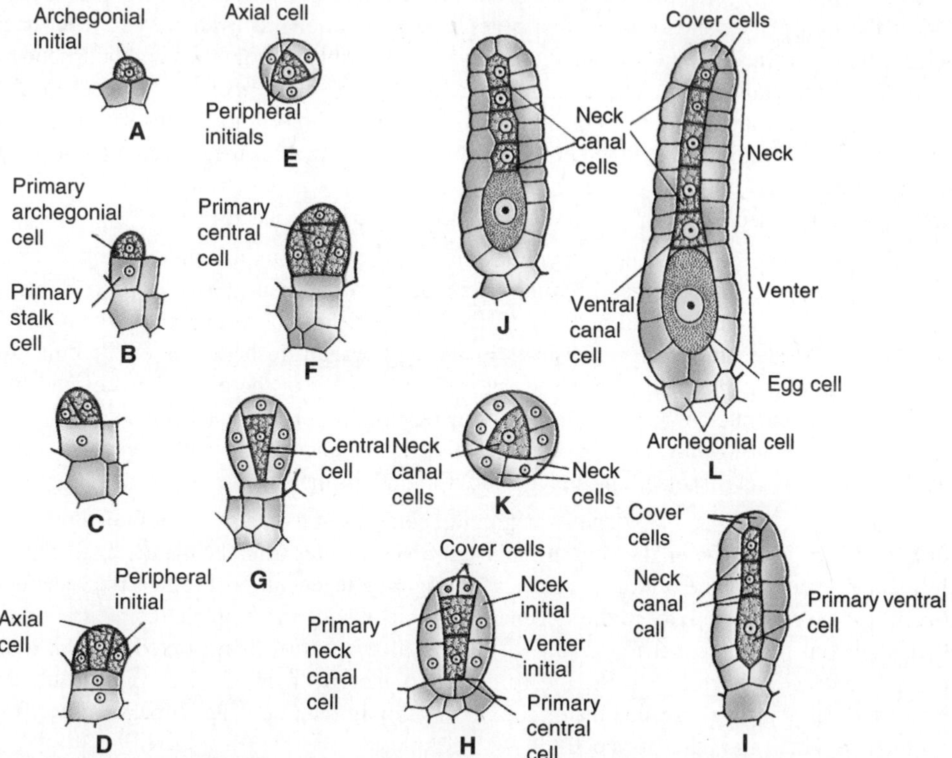

Fig. 5.17. (A—L). ***Marchantia* sp**. A—K, early stages in the development of archegonium; E and K are transverse sections; L, a nearly mature archegonium with four neck canal cells. Explanation in the text.

inner central cell is known as the **primary neck canal cells** (H). The outer cells of the lower tier serve as **venter initials**and inner central cell as **primary ventral cell** (G). The neck initials undergo repeated transverse cleavage to form a tubular neck made up of six vertical rows of **neck cells**. The neck cells enclose a long neck canal. The neck canal is filled with a row of about eight thin-walled **neck canal cells** (L). The neck canal cells are formed by the repeated transverse division of the primary neck canal cell ((I—J). At the top of the neck is a distal rosette of four **cover** or **lid** cells formed by the divisions of the primary cover cell (L). Meanwhile the transverse divisions of the venter initials have produced a **venter wall**. It is one cell thick. It encloses the **venter cavity**. The latter contains a small, upper **ventral canal cell** and a lower **larger egg** or **ovum**. The two are separated by a thin wall. They are formed from the primary ventral cell (J-L). Ultrastructurally the *immature egg* has plastids with one or two discrete lamellae. The numerous mitochondria are generally smaller than the plastids. Some of them lie in close association with them. There is fairly extensive endoplasmic reticulum especially near the periphery of the cell. Scattered apparently active dictyosomes also occur here and there in the cytoplasm. Small vacuoles and isolated lipid bodies are as well found. The large roughly spherical nucleus is centrally located. It has a prominent nucleolus in a central position.

Oogenesis. The cytoplasmic modifications and nuclear changes which take place in the egg, as it matures constitute *oogenesis*. The fine structure of oogenesis in *M. polymorpha* was studied by Zinmeister and Carothers (1974). The account given here is based on their investigation. It is described under two heads namely (*i*) cytoplasmic modifications and (*ii*) nuclear changes.

(i) Cytoplasmic modifications. In the maturing egg there is further simplification of the lamellar system in the plastids. Eventually they have very sparse or no lamellae and are completely devoid of starch. During the expansion phase of the egg numerous small spherical versicles are seen in the cytoplasm. The mitochondria which are fairly abundant in the immature egg do not undergo any change in the maturing egg. Some of them lie in close association with the plastids. There is significant change in the number, size and location of vacuoles in the maturation process of the egg. The vacuoles, which are limited by a single membrane move toward the periphery from the neighbourhood of the nucleus. During migration some of them come together to form clusters or even coalesce to form a large vacuole. The vacuoles are electron-transparent. Most of the lipid bodies in the peripheral region of the cytoplasm also get together to occur in groups. Some of them even coalesce to form larger globules. The lipid clusters are completely encircled by an electron dense fringe. Despite clustering, solitary vacuoles and lipid bodies still occur in the cytoplasm.

(ii) Nuclear changes. Besides the cytoplasmic modifications, significant changes occur in the egg nucleus. The nucleus becomes irregular in shape. Several small, peg-like protrusions, each bounded by a double membrane form on its surface and project into the cytoplasm. Many of these get detached. The detached nuclear vesicles in the egg cytoplasm have contents similar to the nucleoplasm. Some of these have been seen near the periphery of the egg. The centrally located more or less spherical nucleolus, which in the young egg is a loosely compacted mass, separates into fragments in the maturing and mature eggs prior to the appearance of the nuclear evaginations. The nucleolar fragments get dispersed in the nucleoplasm and disappear.

Dehiscence of archegonium. The archegonium dehisces in the presence of moisture. With the maturation of egg in the venter, the ventral canal cell first separates from the mature egg, all the cells of the axial row including the ventral canal cell show signs of degeneration. Progressive vacuolisation and intense dictyosome activity in the degenerating cells results in complete disintegration of the cells of the axial row except the egg. On absorption of water, the disintegrated cellular material changes into mucilage which swells and forces apart the cover or lid cells. A little bit of this disintegrated cellular mucilaginous material extrudes through the opening. A passage way for the sperms to reach the egg is thus formed.

DISTINCTION BETWEEN THE MALE AND FEMALE PLANTS

The thalli of the male and the female plants (Fig. 5.2 A and B) of *Marchantia* are similar. The two may, however be distinguished by the following characteristics of their gametophores:-

1. The antheridiophore is slender comparatively shorter than the archegoniophore.
2. The male receptacle is a flat disc with a scalloped edge, whereas the female is umbrella-shaped when young and star-shaped at maturity.
3. There is no inversion of the receptacular surface of the male receptacle.
4. The antheridia in the male receptacle lie embedded on the upper surface in pits and in rows radiating from the centre. The archegonia hang from the under surface of the female receptacle.
5. The male receptacle lacks accessory structures such as rays, involucres etc.
6. The flattened upper surface of the male disc is slightly concave to serve as a shallow **splash cup** whereas the upper surface of the female disc is markedly convex.
7. The upper surface of the male disc is marked by slightly papillate elevations which indicate the position of antheridia below. These are absent in the female disc.

Fertilization

The sex organs in *Marchantia* are developed in receptacles elevated on long stalks. Besides the male and the female receptacles are borne on different plants. These facts present difficulties in the way of fertilization. Because of uncertainty of fertilization reproduction by vegetative methods is very common, efficient and effective in *Marchantia*.

Fertilization is dependent upon the presence of water and is possible when the male and female plants grow together. It takes place when the plants are wet with rain or dew. Possibly the antheridia and archegonia mature and fertilization occurs before the elongation of the gametophores. The sperms may reach the archegonia in the following ways :

1. Splash cup mechanism. The flattened slightly concave upper surface of the male disc acts as a **shallow splash cup**. The spreading of discharged sperms on the water surface in the splash cup presents an excellent opportunity for dispersal by rain drop splash as all splash droplets falling on the neighbouring sessile female receptacles will contain sperms. Butler showed that sperms may be dispersed in this way from 46—61 cm.

2. The sperms splashed on to the ground by the rain drops from the male receptacle may actually swim the whole way to the archegonia in wet weather.

3. The sperms may swim through the water when the male and the female thalli are actually submerged under the rain water.

The above-mentioned possibilities can become realities only if the male and female plants grow near each other.

4. There is possibility of the sperms being dispersed by the agency of small insects such as the mites. Spring tails and midgets which are attracted by and subsequently feed on the mucilage that exudes from the open archegonial necks and is also secreted by the paraphyses.

A number of sperms may reach the female receptacle in either of the above-mentioned ways. From the female receptacle they are attracted towards the archegonia. The source of attraction is some chemical protein or potassium salts present in the drop of mucilage that oozes through the open necks of the archegonia. A number of sperms may enter the open necks of archegonia and swim downwards in the neck canals. Normally one unites with the egg in the venter.

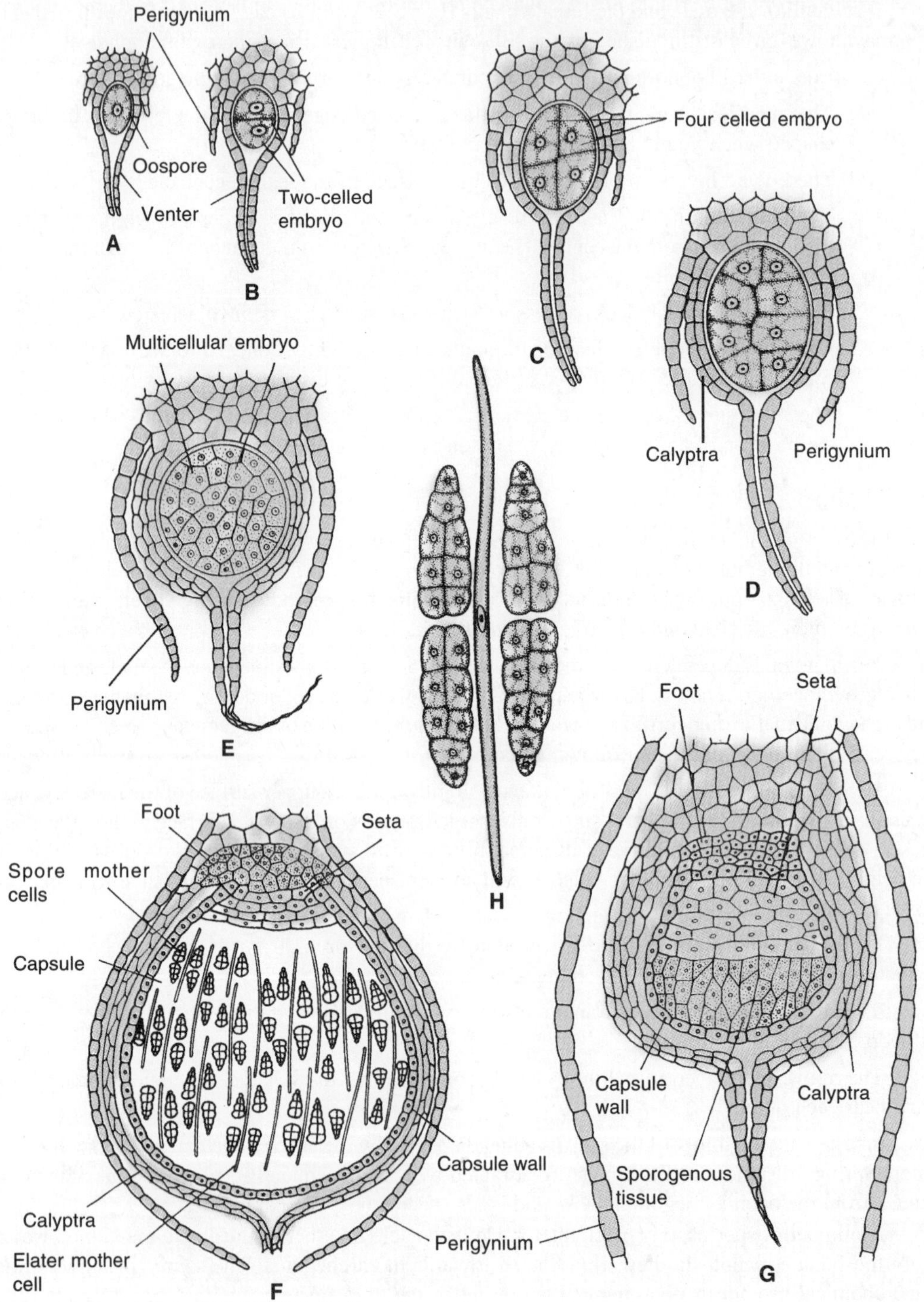

Fig. 5.18. (A—D). ***Marchantia* sp.** Stages in the development of sprorophyte. A, zygote located in the venter; B—E, early stages in the development of embryo; F; young sporophyte showing differentiation into foot, seta and capsule; G, later stage with the capsule containing groups of spore mother cells alternating with elater mother cells; H, groups of spore mother cells with a young elater mother cell in between.

Post-fertilization changes (Fig. 5.18 A—G). Following fertilization the stalks of the archegoniophores elongate. From the upper surface of the disc develop, green cylindrical processes called the **rays**. A number of archegonia may be fertilised in each receptacle. All of them, however, do not develop into sporogonia. The act of fertilisation originates the diploid condition in the female nucleus of the zygote. The zygote secretes a wall around it and enters upon active segmentation to form a spherical **embryo**. The venter enlarges with the growth of embryo. A cylindrical sheath called the **perigynium** grows from the base of each archegonium and surrounds it. A two-lipped membrane, the perichaetium with the lower edge fringed also grows downward on either side of a row of archegonia.

SPOROPHYTE PHASE

With the formation of the zygote the sporophyte or diplophase in the life cycle starts. It consists of the **zygote, embryo** and the **sporogonium. Spore mother cells** and **elaters** are the last structures of this phase.

Development of the sporogonium (Fig. 5.18). The zygote (A) probably starts dividing within 48 hours of fertilisation. It divides by a horizontal wall at right angles to the long axis of the archegonium (B). This division delimits the outer or distal **epibasal** and the inner or proximal **hypobasal** regions. Since the capsule which constitutes the apex of sproophyte, is formed from the outer or epibasal region embryogeny is described as **exoscopic**. The next cleavage is at right angles to the first. The globular embryo at this stage consists of four cells. It is the **quadrant stage** (C). There are variations in the early development of the embryo in different species. McNaught reported the formation of a three celled filamentous embryo in *M. chenopoda*. Typically the next division produces the **octant stage**. Only four cells are visible in a section (C). After the octant stage the embryo grows vigorously. The divisions are in an irregular sequence. Associated with the changes taking place in the developing embryo the following changes take place in the surrounding gametophyte tissue :-

(*i*) The stalk of the archegoniophore elongates considerably.

(*ii*) The venter cells divide by periclinal walls to form a two to three-layered **calyptra** (C—D). The latter forms a close investment around the developing embryo sporophyte.

(*iii*) The collar-like **perigynium** eventually forms a cylindrical sheath. It is one cell in thickness and few cells in height. The perigynium encloses both the archegonium and the sporogonium.

(*iv*) The development of a two-lipped curtain-like **perichaetium** or **involucre** forming a protective covering around the whole group of archegonia.

(*v*)The development of **rays** from the margin of the female disc between the lobes. Their development is intercalary.

The four epibasal octants (nearest the neck of the archegonium) by repeated cell division accompanied by cell differentiation and continued growth give rise to the **capsule**. The four hypobasal octants form the **foot** and the **seta** (F). During further development the embryonic sporophyte elongates vertically at the expense of nutrients drawn from the gametophyte. Periclinal divisions appear in the embryonic capsule portion. These separate an outer single layered **amphithecium** from the inner mass of cells which constitutes the **endothecium**. The ampnithecium cells divide anticlinally to give rise to the single layered **capsule wall** (F). It remains one cell in thickness. At maturity, the walls of these cells develop ring-like thicknenings on their inner surface. The entire endothecium forms the **archesporium**. The archesporial cells divide and redivide mitotically to form a massive tissue. It is known as the **sporogenous tissue** (F). The cells of the sporogenous tissue are, at first, all alike and vertically elongated. They divide diagonally. Later they become differentiated into the following two kinds of cells (G, H) :-

(*a*) **Elater mother cells**. Practically half of the sporogenous cells elongate still further. They become narrow and remain sterile. These are the **elater mother cells**. The latter elongate considerably to form long, slender, diploid, fusiform cells tapering at both the ends (G). Each of these develops two spirally thickened bands on the inner surface of its walls and loses its protoplasmic contents to become the **elater**. The diploid bispiral elaters are hygroscopic. They help in the dispersal of spores.

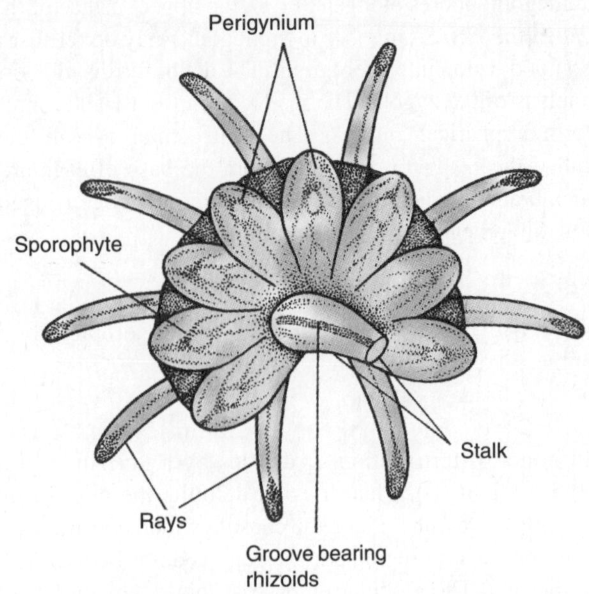

Fig. 5.19. ***Marchantia.*** Female disc seen from below with the nearly mature slightly emergent sporophytes.

(*b*) **Spore mother cells**. The other half of the sporogenous cells divide and redivide by transverse cleavage to form vertical rows of cells. These are the **spore mother cells** (G). There is a good deal of evidence to support the view that the elater and spore mother cells do not belong to the same cell generation. There is a difference of 3-4 or 5 successive cell generations. The diploid elaters are differentiated earlier from the sporogenous tissue. The spore mother cells are, at first, somewhat cubical. Later they grow equally in all directions to become rounded. They contain dense cytoplasm and a conspicuous diploid nucleus. Each spore mother cell undergoes meiosis to form four meiospores as in *Riccia*. The haploid number of chromosomes in each meiospore is reported to the 8 or 9 in *M. polymorpha*. The average output of spores per capsule in *Marchantia polymorpha* is estimated to be about 300,000. O'Hanlou (1926) estimated that there is one elater produced for every 128 spores in *M. polymorpha*.

The young sporogonia are effectively protected by three protective sheaths developed from the tissue of the female receptacle. These are the **perigynium**, the **calyptra** and the **perichaetium** or the **involucre**. The first and the third are absent in *Riccia*. The development of the capsule is accompanied by the growth of the foot and the seta. The absorptive foot is embedded in the tissue of the lower surface of the female disc and is differentiated early. With the differentiation and the maturation of spores in the capsule the constriction-like seta elongates slightly. *The slight elongation of the seta in Marchantia is an anatomical necessity*. The sporogonium hangs downwards. Greater elongation of the seta will carry the capsule nearer to the ground and thus hinder efficient dispersal of spores. The role of short seta in *Marchantia* is simply to clear the pendant capsule of the calyptra and enveloping sheaths.

Structure of Sporogonium (Fig. 5.20 A). It is differentiated into the following three regions:

(*a*) **Foot**. It is an absorptive anchoring organ forming the basal broad portion of the sporogonium. It consists of parenchymatous cells and is embedded in the tissue of the female receptacle on its lower surface. It absorbs all the nourishment from the gametophyte for the developing sporogonium.

(*b*) **Seta**. It is at first very short and constriction-like. It connects the foot and the capsule. The cells constituting it are arranged in vertical rows. With the formation of spore tetrads in the capsule the seta elongates slightly. The slight and sudden increase in the length of the seta ruptures the calyptra. It pushes the mature capsule through the sheaths enclosing the venter. These are **perigynium** and the **prichaetium** (involucre).

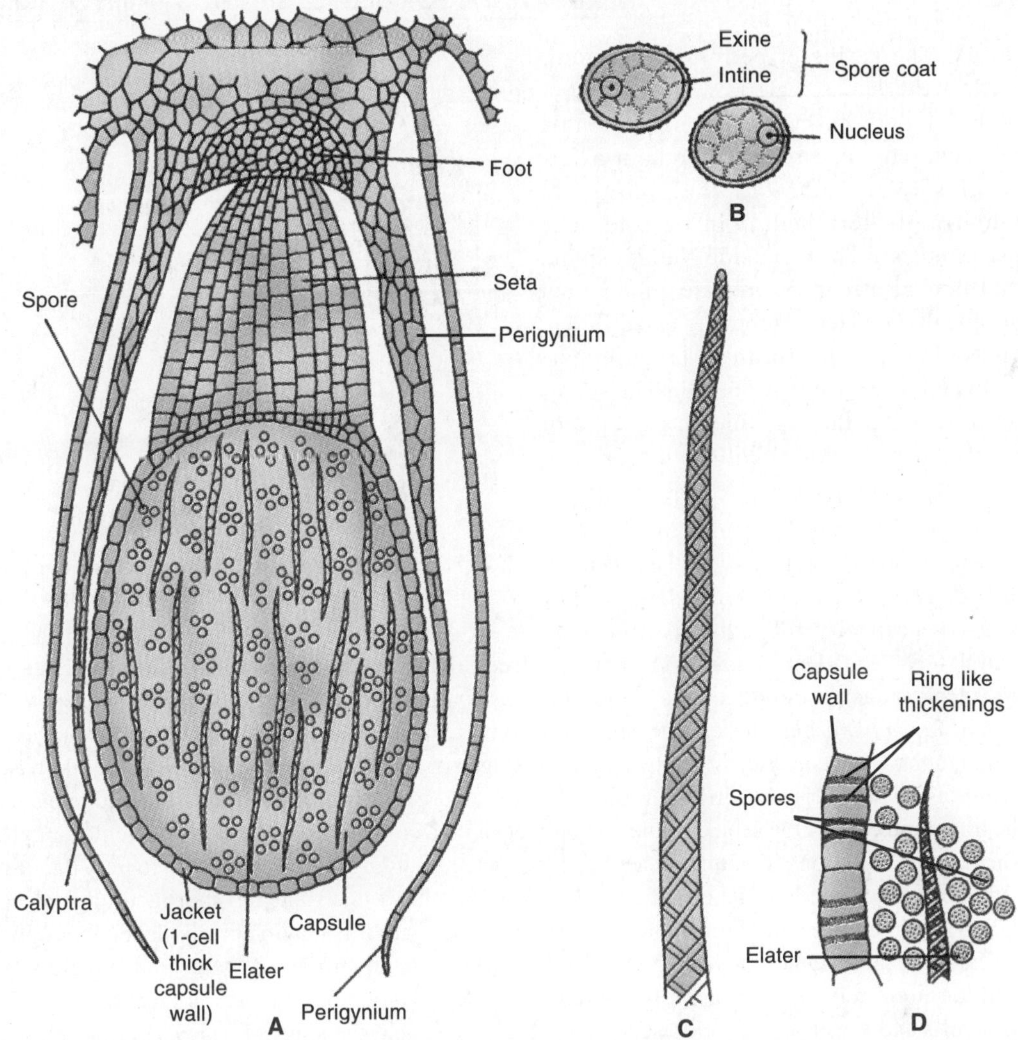

Fig. 5.20. (A—D). ***Marchantia* sp.** A, L.S. mature sporogonium; B, spores showing structure; C, part of the elater with a double spiral band of thickening; D, portion of capsule showing a few cells of the single layered capsule wall with ring-like thickening on their cell walls, spores and a portion of the elater.

(*c*) **Capsule**. It is oval in form and yellow in colour when mature. It has an outer layer of sterile cells constituting the **capsule wall**. Ring-like thickening bands run anticlinally across the wall cells (Fig. 5.20 D). A cap of cells more than one cell-layer thick is developed in some species at the apex of the capsule. It is formed from the sporogenous cells. It projects into the cavity of the capsule. Enclosed within the capsule wall, at maturity, is a mass of **meiospores** and **elaters**. The elaters are exceptionally long, slender cells with tapering ends. They have double spirally thickened bands on their walls. The mature elaters lack protoplasm. They are thus dead and are hygroscopic.

(a) Spore morphology. The meiospores of *Marchantia* (B) are small in size and vary in form ranging from 0.012 to 0.03 mm in diameter. They are globose in form in some species (*M. polymorpha*) and have no distinct polar axis. The spore wall is differentiated into the outer smooth or reticulate comparatively thicker **exospore** or **exine** and inner, thin **endospore** or

intine. The perine or perinium is **absent**. Within the spore wall is a tiny mass of granular cytoplasm. It contains a single nucleus and some reserve food. In a few species (*M. cuneiloba*) the spores are indistinctly tetrahedral in outline. The perinium is present outside the exospore. Morphologically the spores are all alike but genetically each tetrad produces two different kinds of spores. Two of these produce male thalli and other two female thalli. The spores of *Marchantia* thus provide an example of *functional* or *physiological heterospory*.

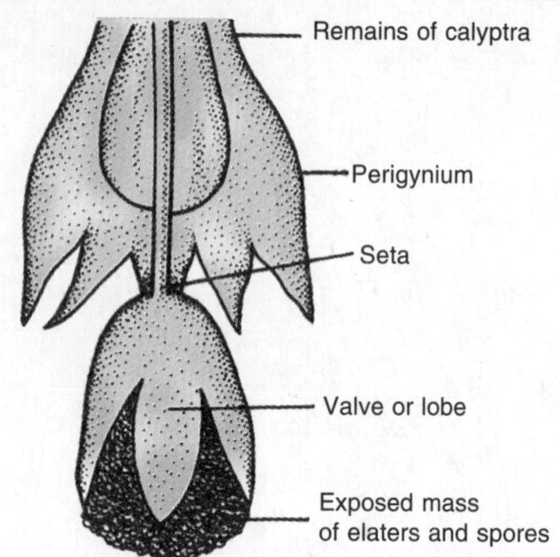

Fig. 5.21. *Marchantia* sp. Showing dehiscence of capsule. (Based on Bischoff but slightly modified).

(b) Nutrition of sporophyte (sporogonium). The older morphologists held that the hepatic sporophyte (with the exception of *Anthoceros*) is basically colourless and thus lacks the capacity for self-nutrition. It is completely dependent or parasitic upon the green thallose gametophyte, to which it remains organically attached throughout its life for water and carbohydrate food. Bold (1938) also reported that in *M. polymorpha* the egg before and after fertilization is colourless and so is the few-celled embryo sporophyte. Even the spherical stages of the developing sporophyte are likewise colourless. However with differentiation of the young sporophyte into foot, seta and capsule, the immature cells of the seta, capsule wall, elaters and even those of the foot develop chlorophyll. These green cells contain abundant active chloroplasts enabling the sporogonium to manufacture a greater part or whole of its organic food such as starch. At this stage the sporogonium is deep dull green in colour and autotrophic to a considerable extent. It may be partly dependent upon the parent plant (gametophyte) for its food supply. For the supply of water and minerals in solution it entirely depends upon the parent plant. Sporophyte remains green until the capsule wall cells and the elaters develop secondary thickenings and the spores form. The chloroplasts, however, disintegrate as the sporophyte reaches matuirty (the time of capsule dehiscence approaches). The mature sporogonium is, therefore, yellowish in colour and is totally dependent (parasitic) for its nutrition on the parent gametophyte (thallus).

(*c*) **Dehiscence of capsule** (Fig. 5.21). With the ripening of spores there is slight elongation of the seta. The capsule breaks through the calyptra. It projects beyond the perigynium and the perichaetium. As the exposed capsule dries the apical cap, if any, ruptures along an irregular line. The capsule wall then splits open along four to six lines. Each split starts from the apex to about the middle of the capsule. Since there are no regular lines of dehiscence on the capsule wall the latter splits in an irregular manner by four to six lobes or valves. The mass of spores and elaters is consequently exposed.

(*d*) **Dispersal of spores**. There is ready and efficient dispersal of spores by wind in *Marchantia*. It is aided by the following two structural features :

COMPARISON WITH RICCIA

Sporogonium of Riccia	Sporogonium of Marchantia
1. In *Riccia* the sporogonium is the simplest known sporophyte among the bryophytes. It lacks both the **foot** and the **seta**. It is just a spore case or capsule globular in outline.	1. In *Marchantia* the sporogonium is larger and more complex. It is differentiated into the **foot**, the **seta** and the **capsule**.
2. The globular sporogonium consists of a jacket layer of simple sterile cells constituting the **wall** which surrounds a mass of fertile cells known as the **spore mother cells**. There are no elater mother cells.	2. The cells of the single layered capsule wall develop ring-like thickenings on their walls and surround a mass of **spore mother cells** and **elater mother cells**.
3. Excepting the single layered sporogonium wall and a few of the **nurse cells** that undergo degeneration, major portion of the sporogonium is devoted to spore formation.	3. Much of the sporogonium produces the sterile tissue in the form of foot, seta and capsule wall. Half of the sporogenous tissue forms the **elater mother cells** and the rest by a few more divisions constitute the **spore mother cells**. Nurse cells absent.
4. The nurse cells which eventually disintegrate to form the nutritive fluid are considered by some bryologists as the **forerunners** of the elaters of the more advanced members of the Marchantiales. The elaters are thus absent in the sporogonium of *Riccia*.	4. The elater mother cells form long, slender, fusiform cells with tapering ends and are called the **elaters**. They are hygroscopic and help in the dispersal of spores.
5. In fact at maturity it has no diploid tissue at all. The outer layer of the spore sac which houses the spores represents parent gametophyte and the spores represent the future gametophyte.	5. The mature sporogonium wholly consists of diploid tissues except the spores which represent the new gametophyte.
6. The sporogonium remains embedded in the thallus and is protected and surrounded only by the two-layered **calyptra**. The perigynium and perichaetium are lacking.	6. The sporogonium hangs from the undersurface of the female receptacle and is surrounded by the two-layered **calyptra, perigynium** and the **perichaetium**. Later by the rapid elongation of the seta, the capsule breaks through the calyptra and projects beyond the perigynium and the perichaetium.
7. The mature spores are released simply by the disintegration of the cells of the capsule wall, calyptra and finally by the death and decay of the surrounding thallus tissue. The sporogonium never dehisces.	7. The capsule dehisces in a more regular manner by 4—6 valves to allow the spores to escape into the air.
8. The mature meiospores are simply left behind on the soil by the decay of the surrounding tissues and are not dispersed. In that condition they may be carried by the wind.	8. The elevation of the hanging sporogonium on a long stalk of the archegoniophore and the presence of hygroscopic elaters in the spore mass constitute an efficient provision for the distribution of meiospores by the wind.

(*i*) *Presence of elaters*. The hygroscopic elaters facilitate dispersal of spores from the exposed spore mass. They coil and uncoil with the changes in the moisture content of the surrounding air (atmospheric humidity). As the elaters dry they stretch and twist undergoing wriggling movements. These movements in response to changes in the moisture content of the surrounding air "fluff-up" the exposed mass of spores facilitating their gradual removal into the air where they are readily caught up by the air currents and dispersed.

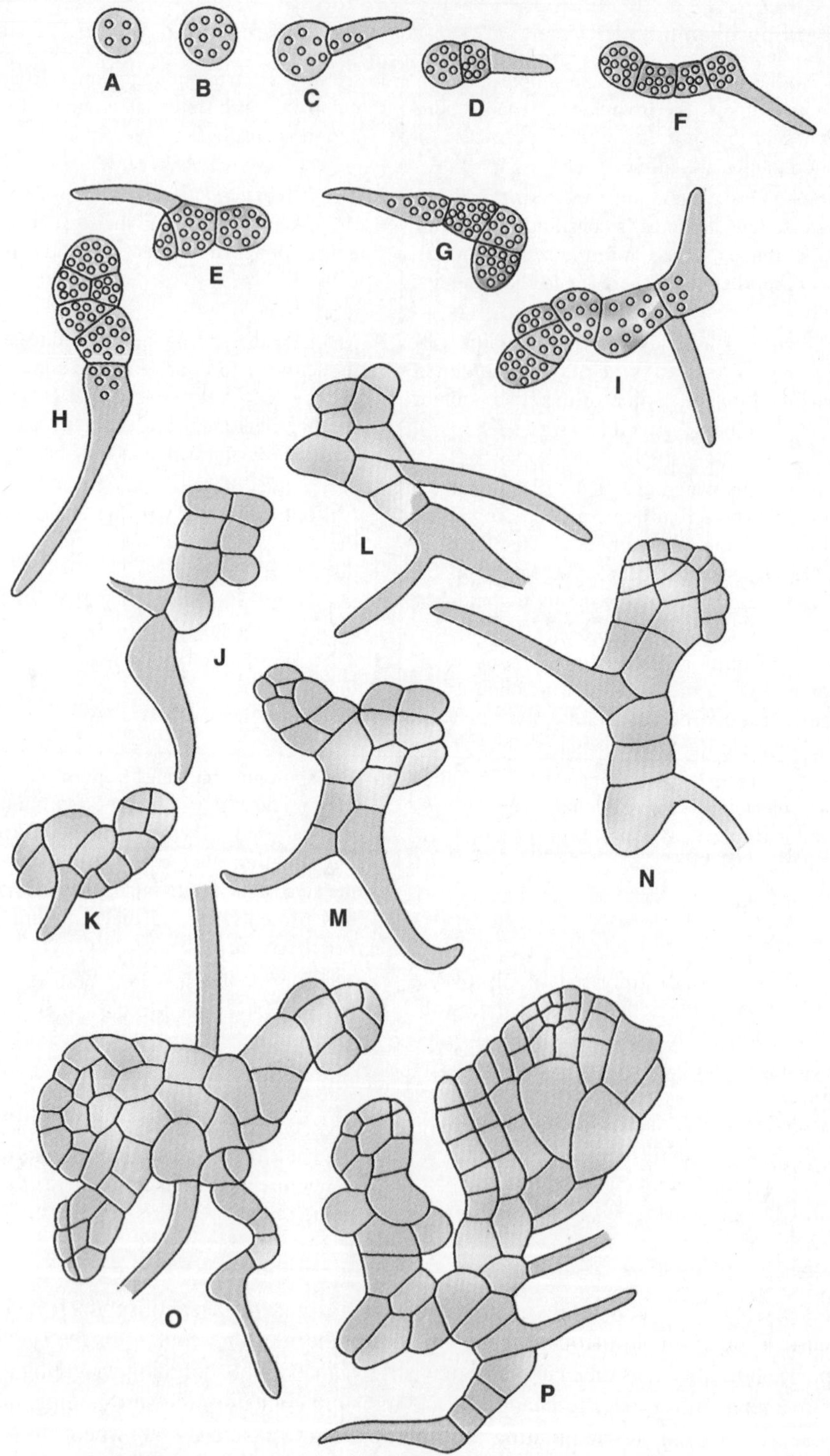

Fig. 5.22. (A—P). ***Marchantia* sp.** Stages in the germination of a spore. Explanation in the text (After O'Hanlon).

(ii) Elevation of the hanging sporophyte on the long archegoniophore. The elevated position of the hanging sporogonium is an additional advantage. It favours the dispersal of spores by air currents. The small spores ejected into the air by the squirming movements of the elaters are readily caught up and distributed by the air currents. The greater elongation of the seta would not have helped spore dispersal. On the other hand it would have hindered it by bringing the capsule nearer to the ground.

Germination of spore or meiospore (fig. 5.22). According to O'Hanlon (1926), who studied meiospore germination in *M. polymorpha*, the spores remain viable for about a year. On falling on a suitable moist substrate, they germinate immediately. Germination begins with the imbibition of water by the meiospore (A). The latter increases considerably in size (B). The increase in size of the spore protoplast is accompanied by the reappearance of chlorophyll (B). Unlike *Riccia* no germinal tube is formed. Instead the green spore protoplast immediately divides (D). At first the cell divisions are in one plane only. Consequently a short filament of green cells in formed (D—F). The primary (first) rhizoid appears after uniform increase in the size of the spore and simultaneous appearance of chloroplasts (C). Occasionally a second rhizoid may appear early even at the 2-celled stage but usually it does not appear untill the young gametophyte has advanced considerably (I). All the rhizoids which appear on the young gametophyte are of smooth-walled type. The divisions in the second plane usually occur when the filament is 3 or 4 cells in length (G-I). A variety of forms appear in these early stages (D-I). According to O'Hanlon, a marginal row of cells appears in the apical region of the plantlet when it is still young and consists of less than a dozen cells (J-L). This marginal row of embryonic cells persists through subsequent growth of the young thallus (M,N). When the young thallus consists of about 30-40 cells, characteristic apical notch appears by the differential growth of the embryonic cells at the margin of the thallus (O,P).

Menge (1930), however, reported the establishment of an apical cell at an early stage in the development of gametophyte of *M. polymorpha.* According to him a cell at the apex begins to function as an **apical cell** when the young gametophyte consists of a row of 6-8 green cells which may be two cells broad at the apex. The apical cell is wedge-shaped with two lateral cutting faces. It cuts off about 5-7 segments right and left alternately. These divide and redivide to produce the thallus tissue. After cutting off a few segments, the apical cell divides and the derivatives redivide to produce a sheet of many cells in which a transverse row of apical initials constituting the apical meristem typical of the Marchantiales is soon established.

IMPORTANT FEATURES

1. The plant body is a repeatedly forking, flat, green, broad dorsiventral **thallus** with a distict broad, central **midrib** which is more pronounced on the ventral side.
2. Dorsally the thallus surface is marked by rhomboidal or polygonal areas called the **areolae**. Each areole has a distinct dotlike **air pore** in its centre.
3. Small, shallow **gemma cups** with frilled, membranous margins are usually present on the upper surface of the thallus in the midrib region. The cups contain numerous, green, lens-shaped objects, the **gemmae**. When detached each gemma develops into two new thallus plants.
4. From the ventral surface of the thallus, in the midrib region, arise unicellular, unbranched smooth-walled and tuberculate attaching filaments, the **rhizoids**. They secure the thalloid gametophyte to the substratum.
5. Associated with the rhizoids on the lower surface of the thallus are the membranous **scales**. They are arranged in two to four alternating rows on either side of the midrib. Each scale typically consists of a **body**, a **constriction** and an **appendage**.
6. The growth in length of the thallus lobes takes place by the activity of a group of meristematic cells and not by an apical cell. The former are situated in a notch at the apex of each lobe.

7. Externally the plant body is simple but in its internal structure it is the most complex gametophyte body developed by any liverwort. It is many cells in depth in a vertical section. There is the upper epidermis in which are embedded the barrel-shaped pores. The outer walls of the epidermal cells are practically water-proof. Beneath the upper epidermis are the air chambers arranged in a single layer. Each chamber opens to the outside by an air pore. The shallow cavity of each air chamber is filled with green, frequently branched, assimilatory filaments which arise from its floor. The neighbouring chambers are separated from each other by groups of vertically arranged green cells which serve as pillars supporting the upper epidermis. The ventilated, green chambered upper portion of the thallus is called the **photosynthetic region**. The portion of the thallus below the air chambers consists of several layers of compactly arranged parenchymatous cells forming the **storage region**. Rhizoids and scales grow from the lower epidermis.
8. Without exception sexual reproduction is on **oogamous** type. The plants are **dioecious**. The sex organs are **antheridia** and **archegonia**. They are developed in disc-shaped receptacles elevated on long stalks. They are the **gametophores**. The gametophores are terminal in position and in direct continuation of the midrib. The stalks have two rhizoidal furrows each running the whole length.
9. The male receptacle is a lobed disc with a wavy margin. The antheridia are deeply sunk on the upper surface of the receptacle each in an **antheridial pit** opening to the outside by an **ostiole**. The antheridial pits alternate with the air chambers. The sperms are flagellate, curved structures. The male receptacles lack rays characteristic of the female receptacles and are usually eight lobed.
10. The female receptacle is eight lobed. The lobes are not very conspicuous. Alternating with the lobes grow out the stout finger-like rays from the periphery of the disc. The rays are nine in number. In young receptacles they hang downwards like the ribs of a tiny umbrella. At maturity they spread widely apart giving the female receptacle a star-shaped appearance.
11. The archegonia are pendulous. They hang downwards from the under surface of the lobes of the female receptacle.
12. Fertilization takes place in the presence of water furnished by rain or dew and when the female receptacles are sessile.
13. The two-lipped, curtain-like **perichaetium** may enclose several young sporogonia each enclosed by the **calyptra** and surrounded by the **perigynium**.
14. The sporogonium, at maturity, is differentiated into a foot, a small seta and a capsule. The cells of the single layered capsule wall develop annular bands. Inside the wall is a mass of meiospores and elaters.
15. The ripe capsule wall dehisces by 4-6 irregular teeth or valves.
16. The elaters are simple, long cells tapering towards both ends. Each has two spiral bands on the wall.
17. The elaters are hygroscopic and thus help in the dispersal of spores.
18. The ready dispersal of spores is aided by the pendulous sporogonium being elevated on a long archegoniophore.
19. The short seta of the hanging sporogonium serves as an additional aid in the dispersal of spores. It carries the capsule clear of the calyptra and the enveloping sheaths.
20. Each spore, on germination, produces a tiny gameophyte which, at first, grows by an apical cell with two cutting faces. Soon the apical cell is replaced by a group of meristematic cells.

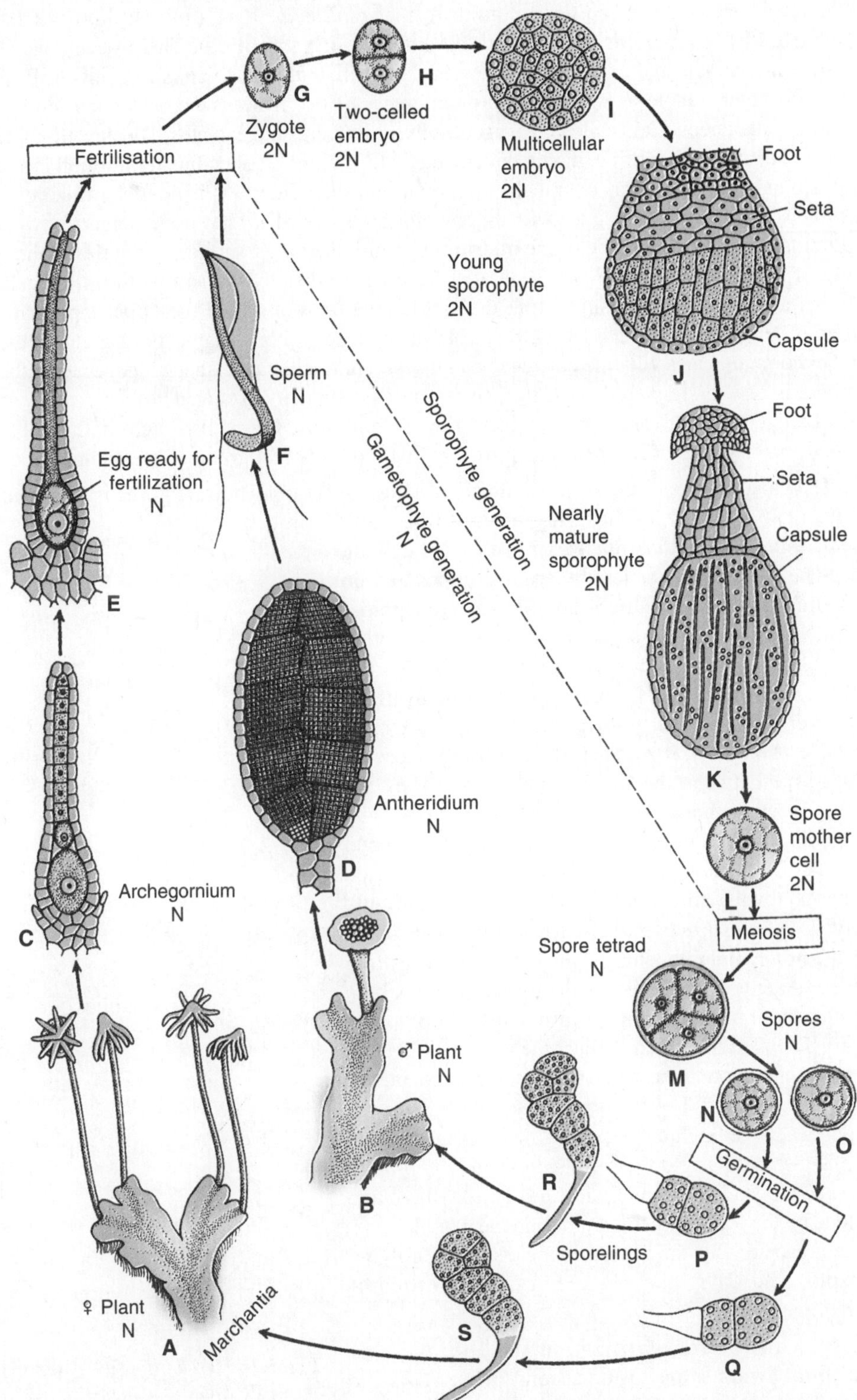

Fig. 5.23. (A—S). ***Marchantia* sp**. Diagrammatic representation of the sexual life cycle.

SUMMARY OF THE LIFE HISTORY OF *MARCHANTIA* (Fig. 5.23)

Life history of *Marchanitia* is similar to that of *Riccia*. It is **diplohaplontic** and thus is characterized by **sporogenic meiosis** and **alternation of generations** There occur two distinct vegetative individuals in the life cycle. They are the green, thalloid *Marchantia* plant (A, B) and the radially constructed more or less solid sporogonium (K). The former is the most conspicuous of the two and is independent. It is called the **gametophyte**as it bears the gametes. The gametophyte plant is a green, dorsiventral, forking, highly developed thallus with a distinct, broad midrib. It is anchored to the ground by unicellular, unbranched, smooth and tuberculate **rhizoids** The rhizoids absorb water and solutes for it. Associated with the rhizoids are the **scales** They are arranged in two to four longitudinal rows on either side of the midrib. Internally the upper surface of the fleshy thallus has a layer of **air chambers** They are separated from each other by vertical partitions of cells. The partitions also act as pillars supporting the single layered roof called the upper **epidermis** The cavities of air chambers are filled with simple or branched, short, filaments of green cells. Each chamber communicates with the outside through a well defined, barrel-shaped **pore** Beneath the air chambers is a several layered thick storage region of compactly arranged colourless parenchyma cells. Scattered in the storage region are a few **oil** and **mucilage** cells. Each thallus lobe has a growing point situated at its apex. The growing point consists of a group of meristematic cells.

The gametophyte or the sexual thallus bears the sex organs. They are borne in localised areas which are disc-shaped. These are **receptacles** The receptacles in *Marchantia* are invariably elevated on long stalks. The stalked receptacles are terminal in position on the thallus lobes. The antheridial (B) and archegonial receptacles (A) occur on separate plants. Together with their stalks the receptacles are called the **antheridiophores** and the **archegoniophores** respectively. *Marchantia* is thus **dioecious** The female receptacle, at maturity, is star-shaped. The archegonia occur in the tissue between the finger-shaped rays. They are pendulous with the necks directed downwards. The archegonia of each group are protected by a two-lipped involucre. The male receptacle has a lobed margin. Each lobe has a growing point at its tip. The antheridia are sunk deeply on the upper surface. Each lies in its own flask-shaped **antheridial pit**opening at the surface by an **ostiole** All these structures produced by the thallus gametophyte constitute the **gametophyte generation**or the **haplophase** (A—F). They are the green thallus, the antheridiophores, the archegoniophores, the antheridia, the archegonia, the sperms and the eggs. The first structures of this phase are the spores and the last are the gametes. With the formation of the gametes the haplophase ends. In *Marchantia* there is provision for additional multiplication of the thallus plant. It is done by the production of gemmae in the gemma cups. The gemmae are thus the accessory means of multiplying the haplophase. They play no role in the alternation of generations.

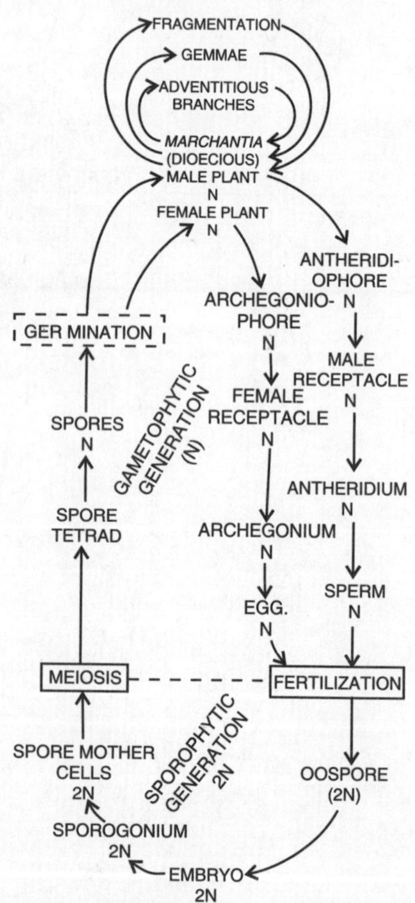

Fig. 5.24.*Marchantia* sp.—word diagram of the life cycle.

With the act of fertilization the life cycle of *Marchantia* switches on to the second phase. It is the

diplophaseor the **sporophyte phase**. It originates with the **zygote**(G). The latter undergoes cleavage to form the **embryo**(H—I). The embryo in the bryophytes is a short-lived structure. Soon, by further cleavage and differentiation it forms the second vegetative individual in the life cycle. It is the **sporogonium**(J). All the young sporogonia in a particular group are protected by the common, two-lipped **involucre**. Besides, each sporogonium is closely invested by the calyptra. External to it is the **perigynium**. The sporogonium is more or less a solid, radially symmetrical object without any appendages. It is incapable of self-nutrition. It consists of three regions, the **foot,** the **seta** and the **capsule** (K). The latter produces the meiospores and elaters. The elaters help in the dispersal of spores. The sporogonium of *Marchantia* which produces the spores, is called the **sporophyte**. It is concerned with spore production. The structures produced after fertilization such as the **zygote**, the **embryo** and the **sporogonium** with its foot, seta and capsule constitute the **sporophyte phase** or the **diplophase**(G—K). It ends with the **spore mother cells**(L) and elaters. The spore mother cells by meiosis (M) produce meiospores (N, O) which are the first structures of the future gametophyte generation.

From the account of the life cycle of *Marchantia* given above it is clear that the gametophyte and the sporophyte phases are very closely connected. In the single life cycle they alternate with each other. The reproductive cells of one generation, on germination, produce the alternate plant. The two critical points in the life cycle are **fertilisation** and **meiosis**. With the former starts the diplophase or the sporophyte generation. The meiosis originates the gametophyte phase or the haplophase. The regular alternation in a single life cycle of one phase with the other is expressed by a biological phrase, 'Alternation of Generations'. Since the alternating plants in life cycle are dissimilar the alternation of generations is of **heterologous type**.

DISCUSSION

The gametophyte plant of *Marchantia* is independent and photosynthetic. It is simple externally being a dorsiventral thallus. The elaboration is internal rather than external. Internally it has reached the highest level of differentiation achieved by a thalloid gametophyte. The sex organs are borne on stalked receptacles. The sporophyte is complex being differentiated into foot, seta and capsule. The question arises which of the two is primitive, *Marchantia* or *Riccia*?

There are two opposite hypotheses with regard to the evolutionary position of *Marchantia*. Some bryologists consider *Marchantia* as the most advanced member of the group. They hold that it has evolved from *Riccia* which is simple and thus primitive as shown by the following characteristics :-

(*a*)Thallus much smaller in size and relatively simple both externally as well as internally.

(*b*)Photosynthetic region less elaborate and less water conserving than the photosynthetic system in the form of air chambers as in *Marchantia*.

(*c*)Absence of well defined upper epidermis and definite air pores.

(*d*)Absence of stalked gametophores, the sex organs developing in pits on the upper surface of the thallus.

(*e*)Sporophyte completely dependent on the gametophyte for its nutrition.

(*f*) Simple sporophyte consisting of little more than a capsule without foot and seta.

(*g*)At maturity it is simply a spore case with no diploid tissue.

(*h*)Absence of any mechanism for dispersal of spores which must thus await the decay of surrounding gametophyte tissues.

The changes involved are :

(*a*)Gradual and progressive widening of the air canals till they form well developed air chambers.

(*b*)Associated with the above change are the development of assimilatory filaments from the floor of each chamber and the elaboration of air pores into well defined barrel-shaped structures.

(*c*)Development of sex organs in restricted areas of the thallus called the receptacles.

(*d*)Elevation of receptacles on long stalks.

(*e*)Cessation of apical growth of the thallus lobes after the development of sex organs so that the gametophores become terminal in position.

(*f*) Gradual and progressive sterilisation of the potentially fertile cells of the sporogenous tissue in the sporophyte.

This theory of progressive sterilisation was first proposed by Bower and later elaborated by Cavers. On the basis of this theory the fertile cells devoted to spore formation become gradually progressively diverted to vegetative functions such as protection, nutrition and spore dispersal. This resulted in the differentiation of the sporophyte into the foot, seta and the capsule. Some of the potential spore mother cells become sterile to form narrow, pointed, hygroscopic elaters which help in spore dispersal.

The supporters of this hypothesis consider *Riccia* as primitive and *Marchantia* as a highly evolved or advanced genus.The other genera of the order form a complete ascending series of intergrading forms. So seriated they say the series forms an excellent example of **progressive evolution** or natural advance. Smith is another ardent supporter of this hypothesis.

There is another school of thought led by Goeble.They hold that the genera of Marchantiales seriated as above illustrate a case of **retrogressive evolution** and form the descending series. According to them *Marchantia* is primitive. They consider *Marchantia* to have given rise to *Riccia* by progressive simplification or reduction. The changes involved are :

(*a*)The air chambers become progressively reduced in width till they become deep narrow canals. This change is accompanied by the disappearance of assimilatory filaments from the air chambers and simplificationof air pores.

(*b*)Loss of stalks and receptacles of the gametophores. With this the growth of the growing points is continued forward. Consequently the sex organs become scattered on the upper surface of the thallus.

(*c*)Elimination of protective sheaths (involucre and perigynium) around the sporogonium. This is accompanied by reduction in the complexity of the structure of the sporophyte. The evolutionary trend has been the gradual and progressive simplification of the sporophyte. First the seta and later the foot also disappears. The sporogonium becomes simply a spore case. The ringlike thickenings disappear from the walls of the cells of the capsule wall. All the inner (endothecium) cells become fertile so that the elaters are eliminated. The nutrition to the numerous developing spore tetrads is supplied by the degeneration of some of the potential spore mother cells, capsule wall and inner layer of the calyptra.

All the changes enumerated above finally resulted in the origin of forms like *Riccia* from primitive ancestors like *Marchantia*.

The hypothesis of progressive evolution as advocated by Bower, Cavers and others appears plausible but the breeding experiments carries out by Bergeff (1943) with *Marchantia* support the theory of progressive simplification or reduction. In his cultures of *Marchantia* he observed a number of mutants which he hybridized in various ways and obtained a *Marchantia* thallus of *var. riccioides*. It resembles *Riccia* in having narrow thallus lobes and immersion of sex organs in the thallus tissue.

The striking results of these breeding experiments suggest the way forms like *Marchantia* may have yielded genera like *Riccia* by a process of simplification. On the basis of this *Riccia* wouldbe considered an advanced but a reduced form and *Marchantia*—a primitive genus.

Systematic Position of Marchantia

Division	:	Bryophyta
Class	:	Hepaticopsida
Order	:	Marchantiales
Family	:	Marchantiaceae
Genus	:	*Marchantia*
Species	:	*palmata*

QUESTIONS

ESSAY TYPE

1. Describe sexual reproduction in detail in *Marchantia.* How does fertilization take place in this genus?
2. Give an illustrated account of the development of antheridium and spermatogenesis in *Marchantia.*
3. Describe the development of archegonium of *Marchania.*
4. Give an illustrated account of the development of sporogonium of *Marchantia*. Compare it with that of *Riccia.*
5. Describe the structure of mature sporophyte (sporogonium) of *Marchantia* and compare it with that of *Riccia.*
(Gorakhpur, 1999; Poorvanchal, 1997; Kumaon, 1995)
6. With the help of a series of diagrams describe the life history of *Marchantia.* *(Agra, 1954, 1956)*
7. Give a comparative account of the structures of gametophytes of *Riccia* and *Marchantia* & *Pellia.*
(Kanpur, 1998; Rohilkhand, 1992; Gorakhpur, 1994)
8. Give a comparative account of the structure of vegetative thalli of *Marchantia*, *Pellia* and *Frullania.* *(Lucknow, 1997, 1999)*
9. Give a detailed account of the structure of antheridiophore and archegoniophore of *Marchantia*, with the help of labelled diagrams.
(Lucknow, 1998, 2001; Gorakhpur, 1997)
10. Give a comparative account of the structures of sporophytes of *Marchantia* and *Anthoceros.*
(Meerut, 1997; Awadh, 1997)
11. With the help of labelled diagrams compare the structure of sporophytes of *Riccia* and *Marchantia.*
(Meerut, 1998, 1999; Mahatma Gandhi, 1998; Mahatma Dayanand Saraswati, 1998)
12. With the help of labelled diagrams, describe the vegetative reproduction in *Marchantia.* *(Rohilkhand, 1992)*
13. (*a*) With the help of labelled diagrams, describe the structure of sporophytes of *Marchantia* and *Pellia.*
(Rohilkhand, 1993)
(*b*) With the help of labelled diagrams, describe the archegoniophore of *Marchantia.*
(Rohilkhand, 1993; Virkumar Singh, 1994)
14. Describe the sporophyte of *Marchantia* and compare it with that of *Pellia.*
(Lucknow, 2007)
15. (*a*) Describe the strucutre of thallus in *Marchantia* and *Anthoceros*. Point out the features of differences in the two. *(Awadh, 1993)*
(*b*) Describe the gametophyte of *Marchantia.* *(J.P. Univ., 1999)*
16. Describe the structure of thallus in *Marchantia* or give an account of gametophyte in *Marchantia.*
(Awadh, 1994; Mahatma Gandhi, 1998)

17. (*a*) Give a comparative account of the gametophytes of *Riccia* and *Marchantia* and *Anthoceros*.
    (Awadh, 1995, 1999; Gorakhpur, 1991, 1995)
    (*b*) Give a comprative account of thallus structure of *Riccia*, *Marchantia* and *Anthoceros* *(Allahabad 2008)*
18. Give a comparative account of the structure of sporophytes of *Riccia*, *Marchantia* and *Anthoceros* with the help of labelled diagrams
    (Awadh, 1998; Gorakhpur, 1992; Kerala, 1997; Magadh, 1995)
19. Compare the sporophytes of *Marchantia* and *Anthoceros* on the basis of
    (*i*) Origin of sporogenous tissue
    (*ii*) Capsule wall
    (*iii*) Extent of dependency on the gametophyte. *(Allahabad, 1998)*
20. Compare the internal structure of vegetative thalli of *Riccia*, *Marchantia* and *Anthoceros.*
    (Allahabad, 1999; Kerala, 2000)
21. With the help of labelled diagrams describe the life-cycle of *Marchantia.*
    (Gorakhpur, 1990; Bihar, 1990)
22. Give an account of external morphology and anatomy of gametophytic thallus of *Marchantia* and *Pogonatum*.
    (Kumaon, 2000)
23. What do you understand by alternation of generation? Illustrate it with the help of the life history of *Marchantia*.
    (Bundelkhand, 1994, 1997)
24. Compare the sporophytes and gametophytes of *Marchantia* and *Anthoceros and Pellia.*
    (Bundelkhand, 1995, 1999)
25. Give an account of vegetative propagation in *Marchantia.* *(Mahatma Gandhi, 1997)*
26. Give an account of T.S. of *Marchantia* thallus and compare it with that of *Anthoceros.* *(Vinoba Bhave, 1998)*
27. Describe the gametophytic generation in *Marchantia*
    (Vinoba Bhave, 1999; Magadh, 1997)
28. Draw diagrams of antheridia and archegonia of *Marchantia* and *Anthoceros* and give structural differences in the sex organs of the two plants.
    (Himachal Pradesh, 1992)
29. Describe the sporophyte of *Marchantia.*
    (Vir Kumar Singh, 1990, 1992, 1996, Bihar, 1991; Magadh, 1990)
30. Describe the structure and development of sporogonium of *Marchantia*.
    (Virkumar Singh, 1993)
31. *Marchantia* has well defined assimilatory zone in its thallus. Explain the statement and also give its reproductive structures.
    (Magadh, 1997)
32. Describe sexual reproduction in *Marchantia*. How does fertilisation take place in this genus?
    (Virkumar Singh, 1998)
33. Give an account of reproductive structures in *Marchantia.* *(Virkumar Singh, 1999)*
34. Describe the morphological and internal structures of gametophytic thallus of *Marchantia.* Give an account of mode of vegetative reproduction in the plant.
35. Give a brief account of the structure of thallus of *Marchantia* and modes of vegetative reproduction in this genus.
    (Vikram, 1990)
36. Define alternation of generation and explain it with reference to the life cycle of *Marchantia.* *(Rohilkhand, 2001)*
37. (a) Give an illustrated account of sex organs of *Marchantia.*
    (Poorvanchal, 2001)
    (b) With the help of suitable illustrations describe the position and structure of sex organs in *Marchantia.*
    (Poorvanchal, 20014, 2008)
38. With neat labelled sketches compare antherdiophore and archegoniophore of *Marchantia.*
    (Lucknow, 2006; Bangalore, 2002)
39. Describe sexual reproduction in *Marchantia.* How does it differ from *Funaria.* *(Gharwal, 2003)*

SHORT ANSWER TYPE

40. Write short notes on :

(*i*) Structure and function of scales of *Marchantia.*
(Kanpur, 1997; Meerut, 2000; Himachal Pradesh, 1992)

(*ii*) Antheridiophore of *Marchantia.*
(Lucknow, 1995, 2003, 2005; Allahabad, 1994).

(*iii*) Archegoniophore of *Marchantia.*
(Lucknow, 1996, 2003, 2008; Allahabad, 1992, 1993, 1995, 1996, 1999; 2002, 2003, 2005; Gorakhpur; 1998; Kerala, 1997; Virkumar Singh, 1994, 1997; Bhagalpur, 1990; Nagpur, 2002; Kanpur, MSc., 2007)

(*iv*) Gemma
(Lucknow, 1997, 1998, 1999, 2000, 2001, 2004; Rohilkhand, 1995; Awadh, 1998, Allahabad, 1991; Gorakhpur, 1992 Poorvanchal, 1997, 2000; U.P. College, 2000; Kanpur Msc, 2002, Kerala, 1998, 2001; Himachal Pradesh, 1997; Rajasthan, 1988); Andhra Pradesh, 2002)

(*v*) Elaters
(Rohilkhand, 1992, Allahabad, 1997; Bhagalpur, 1990; I.A.S. 1994; Kanpur MSc., 2003)

(*vi*) Vegetative reproduction in *Marchantia.*
(Kanpur, 2002; Rohilkhand, 1993, 1997, 1999; Poorvanchal, 1999; Kerala, 1996).

(*vii*) Gemma Cup.
(Rohilkhand, 1998; Allahabad, 1995; Gorakhpur, 1990, 1995; Poorvanchal, 1996,1998; Kerala, 2000; Virkumar Singh, 1991, 1996, 1997, 1998; Ravi Shankar Shukla, 1996; Bhagalpur, 1996; Kanpur, 2005, 2007 Lucknow, 2007)

(*viii*) Air pore and Air Chambers in *Marchantia* .
(Allahabad, 1998; Kerala, 1998)

(*ix*) Internal structure of *Marchantia* thallus. *(Kumaon, 1997)*

(*x*) Sexual reproduction in *Marchantia.*
(Kumaon, 1999)

(*xi*) Thallus of *Marchantia.*
(Rohilkhand, 2002, Bangalore, 2001, Nagpur, 2002)

(*xii*) Sex organs of *Marchantia.*
(Nagpur, 1995)

(*xiii*) Carpocephalum of *Marchantia.*
(Virkumar Singh,1991)

(*xiv*) Structure of Sporogonium in *Marchantia.(Virkumar Singh, 1994)*

(*xv*) Habit and distribution of *Marchantia.*

(*xvi*) External morphology of *Marchantia* thallus.

(*xvii*) Structure and function of Gemmae.
(Rohilkhand, 2001)

(*xviii*) Sperms of *Marchantia.*

(*xix*) *Antheridium* – Development and Structure.

(*xx*) Perichaetium

(*xxi*) Perigynium

(*xxii*) Capsule in *Marchantia.*

(*xxiii*) Fructifications of *Marchantia.*
(Nagarjuna, 1991)

(*xxiv*) Spore and its germination in *Marchantia.*

(*xxv*) Archesporium
(Lucknow, 2002, 2003)

(*xxvi*) Structure and function of gemma cups *(Poorvanchal, 2006)*

41. Name the bryophyte in which

(*i*) Elaters are present.

(*ii*) Inverted archegonium occurs.

(*iii*) Rhizoids are dimorphic.

(*iv*) Appendiculate scales are present.

(*v*) Barrel shaped air pores are present.

(*vi*) Half of the archesporium gives rise to spores while the remaining half is converted to elaters.

(*vii*) Six longitudinal rows of neck cells are present in the archegonium.

(*viii*) Gemma cups are present.

42. Classify *Marchantia* according to a recognised system of classification giving reasons. *(Kumaon, 1996)*

43. Where are the archegonia situated in *Marchantia* ? *(Gorakhpur, 1997)*

44. Name the types of scales found in *Marchantia*. *(Rohilkhand, 1992)*

45. Give the number of cells found in each tier of the air pore of *Marchantia* thallus. *(Rohilkhand, 1992)*

46. Give the number of plants formed by the germination of a gemma in *Marchantia*. *(Rohilkhand, 1993)*

47. Give the length of the stalk of antherediophore of *Marchantia*. *(Rohilkhand, 1994)*

48. Draw neat and labelled diagrams of the following :

(*a*) Appendiculate scale. *(Kanpur, 2000)*

(*b*) L.S. sporophyte of *Marchantia* *(Rohilkhand, 2000; Awadh, 1995; Kumaon, 2000)*

(*c*) Tuberculate rhizoid. *(Kanpur, 2000)*

(*d*) Single Gemma. *(Kanpur, 2000)*

(*e*) T.S./V.S. thallus of *Marchantia* passing through gemma cup. *(Kanpur, 2001; Rohilkhand,1999; Allahabad, 1994, 1996, 2002; Gorakhpur, 1994, 1998; Poorvanchal, 2000; U.P. College, 1998; Bundelkhand, 1993, 1999; Osmania, 1991; Lucknow, 2003; Kanpur MSc., 2004)*

(*f*) V.S./L.S. of archegoniophore of *Marchantia*. *(Kanpur, 1999, 2002; Rohilkhand, 1995, 1999; Awadh, 1992, 1994, 1997,1998; Allahabad, 1991; Gorakhpur, 1991, 1995; Lucknow, 2000; Poorvanchal, 1998, 2003; Bundelkhand, 1996; Gharwal 2003, 2004)*

(*g*) L.S. Sporogonium/sporophyte of *Marchantia*. *(Lucknow, 1995, 2001; Awadh, 1995; Gorakhpur, 1996; Poorvanchal, 1996, 1999, 2005; Vinoba Bhave, 1999; J.P. Univ., 1999; Kanpur, 2004)*

(*h*) V.L.S. Gemma Cup of *Marchantia*. *(Lucknow, 1996, 1999; Meerut, 2000)*

(*i*) T.S. Thallus of *Marchantia*. *(Meerut,1998, 1999; Awadh, 1993, 1998; Gorakhpur, 1999; Poorvanchal, 2000; Mahatma Gandhi, 1998; Himachal Pradesh, 1996; Bhagalpur, 1992)*

(*j*) V.S./L.S./V.T.S antheridiophore of *Marchantia*. *(Meerut, 2000, 2002; Rohilkhand, 1996; Awadh, 1996; Allahabad, 1997, 2006; Gorakhpur, 1992, 1993; Poorvanchal, 1997; Bundelkhand, 1995; Bhagalpur, 1991; Kanpur 2003, 2006; Garhwal, 2000)*

(*k*) Sporophyte of *Marchantia*. *(Kanpur, 2007; Rohilkhand, 1998)*

(*l*) V.L.S. of an archegoniophore and a portion of thallus *Marchantia*. *(Allahabad, 1998)*

(*m*) T.S. of ventral scale in *Marchantia*. *(Gorakhpur, 1996)*

(*n*) Capsule of *Marchantia*. *(Kanpur, 2007)*

(*o*) Sperm of *Marchantia*.

(*p*) Gemma Cups of *Marchantia* *(Lucknow, 2008)*

49. Draw only labelled diagrams of Transverse section of the thallus/ gametophytes of *Riccia, Marchantia, Pellia* and *Anthoceros*. *(Awadh, 1991; Allahabad, 1995)*

50. Differentiate between :

(*a*) Smooth walled and tuberculate rhizoids. *(Kanpur, 2008)*

(*b*) Antheridiophore and Archegoniophore of *Marchantia*. *(Awadh, 1998)*

(*c*) External features of thallus of *Riccia* and *Marchantia*.

(*d*) Male sex organs of *Marchantia* and *Polytrichum* . *(Madras, 2000; Trichy,1995)*

(*e*) Rhizoids of *Marchantia* and *Funaria*.

(*f*) Thallus of *Marchantia* and *Anthoceros*. *(Allahabad, 2003)*

(*g*) Sex organs of *Marchantia* and *Cyathodium*. *(Virkumar Singh,1993)*

(*h*) Sporogonium of *Riccia* and *Marchantia*.

(*i*) Elaters and pseudoelaters *(Lucknow, 2004; Allabahad, 2006; Lucknow, 2008)*

(*j*) Structure of *Riccia* and *Marchantia* thallus *(Kanpur, 2005)*

(*k*) Perichaetium and Perigynium *(Allahabad, 2006)*

(*l*) Barrel shapedpores and simplepores *(Allahabad, 2006)*

51. Draw labelled sketches only to show the distinguishing characters of Sporogonium and Gemma cup of *Marchantia*. *(Awadh, 1993)*

52. Give only labelled diagrams of L.S. of mature sporophytes of *Marchantia* and *Porella* (*Madotheca*). *(Allahabad, 1995)*

53. What are (*i*) Gemmae and (*ii*) Archesporium ? *(Allahabad, 1998)*

54. Describe and draw a gemma of *Marchantia*. *(Calicut, 2001)*

55. Explain the internal structure of *Marchantia* thallus. *(Kerala, 2001)*

56. Briefly explain the vegetative propagation in *Marchantia* or What are the modes of vegetative propagation in *Marchantia*? *(Kerala, 1997, 2000)*

57. With suitable diagrams, explain the structure and function of gemmae in *Marchantia*. *(Kerala, 2000)*

58. Describe sex organs in *Riccia* and *Marchantia*. *(Kerala, 1997)*

59. Describe the organisation of antheridiophore and archegoniophore in *Marchantia*. *(Calicut, 1998)*

60. Answer briefly the following :

(*a*) Gemmae in *Marchantia*. *(Kerala, 1999)*

(*b*) *Marchantia* thallus. *(Kerala, 1999)*

(*c*) Antheridium in *Marchantia*.

(*d*) Antherozoid in *Marchantia*.

(*e*) Fertilization in *Marchantia*. *(Mahatma Gandhi, 1996)*

61. Describe the structure and function of chimney pores in *Marchantia*. *(Kerala, 1995)*

62. (*a*) What is the structure of Gemma in *Marchantia*?

(*b*) What is meant by Perichaetium in *Marchantia*? *(Mahatma Gandhi, 1998)*

63. (*a*) Compare the structure and position of Archegonia in *Riccia*, *Marchantia* and *Funaria*.

(*b*) Compare the rhizoids of *Marchantia*, *Funaria* and ferns. *(Himachal Pradesh, 1993)*

(*c*) Compare the structure and position of antheridia in *Marchantia, Riccia and Funaria*.

64. Explain the inversion of archegonia in *Marchantia*. *(Himachal Pradesh, 1997)*

65. What is anchesporium ? What does it contribute in *Marchantia*?

66. What is perichaetium ? What are its functions ?

67. Write the distinctive features of *Marchantia*.

68. Justify the truth or falsity of the following statements giving reasons :

(*i*) The air pores on the thallus of *Marchantia* are homologous to the stomata of higher plants.

(*ii*) The short seta of *Marchantia* sporogonium is an anatomical necessity.

(*iii*) The gemmae of *Marchantia* are reproductive structures which do not play any role in the phenomenon of alternation of generations.

68. Arrange the following in sporogonium of *Marchantia* from outside to inside:

(*i*) Capsule wall (*ii*) Perigynium (*iii*) Calyptra (*iv*) Elaters.

70. Describe the process of spermatogenesis in *Marchantia*.

71. Give a brief illustrated account of the structure of sperms in *Marchantia*.

72. Describe vegetative reproduction in *Riccia* and *Marchantia*. *(Kanpur, 2004)*

73. What do you mean by elaters. *(Poorvanchal, 2001)*

74. Give a brief account of T.S. thallus of *Marchantia*. *(Poorvanchal, 2002)*

75. The air pores in the thallus of *Marchantia* are homologous to the stomata of higher plants. Give appropriate reasons. *(Poorvanchal, 2003)*

76. Name the class to which *Marchantia* belongs. *(Meerut, 2002)*

77. What is perianth ? Name a few liverworts which show this structure. *(Kanpur, MSc., 2004)*

78. What is antheridophore ? *(Kerala, 2001)*

OBJECTIVE TYPE

79. Describe vegetative reproduction in *Riccia* and *Marchantia* *(Kanpur, 2007)*

80. Name the bryophyte in which elaters are found *(Kanpur, 2007)*

81. Write short notes on reduction theory of origin of marchantiales *(Kanpur, M.Sc. 2005)*

82. Select the correct answer :

(*i*) Calyptra in *Marchantia* is found in
(*a*) Antheridiophore
(*b*) Archegoniophore
(*c*) Gametophyte
(*d*) Sporophyte.

(*ii*) In *Marchantia* the archegonia are surrounded by a common involucre which is called as
(*a*) Operculum
(*b*) Perichaetium
(*c*) Peritoneum
(*d*) Perigynium.

(*iii*) Archegonium of *Marchantia* has
(*a*) 6 rows of neck cells
(*b*) 5 rows of neck cells
(*c*) 4 rows of necks
(*d*) 2 rows of neck. cells.

(*iv*) Which of the following is not found in Marchantia?
(*a*) Perigynium
(*b*) Perichaetium
(*c*) Calyptra
(*d*) Paraphysis.

(*v*) Barrel shaped pores are found in
(*a*) *Riccia* (*b*) *Marchantia*
(*c*) *Pellia* (*d*) *Anthoceros.*

(*vi*) Which of the following has five rows of neck canal cells in the archegonium?
(*a*) *Marchantia* (*b*) *Pellia*
(*c*) *Pogonatum* (*d*) *Funaria.*

(*vii*) Which of the following is a sporophytic structure in *Marchantia*?
(*a*) Calyptra (*b*) Spores
(*c*) Elaters (*d*) Rhizoids.

(*viii*) The stalk of gemmae of *Marchantia* is
(*a*) Unicellular (*b*) Bicellular
(*c*) Multicellular (*d*) Acellular.

(*ix*) Elaters of *Marchantia* are
(*a*) Haploid (*b*) Diploid
(*c*) Triploid (*d*) Polyploid.

(*x*) Female sex organs in *Marchantia* are borne in
(*a*) Elateropore
(*b*) Sterile tissue
(*c*) Antheridiophore
(*d*) Archegoniophore.

(*xi*) Gemma cup is found in
(*a*) *Marchantia* (*b*) *Anthoceros*
(*c*) *Sphagnum* (*d*) *Riccia.*

(*xii*) Elaters of *Marchantia* exhibit
(*a*) Xerochasy
(*b*) Hydrochasy
(*c*) Mutation
(*d*) Circumnutation.

(*xiii*) Perichaetium is observed in
(*a*) Archegoniophore
(*b*) Antheridiophore
(*c*) Sporogonium
(*d*) Thallus.

(*xiv*) In *Marchantia* the chloroplast is
(*a*) Cup shaped
(*b*) Disc-shaped
(*c*) Star shaped
(*d*) Ribbon shaped.

(*xv*) In *Marchantia* the archegonia are situated
(*a*) On the disc
(*b*) Below the disc
(*c*) In the middle of the disc
(*d*) On the sides of the disc.

(*xvi*) Male sex organs in *Marchantia* are borne on
(*a*) An elaterophore
(*b*) A rhizophore

(*c*) An antheridiophore
(*d*) An archegoniophore.

(*xvii*) The sporophyte in *Marchantia* is protected by
(*a*) One protective sheath
(*b*) Two protective sheaths
(*c*) Three protective sheaths
(*d*) Four protective sheaths.

(*xviii*) Perigynium is seen in
(*a*) Archegonium (*b*) Antheridium
(*c*) Gametophyte (*d*) Sporophyte.

(*xix*) Spore mother cells in *Marchantia* are
(*a*) haploid (*b*) diploid
(*c*) triploid (*d*) tetraploid.

(*xx*) Formation of elaters is characteristic of
(*a*) *Riccia* (*b*) *Anthoceros*
(*c*) *Funaria* (*d*) *Marchantia.*

(*xxi*) In *Marchantia* the gametophores are the elongation of
(*a*) Thallus (*b*) Calyptra
(*c*) Sporogonium (*d*) Leafy plant.

(*xxii*) Archesporium develops from endothecium in
(*a*) *Riccia* (*b*) *Marchantia*
(*c*) *Funaria* (*d*) *Anthoceros.*

(*xxiii*) Air pores in *Marchantia* are surrounded by
(*a*) one tier of four cells
(*b*) 2 tiers of 5 cells
(*c*) 3 tiers of four to five cells
(*d*) 4 tiers of 4-5 cells.

(*xiv*) Antheridiophore and archegoniophore are modified branches of :
(*a*) Antheridium and Archegonium
(*b*) Vegetative thallus
(*c*) Gemma Cup
(*d*) Rhizoids.

(*xxv*) How many layers of protective coverings envelope the sporophyte of *Marchantia ?*
(*a*) 2 (*b*) 3
(*c*) 4 (*d*) 5

(*xxvi*) In which of the following tuberculate rhizoids are present. ?
(*a*) *Funaria*
(*b*) *Anthoceros*
(*c*) *Marchantia*
(*d*) None of the above.

(*xxvii*) Gemmae are sexual reproductive bodies of which of the following ?
(*a*) *Riccia* (*b*) *Selaginella*
(*c*) *Marsilea* (*d*) *Marchantia.*

(*xxviii*) Elaters of________help in dispersal
(*a*) *Riccia* (*b*) *Selaginella*
(*c*) *Marsilea* (*d*) *Marchantia.*

83. Fill in the blanks :

(*a*) The structure which surrounds the group of archegonia in the archegoniophore is called ________________.

(*b*) An aerial reproductive stage in *Marchantia* is __________.

(*c*) Barrel shaped pores are present in ____________.

(*d*) In *Marchantia* asexual reproduction is brought about by __________.

(*e*) Gametophores in *Marchantia* are elongation of __________.

(*f*) In *Marchantia* the tissue of calyptra grows to form a covering called __________.

(*g*) Specialised branch systems of the thallus carrying antheridia in *Marchantia* are called ______________.

(*h*) Elaters are __________ in nature and help in ________ dispersal.

(*i*) In *Marchantia* archesporium develops from __________.

(*j*) Calyptra in *Marchantia* is ____________.

(*k*) Archegonium in *Marchantia* has __________ rows of neck cells.

(*l*) Formation of elaters is characteristic of __________.

(*m*) First cell of the gametophytic generation in *Marchantia* is __________.

(*n*) The sperm in *Marchantia* has ______________ flagella and a long narrow rod like ______________.

(*o*) Appendiculate scales are present in____________.

Image of *Targionia*

CHAPTER 5(II)

MARCHANTIALES
Targioniaceae
Targionia and Cyathodium

- Family Targioniaceae
- Targionia
- Cyathodium

FAMILY TARGIONIACEAE

General characteristics

The family Targioniaceae includes some complex members of the order Marchantiales. They are characterised by —

1. The gametophytic plant body is thalloid. Thallus is prostrate and dichotomously branched.

2. The air chambers open outside on dorsal surface through semi-barrel shaped air pores.

3. Semi-barrel shaped air pore is formed by several concentric rings of cells on dorsal surface of each air chamber.

4. Air chambers are either empty or filled with photosynthetic filaments.

5. The antheridia are restricted to special short ventral adventitious shoots branches produced from the main thallus.

6. The archegonia are shifted backward near growing point.

7. The archegonia are enclosed and protected by two valved boat shaped or oval - tumblar shaped

involucre. The sporophyte has foot, seta and capsule.

8. Seta is very short.
9. Lid or operculum is present on the top of capsule.
10. The capsule contains both spores and elaters.

The family includes three genera. These are *Targionia, Cyathodium* and *Aitchisoniella*. The later genus was discovered by Kashyap (1914, 1929) from Mussoorie, Simla & Kulu. The genus is endemic to India and listed as one of the endangered genera of the world. *Aitchisoniella* is a monotypic genus and is represented by a single species *A. himalayensis*. Two genera, *Targionia* and *Cyathodium* are discussed here in brief.

TARGIONIA

The Gametophyte

Distribution. The genus is represented in India by five species (Udar & Gupta, 1983). Out of which three species are most common. These are *T. hypophylla*, *T. indica* and *T. lorbeeriana*. The species are distributed in various bryological territories of the country ranging from high altitude to plains.

External characters (Fig. 5.25 A-E). The plants of *Targionia* are gametophytic and has a very simple strap-shaped thallus, sparingly dichotomously branched with two rows of ventral scales on either side of midrib (Fig. 5.25 B). The scales may be simple or appendaged. The air pores on the dorsal surface are simple or raised consisting of several layers of concentric cells (Fig. 5.25 D). Numerous ventral adventitious shoots are produced from ventral surface of midrib (Fig. 5.25 A). These on detachment help in vegetative propagation. The rhizoids are typical of the order Marchantiales *i.e.* smooth walled and tuberculate.

The mid-dorsal groove (as found in *Riccia*), polygonal area and gemma cups (as found in *Marchantia*) are absent on dorsal surface of thallus.

Internal structure (Fig. 5.25 E). In anatomy thallus shows two distinct regions : (*i*) *Photosynthetic* or *assimilatory* zone and (*ii*) *Storage zone*. The upper photosynthetic zone consists of a single row of air chambers which are packed with branched and unbranched photosynthetic filaments. Each chamber opens outside through a simple or upper half raised air pores also called half barrel shaped air pore. The lower storage zone is similar to what we have in *Riccia.*

Sexual reproduction. The plants are usually monoecious (homothallic). The antheridia are produced on the dorsal surface of adventitious shoots forming spherical cushion like areas which are also called *sessile male receptacles* (Fig. 5.25 F). The archegonia are initially produced at the apex of thallus from growing point but subsequently shifted downwards. As result of this, in a mature thallus the archegonia are found enclosed within a boat shaped two lobed involucre at the ventral surface near the apex (Fig. 5.25 B and G). This is a diagnostic feature of the genus. The fertilization is similar to other members of Hepaticopsida.

The sporophyte. The sporophyte has three parts : (*i*) foot (*ii*) seta (*iii*) capsule. The capsule has a lid or operculum at the apex and some of the elaters get fixed at the apex (Fig. 5.25 H and I). The fixed elaters are short, stumpy and with annular or spiral thickening bands (Fig. 5.25 J). The free elaters are relatively larger with two or three spiral thickenings (Fig. 5.25 K). After the removal of lid (operculum) the capsule dehisces into 4-8 irregular valves. The capsule wall is one cell thick and with annular or semi annular thickening bands on inner surface (Fig. 5.25 L and M).

The spores are haploid and produced after meiosis from sproe mother cells. The spores germinate to form the gametophyte.

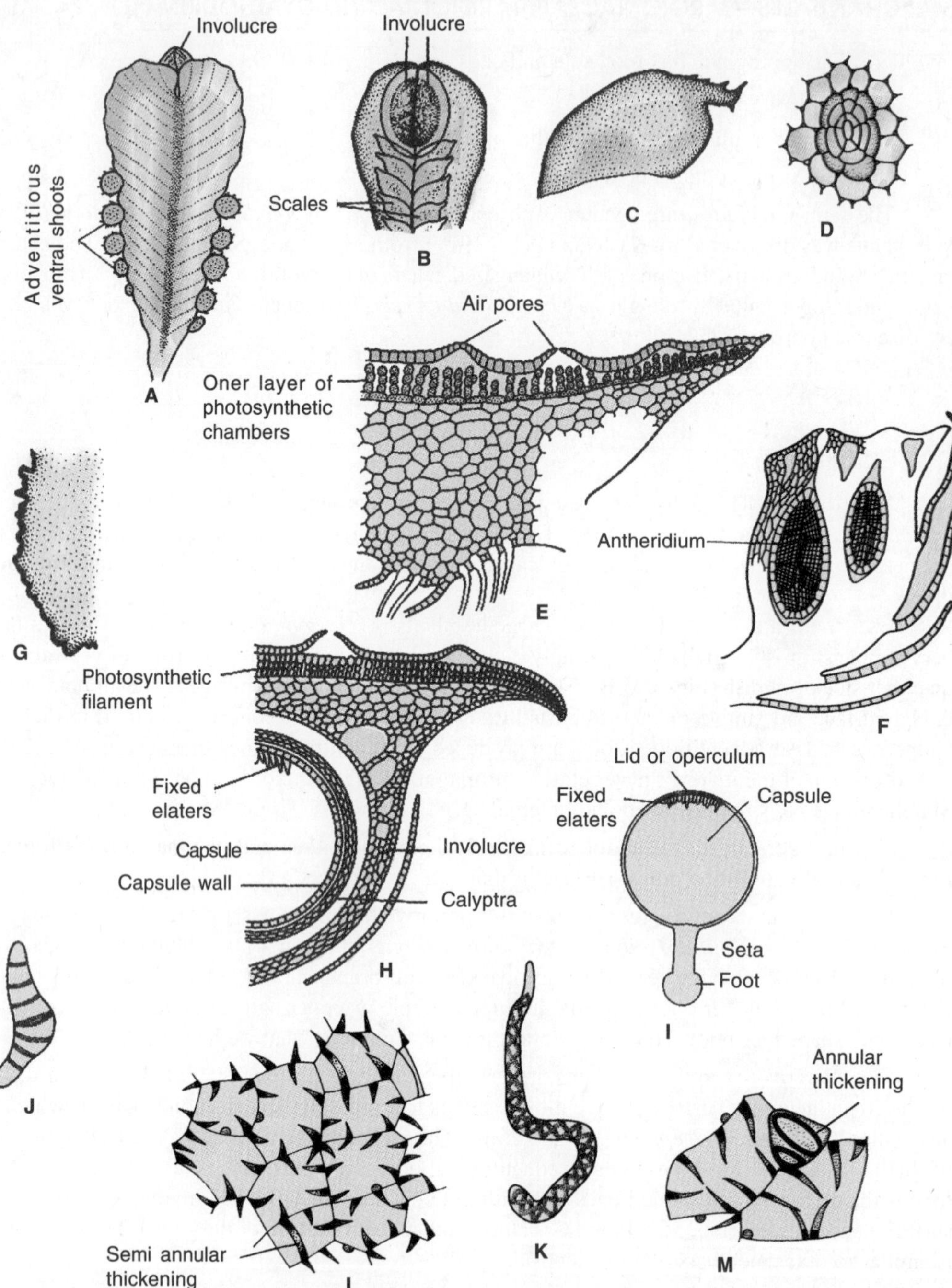

Fig. 5.25. (A—M). ***Targionia* sp.** A, dorsal surface of thallus; B, ventral surface of thallus; C, scale; D, air pore; E, V.T.S. of thallus; F,V.L.S. of sessile male receptacle showing single antheridium in each antheridial chamber; G, Margin of involucre; H, V.T.S. of thallus passing through sporogonium (capsule); I, sporophyte, J, fixed elater with annular thickening; K, free elater with 3 spiral thickenings. L, and M, capsule wall-cells showing thickenings.

CYATHODIUM

The Gametophyte

Distribution. *Cyathodium* is a very common genus of the family Targioniaceae. Udar and Singh (1976) have reported seven species from India. The common species are : *C. tuberosum* and *C. cavernarum*. The plants prefer moist, shady and dark areas receiving dim light. *C. cavernarum* grows in caves and has a peculiar quality of exhibiting flourescence. It appears golden yellow inside the caves and when taken out appears yellowish green or green. The genus has been reported from all the bryological regions of the country.

External characters (Fig. 5.26 A—D) . Almost all the species of *Cyathodium* are relatively delicate with a thin dichotomously branched thallus. The dorsal surface of thallus bears prominent polygonal areas each with an air pore. The ventral scales are highly reduced or often absent. The reduced ventral scales are few celled, chlorophyllous, filamentous, uniseriate or biseriate and found near the growing point Fig. 5.26 D. The rhizoids are smooth walled and tuberculate.

Internal structure (Fig. 5.26 E_1 and E_2). Majority of species of the genus exhibit highly reduced thallus consisting only of photosynthetic zone showing one row of large and empty air chambers Fig. 5.26 E_1. The pores are simple or half-barrel shaped consisting of several layers of concentric cells. The storage zone is absent or reduced in majority of species except *C. denticulatum* and *C. foetidissimum* where photosynthetic zone has 2-3 layers of empty photosynthetic chambers (also called air chambers). The storge zone is also few cell layer thick Fig. 5.26 E_2.

Vegetative reproduction. Some of the species like *C. tuberosum* develops prominent tubers at the apex of the thallus which help in vegetative propagation of the plants.

Sexual reproduction. *Cyathodium* may be monoecious (homothallic - both antheridia and archegonia are produced on same plant) or dioecious (heterothallic - antheridia and archegonia are produced on separate plants). The antheridia are produced on antheridiophore (male receptacle) which is either sessile or stalked with two to several lobed disc. The stalk has single shallow rhizoidal furrow (Fig. 5.26 H). Antheridia are formed in acropetal succession. The archegonia are found on ventral suface near growing point at the apex of the thallus. They are enclosed within a single oval or tumblar shaped bi-lipped involucre, the surface of involucre is either smooth or hairy-the diagnostic feature of the genus *Cyathodium.* Based on the characteristic feature of involucres, Udar and Singh (1976) have recognised two groups of all the seven species.

Group 1. Species having smooth involucres e.g. *C. cavernarum, C. denticulatum, C. smaragdinum*

Group 2. Species having hairy involucres e.g. *C. aureonitens, C. acrotrichum, C. flabellatum, C. tuberosum.*

Fertilisation takes place in presence of water.

The sporophyte (Fig. 5.26 I, J.K.). The sporophyte consists of a very small foot of few cells, a small seta and a spherical capsule. There is a prominent lid or operculum at the apex which is bistratose consisting of usually 4 cells on outer side and 8 or more cells on the inner side. The upper half of the capsule wall shows semiannular thickening bands while lower half is without thickening bands. The dehiscence of capsule is by throwing off of the lid and rupturing of capsule wall into 4-8 irregular valves. The number of elaters in each capsule is much less than the number of spores.

Spores are haploid and produced from spore mother cells (I) after reduction division. The spores germinate in presence of water to form the thallus.

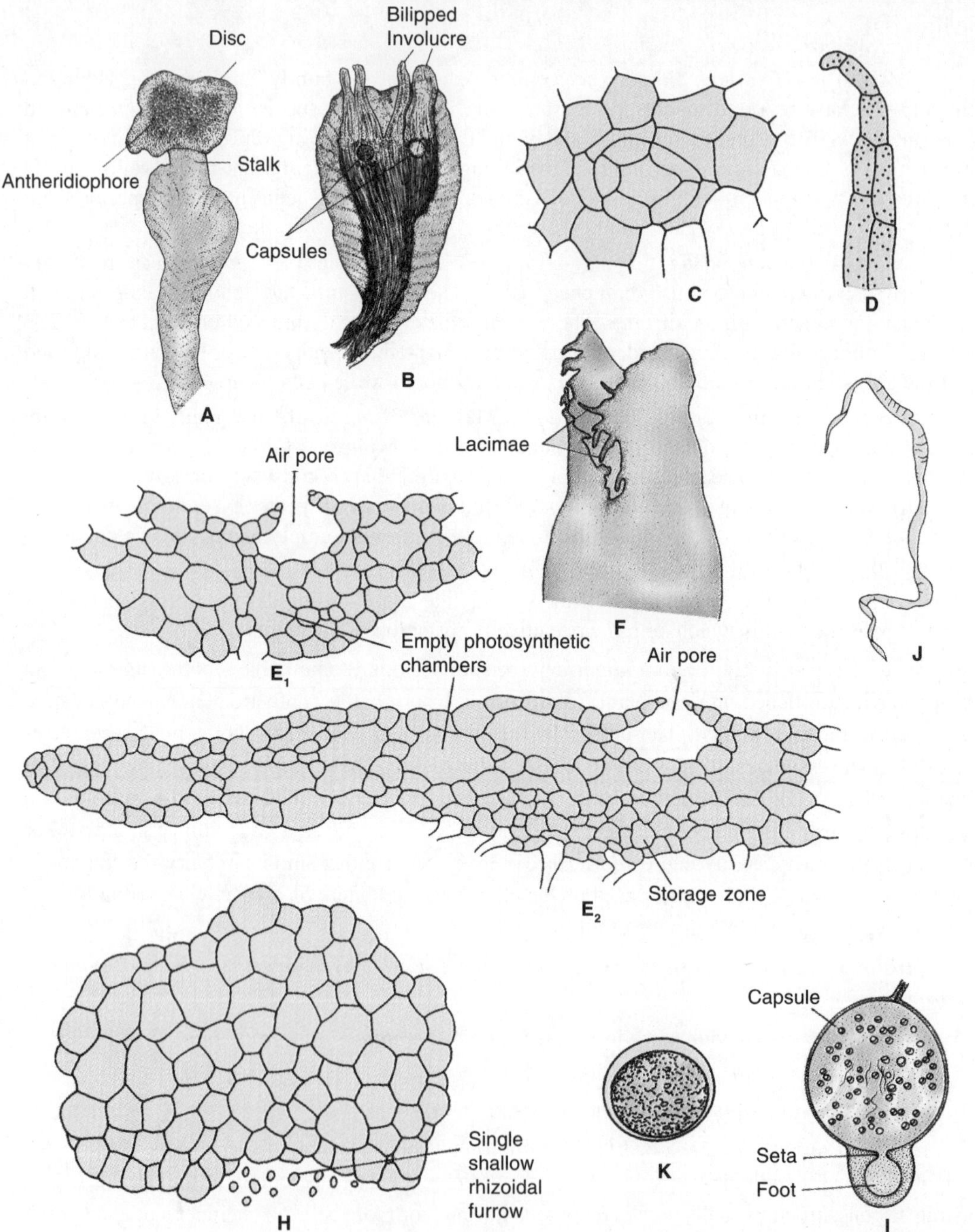

Fig. 5.26. (A–K) ***Cyathodium* sp.** A, dorsal surface : male plant with stalked male receptacle (antheridiophore); B, ventral surface of female plant showing involucres containing sporophyte; C, airpore; D, scale and E_1 and E_2, V.T.S. of thallus; F. involucre; G, lacina of involucre; H,T.S. of stalk of antheridiophore showing shallow rhizoidal furrow; I; young sporophyte; J, an elater ; K, young spore.

SYSTEMATIC POSITION OF *TARGIONIA*

Division	:	Bryophyta
Class	:	Hepaticopsida
Order	:	Marchantiales
Family	:	Targioniaceae
Genus	:	*Targionia*
Species	:	*hypophylla*

SYSTEMATIC POSITION OF *CYATHODIUM*

Division	:	Bryophyta
Class	:	Hepaticopsida
Order	:	Marchantiales
Family	:	Targioniaceae
Genus	:	*Cyathodium*
Species	:	*tuberosum*

QUESTIONS

ESSAY TYPE

1. Describe the salient feature of the family Targioniaceae. How does it differ from Marchantiaceae?
2. With the help of labelled diagrams describe the life history of *Targionia.*
3. Give an illustrated account of the life cycle of *Cyathodium.*
4. Describe the sex organs of *Targionia* and compare it with that of *Cyathodium*.
5. With the help of labelled diagrams compare the thallus structure of *Cyathodium* with that of *Targionia.*
6. Give a brief account of reproduction in *Cyathodium* and *Targionia*.

SHORT ANSWER TYPE

7. **Write notes on the following :**

(*a*) *Cyathodium*
(Kanpur, 1992, 1994, 1996; Rohilkhand, M.Sc. 1995, 2000; Bihar, 1990)

(*b*) *Targionia*
(Kanpur, 1993, 1995, 2000)

(*c*) Reproduction in *Targionia*

(*d*) Sexual reproduction in *Cyathodium*

(*e*) Thallus structure in *Cyathodium*

(*f*) Sporophyte of *Cyathodium*
(Virkumar Singh, 1991)

8. Differentiate between the following :

(*a*) *Cyathodium* and *Anthoceros*
(Kanpur, 1993)

(*b*) *Cyathodium* and *Pellia*
(Awadh, M.Sc. 2001)

(*c*) *Targionia* and *Plagiochasma*
(Awadh, M.Sc. 2001).

(*d*) Sex organs of *Marchantia* and *Cyathodium*. *(Magadh, 1993)*

OBJECTIVE TYPE

9. Select the correct answer :

(*i*) *Targionia* belongs to the family
- (*a*) Ricciaceae
- (*b*) Anthocerotaceae
- (*c*) Pelliaceae
- (*d*) Targioniaceae.

(*ii*) Antheridia are restricted to special short ventral adventitious shoots in the plants belonging to the family
- (*a*) Ricciaceae
- (*b*) Anthocerotaceae
- (*c*) Pelliaceae
- (*d*) Targioniaceae.

(*iii*) Two valved boat shaped involucre protecting the archegonia are present in
- (*a*) *Riccia* (*b*) *Anthoceros*
- (*c*) *Pellia* (*d*) *Targionia.*

(*iv*) In *Targionia* the elaters are
- (*a*) fixed and free
- (*b*) freely distributed in the capsule
- (*c*) not true but pseudoelaters
- (*d*) absent.

(*v*) In *Cyathodium* the thallus has large photosynthetic zone and the storage is
- (*a*) either reduced or completely absent
- (*b*) larger than the photosynthetic zone
- (*c*) more developed than the photosynthetic zone
- (*d*) equal in size of the photosynthetic.

Image of Plagiochasma

CHAPTER 5(III)

MARCHANTIALES

Rebouliaceae

Plagiochasma

- Rebouliaceae
- Plagiochasma
- Reproduction

REBOULIACEAE

GENERAL CHARACTERISTICS

The family Rebouliaceae is very close to family Marchantiaceae. However, the family Rebouliaceae is characterised by the following features :

1. The ligulate scales are absent.
2. Only appendicular scale are found.
3. The air pores on the thallus are simple or half barrel-shaped.
4. The air pores on disc of receptacle retain the structure of barrel shaped structure as found in family Marchantiaceae.
5. The operculum is present in capsule.

The family Rebouliaceae is represented in India by five genera which are : 1. *Reboulia,* 2. *Asterella* (*Fimbriaria*), 3. *Plagiochasma*, 4. *Mannia* 5. *Cryptomitrium*. The genus *Plagiochasma* is being described here.

PLAGIOCHASMA

HABIT AND DISTRIBUTION

The plants of *Plagiochasma* usually grow on exposed conditions and always prefer calcium rich substrate. About 20 species have been reported which are distributed in most part of the world. The important species which have been reported from India are : *P. intermedium, P. simalensis, P. appendiculatum* and *P. articulatum*.

Gametophyte

External feature (Fig. 5.27 A—K). The gametophytic plant body is thalloid. Thallus is prostrate, dorsiventrally flat and dichotomously branched. The dorsal surface of young thallus is more or less smooth with dot like air pores. The midrib is ill-defined. The apical notch is promiment from which arises apical innovations (adventitious branch of young thallus). In older thallus several apical innovations may be produced one after the other. These apical innovations actually help in vegetative propagation of the genus. On the ventral surface of the thallus, there are present two rows of ventral scales of which one row is on either side of the midrib. The ventral scales are only appendicular type. Each scale has one (Fig. 5.27 B) or two linear appendages (Fig. 5.27 C) over large body. The ligulate scales are absent. The rhizoids are of two types : (*i*) Smooth-walled simple rhizoids and (*ii*) Tuberculate rhizoids.

Internal structure of thallus (Fig. 5.27 F, G). In anatomy (V.T.S. of thallus) the thallus is typical *Reboulia* - type. The photosynthetic zone consists of 2-3 or 4 layers of empty air chambers (Fig. 5.27 F,G). The chloroplasts are confined in the cells of partition walls of the chamber. The photosynthetic filaments are absent within chambers. The upper most layer of photosynthetic chambers bears half barrel-shaped or simple air pores (Fig. 5.27 G,E). The air pore is formed by aggregation of several concentric rings of cells. The epidermal cells surrounding the air pore are thickened at the corners. The thickenings are called trigones (Fig. 5.27 E). The storage region is well developed and made up of mostly thinwalled parenchymatous cells having starch grains as reserve food. Few oil-cells are also found. A few cells contain crystals of calcium oxylate.

REPRODUCTION

Regarding the sexuality, the genus *Plagiochasma* has both the type of species:

1. Monoecious (Homothallic) - *P. appendiculatum*
2. Dioecious (Heterothallic) - *P. intermedium*

(a) Antheridia (Fig 5.27 A, H,I). The sessile male receptacles (antheridiophores) are produced on ill-defined midrib of dorsal surface in an acropetal fashion. The shape of sessile male receptacle is horse shoe-shaped (diagnostic feature of the genus) (Fig. 5.27 A). The receptacle bears two type of chambers, (*i*) Air chambers, (*ii*) Antheridial chambers. Antheridial chamber contains single large subglobose antheridium. The opening of this chamber is simple and called ostiole (Fig. 5.27 H). The development and dehiscence of antheridium is more or less similar to *Marchantia*.

(b) Archegonia (Fig. 5.27 A,J,K). The stalked female receptacles (archegoniophores) are also born on ill-defined midrib of dorsal surface (Fig. 5.27 A). In case of *Plagiochasma* the archegoniophore is never produced from apical cell. Therfore, their position is strictly on dorsal surface and not in apical notch. Because of this fact, the stalk of archegoniophore has no rhizoidal furrow (diagnostic feature of the genus). The disc of archegoniophore has only air chambers and each air chamber has barrel - shaped air pores as found in *Marchantia*. It is a primitive character which appears during the development of archegoniophore.

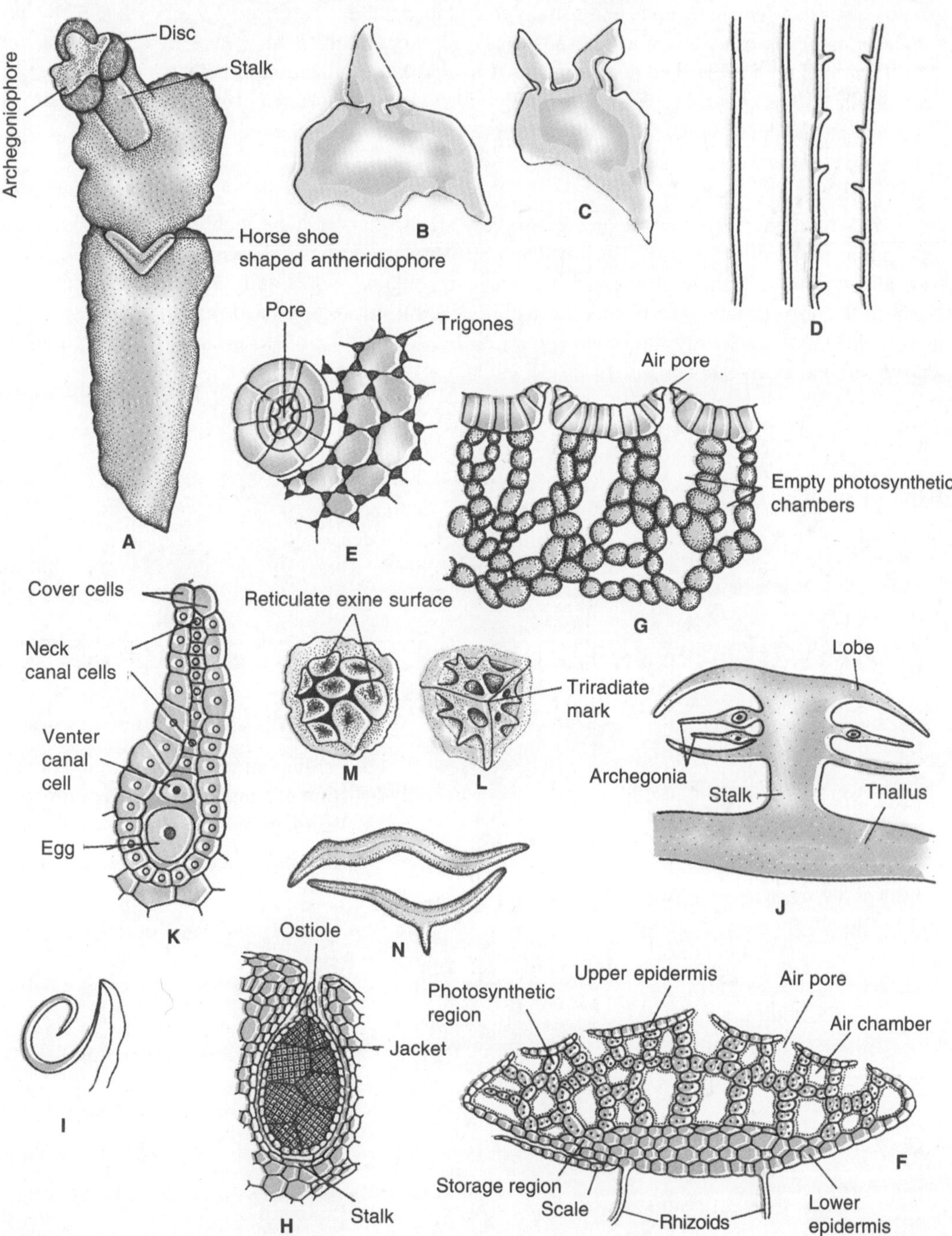

Fig. 5.27. (A—N) ***Plagiochasma* sp.** A, monoecious thallus with horse shoe shaped sessile antheridiophore (male receptacle) and stalked archegoniophore (female receptacle); B. and C, scales; D, rhizoids; E, upper epidermis of thallus with air pore and trigones in epidermal cells; F, V.T.S. of thallus; G,V.T.S. of thallus showing only photosythetic zone having empty photosynthetic chambers ; H, an antheridum; I, antherozoid; J,V.L.S. of archegoniophore; K, an archegonium; L, a spore in proximal view; M, a spore in distal view; N, elaters.

The disc of female receptacle is usually three lobed but it varies from 2-9 lobes. Each lobe has single or rarely two archegonia. The position of archegonium is horizontal (not pendant as in *Marchantia*) (Fig. 5.27 J). The development, structure and fertilization of archegonium is more or less similar to *Marchantia* type. In case of *Plagiochasma* the horizontally placed archegonium is protected by the development of involucre.

Sporophyte

The sporophyte has very reduced foot, very small seta and large globose capsule having an operculum on its anterior side. The capsule wall is one cell thick. The cells of capsule wall are isodiametric and thickened at corners. The capsule contains spores and elaters. The spores (Fig. 5.27L, M) are reticulate. The elaters are with 2-3 spiral thickening bands except *P. intermedium* where elaters are uniformly thickened (Fig. 5.27 N). At the time of dehiscence, the operculum is thrown off and then rest part of the capsule splits in several irregular valves.

SYSTEMATIC POSITION OF *PLAGIOCHASMA*

Division	:	Bryophyta
Class	:	Hepaticopsida
Order	:	Marchantiales
Family	:	Rebouliaceae
Genus	:	*Plagiochasma*
Species	:	*intermedium*

QUESTIONS

ESSAY TYPE

1. Describe the life history of *Plagiochasma*.
2. Compare the life-cycles of *Marchantia* and *Plagiochasma.*
3. Give a diagrammic representation of the structure of gametophyte and sporophyte of *Plagiochasma.*
4. Describe the structure and position of sex organs in Marchantiales.

(Allahabad, MSc., 2000)

SHORT ANSWER TYPE

4. Write short notes on

   (*a*) *Plagiochasma.*

   (*b*) Differences between *Plagiochasma and Marchantia.*

OBJECTIVE TYPE

5. **Select the correct answer :**

   (*i*) *Plagiochasma* differs from *Marchantia* in the absence of

   (*a*) Simple rhizoids
   (*b*) Tuberculate rhizoids
   (*c*) Ligulate scales
   (*d*) Appendiculate scale.

   (*ii*) The antheridiophore in *Plagiochasma* is

   (*a*) Horse shoe shaped
   (*b*) Barrel shaped
   (*c*) Square shaped
   (*d*) Oval shaped.

Image of Lunularia cruciata

CHAPTER 5(IV)

MARCHANTIALES
LUNULARIACEAE
Lunularia

- Lunulariaceae
- Lunularia
- Gametophyte
- Reproduction
- Sporophyte

General Characteristics

The family Lunulariaceae is a monotypic family with a single genus **Lunularia**. The family is characterised by the following features :

1. The presence of crescent or lunate - shaped gemma - cups on dorsal surface on the thallus, with entire margin. The gemmae are discoid.

2. The ligulate or marginal scales -are absent on ventral surface. Only rotundate appendiculate scale are present in two longitudinal rows.

3. The air chambers are in a single layer with simple or branched photosynthetic filaments.

4. The air pores on the thallus are simple or half barrel-shaped.

5. The antheridial receptacles are disciform, sessile and lack pores.

6. The archegonial receptacles (archegoniophores) are stalked; stalk is without rhizoidal furrows where as disc is deeply four lobed and without pores and photosynthetic tissues. Each lobe of the disc is covered by horizontal, tubular involucres.

LUNULARIA

Habit and Distribution

The plants of **Lunularia** prefer moist, shady and cold places of rocky soil. The genus is represented in India by a single species *L. crusiata* which is found in Darjeeling (eastern himalayas), Simla (western himalayas) and Kodaikanal and Madras (southern India).

Gametophyte

External feature (Fig. 5.28 A–C). The plant body is gametophyte and thalloid. The thallus is prostrate, dorsiventrally flat, large (5-20 cm long and 1-2 cm wide), more or less, irregularly dichotomously branched and forms apical innovations (Fig. 5.28 A). The margin of the thallus is undulate and its apex is emarginate. The dorsal surface of the thallus has polygonal area each with an air pore and characteristic crescent or lunate shaped gemma-cups of which margin is entire. The gemmae are discoid (diagnostic feature of *Lunularia*). The ventral surface has smooth-walled (simple) and tuberculate rhizoids. The ventral scales are in two longitudinal rows. The scales are only rotundate appendiculate (ligulate scales are not found).

Internal structure of thallus (Fig. 5.28 D). It has two distinct zones. The dorsal-upper photosynthetic zone is made up of a single layer of air chambers which open out side through simple or half barrel-shaped air pores. Each air pore is formed by five concentric rings and each ring is made up of six cells. Each air chamber has unbranched rarely branched photosynthetic filaments which are green, chlorophyllous and 2-3 cells in height. The vertral-lower zone of thallus is called storage zone which is made up of parenchymatous cells containing starch grain and numerous oil-cells containing single large oil body which is brown in colour.

Reproduction

The reproduction is of two types as found in *Marchantia*.

1. Vegetative reproduction. The plants of *Lunularia* mostly reproduce vegetatively in favourable conditions by following method:

(*a*) **Fragmentation.** Any fragment, containing growingpoints, when detached from main thallus either by external means on by death and decay of older part of the thallus, develops into an independent plant.

(*b*) **Gemmae formation.** The most elegant and interesting method of vegetative reproduction is by the formation of discoid green gemmae which are produced inside crescent or lunate-shaped gemma cup, whose margin is entire. Infact it is not a cup-like structure (as found in *Marchantia*). In *Lunularia* it is pocket like structure which is semilunar in shape. The detached gemmae, when come out from these pocket like semilunar gemma cup, are dispersed on soil either by wind or by water. Each gemma soon germinates and forms a new thallus.

2. Sexual reproduction. Similar to *Marchantia*, the plants of *Lunularia* are also dioecious (heterothallic).

(*a*) **Antheridia** (Fig. 5.28 B). They are produced on disciform, sessile antheridial receptacle present at apices of short branch of main thallus. The antheridia are formed in acropetal order in median region of male receptacle. Each antheridium is found enclosed with in a chamber called antheridial chamber which opens out side through an opening called ostiole. The development, structure and dehiscence of antheridium is *Marchantia* type.

(*b*) **Archegonia** (Fig. 5.28 F). They are produced on deeply four lobed, stalked female receptacle (archegoniophore) which emerges from the sinus of the thallus. The stalk of archegoniophore is short hairy and without rhizoidal furrow and photosynthetic tissue (similar to *Plagiochasma*). It is

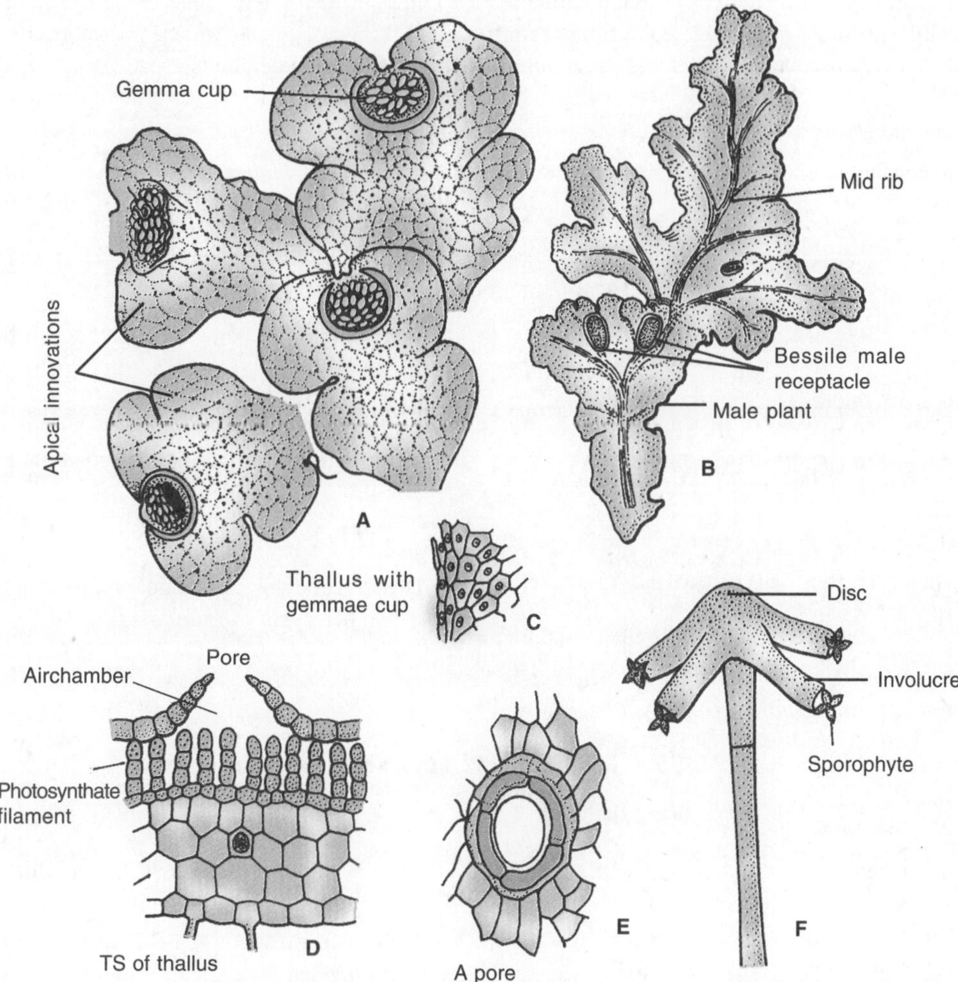

Fig. 5.28. (A—F). ***Lanularia cruciata* A,** Thallus showing crescent-shaped Gemmae caps; B- Male plant showing antheridia (sessile); C. View of thallus; D. T.S. of thallus through a pore; E, A pore with 3 rings; F. Archegoniophre beaning the sporophyte

surrounded at base with scales. The disc is small each with a row of archegonia which are acropetally arranged. The archegonia are covered and protected by horizontal, tubular involucre having wide mouth which facilitates in fertilization. The disc has no pores and photosynthetic tissue. It is a characteristic feature of the monotypic family Lunulariaceae.

Sporophyte

It has small foot, long seta and globose capsule. The sporophyte, which is horizontal in position and found attached on each arm of female receptacle (disc) is covered and protected by involucre. The pseudoperianth (Perigynium) is absent. The capsule dehisces by detachment of its apical portion and spliting of one cell layer thick capsule wall from apex to near the base into four irregular valves. The apical portion of capsule which detaches from capsule is operculum or lid and is bistratose (two cell layer thick). The cells of capsule wall lack any type of thickenings. The spores and free elaters are found within capsule. The spores are yellowish green or yellowish brown, 14-20 μm in diameter. The exine surface is smooth or verucose. The free elaters are thread like, spring like due to presence of two spiral thickenings which help in dispersal of spores.

The spores, which are haploid and called as first cell of gametophyte when come in contact with rocky soil, under favourable conditions, germinate and form new plants. Infact, two spores of a spore tetrad form two male plants and remaining two spores form female plants.

Systematic Position of Lunularia

According to classification of Grolle the taxonomic position of *Lunularia* is:

Class	:	Hepaticopsida
Order	:	Marchantiales
Family	:	Lunulariaceae
Genus	:	*Lunularia*
Species	:	*Cruciata*

The above classification is based on Grolle's classification (1983).

QUESTIONS

Essay Type

1. Describe the structure of thallus and sporophyte in *Lunularia*
2. Give Labelled diagram of T.S. Thallus of *Marchantia* and *Lunularia* passing through *archegoniophre*.(*Kanpur, 2004*)
3. Describe the diagrammatic representation of the life cycle of *Lunularia*.

SHORT ANSWER TYPE

4. **Write short-notes on :**
   (*a*) Gemma cups of *Lunularia* (*Kanpur, M.Sc., 2007*)
   (*b*) *Lunularia*
   (*c*) Gametophyte of *Lunularia*
   (*d*) Sex organs of *Lunularia*
5. Compare the gametophyte of *Lunularia* and *Marchantia.*
6. Give a brief account of sporophyte of *Lunularia*.

OBJECTIVE TYPE

7. **Select the correct answer :**
   (*i*) *Lunularia* is characterised by :
   (*a*) Lunate gemma cups
   (*b*) Simple gemma cups
   (*c*) Mixed gemma cups
   (*d*) Circular gemma cups
   (*ii*) Rotundate appendiculate scales are formed in
   (*a*) *Reccia*
   (*b*) *Marchantia*
   (*c*) *Funaria*
   (*d*) *Lunularia*
   (*iii*) Sessile disc in antheridial neceptales are present in
   (*a*) *Reccia*
   (*b*) *Funaria*
   (*c*) *Lunularia*
   (*d*) *Marchantia*
   (iv) In *Lunularia* archegonial receptacles have stalks which
   (*a*) Have rhizoidal furrows
   (*b*) Do not have rhizoidal furrows
   (*c*) Species have rhizoidal furrows
   (*d*) May not have rhizoidal furrows

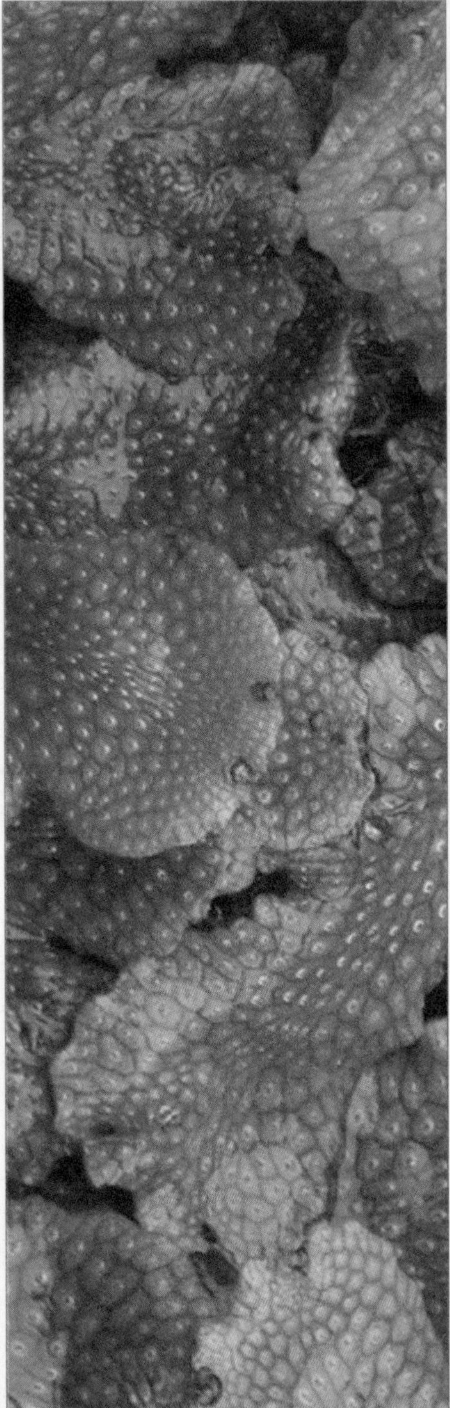

Image of *Conocephalum*

CHAPTER 5(V)

MARCHANTIALES : CONOCEPHALACEAE
Conocephalum

- Conocephalaceae
- Conocephalum
- Gametophyte
- Reproduction
- Sporophyte

CONOCEPHALACEAE

General Characteristics

The family is characterised by following features:

1. The dorsal surface of the thallus has prominent, large polygonal areas (areole), each with simple or half-barrel shaped air pore. It is an advanced and acquired character.

2. Gemma -cups are not found on the dorsal surface.

3. The ventral surface has two longitudinal rows of appendicular scales. The shape of appendage is either orbicular or reniform.

4. In addition to parenchymatous cells containing starch and oil cells containing single large brown oil body, the storage zone also has some slime cells or slime sacs.

5. The antheridial receptacles are disciform, sessile and with large prominent barrel-shaped-air pores as found in *Marchantia*. The remarkable feature is its sessile nature because in *Marchantia* male receptacle is stalked and with two horizontal furrows.

6. The female receptacles (archegoniophoves) are stalked; the stalk has one rhizoid furrow (rhizoidal furrow is absent in family Lunulariaceae where as two rhizoidal furrows are found in *Marchantia* and *Dumortiera*). The disc is conical in shaped which is so peculiar that the name of the genus *Conocephalum* has been derived from it. The disc has 5-8 short feebly developed lobes and air chambers with prominent barrel-shaped air pores on its surface.

7. The retention of primitive character of barrel shaped air pore on the disc of male and female receptacles.

The type genus *conocephalum* is discussed here.

CONOCEPHALUM

Habit and Distribution

The plants are found at high altitude of mountains and prefer moist, shady and cold areas. Only two species of the genus are found in our country.

C. conicum **:** This species is found in western himalayas and eastern himalayas

C. japonicum **:** This species is found only in eastern himalayas. Grolle (1990) has merged to *Conocephalum supradecompositum* under this species.

Gametophyte

External feature (Fig. 5.29 A–G) : The plants are gametophytic and thalloid. The thallus is bright green, large 10-25 mm long and 8-12 mm wide, margin undulate, dichotomously branched, oblong to linear. The apex of the thallus lobe is emarginate. The apical innovations are common which help in vegetative reproduction. The dorsal surface of plant has conspicuous hexagonal or polygonal areas (aeroles) forming a regular net configuration. Each aerole possesses single simple or half barrel-shaped-air pore (in *Marchantia* lach hexagonal or polygonal area possesses single barrel shaped air pore). The gemma cups are absent on dorsal surface. The ventral surface has simple (smooth-walled) and tuberculate rhizoids. The ventral scales are in two longitudinal rows, each on either side of midrib. The scales are appendiculate with orbicular on reniform appendix.

Internal structure of thallus (Fig. 5.29 D) : The vertical transverse section of thallus exhibits two regions. The upper dorsal green photosynthetic regions is made up of single layer of large, broad-air chambers (also called photosynthetic or assimilatory chambers) which open on dorsal surface through prominent elevated simple or half barrel-shaped-air pore. Each air pore is made up of 5-6 concentric rings of small narrow cells of which each ring is made up of 6-7 cells. Each air chamber has branched or unbranched photosynthetic or assimilatory filaments of 2-5 cells long. In young portion of thallus the filaments of large inflated basal cells which form the floor of air chamber. The terminal cell of photosynthetic filament is long pointed and beak shaped. The midrib is conspicuous and passes suddenly into thin undulate lamina, its margin is often two cells layer thick. The presence of mycorrhiza in midrib has been reported in *C. Japonicum.* The lower ventral region of thallus is called storage region which is made up of mostly parenchymatous cells containing starch grains, numerous oil-cells containing single large brown oil body and a few slime cells or slime sacs.

Reproduction

The plants mostly reproduce by sexual process. However, vegetative reproduction takes place either by apical innovation (*C. conicum*) or by multicellular gemmae at apex of thallus (*C.Japonicum*).

The gemma cups are not found on the dorsal surface. Gemmae, which are oval, elliptical or subspherical, are produced directly in large quantity from lateral margin of thallus towards apex.

Sexual reproduction Plants are dioecious *i.e.*, male and female plants are separate.

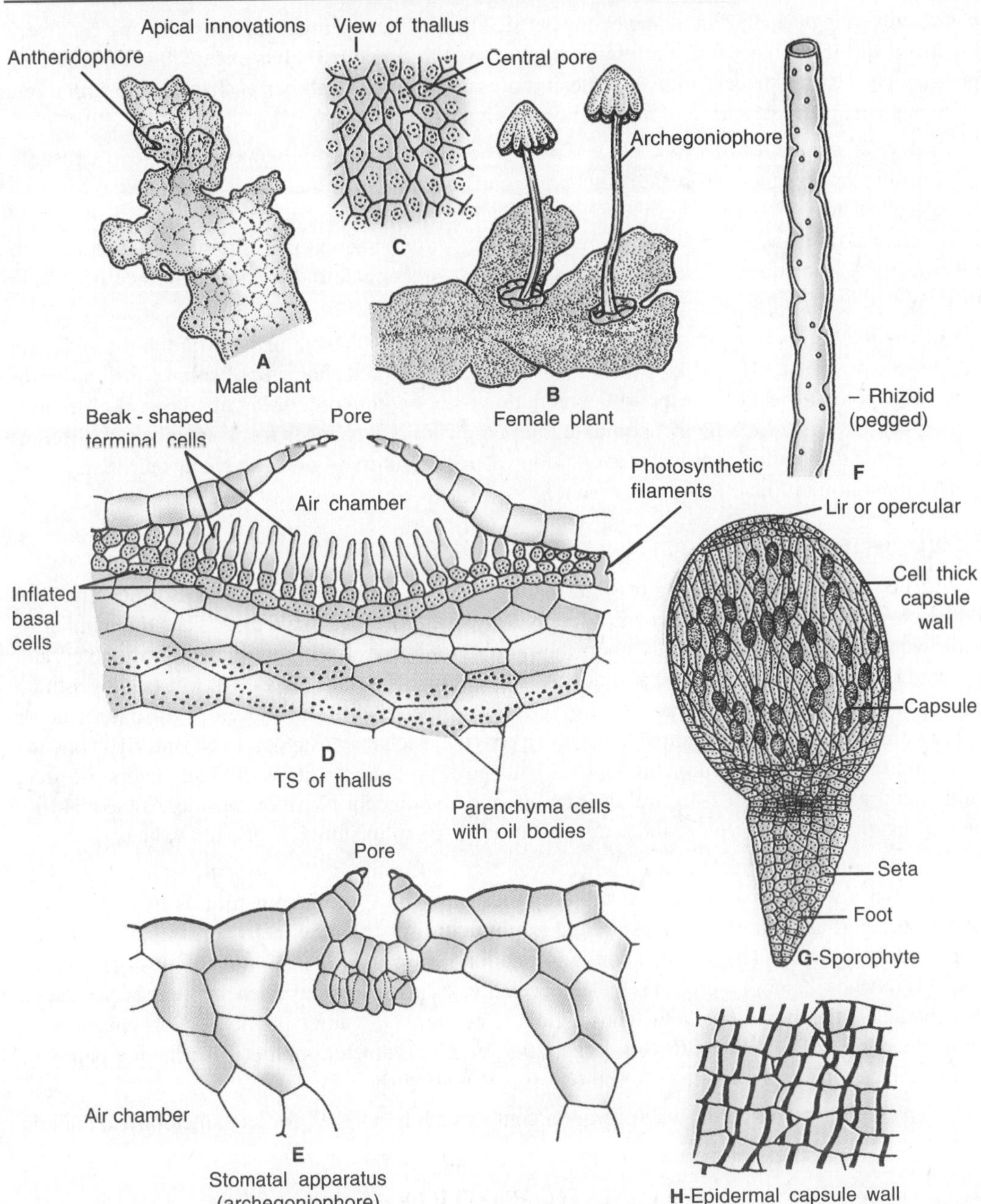

Fig. 5.29. (A—H). ***Conocephallum conicum*** A,–A.male plant; B. female plant showing archegoniophore; C, view of thallus (close up of hexagonal areas with central pore); D.T.S. of thallus through a pore; E, archegoniophore stomatal appartus; F, A Rizoid (peg-like; G. Sporophyte; H, cells of cupsule wall (Epidermal); showing thickening by dark bands.

(a) Antheridia (Fig. 5.29 A). They are produced on disciform, sessile, papillose male receptacle present on apical innovation. The disc is slightly raised unlobed and surrounded by thin out growth of thallus. Antheridial chambers and air chambers are scattered on dorsal surface (similar to *Marchantia*). Anteridial chambers, are arranged acropetally in 6-8 indefinite rows. Each antheridial chamber has single antheridium and opens out side through an opening called ostiole. Air chambers on dorsal surface of male disc has similar organization as found in thallus except in structure of air pore which is barrel-shaped (in thallus the air pores are simple or half barrel shaped. The structures, developement and dehiscence of antheridium is similar as in *Marchantia.*

(b) Archegonia (Fig. 5.29 B). The archegonia are produced on female receptacle (archegoniophore) which has two distinct parts: stalk and disc. The stalk arises from apical notch of female plant. It is 5-10 cm long with one rhizoidal furrow. The disc is characteristic of the genus being conical in shape (diagnostic feature of *Conocephalum*) and with 5-8 short lobes at base. Each lobe has tubular or bilipped involucre which protects archegonium. The dorsal surface of female disc is lined up by air chambers having barrel shaped air pores.

The retention of primitive-archaic character of barrel – shaped air pore on the disc of male and female receptacles (Fig. 5.29 E) where as advance – acquired character of simple or semi-barrel shaped air pore on the thallus support the reduction theory within order Marchantiales. It is because of the fact that first of all the gametophyte thalloid plant body changes it self to adjust in different adverse climatic condition for better adoptation whereas primitive – archatic characters are retained and visible during production of sex organs.

Sporophyte

The sporophyte has small foot slightly long seta and pyriform or ellipsoid capsule (Fig. 5.29 G). Each sporophyte is present on short feebly developed lobe of female disc. Thus the number of sporophytes on each disc depends upon the number of lobes. Each sporophyte is protected and covered by tubular involucre. The pseudoperianth is absent. The capsule well as one cell layer thick except at apex where it is bistratose forming a lid or operculum. The capsule wall (except lid or operculum) has annular thickening bands which provide mechanical support to capsule that contains large, multicellular and germinating spores causing a pressure on its wall. The elaters are free, elongated, spring like with 2-4 spiral thickenings and help in debisclerel of capsule. At the maturity of capsule, the lid is thrown off and remaing capsule wall splits into 4-8 reflexed values.

The spore mother cell is a flattened oval body differing from that of the other species of Marchantiales which have a globose spore mother cell. The spore germination is **in situ** *i.e.*, the spores start germination with in capsule. In **C-japonicum** spore mother cells are cylindrical show a distinct dimorphism in shape. The spore germination is also unique in **Conocephalum** (pattern is known as conocephalum-type), that is the germ cell divides in capsule and when the spore is discharged it is characteristically multicellular. Thus a globose cell mass of gametophytic tissue is present with in the spore coat. The spores are very large, 70-90 mm in diameter, multicellular having papillose exine surface. The haploid number of chromosomes with in spore is n = 9.

The multilocular spores, when come in contact with rocky soil, forms gametophytic thalloid plant body.

SYSTEMATIC POSITION

As per classification of Grolle (1983) the systematic position of *Conocephalum* is as follows:

Division	:	Bryophyta
Order	:	Hepaticopsida
Family	:	Conocephalaceae
Genus	:	***Conocephalum***
Species	:	***conicum***

QUESTIONS

Essay Type

1. Describe the habit-habitat and structure of thallus of *Conocephalum*.
2. Give an account of structure of thallus and reproduction in *Conocephalum*.
3. Describe the sporophyte of *Conocephalum*.

SHORT ANSWER TYPE

4. **Draw labelled diagrams of the following:**
   (*a*) T.S. thallus of sporophyte in *Conocephalum*
   (*b*) V.S. sporophyte of *Conocephalum*
5. Compare the thallus structure of *Marchantia, Lunularia* and *Conocephalum.*
6. **Write Short notes on :**
   (*a*) Conocephalum
   (*b*) satomy of Thallus of *conocephalum*
   (*c*) Sporophyte of *conocephalum*
   (*d*) *Lunulabria* and *conocephalum*

OBJECTIVE TYPE

7. **Select the correct answer :**

(*a*) Gemma cups are absent in
(*i*) *Lunularia*
(*ii*) *Marchantia*
(*iii*) *Conocephalum*
(*iv*) All the above

(*b*) In *Conocephalum* the archegonial disc is
(*i*) Conical
(*ii*) Lunate
(*iii*) Circular
(iv) Irregular

(*c*) The stalk of archegonia has one rhizoial furrow in
(*a*) *Riccia*
(*b*) *Marchantia*
(*c*) *Lunularia*
(*d*) *Conocephalum*

(*d*) *Conocephalum* is
(*a*) Monoecious
(*b*) Dioecious
(*c*) Bisexual
(*d*) Neutral

(*e*) *Simple or semi-barrel shaped air pore on thallus and barrel shaped air pore on disc of male and female receptacles are found in*
(*i*) *Riccia*
(*ii*) *Marchantia*
(*iii*) *Conocephalum*
(*iv*) *Targionia*

Image of *Sphaerocarpos*

CHAPTER 6(I)

HEPATICOPSIDA
Sphaerocarpales
Sphaerocarpos, Riella

- General Characteristics
- Family - Sphaerocarpaceae
- Gametophyte
- Sporophyte
- Family Riellaceae

GENERAL CHARACTERISTICS

The order sphaerocarpales is one of the important orders of the class Hepaticopsida because it shows some affinities with order Metzgeriales in thallus organisation, with order Marchantiales in structure and development of sex organs, in early stage of embryogeny and in the presence of 1-cell thick capsule wall. The most peculiar and diagnostic feature of the order is the presence of bottle or involucre around each antheridium or archegonium. The general characteristic features of the order Sphaerocarpales are as follows:

1. The plant body is thalloid but sometimes it also shows a tendency towards the development of leaves on the dorsal surface of axis (midrib). The leaves are *succubously* arranged.

2. Ventral scales are absent but mucilaginous hairs are found near growing points.

3. The tuberculate rhizoids are absent.

4. Only smooth-walled (simple) rhizoids are present.

5. In vertical transverse section the thallus shows neither photosynthetic zone nor storage zone.

6. All the cells are uniformly green in thallus.

7. Photosynthetic chambers, air pores and photosynthetic filaments are not found.

8. Each antheridium or archegonium is enclosed with in a special covering known as involucre or bottle.

9. The sporophyte has small foot, very small seta and a globose capsule.

10. The capsule wall is one cell-layer thick.

11. The thickening bands are absent on the cells of capsule wall.

12. The elaters are absent.

13. The nurse cells are present within capsule along with developing spores. The nurse cells provide nourishment to developing spores.

14. The capsule is cleistocarpous. The dehiscence of capsule is irregular.

The order Sphaerocarpales is comparatively a small order than Marchantials, Jungermanniales and Metzgeriales. It has only two families:

Family 1. Sphaerocarpaceae

Family 2. Riellaceae

FAMILY - SPHAEROCARPACEAE

The thalloid plant body is bilaterally symmetrical. The family has two genera *Sphaerocarpos* and *Geothallus.* Of these the former is being discussed here briefly.

SPHAEROCARPOS

Distribution. The genus *Sphaerocarpos* is not found in India but it shows its luxuriant growth in U.S.A., chiefly in the Gulf and the Pacific Coast.

Habitat. The plants prefer very moist and colder place for their luxuriant growth. The morphological characters of the thallus vary if habitat is changed.

GAMETOPHYTE

External features (Fig. 6.1A, B). The gametophytic plant body is thalloid. The thallus is prostrate, dorsiventrally flattened, dichotomously branched and dark green in colour. Most of the species have notched margin and each notch bears a growing point.

In some species the margin of the thallus is entire and smooth. It is slightly curved upwardly. Some other species of *Sphaerocarpos* have very prominent midrib which looks like an axis. It bears succubously arranged and dorsally appressed leaf like lobes. Proskauer (1954) considered the genus as a member of leafy liverworts. The dorsal surface of the thallus is smooth. There is no polygonal areas and air pores as found in *Marchantia.* On ventral surface any type of appendages (scales) is not present except at the apex, near the growing point, where mucilaginous hairs are present. The terminal end of each mucilagenous hair has large swollen terminal cell. The tuberculate rhizoids are also absent. The entire ventral surface is covered by only smooth - walled (simple) rhizoids. Thus, in external morphology, *Sphaerocarpos* resembles both thalloid (*Pellia*) and leafy (*Fossombronia*) forms of order Metzgeriales.

Anatomy of the thallus (Fig. 6.1 H). Anatomy ofthe thallus of *Sphaerocarpos* is also very simple. The thallus has neither photosynthetic zone nor storage zone. The photosynthetic chambers, photosynthetic filaments and air pores are also absent. The mid-rib (axis) is multistratose but wings or leaf lobes are unistratose. All the cells of the thallus possess chloroplasts except the rhizoidal cells.

Reproduction. *Sphaerocarpos* reproduces vegetatively and very well by sexual process which is controlled by sex chromosomes - also named as "X" and "Y" chromosomes.

1. *Vegetative reproduction.* It is a common method of propagation in the genus *Sphaerocarpos*. It takes place by following methods.

(a)Adventitious branches. The plants have tremendous capacity to produce advertitious branches from lower surface of the midrib (axis), lateral wings or from involucres (bottles). The involucres (bottles) are the coverings around each sex-organ.

(b) Dichotomous branches. It takes place by progressive death and decay of posterior old parts of the thallus reaching up to the dichotomy. It results into separation of two branches which now grow independently and form two independent plants :

2. *Sexual reproduction.* All the species of the genus are dioecious (heterothallic). Both male and female plants are separate and differ from each other in external morphology which is controlled genotypically by sex chromosomes.

Male plant. (Fig. 6.1A, C). The male plants are relatively smaller in size than female plants. The dorsal surface of thallus has several flask-shaped sessile involucres which open outside by a mouth. The involucre is one cell layer thick and formed by elevation of dorsal surface. Each involucre has a single antheridium. The body of which is large and globose and situated on short stalk. The body of antheridium has a single cell layer thick sterile covering, the cells of which contain chromatophores providing deep orange-red colour to the mature antheridium. In side the sterile covering there is present biflagellated spindle-shaped or coiled antherozoids (sperms). Out of the two flagella, the lower is slightly longer. The development of antheridium is same as found in order Marchantiales.

Female plant (Fig. 6.1B, D). The female plants are larger in size than male plants. The dorsal surface of female thallus bears numerous oval involucres with a wide mouth at its top. The involucres of female plant are also one cell layer thick and all the cells contain chloroplasts. Each oval-shaped involucre loosely covers a single archegonium. Each archegonium is sessile and short. The neck of archegonium has six vertical rows of cells (Fig. 6.1, E) that enclose an axial row of only four neck canal cells. The venter of archegonium which contains a venter canal cell and a large egg, is one cell layer thick. The development of archegonium is also Marchantiales type.

Fertilization : The process of fertilization is similar to that found in the plants of the order Marchantiales.

SPOROPHYTE

Development. After fertilization, the zygote divides by mitosis and forms two daughter cells - the upper cell, which is diploid, is called epibasal cell and the lower cell which is also diploid, is called hypobasal cell. Both the cells again divide by transverse division and form a four celled uniseriate filamentous pro-embryo. Now each cell of pro-embryo divides by two longitudinal divisions at right angle to each other. Thus a sixteen celled embryo is produced in which eight cells are arranged in two tiers in the epibasal part and the remaining eight cells are arranged in the hypobasal part. The former forms the capsule and the later forms small foot and very small seta.

Sporophyte (6.1 F,G,H). The sporophyte of *Sphaerocarpos* has three parts :-

(i) Foot. It is small, slightly bulbous and lower most part of the sporophyte which is found embedded in the gametophytic thallus tissue. Its function is absorption of food from thallus and to fix the sporophyte within the female involucre.

(ii) Seta. It is very small and middle part of the sporophyte which is connected with foot on one end and with capsule on the other end. The seta of *Sphaerocarpos* never elongates and always remains only few cells in height.

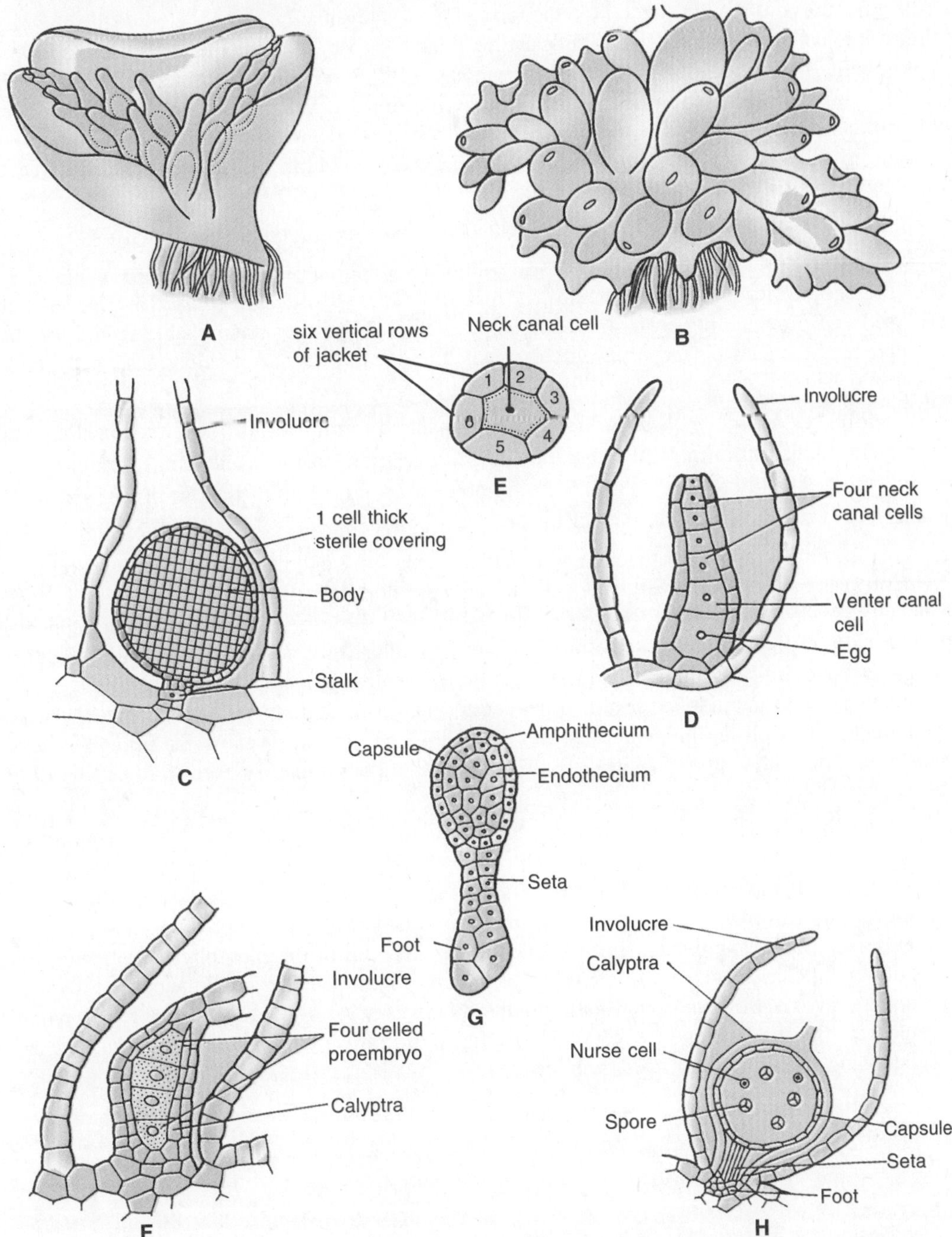

Fig. 6.1. (A–H) ***Sphaerocarpos***. A, male plants; B, female plants C, an antheridium; D, an archegonium; E, T.S. neck of archegonium; F—G, developing sporophyte; H,V.T.S. of sporophyte.

(*iii*) *Capsule*. The upper most spherical or globose part of the sporophyte is called capsule. It has one cell layer thick capsule wall which is derived from amphithecium. The cells of capsule wall contains chloroplasts. The cavity of capsule is filled by spores and nurse cells which are produced from endothecium. In some species, the four spores produced from a spore mother cell by meiosis (reduction division) remain adherent in the form of a tetrad even at maturity. Actually, the majority of the diploid cells of endothecium divide and redivide and form spore mother cells while a few of diploid cells of endothecium fail to act as spore mother cells. Such cells remain sterile. The nature of these sterile cells is changed and finally they provide nutrition to developing young spores. Therefore, they are called *nurse cells*. The diploid nucleus of a nurse cell in *S. donnelli* shows free nuclear division by mitosis. In *S. cristatus* the four diploid nuclei of a nurse cell are separated from each other by formation of internal partition walls.

It is interesting to note that the nurse cells of *Sphaerocarpos* contain chloroplasts.

The young sporophyte remains enclosed within the calyptra-a gametophytic covering produced from venter of the fertilized archegonium. The mature sporophyte of *Sphaerocarpos* always remains enclosed and protected by oval-shaped female involucre. The most remarkable feature of the sporophyte of the genus is its partial autotrophic nature due to presence of chloroplasts in the cells of capsule wall and sterile nurse cells.

Spores. *Germination of spores*. Two spores of a tetrad germinate and form two small thallii of male plants. Adjacent to male plants, the remaining two spores of the same tetrad germinate and form two large thallii of female plants. Thus, a spore tetrad, after germination, form four groups of plants. Out of which two plants are male and two are female.

At the time of spore germination a germ tube appears through the germ pore. The germ tube divides by a transverse wall at terminal end and forms two unequal cells. The lower larger cell which contains scanty cytoplasm forms a rhizoid called first rhizoid. The terminal smaller cell which contains dense cytoplasm divides by successive transverse and longitudinal divisions - resulting in the formation of two cells thick and about four cells in height short filamentous gametophytic plant body. The cells in distal tier divide and redivide several times and form a germinal disc which is obconical in shape and looks like a "Golf-tee". Now further growth of the disc is asymmetrical which forms a male or female plant depending upon the presence of "Y" or "X" chromosomes respectively in each cell of the plant.

Allen (1919) reported the haploid number of chromosomes in each cell of the gametophytic plant body as eight (n=8). In male plant each cell has seven chromosomes of normal size and one chromosome is very small and is known as "Y" chromosome. The female plant has seven chromosomes of normal type and one chromosome is considerably large and is known as "X" chromosome. The zygote, which is also called as the first cell of the sporophyte, contains seven pairs of normal chromosomes and one pair of sex chromosomes as "XY". All the cells of a young sporophyte have same chromosomal configuration. At maturity, the diploid spore mother cells within capsule wall divide by meiosis (reduction division) and form two spores with "Y" chromosome and the remaining two spores with "X" chromosome.

SYSTEMATIC POSITION

Division	:	Bryophyta
Class	:	Hepaticopsida
Order	:	Sphaerocarpales
Family	:	Sphaerocarpaceae
Genus	:	*Sphaerocarpos*
Species	:	*cristatus*

FAMILY-RIELLACEAE

The family Riellaceae is characterised by its aquatic habitat and asymmetric plant body. The monogeneric family has a single genus *Riella* which is being described here briefly.

RIELLA

Distribution. The genus *Riella* has been reported from Texas, California, Canary Island, N. Africa and India. The genus has about 19 species out of which three species occur in India viz. *R. affinis*, *R. cosoniana* and *R. paulsonii*. Pande *et al.* (1954) had reported a new species of the genus as *R. vishwanathai* from Varanasi in shallow fresh waters of lake Latif Shah. Later, in 1955 Proskauer has reduced *R.vishwanathai* as synonym of *R. affinis* earlier reported from Africa. Kachroo (1969) made a remark on the distribution of *R. affinis* from America, Canary Island, Africa and India that it shows disjunct distribution.

Habitat. It is an aquatic liverwort which is found submerged under the shallow waters. The plants grow vertical in water and have been found associated with a number of algae and aquatic angiosperms. When water receedes from banks, the plants remain attached within the mud and become prostrate. At this stage it is found associated with *Riccia frostii*, with smooth walled rhizoids and without or poorly developed ventral scales, with which it sometimes creates a confusion.

Gametophyte

External features. (Fig. 6.2 A). The plants of *Riella* has a prominent thickened midrib (axis) with usually a wing that develops only on one side except in *R. bialata* in which the wings are present in both the sides of the midrib. The rhizoids are simple occuring at the base of the midrib when plants become prostrate. The plants also have several minute lanceolate ventral scales present on ventral surface of the midrib (axis). Sometimes lateral scales are also present at the juncture of midrib (axis) and wing.

Anatomy of thallus. Anatomy of the thallus of *Riella* is more or less similar to that of *Sphaerocarpos*.

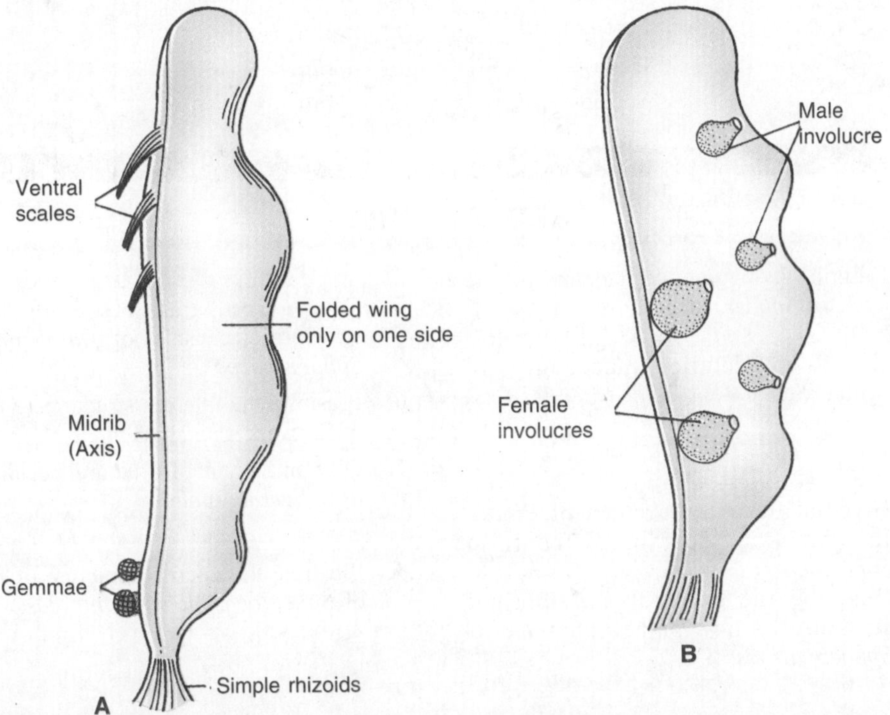

Fig. 6.2. (A-B) ***Riella*** A, vegetative plant with folded wing only on one side of midrib; B, monoecious plant with male involucres at margin and female involucres on midrib (axis).

Reproduction. *Riella* reproduces by both vegetative and sexual methods.

1. *Vegetative reproduction.* In *Riella* the vegetative propagation takes place either by one celled or by many celled spherical gemmae produced at the older part of midrib. Sometimes, gemmae are also found in between ventral and lateral scales.

2. *Sexual reproduction.* *Riella* is both monoecious and dioecious. Some species of *Riella* are monoecious (homothallic) i.e. both antheridia and archegonia are produced on the same plant and other species are dioecious (heterothallic) i.e. both antheridia and archegonia are produced on separate independent plants.

Antheridia. (Fig. 6.2B). They are found at the margin of wing. Each antheridium is enclosed within a flask-shaped male involucre which opens outside through a mouth. The structure and development of antheridium and its involucre is same as in case of *Sphaerocarpos*.

Archegonia (Fig. 6.2B). The archegonia are borne on midrib (axis). Each archegonium is found enclosed within globose or subglobose female involucre having an opening called mouth. The other details are also similar to that of *Sphaerocarpos*.

Sporophyte

The sporophyte has foot, seta and capsule which remains enclosed within calyptra and female involucre. The other details including development of sporophyte from zygote is same as in case of *Sphaerocarpos*.

SYSTEMATIC POSITION

Division	:	Bryophyta
Class	:	Hepaticopsida
Order	:	Sphaerocarpales
Family	:	Riellaceae
Genus	:	*Riella*
Species	:	*affinis*

QUESTIONS

ESSAY TYPE

1. Describe giving suitable diagrams, the life cycle of *Sphaerocarpos*. *(Kanpur M.Sc., 1990, 1994)*
2. Give a detailed account of Sphaerocarpales and discuss its phylogeny. *(Poorvanchal, M.Sc., 1998; Rohilkhand M.Sc., 1992)*
3. Give an illustrated account of *Riella*. In what way does it differ from *Sphaerocarpos* ?
4. Describe the external and internal structure of gametophyte of *Sphaerocarpos.*
5. Give a comparative account of the structure of capsules of *Marchantia* and *Sphaerocarpos*.
6. Illustrate the internal structure of thallus of *Sphaerocarpales*. *(Kanpur, M.Sc., 2003)*
7. Give an account of structural peculiarities in *Sphaerocarpales* *(Lucknow M.Sc., 2006)*
8. Illustrate the internal structure of thallus of *Sphaerocaspales(Kanpur M.Sc., 2007)*

SHORT ANSWER TYPE

9. **Write short notes on :**
   (*a*) Affinities between Sphaerocarpales and Marchantiales. *(Riohilkhand M.Sc., 1994)*
   (*b*) Relationships of *Sphaerocarpales.* *(Awadh M.Sc., 2001)*
   (*c*) Male gametophytes of *Sphaerocarpos.* *(Kanpur M.Sc., 1992)*
   (*d*) *Sphaerocarpos.* *(Kanpur M.Sc., 1995, 1997; Rohilkhand M.Sc., 1998)*
   (*e*) Differences between *Anthoceros* and *Sphaerocarpos.* *(Kanpur M.Sc., 1995)*
   (*f*) *Riella.* *(Rohilkhand, 1991)*
   (*g*) *Sphaerocarpos.* *(Allababad M.Sc., 2000)*
   (*h*) Affinities of Sphaerocarpales *(Kanpur M.Sc., 2006)*
10. **Differentiate between :**
   (*a*) *Anthoceros* and *Sphaerocarpos.* *(Kanpur M.Sc., 1993; Rohilkhand, 1999)*
   (*b*) *Riella* and *Sphaerocarpos.* *(Kanpur M.Sc., 1999)*
11. Discuss the reasons for and against the separation of *Sphaerocarpos* from *Marchantiales* and its inclusion in Sphaerocarpales. *(Kanpur M.Sc., 1998)*
12. Describe structure and position of sex organs in *Sphaerocarpos* and *Monoclea* *(Lucknow, M.Sc., 2006)*

OBJECTIVE TYPE

13. **Select the correct answer :**
   (*i*) In which of the following ventral scales are not present ?
   (*a*) *Riccia* (*b*) *Marchantia*
   (*c*) *Sphaerocarpos* (*d*) *Lunularia.*
   (*ii*) Rhizoids are single celled and smooth walled in
   (*a*) *Sphaerocarpos* (*b*) *Riccia*
   (*c*) *Marchantia* (*d*) *Funaria.*
   (*iii*) Nurse cells are present in the capsules of a
   (*a*) *Sphaerocarpos* (*b*) *Anthoceros*
   (*c*) *Pellia* (*d*) *Marchantia.*
   (*iv*) Which of the following is an aquatic genus ?
   (*a*) *Sphaerocarpos* (*b*) *Riella*
   (*c*) *Riccia* (*d*) *Marchantia.*
   (*v*) The thallus is not differentiated into photosynthetic and storage zones in.
   (*a*) *Riccia*
   (*b*) *Marchantia*
   (*c*) *Plagiochasmia*
   (*d*) *Sphaerocarpos.*

Image of *Metzgeria*

CHAPTER 6(II)

HEPATICOPSIDA
(Hepaticae) Metzgeriales

- General Characteristics
- Distribution
- Vegetative Reproduction
- Sporophyte

GENERAL CHARACTERISTICS

The order Metzgeriales includes forms in which the archegonia usually occur in groups on the upper surface of the thallus (Fig. 6.3 E) or its lobes. They originate behind the apical cell from the segments derived from it but the apical cell itself never develops into an archegonium. Because of this the thallus continues to grow with the result that archegonia and sporophytes in this group are always dorsal in position. The plant body (gametophyte) is diversified in form. All are prostrate, dorsiventral and generally thallus-like in construction. It, however, is not characteristic of the order as a whole. *Pellia* (A), *Riccardia* (B), and *Pallavicinia lyelii* (E) are typical examples of thalloid forms with a wavy margin and dichotomous branching. *Fossombronia* (I) is a leafy form in which the gametophyte is differentiated into stem and lateral leaves. Besides, the order also includes genera which are intermediate between the thallose and leafy forms. In them the thallus has a distinct midrib and the wings are deeply and regularly incised to form lateral appendages (lobes) which are not distinct enough to be called leaves. Best examples of these transitional

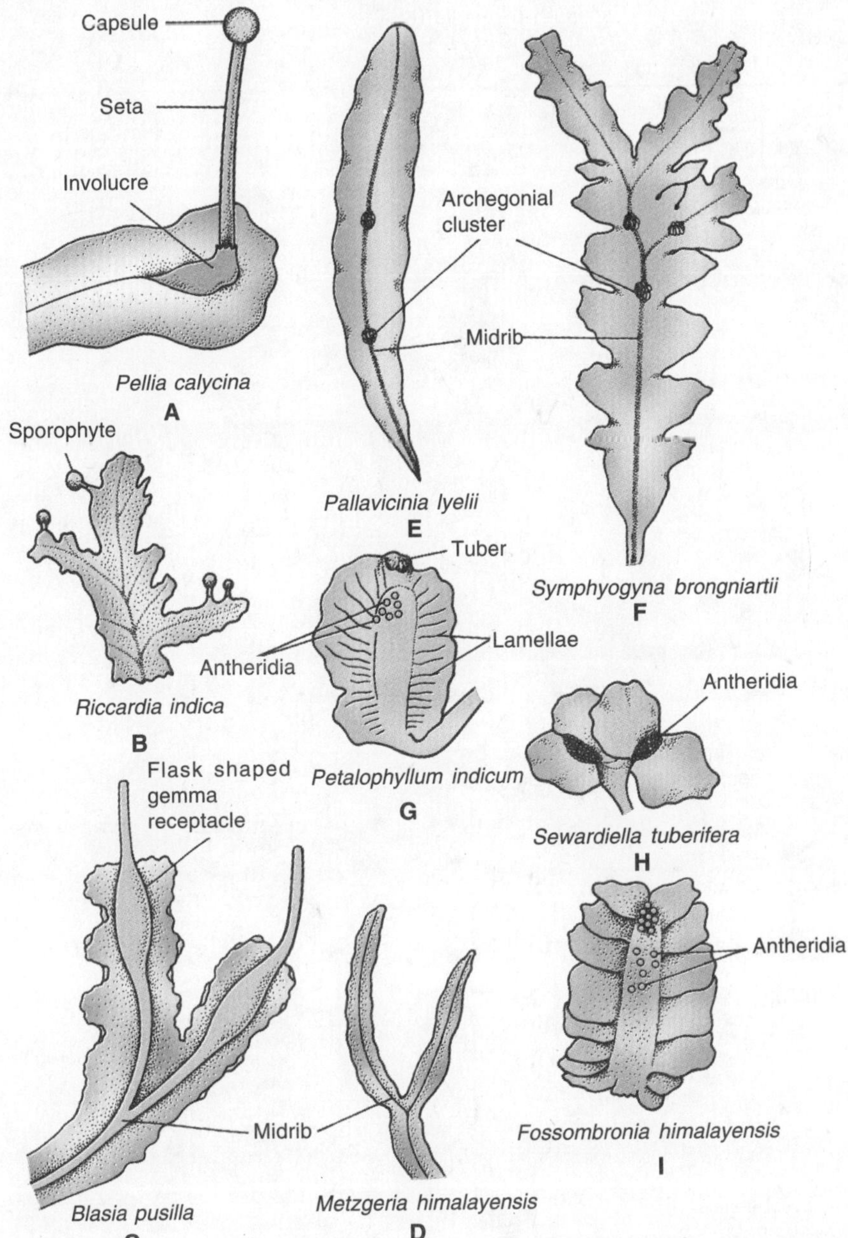

Fig. 6.3. (A-I) Metzgeriales. Some of the important genera (A–D, and G–I after Kashyap; E–F after Haupt).

forms are *Symphyogyna brongniartii* (F) and *Pallavicinia crispula*. They are on the road leading to the leafy habit exemplified by *Treubia* and *Fossombronia*. The display of this remarkable range in structure from the simple thalloid forms through the transitional forms with a distinct midrib and wings deeply incised to distinctly leafy forms has provoked considerable phylogenetic speculation. Two major and diametrically opposed views have been advanced. The most modern view advocated by Schuster (1966) supports the hypothesis that the thalloid forms arose by reduction from the ancestral (primitive) leafy forms. The alternate hypothesis put forth by Leitgeb (1877) and Cavers

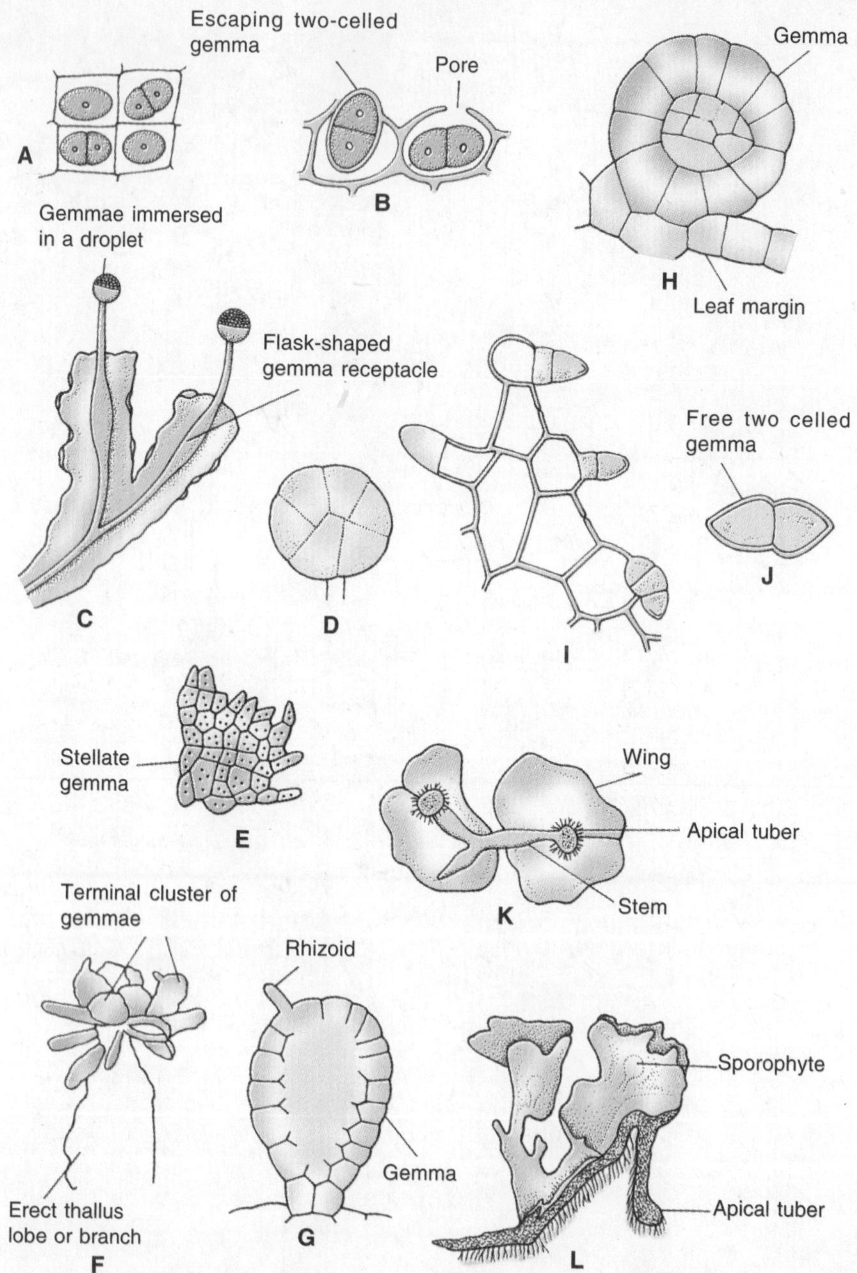

Fig. 6.4 (A–L) Chief methods of vegetative reproduction in the Metzgeriales (A–G, K–L) and Jungemanniales (H–J). A–B, Stages in gemma formation in the cells of the thallus (A) and subsequent release of 2-celled gemma through a pore (B) in the outer wall in *Riccardia multifitida*; C, thallus of *Blasia pusilla* with flask-shaped gemma receptacles; D, single gemma; E, stellate gemma of *B. pusilla*; F, clusters of gemmae formed at the tip of a thallus lobe in *Metzgeria fruticulosa*; G, single gemma of F; H, gemma of *Radula complanata* on leaf margin; I, gemmae arising from the marginal cells of the leaf of *Lophozia ventricosa*; J, single free gemma of I; K, forked male thallus of *Sewardiella tuberifera* with apical tubers; L, female plant of *Fossombronia himalayensis* with a characteristic bend on stem bearing an apical tuber (A, B after Cavers, C–E, K, L, after Kashyap; F, G, I, J after Watson and H after Fullford).

(1910) and supported by many others including Mueller (1954) is equally plausible. They hold that the series represents a progressive development of the thallose to the leafy (foliose) forms. The sex organs occur singly or in groups on the upper surface of the thallus (*Pellia*) or on short branches (*Metzgeria* and *Riccardia*) which may arise ventrally or are typical side branches but never on stalked receptacles. The archegonia in the cluster are surrounded and thus protected by a tubular or funnel-like outgrowth of the adjacent thallus tissue. It is termed the *involucre*. The capsure wall is 2–5 layers of cells thick.

Distribution

The Metzgeriales are widespread in their distribution. They occur both in the temperate and tropical regions of the world extending far north and south up to the polar regions. About ten genera of this order have been reported from the Himalayas and South India. Combination of shade and abundant moisture is a precondition for their successful growth. The majority of the species are hygrophytic or mesophytic. They grow on damp soil, moist rocks, and bark of trees.

Vegetative reproduction. (Fig. 6.4)

Vegetatively the Metzgeriales reproduce by the following methods :-

1. Gemmae (A–H). Many Metzgeriales reproduce by gemmae. These are bud-like structures variable in form and size. In the thallose forms the gemmae may be produced exogenously or endogenously from or within any specialized cell on the dorsal surface of the thallus. Certain genera produce them on special gemmiferous branches or in flask-shaped receptacles. In *Riccardia* the gemmae are small, two-celled structures. They are produced endogenously in the superficial cells on the dorsal side of the thallus near the tip (A). They are expelled from the parent cells through a pore (B). One-celled marginal gemmae were described by Yang and Heu (1967) for *R. multifitida*. In 1971 Proskauer (1971) reported globose superficial multicellular gemmae on a *Riccardia* species. They are stalked, terete or flattened and occur on the upper surface just behind the apex on narrow thallus branches. The stalk is one or two celled. The gemmae of *Blasia pusilla* are multicellular and of two types. One kind are multicellular and star-shaped (E). These are produced usually behind the apex from a single cell on the upper surface of the thallus. The second type are also multicellular but globose or spherical and stalked (D). These are produced in large numbers in flask-shaped receptacles arising from the upper surface of the thallus (C). The gemmae are readily detached and dispersed by water or wind. In *Metzgeria uncigera* flat, roughly circular, plate-like, multicellular gemmae are developed on special erect branches of the thallus (F). They are called the **gemmiferous branches**. Each gemma originates from a single superficial cell (G). Gemmae in *Treubia* arise in the axils of the leaves. They are 3 to 4-celled structures.

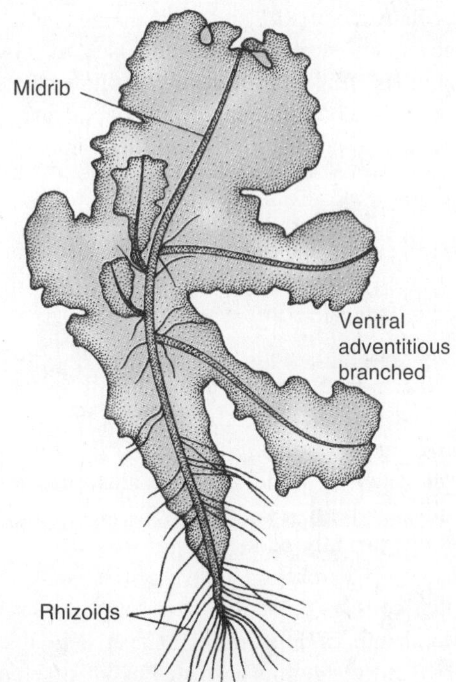

Fig. 6.5. Metzeriales. Formation of ventral adventitious branches in *Calycularia crispula.* (After Pande and Udar).

2. Fragmentation. By progressive growth followed by the death of the older regions of the thallus the younger thallus lobes or branches of a dichotomy become isolated. The isolated branches are called the **fragments**. Each fragment by apical growth and branching grows into a new plant.

3. Some thallose Metzgeriales produce specialised adventitious **branches** (Fig. 6.5). Ventral adventitious branches arising from the midrib have been reported by Pande and Udar (1956) in *Calycularia crispula* and by Pande and Srivastava (1953) in *C. canarana*. The ventral adventitious branches get detached and serve as means of vegetative propagation.

4. Tubers (Fig. 6.4; K—L). *Fossombronia tuberifera, F. longista, F. himalayensis* (L), *Petalophyllum indicum* (Fig. 6.1 G), *Sewardiella tuberifera* (K) and *Symphyogyna* develop apical tubers at the end of the growing season. The tip of the plant grows downwards into the soil and thickens to form a globose or cylindrical mass of cells called the **tuber**. The cells of 2 or 3 surface layers of the tuber develop corky walls which protect it form desiccation. The inner tissues store reserve food in the form of starch, oil globules and protein granules. With the onset of dry season, the thallus perishes leaving behind the tubers fixed to the substratum by rhizoids. The tubers remain dormant over the dry period. With the return of conditions favourable for growth, the tuber resumes activity. The young tubers have been reported to contain large quantities of starch within the chloroplasts and have mitochondria, golgi bodies and endoplasmic reticulum. The mature ones lack starch. The food reserve in them is in the form of oil droplets and protein bodies. The mitochondria, golgi bodies and endoplasmic reticulum are also absent.

Sex organs. The sex organs in the Metzgeriales are similar in essential respects but differ in detail from those of the Marchantiales. Their diverse position in the Metzgeriales is an important feature on which family distinctions are based. The antheridia in thallose forms may occur singly or scattered in rows (*Pellia*) or in groups (*Calycularia crispula*) on the dorsal surface of the thallus or its lobes (branches). The lobes are specialized short branches which arise ventrally in *Metzgeria* but are typically side branches in *Riccardia pinguis*. Unlike *Marchantia* the sexual branches are not specially modified. The sex organs are thus never borne on stalked receptacles. In *Pellia* and *Riccardia* the antheridia occur in sunken pits formed by the upward growth of adjacent vegetative tissue. This provides efficient protection and allows violent discharge of sperms. The scattered and unprotected occurrence of antheridia on the upper surface of the central axis of a leafy genus *Fossombronia* is considered ancestral or primitive from which the sunken or embedded state has been derived by reduction.

The antheridium is nearly globose in form and stalked. The stalk is short but multicellular. The sac-like body of the antheridium encloses a mass of androcyte mother cells and eventually the sperms. The wall of the antheridial sac is one layer of cells thick. The sperms like those of the Marchantiales are biflagellate but they are larger in size with more coils.

The archegonia in the thallose Metzgeriales occur singly (*Riccardia*) or in groups (*Pallavicinia lyelii*) on the upper surface of thallus or its lobes but never on stalked receptacles. They originate behind the apical cell from the segments derived from the latter but the apical cell itself never develops into an archegonium. The Metzgeriales are thus **anacrogynous**. Because of this (anacrogynous) condition the thallus continues to grow with the result that archegonia and sporophytes in the Metzergiales are always dorsal in position. In a leafy form *Fossombronia* they occur in small groups laterally on the central axis. They originate near the growing point at the bases of young leaves. The archegonia have distinct stalks. The venter is only slightly broader than the neck. The latter consists of five vertical rows of neck cells (Fig. 7.7 H) instead of six characteristic of the Marchantiales (Fig. 5.17 K). The archegonial group in some of the thallose Metzgeriales is generally surrounded and thus protected by an envelope known as the **involucre** or **perichaetium** formed as a result of the upward growth of the adjacent thallus tissue and not from the fusion of leaves.

SPOROPHYTE

As in the majority of liverworts, the sporophyte in the Metzgeriales is differentiated into the usual three parts, namely (*i*) the absorbing and anchoring swollen base known as the **foot**, (*ii*) a long stalk-like **seta**, and (*iii*) the terminal sac-like structure, the **capsule** containing spores and elaters. The foot is usually anchor-shaped in logitudinal section. Its dagger-like tip burrows deep in the gemetophyte tissue. It absorbs nutrients from the gametophyte. A long, transparent, fragile seta is characteristic of the sporophyte of the Metzgeriales. The dark mature capsule is variable in form. It is globose in *Pellia* and *Fossombronia* but ovoid-cylindrical in *Blasia* and *Riccardia*. The capsule wall is two or more layers of cells thick. The cells of the capsule wall develop annular or rod-like thickenings on their walls. The sporogenous tissue within is devoted to the formation of spore mother cells and sterile cells. There is no **columella.** The spore mother cells usually become four-lobed prior to sporogenesis. The sterile cells get metamorphosed into elaters. In some genera a tuft of fixed elaters occurs at the base of the capsule (*Pellia* Fig. 7.10A) or at the apex (*Riccardia*) in addition to the free elaters which occur intermixed with the spores. The ripe capsule, as a rule, dehisces in a regular manner. It splits by four-valves usually to the base but in *Cryptothallus* the valves fail to separate distally. In *Pellia* the tuft of fixed elaters which is usually but erroneously called the elaterophore stands at the base of the dehisced capsule whereas in *Riccardia* they (fixed elaters) remain attached to the tip of each valve and stand nearly erect.

Classification. Metzgeriales was formerly recognised as a suborder of the order Junger–manniales, which was divided into two main groups: *Anacrogynae* (archegonia borne on the dorsal surface of the prostrate shoot) and *Acrogynae* (archegonia borne at the apex of the shoot). It was Verdoorn (1932) who gave each group the status of an order and named these as Jungermanniales *Anacrogynae* and Jungermanniales *Acrogynae*.

Schuster in 1958, 1961, gave each group the status of an order and named them as *Metzgeriales* and *Jungermanniales*.

Evans (1939) divides the order Jungermanniales into three suborders : Haplomitrinae, Jungermanniae and Metzgerinae. However Campbell (1936) recognised only two orders : *Metzgeriales* and *Jungermanniales*.

The order Metzgeriales is a group of medium size comprising 23 genera and more than 550 species. The chief among the former are *Pellia, Riccardia, Metzgeria, Pallavicinia*, *Calycularia, Blasia, Sewardiella, Petalophyllum, Fossombronia, Moerckia, Androcryphia* (*Noteroclada*), *Hymenophytum, Symphyogyna, Treubia, Cryptothallus* and some others. In India the suborder is represented by the first ten genera. A species of *Cryptothallus* known as *C. mirabilis* is of unique interest. It is mycorrhizal in habit and the fleshy thallus lacks chlorophyll. This saprophytic liverwort grows under the surface of litter of *Betula*. The classification of Metzgeriales is based on two important characteristic features of the gametophyte besides others from the sporophyte generation. These are, (*i*) the presence or absence of mid-rib and leaf-like appendages, and (*ii*) the diverse position of the sex organs. Mueller (1954) recognized six families Pelliaceae, Blasiaceae, Pallaviciniaceae, Metzgeriaceae, Riccardiaceae and Monocleaceae but Schuster (1966) listed eight. The important among these are Pelliaceae, Riccardiaceae. Blasiaceae, Metzgeriaceae, Pallaviciniaceae, Treubiaceae and Fossombroniaceae. Of these Pelliaceae, Riccardiaceae and Fossombroniaceae have been discussed in this edition of the text.

QUESTIONS

ESSAY TYPE

1. Give an account of general characteristics, distribution and reproduction of the order Metzgeriales.
2. With the help of diagrams, write in detail the vegetative reproduction in Metzgeriales.
3. Describe sexual reproduction in the order Metzgeriales.
4. Write explanatory notes on thallus structure in metzgeriales. *(Allahabad M.Sc., 2000)*

SHORT ANSWER TYPE

5. **Write short notes on :**
   (*a*) Vegetative reproduction in Metzgeriales.
   (*b*) Characteristics of Metzgeriales.
   (*c*) Sex organs in Metzgeriales.
   (*d*) Sporophyte of Metzgeriales.
   (*e*) Classification of Metzgeriales.
   (*f*) General characters of Metzgeriales *(Lucknow, 2007)*

OBJECTIVE TYPE

6. **Select the correct answer :**
   (*i*) The status of an order to Metzgeriales was given by
   (*a*) Parihar (*b*) Evans
   (*c*) Schuster (*d*) Kashyap.
   (*ii*) *Cryptothallus mirabilis* is a liverwort which is
   (*a*) Autophyte (*b*) Parasite
   (*c*) Symbiotic (*d*) Saprophyte.
   (*iii*) Sex organs occur singly or in groups on the dorsal surface of the thallus in the members of the order
   (*a*) Marchantiales (*b*) Metzgeriales
   (*c*) Bryales (*d*) Anthocerotales.
   (*iv*) Vegetative reproduction in Metzgeriales takes place by
   (*a*) Gemmae
   (*b*) Tubers
   (*c*) Fragmentation
   (*d*) All of the above.
   (*v*) One celled gemmae have been recorded in
   (*a*) *Riccardia* sp.
   (*b*) *Pellia* sp.
   (*c*) *Blasia pusilla*
   (*d*) *Riccardia multifitida*.

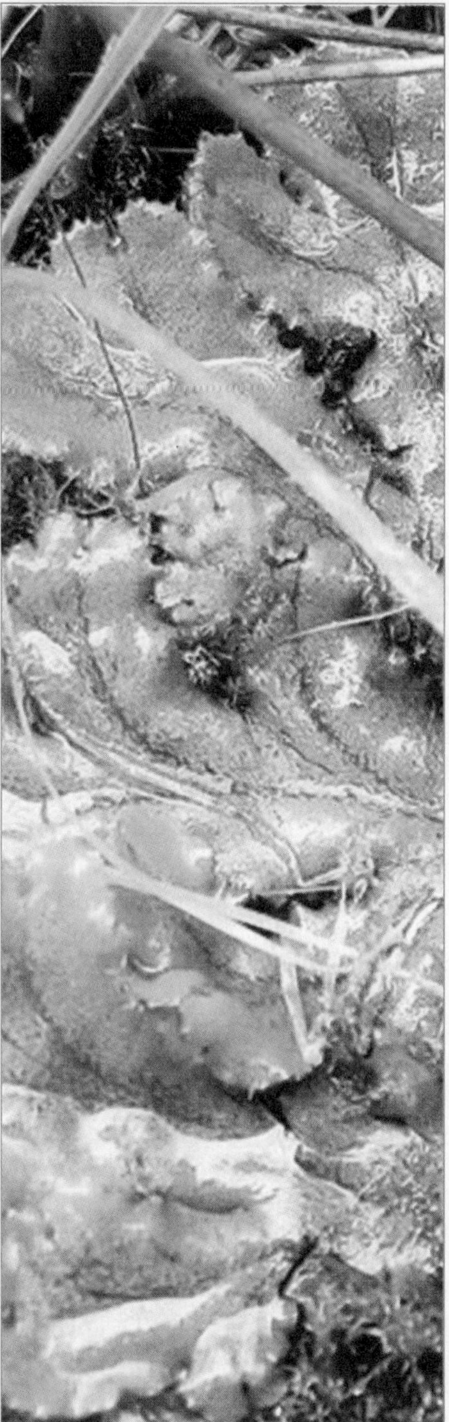

Image of *Pellia epiphylla*

CHAPTER 7 (I)

METZGERIALES

Pelliaceae

Pellia

FAMILY PELLIACEAE

General characteristics

The family includes thalloid liverworts in which the thallus shows no special differentiation beyond a mid-rib and smooth-walled rhizoids on the ventral surface. The thallus is prostrate and dorsiventral often lobed by irregular incisions. It is secured to the ground by means of simple, unseptate, smooth and thin-walled rhizoids only. The scales are absent and so are the tuberculated rhizoids. The antheridia occur scattered and archegonia in a group on the upper surface of the thallus. The archegonial cluster is always surrounded by an involucre which is an outgrowth of the thallus. The capsule is usually spherical or oval in outline and elevated on a long, slender stalk, the **seta**. The capsule wall is generally two to four layers of cells in thickness. There is a coherent mass of elaters, the so-called **elaterophore** attached to the floor of the cavity of the capsule. It is termed the **basal elaterophore.** In addition, there are free elaters. Each elater has two to four rarely even six spiral bands. The spore mother cells become fourlobed before entering upon meiosis.

The lobes are arranged tetrahedrally. The conventional treatment was to place two genera, *Pellia* and *Noteroclada* (*Androcryphia*) in this family. Evans (1939) added a third to the list. It is *Calycularia*. Pande and Udar (1956) considered the inclusion of *Calycularia* in this family untenable and suggested its separation from this assemblage. Thus, the family includes 2 or 3 genera. All are thallose. *Pellia*, the best known genus of this family is taken as a type.

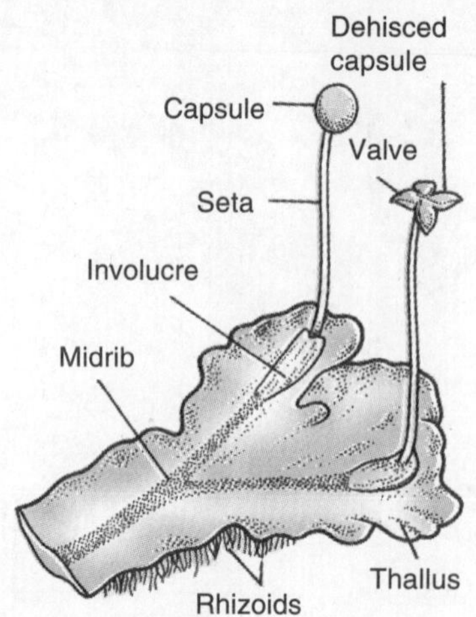

Fig. 7.1. ***Pellia* sp.** Thallus bearing a mature sporophyte.

PELLIA Raddi (Fig. 7.1)

Habitat. It occurs in diverse situations commonly on damp soil. Generally it occurs by the sides of streams, springs, wells, and in damp woods, sometimes, actually under water. Rarely it is found on moist rocks. The aquatic forms usually remain sterile. The form and texture of the thallus varies according to the habitat. The individuals growing on damp soil have a robust thallus with broad, elongates lobes. When growing submerged or in very humid, damp, shady places the thallus is delicate, long, narrow, ribbon-shaped with a distinct mid-rib and thin margin. Three species of this genus are found in India. These are *P. epiphylla* (Fig. 7.4 A), *P. neesiana* and *P. calycina* (Fig. 7.4, B—C).

Distribution. *Pellia calycina* (*P. fabbroniana*) has been reported by Kashyap from Kumaon, Western Himalayas, Mussoorie, Kulu, Simla, Dalhousie, etc. It occurs between 5,000 to 8,000 ft. on moist soil or actually under water. *P. epiphylla* is common in Sikkim and eastern Himalayas. *P. neesiana* is not commonly found. All the three species of *Pellia* are commonly found in the North Temperate Zone.

External characters (Fig. 7.1). The plant body is a small simple, dorsiventral thallus. It is dichotomously branched as in *Marchantia* but differs in its external form. The thallus is thin, flat, green and lobed. The margin is sinuous and irregularly lobed. The lobes often overlap one another. The upper surface of the thallus is smooth without areolae. It appears deep green and opaque as that of *Marchantia*. Since many plants grow together it is difficult to distinguish the individuals in the patch. The central portion of each lobe is thicker than the margins. It constitutes the **midrib**. The broad poorly defined midrib extends to the apex of each lobe and slightly projects below. From the ventral side of midrib arise numerous smooth-walled **rhizoids**. They attach the plant to the substratum. Scales and tuberculate rhizoids are absent. Each lobe of the thallus has a terminal notch. At the bottom of this notch lies the growing point.

Structure of the thallus (Fig. 7.2). Internally the thallus is simple but several cell layers deep. However there is no cell differentiation. Entire thallus is thus composed of thin, polyhedral, parenchyma cells. The cells are joined together in a honey-comb-like manner. The thallus is several layers of cells thick along the median line or midrib region. In some species (*R. epiphylla* and *P. neesiana*) the cells in the midrib region are elongated in the direction of the long axis of the thallus lobes. The cell walls of these elongated cells are thickened by brown or yellow layer of thickening bands forming a kind of network (C). The thallus gradually thins out towards the margins where it may be one cell layer thick (A). The cells near the surface contain abundant chloroplasts (B). The starch grains, however, occur in all the cells. A few cells may, sometimes, contain oil. The single layer of regularly arranged cells which covers the upper and the lower surface of the thallus are sometime referred to as the **epidermis**. The pores and air chambers characteristic of *Marchantia* are absent. The unicellular rhizoids grow out as tubular outgrowths from the cells of the under sruface in the midrib region (B).

Apical growth. It takes place by means of a single, large, apical cell. It lies in a depression at the anterior end of each thallus lobe. In *P. epiphylla* the apical cell is lenticular and cylindric. It cuts off segments parallel to its two sides and the posterior convex base. The former by repeated divisions give rise to the wings of the thallus. The latter build up the broad, thickened median portion. Owing to more rapid growth of the marginal cells the growing apex becomes sunk in a depression. There it is protected from damage. Near the growing point certain cells of the lower surface grow into glandular hairs. They secrete mucilage which protects the gowing point from drying. At the time of dichotomy the apical cell divides by a longitudinal wall into two equal cells. Each of the latter functions as an apical cell of a branch.

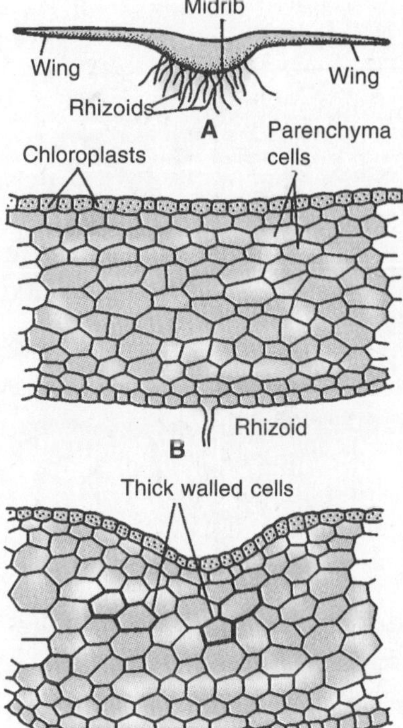

Fig. 7.2 (A—C). *Pellia* sp. Structure of the thallus. A, outline sketch of a vertical transverse section of the thallus of *P. epiphylla*; B, portion of a T.S. of a thallus of *P. calycina* showing internal structure; C, part of a T.S. of thallus of *P. epiphylla* showing internal structure.

Reproduction. The thallus or the **gametophyte** of *Pellia* reproduces by two methods, **vegetative** and **sexual.**

1. Vegetative Reproduction. Vegetatively, *Pellia* reproduces by *adventitious branches* and *fragmentation*. The gemmae have not been reported so far.

(*i*) *Adventitious branches*. These arise from the upper surface of the thallus or the margin. Eventually these branches separate from the parent thallus by the decay of the connecting tissue. On separation each branch grows as an independent plant.

(*ii*) *Fragmentation*. The cells in the basal, older regions of the thallus die and disintegrate leading to the separation of the lobes or the fragments from the parent thallus. Each fragment by apical growth and branching develops into an independent individual.

(*iii*) *Regeneration*. Cavers (1930a) and Kreh (1909) reported regeneration in *P. epiphylla* and *P. fabbroniana* (*P. calycina*) from bits of thallus in culture.

2. Sexual Reproduction (Fig. 7.3). The thallus is the sexual plant. It bears the sex organs. These are **antheridia** and **archegonia.** Some species of *Pellia* are **dioecious** and others **monoecious**. Examples of dioecious species are *P. calycina* (B, C) and *P. neesiana*. The third species, *P. epiphylla*, is monoecious (A). The monoecious species are **protandrous**.

(*a*) **Antheridia** (*i*) *Position* (Fig. 7.3 A). Mature antheridia are seen as circular spores on the upper surface of the thallus (A). They occur singly and lie irregularly scattered in two or more rows in the broad midrib region. Each antheridium is immersed in the thallus. It lies in a cavity called the **antheridial chamber** (fig. 7.4). The latter opens on the upper surface of the thallus by means of a small opening, the **ostiole**. The sunken condition of antheridia in *Pellia* serves a double purpose. It provides efficient protection and facilitates discharge of sperms.

(*ii*) *Structure*. The antheridium is a stalked, globular structure (Fig. 7.5 K). The stalk is short, slender and multicellular. The globular body of the antheridium has an outer wall. It is one cell-layer thick and surrounds a central mass of **androcyte mother cells**. Each androcyte mother cell divides diagonally into two **androcytes** or **spermatids**. The protoplast of the androcyte metamorphoses into a biflagellate sperm. The liberated sperm is an elongated, spirally coiled biflagellate structure

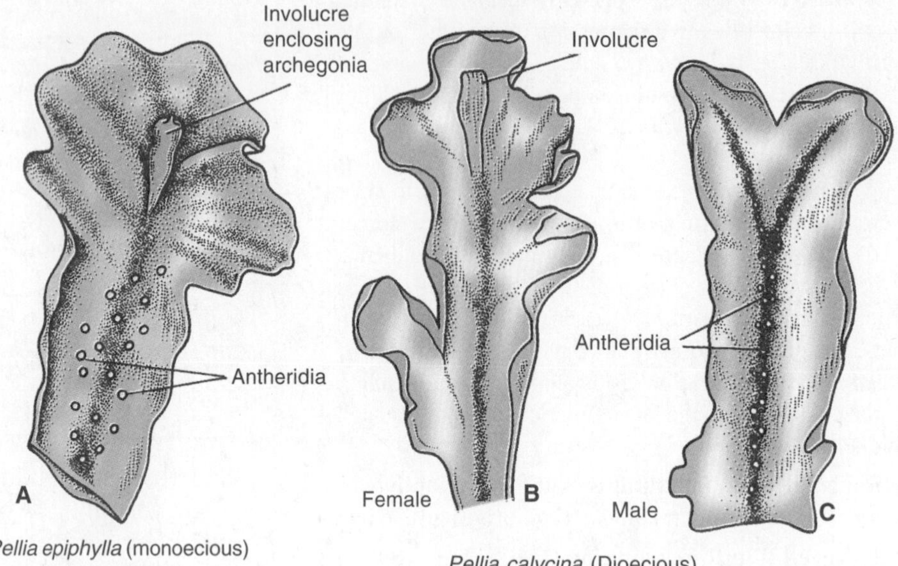

Fig. 7.3. (A—C), ***Pellia* sp.** A, monoecious thallus of *P. epiphylla;* Female (B) and Male (C) thalli of *P. calycina* (Dioecious) (After Kashyap).

(Fig. 7.5 L). The two flagella are inserted at different points at the anterior thin end. The tapering coiled body of the sperm is entirely nuclear in origin.

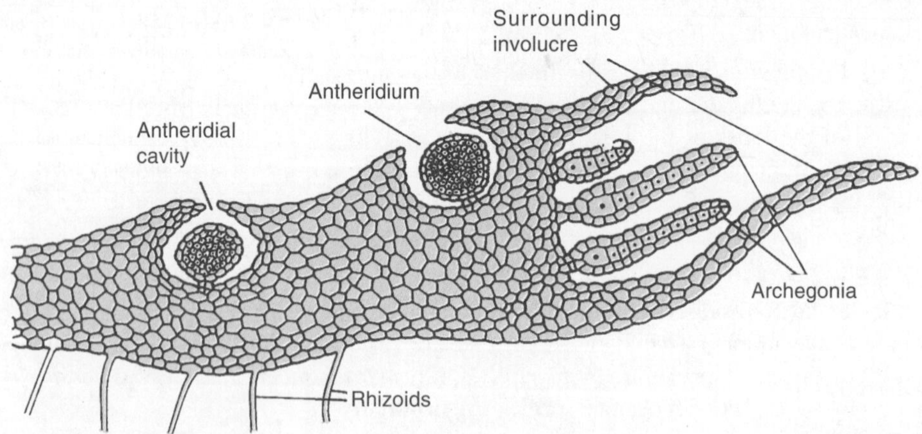

Fig. 7.4. *Pellia epiphylla.* V.S. monoecious thallus showing the position of sex organs.

(iii) Development of antheridium. (Fig. 7.5). Each antheridium arises as a single superficial cell. It is called an **antheridial initial** (A). It lies on the upper surface of the thallus close to the growing apex. The antheridial initial increases in size and projects above the surface of the thallus. It then divides by a transverse wall into two (B). Of these the lower or basal cell remains as an **antheridial mother cell.** It divides transversely into a lower **primary stalk cell** and an upper **primary antheridial cell** (C). The former undergoes a few divisions to form the short mutlicellular stalk.

The primary antheridial cell develops into the body of the antheridium. It first divides by a longitudinal wall into two daugher cells (D). They are of equal size. The next wall in each daughter cell is in a plane diagonal to the first division. It is nearly periclinal (E). It divides each daughter cell

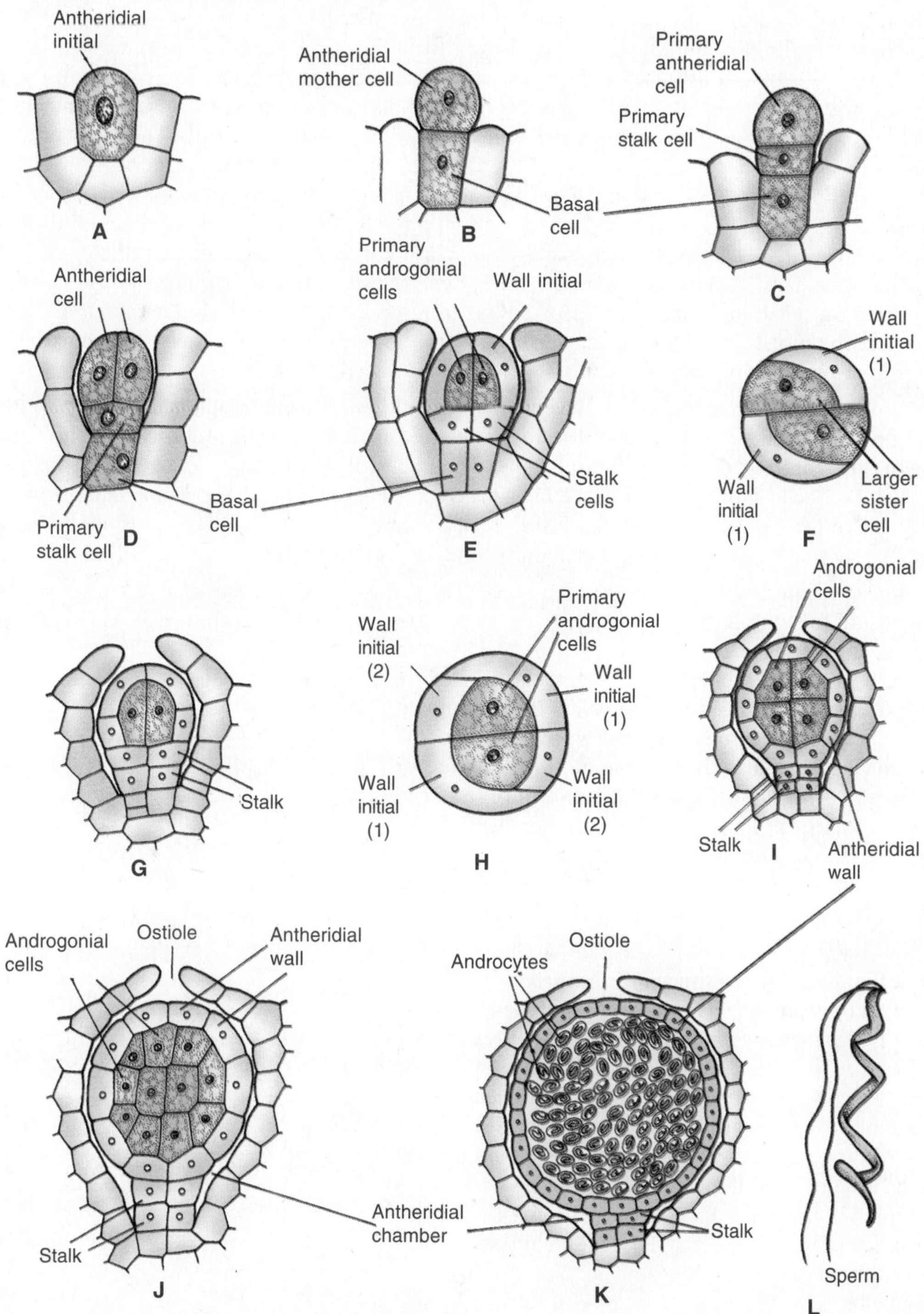

Fig. 7.5 (A—L). ***Pellia* sp**. Stages in the development of antheridium (A—J); K, mature antheridium; L, sperm.

into a pair of unequal cell (F). The smaller of the pair constitutes the **jacket** or **wall initial**. The larger sister cell again divides periclinally into an outer and an inner cell. The outer cell is the **second jacket** or **wall initial**. The inner cell functions as the **primary androgonial cell**. These divisions can best be seen in transverse sections (F,H). At this stage the body of the young antheridium consists of four wall initials (H). They enclose the two primary androgonia cells. The jacket or wall initials divide only by anticlinal walls to form the one cell thick wall of the antheridium (I). The primary androgonial cells divide and redivide several times (J). The cells of the last cell generation consitute the **spermatocytes** or the **androcyte mother cells**. Each androcyte mother cell divides diagonally into two **androcytes** or **spermatids**. Each androcyte produces a single antherozoid (K). It is formed mainly from its nuclear material. It is furnished with two longer whiplash flagella. They are inserted at the thin, anterior end of the tapering coiled body of the antherozoid (L). The development of the antheridium is accompanied by the upward growth of the surrounding tissue. It completely encloses it except for a small opening at the top (K).

Dehiscence. On the access of moisture the wall cells of the mature antheridium imbibe water and become distended. The distended wall cell abutting against the walls of antheridial pits cause pressure to bear on the contents within the antheridium. Consequently the mature antheridium ruptures at its apex. The adndrocytes are extruded in a mass of mucilage through the opening into the water that caused the rupture. They rise to its surface and spread apart. Finally the sperms are liberated into the surrounding water by the dissolution of the walls of androcytes.

(*b*) **Archegonia** (*i*) *Position* (Fig. 7.6 B). The archegonia are produced in a cluster on the upper surface of the thallus lobes. The archegonial cluster lies close to the growing apex (B) but the apical cell itself persists. All the four to twelve **anacrogynous** archegonia in the cluster stand on a slightly raised transverse ridge of tissue called the **receptacle**. The latter faces the growing apex. The archegonia of the cluster are surrounded by a complete collar-like or incomplete flap-like sheath, the **involucre** (B). The involucre is green and protective in function. It is tubular in *P. calycina*, short and cylindrical in *P. neesiana* and reduced to a pouch open in front in *P. epiphylla*. Amidst the archegonia in the cluster occur the mucilage hairs.

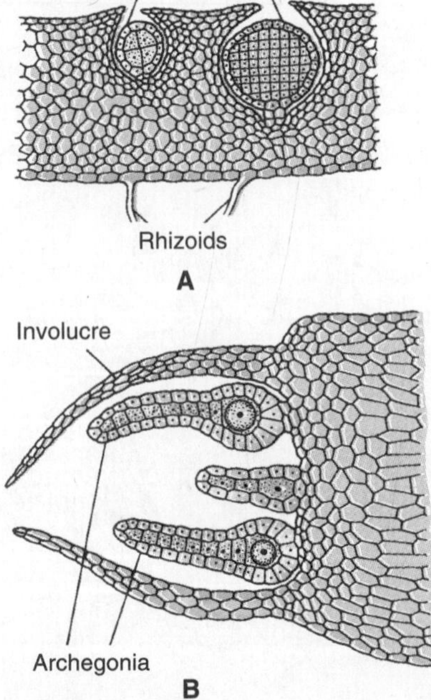

Fig. 7.6 (A—B). ***Pellia calycina.*** A, V.S. male thallus; B, V.S. female thallus.

(*ii*) *Structure* (Fig. 7.7 J). The archegonium is typically a flask-shaped structure. It is essentially the same as the corresponding organ in the Marchantiales but usually more massive. The differences are only in detail. It is seated on a short but stout and a massive **stalk**. The venter consists of a single layer of cells in thickness but prior to fertilization it becomes two cells layers thick (Fig. 7.8 A). The venter cavity contains an **egg** and a small **ventral canal cell** above it. The elongated neck is not sharply marked off from the venter. It consists of five lingitudinal rows of cells (H). They enclose a canal containing a row of usually 6—9 **neck canal cells** (J). A rosette of four rather large **cover** or **cap cells** are located at the top of the neck. Sometimes the lower portion of the neck also becomes two cell layers thick.

(*iii*) *Development* (Fig. 7.7). The archegonia arise from a group of cells on the upper side of the thallus lobes. These are the surface cells of the younger segments of the apical cells. The apical cell itself is not directly concerned in their development. A variable number of cells in this group function as **archegonial initials**. The result is that the anacrogynous archegonia stand in a group on the upper surface of the thallus lobes near the growing point.

Any surface cell in the group may function as an **archegonial initial** (A). It enlarges into a papilla-like out-growth. The papillate archegonial initial divides horizontally into a basal **pedicel cell** and an upper or outer **archegonial mother cell** (B). The latter undergoes the usual divisions to produce an archegonium. The basal pedicel cell divides to form the short, multicellular stalk.

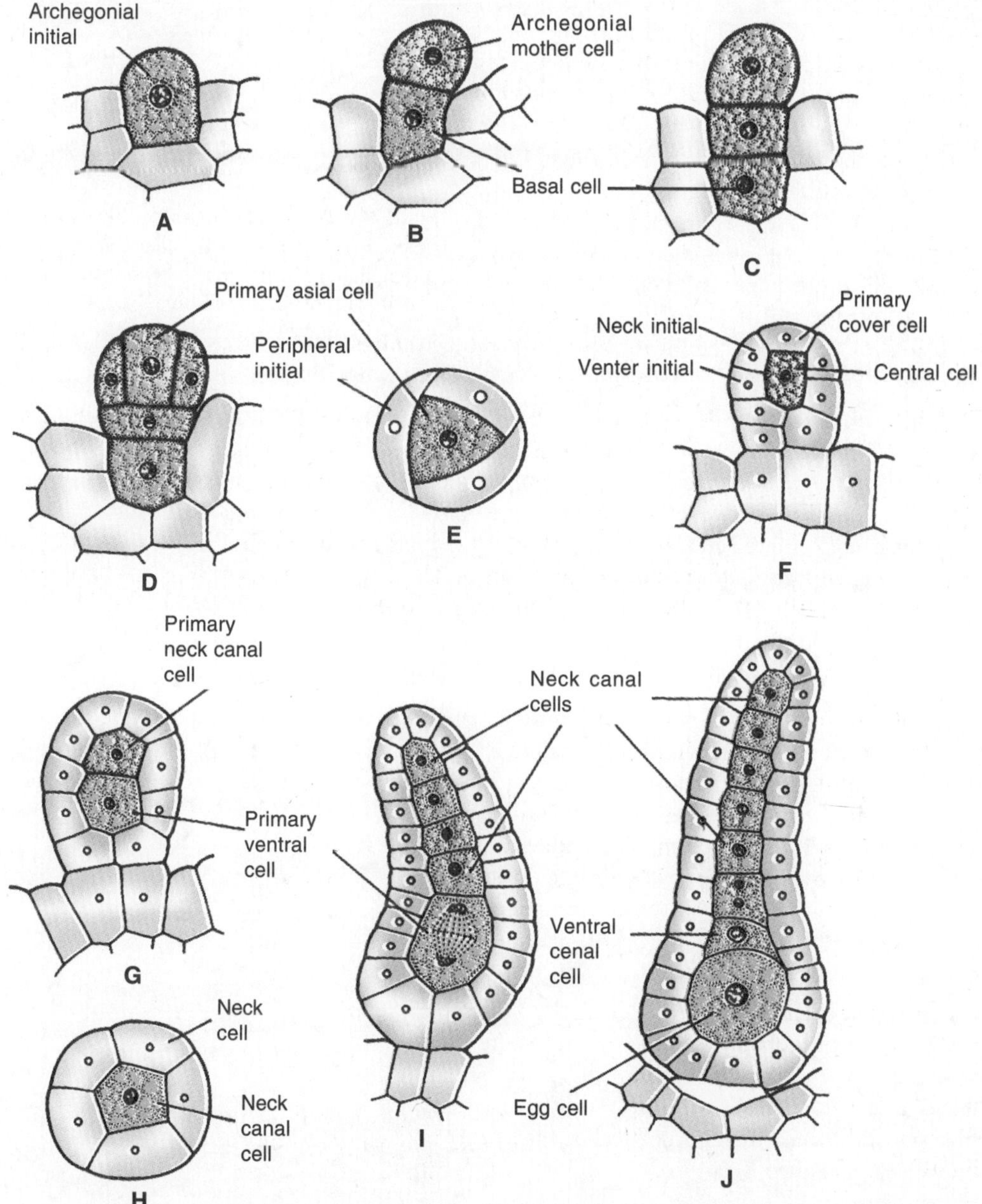

Fig. 7.7 (A—J). ***Pellia* sp.** A—I, stages in the development of archegonium; E and H, are transverse sections; J, nearly mature archegonium. Explanation in the text.

The archegonium mother cell divides by three interesting vertical walls so as to cut off three lateral of **peripheral initials** or **cells** (D). Of these one is the smallest (E). They surround an internal, middle cell called the **primary axial cell**. The latter slightly overtops the peripheral initials. The primary axial cell divides transversely to form a small, outer **primary cap** or **cover cell** and a lower, larger **central cell** (F). The two larger, peripheral initials or cells divide by vertical walls. The smallest peripheral cell does not divide. The central cell now becomes enlcosed in a ring of five cells. They are the **envelop cells** or the **jacket initials**. All the cells constituting the young archegonium including the central cell divide transversely. The young archegonium is now divided into two halves (F). Each half consists of five envelope cells and one cnetral cell. The five envelope cells of the upper half constitute the **neck initials**. Its central cell is the **primary canal cell**. The five envelope cells of the lower half constitute the **venter initials**. Its central cell functions as the **primary ventral cell** (G).

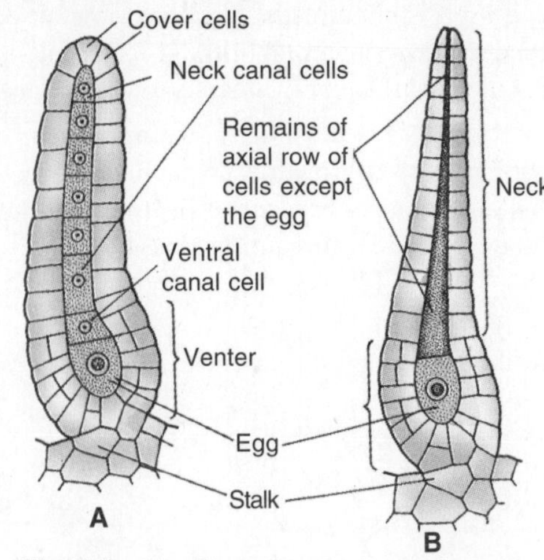

Fig. 7.8. (A—B). *Pellia* sp. A, nearly mature archegonium in section; B, Mature archegonium at the time of fertilisation and with the axial row of cells except the egg disorganised.

The neck initials divide repeatedly by transverse walls to form the archegonial neck (I, J). It consists of five vertical rows of **neck cells**. In the meanwhile the priamry neck canal cell divides to form a row of six to nine or more **neck canal cells** (G, I-J). They fill the neck canal. The venter initials divide to form the venter wall. It encloses a **venter cavity**. Before fertilization the venter wall becomes two or three cell layers thick (Fig. 7.8 A). The primary ventral cell divides **unequally** to form a small, upper **ventral canal cell** and a lower, large **egg** or **oosphere** (Fig. 7.8, I-J). Finally the primary cover cell divides by two intersecting walls to form the four **cover** or **lid cells**.

Coincident with the development of the archegonia a delicate membrane grows from the top of the archegonial receptacle. It arches over the archegonia to form an **involucre**.

(*c*) **Fertilization.** It takes place in the usual manner in the presence of water. The axial row of cells excpet the egg disorganises in the mature archegonium (Fig. 7.8 B). A mass of mucilage is formed. It now fills the neck canal. The mucilage absorbs water and wells up. The pressure exerted from within separates the cap cells. At the same time water finds access to the antheridium. The antheridial wall ruptures at its apex. The androcytes emerge through the opening into the water.

Finally the sperms are liberated from the androcytes. They swim to the archegonia and enter the open archegonial necks and swim down the canals to reach the egg. One of them probably the first to reach there loses its flagella and penetrates the egg to fuse with the female nucleus to accomplish fertilization. The fertilised egg secretes a wall around it and is now called the **zygote** or the **oospore**.

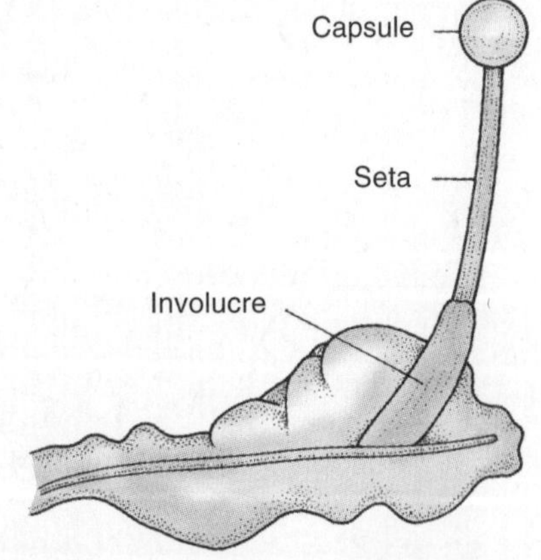

Fig. 7.9. *Pellia neesiana* (Dioecious). The female plant bearing the sporogonium.

Sporogonium (Fig. 7.9). At maturity the sporogonium consists of the **foot**, the **seta** and the **capsule**. The foot forms the basal, absorbing region of the sporogonium. It is distinct and conical in form. Its edges project upwards forming a collar-like structure around the base of the seta (Fig. 7.11 A). The seta is of pure white colour. It is almost transparent, at maturity and terminates in a dark green or black nearly globular capsule. In *Pellia* the seta attains a great length upto 5 cm. It is delicate structure composed chiefly of thin-walled cells.

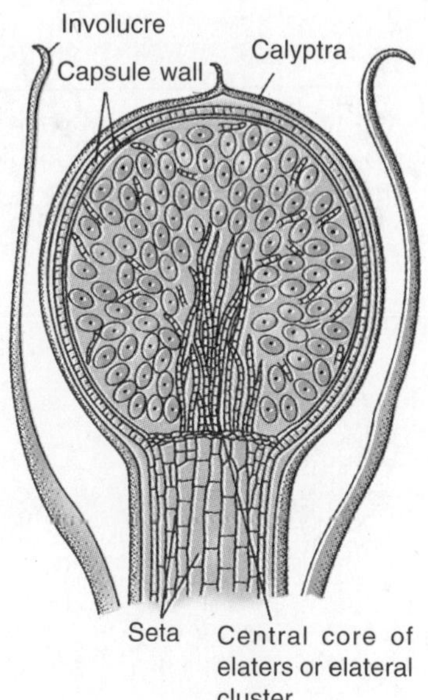

Fig. 7.10. ***Pellia*** **sp.** A longitudinal section of the maturing capsule.

(i) Structure of capsule (Fig. 7.10). It is globular in outline with a diameter of about 1.5 mm. The capsule wall is two or more cell layers thick. The outer layer of the capsule consists of polygonal cells. Their radial walls possess rod-like thickening bands (Fig. 7.12 A). The cells of the second layer are flattened. They are, somewhat, reticulately thickened. Within the capsule wall is the spacious spore cavity which contains free elaters intermixed with spores. The spores are large. Jack (1895) estimated that about 4,500 spores occur in one capsule of *P. epiphylla*. They begin to germinate before they are shed. The mature free elaters are empty, considerably long, slender, spindle-shaped cells with 2 or 3 sometimes more up to six, bands of spiral thick-ening on their walls. They are hygroscopic and thus well known as organs of spore dispersal. Besides the free elaters, there is a prominent basal central core or tuft of 50-100 elaters attached to the centre of the base of capsule. This elateral cluster is often but erroneously termed the **elaterophore**. At the point of attachment of the elateral cluster, the base wall structure aggregates into a small, basal columnar thickening of indistinct tissue. The central elateral tuft and the upheaved

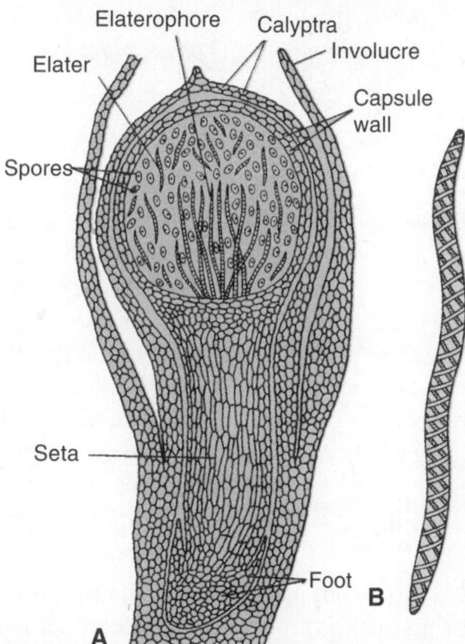

Fig. 7.11. (A—B). *Pellia* sp. A, longitudinal section of a mature sporogonium; B, elater with a double spiral band of thickening.

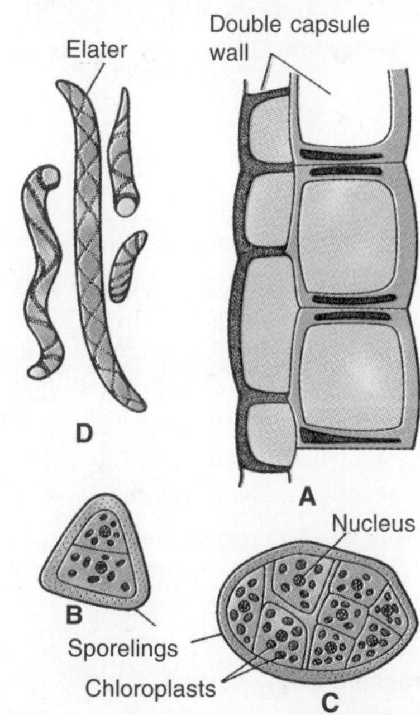

Fig. 7.12. (A—D). *Pellia* sp. A, part of the capsule wall showing thickening of the walls; B—C, sporelings; D, elaters.

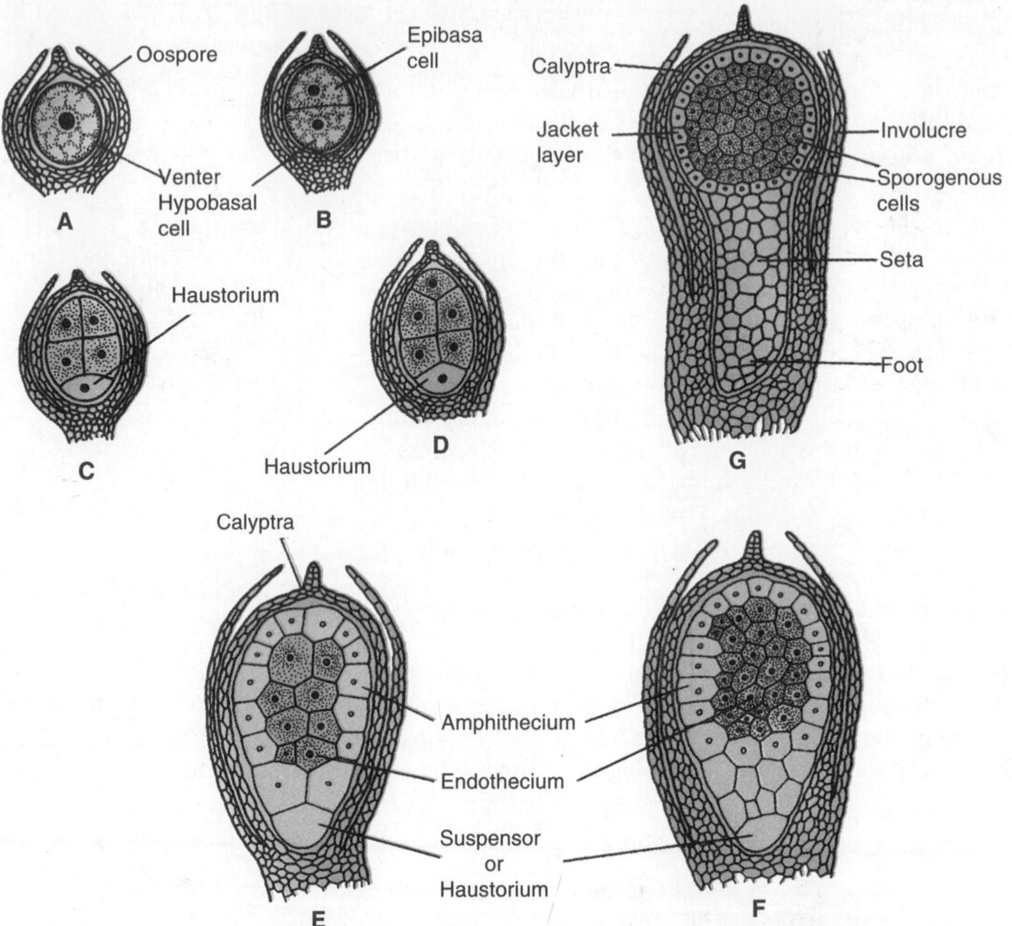

Fig. 7.13. (A—G). *Pellia* sp. Various stages in the development of sporogonium. Explanation in the text.

base wall sturcture together form a cylinder of pure sterile tissue which often extends nearly to the upper end of the spore cavity (Kuwahara, 1978). A remarkable feature of *Pellia* sporogonium is the absence of spores in the central part of the elateral cluster. The upper free ends of these fixed elaters radiate into the spore cavity intermingling with the spores and free elaters. Smith holds that the basal elateral tuft or the so-called elaterophore helps in bringing about a gradual shedding of the spores. Others believe that it functions as a primitive **sort** of vascular system. The capsule wall has on its surface four vertical strips of thinwalled cells. These are called the **lines of dehiscence** (Fig. 7.15 A). The mature capsule splits as a rule into four sectors along the lines of dehiscenee. The split starts at the top and extends right up to the base. The four valves spread and become everted (Fig. 7.1). This regular method of dehiscence is also a feature in sharp contrast to the capsule of Marchantiales which opens irregularly.

Morphology of elaterophore. Evans (1939), Bold (1967) and many others applied the term elaterophore to the cluster of persistent elaters (basal or apical) formed in the capsule of certain Metzgeriales. In the glossary of botanical terms it is defined as a region of attachment of elaters in certain liverworts. Bower (1908 and 1938) used the term for the whole structure consisting of the elateral cluster and the region of attachment which in *Aneura* (*Riccardia*) is cylindrical structure. Cavers (1910) applied the term elaterophore appropriately to the cylindrical structure in *Aneura* to which the persistent elaters are attached. Smith (1955) and Schuster (1966) also used the term for the structure to which the persistent elaters are attached. Kuwahara (1978) pointed out this inconsistency in the use of this term elaterophore. He reported that the anatomical data suggest a common histological origin of elaterophore and the capsule wall. In fact the former may be considered an extension of latter. On the basis of this fact he emphasized that the term elaterphore should be applied to the *sterile elater bearing structure* in the capsule and the term *sessile elaters* for the elateral cluster (basal or apical) attached to it.

It is evident that the capsule of *Pellia* contains more sterile tissue as compared with that of *Marchantia*. It consists of the foot, the long seta, more than one cell-layer thick capsule wall, basal elaterophore and the sessile and free elaters. In short the sporophyte of *Pellia* is a more elaborate object. It has a more complex structure as compared with that of *Marchantia*. Of course the elaboration is internal rather than external.

The sterilisation of potentially fertile tissue (sporogenous tissue) has advanced. The fertile tract is partially decentralised by the substitution of a sterile, basal elaterophore and central elateral cluster of sessile elaters. The absence of spores in the central part of the elateral cluster is a noteworthy feature of *Pellia* capsule. Some people look upon the elaterophore and the elateral cluster as the forerunner of the columella. This view is disputed by others.

Nutrition and protection. Like that of *Marchantia* the mature sporophyte lacks photosynthetic tissue. The foot which is housed in the thalloid gametophyte absorbs adequate nutrition from the later for the entire sporogonium. Protection to the developing sporophyte is provided by the calyptra (an enlargement of the archegonial venter tissue) and involucre. Usually only a single sporogonium is developed within each involucre.

(*ii*) **Development of sporogonium** (Fig. 7.13). Five or six days after fertilization the oospore or the zygote (A) undergoes segmentation. The first division wall is transverse (B). It separates an upper **epibasal** cell from a lower **hypobasal cell**. The hypobasal cell undergoes no further division. It usually remains as a one-celled appendage called the **haustorium** (C). Some people called it **suspensor**. It helps the growing embryo to go deeper into the tissue of the receptacle. The entire sporophyte (foot, seta and capsule) is derived from the epibasal cell. The latter divides first by a vertical wall and then by a transverse wall (C). The transverse division is at right angles to the first. The embryo at this stage consists of four cells. Each of these divides by a vertical wall. The embryo now consists of two tiers of four cells each (C). The cells of both the tiers divide and redivide. The derivatives of the upper tier form the capsule (G). The lower tier develops into the stalk or the seta (G). The seta at its lower end differentiates into a distinct, conical absorbing organ, the '**foot**'. The foot attaches the seta to and is embedded in the tissue of the thallus. The conical foot has its edges projecting upwards forming a collar-like structure at the base of the seta. In outline it looks a barbed arrow head (Fig. 7.11 A). The seta consists of uniform, small-celled parenchyma.

Each of the four cells of the upper tier of the octant stage divides periclinally separating a single layered **amphithecium**. The latter surrounds an inner mass of cells constituting the **endothecium** (B). The endothecium functions as the **archesporium** or the **primary sporogenous tissue**. As the capsule advances towards maturity the amphithecium divides by anticlinal walls to form the **capsule wall** (G). Later the wall becomes two or more cell layers thick by further periclinal divisions. The archesporium cells divide and redivide to give rise to a mass of **sporogenous cells** (Fig. 7.13 F and G). Quite early a central mass of sporogenous cells at the base of the capsule becomes differentiated into sterile cells. These sterile cells elongate considerably and develop spiral thickening on their walls. These elater-like cells radiate from the base upwards and outwards. This basal structure is usually but inappropriately called an **elaterophore** (Fig. 7.11 A). In the meanwhile the remaining sporogenous cells which surround the elaterophore become differentiated into the **spore mother cells** and the sterile **elater cells**. The later elongate considerably. The elongated cells develop into long, thin, doubly pointed tubular structures with a double spiral thickening on their walls. These are the **elaters** (Fig. 7.11 B). The upper free ends of the elater-like cells of the elaterophore pass between the spore mother cells and elaters in the upper part of the capsular cavity.

(*iii*) **Sporogenesis** (Fig. 7.14). As described before sporogenesis comprises a complicated integrated series of events involving a special type of nuclear division leading to the conversion of the diploid protoplast of the sporocyte (spore mother cell) into the haploid dispersal units with resistant walls termed the **spores** or more appropriately **meiospores**. The nuclear division involved in sporogenesis is called **meiosis**. In meiosis the diploid nucleus divides twice but the chromosomes are replicated only once. The spherical spore mother cell (A) during prophase of meiosis becomes a deeply, four-lobed structure (D). The lobes are tetrahedrally arranged. They are connected in the middle by a narrow neck. The latter contains the **diploid** nucleus. The nucleus divides twice by **meiosis** into four haploid nuclei (E). These migrate into the lobes (F), one each. The lobes finally separate by cell walls extending inwards and laid simultaneously between them (G). A tetrad of haploid spores is formed. It is surrounded by a common sheath. The latter ruptures and the ripe spores are separated (H). They contain chlorophyll. The exospore is poorly developed. The spores are unicellular and haploid structures. The haploid number of chromosomes is nine (n=9). The unicellular spores later develop into multicellular structures before they are shed (Fig. 7.12 B-C). Towards maturity most of the wall cells in the two layered capsule wall become thickened. There is, however, no thickening of the wall cells in the four vertical apical strips. These constitute the lines of dehiscence (Fig. 7.15 A). They extend right from the apex down to the middle or the base of the capsule.

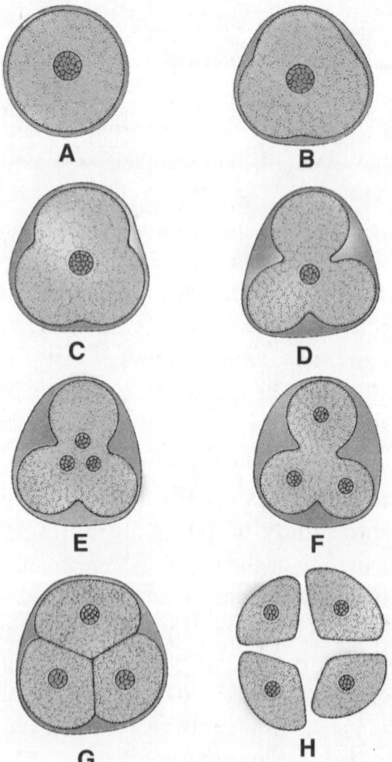

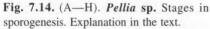

Fig. 7.14. (A—H). ***Pellia* sp.** Stages in sporogenesis. Explanation in the text.

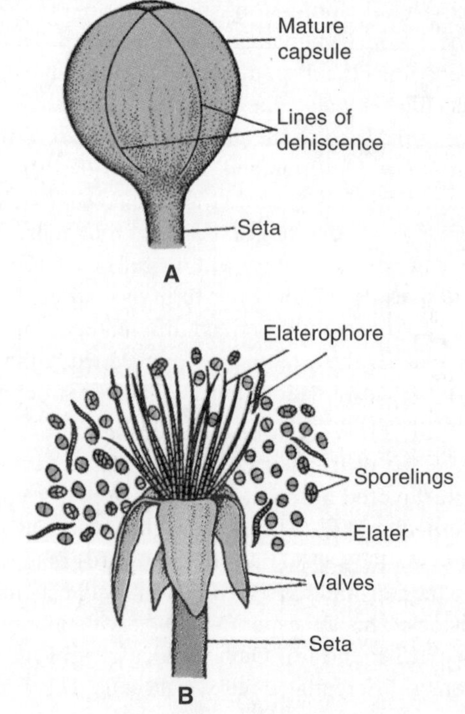

Fig. 7.15. (A—B). ***Pellia* sp.** A, ripe capsule showing lines of dehiscence; B, dehisced capsule showing recurved valves, elaterophore and discharged sporelings.

All the above-mentioned developmental changes take place within the venter. The latter in the meantime has enlarged keeping pace with the growth of the sporophyte inside. It forms a complete envelope, the **calyptra** around the young sporogonium (5.13 G). The seta at this stage is quite short. It remains so until the spores are ripe. With the ripening of the spores the seta elongates rapidly. The calyptra ruptures and remains around the base of the seta as a torn membrane.

(*iv*) **Dehiscence of the capsule** (Fig. 7.15). The dehiscence of the capsule is attained by the elongation of the seta. The calyptra is ruptured and the capsule is carried above the surrounding

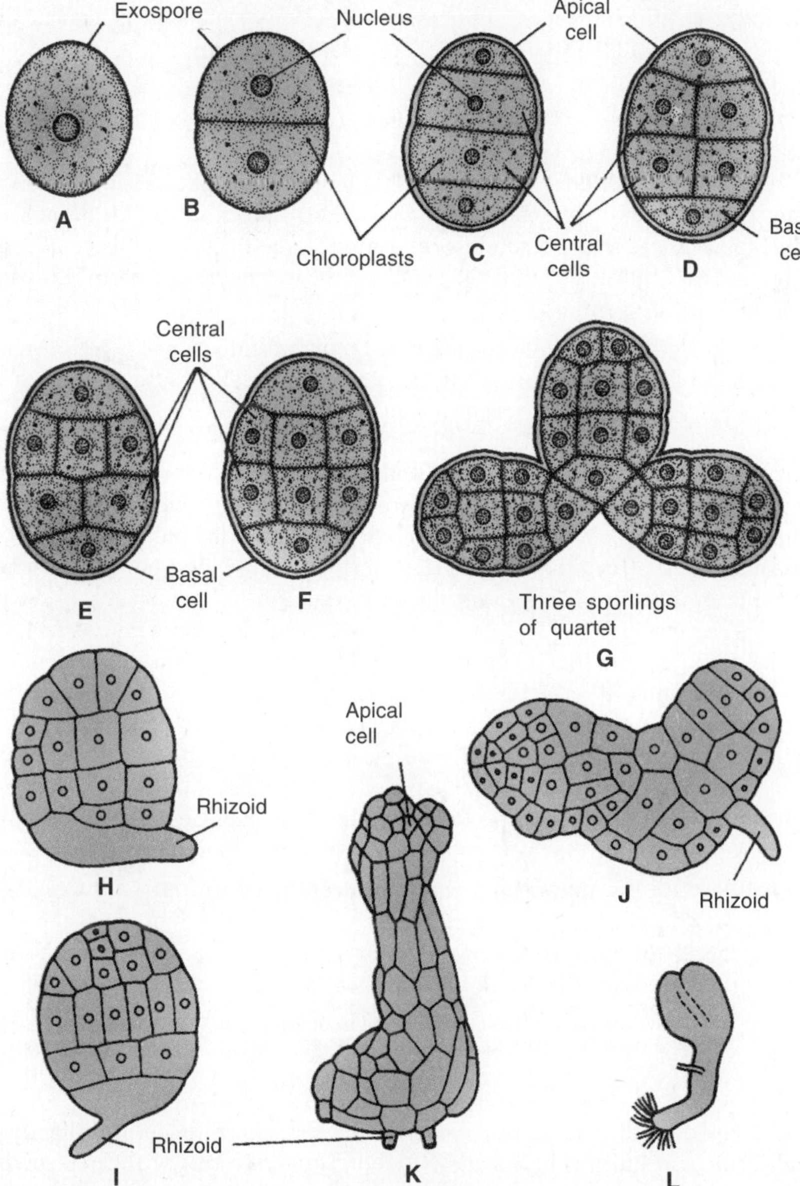

Fig. 7.16. (A—L). *Pellia* sp. Stages in the germination of spore and development of thallus. Explanation in the text. (A—I), stages in the development of sporeling of *P. epiphylla* and J, development of thallus from the side of sporeling (A—J after Wolfson, K—L after Gottache).

involucre (Fig. 7.9). It is now exposed to the drying effect of the surrounding air. Drying out of the capsule initiates the hygroscopic movements in thickened cells of the capsule wall. This splits the capsule by crossed cleavages from the apex along the lines of dehiscence to the base into four parts or valves (A). The four segments or valves bend back upon themselves (B). This exposes the mass of spores and the free elaters held round the basal tuft of fixed elaters.

(*v*) **Dispersal of spores.** The separation of spores from the exposed mass is assisted by the hygroscopic movements of the elaters. They coil and uncoil with the changes in the moisture content of the air. The loss of moisture stretches out the elaters. This stirs up and separates the spores in the exposed spore mass. The flicking to and fro of the sessile elaters facilitates the gradual dispersal of the loosened spores. When all the spores are shed, the elaterophore persists. It stands like a column in the centre of the four spreading valves (Fig. 7.15 B).

Germination of spores (Fig. 7.16). The spores of *Pellia* begin to germinate before they are shed. This precocious germination of spores is an exceptional feature. By the time the capsule dehisces several cells of protonema are already formed within the exospore. According to Fulford (1975), this has led to the erroneous interpretation of multicellular spores in *Pellia*. Before the capsule dehisces the spores begin to divide and the germination starts. In fact they become multicellular long before the seta has lengthened. The divisions take place within the exospore. This type of spore germination is called *in situ* germination.

At first the spore (A) divides by two successive transverse divisions (B—C). An oval object consisting of number of tiers of cells is formed (C). It may be called **sporeling**. Each cell of the sporeling contains chloroplasts, a nucleus and abundant protoplast. The whole structure, in fact, is a minute thallus. Excepting the basal and the end cells, the others divide vertically (D). Sometimes the apical or end cell may also divide by a vertical wall. On liberation from the capsule, the sporlings rather the young gametophytes, are 6-9 celled ovoid masses (E-F). Under favourable conditions (moist soil) the cell divisions continue in the central cells within the old exospore for some time until a globose mass of 20-30 cells is produced (H). The expanding endospore stretches the exospore so much that the latter remains no longer visible. At this stage basal cell of the globose protonema which has less cytoplasm and few chloroplasts, grows outside the exospore into a small rhizoid (H). The central cells undergo more longitudinal divisions (I). The cells in the apical region divide by oblique cell walls. Wolfson (1928) stated that one of these wedge-shaped cells in the apical region continues to function as an apical cell. It cuts off segments which divide and redivide outside the exospore to build at first, a cylindrical stem (K) which soon expands into the typical flattened *Pellia*-like thallus (L). The apical cell, at this stage, lies deep at the bottom of the notch of the growing cordate end. It is well protected by the two lobes and the slime papillae around it. Wolfson as well reported the development of the thallus from the side of the sporeling in *P. neesiana* (J).

Salient features. 1. The flat, deep green translucent dorsiventral **thallus** of *Pellia* grows dichotomously as *Marchantia* but differs in external appearance. It is thinner and simpler than the light green and opaque thallus of *Marchantia* and shows no differentiation beyond a poorly defined mid-rib and a crop of rhizoids on the lower surface.

2. The upper surface of the thallus is **smooth**. There are no hexagonal area (**areolae**) marked by dot-like central **air pores** characteristic of *Marchantia*.
3. There are no **scales** on the lower surface of the thallus.
4. The rhizoids that arise from the lower side of the braod, poorly defined slightly projecting midrib are unicellular, simple and of **smooth, thin-walled** type. Tuberculate rhizoids are absent.
5. Internally the thallus of *Pellia* is much simpler than that of *Marchantia*. There is no or little differentiation of tissues. The **air chambers** and **air pores** characteristic of *Marchantia* are absent. The epidermal layers are not well-defined. There is lack of

differentitation between the different cells except that the superficial cells of dorsal and ventral surface. The cells of dorsal surface contain abundant chloroplasts.

6. The apical growth is by means of a single **apical cell**.
7. Some species of *Pellia* are **monoecious** and others **dioecious**. The former are markedly **protandrous**.
8. The sex organs are never borne on **stalked receptacles**.
9. The shortly stalked, globular antheridia are immersed singly in **antheridial chambers** on the upper surface of the thallus. They are either scattered or arranged in two or more rows in the board **midrib** region.
10. The body of the antheridium has a usual structure. It consists of a single layered **antheridial wall** enclosing a mass of **androcytes**.
11. The **biflagellate sperms** are larger in size than those of most of the Marchantiales. They have more coils. The two flagella are inserted at different points of the thin, anterior end.
12. The early stages of development of the antheridium differ from those of the Marchantiales. The primary antheridial cell divides by a **vertical** instead of a transverse division. The succeeding divisions are **diagonally vertical**.
13. The archegonia occur in cluster on the upper surface of the thallus just back of the growing point. They are stalked. The stalk though short is distinct. The archegonial neck consists of **five** vertical rows of neck cells instead of six characteristics of the Marchantiales. Before fertilisation the venter wall consists of two layers of cells. In other respects the archegonia are similar to those of the Marchantiales.
14. Of the three lateral or **peripheral cells** surrounding the primary axial cell only **two** divide by vertical walls to give rise to five jacket initials in stead of six as in the Marchantiales.
15. The early development of embryo in *Pellia* differs from that of the Marchantiaceae. The **hypobasal cell** formed as a result of the first transverse division of the zygote takes no further part in the development of the sporogonium. It remains as a single-celled appendage at the base of the sporogonium. The sporogonium is entirely developed from the **epibasal region** of the two-celled embryo.
16. The capsule is raised on a long, slender stalk, the **seta**.
17. The capsule of *Pellia* shows greater **internal elaboration** than that of the Marchantiales. The capsule wall is two or more cell layers thick. The cells of the two layers of the capsule wall develop **strengthening bands**. The mature capsule dehisces in a regular and definite manner along the four **lines of dehiscence** into four **valves** which become reflexed. The sporogenous tissue is differentiated into spore mother cells, the free elaters and the cluster of sessile elaters attached to the basal elaterophore. The spore mother cells become **four lobed** before entering upon meiosis. The presence of a **basal elaterophore** bearing a cluster of sessile elaters is a disinctive feature.
18. The *in situ* germination of the spores before being discharged is another exceptional feature.
19. The development of a globose protonema is a feature in which *Pellia* differs from *Marchantia*.

SUMMARY OF LIFE CYCLE OF *PELLIA* (FIG. 7.17)

In general the life cycle of *Pellia* is similar to that of the other liverworts. There are differences in the details of the sex organs and sporogonium. As in other liverworts the life cycle consists of two generations, the **sexual** (gametophyte) and the **asexual** (sporophyte). The two are closely connected. As a matter of fact, the **asexual individual** (sporogonium, I) remains organically connected with the **sexual plant** (A) throughout its life and is dependent upon it for its nutrition.

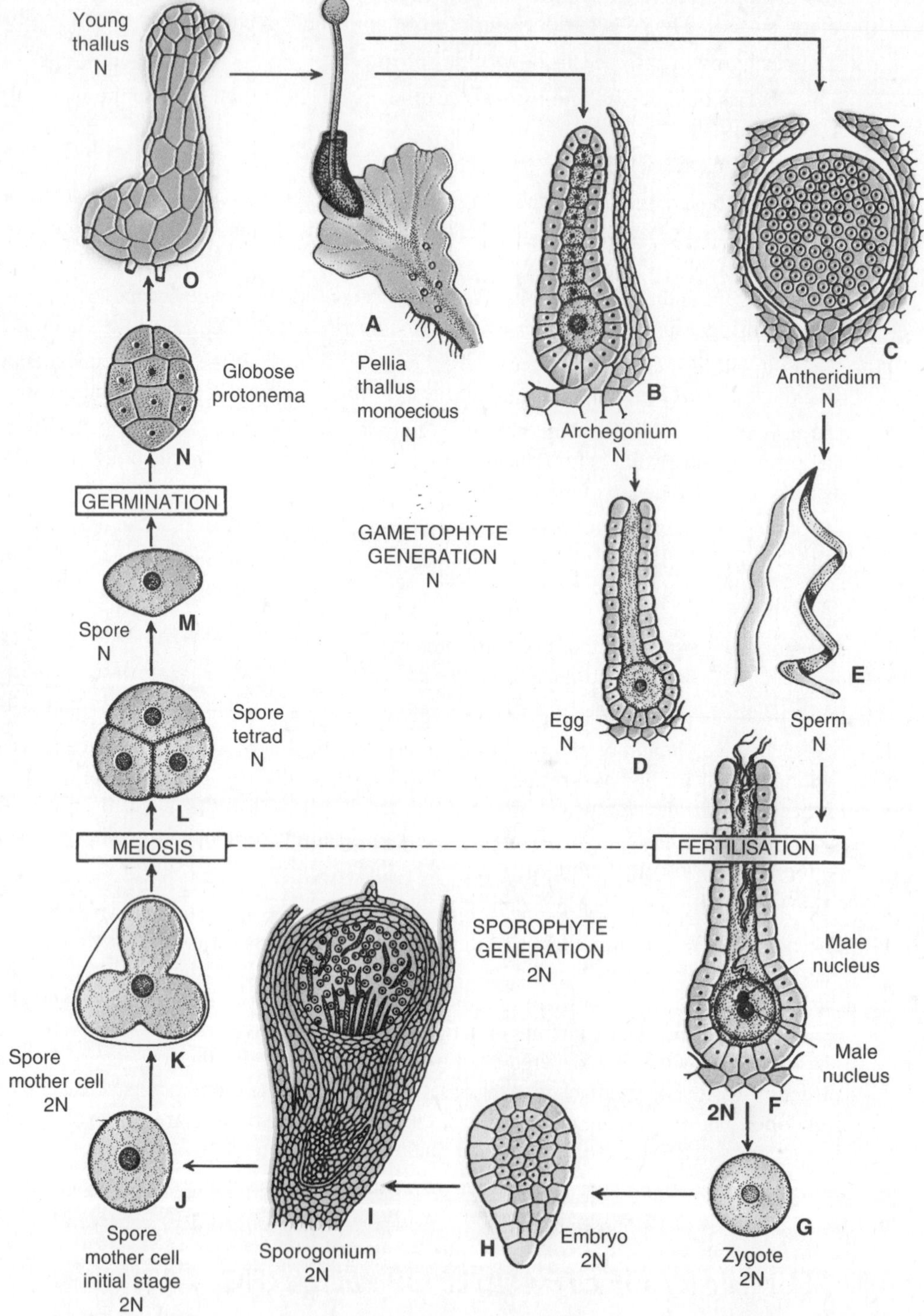

Fig. 7.17. (A—O). *Pellia* sp. Pictorial sketch of the sexual life cycle.

The sexual plant (**gametophyte**) is independent (A). It is a thin, flat, green dichotomously branched **thallus**. Each thallus lobe has a broad, slightly thickened, median portion, the **midrib**. The latter gradually thins out to a thin layer at the margins which are **sinuous**. The upper surface of the thallus is **smooth**. The ventral surface has no **scales**. The thallus is secured to the moist substratum by numerous, **smooth-walled rhizoids**. The later spring from its lower surface in the midrib **region**. Internally the thallus shows no differentiation into the upper photosynthetic and the lower, compact, storage region. It entirely consists of similar cells except that the superficial layers of the cells of the dorsal and ventral surfaces. The cells of dorsal surface are rich in chloroplasts. There are no air chambers and no air pores.

The thallus bears the **sex organs**. It may be **monoecious** or **dioecious**. The male sex organs or the **antheridia** (C) are borne on the upper surface of the thallus either scattered or in two or more rows. Each antheridium lies in a pit. It is shortly stalked and has a globular body. The body consists of a single layered antheridial wall enclosing a mass of androcytes. The latter get metamorphosed into biflagellate **spermatozoids** or **sperms** (E). The body of the sperm is entirely made up of nuclear material. It is tapering and spirally coiled. The coils are more numerous. The two flagella are inserted at the thin, anterior end. The **archegonia** occur in a cluster on the upper surface of the thallus just back of the growing apex. They are typically flask-shaped structures (B). The archegonial neck consists of **five** vertical rows of neck cells. The neck canal is filled with 6 to 9 or even more neck canal cells. The venter is two cell layers thick even before fertilization. The cavity of the venter is occupied by a large egg or oosphere (D) and a smaller ventral canal cell. the sperms and the eggs are the last structures of the **gametophyte generation**. The later comprises the *meiospores,* the green *thallus*, the *antheridia,* the *archegonia,* the *sperms* and the *eggs*. It starts with meiosis and ends with fertilisation in the life cycle (F). The sexual generation is characterised by the haploid number of chromosomes in the nuclei of its cells which is n=9.

The fertilised egg secretes a wall around it (G). It is the first structure of the sprophyte generation in the life cycle. Lodged in the venter it soon enters upon segmentation. By repeated mitotic division and differentiation it forms the **asexual plant** also called the **sporogonium** or the **sporophyte** (I). It is characterised by the presence of **diploid** number of chromosomes in the nuclei of its cells. The sporogonium is differentiated into a **foot**, a long **seta** and a spherical **capsule**. The capsule shows greater **sterilisation** of the potentially fertile tissue. Associated with this is a corresponding more efficient mechanism for dispersal of meiospores as compared with the Marchantiales. The capsule wall is two or more layers of cells in thickness. The wall cells are stengthened by bars of thickening material. The sporogenous cells are differentiated into the **spore mother cells**, the free **elaters** and the basal cluster of sessile elaters. The spore mother cells are the last cells of the sporophyte generation (J, K). They become four-lobed (K) and undergo meiosis. Each spore mother cell thus forms a tetrad of spores (L). The spores are haploid. The ripe capsule dehisces in a regular manner. It opens by crossed cleavage along four lines of dehiscence right up to the base into valves. The latter bend back upon themselves exposing the erect, basal elaterophore holding around it the mass of spores and free elaters. The later by their hygroscopic movements help in the dispersal of spores. The **sporophyte** generation thus consists of the *zygote*, the *sporogonium*, and the *spore mother cells*. It ends with **meiosis**. The haploid spores (meiospores) are the pioneer structures of the next gametophyte phase (M). The accompanying diagram (Fig. 7.17) shows that the two generations occur regularly one after the other in the life cycle. The reproductive cells of one generation give rise to the alternate plant in the life cycle. This phenomenon is expressed by the phrase '**Alternation of Generations**'.

SYSTEMATIC POSITION

Division	:	Bryophyta
Class	:	Hepaticopsida
Order	:	Metzgeriales
Family	:	Pelliaceae
Genus	:	*Pellia*
Species	:	*calycina*

QUESTIONS

ESSAY TYPE

1. List the interesting features in the life history of *Pellia*.
2. Give an illustrated account of the life history of *Pellia*.
3. Describe the reproductive phase of *Pellia*.
4. Describe in detail the structure of the sporogonium of *Pellia*. In what respects do you consider it to be more advanced than that of *Riccia* and *Marchantia*?
5. Compare the stages in the development of sporognium of *Pellia*; *Riccia* and *Marchantia*.
6. Give a comparative account of the strucutre of vegetative thalli of *Marchantia, Pellia* and *Frullania*. *(Lucknow, 1995, 1997, 1999, 2000; Gorakhpur, 1994, 1997; Allahabad 1995; Rohilkhand, 1992, 1998)*
7. (*a*) Describe the sporogonium of *Pellia* and compare it with that of *Marchantia*. *(Lucknow, 1997; U.P. College, 1997; Rohilkhand, 1993)*

   (*b*) Give an illustrated account of sporognium of *Pellia* *(Lucknow, 2005)*
8. Give a comparative account of the structure of sporophyte of *Marchantia Anthoceros* and *Pellia*. *(Gorakhpur 1990, 1993, Allahabad, 1997; Awadh, 1996, 2000; Kumaon, 1995; Rohilkhand, 2001, 2003)*
9. Give a comparative account of the sporophytes of *Pellia* and *Porella* or *Anthoceros*. *(Gorakhpur, 1999, Awadh; 1993; Kanpur, 1998)*
10. With the help of labelled diagrams only illustrate the life history of *Pellia*. *(Allahabad, 1991; Awadh 1997; Kanpur, 1998)*
11. Describe sexual reproductive organs of *Riccia* and *Pellia*. *(Awadh, 1995; Rohilkhand, 1997)*
12. With the help of labelled sketches, compare the thallus structure of *Riccia* and *Pellia*. *(Awadh, 1998)*
13. Describe the identifying characters of *Riccia*, *Marchantia*, *Pellia* and *Anthoceros*. *(Kanpur, 1996; Rohilkhand, 1997, 1999)*
14. Give an account of life-cycle of *Pellia* with the help of diagrams and explain the characters by which it is different from that of *Marchantia*. *(Kanpur 2000)*
15. Write a comparative account of the gametophytes of *Pellia, Anthoceros, Riccia* & Marchantia. *(Rohilkhand, 1994, 2000, 2002)*
16. Describe in brief the life cycle of *Pellia*. *(Rohilkhand, 1996; Saugar, 1988)*
17. Describe the post fertilization changes in *Pellia*. *(Bhopal, 1992)*
18. Describe the mode of sexual reproduction in *Pellia*. *(Bundelkhand, 1995)*
19. Compare the gametophyte and sporophyte of of *Pellia* and *Marchantia*. *(Bundelkhand, 1999)*
20. Describe the structure of the gametophyte and sporophyte in *Pellia*. In what respects do you consider its Sporogonium to be more advanced than that of *Marchantia* ? *(Poorvanchal, 2003)*
21. With the help of labelled sketches only illustrate the life-history of *Pellia*. *(Allahabad, 2005)*

SHORT ANSWER TYPE

22. In what respects does the sporogonium of *Pellia* show an advance over that of *Marchantia*?
23. Compare the development of sex organs in *Pellia* and *Marchantia*.

24. Write the systematic position of *Pellia.* *(Lucknow, 1993, 1998, 2001)*

25. Write short notes on :

(*a*) Function of elaterophore. *(Lucknow, 1994, 1999)*

(*b*) Elaterophore *(Lucknow 1995, 1998, 2002, 2006, 2007; Gorakhpur, 1992; Allahabad 1992, 1994, 1999; Rohilkhand, 1998; Bundelkhand, 1995)*

(*c*) Elaterophore and columella. *(Gorakhpur, 1996)*

(*d*) Sporophyte of *Riccia* and *Pellia.* *(Gorakhpur, 1997)*

(*e*) Sex organs of *Pellia.* *(Gorakhpur 1997)*

(*f*) Mechanism of spore dispersal in *Pellia.* *(Kanpur, 1996; Rohilkhand, 1994, 1997; Agra, 1995)*

(*g*) Sporophyte of *Pellia.* *(Kumaon, 1997, 1999)*

(*h*) Fertilization in *Pellia.*

(*i*) Vegetative reproduction. *(Kanpur, 2002)*

(*j*) Capsule of *Pallia* *(Lucknow, 2007)*

(*k*) Pellia thallus bearing mature sporophyte *(Lucknow, M.Sc., 2007)*

26. How will you identify *Pellia* on the basis of internal structure ? *(Kanpur, 2000)*

27. Draw labelled sketches of the following :

(*i*) V.L.S. thallus of *Pellia* passing through the involucre. *(Lucknow, 1993; Gorakhpur, 1992)*

(*ii*) V.L.S. sporogonium of *Pellia.* *(Lucknow, 1997, 2000, 2001; Poorvanchal, 1996, 2000; Gorakhpur 1991, 1992, 1995; Allahabad, 1998)*

(*iii*) V.L.S. of thallus of *Pellia* showing the position of sex organs. *(Kanpur, 2003; Poorvanchal, 1998, 1999; Rohilkhand, 1996; Bundelkhand 1993; Allahabad, 2006)*

(*iv*) V.L.S. sporophyte of *Pellia.* *(Gorakhpur, 1998; Rohilkhand, 1992; Kumaon, 2000; Bundelkhand, 1994, 1997; Kanpur, 2002, 2005, 2006; Lucknow, 2003, Poorvanchal, 2002)*

(*v*) T.S. of thallus of *Riccia, Marchantia, Pellia* and *Anthoceros.* *(Awadh, 1991; Kanpur 1995)*

(*vi*) V.S. thallus of *Pellia.* *(Awadh, 1992, 1994, 1997)*

(*vii*) Sex organs of *Pellia.* *(Rohilkhand, 1995)*

28. Differentiate between *(Rohilkhand, 2000)*

(*a*) Elaters and elaterophore *(Kanpur, 2006)*

(*b*) Elaters and Pseudoelaters . *(Allahabad, 2002)*

29. Write two characters to differentiate the sporophyte of *Pellia* and *Riccia* *(Gorakhpur, 1994)*

30. Name a bryophyte which has elatcrophore in its sporogonium. *(Gorakhpur, 1995; Allahabad, 1993)*

31. Name a bryophyte in which spores start germination within the capsule. *(Allahabad 1991; Awadh, 1993; Bundelkhand, 1998)*

32. Give the significance of elaterophore. *(U.P. College, 2000)*

33. Differentiate by means of labelled diagrams between

(*i*) Thallus of *Anthoceros* and *Pellia.* *(Allahabad, 1993)*

(*ii*) Male thalli of *Anthoceros* and *Pellia.* *(Allahabad, 1992)*

(*iii*) Gametophytes of *Anthoceros, Porella & Pellia.* *(Allahabad, 1994)*

(*iv*) Archegonium of *Pellia and Marchantia,* *(Kanpur, 2002)*

(*v*) Spore germination in *Riccia* and *Pellia.* *(Allahabad, 2003)*

(*vi*) Sporogonium of *Pellia and Marchantia.* *(Lucknow, 2002)*

34. Name the bryophyte in which archegonia are enclosed in involucre. *(Rohilkhand, 1992)*

35. (*a*) Give the member of elaterophores found in the capsule of *Pellia.*

(*b*) Give the number of monoecious species of *Pellia.*(*Rohilkhand, 1993)*

36. Compare spore dispersal in *Pellia, Anthoceros* and *Sphagnum.* *(Rohilkhand, 2004)*

37. Name important species of *Pellia*. *(Poorvanchal, 2002)*

38. Distinguish between :
(*a*) Capsules of *Pellia* and *Riccaridia* *(Kanpur, M.Sc., 2004)*
(*b*) Gametophyte of *Pellia and Riccia.*

39. Describe the structure of Gametophytic phase of *Pellia.* *(Kanpur, M.Sc., 2002)*

40. What is the position of elaterophore in *Pellia.* *(Kanpur, M.Sc., 2003)*

41. Name important spceies of *Pellia.* *(Kanpur, 2007)*

42. Describe in brief the life cycle of *Pellia.* *(Kanpur, 2006)*

43. Distinguish between gametophyte of *Pellia* and *Reccia.* *(Kanpur, 2007)*

OBJECTIVE TYPE

44. **Select the correct answer :**

(*i*) The capsule of *Pellia* dehisces into
(*a*) 2 valves (*b*) 4 valves
(*c*) 5 valves (*d*) 6 valves.

(*ii*) The masses of sterile cells located at the base of the capsule of *Pellia* are known as
(*a*) Elaters
(*b*) Pseudoelaters
(*c*) Elaterophores
(*d*) Elaterites.

(*iii*) All the plants are thallose in the family
(*a*) Funariaceae
(*b*) Polytrichaceae
(*c*) Jungermanniaceae
(*d*) Pelliaceae.

(*iv*) The antheridia in *Pellia* open to the dorsal surface bymeans of
(*a*) Specialized pores
(*b*) An ostiole
(*c*) Sutures
(*d*) All of the above.

(*v*) Archegonia in *Pellia* appear
(*a*) Singly
(*b*) In groups of four to twelve
(*c*) Both of the above
(*d*) None of the above.

(*vi*) In *Pellia* the neck is made up of longitudinal rows of cells which are
(*a*) 3 in number (*b*) 5 in number
(c) 7 in number (*d*) 9 in number.

(*vii*) The function of elaterophore is to help
(*a*) In gradual shedding of the spores,
(*b*) In shedding of spores in groups,
(*c*) In escape of the spores one byone,
(*d*) In nourishment of the developing capsules.

(*viii*) The elaters in *Pellia* have
(*a*) Single spiral band
(*b*) Double spiral band
(*c*) Three spiral bands
(*d*) Four spiral bands.

(*ix*) In which of the following genera spores begin to germinate even before shedding?
(*a*) *Riccia* (*b*) *Marchantia*
(*c*) *Pellia* (*d*) *Funaria.*

(*x*) The gametophyte of *Pellia* is characterised by the presence of
(*a*) Apical notch (*b*) Midrib
(*c*) Rhomboidal areas
(*d*) Sinuous margins.

(*xi*) *Pellia* belongs to
(*a*) Metzgerinae
(*b*) Jugemanniae
(*c*) Anthoceratae
(*d*) Bryidae

(*xii*) Basal elatophore is found in the capsule of
(*a*) *Pellia* (*b*) *Marchantia*
(*c*) *Anthoceros* (*d*) *Funaria*

45. Fill in the blanks :

(*i*) Elaterophore is found in ________ .

(*ii*) Elaterophore is found in the capsule of ________ .

(*iii*) The capsule of *Pellia* dehisces into ________ valves.

(*iv*) *Pellia epiphylla* is a ________ species.

(*v*) In *Pellia* the antheridium opens on the dorsal surface by means of ________ .

(*vi*) In *Pellia* the number of neck canal cells range from ______ to ________.

(*vii*) The spores germinate before shedding in ________ .

(*viii*) The elaters in *Pellia* have ________ spiral band of thickening.

(*ix*) The elaterophore helps in ________ of spores.

Image of *Riccardia*

CHAPTER 7 (II)

METZGERIALES
Riccardiaceae (Aneuraceae) Riccardia

- Family Riccardiaceae
- Riccardia
- Sporophyte

FAMILY RICCARDIACEAE

General characteristics

Family Riccardiaceae (Aneuraceae) is one of the important families of order Metzgeriales (anacrogynous Jungermanniales) and shows worldwide distribution. The family is characterised by :

1. The gametophytic plant body is strictly thalloid.

2. Thallus is compact without air pores on dorsal surface and ventral scales on the lower surface.

3. Rhizoids are only smooth walled or simple.

4. Thallus cells have distinct oil-bodies.

5. The sex organs are produced on specialized abbreviated lateral branches on dorsal surface of thallus

6. The involucre is absent.

7. As involucre is absent, the sporophyte is protected by the development of the *fleshy-shoot calyptra.*

8. The capsule is never spherical. It is either ovoid or cylindrical.

9. Apical elaterophore is present within the capsule.

10. Capsule dehisces in four valves and each valve at its apex carries a bunch of fixed elaters called apical elaterophore.

The family has only three genera which are 1. *Cryptothallus,* 2. *Aneura* 3. *Riccardia*. Out of these three genera, *Cryptothallus* is monotypic genus with a single species *C. mirabilis* which is confined only in Europe. It is an example of saprophytic liverwort in which nutrition is mycorrhizal as the cells of the plant lack chloroplasts. The other two genera are ignorently treated congeneric as in case of *Calobryum* and *Haplomitrium*. Infact *Aneura* Dumort. and *Riccardia* Gray emend Schust. are two distinct genera which differ from each other in several respects. Differences between the two genera are given below:

Differences between Aneura and Riccardia.

Aneura Dumort.	Riccardia Gray emend Schust.
1. Plant has a broad thallus which is scarcely branched.	1. Plant has thin and narrow thallus which is profusely branched.
2. Oil-bodies in the cells of thallus are numerous, small, smooth and spherical	2. Oil-bodies in the cells of thallus are 1-2 per cell, large and rough due to presence of prominant granules.
3. Gemmae absent.	3. Gemmae present. These are endogenous in origin and are 1-2 celled.
4. Seta is massive in cross section. The cells are not arranged in any specific manner.	4. Seta is four celled across. It has four large central cells surrounded by 16 smaller peripheral cells.
5. The cells of capsule wall in inner layer show distinct annular or semiannular thickenings.	5. The cells of capsule wall in inner layer show uniform thickenings restricted only on radial-walls. Annular and semiannular thickenings are altogether absent.

The genus *Riccardia* is being described as the type genus of the family Riccardiaceae.

RICCARDIA

Habit and Habitat. Plants grow profusely on moist, shady cold rocks as well as on wet sandy ground or near streams and ditches. Some species of *Riccardia* are epiphytic.

Distribution. *Riccardia* is the largest genus of the family with about 280 sp. *R. pinguis* and *R. multifida* are cosmopolitan. About 11 sp. have been reported from India.

GAMETOPHYTE

Thallus (Fig. 7.19A). It is strictly thalloid. Thallus is completely prostrate or semi-prostrate or partially erect forming dense and compact patches. The plants are thin, narrow and closely pinnately branched as in *R. santapaui* reported from Chhindwara (M.P.) by Udar and Srivastava in 1973. The dorsal surface is all over smooth. The polygonal areas and air pores are absent. The ventral surface lacks ventral scales. The rhizoids are only smooth walled (simple) and few.

Anatomy (Fig. 7.19C). The vertical transverse section of thallus shows that there is no demarcation of photosynthetic zone and storage zone. Thallus is compact with thick multistratose middle part and gradually thin at lateral margin. The cells contain chloroplasts which are without pyrenoids.

The epidermal cells contain 1-2 (-3) large and prominent oil-bodies with different refractive index by which they can be distinguished from chloroplasts which are green in colour. The surface of each oil-body is rough due to presence of prominent globules. The oil bodies are visible only in living and fresh material. The content of oil-bodies is extremely volatile hence in herbarium specimen or in preserved materials they are totally absent.

Vegetative reproduction. It takes place by death and decay of older part of the thallus. The other mode of vegetative reproduction in *Riccardia* is stolons. The stoloniferous branches are produced from older part of thallus and they serve as organs of vegetative reproduction. The third method, which is very common and characteristic feature of the genus *Riccardia*, is development of endogenous gemmae. The superficial cell, first of all, rounds up its protoplast in the center and secretes a new wall arround it which may or may not soon divide by a transeverse wall and forms two daughter cells which are firmly cemented to each other. One celled or two celled gemmae thus produced are present and enclosed within superficial cells. When superficial wall ruptures, the endogenous gemmae come out and germinate to form new plant-body.

Sexual reproduction. The species of *Riccardia* may be monoecious or dioecious. The monoceious species are *R. multifida, R. sinuata and R. decolyana* while the dioecious species are *R. palmata, R. pinguis* and *R. indica*. The position of sex organs is peculiar and shows the characteristic feature of the family as both antheridia and archegonia are produced on special, abbreviated, short lateral branches which mostly arise at the margin of thallus.

Antheridia (Fig. 7.19 F, G): They are found singly enclosed within antheridial chamber which opens out side through an opening called ostiole. Such openings are found on upper surface of short, abbreviated lateral branches. Antheridia are produced in acropetal succession. Each antheridium has large globose body which is present upon very short stalk.

Development of the antheridium is typical of the order Metzgeriales described in earlier pages.

Archegonia (Fig. 7.19 B, D, E): The archegonia are produced on dorsal surface of abbreviated lateral archegonial branches shorter than the antheridial branches. A dozen archegonia are borne in two alternating rows and are enclosed within incurved lacinate margins of female branch. The archegonia are short in height. The venter is massive *i.e.* 2-3 cell layer thick. The neck is made up of five vertical rows of neck cells (characterisitic feature of order Metzgeriales). The sterile covering of neck at basal region is usually 2 cell layer thick.

Development of archegonium is typical of the order Metzgeriales and has been described earlier.

Fertilization is typical of Hepaticae.

Sporophyte

After fertilization, the abbreviated short lateral archegonial branch develops a fleshy and massive shoot calyptra (characteristic feature of the family) around the young sporophyte. The surface of shoot-calyptra shows variety of scaly out growths depending on the species. The development of sporophyte in *Riccardia levieri* was studied by K.P. Srivastava in 1960. The zygote divides by a transeverse wall (mitotic cell division) and forms two daughter cells of which upper cell is called epibasal and lower cell called hypobasal. The hypobasal cell elongates and forms haustorium. The entire sporophyte (including foot, small seta and cylindrical capsule) develops from the epibasal cell.

In sporophyte (Fig. 7.19 H) the foot is extremely reduced and represented by a club-like swelling at the lower end of seta. The first function of foot, to attach sporophyte with gametophyte, is performed by massive shoot calyptra (Fig. 7.19 B) and the second function, to absorb food material from gametophyte, is taken over by the entire surface cells of the sporophyte from inner surface of shoot calyptra. Seta is very short and four celled across the diameter. The cells in seta are arranged in two concentric rings. The inner ring consists of 4 larger cells surrounded by 16 smaller peripheral cells (Fig. 7.19 I) The capsule is ovoid to cylindrical in shape (never globose or spherical) and two cell layer thick. The cells of capsule wall in inner layer have uniform thickenings restricted only on radial walls. The cavity of capsule is filled by spores and elaters. The elaters are of two types : free elaters and fixed elaters. The position of fixed elater is very unique. They are found attached at the apical part of capsular cavity and collectively known as *apical elaterophore* (Fig. 7.19 H) (basal elaterophore is found in *Pellia*). The capsule dehisces in four valves and each valve at its apex carries a bunch of fixed elaters of apical elaterophore.

Germination of spores. The spores are small and range between 10-30 μm in diameter. The exine surface is usually papillose or granulose. The spores show quick germination after coming out from the capsule. The spore divides by a transverse wall into two unequal daughter cells. The smaller cell divides by a diagonal wall. Now an apical cell originates which is wedge shaped. It soon becomes meristematic and starts to produce the new gametophytic tissue. The smooth walled (simple) rhizoids are also produced from the lower side of gametophyte which is in contact with the soil.

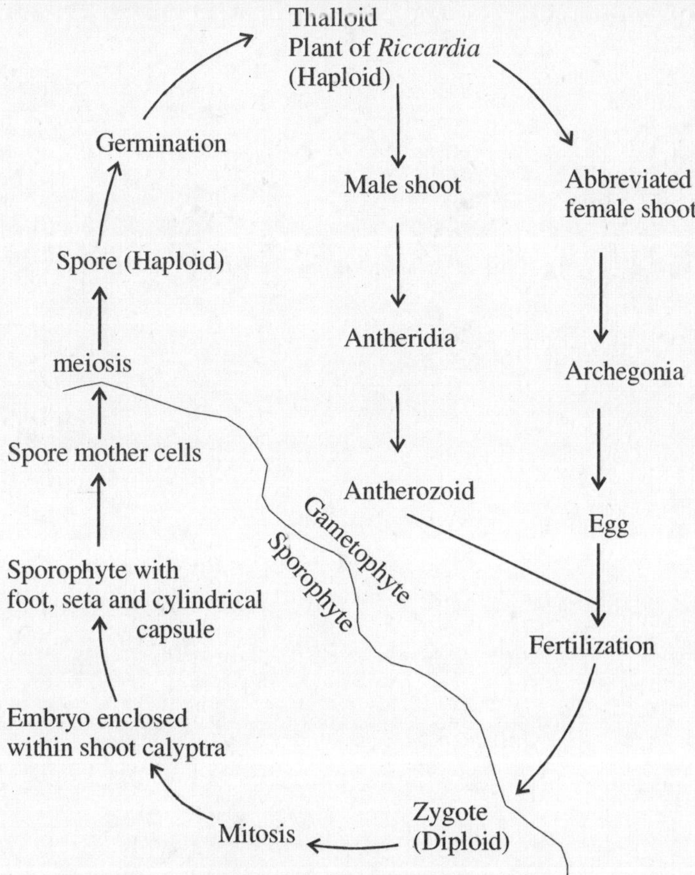

Fig. 7.18. ***Riccardia* sp.**: Word diagram of life cycle.

SYSTEMATIC position

Division	:	Bryophyta
Class	:	Hepaticopsida
Order	:	Metzgeriales
Family	:	Riccardiaceae
Genus	:	*Riccardia*
Species	:	*santapaui*

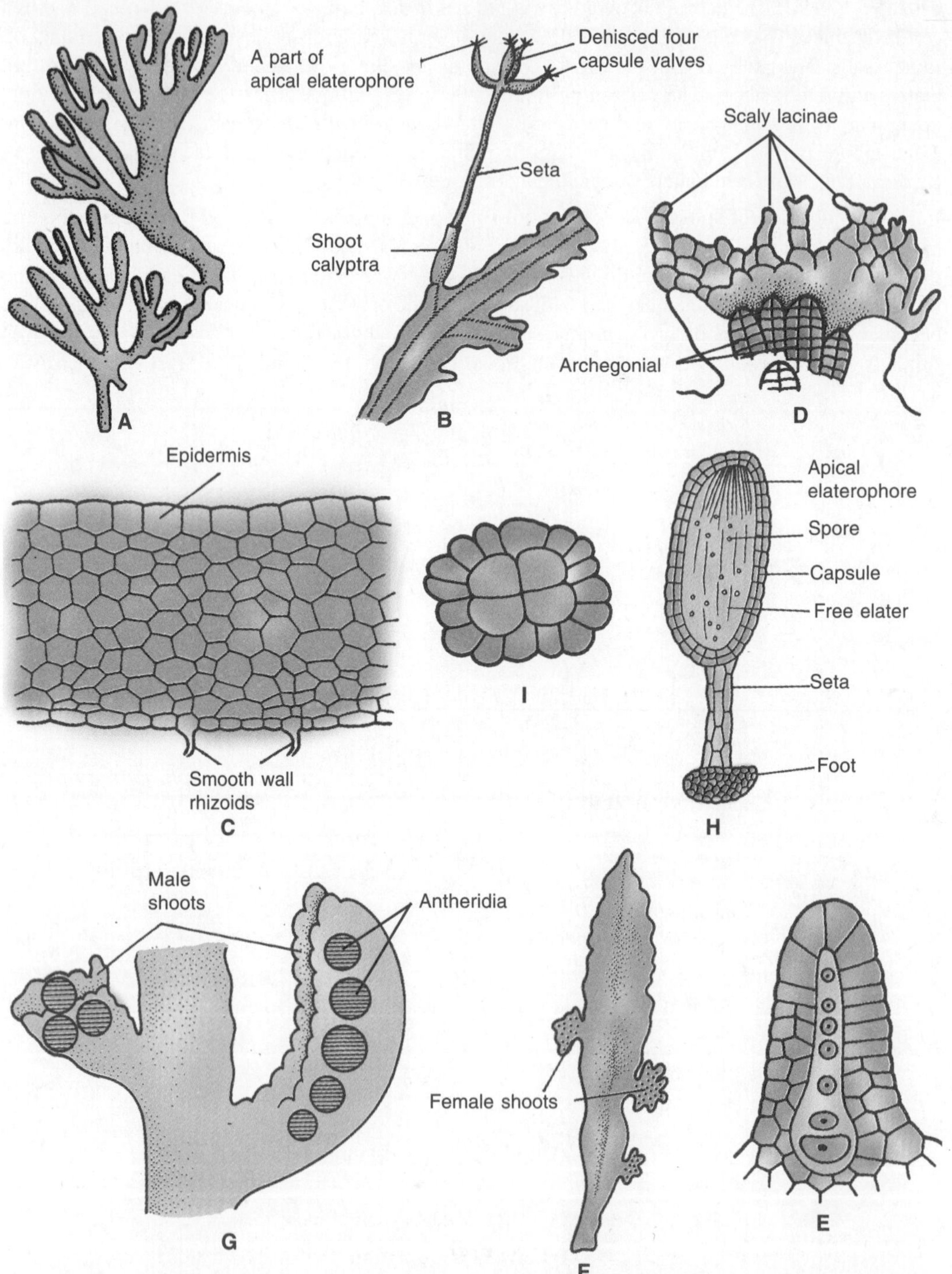

Fig. 7.19. (A-I) ***Riccardia* sp**. A, vegetative thallus; B, thallus with dehisced capsule; C, V.T.S. of thallus; D, abbreviated female shoot with archegonia; E, an archegonium; F, female thallus with abbreviated female shoots; G, male thallus with male shoots; H, sporophyte; I, T.S. of seta showing four inner cells surrounded by sixteen peripheral cells.

QUESTIONS

ESSAY TYPE

1. Give a detailed account of the gametophyte *Riccardia.*
2. With the help of suitable diagrams, describe the sporophyte of *Riccardia.*
3. With help of suitable illustrations describe life cycle of *Riccardia.*
4. Give a general account of *Riccardia.*
5. How many genera have been placed in the family *Reccardia* ? Give a list of these and describe the structure of gametophyte and sporophyte of the genera studied by you.

SHORT ANSWER TYPE

6. **Write short notes on :**
   (*a*) *Riccardia*
   (*Kanpur, M.Sc., 1993, 2000*)
   (*b*) Differences between *Aneura* and *Riccardia*
   (*c*) Vegetative reproduction in Riccardiaceae.
   (*Rohilkhand, M.Sc., 2003*)
   (*d*) *Aneura*
   (*Allahabad M.Sc., 1999*)
   (*e*) sporogonium of *Aneura.*
   (*Allahabad M.Sc., 1999*)
7. Give a brief account of *Riccardia.*
   (*Kanpur M.Sc., 2002*)

OBJECTIVE TYPE

8. **Select the correct answer :**
   (*i*) *Riccardia* differs from *Pellia* in
   (*a*) The presence of involucre.
   (*b*) The presence of archegonia.
   (*c*) The absence of involucre.
   (*d*) The absence of archegonia.
   (*ii*) One of the members of *Riccardiaceae* is a saprophyte. It is
   (*a*) *Riccardia* (*b*) *Aneura*
   (*c*) *Cryptothallus* (*d*) *Riccia.*
   (*iii*) In which of the following genera, seta has four large central cells surrounded by 16 smaller peripheral cells?
   (*a*) *Riccardia* (*b*) *Riccia*
   (*c*) *Marchantia* (*d*) *Notothylus.*
   (*iv*) Oil bodies are present in epidermal cells in
   (*a*) *Riccia* (*b*) *Marchantia*
   (*c*) *Anthoceros* (*d*) *Riccardia.*
   (*v*) Development of sporophyte in *Riccardia* was described by
   (*a*) Ram Udar (*b*) S.K. Pande
   (*c*) K.P. Srivastava (*d*) P.N. Mehra.

Image of *Fossombronia*

CHAPTER 8

METZGERIALES
Fossombroniaceae
Fossombronia

- Family Fossombronicaeae
- Gametophyte
- Sporophyte

FAMILY FOSSOMBRONIACEAE

The family Fossombroniaceae includes four genera, namely, *Fossombronia* Raddi, *Simodon* Lindb, *Petalophyllum* Gottsche and *Sewardiella* Kashyap (Pande *et al*, 1954). Of these *Fossombronia* is widely distributed and is best known. It is thus studied as a representative of the Metzgeriales in which the gametophyte is distinctly foliose.

FOSSOMBRONIA Raddi (Fig. 8.1)

Fossombronia comprises about 50 sp. of worldwide distribution. Pande *et al* (1954) stated that two species namely, *F. indica* St. and *F. himalayensis* Kash. (*F. levieri* St.) occur in India. The former is confined to South India whereas the latter is common in the Himalayas (5,000-7,000 ft), Pachmarhi (Madhya Pradesh) and South India. Udar and Srivastava (1969) added another species *F. cristula* to our flora. A new species. *F. foreauii* was discovered from Kodaikanal (Palni Hills), South India by Udar and Srivastava (1972 a). Pande, Mahabale, Raje and Srivastava (1954) studied the life history of *F. himalayensis* Kash. in detail. The account given here is mainly based on their investigation.

GAMETOPHYTE

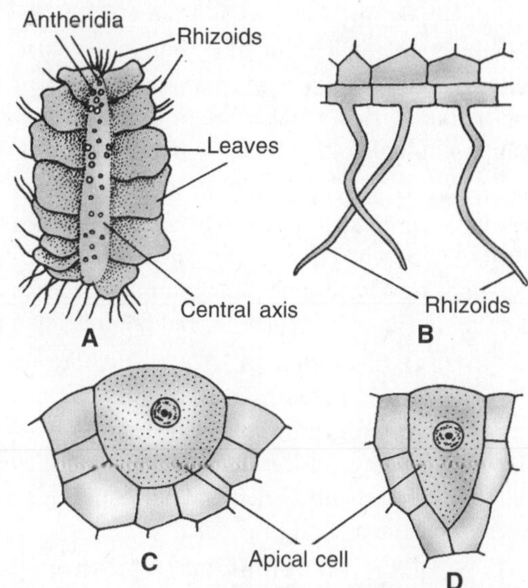

Fig. 8.1. (A—D). ***Fossombronia* sp.** A, male plant of *F. himalayensis*; B, smooth walled rhizoids arising from the lower epidermis of the midrib; C, M.L.S. apical cell midrib; D, M.T.S. of the same (A after Kashyap, B-D, after Haupt).

Habit and habitat : *Fossombronia* is distinctly foliose (A). It grows in compact clusters over the substratum among grass and mosses or occurs singly in exposed places on moist soil. In the later case the thalli are comparatively larger than those growing in dense mat-like outgrowth. The gametophyte is light-green and annual. *F. himalayensis* completes its life history in about 5 months. Sporogonia appear in early September and the spores mature by the end of September-October. During winter the spores remain dormant and germinate about a fortnight after the onset of the monsoon season in the following year.

Thallus (Fig. 8.1). It is dorsiventral in configuration and prostrate or almost semi-prostrate in habit (A). The thallus consists of a well-defined elongated central axis or midrib bearing leaf-like structures in two lateral rows. The midrib is more or less flattened above and convex below. From the ventral surface of the midrib (so-called stem) arise numerous long simple, smooth-walled, violet coloured or hyaline, unicellular rhizoids which penetrate and thus anchor the plant to the substratum (B). Ventral scales of Marchantiales and under-leaves (amphigastrium) of Jungermanniales and tuberculate rhizoids are absent.

Usually the stem is sparsely branched. The branching is strictly apical. It is initiated by the differentiation of a second apical cell in a young segment derived from the apical cell and not by the vertical division of the apical cell itself into two daughter cells of equal size.

The leaves are thin, translucent, light green or pale and alternate. They are more or less erect, obliquely inserted and decurrent with the outer margin irregularly sinuate and indistinctly toothed or lobed. They are closely set and imbricate with the posterior margin of each leaf overlapping the anterior margin of the next older leaf. This kind of leaf arrangement is described as **succubous**. In some species of *Fossombronia* (*F. longiseta*), the leaves are so much convoluted that the overlapping arrangement becomes obscure.

The leaf is one cell thick except the basal portion which is 2 or 3 cells in thickness. The cells are thin-walled and contain numerous chloroplasts. Some of the marginal cells in the leaf of *F. himalayensis* bear mucilage secreting papillae (Fig. 8.2 A).

Structure of midrib region (Fig. 8.2 B,C) The midrib (so-called stem) has a simple organisation. It shows little or no internal differentiation and is composed of similar thin-walled parenchymatous cells with slight difference in size. They are compactly arranged to form almost a uniform tissue with no indication of a central strand (C). A section through the posterior part of the older thalli of *F. himalayensis* shows abundant mycorrhiza (C). According to Pande *et al.* (1954) infection probably takes place through the rhizoids (D). The actively growing regions of the thallus invariably do not show any fungal infection.

Growth (8.1 C-D). It is apical. The central axis and the branches grow by the activity of an elaborate apical cell with two cutting faces (C). It cuts off segments alternately right and left. According to Cavers (1910) each lateral segment divides by two transverse divisions (horizontal walls) into 3 horizontal cells (D). Of these the upper and the lower produce the stem and the middle one develops into a leaf. Associated with the growing point are the young leaves and mucilage hairs which encircle it. The mucilage hairs are ventral in position, simple, short-lived and several cells in length (Fig. 8.2 B). Pande *et al.* compared them to the amphigastria of the Acrogynae and scales of the Marchantiales. All the tissues of the thallus are derived from this apical cell. It is lenticular and bulges out in the middle of the growing point.

Vegetative reproduction. Regeneration and tuber formation are the two common methods of vegetative propagation in *Fossombronia*. Pande *et al.* (1954) reported that the thalli of *F. himalayensis* are endowed with the great capacity for withstanding desiccation. Even after a few months of drying, the thalli readily resume their form and activity if immersed in water. The two contributing factors are the mucilage cell contents and the mucilage papilae.

Tuber formation (8.2 E). *F. himalayensis* and *F. tuberifera* form tubers. At the end of the growing season, the stem apex of the plant in *F. himalayensis* ceases to form leaves. It elongates, bends downwards, grows more or less vertically into the soil (S) and becomes thickened at the tip due to the storage of starch and other food materials in the cells. This thickened structure is called the **tuber**. It remains buried and dormant in the ground during winter. The tuber germinates to form a new plant next spring.

Sexual reproduction (Fig. 8.3). Most of the species (*F. cristula, F. longiseta* and *F. pusilla*) are monoecious (B). The sex organs develop in acropetal succession on the dorsal side of the midrib and occur scattered or in groups. Each originates from a single, superficial cell behind and close to the apical cell. The antheridia may precede (A) or follow the archegonia. *F. himalayensis* is monoecious but protandrous. Rarely it may be dioecious (Pande *et al.* 1954).

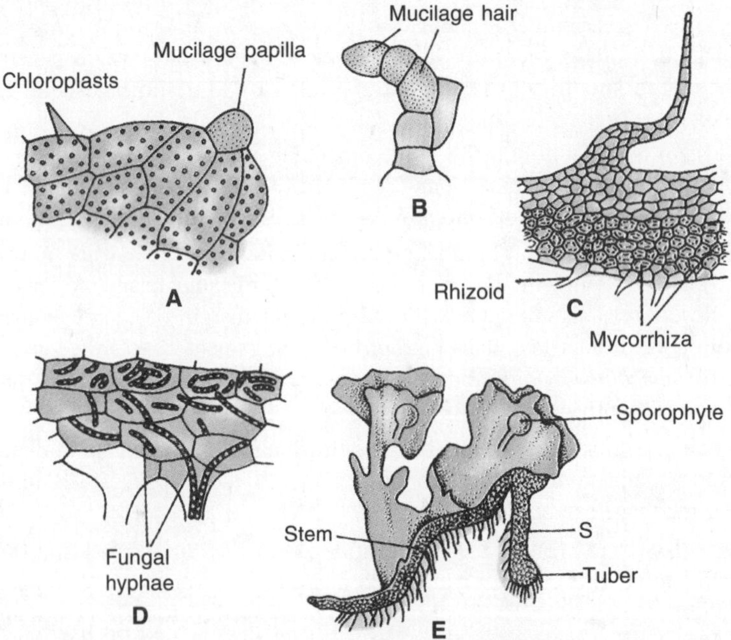

Fig. 8.2. (A—E). ***Fossombronia himalayensis***. A, marginal leaf cell bearing a mucilage papilla and containing chloroplasts; B, mucilage hair; C, thallus in section showing structure and mycorrhiza in the ventral region of midrib; D, few cells from the mycorrhizal region of C enlarged to show the fungal hyphae; E, female plant showing the characteristic bend in the stem and the apical tuber (E after Kashyap and the rest after Pande *et al.*).

Antheridia. They develop in acropetal succession scattered (singly) or in small groups of 2 or 3, sometimes up to 6, unprotected on the upper surface of the thallus in the midrib region near the insertion of leaves. The antheridial groups mostly occur near the anterior end, each separated from its neighbour by a small scale. The latter represents a reduced leaf which subtends the antheridial

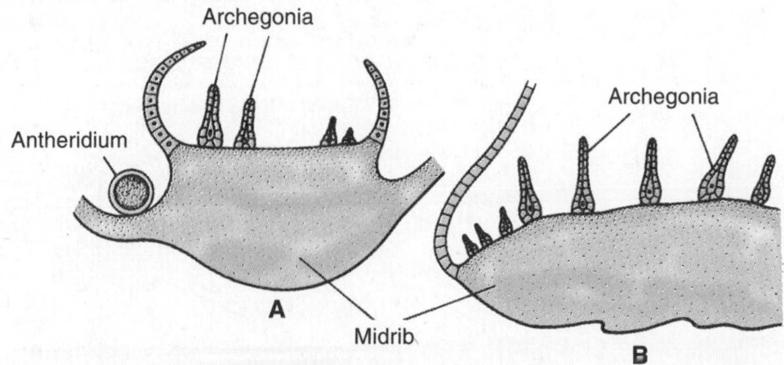

Fig. 8.3. (A—B). ***Fossombronia himalayensis***. A, monoecious thallus in section bearing both antheridia and archegonia; B, dioecious thallus in section bearing archegonia only (after Pande *et al.*)

group. Usually the antheridia and archegonia separately grouped (A) but sometimes both may occur mixed in the same group as in *F. longiseta*. The mature antheridia are rounded, shortly stalked and orange in colour (Fig. 8.4 K). The antheridial wall is one-cell thick. The wall cells towards the terminal part of the antheridium are generally larger than those in the lower part.

Development of antheridium (fig. 8.4). The antheridium arises from a single superficial cell derived from the lateral segment of the apical cell. It is located behind and close to the latter. It is termed the **antheridial initial** and is different from the adjacent cells in its elongated shape, dense cytoplasm and large nucleus (A). The antheridial initial becomes papillate and projects above the general level of the thallus. It then divides by a transverse wall which separates an outer cell from the basal cell (B). A second transverse wall appears in the outer cell dividing it into two equal daughter cells, the upper and the lower (C). The upper daughter cell functions as the **primary atheridial cell** and the **lower primary stalk cell**. The third division in both the cells in a median vertical one (D). The two terminal segments derived from the primary antheridial cell are hemispherical in shape in a cross section (E). Each of these divides by a periclinal wall (Fund G). The division is asymmetrical. The smaller of these constitutes the first **jacket initial**. The larger sister cell of each segment again divides by a periclinal wall but at right angles to the first one intersecting both it and the median wall (G). The relation of periclinal walls to the median vertical wall can best be seen in a cross section of the young antheridium at these stages (G). The stalk cells do not divide by periclinal walls. Figures F and H represent vertical longitudinal sections of the antheridium at these stages. The antheridium at this stage consists of two central **primary androgonial cells** surrounded by 4 **jacket initials** or **primary wall cells** (G and H). The latter, henceforth, divide by anticlinal walls only, to complete the one cell-thick jacket layer of the antheridium (J). The primary androgonial cells divide and redivide rapidly as in *Pellia* to form a large number of small, cubical androgonial cells by lying within the one-cell thick wall antheridium (J & K). The small sized cells of the last cell generation of the fertile, androgonial cells constitute the **sperm mother cells** which are recognised by their dense cytoplasm and prominent nuclei and nucleoli.

The stalk cells of the antheridium divide and redivide to form the short stalk of the mature antheridium consisting of 4 longitudinal rows of cells usually 4 or 5 cells (sometimes only 2 or 3 cells) high. Each sperm mother cell eventually divides diagonally to form two small wedgeshaped cells separated by a thin membrane. These are known as the **androcytes**. The protoplast of each androcyte metamorphoses into a biflagellate sperm. According to Pande *et al.* (1954), the haploid number of chromosomes in the dividing antheridial cells of *F. himalayensis* is nine.

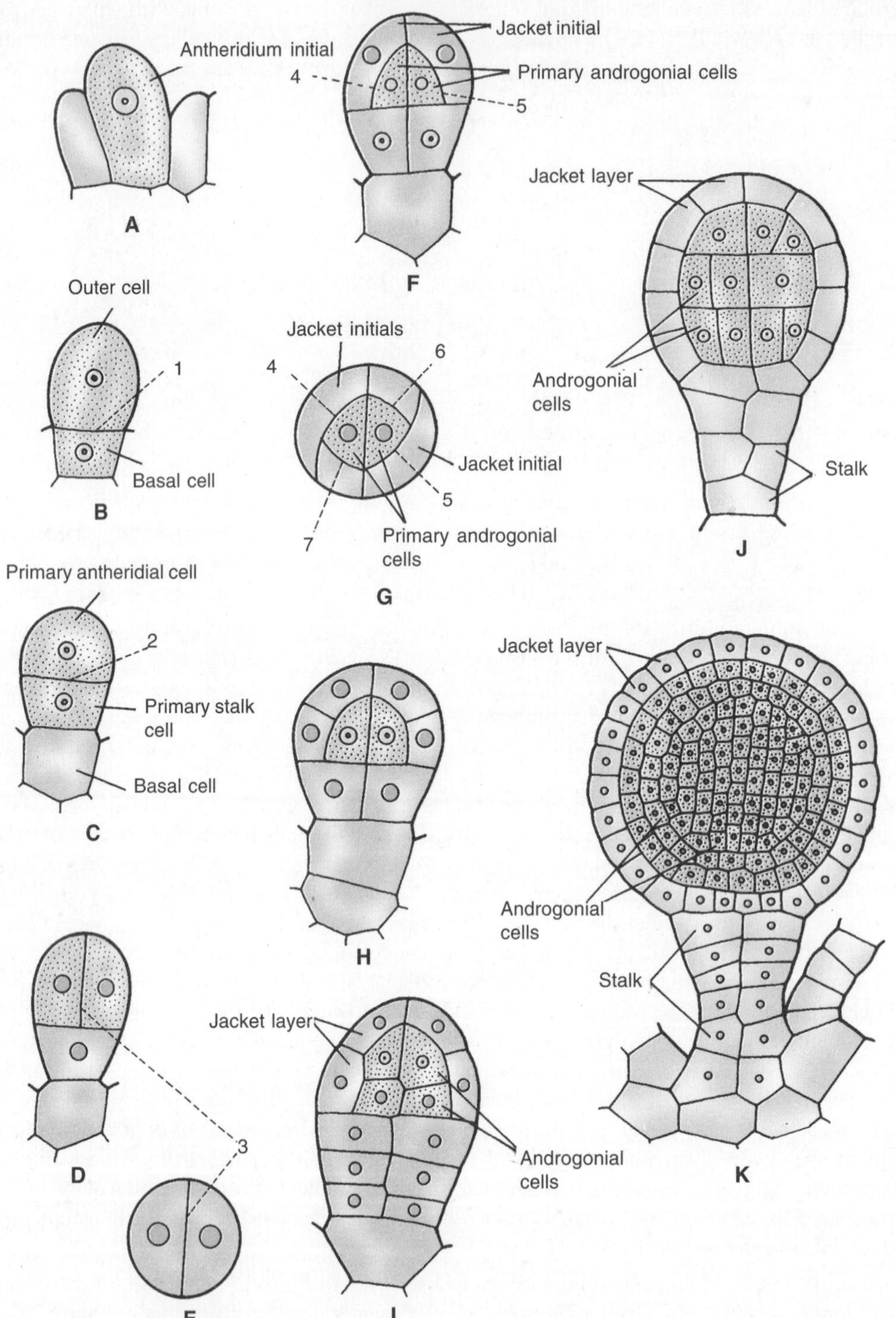

Fig. 8.4. (A—K). ***Fossombronia* sp.** Stages in the development of antheridium. E and G are cross sections of the antheridium and the rest longitudinal sections; K, L.S. nearly mature antheridium showing structure. Explanation in the text (K after Smith and rest after Haupt).

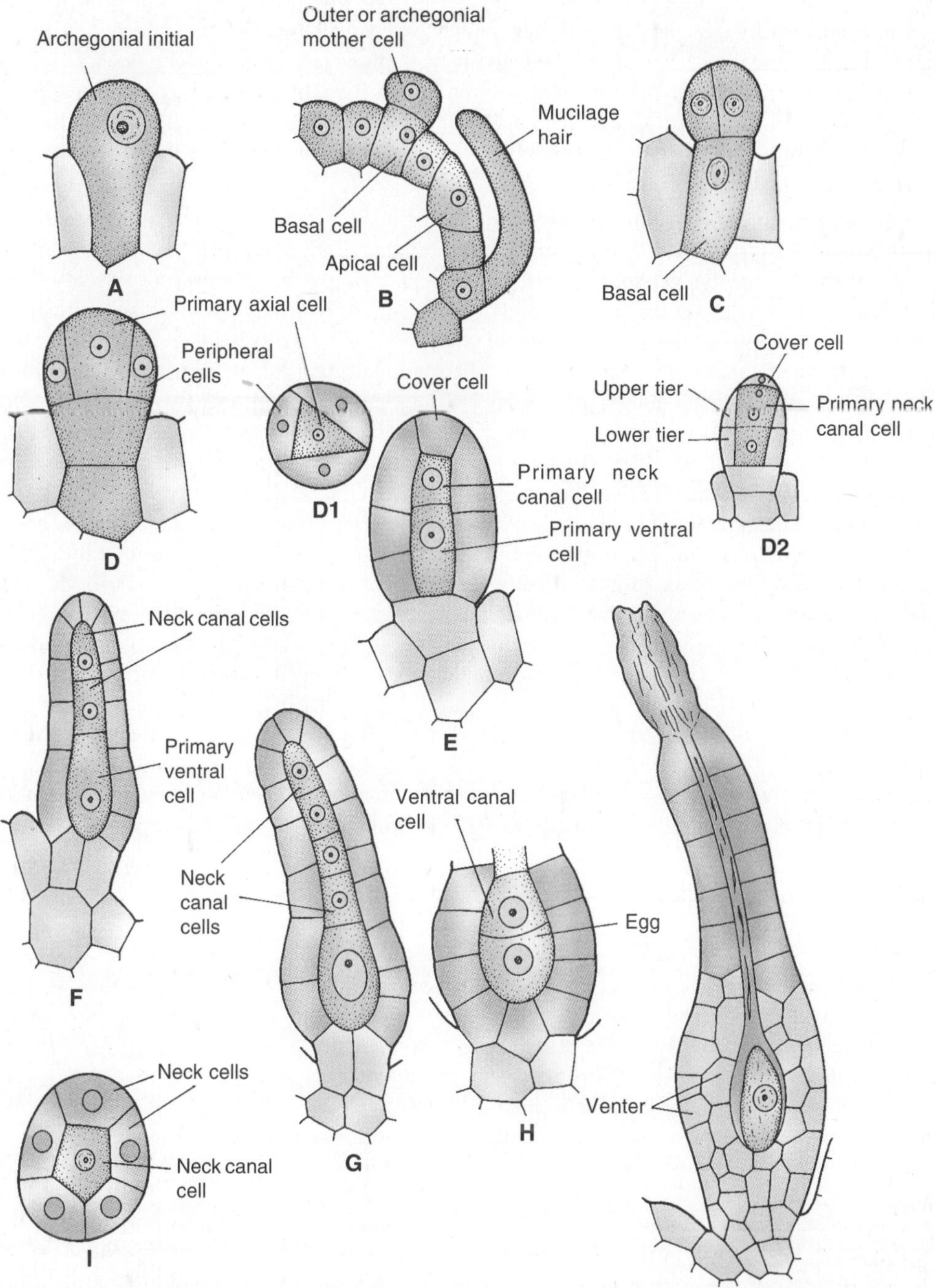

Fig. 8.5. (A—J). ***Fossombronia* sp.** Stages in the development of archegonium. A, archegonium initial; B, first division of archegonium initial; C, formation of first vertical wall; D, appearance of 2nd and 3rd vertical walls; D_1 cross-section of the same; D_2 separation of cover cell and transverse division of peripheral cells and central cell; E, young archegonium consisting of primary ventral cell, primary neck canal cell and cover cell; F—G, formation of neck canal cells, but primary ventral cell undivided; H, primary ventral cell divides to form ventral canal cell and egg; I, cross section of neck; J, mature archegonium (A—D, E—H and J after Haupt).

Archegonia (Fig. 8.5). They generally occur in small groups laterally on the midrib near the growing point protected by the over arching young leaves at the base of each of which they originate. The mature archegonium has a slightly twisted base, a broad venter and a long neck usually with 6-8 neck canal cells. The neck consists of 5 longitudinal rows of neck cells, each being 7-8 cells hgih. The venter wall is 2-cells thick. The neck cells in the mature archegonium are elongated and the neck is slightly bent towards the subtending leaf. After fertilization each archegonial cluster is invested by a bell-shaped perianth.

Development of archegonium (Fig. 8.5). The archegonium initial lies very close to the apical cell. In fact it arises from the dorsal cell of a lateral segment of the apical cell but in no case from the apical cell itself. It becomes papillate and has granular cytoplasm. It stains more deeply than the surrounding cells (A). Soon the papillate archegoium initial divides by a transverse wall appearing above the general level of the thallus. An outer and a basal cell result (B). A second transverse wall appears in basal (D) and not in the outer cell. The outer cell function as the **archegonium mother cell**. A vertical wall appears in the archegonium mother cell dividing it into two sister cells. One of these is much larger than the other (C). Two vertical eccentric walls appear in the larger sister cell (D). At this stage the young archegonium consists of four cells, 3 peripheral and one axial cell. One of the peripheral cells is smaller than the other two (D_1). In a longitudinal section only two peripheral and an axial cell can be seen (D). Figure D_1 shows a transverse section of the young archegonium in which the three vertical walls have appeared in the archegonial mother cell dividing it into the axial cell surrounded by the three peripheral cells. The axial cell is termed the **primary axial cell**. A transverse division of the axial primary cell at the upper level cuts off a small **primary cover** or **cap cell** from the lower central cell (D_2). Meanwhile each of the two larger peripheral cells divides by a vertical wall resulting in 5 peripheral cells surrounding the central cell. Subsequent transverse division of the 5 peripheral cells and the lower larger central cell results in a 2-tiered young archegonium (D_2). Besides the cover or cap cell, the upper tier consists of 5 peripheral cells and an upper segment of the central cell. The former function as the **neck initials** and the latter **primary neck canal cell**. The lower tier consists of 5 perimpheral cells which function as the **venter initials** and a lower larger segment of the central cell termed the **primary ventral cell**.

The 5 neck initials and the primary neck canal cell divide repeatedly by transverse walls only to produce an axial row of 6—8 **neck canal cells** surrounded by 5 vertical rows of neck cells. Meanwhile the primary cover cell divides by two vertical intersecting walls producing 4 cap cells. It never functions as an apical cell and thus does not contribute to the development of the neck in the liverworts. Figure F shows a young archegonium in which the primary neck canal cell has divided once. The venter initials divide transversely as well as periclinally to form the venter which in older archegonia becomes 2-cells in thickness (J). The primary ventral cell divides by a horizontal wall into an upper **ventral canal cell** and a lower **egg cell.** Both are located in the venter cavity and are almost equal in size (H). Figure G shows 4 neck canal cells and an undivided primary ventral cell.

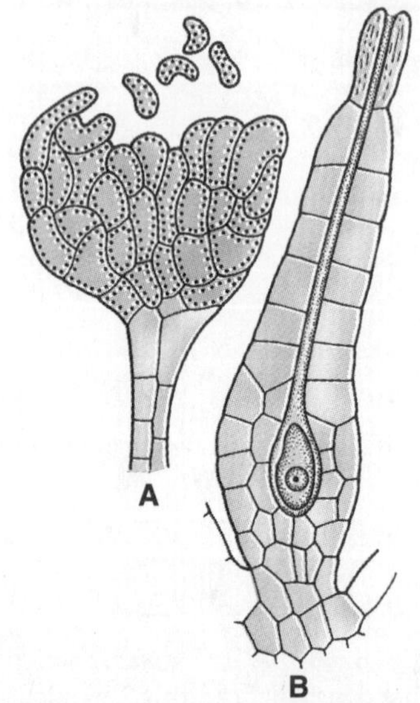

Fig. 8.6. (A—B). ***Fossombronia***, Dehiscence of sex organs. A, dehisced antheridium; B, mature archegonium ready for fertilization (A after Pande *et al*, B after Haupt).

Dehiscence of sex organs (Fig. 8.6). The sex organs dehisce in the presence of moisture. According to Horne (1909) the larger cells of the distal part of the wall of the mature antheridium have mucilaginous contents. These imbibe water with great avidity. The consequent increase in turgidity of these cells causes rupture of the antheridial wall into a number of irregular lobes which instantly curl out resulting in rapid discharge of sperms with a force (A).

Excepting the egg, the axial row of cells in the mature archegonium disintegrates. Their mucilaginous contents imbibe water and swell forcing apart (B) or casting off the cap cells at the tip of the archegonium. A passage way leading to the egg in the venter results. (B)

Fertilization. It takes place, as in other liverworts, in the presence of water provided by rain or dew. Even in the monoecious species, on account of their pronounced protandry, there are great chances of cross fertilization. With the fertilization of some of the archegonia on the thallus, the development of new ones ceases. The act of fertilization provides added stimulus to the thallus tissue, adjacent to the base of the fertilized archegonium to grow into a bell-shaped or tubular organ called the **perianth**.

Sporophyte (Fig. 8.7)

The sporophyte of *Fossombronia* is differentiated into **foot**, **seta** and **capsule** (A). The cells of the surface layer of the foot are elongated and have denser cytoplasm. These features apparently suggest that they have haustorial function. The seta is fairly long in some species and short in others. It is composed of parenchymatous cells and is stalk-like in form (B).

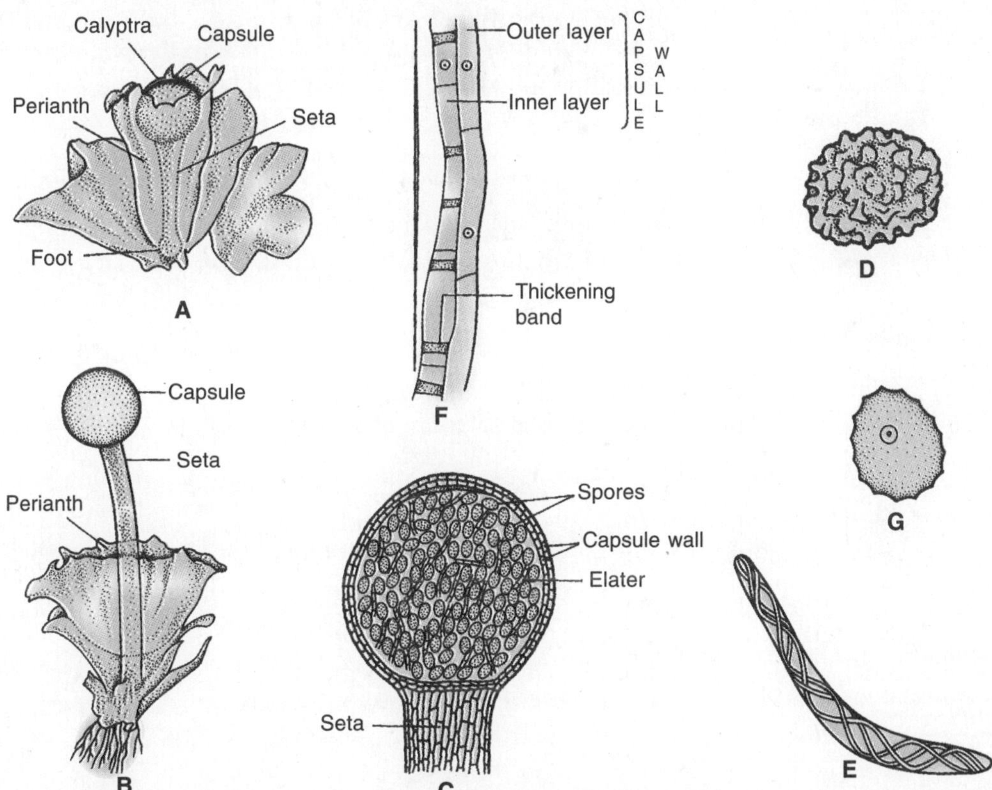

Fig. 8.7. (A—G). ***Fossombronia* sp.** A, sporophyte still enclosed, within the calyptra and surrounded by the perianth; B, mature sporophyte projecting beyond the perianth; C.L.S. capsule showing structure; D, mature spore in surface view; E, elater with three spiral bands; F, capsule wall in L.S. showing thicknening bands on the cells of the inner wall layer; G. nearly mature spore in section (E after Kashyap, D after Campbell; A, B, F, G after Pande *et. al.*).

The nature capsule is more or less globular in form (C). It has a wall which is invariably two cells in thickness excpet its apical end where it may be three cells thick. The spore cavity contains elaters and spores which when young contain chloroplasts and are green but turn brown at maturity. The elaters are scattered irregularly and are mixed up with the spores. There is no elaterophore. The elaters in *F. himalayensis* are 140 μ long and have 2 (sometimes 3) spiral bands on their walls (E). The brown spores are usually 36—45 μ in diameter and have thick projecting lamellate markings on the exosporium (D). The cells of the outer layer of the capsule wall have thin walls and are transparent. Those of the inner layer develop small annual or half ring fibres on their inner side (F).

The mature sporophyte is surrounded and thus protected by a bell-shaped sheathing organ called the **perianth** (B). The later develops after fertilisation by the upgrowth of the thallus tissue adjacent to the base of the fertilized archegonium. The remnants of the ruptured calyptra are seen at the base of the mature sporophyte within the perianth.

Development of sporophyte (Fig. 8.8). Six to nine days after fertilization, the zygote in the venter enters supon segmentation. The first division wall is transverse. It divides the zygote into two unequal cells, the upper larger **epibasal cell** and the lower smaller **hypobasal cell** (A). The latter

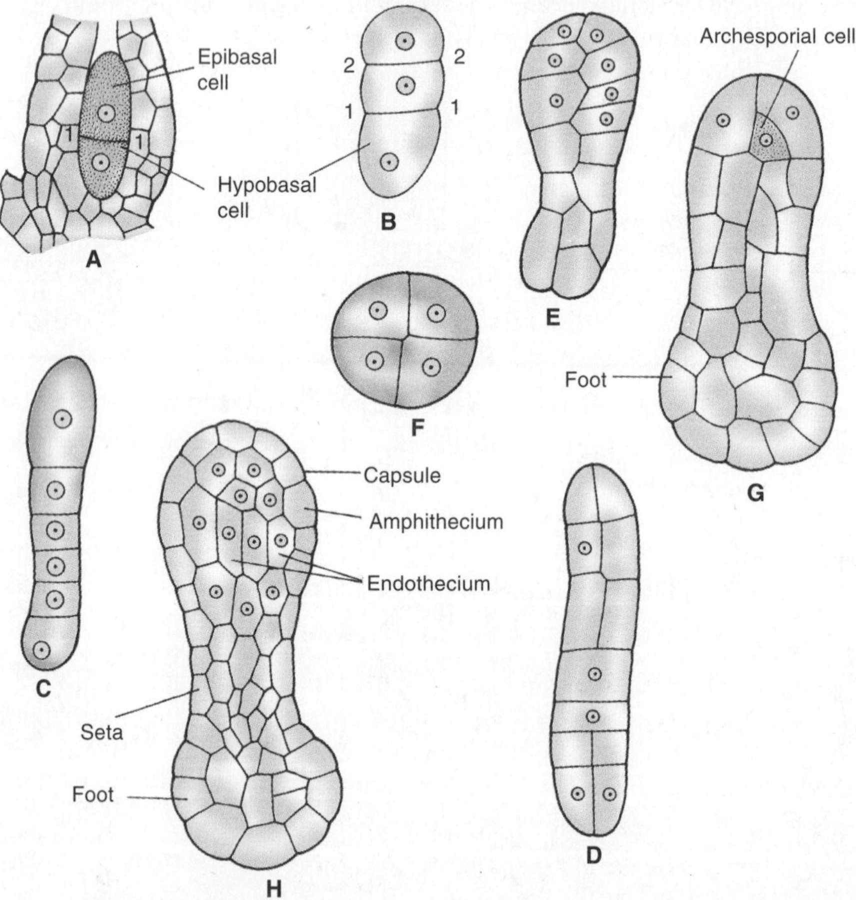

Fig. 8.8. (A—H). ***Fossombronia sp.*** Early stages in the development of sporophyte. A, 2-celled embryo; B, 3-celled embryo; C, filamentous embryo; D, later stage showing appearance of vertical walls; E, still later stage; F, T.S. cross section of E; G, differentiation of archesporial cell starting; H, young sporophyte shows differentiation of amphithecium and endothecium in the capsule region (A, C after Haupt; B, E, H after Smith, D after Pande *et al.* and F-G after Campbell).

undergoes repeated transverse and longitudinal divisions to produce the bulbous **foot** which, at first, is larger than the capsule region. (Fig. 8.7). The division of cells in the foot region is not regular. It is thus difficult to follow the sequence. It is worth while to note that the hypobasal cell in *Fossombronia* develops into foot of the mature sporophyte and not merely to the appendage of the foot called haustorium or suspensor as is the case in *Pellia*, or *Riccardia*.

The second wall, which appears in the larger epibasal cell, is also transverse. Two cells result, the upper and lower (B). The upper segment of the epibasal cell forms the capsule and the lower develops into the seta (Chaland, 1929—31). According to Humphrey (1906), Haupt (1920), Showalter (1927) the first few divisions in the epibasal cell are transverse resulting usually in a 5 or 6-celled filamentous embryo (C). A vertical wall then appears intersecting the transverse walls (D). It is followed by another vertical wall at right angles to the first one. At this stage four cells are seen in a cross section of the upper part of the embryo (F) but only two in a longitudinal section (D, E). According to Pande *et. al.* (1954) divisions in the middle part of the embryo are slow. Those in the

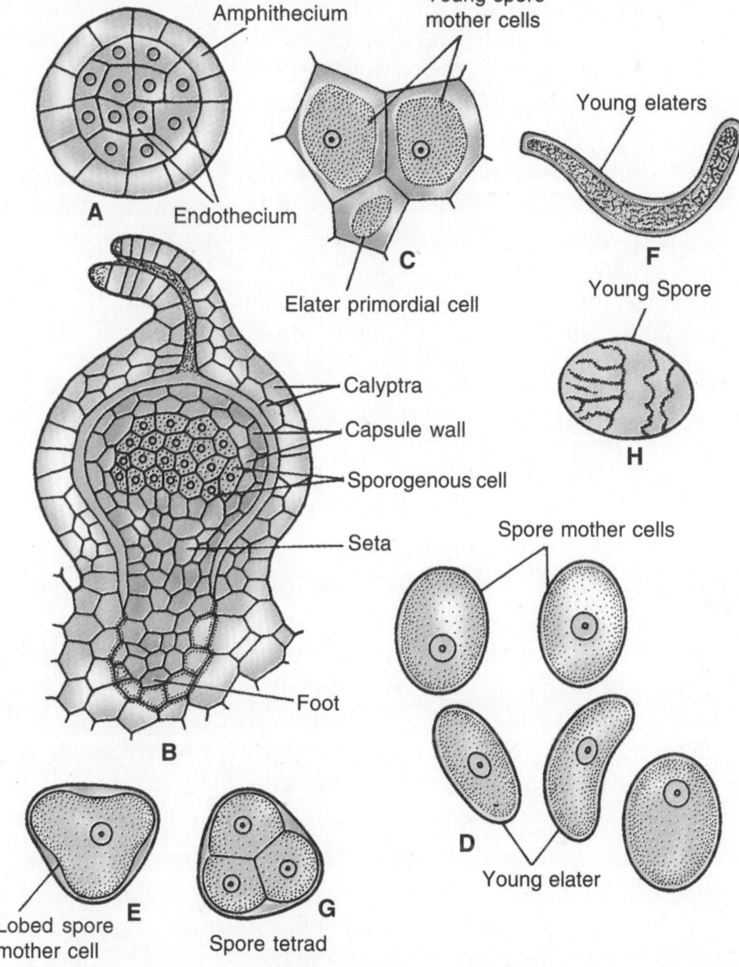

Fig. 8.9 (A—G). ***Fossombronia sp.*** Later stages in the development of sporophyte. A, T.S. young capsule showing differentiation of amphithecium and endothecium; B, L.S. young sporophyte enclosed within the calyptra; C, two young spore mother cells and an elater primordial cell; D, three spore mother cells and two young elaters; E, indistinctly lobed spore mother cell; F, young elater; H, young spore (B,D,E, G after Haupt; C after Pande *et al.*; and A, F, after Campbell).

upper part are rapid and eventually produce the terminal capsule. Periclinal walls (G) appear early in this region (upper part of embryo) separating an outler layer of sterile cells constituting the **amphithecium** from a central group of fertile cells, the **endothecium** or **primary archesporium** (H). These cells are large and have dense cytoplasm. Each cell has a prominent nucleus. By repeated successive divisions the archesporial cells increase in number. The cells of the last cell generation of the archesporium are called the **sporogenous cells** (Fig. 8.9 B). Meanwhile the periclinal divisions of the one-cell thick amphithecium result in a double layered capsule wall (B). At the distal end, however, the capsule wall may become 3 cells in thickness by further periclinal division in the wall cells of this region.

Eventually the sporogenous cells (Fig. 8.9 B) which completely fill the cavity of the capsule differentiate into two-types of cells, namely, (*i*) the **spore mother cells**, (D) and (*ii*) **elater primordial cells** (C). At the time of their differentiation, the protoplasts of the sporogenous cells withdraw from the cell walls. The protoplasts which are destined to form the spore mother cells become more or less spherical and those of the elaters somewhat elongate (C). Both secrete new walls. The original walls of the sporogenous cells are finally dissolved.

Each spore mother cell develops four inconspicuous lobes and has granular and vacuolated cytoplasm (E). The nucleus which is located int he centre undergoes meiosis. The resultant four haploid nuclei are arranged in a tetrahedral manner. Walls are finally laid between the nuclei to separate the four members of the tetrad (G). The seta at this stage, is not yet elongated. The nearly mature sporophyte is thus still completely enclosed by the **calyptra**, external to which is **perianth** (Fig. 8.7 A). The elater primordial cells (C) stretch towards both ends to form short **elaters** (D). An unusual feature of the elaters of *Fossombronia* is that the local thinkenings on their walls may consist of from 5 to 9 rings instead of the usual 2 or 3 longitudinal spirals. These rings, however, become connected to form a single rudimentary spiral. Kashyap (1929) and Pande *et al* (1954) reported short elaters with bi or tri-spiral bands (8.7 E) in *F. himalayensis*.

Dehiscence of capsule and dispersal of spores. As the spores mature in the capsule, the seta elongates rapidly by intercalary growth of its cells. Increase in length of the seta ruptures the calyptra and elevates the capsule far above the perianth (Fig. 8.7 B). The exposed capsule dries up. The loss of water sets up tension in the cells of the capsule wall. Consequently the capsule wall according to the species, splits into 4 valves or dehisces irregularly, the wall being torn into pieces. The ripe spores, which are mixed with the elaters in the exposed spore mass, are dispersed by the hygroscopic movements of the later.

Germination of spores. The spores of *F. himalayensis* remain dormant in the dry season and germinate in about a fortnight after the first shower in June (Pande *et al.*, 1954). On germination, the spore of *Fossombronia* forms a green filamentous protonema which consists of 2—12 cells. The first rhizoid originates from the cell nearest to the germinated spore. By the activity of the terminal cell of the peripheral cells in the globose mass beings to function as an apical cell. It has two cutting faces which cut off segments alternately left and right. The segments cut off early in development form a thallus-like structure. In the later formed portions of the thallus, the derivatives of each segment cut off by the apical cell develop into a leaf and a portion of the stem.

Systematic Position of Fossombronia

Division	:	Bryophyta
Class	:	Hepticopsida
Order	:	Metzgeriales
Family	:	Fossombroniaceae
Genus	:	*Fossombronia*
Species	:	*himalayensis*

QUESTIONS

ESSAY TYPE

1. List the salient features of the life hisotry of *Fossombronia*.
2. In what respects does the sporophyte of *Fossombronia* show an advance over that of *Marchantia*?
3. Give an illustrated account of the life cycle of *Fossombronia*.
4. Compare and contrast the structure and development of sex organs of *Fossombronia* with that of *Marchantia*.
5. Describe in detail the strucutre of the sporogonium of *Fossombronia*. In what respects do you consider it to be more advanced than that of *Riccia* or *Marchantia*?
6. Give an illustrated account of the external and internal features of *Fossombronia* thallus.
7. Describe by means of diagrams only the life-cycle of *Fossombronia*.

SHORT ANSWER TYPE

8. **Write short notes on :**
   (*a*) Thallus of *Fossombronia*.
   (*b*) Development of sex organs in *Fossombronia*.
   (*c*) Sporophyte of *Fossombronia*.
   (*d*) Sexual reproduction in *Fossombronia*.
   (*e*) *Fossombronia*
   (Allahabad, Msc, 2000)
9. **Draw labelled diagrams of :**
   (*i*) T.S. thallus of *Fossombronia*.
   (*ii*) A mature antheridium
   (*iii*) A mature archegonium
   (*iv*) V.S. sporogonium
10. Distinguish between archegonicum of *Marchantia* and *Fossombronia*.
   (Rohilkhand Msc, 2003)

OBJECTIVE TYPE

11. **Select the correct answer :**
   (*i*) Which of the following is a leafy member of Metzgerials?
   (*a*) *Pellia* (*b*) *Riccardia*
   (*c*) *Fossombronia* (*d*) *Riccia*.
   (*ii*) In which of the following bryophyte mycorrhiza is present in ventral zone of thallus?
   (*a*) *Pellia* (*b*) *Riccardia*
   (*c*) *Fossombronia* (*d*) *Riccia*.
   (*iii*) In *F. himalayensis* the life cycle is completed in
   (*a*) A year (*b*) 2 years
   (*c*) 3 months (*d*) 5 months.
   (*iv*) Mucilage papilla is borne on marginal leaf cell in
   (*a*) *Pellia*
   (*b*) *Riccardia*
   (*c*) *Riccia*
   (*d*) *Fossombronia*.
   (*v*) The hypobasal cell in *Fossombronia* gives rise to
   (*a*) Foot of the mature sporophyte
   (*b*) Hanstorium of the sporophyte
   (*c*) Foot and seta of the mature sporophyte
   (*d*) Foot and capsule of the mature sporophyte.

Image of *Calypogeia fissa*

CHAPTER 9

HEPATICOPSIDA (Hepaticae) Jungermanniales

- Gametophyte
- Sporophyte
- Comparison Between the Jungermanniales and the Marchantiales

Characteristic features.

The order Jungermanniales includes liverworts in which the plant body is differentiated into a central axis, the so called **stem** bearing leaf-like appendages. (Fig. 9.1 A). Popularly they are called the *leafy* or *foliose* liverworts. Despite this external elaboration, the plant body of the foliose liverworts is still called a thallus. Like thallose liverworts, it is prostrate in habit, dorsiventral in configuration and simple in structure showing no internal differentiation. The sex organs are superficial and projecting. They are never sunken. Some species are monoecious and some dioecious. The sex organs occur either singly or in small groups. The antheridia are axillary in position whereas archegonia are apical. The archegonial cluster is enclosed and thus protected by a special envelope called the **perianth** formed by the fusion of 2 or 3 terminal perichaetial bracts. The archegonia develop from the segments derived from the apical cell. In fact the apical cell itself also develops into an archegonium. The Jungermanniales are thus **acrogynous**. As a result of this the growth in length of the axis ceases. Consequently the archegonia are always apical in position. This acrogynous condition of archegonia subsequently results in the sporophytes being always terminal.

Distribution and habitat. The leafy liverworts are by far the richest in species and thus comprise about 90% of the Hepaticae. The Jungermanniales are widespread in their distribution, occurring both in the cold climates and in the tropics. They are, however, abundant in the tropics but extend north and south up to the polar regions. Himalayas, particularly the eastern part and South India are the treasure houses of the leafy Jungermanniales. Mussoorie, Darjeeling, Almora, Garhwal, etc., are some of the places rich in these hepatics. Combination of shade and abundant moisture is a precondition for their successful growth. A few species are aquatic but the majority are hygrophytic or mesophytic. They grow on damp soil, moist rocks, logs of wood, bark of trees and their leaves in the damp tropical forests. Most of the foliose forms are epiphytic.

Gametophyte (Fig. 9.1)

The gametophyte is a leafy thallus. With few exceptions (*Herberta* and *Anthelia*) it is prostrate to decumbent in habit and dorsiventral in configuration. The central axis or stem which bears the leaves is generally branched. The branching is **monopodial** and never dichotomous. The branch arises besides the leaf and is never axillary. The external elaboration of the thallus is not accompanied by internal differentiation of cells. The whole thallus consists of uniform green parenchyma cells. The air chambers and air pores characteristic of the marchantiaceous thallus are conspicuous by their absence. The thallus is usually attached to the substratum by rhizoids which are simple, unicellular and smooth-walled. The scales and tuberculate rhizoids, as a rule, are lacking on the ventral surface of the thallus.

Leaves. The central axis (stem) and its branches bear leaf-like expansions, the so-called **leaves**. The leaf is invariably without a midrib and consists of a single layer of cells containing chloroplasts. Majority of the Jungermanniales are **anisophyllous**. They bear leaves of two sizes of shapes arranged in a spiral manner in three rows on the stem (Fig. 9.1 C). Two of these rows consist of large, dorsal leaves placed laterally one on each side of the stem. The third row consists of small more or less reduced ventral leaves usually called the **amphigastria** or **underleaves**. The common examples of anisophyllous Jungermanniales are *Porella* (Fig. 10.1 A), *Frullania*, (Fig. 11.1, D); *Calypogeia* (Fig. 9.1 C), *Mastigobryum* and *Lejeunia* (Fig. 9.2 D). Some Jungermanniales are distichous leaved. In them the ventral row of small leaves is absent, so that the leaves on the stem are arranged in two lateral rows only.

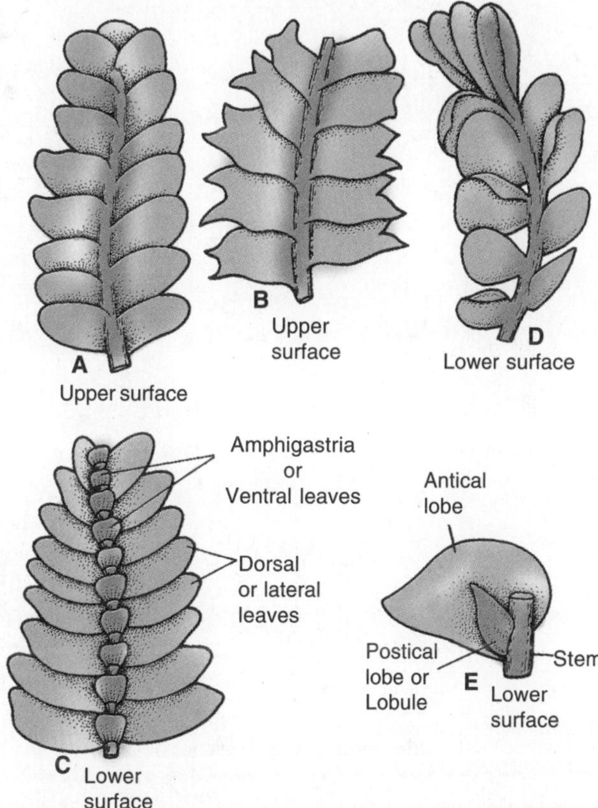

Fig. 9.1. (A—E). **Jungermanniales**. Leaf arrangement. A, dorsal view of incubous arrangement of leaves of *Calypogeia neesiana*; B; dorsal view of succubous leaves of *Chiloscyphus rivularia*; C, ventral view of incubous leaves of *Calypogeia neesiana*, note the third row of ventral leaves; D, ventral view of *Plagiochila asplenioides*—a species without under-leaves; E; ventral view of a lateral leaf of *Porella* attached to the stem (A,C,D, after Steare).

Pleurozia, Radula (Fig. 9.2 G), *Scapanic* (Fig. 9.2 H-I) and *Plagiochila asplenioides* (fig. 9.1 D) are the common examples of distichous leaved acrogynae. *Herberta* (Fig. 9.2 J) and *Anthelia* are a class by themselves. In them the erect gametophyte is radially symmetrical. The erect stem bears three rows of similar, radially arranged leaves. The leaves are alike, in size (**isophyllous**) and each is cleft to the base into two tapering lobes.

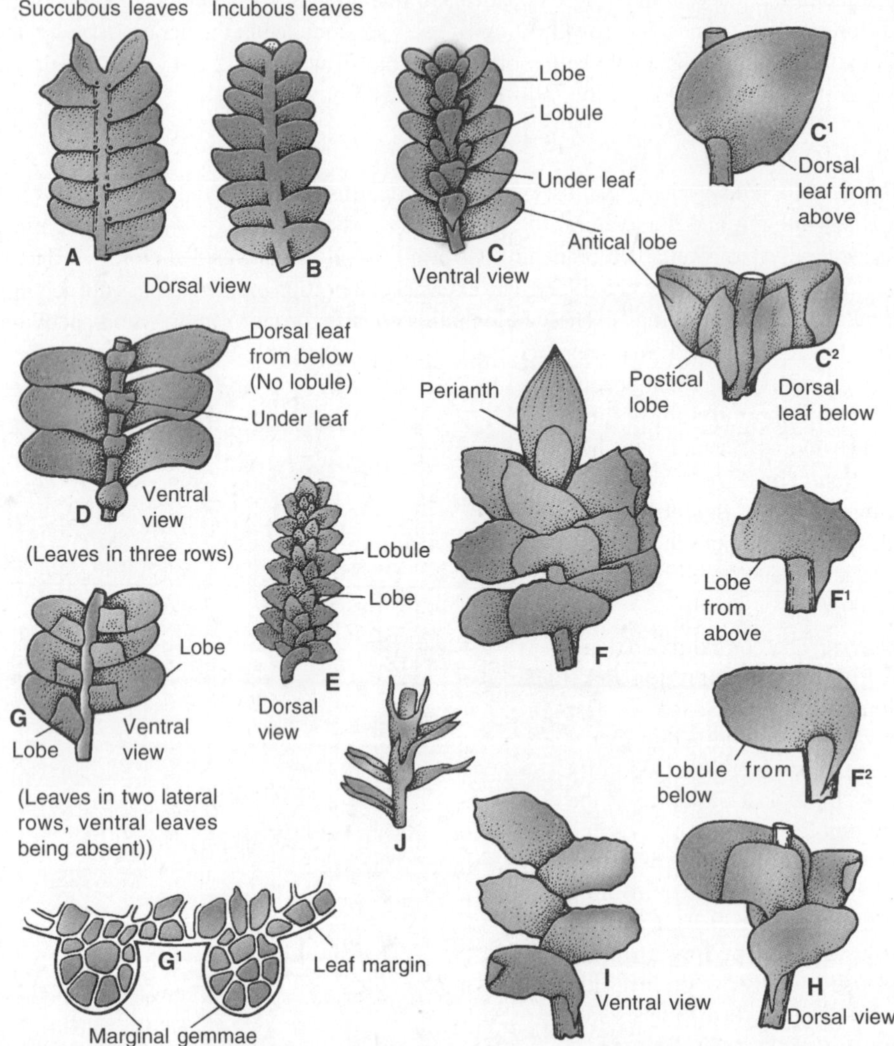

Fig. 9.2. (A—J). **Jungermanniales.** A, shoot of *Chiloscyphus himalayensis* showing succubous arrangement of leaves; B, incubous leaves in *Calypogeia neesiana*; C, ventral view of a shoot of *Porella* showing a ventral row of under leaves in addition; C^1 dorsal view of a single leaf of *Porella gracillima* attached to the stem; C^2, ventral view of leaves with their lobules of *P. gracillima*; D, ventral view of a shoot of *Lejeunea chinensis* showing leaves in three rows with the lobules obsolete; E, dorsal view of a shoot of *Scapania nemorosa* with the lobes smaller than the lobules; F, fertile shoot of *Diplophyllum oriental*; F^1, dorsal lobe of F from above; F^2, ventral lobe (lobule) of F from below; G, ventral view of *Radulla complanate* with leaves in two lateral rows, the ventral leaves being absent; G^1, gemmae arising from the leaf margin in G; H, dorsal view of shoot of *Scapania purpurea*, leaves in two rows; I, ventral view of H showing absence of under leaves; J, isophyllous leaves of *Herberta* arranged in three rows on erect axis. (B and E after Steare, J after Muller and the rest after Kahsyap).

Arrangement of leaves. The dorsal or lateral leaves are close set on the central axis and its branches and thus overlap. The overlapping is of two types, **succubous** and **incubous**. In the former, the posterior margin of each leaf overlies the forward edge of the next older leaf on the same side in dorsal view. The common examples of succubous arrangement of leaves are *Cephalozia, Lophocolea, Lophozia, Plagiochila* and *Chiloscyphus* (Fig. 9.1 B). In these plants the water run off from the surface of succubously-arranged leaves. The overlapping is reversed in the incubous arrangement of leaves. The posterior margin of each underlies the forward edge of the next older leaf in dorsal view. The best known genera with incubous arrangement of leaves are *Frullania, Lejeiunia, Porella* (Fig. 10.1 B), *Radula, Bazzania* and *Calypogeia* (Fig. 9.2 B). In these plants the water is retained from the surface of incubously arranged leaves.

In majority of genera, the leaves are arranged in three rows: two rows in lateral side and third row on ventral side. The leaves of all the three rows are similar in structure (Isophyllous) as in *Herberta* and *Anthelia* where plants are erect and straight. But in prostrate or suberect plants, the third row of ventral leaves goes down ward and come in contact with soil. These ventral leaves are called underleaves or amphigastria. In such plants the leaves are not similar in structure (Anisophyllous) as in *Frullania* and *Porella*. The underleaves show gradual reduction and finally disappear. In such plants (*Jungermannia*) the leaves are only in two lateral rows. The leaves of lateral row also show variation in size, shape, structure and their attachment on axis.

The dorsal or lateral leaf is bilobed, sometimes cleft at maturity. More frequently the two lobes are unequal in size (Fig. 9.1 E), rarely they are equal. In the former case the dorsal or antical lobe is large (*Porella*, Fig. 10.2 C) and *Radula* (Fig. 9.2 G). It is often referred to as the "lobe". The smaller postical or ventral lobe is designated as "lobule". In some genera such as *Frullania* and *Jubula*, the lobule further shows distinction into an appendage known as the **stylus** and the **lobule proper** (Fig. 11.1 E). *Scapania nemorosa* (fig. 9.2 E) and *Diplophyllum* are examples of the foliose forms in which the ventral or postical lobe is larger than the antical lobe. In some species the lobule is obsolete (*Calypogeia neesiana*, (Fig. 9.1 C) and *Lejeiunia chinensis* (Fig. 9.2 D).

Apical growth. It always takes place by means of a single apical cell which is pyramidal in shape. It has a base and three cutting faces (sides). Segments are cut off parallel to it three segmenting faces, two dorsal and one ventral. Each dorsal segment gives rise to a single leaf and to the portion of the stem subtending it. So is the case with the ventral segment. Each ventral segment produces the ventral leaf and the portion of the stem subtending it.

Vegetative reproduction. Vegetatively the leafy liverworts (Jungermanniales) reproduce by fragmentation, gemmae, and leafy propagula.

1. Fragmentation. By progressive growth followed by the death of the older regions of the leafy thallus, the younger branches become separated. These isolated branches are called the **fragments**. Each fragment by apical growth and branching grows into a new plant.

2. Gemmae. Many Jungermanniales reproduce vegetatively by **gemmae.** The gemmae produced in *Radula* are small, discoid, multicellular structures. They are budded off from the margins of leaves (9.2 G). At maturity they break away and under suitable conditions each grows into a new plant. *Lophozia*, (Fig. 6.2 I), *Cephalozia* and *Scapania* have 1 to 3-celled gemmae developed on the stem apex.

3. Many of the Jungermanniales produce specialised *leafy propagula*. Udar and Asha Gupta (1977) reported copious formation of leafy propagula on the under surface of the leaves of *Plagiochila* sp. from Nepal.

4. Several species of leafy liverworts withstand drying for a considerable period without apparent injury. With the return of favourable conditions the apparently dried up specimens resume growth and become green.

Sex organs (Fig. 9.3, A—F). Some Acrogynae (Jungermanniales) are monoecious and some dioecious. The monoecious forms may be **autoicous (autoecious)** or **paroicous (paroecious)**. In

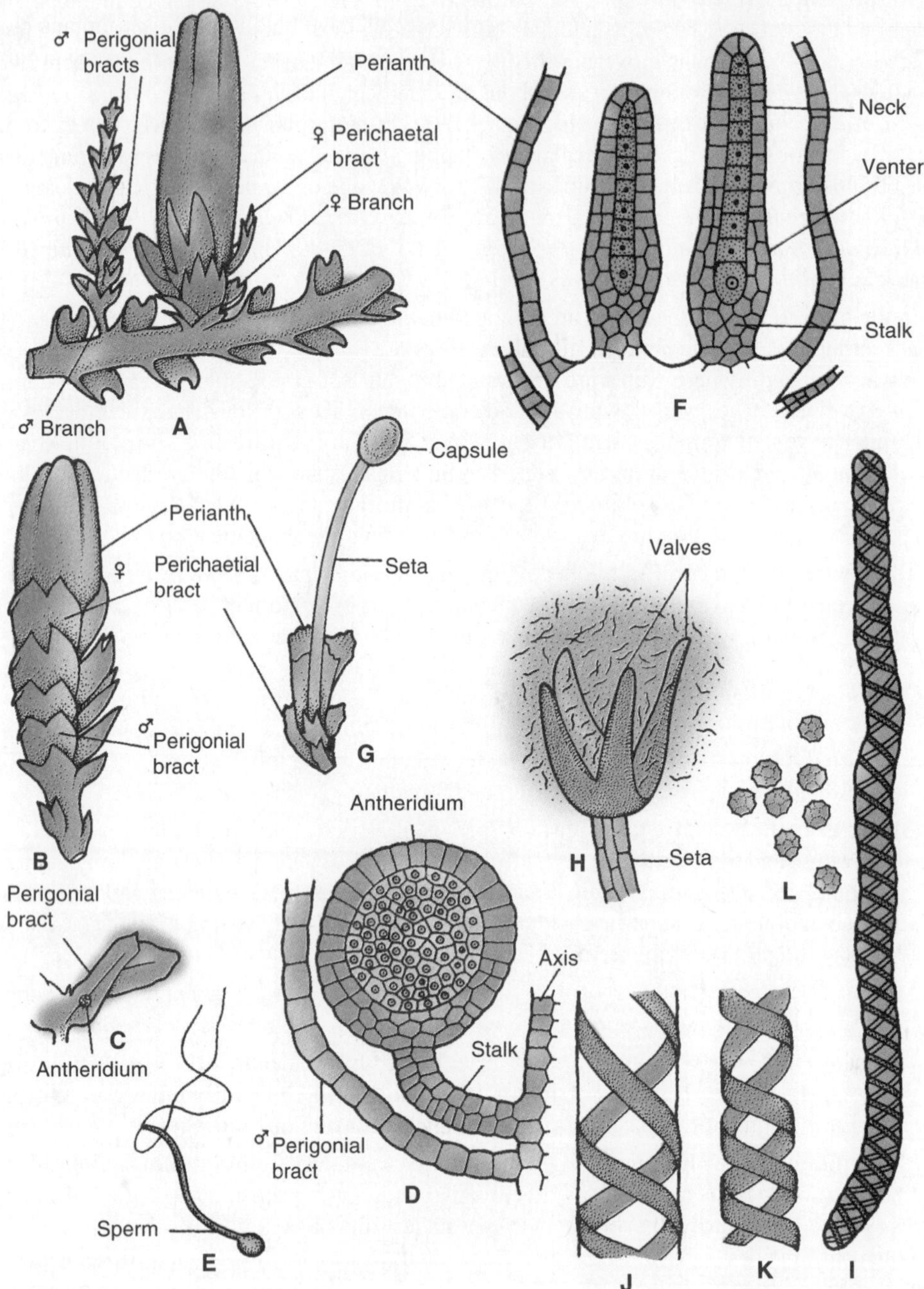

Fig. 9.3. (A—L). **Jungermanniaceae**. A, *Cephalozia pleniceps,* monoecious autoicous species; B, *Cephaloziella rubella*, monoecious paroicous species; C, portion of antheridial branch of *Diplophyllum albicans* with an antheridium in the axil of a perigonial bract; D, L.S. antheridium of *Porella*; E, Liberated sperm of *Porella*; F, L.S. perianth of a leafy liverwort *Frullania*; G, apical region of a female branch of *Lophocolea heterophylla* with a perianth and the sporogonium; H—L, *Cephalozia bicuspidata*; H, dehisced empty capsule; I, elater with a double spiral band of thickening; J, part of an elater filled with water; K, part of an elater after partial evaporation of contained water; L, a few spores (A—B after Schuster, C and G after Watson, H—L after Ingold).

the autoicous species, antheridia and archegonia occur on different branches of the same plant (*Cephalozia pleniceps,* A). Monoecious paroicous species have both kinds of sex organs close to one another on the same branch (*Cephalozia rubra*, B). The sex organs are superficial and projecting. They are never sunken.

Antheridia. The antheridia occur in groups of 2-5, sometimes singly in the axils of modified leaves called the **perigonial bracts** (Fig.9 3. C, D), on ordinary branches (*Lophazia, Nardia*) or specially modified antheridial branches. The mature antheridium is globose in form and is raised on a long stalk (Fig. 9.3 D). The antheridial wall which encloses the sperm mother cells is usually one cell layer thick in the upper part and 2-3 cells thick in the basal part.

Archegonia (F). They occur singly or in a small group (F), and are apical in position. The apical cell itself is involved (used up) in the formation of the archegonium. The archegonia are surrounded and thus protected by a special envelop known as the **perianth** (A). It is formed by the lateral fusion of 2 or 3 terminal perichaetial bracts. In some species there is, in addition, another envelope external to the perianth. It is known as the **involucre** Perianth varies in shape in different species.

Sporophyte (Fig. 9.3, G—L)

The terminal sporophyte is differentiated into the **foot**, the long **seta** and commonly narrowly ovoid **capsule** (G). The ripe capsule contains spores (L) and free elaters (I). There is no elaterophore except in *Gotschea*. The spore mother cells are conspicuously four-lobed and dehiscence is by means of 4-valves (H). The capsule wall is two or more cell layers in thickness. The cells of the inner layer generally develop spiral thickenings.

The order Jungermanniales is a large group comprising about 220 genera and 8,500 species. They are allotted to seventeen families but Schuster recognizes 36. Of these Porellaceae and Frullaniaceae are discussed in this book.

SALIENT FEATURES OF JUNGERMANNIALES

1. The thallus is always differentiated into the central axis, the so called stem bearing leaf-like expansion, the leaves.

2. This external elaboration of the thallus is not accompanied by internal differentiation of cells. The thallus thus consists of similar paranchyma cells.

3. The thallus like the thallose liverworts is distinctly dorsiventral.

4. The leaf lacks the midrib and consists of a single layer of cells containing chloroplasts and oil-bodies.

5. Majority of them are anisophyllous in which the two kinds of leaves are arranged in a spiral manner in three rows, two rows of large dorsal or lateral leaves and one of small ventral leaves.

6. The close set leaves overlap each other in a succubous or incubous manner.

7. The rhizoids which function as anchoring organs are unicellular, simple, smooth, thin-walled type.

8. The scales are usually absent and so are tuberculated rhizoids.

9. The apical growth in all the Jungermanniales takes place by means of a single apical cell which is pyramidal in shape.

10. The sex organs are superficial and projecting but never borne on stalked receptacles.

11. The archegonia usually occur in groups and are distinctly stalked. The venter is almost as broad as the neck or only slightly broader than the neck. The neck consists of only five vertical rows of neck cells.

12. The antheridia are oval or globular in outline and usually elevated on long, slender stalks. They are lateral and axillary in position.

13. The sperms are biflagellate but larger and show more numerous coils than those of the Marchantiales.

14. The zygote invariably divides by a transverse or approximately transverse wall to give rise to an upper epibasal cell and a lower hypobasal cell.

15. The hypobasal cell takes no further part in the development of the sporogonium, the entire sporogonium develops from the epibasal cell. It is differentiated into foot, seta and the capsule. The seta is much elongated at maturity.

16. The capsule wall is two or more cell layers in thickness. The cells of the jacket layer are always sclerified.

17. The sporogenous cells are differentiated into spore mother cells and the sterile cells.

18. The spore mother cells become four-lobed before further division.

19. The sterile cells in most genera develop into elaters.

20. The ripe capsule usually dehisces in a regular and a definite manner along lines of dehiscence. It splits into four valves which become reflexed.

21. The elaters after dehiscence 'fluff up' the exposed mass of spores by their hygroscopic movements in response to changes in the atmospheric humidity and thus facilitate dispersal of spores.

22. Formation of a protonema stage is characterisitc of the foliose forms. It is generally short lived and ephemeral but sometimes long lived.

COMPARISON BETWEEN THE JUNGERMANNIALES AND THE MARCHANTIALES

The general life history is the same in both the *Jungermanniales* and the *Marchantiales*. There are differences in detail. The *Jungermanniales* **differ** from the *Marchantiales* in the following respects :

1. Greater external elaboration of the gametophyte.

2. No or little histological differentiation so that there are neither any air chambers nor any air pores. The entire thallus usually consists of similar parenchyma cells.

3. Absence of tuberculate rhizoids.

4. Absence of scales. Evans, however, likens the scales of Marchantiales to the ventral leaves of the foliose Jungermanniales. This view is supported by the fact that both are one cell thick and are attached by a broad base. Besides, scales of the Marchantiales, in many members of the order, contain chloroplasts, at least, in early stages of development.

5. Growth always by means of a single apical cell.

6. Sex organs never borne on stalked receptacles.

7. Archegonia usually in groups, apical in position and distinctly stalked.

8. Venter nearly as broad as the neck or only slightly broader than the neck.

9. Neck of five vertical rows of neck cells.

10. Antheridia always superficial and projecting. They are lateral and axillary in position.

11. Larger sperms with more numerous coils.

12. Development, in most genera, of the entire sporogonium from the epibasal cell.

13. Greater internal elaboration of the sporogonium.

14. The capsule wall two or more cells thick with the cells of the jacket layer always sclerified.

15. Presence of perfect elaters in most if not all the Jungermanniales.

16. Dehiscence of the ripe capsule in a definite and regular manner along four lines of dehiscence.

17. Presence of protonematal stage in all the foliose forms.

The *Jungermanniales* **resemble** the *Marchantiales* in the following features :

1. Prostrate habit and dorsiventral configuration.

2. Presence of unicellular, simple, smooth-walled rhizoids.

3. Sex organs similar in essential respects in both, differing only in details.

4. Presence of perianth in both. It is widespread in the Jungermanniales and is represented in some of the Marchantiales.

5. The same basic chromosome complex of n=9 chromosomes (Mehra).

6. Similar radial and general plan of construction of the sporogonium into foot, seta and capsule in both. The elaboration in the Jungermanniales is internal rather than external.

7. Similar type of elaters.

8. Presence of intercalary growth in the sporophytes of both.

9. Absence of ventilated photosynthetic tissue in both so that the sporophyte is physiologically dependent on the gametophyte.

QUESTIONS

ESSAY TYPE

1. Give a brief account of the habitat, distribution and external features of the gametophyte of Jungermanniales.
2. In what respects do the Jungermanniales (a) differ from, and
   (b) resemble the Marchantiales?
3. Give a brief account of the vegetative reproduction in the Jungermanniales.
4. List the salient features in the life cycle of Jungermanniales.
5. Give a general account of Jungermanniales and discuss its relationship with other orders of Hepaticopsida.
   (Rohilkhand, M.Sc. 1989)
6. Give a comparative account of anatomy and reproduction in Jungermanniales and Marchantiales.*(Rohilkhand, M.Sc. 1996)*
7. Describe the salient features of Jungermanniales. How does it differ from Metzgeriales?
8. (*a*) With suitable diagrams, describe the arrangement and structure of leaves.
   (*b*) Compare the salient features of Jungermanniales with that of Marchantiales. *(Awadh, M.Sc. 1997)*
9. In what respects do the sex ograns of Jungermanniales differ from those of Marchantiales. *(Kanpur, M.Sc. 2007)*

SHORT ANSWER TYPE

10. Write in brief on the following :

(*a*) Archegonium in Jungermanniales and Marchantiales.*(Kanpur, M.Sc. 1992)*

(*b*) Differences between Acrogynae and Anacrogynae. *(Kanpur, M.Sc. 1997)*

(*c*) Range of thallus structure in Jungermanniales. *(Kanpur, M.Sc. 2000)*

(*d*) General characteristics of Jungermanniales. *(Rohilkhand, M.Sc. 1991)*

(*e*) Differences between Jungermanniales and Marchantiales. *(Rohilkhand, M.Sc. 1995)*

11. Compare the Jungermanniales with Marchantiales.

12. Draw a suitable comparative account of the study of *Jungermanniales* and *Marchantiales*. *(Punjab 1992)*

13. Write a brief account of vegetative reproduction in Jungermanniales.

14. What do you know of sex organs in Jungermanniales?

15. Give important characters of Jungermanmiles. *(Garhwal, 2003)*

OBJECTIVE TYPE

16. Select the correct answer :

(*i*) In the autoecious species, antheredia and archegonia occur on

(*a*) Different branches of the same plant

(*b*) The same branch close to each other

(*c*) Same branch of different plants

(*d*) Different branches of different plants.

(*ii*) The antheridia occur in the axil of modified leaves called.

(*a*) Perigynium

(*b*) Perichaetium

(*c*) Perigonial bracts

(*d*) Perianth.

(*iii*) The order Jungermanniales has been divided by Schuster into

(*a*) 16 families (*b*) 26 families

(*c*) 36 families (*d*) 46 families.

(*iv*) The Jungermanniales differ from Marchantiales in the

(*a*) Presence of leafy gametophyte

(*b*) Greater elaboration of the gametophyte

(*c*) Absence of scales

(*d*) Presence of archegonia in groups.

(*v*) Which one of the following is a character which is characteristic of Jungermanniales in Hepaticopsida?

(*a*) Spores germinate to form protonema

(*b*) Zygote develops into a sporophyte

(*c*) Presence of rhizoids

(*d*) Gametophyte is haploid.

(*vi*) The underleavs in leafy Junger manniales are knownas

(*a*) Antieal lobe (*b*) Postical lobe

(*c*) Amphigastna (*d*) Scale leavs

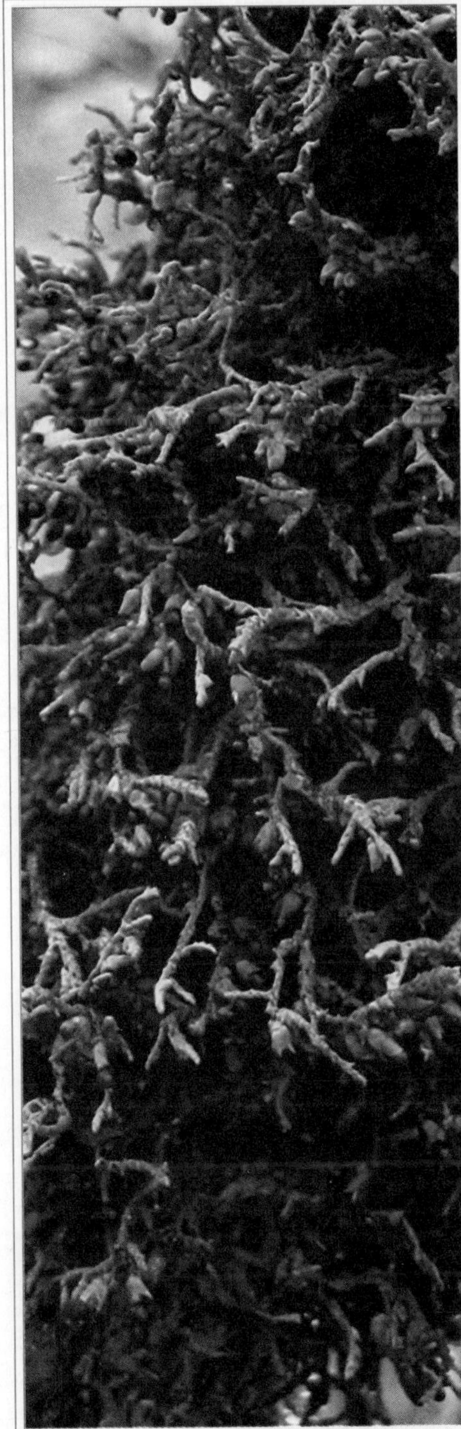

Image of *Porella cordeana*

CHAPTER 10

JUNGERMANNIALES : Porellaceae (Madothecaceae) : Porella

- Family porellaceae
- Porella L. Madotheca Dum.
- Summary of the Life-cycle of Porella
- Systematic Position of Porella

FAMILY PORELLACEAE

GENERAL CHARACTERISTICS

The family Porellaceae includes advanced **foliose** forms with leaves arranged in three rows. The ventral leaves are well developed and usually decurrent at the base. The dorsal leaves are **incubous** and **bilobed**. The ventral lobe lies more or less parallel to the axis. The rhizoids are scarce and spring from the lower side of the stem in tufts generally near the base of the ventral leaves. The antheridia are **solitary**. The archegonia arise in a **terminal cluster** on small lateral branches. All the archegonia in the cluster are surrounded by a common **perianth** with a bilabiate and dorsiventrally compressed mouth. The globose capsule dehisces by four valves separating only halfway down to the base. The seta is short. The elaters are short, each with two or three spiral bands. The family is represented by a single genus *Porella* (*Madotheca*).

PORELLA L. (*MADOTHECA* DUM.)

GAMETOPHYTIC PHASE

Distribution. It is the best known and widely distributed genus of the advanced Jungermaniales with more than 180 species. They flourish the most in the tropics. Many species, however, are found in the cold temperate regions also. *Porella platyphylla* appears to be cosmopolitan in its distribution. It has been reported from Europe, America, Asia and India. About 34 species of *Porella* have been found in India. They mostly occur at various places in the Himalayas such as Simla, Dalhousie, Mussoorie, Garhwal, Sikkim, Chamba, Tehri Garhwal, Kullu valley and Kumaon. Chopra (1943) recorded a few species from South India.

Habit and habitat. *Porella* (*Madotheca*) is generally found in the moist, shady places growing flat on logs, trunks of trees and rocks over which water trickles. It grows in dense layers forming large mats closely covering substratum.

External characters (Fig. 10.1). The plant body is greenish, leafy and fairly large up to 15 cm. or even more in length. It grows flat on the substratum and is thus **dorsiventral** in configuration. It consists of a branched central axis. Both the central axis or stem and the branches bear leaf-like *expansions* (*A*). The stem is thin and cylindrical. It bears branches in a bipinnate or tripinnate manner. The branching is **monopodial**. The branch primordium lies close to the apical cell. It takes the palce of the ventral lobe of a dorsal leaf. The stem and the branches bear two kinds of leaves, large **dorsal** and small **ventral**. They are arranged in three rows (C).

The dorsal leaves are closely set in two lateral rows (B). They cover the stem from above and overlap each other. The anterior edge of each leaf covers the posterior edge of the leaf in front.

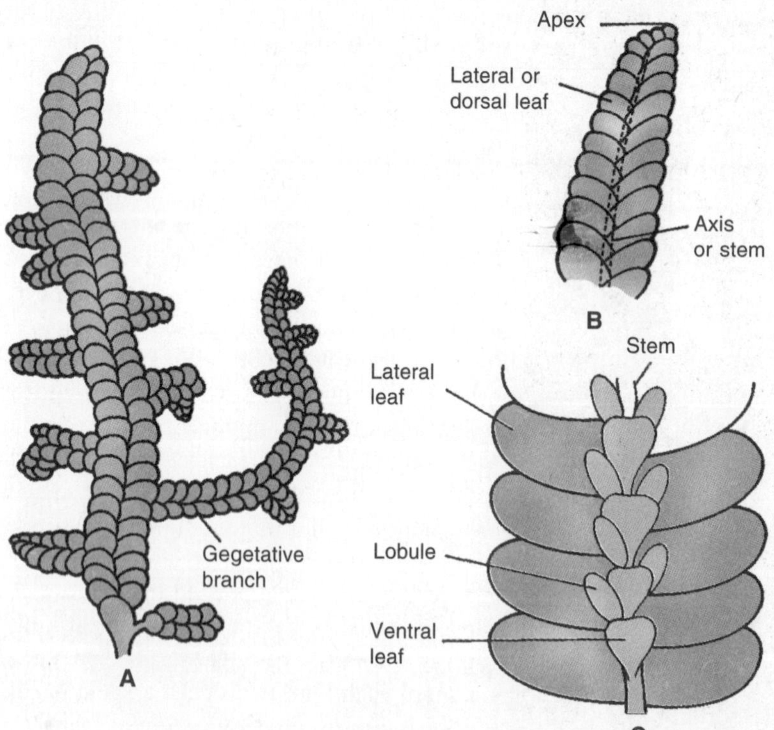

Fig. 10.1. (A—C). ***Porella* sp.** A, part of the plant showing habit; B, a branch seen from the upper surface showing incubous arrangement of leaves; C, ventral view of B showing ventral leaves and lobules of dorsal leaves.

Such an overlapping arrangement of the leaves is described as **incubous** (B). Each dorsal leaf is **bilobed** (Fig. 10.2 C). Of the two lobes the upper or dorsal is large and usually oval in outline. It has a rounded apex and is called the **antical lobe**. The ventral smaller lobe is called the **postical lobe** or the **lobule**. It is folded back and has an acute apex. It is closely appressed to the lower surface of the dorsal lobe and runs more or less parallel to the stem so as to appear like an extra leaf (Fig. 10.2 A). The small ventral leaves which are usually decurrent at the base are also called the **amphigastria**. They are simple and are arranged in a single row on the ventral side of the stem. Together with the postical lobes to which they resemble in form and size they appear to form three rows on the lower surface of the stem. The leaves of *Porella* like other foliose liverworts regularly lack nerves. Even the midrib is absent. Each leaf consists of a single layer of cells.

Dalton and Chatfield (1985) reported that numerous saccate, loosely attached ectophytic *Nostoc* colonies occur in the crevices and curled margins of overlapping leaves and underleaves of *Porella navicularis*. They suggest that this alga-hepatic association is a specialized form of association in which both the partners are mutually beneficial to each other. The alga fixes atmospheric nitrogen and reduces acetylene. Some of the products are rapidly absorbed by the host (*Porella*). *Nostoc*, on the other hand, has reduced carbondioxide fixation capcity and is thus dependent on the liverwort (*Porella*) for fixed carbon.

The rhizoids arise from the lower surface of the stem near the bases of the ventral leaves. They are few in number and are thin-walled. Their chief function is to fix the plant to the substratum. Absorption is believed to take place directly through the leaves.

Mehra and Pathania (1959) studied the cytology of four species of *Porella* (*Madotheca*) viz. *M. gollani* St., *M. denticulatum* Kash, *M. macroloba* St., *M. appendiculata* St. They found that all the four species of *Porella* have n=8 and all of them also have an additional "m" chromosome in the gametophyte.

Internal structure of stem. The young stem consists of a perfectly uniform tisue of green parenchyma cells. Even the epidermal layer is not well defined. The central strand also cannot be made out. The stem of *Porella*, therefore, is very simple in its internal structure as it shows no differentiation of tissues. In the older portions of the stem there is differentiation of tissues. It consists of an outer **cortical** and an inner **medullary region**. The cortex is made of small cells with slightly thickened walls. The medulla is composed of comparatively larger cells with thinner walls.

The leaf consists of a thin plate of uniform cells, one cell layer in thickness. The cells contain abundant chloroplasts and are polygonal in outline. There is no midrib.

Growth (Fig. 10.2 D). Increase in size takes place by means of an apical cell. It is pyramidal in shape

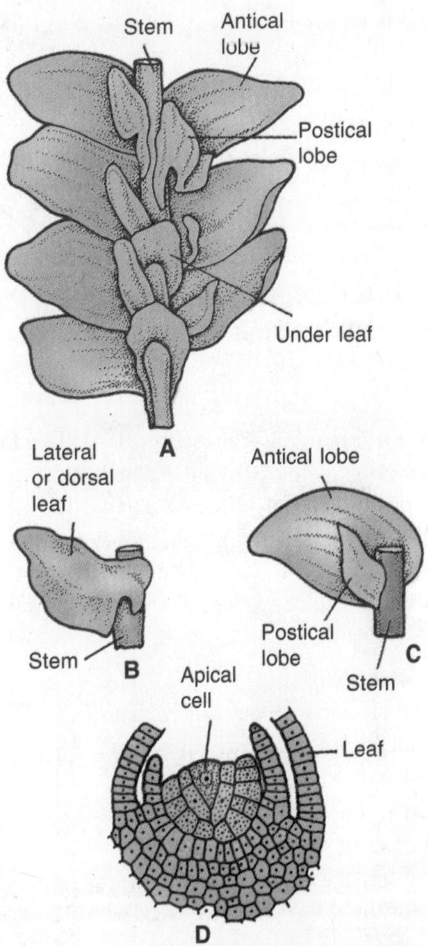

Fig. 10.2. (A—D). ***Porella***. A, ventral view of incumbous leaves of *P. platyphylla*; note the under leaves and postical lobes of dorsal leaves; B, leaf attached to the stem seen from above; C, a leaf with its lobule attached to the stem seen from the ventral side; D, V. S. through the shoot apex. (A—C after Kashyap).

with three cutting faces. One of these is towards the ventral side and the other two towards the dorsal side.

Reproduction

1. *Vegetative reproduction.* The species growing under the humid conditions propagate by **fragmentation**. Vegetative reproduction by the formation of discoid gemmae developed on the lower surface of the leaves of *Porella rotun-difolia* was recorded by Schiffiner from Brazil. This was denied by Degenkolbe in 1938 who discovered that the so-called discoid gemmae, were in reality the thin-walled, rounded structures containing blue green algae.

The leafy thallus of *Porella* has a great power of regeneration. Even the dried up specimens resume growth on being moistened.

2. *Sexual reproduction* (Fig. 10.3). All species of *Porella* are **dioecious.** The sex organs occur on short, side branches. The male plants are generally smaller (A). They bear special, side branches apparently arising at right angles from the main stem (A).

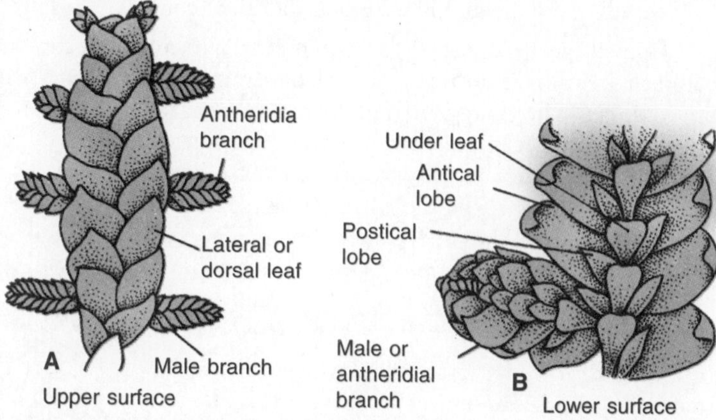

Fig. 10.3. (A—B) ***Porella* sp.** A, dorsal view of a portion of the male plant bearing antheridial branches; B, ventral view of A showing the origin of an antheridial branch (Based on Campbell).

(*a*) **Antheridia.** (*i*) *Position and structure* (Fig. 10.4). The antheridia usually occur singly in the axils of small leaves or bracts of the special side branches of the male plant (Fig. 10.3 A). The antheridial branches differ from the sterile branches in two respects. In the first instance the special male branches stand approximately at right angles to the main stem. Secondly, they bear light-green leaves or bracts which are closely imbricated and bear antheridia singly in the axils (A). These two features make them conspicuous and different from the sterile vegetative branches.

(*ii*) *Structure of antheridium* (Fig. 10.4 B). The antheridia are long stalked. The stalk bears the nearly spherical body. It consists of two rows of cells. The globular body has a **jacket** or **wall** one cell thick in the upper part and two to three cells thick towards the base. The wall cells contain numerous chloroplasts. Inside the wall is a mass of colourless **androcytes** or **spermatids.** Each androcyte gives rise to spirally coiled, biflagellate **sperm** (Fig. 10.5 K).

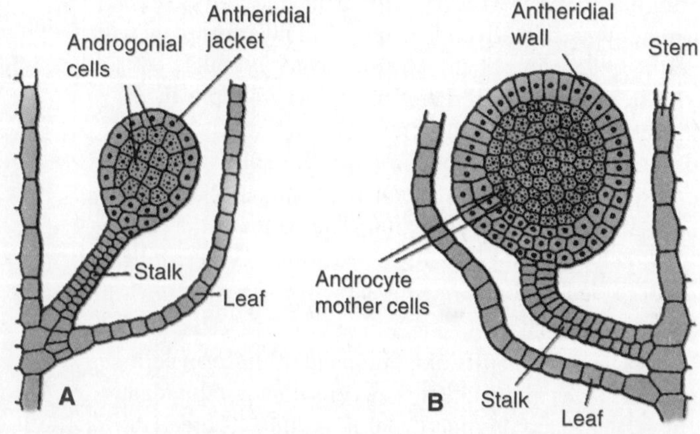

Fig. 10.4. (A—B). ***Porella* sp.** A young antheridium in section arising in the axil of antheridial bract; B, nearly mature antheridium showing structure.

(*iii*) *Dehiscence* (Fig. 10.5 I). On the access of water the mature antheridium dehisces in a very characteristic manner. The cells of the wall absorb water. The thinner upper part bursts open into a number of irregular lobes. The latter curl back to allow the androcytes to escape *en masse* into the water that causes the rupture. With the dissolution of the walls of the androcytes the sperms are set free.

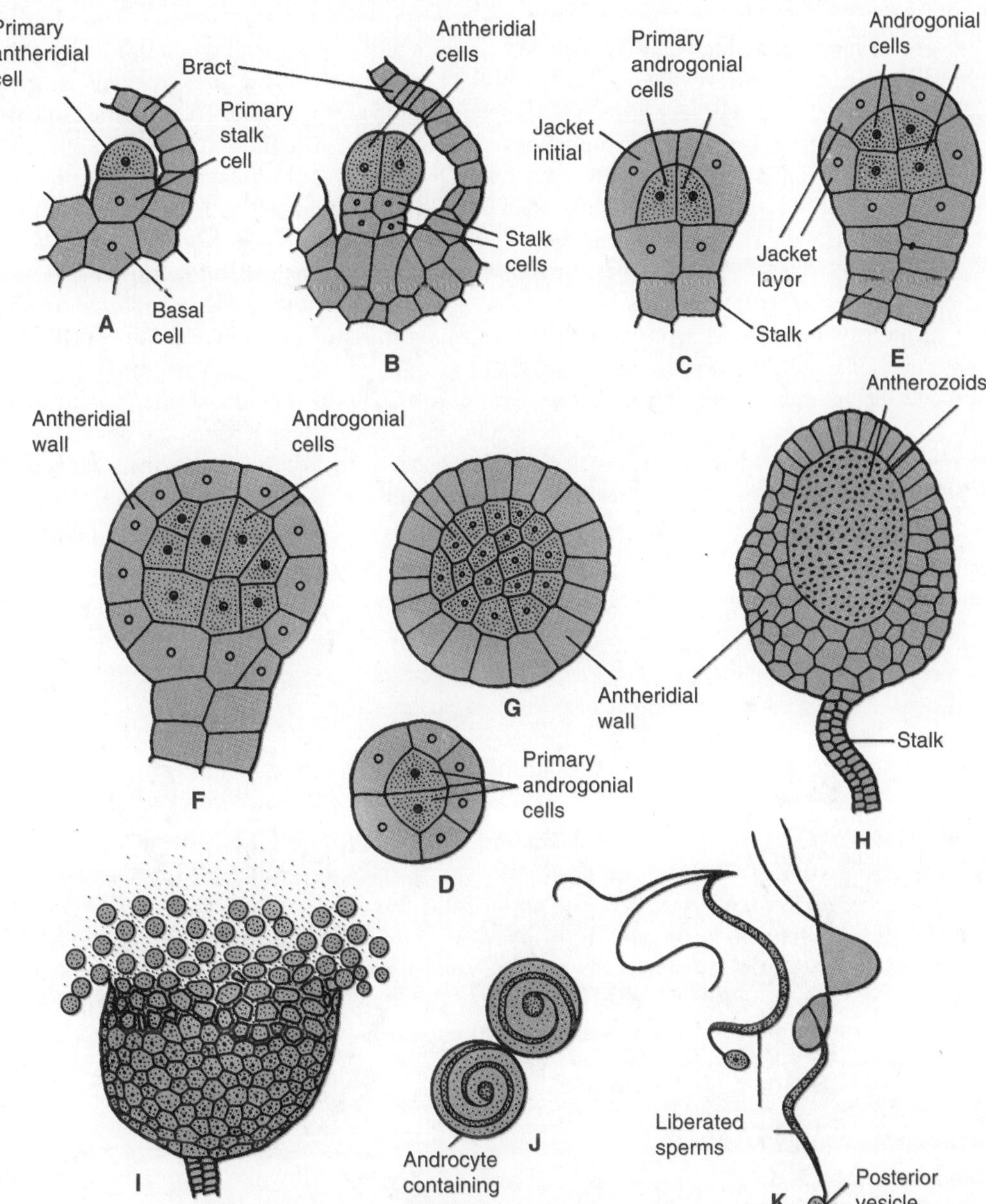

Fig. 10.5. (A—K). ***Porella* sp.** A—F, early stages in the development of antheridium; D and G are transverse sections; H, mature antheridium; I, dehisced antheridium; J, sperm enclosed in the androcyte vesicle; K, liberated sperm (Based on Cambpell).

(*iv*) *Development of antheridia* (Fig. 10.5). Each antheridium arises from one of the surface cells close to the growing apex of the male branch. It is called an **antheridial initial**. It lies at the base of the leaf and enlarges to become **papillate.** The papillate autheridial initial divides transversely into an outer and inner (basal) cell. The basal cell remains embedded. The outer cell projects above the surrounding tissue. It is called the **antheridial mother cell.** The latter divides by a horizontal wall into two cells. Of these the upper one functions as a **primary antheridial cell** and the lower as a **primary stalk cell** (A). The latter undergoes segmentation to give rise to a stalk two cells in width and several cells in height.

The primary antheridial cell (A) develops into the body of the antheridium. It undergoes a vertical division to produce two equal sister cells (B). Each sister cell divides by two intersecting walls. These divisions can best be seen in cross-sections of the antheridium. They separate a **central androgonial cell** from the two outer **jacket** or **wall initials** (C). The former is tetrahedral in form. The first jacket initial in each half has by now divided by an anticlinal wall into two. The body of the antheridium in a cross-section, at this stage, shows two **androgonial cells** surrounded by six **jacket** or **wall initials** (D). The latter divide and redivide by anticlinal divisions to produce a single layered **antheridial wall** (F—G). Later on periclinal divisions appear in the cells of the lower part of the antheridial wall (G). The latter thus becomes 2 to 3 layers thick at the base (H). The androgonial cells in the meantime divide and redivide to produce a **mass of androcyte mother cells**. Each androcyte mother cell divides by a diagonal wall to form two **androcytes**.The protoplast of each androcyte metamorphoses into a biflagellate sperm (H—I). The sperm has a slender, spirally coiled body (K). It shows two complete coils. The flagella are somewhat longer than the body. They are inserted at the anterior thin end. A small vesicle is attached to the posterior end of the spirally coiled body.

(*b*)**Archegonia.** (*i*) *Position* (Fig. 10.6 A, B). The archegonia are produced on the lateral branches of plants other than the males. These **female plants** (A) are larger than the males. The side branches bearing archegonia are exceptionally short (B). Each archegonial branch usually bears a few usually four or five leaves. After these the segments cut off by the apical cell of the archegonial

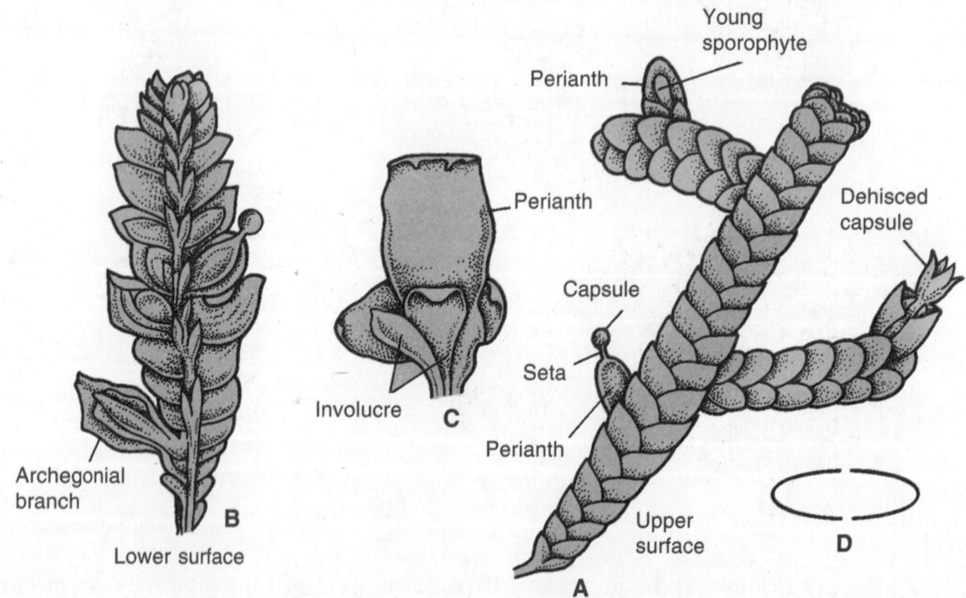

Fig. 10.6. (A—D). ***Porella***. A dorsal view of a portion of the female plant bearing archegonial branches; B, ventral view of a portion of the female plant showing the position of archegonial branches; C, female branch of *P. platyphylla* enlarged; D, ground plan of a dorsiventrally compressed perianth. (B based on Campbell, C on Kashyap).

branch produce archegonia. The latter arise in acropetal order. Eventually the apical cell itself is used up. It is transformed into an archegonium. *Porella* thus is acrogynous. The archegonia occur in a terminal cluster (Fig. 10.7). The further growth of the archegonial branch is arrested after the formation of the terminal archegonium in the cluster. Later the whole cluster of archegonia is surrounded by a common protective envelope, the **perianth** (Fig. 10.6 C).

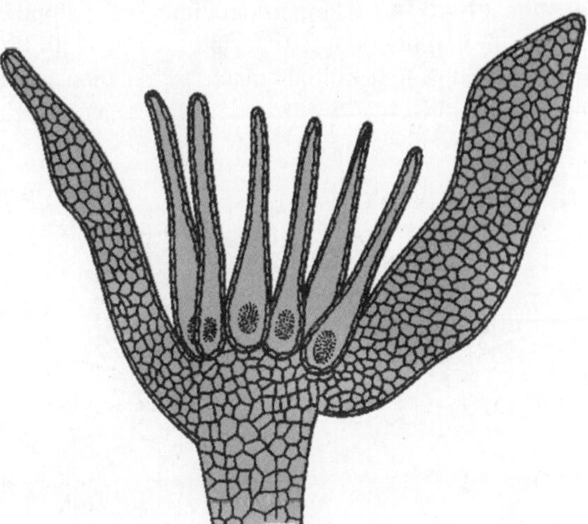

Fig. 10.7. ***Porella* sp.** A female branch bearing a terminal cluster of archegonia.

(*ii*) *Structure of archegonium* (Fig. 10.8 H). The mature archegonium is stalked. It is more or less a cylindrical object (H). The neck consists of five vertical rows of **neck cells** (I). They enclose the **neck canal.** The neck canal is usually filled with 8 broad **neck canal cells**. The basal portion of the archegonium is called the **venter**. It is but little enlarged. It has a two cell-thick wall surrounding the **venter cavity**. The latter contains a small **egg** with the **ventral canal cell** above it.

(*iii*) *Development of archegonium* (Fig. 10.8). The first three to four segments cut off by the apical cell of the female branch develop into leaves. Thereafter the derivatives of the apical cell function as **archegonium initials**. They thus lie very close to the growing apex. Each archegonium initial enlarges into a papillate outgrowth. The latter divides horizontally into a **basal cell** and a **distal cell** (A). The former is called the **pedicel cell**. It undergoes repeated segmentation to form the **stalk** of the archegonium. The distal cell functions as the **archegonium mother cell**. It undergoes segmentation on the lines usual for the Metzgeriales (*Pellia*) to produce the archegonium.

The archegonium mother cell divides by three eccentric vertical walls (C). Of these the last division wall is the shortest. In this way three **lateral** or **peripheral cells** are separated from the **primary axial cell** surrounded by them (C). Two of the peripheral cells are large and the third is the smallest. Each of the former two again divides by a vertical wall (E). The smaller cell remains undivided. A ring of five peripheral cells is formed. They are the **jacket initials**. They surround the middle **primary axial cell**. The latter overtops the jacket initials and divides transversely to produce an outer cell and an inner cell (D). The former is called the **primary cap cell** and the latter **central cell**. The central cell is enclosed by the five jacket initials. From this stage onward the development is exactly similar to that of *Pellia* and other heptics. It is described on page 140.

(*iv*) *Dehiscence of archegonium*. On the access of water the mature archegonium opens at its tip. The cover cells are separated from each other and folded back. All this is brought by the hydrostatic pressure set up within the archegonium by the mucilage mass resulting from the disintegration of the axial row of cells except the egg.

(*c*) *Fertilization*. It takes place in the presence of water as in the other liverworts. It is provided by the rain or dew. The transportation of the sperms is facilitated by the fact that the male and the female plants grow in company in dense patches closely covering the substratum. The sperms from the dehisced antheridia swim in thin films of water covering the male and the female plants and reach the archegonia to bring about fertilization in the usual way.

SPOROPHYTIC PHASE (Fig. 10.9)

This phase in the life cycle is concerned with the production and efficient scattering of meiospores. It is the function of the asexual individual in the life cycle called the **sporogonium** or the **sporophyte** (A). The sporogonium is developed from the diploid zygote by repeated mitotic divisions, differentiation of cells and their growth. For its nutrition the adult sporogonium depends entirely upon the archegonial branch (sexual plant) to the top of which it remains organically attached throughout its life.

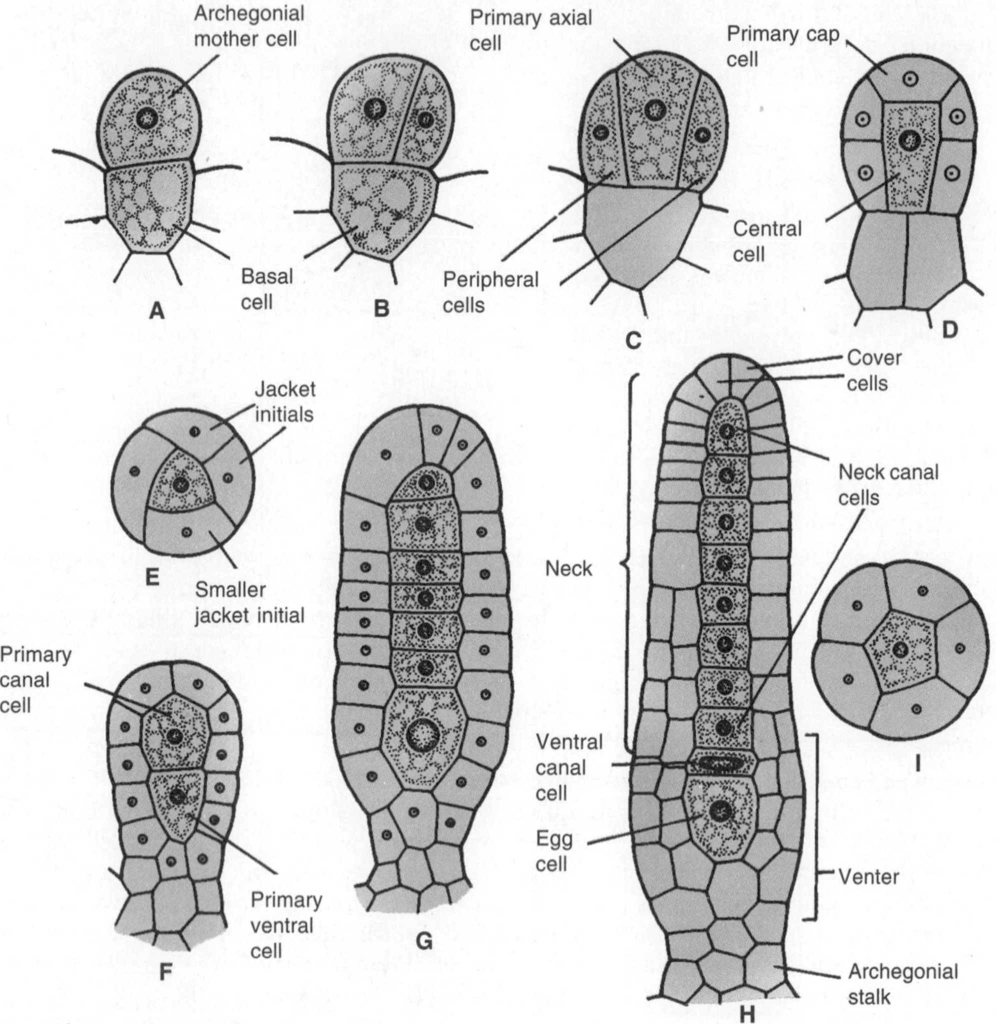

Fig. 10.8. (A—H). ***Porella* sp.** A—G, early stages in the development of archegonium; H, nearly mature archegonium; I,T.S. archegonium. Explanation in the text (Based on Campbell).

Sporogonium (Fig. 10.9 A). The sporogonium at maturity, is differentiated into the **foot**, the **seta** and the **capsule**.

Foot. It is merely a somewhat enlarged base of the seta. It is indistinct.

Seta. It is short. It carries at its top the spherical capsule.

Capsule (A). The spherical capsule at maturity has two to four cells thick wall. Within the capsule wall are the spores and elaters. The elaters are short, each with one to three spiral bands (D). The elaterophore is absent. With the maturing of the spores within the capsule the seta suddenly elongates carrying the capsule upward. With the elongation of the seta the capsule breaks through the surrounding calyptra and projects beyond the perianth and the involucre (A). The exposed capsule dries and opens into four spreading lobes called the **valves**. The latter do not extend down to the base of the capsule.

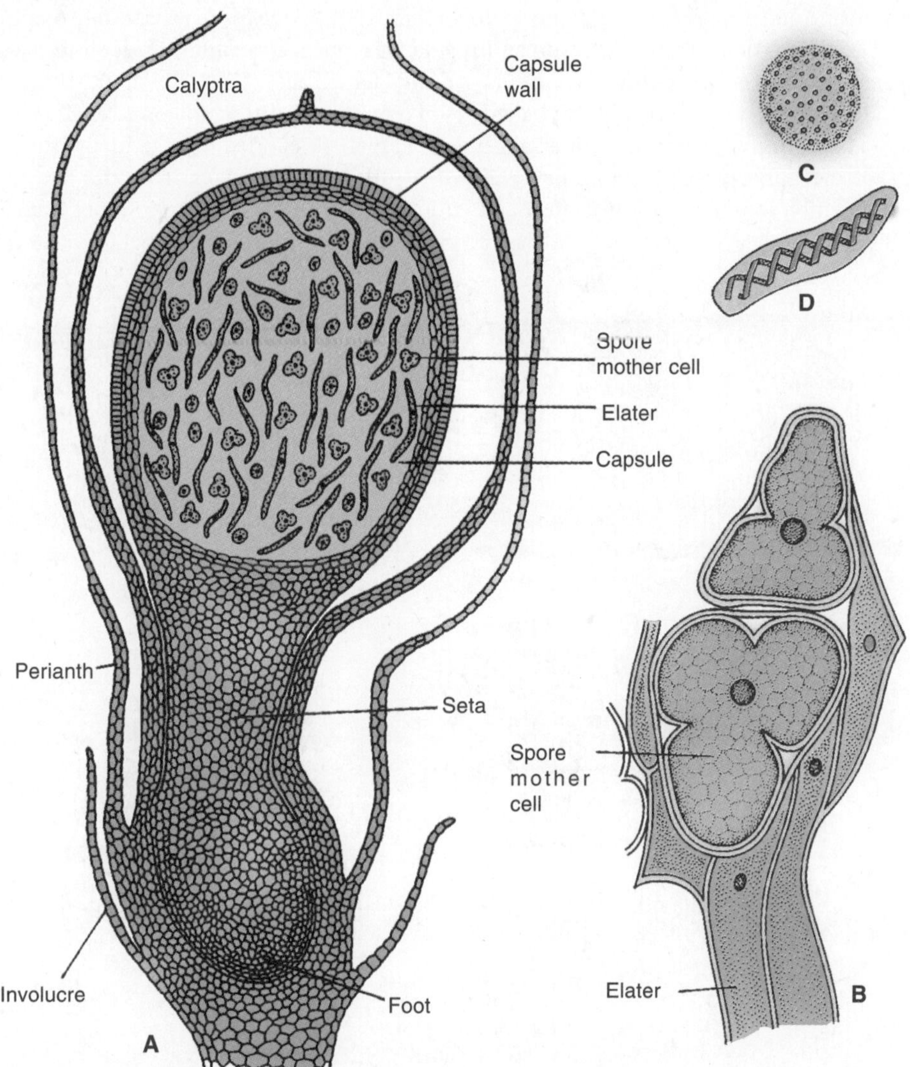

Fig. 10.9. (A—D). ***Porella* sp**. A, L.S. through a nearly mature sporogonium showing structure; B, portion of capsule enlarged to show the lobed spore mother cells and elater cells; C, a mature spore; D, an elater with a double spiral band (B after Campbell, C—D after Kashyap).

In some other leafy Jungermanniales the tip of the female branch becomes enlarged into a pouch-like structure. It is called the **marsupium**. It is the store-house of water and food. The foot of the sporophyte is embedded in it.

(*a*) *Development of the sporogonium* (Fig. 10.10). The zygote (A) divides by a transverse wall into two halves (B). The upper is called an **epibasal half** and the lower **hypobasal**. The former enters upon active segmentation. It divides by a transverse wall into two cells (C). The young embryo, at this stage, consists of a row of three superimposed cells. This linear stage of the embryo is typical of the Jungermanniales and contrasts with the octant stage typical of the Marchantiales in general. The basal cell of the row is the hypobasal cell. It takes no further part in the development of the embryo. It remains as a small appendage at the base of the developing sporophyte and is called the **haustorium**. Some writers call it **suspensor** (D and E). The upper two cells of the row (C) derived from the epibasal half develop into the entire sporogonium. They divide by transverse and longitudinal divisions. These divisions, however, are in an irregular sequence. It becomes difficult to make out the number of segments which form the capsule. As a matter of fact the distinction into the seta and the capsule regions is obscure. The embryo consists of a mass of undifferentiated cells (I). The cells show a good deal of irregularity in their arrangement. Campbell reported that the first periclinals in the cells of the upper part of the embryo appear at different distances from the surface (J). The differentiation into the **amphithecium** and **endothecium** regions is therefore not established

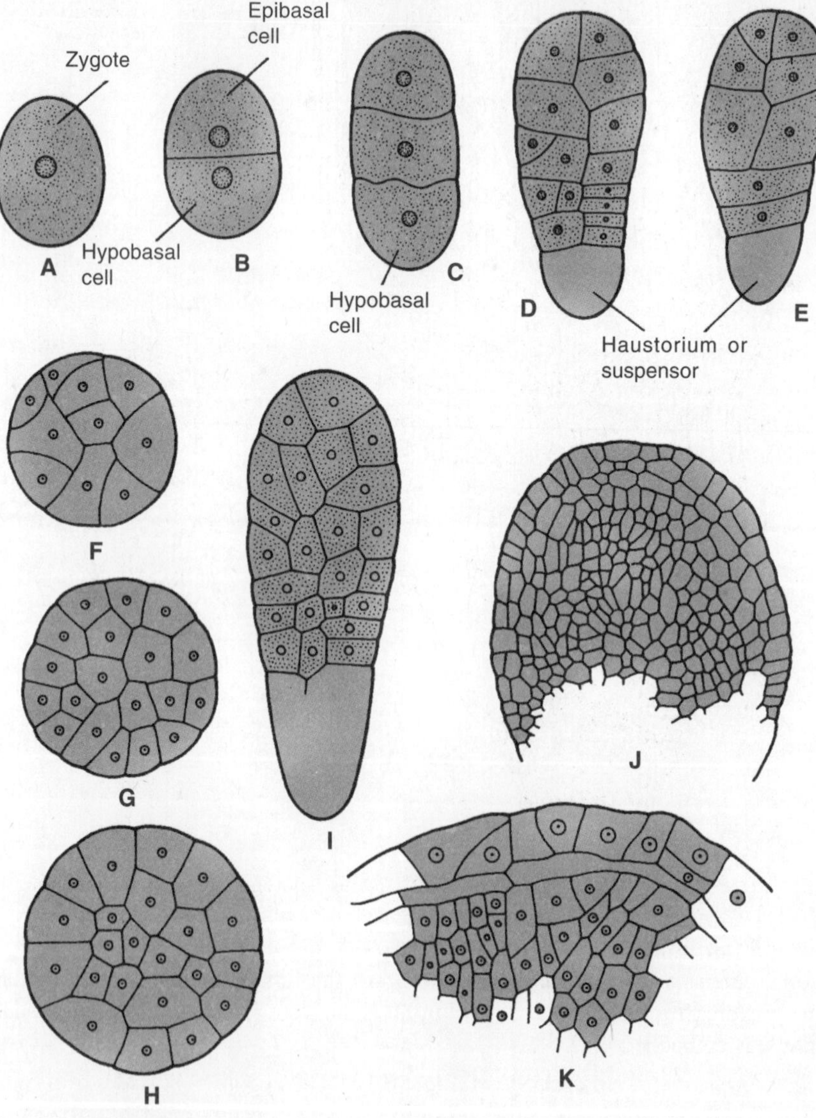

Fig. 10.10. (A—K). ***Porella* sp.** A—I, early stages in the development of embryo; F—H, are transverse sections; J and K, advanced stages of development. Explanation in the text (C-K after Campbell).

by the first periclinals. At a subsequent stage these regions are well-defined. The single layered amphithecium, at first, divides by anticlinal walls and later by periclinal walls to give rise to the capsule wall two or more cells in thickness (K). The entire endothecium mass becomes the **archesporium**. The latter by divisions forms the **sporogenous tissue**.

At a later stage many of the cells of the sporogenous tissue cease to divide. They function as **spore mother cells**. They grow in all directions. The remaining cells of the sporogenous tissue divide and become elongated. They are the **elater cells**. The spore mother cells and the elater cells are intermingled (Fig. 10.9 B). They are not arranged in any regular order. Prior to meiosis the spore mother cells become deeply four-lobed structures. The elongated elater cells lie in between them with their thin tapering ends fitting into the spaces between the lobed spore mother cells (Fig. 10.9 B).

(*b*) **Sporogenesis**. During early prophase the inner layer of the wall of the spore mother cell projects into its cavity to make it a four-lobed structure. The lobes are tetrahedrally arranged and mark the position of the four spores. They are connected in the middle by a narrow neck which contains the **diploid nucleus**. The latter divides by **meiosis** to produce four haploid daughter nuclei. One of these migrates into each of the four lobes. The lobes finally separate by cell walls laid simultaneously between them. A tetrad of spores is formed, it is surrounded by a common sheath. The latter ruptures and the ripe spores are separated. Each spore has a poorly developed exospore. The elater cells develop 1 to 3 spiral bands of thickening material on their wall.

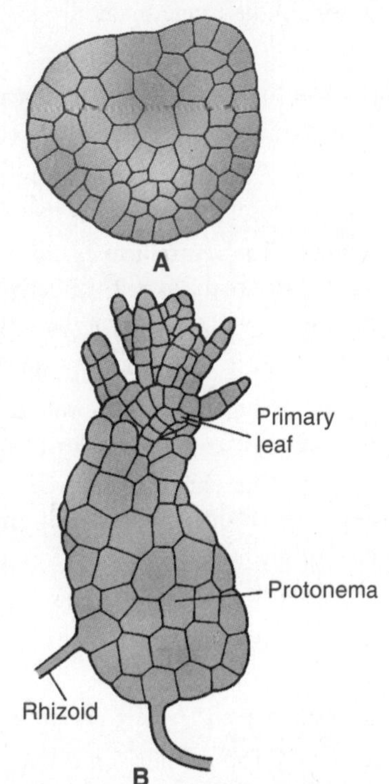

Fig. 10.11. (A—B). ***Porella* sp.** A, disc-shaped protonema; B, sporeling of *P. platyphylla* (B after Goebel).

The seta which is developed from the lower portion of the embryo remains short. It projects a little beyond the surrounding protective envelopes. The latter in *Porella* are the **calyptra**, the **perianth** and the **involucre**. The calyptra is many cell layer thick. The perianth is formed by the fusion of the two distal bracts immediately below the archegonial cluster. The bracts around the perianth become enlarged to form the involucre. The inconspicuous foot is developed from the base of the seta. It is, in fact, the enlarged base of the seta.

(c) Dehiscence of the capsule. As soon as the spores are mature, the seta elongates. By this the calyptra is ruptured. The capsule is raised above the surrounding protective envelopes which are the perianth and involucre (Fig. 10.6 A). Drying out of the exposed capsule opens it at the apex by crossed cleavages into four spreading valves. The valves do not extend down to the base (Fig. 10.6 A). The hygroscopic movements of the elaters help in flicking away the spores to some distance.

Spore structure. The spores are small, spherical and little ornamented in contrast to the relatively large, strikingly ornamented spores of the Marchantiales and the Metzgeriales. The thin spore wall is differentiated into two layers, the outer **exospore** and inner **endospore**. The exospore is either smooth or has a simple architecture. In the latter case it may be papillose or finely echinate.

Germination of spores (Fig. 10.11). The spores begin to germinate immediately after liberation. Precocious division of the spores in *Porella* has also been reported. The development proceeds within the exospore. Neither the exospore ruptures nor the germ tube is formed. With the division of the protoplast, the endospore expands. The expanding endospore stretches the exospore considerably. Eventually the latter no longer remains visible. The repeated division of the protoplast produces a mass of cells which is circular and disclike. It is the **protonema** (A). It develops one or more rhizoids which anchor it to the substratum. Subsequently a large apical cell is established at the edge of the protonema. The apical cell functions as the growing point of the future gametophyte (B). The primary leaves are ovate. The juvenile leaves though not seen are assumed to be of the saccate inflated type.

SALIENT FEATURES

1. The plant body is a **leafy thallus** which is an elaborate, delicate structure. It has the appearance of leaf-like expansions arising from the central axis.

2. The slender, central axis or the stem is branched in a bi- or tri-pinnate manner. The branching is always **monopodial**. Dichotomous branching which is so characteristic of other liverworts is absent int he Jungermanniales.

3. The so-called leaves arising from the stem are of two kinds, large **dorsal** and small **ventral**.

4. The large dorsal leaves are arranged in two lateral rows on the main axis and its branches. Being compactly arranged they cover the axis from above and overlap each other **incubously**.

5. Each dorsal leaf is a **bilobed** structure. The upper larger lobe is oval. The smaller ventral lobe is closely appressed to its lower surface. It lies more or less parallel to the stem.

6. The ventral leaves are small, simple and reduced. They are arranged in a single row on the ventral side of the axis. Together with the ventral lobes of the dorsal leaves they present the appearance of three rows of leaves on the lower surface of the axis.

7. Each leaf generally consists of a single layer of cells and has no **midrib**.

8. Simple, **smooth-walled** rhizoids spring from the ventral side of the axis near the bases of the ventral leaves and fix the plant to the substratum. They are unicellular.

9. The elaborate leafy external form is correlated with simple internal structure. There is slight or no differentiation of tissues. The mature stems are differentiated into outer cortex and central medulla.

10. The **scales** and **tuberculate rhizoids** are absent.

11. Apical growth takes place by means of a single, large **apical cell** pyramidal in shape.

12. All species of *Porella* (*Madotheca*) are **dioecious**. The female plants are distinctly larger than the males. The sex organs are borne on special side branches.

13. The **antheridia** occur singly in the axils of leaves on the **antheridial branches** which spring approximately at right angles from the central axis and bear closely imbricated light green leaves which are often called the perigonial leaves or **bracts**.

14. The spherical **body** of an antheridium is elevated on a long, slender **stalk**.

15. The spirally coiled body of the biflagellate **sperm** shows, at least, two complete coils.

16. The **archegonia** occur in a cluster at the apex of a very short **archegonial branch**. The latter bears only two to four perichaetial leaves.

17. The growth of archegonial branch is arrested by the formation of the terminal archegonium of the cluster.

18. The mature archegonium is more or less a cylindrical object with the **neck** as broad as the **venter**.

19. The neck consists of five vertical rows of **neck cells** enclosing a **neck canal** containing usually 8 broad **neck canal cells**.

20. The venter wall is two cell layers thick before fertilization. The venter cavity contains a small egg and a ventral canal cell above the former.

21. The mature sporogonium is differentiated into an indistinct **foot**, a short **seta** and a spherical **capsule**. It is developed from the epibasal half of the embryo.

22. The capsule wall is two to four cell layers thick. It encloses the spores and elaters. The elaters are short, each with 1 to 3 spiral bands. The elaterophore is absent. The spore mother cells become deeply four-lobed structures before meioses.

23. The mature capsule dehisces by four spreading lobes or **valves** which extend only half way down to its base.

24. The spore, on germination, produces a distinct **protonema stage**.

SUMMARY OF THE LIFE-CYCLE OF *PORELLA* (Fig. 10.12)

The life cycle of *Porella* may be summarized with the help of the accompanying diagram (Fig. 10.12). It is comprised, as usual, of two generations, the **gametophyte** and the **sporophyte**.

1. Gametophyte generation. The conspicuous structures of this phase are the **sexual** or the **gametophyte** plants (A,B). Each of these is produced by the germination of a haploid spore (meiospore). The sproe (N), on falling on a suitable substratum, undergoes segmentation to produce a multicellular, disc-like **protonema** (O). On the edge of the protonema is established an **apical cell**. The latter by active segmentation produces the sexual or gametophyte plant (A or B). It loves to grow on rocks over which water trickles and the bark of trees. It is the most conspicuous and independent plant in the life cycle. It is chiefly concerned with sexual reproduction. The sexual plant grows dorsiventrally upon the substratum and consists of a central axis (the so-called stem) bearing leaf-like expansions. The long, slender stem is branched in a bi- or tri-pinnate manner. The so-called leaves that it bears are of two kinds, **dorsal** and **ventral**. The dorsal leaves are large and nearly oval. They are closely set in two lateral rows on the stem which they completely cover from above. They overlap each other **incubously**. Each dorsal leaf is divided into two lobes. The ventral smaller lobe is closely appressed to the lower surface of the larger lobe. It runs more or less parallel to the stem.

The ventral leaves are small, simple and reduced. They are arranged in a single row on the lower side of the stem. Both kinds of leaves of *Porella* consist of a single layer of cells. There is no **midrib**. The external elaborate appearance of the gametophyte plant is not correlated with histological differentiation. There is slight or no differentiation of tissues.

The sexual plants are **dioecious**. The male palnt (B) is markedly smaller than the female. The male plant bears **antheridia** singly in the axils of leaves (D) on special side branches which spring nearly at right angles from the main stem (B). The long, stalked antheridium has a globular **body**. The wall of the antheridum is single layered in the upper part but 2 to 3 cell layers thick in its basal part (D). On the access of water thinner apical part of the antheridium ruptures. The biflagellate sperms (F) are liberated in the water that causes the rupture.

The **archegonia** occur in a cluster at the apex of a very small side branch arising from the female plant (A). The archegonial branch bears only 2 or 3 leaves. The apical cell of the female branch is also involved in the formation of the terminal archegonium in the cluster. The growth of the female branch thereafter is arrested. Each archegonium is more or less a cylindrical object with the **venter** as broad as the **neck** (C). The neck consists of five vertical rows of **neck cells**. They enclose the narrow neck canal. The latter contains usually a row of 8 **neck canal cells**. The venter contains an **egg** and a **ventral canal cell**. The **ventral wall** is two cell layers thick before fertilization.

The sexual plants (male and female) along with the structures produced on them constitute the **gametophyte generation** in the life cycle. It starts with meiosis and ends with fertilisation. Meiospores are the first structures of this phase (N). The last structures are the gametes (eggs and sperms, E-F). The gametophyte generation therefore comprises the *spores, protonema, leafy plants,* (male and female), *antheridia, archegonia, sperms* and *eggs*. They all are characterised by the haploid number of chromosomes.

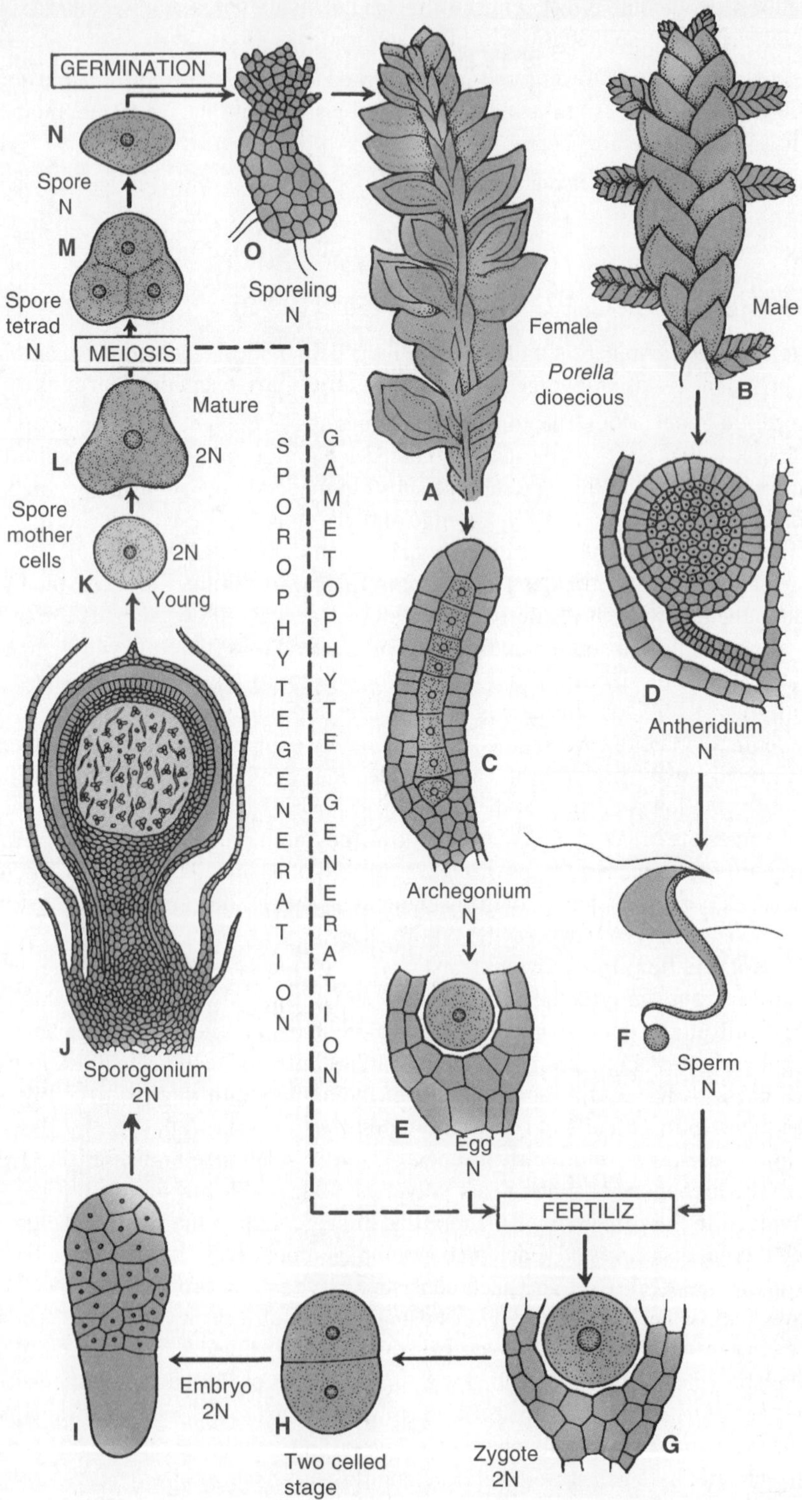

Fig. 10.12. (A—Q). Diagrammatic representation of the sexual life cycle of ***Porella***.

2. **Sporophyte phase**. It starts with the **diploid zygote** which is formed as a result of fertilisation (G). The zygote, by active segmentation (H,I) gives rise to a mass of undifferentiated cells called the **embryo**. The latter by further segmentation, differentiation and growth develops into a radially constructed **sporophyte plant**. It is also called the **sporogonium** (J).

The sporogonium is differentiated into a short **seta** terminating in a globular **capsule** (I). The basal portion of seta forms an indistinct **foot**. The sporogonium is incapable of self-nutrition. It lives parasitically upon the parent gametophyte. In fact it is speciallised to receive nutrition from the parent gemetophyte to which it remains originally connected throughout its life. The capsule region of the sprogonium is devoted to the production and the dispersal of meiospores. It consists of a wall two to four cell layers thick. Within the capsule wall is the solid sporogenous tissue. The latter gets differentiated into spore mother cells and elater cells.

The sporogonium and the structures produced by it constitute the **sporophyte generation**. All these structures have a **diploid** number of chromosomes. The sporophytic generation starts with fertilization and ends with meiosis, so the first structure of this phase is the **zygote** and the last **spore mother cells**. The sporophytic generation therefore consists of the *zygote*, the *embryo*, the *sporogonium,* the *spore mother* and *elater cells*. The spore mother cells (K—L) which are the last structures of this phase become deeply four lobed and each undergoes **meiosis** to produce four haploid spores (M). With meiosis the sporophyte generation ends.

From the account given above it is clear that the reproductive **structures of one phase or generation do not produce the same phase**. On the other hand they give rise to the alternate plant in the life cycle. This results in the regular alternation of the sexually reproducing generation with the asexually reproducing one. This phenomenon is called "**Alternation of Generations**".

SYSTEMATIC POSITION OF *PORELLA*

Division	:	Bryophyta
Class	:	Hepaticopsida
Order	:	Jungermanniales
Family	:	Porellaceae (Madothecaceae)
Genus	:	*Porella* (*Madotheca*)
Species	:	*platyphylla*

QUESTIONS

ESSAY TYPE

1. Describe the vegetative phase of any foliose Jungermanniales.
2. Give a brief account of the structure and development of the sex organs of *Porella* (*Madotheca*).
3. Describe in detail the sporophyte phase of *Porella.* *(Kanpur M.Sc., 2007)*
4. Enumerate the salient features you come across in the life cycle of *Porella* (*Madotheca*).
5. With the help of a sketch give the life cycle of *Porella.*
6. Compare the structure and development of the sporogonium of *Marchantia* and *Pellia* or *Porella*. Which of the two is advanced and why?
7. Describe the development of sex organs in *Riccia* or *Porella.* *(Allahabad, 1991)*
8. What is the difference between sporogonium and sporangium? Write a comparative account of sporogonium of *Porella* and *Sphagnum(Allahabad, 1992)*
9. With the help of labelled diagrams only compare the gametophyte of *Anthoceros, Porella* and *Pellia.* *(Allahabad, 1994, 1996)*

10. Give only labelled diagrams of L.S. of mature sporophytes of *Marchantia*, *Porella* and *Pellia*.
(Allahabad, 1995; Kumaon 1995)

11. With the help of figures, write a comparative account of the structure of sporogonium of *Porella* and *Sphagnum*.
(Allahabad, 1999; Himachal Pradesh, 1993)

12. Draw a series of labelled diagrams to show the life cycle of *Porella*.
(Awadh, 1992; Gorakhpur, 1990; Allahabad, 2001)

13. Write a comparative account of the sporophytes of *Porella* and *Pellia* or *Marchantia*.
(Awadh, 1994; Gorakhpur, 1994, 1999)

14. Give a comparative account of the gametophyte of *Porella* and *Pogonatum*.
(Gorakhpur, 1992, 1996)

15. Give an illustrated account of the external and internal features of the gametophyte of *Porella*.

16. Taking examples of the types studied, compare the arrangement and distribution of sex organs in Marchantiales and Jungermanniales. Illustrate your answer with suitable diagrams.

17. Give an illustrated account of external gametophytic plant body of any two of the following:
(*a*) *Riccia* (*b*) *Anthoceros* (*c*) *Porella*.
Place them in their systematic position.
(Punjab, 1992, 1998)

18. Draw the vegetative structures of *Porella*, *Sphagnum* and *Funaria* plants and compare them.
(Himachal Pradesh, 1994)

19. Describe the structure of mature sporogonium of *Porella*. Compare it with that of *Marchantia*. Which one of the two is advanced and why?
(Himachal Pradesh, 1995)

20. Describe the life cycle of a leafy liverwort studied by you and draw well labelled diagrams of the life cycle.
(Himachal Pradesh, 1999).

21. Describe in detail the gametophyte of *Porella*.
(Bangalore, 2002; Mahatma Gandhi, 1997)

22. Describe briefly the structure and sexual reproduction in *Porella*.
(Vinoba Bhave, 1997)

23. Give an illustrated account of *Poreles.*
(Punjab 2000)

24. Give comparative account of external morphology of *Riccia* and *Porella*.
(Punjab, 2001)

SHORT ANSWER TYPE

25. **Draw labelled diagrams of :**
(*a*) Leaf arrangement in *Porella*.
(Allabhabad, 1993)
(*b*) L.S. sporogonium of *Porella* and *Funaria*. *(Allahabad, 1993)*
(*c*) L.S. sporogonium of *Porella*.
(Allahabad, 1994)
(*d*) L.S. sporophyte of *Porella*.
(Awadh, 1995, 1996)
(*e*) Leaves of *Porella*. *(Gorakhpur, 1999)*
(*f*) L.S. Antheridial branch of *Porella*.
(Allahabad, 2003)

26. Mention the systematic position of *Porella*
(Awadh, 1997)

27. Write short notes on :
(*a*) Leaves in *Porella*,
(Gorakhpur, 1993; Calicut, 1998; Mahatma Gandhi, 1998)
(*b*) Comparative account of external morphology of *Porella*, *Sphagnum* and *Pogonatum*. *Gorakhpur, 1994)*
(*c*) Sporogenous tissue in *Anthoceros* and *Porella*. *(Gorakhpur, 1996)*
(*d*) Antheridium of *Porella*. *(Gorakhpur, 1998; Mahatma Gandhi, 1996)*

(*e*) Arrangement and structure of leaves in *Porella.* *(Guru Nanak Dev, 1992)*

(*f*) Sporophyte of *Porella.* *(Mahatma Gandhi, 1996)*

(*g*) Gametophyte of *Porella.* *(Mahatma Gandhi, 1996; Allahabad, 2002)*

(*h*) Amphigastria. *(Lucknow, 1991; Allahabad, 2002, 2003)*

(*i*) Antheridial Branch of *Porella.* *(Allahabad, 2005)*

(*j*) *Porella* (Madotheca) sporophytes only *(Kanpur, 2009)*

28. Describe the position and development of sex organs in *Porella.* *(Punjab, 1993)*

29. Compare the structure of the gametophyte of *Porella* with that of *Anthoceros.* *(Himachal Pradesh, 1996)*

30. Draw and differentiate between the archegonium of *Porella* and *Funaria.* *(Himachal Pradesh, 1997).*

31. Compare the archegonia of *Porella* with that of *Marchantia* *(Himachal Pradesh, 1999).*

32. Describe the structure of mature sporogonium of *Porella*. How does dehiscense occur in it? *(Punjab, 1996)*

33. What is the peculiarity of *Porella* leaves? *(Mahatma Gandhi, 1998)*

34. Differentiate between

(*i*) *Porella* and *Pellia* *(Awadh, M.Sc. 1999)*

(*ii*) Sporogonia of *Madotheca* (*Porella*) and *Sphagnum* *(Himachal Pradesh, 2000)*

35. (*a*) Name a bryophyte which has amphigastria.

(*b*) Compare the sporophytes of *Porella* with *Pellia.* *(Allahabad, 2004; Kanpur M.Sc., 2003)*

OBJECTIVE TYPE

36. Fill in the blanks :

(*i*) Elaters are sterile structures found alongwith the spores and help in liberation of spores in ________ .

(*ii*) In *Porella* the gametophyte is ____________ .

(*iii*) Archegonia in *Porella* are found in ___________ .

(*iv*) In *Porella*, the antheridia are ____________ .

(*v*) The leaves of the ventral row in *Porella* are called _________ .

(*vi*) Absorption of water in *Porella* takes place by _________ and _________ .

(*vii*) The number of neck canal cells in the Archegonium of *Porella* ranges between _____________.

(*viii*) The capsule is globose in *Porella* _________ .

(*ix*) The dorsal leaves are _________ .

(*x*) The structure of axis is _________ .

37. Select the correct answer :

(*i*) Family Porellaceae is represented by

(*a*) A single genus
(*b*) Two genera
(*c*) Three genera
(*d*) Many genera.

(*ii*) The gametophyte in *Porella* is

(*a*) Thalloid
(*b*) Leafy
(*c*) Both thalloid and leafy
(*d*) Neither thalloid nor leafy.

(*iii*) In *Porella* the branching is

(*a*) Monopodial (*b*) Sympodial
(*c*) Dichotomous (*d*) Absent.

(*iv*) The leaves in *Porella* are arranged in

(*a*) One row (*b*) Two rows
(*c*) Three rows (*d*) Four rows.

(*v*) Amphigastria is the term used for ventral leaves in

(*a*) *Fossombronia* (*b*) *Pellia*

(*c*) *Frullaria* (*d*) *Porella.*

(*vi*) Colonies of which alga have been reported to occur in *Porella*?

(*a*) *Oscillatoria* (*b*) *Nostoc*

(*c*) *Anabaena* (*d*) *Lyngbya.*

(*vii*) Midrib is absent in the leaves in

(*a*) *Funaria* (*b*) *Polytrichum*

(*c*) *Pogonatum* (*d*) *Porella.*

(*viii*) Antheridia in *Porella* occur

(*a*) Singly (*b*) In pairs

(*c*) In groups (*d*) Rarely.

(*ix*) The number of neck canal cells in the archegonium of *Porella* is

(*a*) 4 cells (*b*) 6 cells

(*c*) 8 cells (*d*) 10 cells.

(*x*) The capsule in *Porella* is

(*a*) Oval (*b*) Elongate

(*c*) Spherical (*d*) Irregular.

(*xi*) In *Porella* the amphigastria are

(*a*) Dorsal leaves

(*b*) Ventral leaves

(*c*) Lateral leaves

(*d*) Part of dorsal leaves.

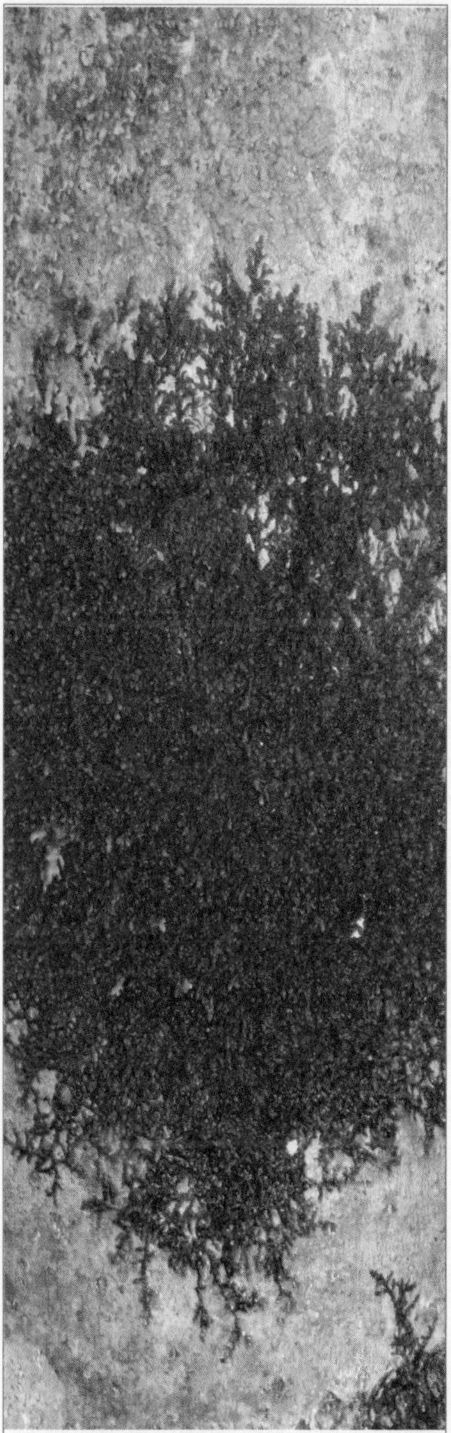

Image of *Frullania digitata*

CHAPTER 11

JUNGERMANNIALES
Frullaniaceae
Frullania

- Family Frullaniaceae
- Frullania Raddi
- Adult Gametophyte
- Systematic Position of Frullania

FAMILY FRULLANIACEAE

The family Frullaniaceae comprises large or medium-sized rarely small green to brown or dark brown pinnately branched foliose liverworts in which the leaves are arranged in three rows on the stem. There are two rows of lateral (dorsal) leaves. They are one cell thick with no midrib. In addition there is a third row of small leaves on the ventral side of the stem. They are better known as the **amphigastria** or **underleaves.** The lateral leaves are close set, imbricate, incubous and complicate-bilobed. The upper, larger **antical lobe** is flat and expanded. The smaller, lower or postical lobe usually known as the **lobule** is cylindrical and sac-like or galeate, sometimes evolute. The amphigastria differ from the lateral leaves in size, shape and usually have a bifid or retuse or entire apex. The rhizoids which are unicellular and unbranched as in other hepatics, arise in a tuft from the base or middle of the underleaf. All of them are smooth-walled. Antheridia usually occur on short lateral branches in the axis of upper perigonial bracts. The archegonia occur in terminal clusters. The upper two or three perichaetical bracts are fused laterally to form a pyriform, protective envelope around the archegonial cluster known as the *perianth*. The perianth is tri- or pluri-keeled with the apex constricted into a short, tubular break. The best known genus of the family is *Frullania*.

FRULLANIA Raddi

The genus *Frullania* includes about 700 species. Kashyap (1932) reported 9 species from India but Chopra, R.S. (1943) raised the list of Indian species to 39.

DISTRIBUTION AND HABITAT

Predominantly the Frullanias are tropical. Many grow in the subtropical regions. The terrestrial species grow on the wet ground and the epiphytic species occur on the **bark** of trees, even on leaves in wet tropical forests. Moist rocks are the favourite habitat of the **lithophytes**. Usually they grow in closely appressed flat patches or form extensive mats.

ADULT GAMETOPHYTE

External features (Fig. 11.1 A—F). The gametothallus is dorsiventral and is differentiated into a branched, prostrate, central stem-like axis and the leaves. The stem is pinnately or bipinnately branched. The branches originate beside the leaves. The leaves on the stem are inserted in three rows. There are two rows of dorsal leaves arranged laterally on the stem. They function as photosynthetic organs. There is a third row of smaller leaves on the lower or ventral side of the stem. These are known as the **underleaves** or **amphigastria (D)**. The closely set lateral (dorsal) leaves are almost transversely inserted on the stem with the anterior edge of each leaf covering the posterior edge of the leaf in front. Such an overlapping arrangement of the leaves is described as **incubous**. Each lateral leaf is bilobed. There is a large dorsal or **antical lobe** and a small ventral or **postical lobule**. The two lobes are free or nearly free from each other. The larger antical lobe is obliquely ovate to suborbicular in shape. It is convex with a decurved apex and entire margin. There is no midrib. The lobule or postical lobe is hood-like (cucculate). In species exposed to periodic drought (such as *F. armitiana* and *F. tamarisci*) it is bladder-like and functions as a water sac in which water enters through more or less distinct openings and is retained by capillarity (F). In some species the lobule bears a short appendage near the point of its attachment. The appendage usually called the **stylus** lies between the stem and the lobule (E). The amphigastria are usually smaller than the leaves. They have a rounded or cordate base with a entire or retuse or bifid apex. The amphigastria together with the stylus form capillary spaces which retain water. The thallus is anchored

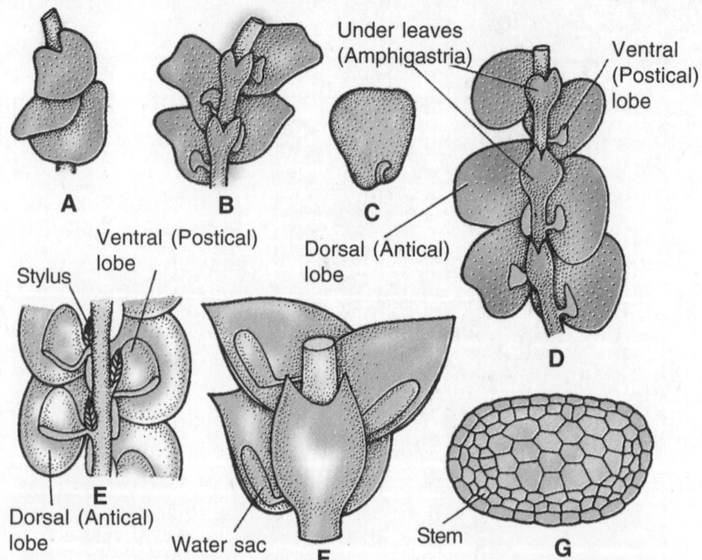

Fig. 11.1. (A—G). ***Frullania***. A, part of a shoot of *F. squarrosa* from above; B, part of a shoot of *F. squarrosa* as seen from below; C, dorsal leaf of *F. squarrosa* with an appendage; D, shoot of *F. musicola* (Ventral view); E, part of a shoot showing stylus; F, part of a shoot of *F. armitiana* (ventral view) showing water sacs on lateral leaves; G, C.S. of *F. dilatata* (A—D after Kashyap; E and G after Cavers and F after Verdoon).

to the substratum by unicellular, unbranched smooth-walled rhizoids which arise in tufts from the bases or middle of the amphigastria.

Anatomy of stem. (Fig. 11.1 G). The stem is very simple in its structure showing little tissue differentiation or cell specialization. There is no well-defined epidermis. The cortical and central medullary zones are recognisable. The cortical cells are smaller in diameter and have thick pigmented walls in the older portion of the stem. The elongated medullary cells have greater diameter and thin colourless walls. The stem has no conducting tissue.

Anatomy of leaf. The leaf is one cell layer in thickness. The cells contain many chloroplasts and a few oil bodies. The cell wall which is thin and colourless at first becomes thick and reddish or purple with age. The leaf has no midrib. However, in some species there is a conspicuous strip of cells (distinct from the other leaf cells) traversing the dorsal or antical lobe. It starts from the base of the lobe and ends a little behind the apex. The stomata and air pores are absent.

Growth. The plant grows by the activity of an apical cell which is located at the tip of the stem. It is pyramidal in shape with three cutting faces. Three sets of segments are cut off in a regular spiral sequence. Two of these are dorsal and the third is ventral. Each segment divides further. The derivatives ultimately produce a single leaf and a portion of the stem subtending it.

Thus the dorsal segments from the lateral leaves and the ventral segments develop into the amphigastria or underleaves along with portions of the stem to which they are attached.

Vegetative reproduction. It takes place by many kinds of propagula besides fragmentation:

(*i*) *Fragmentation*. The older intervening portions of pinnately or bipinnately branched stem die of old age and subsequently undergo decay and decomposition. The branches are thus separated as fragments. Each separated branch or fragment by apical growth grows into a new plant.

(*ii*) *Gemmae formation*. Watson (1955) reported the formation of rounded, multicellular gemmae on the surface and margins of leaves. They become detached from the leaf and under suitable conditions grow into new plants. Cavers (1903) observed the formation of 4-6 celled gemmae on the margin of the leaf in *F. dilatata*. The gemmae were described as discoid to irregular in form.

Hicks (1974) reported the occurrence of marginal gemmae on the dorsal lobes of the leaves of *F. eboracensis*. Each gemma is a red-brown globular mass of about 16-30 thick-walled cells. The gemmae get detached by slightest touch, water or some other environmental agent.

(*iii*) *Caducous leaves and adventitious branches*. Sorenz (1912) described caducous leaves and adventitious branches as a means of vegetative propagation in *F. brittoniae*, *F. reparia*, and *F. plana*. Degenkolbe (1937) stated that the antical lobes of the lateral leaves are shed as **propagules** leaving behind the postical lobes intact along the stem in *F. fragilifolio*. He could induce the detached propagules to give rise the new plants under cultural conditions.

(*iv*) *Perianth tubercula*. Fulford (1956) doubted the formation of true gemmae in *Frullania*. Instead she reported the formation of one to several celled tubercula on the surface of the perianth in *F. dilatata*. These nodular outgrowths are shed as propagules, each giving rise to a new plant.

Sexual reproduction (Fig. 11.2). Some species of *Frullania* are monoecious and others dioecious. The sex organs are borne on special, short, lateral branches. The monoecious species are all autoecious with the two kinds of sex organs borne on separate branches of the same plant. The leaves borne on the fertile branches, particularly those associated with the sex organs are called **bracts**. The bracts differ in shape and size from the vegetative leaves. The bracts occurring on the male branch are called the **perigonial bracts** and those occurring on the female branch are called the **perichaetial bracts**.

Antheridia (A—C). The antheridia occur on special, short lateral branches of limited growth called the male branches or **androecia** (A). Each male branch bears 2—5 or more pairs of usually concave, close set imbricate perigonial bracts. Each perigonial bract is bilobed. The two lobes are

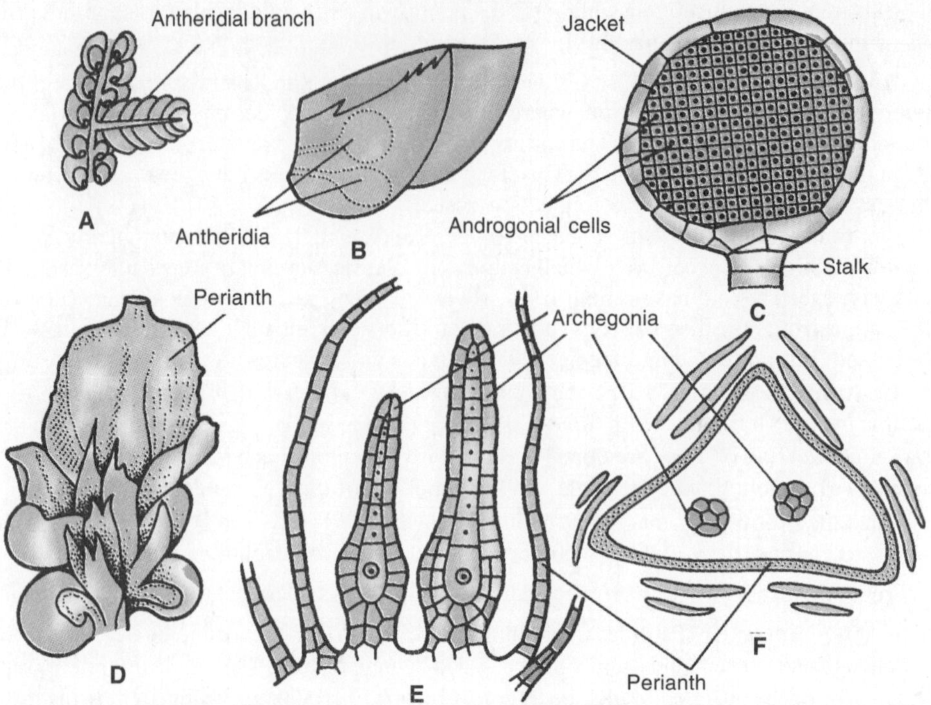

Fig. 11.2. (A—F). ***Frullania dilatata***. A, part of a male plant with an antheridial branch; B, two antheridia arising in the axil of a perigonial bract (ventral view); C, L.S. antheridium; D, female branch with a perianth in ventral view; E, L.S. perianth with two archegonia; F, T.S. perianth (After Cavers).

almost equal in isze. The antheridia develop in the axil of perigonial bracts. Usually there are two antheridia in the axil of each bract (B).

The mature antheridium is differentiated into a long, slender stalk bearing terminally a more or less globose body (C). The stalk consists of a double row of cells. The body of a nearly mature antheridium is differentiated into a central mass of **androcyte mother cells** surrounded by a jacket layer of sterile cells constituting the **antheridial wall**. Each androcyte mother cell divides by a diagonal division into two **androcytes**. The protoplast of the androcyte metamorphoses into a biflagellate antherozoid typical of the bryophytes.

Development of antheridia (Fig. 10.5). Antheridia develop from superficial cells close to the apical cell of the male branch. The **antheridial initial** protrudes above the adjoining cells and divides by a transverse wall into an inner or **basal cell** and an **outer cell**. The basal cell remains embedded in the surrounding tissue and takes no part in the development of the antheridium. The outer cell, which protrudes above the thallus tissue functions as the **antheridial mother cell**. It gives rise to the entire antheridium. At the outset the antheridial mother cell increases in size and divides transversely into an upper primary antheridial cell and a lower **primary stalk cell**. The latter undergoes segementation. The derivatives of the primary stalk cell finally produce the stalk of the antheridium consisting of a double row of cells.

The primary antheridial cell produces the body of the antheridium. It divides by a vertical wall producing two symmetrical sister cells, which in a cross section are nearly spherical each being hemispherical in outline (B). Each sister cell divides by a vertical wall diagonal to the first division producing two daughter cells of unequal size. The smaller daughter cell is the **first jacket initial** (C). The larger daughter cell divides by a periclinal wall into an inner **primary androgonial cell** and an outer **second jacket initial**. Meanwhile the first jacket initial in each half has divided by an anticlinal wall into two. In a cross section the body of an antheridium at this stage consists of two **primary androgonial cells** surrounded by six **jacket** or **wall initials** (D). The latter divide further only by anticlinal divisions to produce the antheridial wall one cell-layer in thickness. The two primary androgonial cells (C) divide and redivide to produce a central mass of fertile cells. The cells of the last cell generation are called the **androcyte mother cells** or **spermatocytes**. Each androcyte mother cell divides diagonally to form two **androcytes** or **spermatids**. The protoplast of each androcyte produces a single, slender, spirally coiled biflagellate sperm.

Archegonia (Fig. 11.2, D—F). The archegonia occur in groups at the apices of short, lateral branches. There are two to four archegonia in the cluster (E-F). The archegonial cluster is surrounded by 2—5 pairs of perichaetial bracts which are larger than the foliage leaves and are dentate or laciniate. The uppermost perichaetial bracts become laterally fused to form a common protective envelope enlcosing the archegonial cluster. It is known as the **perianth** (D). The apex of the pyriform usually trigonous perianth is constricted into a short tubular beak.

The mature archegonium (E) is a flask-shaped structure consisting of a slightly enlarged basal portion called the **venter** and a long, narrow **neck**. The venter encloses a cavity surrounded by a small **egg cell** with a **ventral canal cell** above it. The neck is made up of five vertical rows of **neck cells** surrounding an axial row of up to eight **neck canal cells**.

Development of archegonia. The archegonia develop at the apex of the female branch. The apical cell itself and the last two or three segments cut off by it function as **archegonial initials**. Each archegonial initial grows into a papilla-like outgrowth which divides transversely into a lower **pedicel cell** and an upper **archegonial mother cell**. The pedicel cell divides a number of times to form the **archegonial stalk**.

The archegonial mother cell divides by three centric vertical walls separating three **peripheral cells** from the **axial cell** which they surround. Of the three peripheral cells one is smaller than the other two. The two larger peripheral cells divide by a vertical wall. The resulting five peripheral cells function as **jacket initials**. They enclose the primary axial cell. the latter divides transversely to produce the outer primary **cover** or **cap cell** and the inner **central cell**. The five jacket initials and the central cell divide transversely. The young archegonium at this stage consists of two tiers of cells. The five jacket cells of the upper tier function as **neck initials** and the upper central cell which they enclose is the **primary neck canal cell**. The five jacket cells of the lowr tier constitute the **venter initials** and the lower central cell which they surround functions as the **primary ventral cell**.

The five neck initials divide rpeatedly by transverse divisions to form the archegonial neck consisting of five vertical rows of **neck cells**. They surround an axial row of about 8 **neck canal cells** produced by the division of the primary neck canal cell. The venter initials divide to form the one cell thick **venter wall** enclosing the **venter cavity**. Prior to fertilization the venter wall becomes two cell-layers in thickness. The venter cavity contians a lower large egg cell and an upper ventral canal cell formed by the unequal transverse division of the primary ventral cell (Fig. 11.2E).

Fertilization. Dehiscence of sex organs and fertilisation takes place in the presence of water provided by rain or dew as in the other liverworts. The zygote is retained in the venter where it germinates to develop into the second individual in the life cycle. It is known as the sporophyte or sporogonium.

Development of sporogonium (Fig. 11.3). The zygote divides transversely into an upper **epibasal** half and a lower **hypobasal** half (A). The next two divisions in the epibasal half are transverse but in the hypobasal half, it is vertical (B). The epibasal cells undergo two successive vertical divisions at right angles to one another, resulting in three tiers of four cells each in the epibasal half (C). The two hypobasal cells again divide by a vertical wall at right angles to the first. The hypobasal half of the embryo now consists of four cells arranged in a single tier. The young embryo at this stage consists of four tiers of cells namely, the **upper epibasal tier**, the **mediam**

epibasal tier, the **lower epibasal tier** and the **hypobasal tier** (C). Each tier consists of four cells. The upper epibasal tier gives rise to the **capsule**, the median epibasal tier produces the **seta** and the lower epibasal tier forms the **foot** of the sporogonium. The cells of the hypobasal tier divide repeatedly but irregularly to produce a blunt absorbent structure. With the developemnt of the embryo, the venter cells of the archegonium are stimulated to activity. The growth of the venter keeps pace with the growth of the enclosed embryo. The resulting archegonial structure now called the **calyptra** surrounds the developing sporogonium (sporophyte) until it is nearly mature. External to calyptra is another protective sheath known as the perianth.

The cells of the basal tier divide a number of times in an irregular sequence to form a blunt structure known as the **foot**. It functions as an absorbing organ. The superficial cells of the foot grow into papilla-like outgrowths (D). The cells of the median tier divide longitudinally to form the seta and the basal portion of the capsule. The cells of the upper epibasal tier divide periclinally separating the four outer cells from the four central cells (E). The former constitute the **amphithecium** and the latter **endothecium** (E). The endothecium functions as the **archesporium** (F). The archesporial cells divide and redivide longitudinally to produce the sporogenous tissue consisting of a lens-shaped mass of elongated cells. There are about 200 cells in the sporogenous mass, the central cells

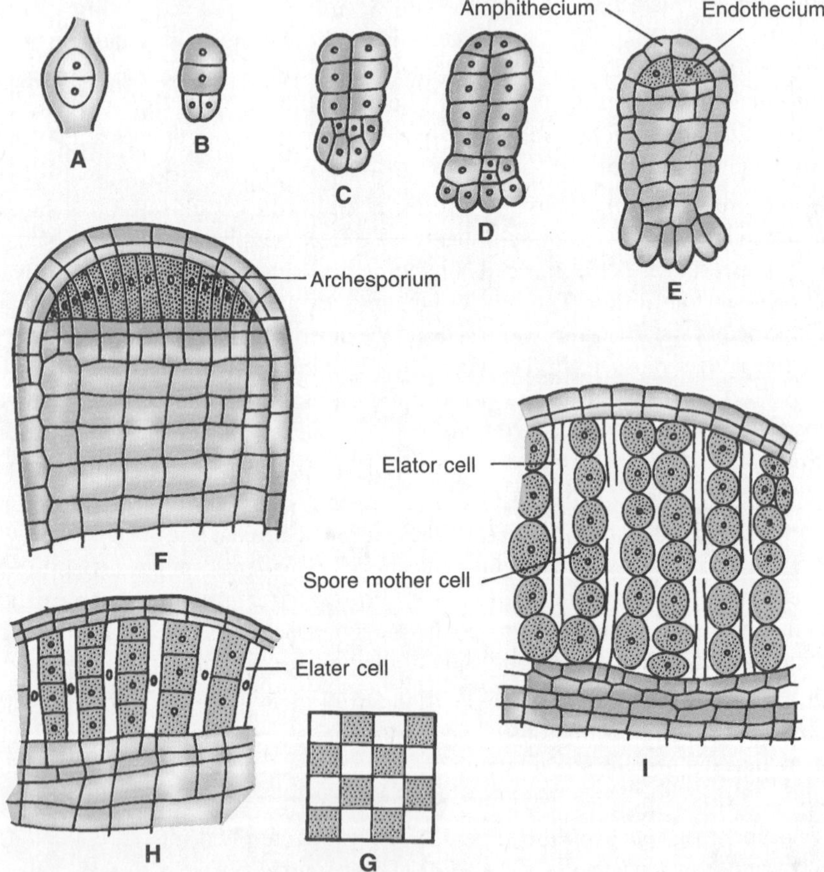

Fig. 11.3. (A—I). ***Frullania dilatata***. Development of sporophyte. A—E, L.S. embryo (sporophyte) at different stages of development; F, H, L.S. older sporogonia showing differentiation of the sporogenous tissue into elater cells and rows of spore mother cells; G, T.S. capsule showing chess board arrangement of sterile elater producing cells and fertile spore mother cells; I, older stage showing rows of spore mother cells (G after Goebel and the rest after Cavers).

in this mass are longer than the peripheral ones. The sporogenous cells differentiate into two kind of cells (H). Nearly half of them remain sterile to produce the elaters. They are called the elater **mother cells**. The other half become fertile. They produce the **spore mother cells**.

The two kinds of cells are intermixed (I). In a cross section of the capsule at this stage they appear to be disposed of like the squares of a chess board (G). The elongated fertile cells undergo repeated transverse division to produce vertical rows of **spore mother cells** (I). They are more or less cubical in form. The sterile cells elongate considerably to give rise to long, slender cells called the **elaters**. Later in their development the protoplasm of each elater cell disppears after it has deposited a single broad spiral band of thickening material on the inner surface of its cell wall. The elaters of *Frullania*, as compared with those of *Marchantia*, are much shorter and flattened with only a single spiral band. The elaters remain attached at both the ends, with their upper ends to the top and lower ends to the floor of the capsule (Fig. 11.4 A). They regularly alternate with the rows of spore mother cells. Towards maturity the spore mother cells separate from one another, become rounded and undergo the meiotic division, each producing four haploid spores (meiospores).

The mature spore is a unicellular, somewhat roundish structure. It ranges from 0.025 to 0.056 mm in diameter. The spore wall is differentiated into two layers, an outer **exospore** and an inner **endospore**. The endospore is thin and the exospore rough and tuberculate. Within the spore wall is the cytoplasm containing a single nucleus and many chloroplasts.

The amphithecium cells meanwhile divide anticlinally a number of times after which each cell divides periclinally. This results in the formtion of the **capsule wall,** two cell layers in thickness. Except the outer walls which remain thin, the cells of the outer layer develop rod-like thickenings on their lateral walls especially at the corner of adjacent cells. The cell walls of the inner layer are reticulately thickened all over. The cells of the capsule wall, however, remain unthickened along four vertical strips. These strips of thin-walled cells constitute the **lines of dehiscence**.

Mature sporogonium (Fig. 11.4 A—D). The fully developed sporogonium is differentiated into the blunt **foot**, the **seta** and the **capsule**. The seta is short (about one millimetre in length) and 8 to 9 cells in thickness until the spores are mature. It supports the globose capsule at its distal end. At the base of the capsule is a mass of thin-walled tissue similar to the apophysis of moss sporogonium. It obscures the sharp distinction between the seta and the capsule. Before the elongation of seta the sporogonium is surrounded by calyptra which in turn is ensheathed by the perianth.

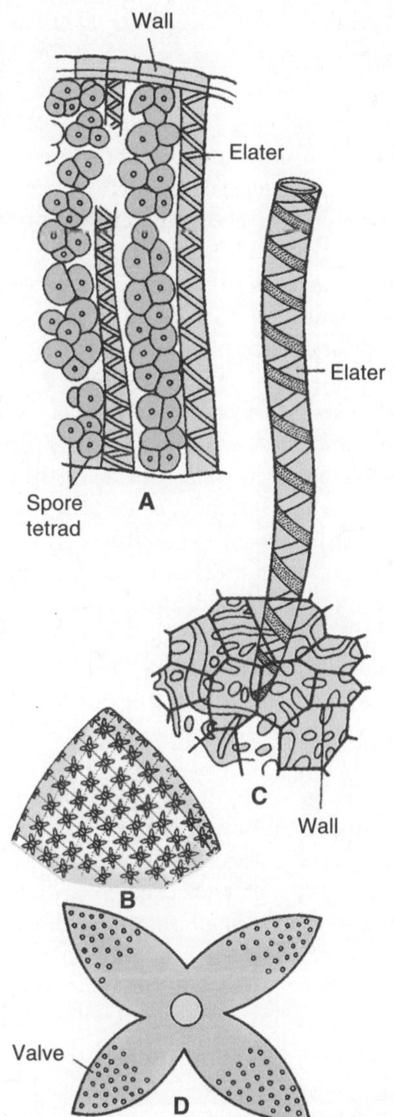

Fig. 11.4. (A—D) ***Frullania dilatata***. Structure of capsule. A, L.S. portion of a nearly mature capsule with spore tetrads and elaters; B, part of capsule wall as seen from outer surface; C, an elater attached to the inner surface of capsule wall, D, four valves of the capsule wall showing the arrangement of elaters (After Cavers).

The capsule wall is two cell layers in thickness. Their walls are sclerified. Those of the outer layer have thick, rod-like thickenings on their lateral walls particularly at the angles between the adjacent cells (B). Their outer walls remain thin. The cell walls of the inner layer are reticulately thickened (C). Within the capsule wall are the numerous spores and the elaters. The spores lie in the vertical series alternating with the elaters which extend from the roof to the floor of the globular capsule (A). The monospiral flattened elaters have a trumpet-shaped lower end (C). At this end they are attached to the floor and at the upper end to the inner surface of the capsule at the top. The elaters in *Frullania* are thus firmly attached at both the ends.

Dehiscence of capsule. With the maturing of spores within the capsule there is rapid elongation of the short seta. This ruptures the calyptra and pushes the globose dark brown capsule above the ensheathing perianth. The torn calyptra remains at the base of the sporogonium as a membranous sheath. There is no further cell division during seta elongation. The increase in length is entirely due to increase in size of the pre-existing cells in the vertical direction. The mature capsule perched at the top of elongated seta is now exposed and situated in a position favourable for wind dispersal of spores upon capsule dehiscence. Dehiscence of capsule depends on the cohesion of water in the lumina of the cell walls of jacket layer of the capsule. As the exposed capsule dries up, it loses water. The thin outer walls of the cells of the outer layer of the capsule wall are pulled inwards. The tension thus set up (due to cohesion mechanism) causes the capsule to open suddenly at the apex along the lines of dehiscence into four valves. The slits between the valves run down from the top of the capsule to two-third of its length. On further drying,each shrinking valve with nearly 20 elaters attached at one end to its tip and at other end to the floor of the capsule bends outwards and then backwards stretching the elaters. Under the extensive stretching strain, the lower ends of the elaters get detached and swing into the air causing the valves to spring back more with a jerk. This sling-like action (rapid upward and outward movement of the freed bases) of elaters expels the spores out of the capsule with a force into the air. This type of violent method of spore dispersal is termed **spiral-spring mechanism** of dispersal of spores. It is characteristic of the Frullaniaceae.

Germination of spores (Fig. 11.5). The germination of spsores, as in *Pellia*, is **precocious** *(in situ)*. It means the spores begin to germinate before they are shed. The development proceeds within the spore wall inside the capsule. Neither the exospore ruptures nor the endospore protrudes in the form of a germ tube. The spore protoplast divides by a transverse wall into an upper and a lower cell (B). The upper cell divides by a vertical division (C). The two daughters divide and redivide. The divisions occur in

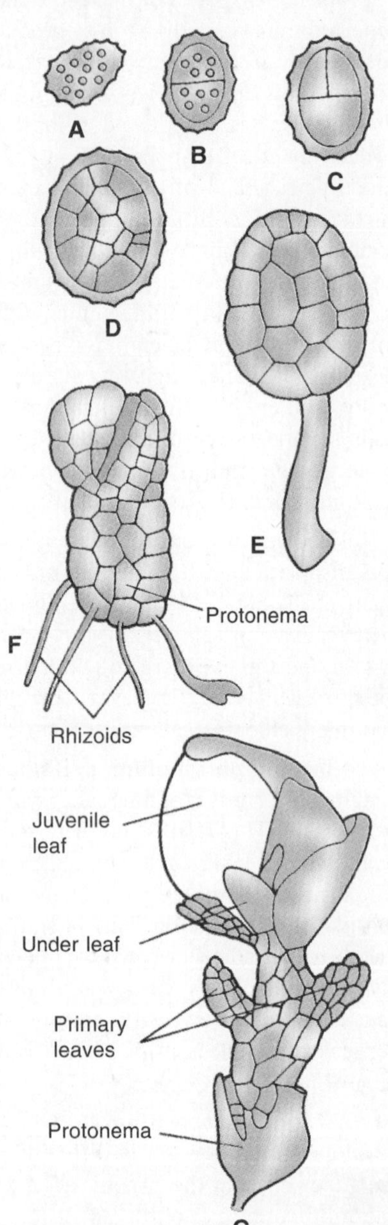

Fig. 11.5. (A—G). ***Frullania dilatata***. Germination of spore. A, spore; B—E, stages in the development of protonema within the exospore; F, a sporeling; G, sporeling at a later stage of development. (A, after Hofmeister; G, after Goebel).

all the three planes resulting in a globose mass of cells called the **protonema** (D). It consists of about 50 or more cells. The expanding protonema stretches the exospore so much that it no longer remains visible as a separate entity. At this stage, the capsule dehisces to liberate the sporelings. On falling on a moist substratum, the thallus-like sporeling (protonema) develops a few rhizoids which anchor it to the substratum (E). Subsequently a leafy gametophyte develops from a superficial cell at one end of the protonema (F). The first formed leaves (primary leaves) are 2-4 cells broad at the base and are ovate to oblong in form (G). Thereafter appear the juvenile leaves. They are saccate and inflated. The under leaves at this stage are narrowly ovate.

SYSTEMATIC POSITION OF *FRULLANIA*

Division	:	Bryophyta
Class	:	Hepaticopsida (Hepaticae)
Order	:	Jungermanniales
Family	:	Frullaniaceae
Genus	:	*Frullania*
Species	:	*squarrosa*

Phyletic evolution of the Metzgeriales and the Jungermanniales. The order Metzgeriales includes members diverse in form. There are genera such as *Pellia* in which gametophyte is a simple, dorsiventral, flat, green, dichotomously branched thallus resembling that of *Riccia* or *Marchantia* in external appearance or even simpler. Besides the strictly thallose forms, the order comprises genera which show foliar development of a rudimentary type. Typical example of this type is *Fossombronia*. Forms like the latter are considered intermediate between the thallose and foliose forms. The Jungermanniales exclusively have gametophytes with a sharp distinction into stem and leaves (*Pellia* and *Frullania*) and for this reason the Jungermanniales are often called the leafy liverworts. It is evident from the above that the representatives of these two orders can be arranged in a series showing progressive development of the creeping thallus to leafy forms with upright stems and radial symmetry. The series starts with the simple, creeping thallus of *Pellia*, runs through thallose types with two rows of ventral scales one on each side of the midrib as in *Blasia* and thallose forms in which the margin of thallus is deeply cranulate so that the lobes resemble leaves as in *Fossombronia* ultimately ends in the leafy forms with upright stems and radial symmetry (*Haplomitrium* and *Calobryum* of the order Calobryales). The tempting hypothesis that the leafy liverworts are transitional to the mosses in the ascending series received much support on this ground but this view has long been discarded.

There has been much argument whether the above series represents generic relationship in the upward direction or in the downward direction. The consensus of opinion at present regards the leafy liverworts as primitive and derive the thallose forms like *Pellia* and *Sewardiella* from them because *Pellia* is so outstandingly simple that it stands under the suspicion of being reduced and specialized. The supporters of this view (retrogressive evolution) have suggested two main lines of evolution towards the development of a thalloid habit in the Anacrogynae (Metzgeriales).

According to one of these lines originally suggested by Church (1919) and Goebel (1930) and elaborated by Evans (1939), the radial forms like *Calobryum* with leaves in three rows adopted a prostrate habit. The change in habit resulted in gradual disappearance of ventral leaves, accompanied by broadening of the axis and dwindling of the dorsolateral leaves. These changes finally resulted in the evolution of forms like *Pellia*. In the second line proposed by Mehra and Vasisht (1950) there was compaction and fusion of dorsolateral leaves resulting in forms like *Petalophyllum* from which later evolved *Sewardiella*. In both these lines there was displacement of sex organs to the dorsal side by continued apical vegetative growth.

QUESTIONS

ESSAY TYPE

1. Give an illustrated account of the gametophyte of *Frullania*.
2. Describe the sexual reproduction in *Frullania*.
3. Describe the structure of sporophyte of *Frullania* with the help of suitable diagrams.
4. Give a comparative account of the gametophytes of *Frullania, Porella* and *Pellia*.
5. Give an illustrated account of leaves in Jungermanniales. *(Allahabad M.Sc., 2000)*
6. Give a comparative account of the structure of vegetative thallii of *Marchantia, Pellia* and *Frullania*. *(Lucknow, 1992, 1997, 1999, 2002, 2004)*
7. Draw labelled diagrams of the V.S. of capsule of *Pogonatum* and *Frullania*. *(Lucknow, 1994, 2001, 2007)*
8. Give a comparative account of the adult gametophyte of *Pogonatum* and *Frullania*. *(Lucknow, 2001)*
9. With the help of diagrams describe the external features of *Frullania*.
10. Give an illustrated account of reproduction in *Frullania*.

SHORT ANSWER TYPE

11. Draw the structure of an elater of *Frullania*. *(Lucknow, 1993)*
12. Name a bryophyte which has androecia. *(Lucknow, 1997)*
13. Give a brief account of phyletic evolution of Jungermanniales.
14. Draw labelled sketches of
    (*i*) Ventral view of vegetative thallus of *Frullania*. *(Lucknow, 1993, 1995, 2000)*
    (*ii*) Mature sporophyte of *Frullania*.
    (*iii*) Antheridium in *Frullania*.
    (*iv*) Leaves of *Frullania*.
    (*vi*) *Frullania* plant. *(Lucknow, 2008)*
15. Write systematic position of *Frullania*.
16. Write short notes on :
    (*a*) Female shoot of *Frullania*. *(Lucknow, 1995, 1996)*
    (*b*) Leaves of *Frullania*. *(Lucknow, 1998)*
    (*c*) Salient features of *Frullania*.
    (*d*) Sporophyte of *Frullania*.
    (*e*) Development of sporogonium in *Frullania*.
    (*f*) Vegetative reproduction in *Frullania*. *(Lucknow, 2004)*
    (*g*) Gametophyte of *Frullania*. *(Lucknow, 2003)*
    (*h*) Features of Jungermanniales *(Lucknow, 2005)*
17. Distinguish between thallus of *Porella* and *Frullania*. *(Rohilkhand M.Sc., 2003)*
18. Differentiate between gametophyte of *Frullania* and *Marchantia*.

OBJECTIVE TYPE

19. **Select the correct answer :**
    (*i*) Which of the following is a leafy member of Hepaticopsida?
    (*a*) *Pellia* (*b*) *Riccia*
    (*c*) *Anthoceros* (*d*) *Frullania*.
    (*ii*) The protective cover around the anchegonial cluster in *Frullania* is also known as
    (*a*) Perianth (*b*) Involucre
    (*c*) Perichaetium (*d*) Bracts.
    (*iii*) In *Frullania* the photosynthetic function is performed by
    (*a*) Dorsal leaves
    (*b*) Ventral leaves
    (*c*) Both of the above
    (*d*) None of the above.

(*iv*) The perichaetial bracts are

(*a*) Smaller than the foliage leaves
(*b*) Large than the foliage leaves
(*c*) Equal to the foliage leaves
(*d*) Nothing but the foliage leaves.

(*v*) Monospiral flattened elaters attached at both the ends are found in

(*a*) *Pellia* (*b*) *Riccia*
(*c*) *Marchantia* (*d*) *Frullania.*

(*vi*) The under leaves in the leafy Jungermanniales are known as

(*a*) Antical lobe (*b*) Postical lobe
(*c*) Amphigastria (*d*) Scale leaves

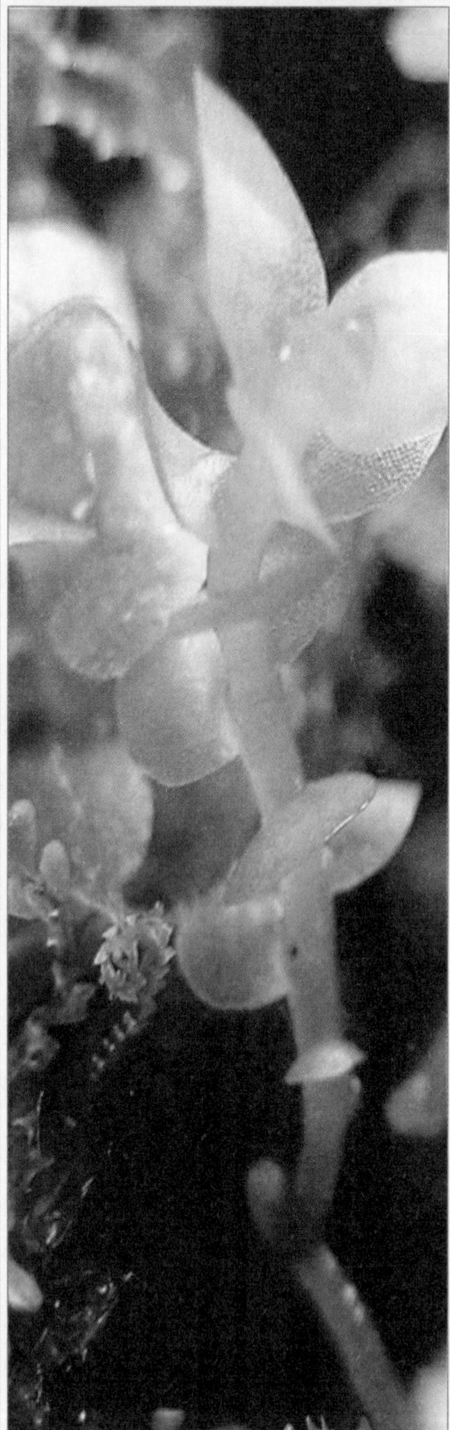
Image of *Haplomitrium*

CHAPTER 12

CALOBRYALES : Calobryaceae : Calobryum (Haplomitrium)

INTRODUCTION

The older taxonomists Campbell (1940) and Jones (1958) placed *Haplomitrium* together with *Calobryum* (then regarded as distinct) in a separate order of the Hepaticae known as Calobryales. *Haplomitrium* is essentially *anacrogynous*. The archegonia even though grouped into a terminal cluster, the apical cell itself is not involved in the development of archegonium. It persists. *Calobryum* is *acrogynous* as the apical cell itself develops into an archegonium in this genus. *Haplomitrium* includes a single species *H. hookeri* which has been recorded from two places in India namely, Jawai (Assam, Eastern Himalayas) by Udar and Chandra (1965) and Vyas Shikhar, Western Himalayas by Udar and Singh (1977). *Calobryum* comprises eight species. Of these 3 have been reported from India. These are : (*i*) *C. blumii* from Jawai (Assam, Eastern Himalayas) by Udar *et al* (1968); (*ii*) *C. indicum* from Darjeeling

(Eastern Himalayas) by Udar and S. Chandra (1961); and (*iii*) *C. dentatum* by Udar and Singh (1976). The other five species of *Calobryum* known so far, are *C. andinum* (Peru, Equador), *C. gibboiae* (New Zealand), *C. giganteum* (Philippines), *C. intermedium* (Australia) and *C. mnioides* (Japan). Of the 8 species of *Calobryum* known, at present, some are anacrogynous like *Haplomitrium* and some acrogynous. Schuster (1963) remarked that the separation of these two genera, on the basis of acrogynous (*Calobryum*) versus anacrogynous (*Haplomitrium*) characteristics, is now untenable. He thus united the two genera under *Haplomitrium*. Therefore, *Calobryum* has been described here under the name *Haplomitrium*.

ORDER CALOBRYALES

Chief Characteristics

The gametophytes are small, rhizomatous and lacking drought resistance. The plant body is differentiated into a basal, branched, creeping, leafless, pale, subterranean rhizome-like structure from which arise the erect green leafy axes or branches termed the **gametophores**. The radially set leaves on the erect gametophore axes are arranged spirally in 3 vertical rows. The leaves may be **isophyllous** or **anisophyllous**. In the latter case, the smaller row of leaves is dorsal. The leaves are variable in form, simple, entire, unistratose but multistratose towards the base only. The soft textured flat lamina is undivided and has no midrib. The total absence of rhizoids both on the leafy axes and the rhizome and the rhizomatous plant body are the features in which the Calobryales differ from all other Hepaticae except Takakiales. The gametophore axes bear slime papillae of non-beaked type. Asexual reproduction is unknown. Sexual reproduction involves two kinds of plants male and female. Calobryales are thus sexually dimorphic and **heterothallic**. The archegonia are large with a neck composed of 4 vertical rows of neck cells. The haploid number of chromosomes is n=9. The developing sporophyte is surrounded and thus protected by a cylindrical green to yellow massive fleshy **shoot calyptra**. The capsule is markedly elongated and has a unistratose capsule wall except at the tip which is bistratose. The order includes a single family CALOBRYACEAE.

FAMILY CALOBRYACEAE

The family includes a single genus **Calobryum (Haplomitrium)** comprising 9 species of which 4 have been reported from India. All the species of *Calobryum* (*Haplomitrium*) are mesophytes. None of them is drought resisting. They avoid calcareous habitats and grow either as individuals or loosely gregarious seldom forming extended patches. In spite of their wide ranging distribution, each species is sharply restricted to a relatively small geographical area. Of the species *H. blumii* is the best known.

HAPLOMITRIUM

HABITAT AND DISTRIBUTION

H. blumii displays a widely scattered pattern of disjunct distribution. Besides Jawai (Assam) it has been reported from Indonesia, Java, Sumatra, New Guinea and Formosa. It is a mesophyte and occurs on forest floor, steepy clay banks and on rotting wood in extremely wet and shady situations.

GAMETOPHYTE (Fig. 12.1)

It is small, green to pale green in colour and differentiated into a creeping leafless basal, branched rhizome-like axis (stem) from which arise the erect leafy shoots or branches known as the **gametophores**. The latter are bright green, green, green to yellowish green in colour, mostly 8-25 mm tall. The robust ones may grow to a height of 3-5 cm. The terete gemetophore axes are fleshy (succulent) but brittle. A newly formed branch may creep over the substratum for a time and then abruptly turns upwards, grows erect and bears the leaves. The branches are dimorphic and exogenous and intercalary in origin. The rhizome and the creeping part of the erect branch completely lack rhizoids. The absence of rhizoids and the rhizomatous gametophyte are the noteworthy features in which *Haplomitrium* (Calobryales) differs from all the Hepaticae except *Takakia* (Takakiales). In some species of *Haplomitrium* (*H. mnioides*) one or more vertically descending leafless branches arise from the base of the erect leafy shoots (Gametophores), grow vertically downward and penetrate the substratum. These positively geotropic, pale green or colourless appendages or structures are variously named as **stolons** or **flagella**. Grubs (1970) who links their presence with the total absence of rhizoids, uses the term roots for them.

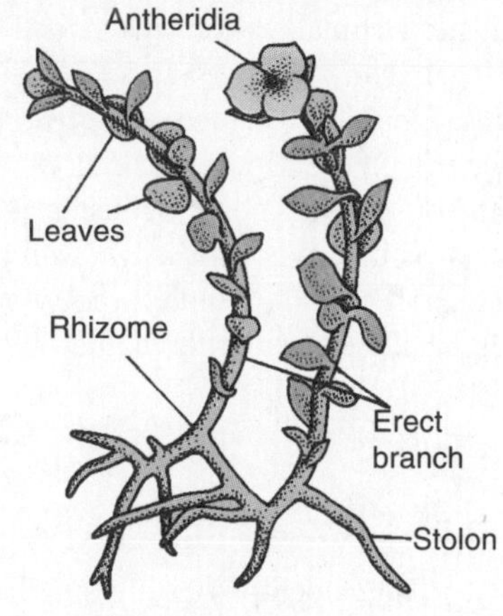

Fig. 12.1. *Haplomitrium* sp. Male plant (after Goebel).

Leaves. The leaves are simple, entire, dorsiventrally flattened, soft textured and without a midrib. They are radially disposed and arranged in 3 vertical rows on the fleshy, terete, erect axis of the gametophores. Grolle (1964) assumed that all the species of *Haplomitrium* have **anisophyllous** leaves. Schuster (1967) reported that the leaves are usually **anisophyllous**, occasionally isophyllous. *H. blumii, H. adinum* and *H. giganteum* are markedly anisophyllous (Fig. 12.2 A) whereas *H. gibbsiae, H. mnioides* and *H. intermedium* are isophyllous (Fig. 12.2 B). It is obvious that in the anisophyllous species, the leaves of one rank (out of the three) are appreciably smaller in size. Some taxonomists equate the smaller leaves with the amphigastrea (ventral leaves) of Jungermanniales and the side bearing them is morphologically considered vertical. Horikawa (1929) reported that the erect shoots (gametophores of *H. rotundifolia*, and *H. mnioides*) bear leaves in 3 rows. The two lateral rows bear equal sized leaves. The third row of smaller leaves alternates with the lateral leaves and is dorsal. This view has been emphasized by Grolle (1963-64) and later by Schuster (1970) and Watson (1971).

Anatomy of leaf. The leaves vary in their structure in the different species. The leaves in *H. blumii* are polystractose in the basal portion. In other species the leaves are unistratose but in *H. mnioides* they are 2-3 stratose towards the base only. The leaf cells are non-collenchymatous, soft, large, thin-walled and contain several to many oil bodies per cell besides chloroplasts (Fig. 12.2 C).

Stem (Fig. 12.2 D). The stem in cross section shows two distinct regions, outer **cortex** and inner **central strand**. There is sharp distinction between the green, starch rich cortex and colourless central strand. The latter consists of smaller elongated leptodermis cells and is 10-15 cells in diameter. The cells of the central strand contain no cell organelles but having lost their protoplasmic contents are empty. Burr *et al* (1974) reported that in *H. gibbsiae* the mature cells of the central strand are axially elongated and devoid of living contents. In this respect they resemble hydroids of mosses. The end walls of these cells are transverse to oblique. Numerous pores occur between the adjacent conducting cells. These are most numerous on the end walls. These perforations are apparently derived from enlarged plasmodesmata (Burr *et al*, 1974). Surrounding the central strand is the massive cortex consisting of large parenchymatous cells containing starch grains. Campbell (1959) reported the occurrence of abundant oil drops in the cortical cells of *H. gibbsiae* (Fig. 12.2 C). Cell organelles are abundant. The peripheral cortical cells may grow into short 2-3 celled *slime papillae* of non-beaked type with a clavate apical cell. The papillae secrete mucilage.

Apical growth. The stem grows by the activity of a tetrahedral apical cell with three cutting faces. In the anisophyllous species one of the faces is narrower than the other two. The segments cut

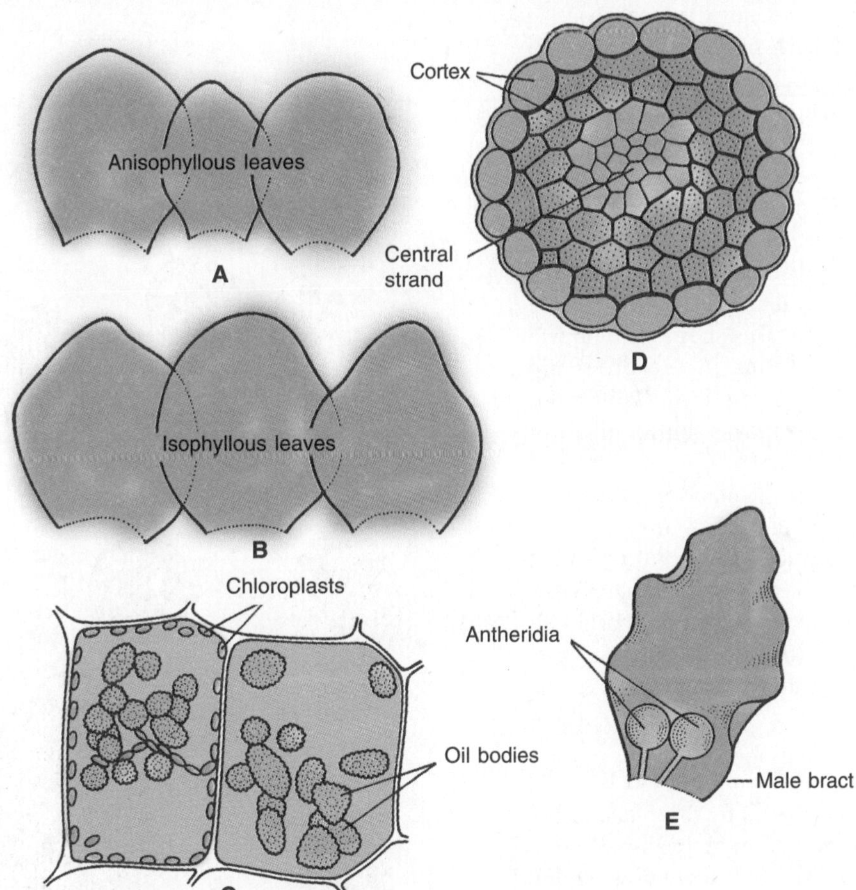

Fig. 12.2. (A—E) **Haplomitrium** sp. A, three leaves from a single cycle showing anisophylly; B, three leaves from a single cycle of *H. gibbsiae* showing isophylly; C, median leaf cells with oil bodies and chloroplasts; D, T.S. stem (*H, intermedium*); E, male bract with antheridia (From Schuster).

off parallel to this face form the rank of smaller leaves. Each segment cut off by the apical cell divides by a transverse division perpendicular to its cutting face. Of the two derivatives, the lower forms the thick multistratose leaf base and the upper portion of the stem between it and the next leaf. The upper derivative forms the unistratose upper part of the leaf.

Reproduction. Asexual reproduction is unknown in the Calobryales.

Sexual reproduction. The gametophyte plants are of two kinds, male and female. *Haplomitrium* is thus *heterothallic* (dioecious). Antheridia and archegonia are produced on the expanded apex of the erect shoots of different plants.

(*a*) *Antheridia* (Fig. 12.1) (*i*) *Position.* The numerous orange yellow antheridia are grouped at the apex of a dilated receptacle formed by the flattening of the tip of the male gametophore (*H. blumii*). The antheridial receptacle is surrounded by an expanded perianth-like structure formed by the closely set, enlarged young male or perigonial bracts which occur in more than three rows. Consequently the male plants look like moss gametophores. In some other species of *Haplomitrium* antheridia occur in the axis of uppermost bracts or scattered on the axis without any relation to the leaf.

(*ii*) *Structure* (12.3.I). The antheridium consists of an ovoid or rounded body raised on a long stalk composed of several superimposed tiers of 4 cells each. In L.S. only two cells are seen in each tier. The body of the antheridium has a jacket layer of cells enclosing a central mass of dividing androgonial cells. The cells of the last cell generation are called the *androcyte mother cells*.

(*iii*) *Development* (Fig. 12.3) The early development of antheridium of *Haplomitrium* is noteworthy. It differs from all other liverworts in the fact that the sequence of early divisions is similar to that in the archegonia. This shows that the two kinds of sex organs in the order are homologous structures. Thus Calobryales are considered the most primitive of any of the liverworts.

Any recently formed segment cut off by the apical cell in the terminal receptacle may function as an **antheridial initial**. It grows into a papillate outgrowth and divides by a transverse division into a basal cell embeded in the thallus and an outer cell projecting above the thallus surface (A). The outer cell again divides by a transverse division to form a lower **primary stalk cell** and a terminal **primary antheridial cell** (B). The latter divides by three successive obliquely vertical eccentric walls, as in the archegonium, so as to separate a set of three **peripheral** or **jacket initials** totally enclosing a single central **primary androgonial initial** (C). A transverse division of the primary androgonial cell results in two **androgonial cells**, upper and lower (E). Each of these divides by a vertical wall (F) into a quartet of **androgonial cells**. From this stage onwards antheridial development is similar to that of other liverworts (Hepaticae). The four androgonial cells divide repeatedly by transverse and longitudinal divisions to form a central mass of androgones (G). The 3 jacket initials meanwhile undergo anticlinal divisions only to form one cell layer thick **antheridial jacket** or **wall** enclosing the dividing androgones. The cells of the last cell generation of the androgonial mass are called the **androcyte mother cells** or **spermatocytes** (1). Each of the latter undergoes the last mitotic division to form two **androcytes** or **spermatids**. The protoplast of each androcyte metamorphoses into a biflagellate sperm.

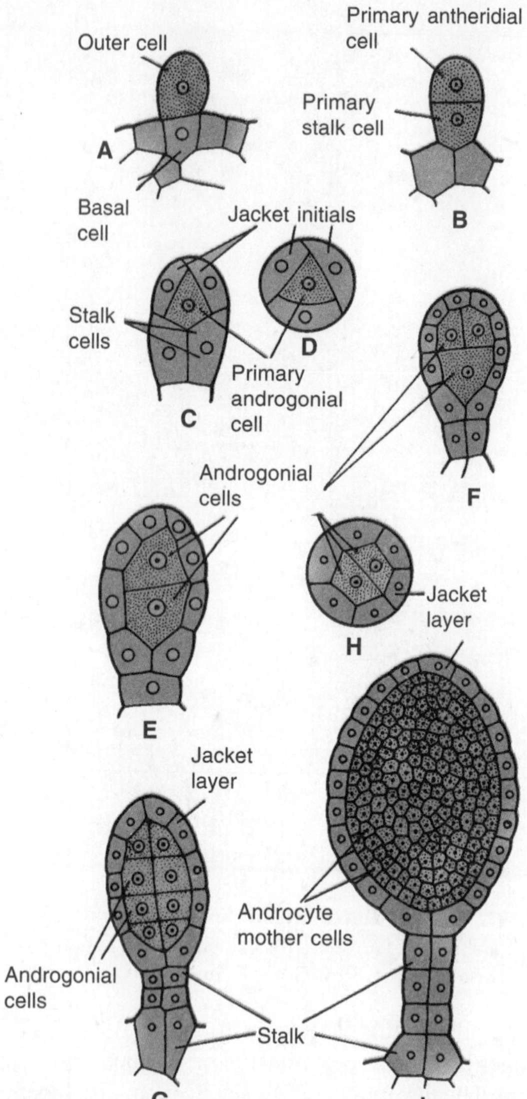

Fig. 12.3. (A—I) ***Haplomitrium*** sp. Development of antheridium. Explanation in the text. A—C, E—G and I are longitudinal sections, D and H are transverse section (B—H based on Smith).

The stalk of the antheridium consisting of 4 rows of cells is formed by repeated division of the primary stalk cell.

(*b*) *Archegonia* (*i*) *Position* (Fig. 12.4 A). The tip of the female gametophore in *H. blumii* becomes expanded to form a receptacle. About 30 or even more archegonia stand crowded to form a cluster on a flat dilated terminal disc which is surrounded by the ascending basis of 3 large perichaetial bracts. It is possible that the apical cell of female gametophore itself may fianlly produce an archegonium. *H. blumii* is thus **acrogynous**. So are *H. adinum* and *H. gibbsiae*, Majority of the species, however are essentially **anacrogynous**. *H. intermedium* and *H. hookeri* are clearly anacrogynous. *H. adinum* and *H. rotundufolium* (*H. mnioides*) bear archegonia in a flattened, dilated terminal disc. In *H. gibbasiae* the archegonia are borne on a terminal convex receptacle which is little or not dilated.

(*ii*) *Structure* (Fig. 12.4 E). The stalked archegonium has a very long, twisted neck which is composed of 4 rows of neck cells surrounding a row of 16-40 neck canal cells. The venter is slightly broader than the neck. At maturity it has a 2 cell layers thick venter wall. The ventral cavity, as usual, contains an egg and a ventral canal cell above it.

(*iii*) *Development* (Fig. 12.4 B—E). A recently formed segment of the apical cell functions as an **archegonial initial**. It projects above the surface level and divides by a transverse wall into a lower or basal cell (Fig. 12.3 A) which remains embedded in the adjacent thallus tissue and an outer or upper cell which projects above the surface level. The outer cell undergoes another transverse division to demarcate an upper **primary archegonial cell** and a lower **primary stalk cell**. The primary stalk cell divides to form the stalk of the archegonium. The primary archegonial cell divides by three vertical oblique eccentric walls to separate three **peripheral** or **jacket initials** from the central **primary axial cell** (B) exactly as in antheridium development. The jacket initials normally completely intersect each other so as to completely encircle the primary axial cell. The later directly functions as the fertile central cell without cutting off the primary cover cell.

Of the three jacket initials normally one undergoes a secondary vertical division. The resultant 4 jacket initials ultimately form the jacket layer of the venter one cell layer thick and the neck consisting of 4 longitudinal rows of neck cells. The venter is only slightly broader than the neck. Mean while the central cell has divided transversally into two cells upper **primary canal cell** and

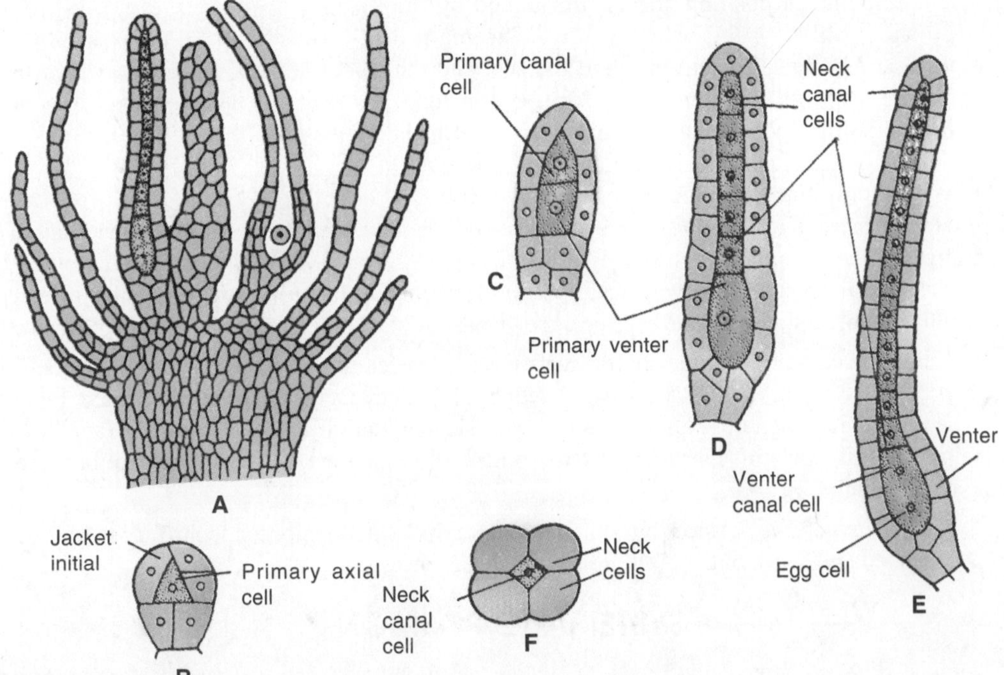

Fig. 12.4. (A—F) ***Haplomitrium*** sp. A, L.S. apex of female gametophore; B—E, showing L.S. of different stages in the development of archegonium; F, T.S. archegonial neck (Based on Smith).

lower **primary ventral cell**. The primary canal cell divides repeatedly by transverse divisions into 16—40 **neck canal cells** (D—E). The primary ventral cell divides to form an upper **ventral canal cell** and a lower **egg cell** (E). Both of these are lodged in the cavity of the venter. Towards maturity the cells of the single layered venter wall divide periclinally (prior to fertilization) resulting in 2—3 cells thick venter wall. There is total lack of any leaf derived protective sheath such as the **perianth** around the archegonial cluster. The archegonia are thus described as naked.

Shoot calyptra (Fig. 12.5 A). Following fertilization, the venter wall cells start dividing extensively, by periclinal divisions resulting in a cylindrical, fleshy green to yellowish green, brittle massive 15—17 mm long calyptra surrounding the developing sporophyte (A). The calyptra is smooth with the unfertilized archegonia usually basal or nearly so. In some species the cells near the venter become meristematic and divide actively resulting in an exceptionally massive calyptra. It is termed the "**shoot calyptra**". The sterile archegonia are elevated on the shoot calyptra. The total absence of any leaf derived protective sheath such as the perianth around the archegonia or marsupium around the developing sporophyte seem to isolate the Calobryales from the Jungermanniales.

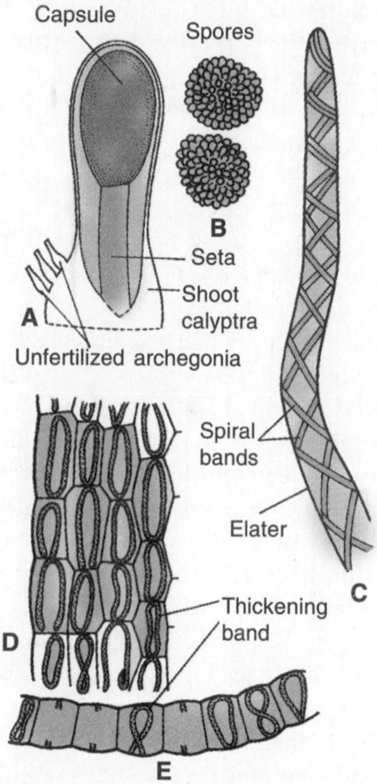

Capsule
Spores
B
Seta
Shoot calyptra
A
Unfertilized archegonia
Spiral bands
Elater
C
Thickening band
D
E

Fig. 12.5. (A—E) ***Haplomitrium hookeri.*** A, L.S. sporophyte still enclosed by the calyptra; B, two spores; C, half of an elater with a bispiral band; D, capsule wall cells showing longitudinal bands; E, capsule wall in cross section (A—C after Macvicer; D—E after Mueller).

Sporophyte (Fig. 12.6)

It is terminal in position and is surrounded by the massive shoot calyptra (A) when young. The mature sporophyte is differentiated into the foot, the seta and the capsule. The seta of *Haplomitrium* is 25—30 mm long, massive and solid. The elongate deep brown capsule is cylindrical and ellipsoidal. It is 4 to 5 mm long. The foot is acuminate in form. Excepting the tip region which is bi-or-tri-seriate, the capsule wall is unistratose (B). The combination of unistratose capsule and massive sporophyte in the *Calobryales* is a noteworthy feature (Watson, 1974). The elongated wall cells have each one (exceptionally two) usually complete, median annular, longitudinally oriented (perpendicular to the surface of the capsule), brown band of thickening material (Fig. 12.5 D and E).

Within the capsule wall, the sporogenous tissue is differentiated into spores and elaters (B). The spores are 18—30μ (Fig. 12.5 B) and elaters 6—10μ in diameter (C). The spore elater ratio is 3:1. There is no elaterophore. Elaters are long, very slender, only feebly and gradually tappered to their tips. They are bispiral (Fig. 12.5 C). The spore wall has numerous, short blunt papillae, more numerous than in *H. gibbsai*.

The mature capsule dehsices by a single, longitudinal slit along one side in *H. blumii* or by 4 longitudinal slits to base along 4 discrete lines of dehiscence.

SYSTEMATIC POSITION

The earlier taxonomists placed the two genera *Haplomitrium* and *Calobryum* (then regarded as distinct) in the order Jungermanniales to which they show superficial resemblance in their erect habit, leafy organisation, basically tri-radiate arrangement and vertically anisophyllous condition of

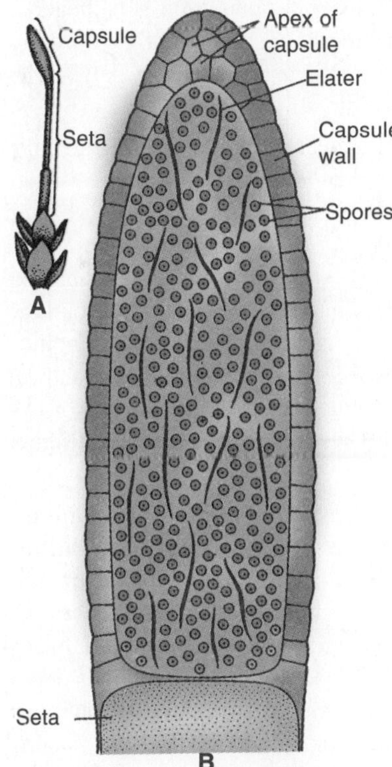

Fig. 12.6. (A—B). ***Haplomitrium*** sp. A, upper part of female gametophore with a terminal mature sporophyte; B, L.S. Capsule showing structure.

leaves. Campbell (1940) and Jones (1958) placed them in a separate order Calobryales. The total absence of any protective sheath such as the perianth around the archegonia, and the archegonial neck consisting of only 4 rows of neck cells and the complete absence of rhizoids are the features, besides many others, which serve to isolate Calobryales from the Jungermanniales. The consensus of opinion favours this view. Thus the systematic position of *Haplomitrium*, (*Calobryum*) at present, is :—

Division	:	Bryophyta
Class	:	Hepaticopsida (Hepaticae)
Order	:	Calobryales
Family	:	Calobryaceae
Genus	:	*Haplomitrium*
Species	:	*blumii*.

PHYLOGENETIC IMPORTANCE

The Calobryales exhibit many synthetic features which are of special interest to the phylogenist. The gametophyte of *Haplomitrium* shows a number of features suggestive of the mosses. The prominent among these are : (*i*) erect leafy shoots with leaves radially disposed; (*ii*) arrangement of leaves in 3 rows, two lateral and one dorsal; (*iii*) leaves either isophyllous or anisophyllous but in the latter case the row of reduced leaves is dorsal in position; (*iv*) development of leaf by means of a single apical cell as in the mosses; (*v*) leaves simple and entire as is usually the case in the mosses; (*vi*) differentiation of a central strand of small, elongated empty cells comparable to the moss hydroids, and (*vii*) very long twisted archegonial neck enclosing a large number of neck canal cells as in the mosses.

The Calobryales are also of interest as they exhibit a strange combination of primitive and advanced features. The primitive characters which the Calobryales possess are: (*i*) radial construction of the erect shoot, (*ii*) exogenous and intercalary origin of branches; (*iii*) lack of drought resistance; (*iv*) absence of asexual reproduction, and (*v*) similarity in the early ontogeny of antheridia and archegonia. The last point is a significant primitive feature which supports the view that the antheridia and archegonia are homologous structures. The Calobryales are thus the most primitives of the Hepaticae and may be placed at the beginning of the Hepaticae between the Jungermanniales and mosses.

Affinities of Calobryales. The Calobryales comprising a single genus *Haplomitrium* with 9 species is a small natural and distinct group. The true affinities of this group with the other liverworts before 1958 were shrouded in mystery.

(*a*) *Relationship with the Jungernammiales*. Its relation to the *Jungermanniales*, the group in which *Haplomitrium* and *Calobryum* (then regarded as distinct) were formerly included, is somewhat doubtful. In their erect habit, leafy organisation, basically triradiate arrangement and anisophyllous condition, the Calobryales show some supreficial resemblance to the primitive Jungermanniales such as *Herberta* and *Anthelia*. Differences however, are markedly fundamental. The chief among these are : (*i*) the absence of any protective sheath such as the *perianth* and *marsupium* around archegonia and later the developing sporophyte, (*ii*) archegonial neck consisting of only four vertical rows of neck cells, (*iii*) total lack of rhizoids, (*iv*) essentially anacrogynous condition of archegonia, and (*v*) the interpretation of Grubs (1970) and Watson (1971) that the smaller leaves of the third row represent the dorsal row and thus are not to be equated with the amphigastria, separate Calobryales from the Jungermanniales which are exclusively acrogynous.

(*b*) *Relationship with the Metzgeriales.* The Calobryales appear closer to the Metzgeriales than to the Jungermanniales in, (*i*) anacrogynous condition of archegonia, (*ii*) almost no resistance to drought, (*iii*) scattered arrangement of antheridia in some, (*iv*) lack of collenchyma, (*v*) often large cells, (*vi*) occasional copious secretion of mucilage, and (*vii*) similarity in elaters which in both of them are long, narrow, tapering towards both ends as compared with those of Jungermanniales which are much shorter. Despite these similarities Schuster (1967) pointed two features which prohibit direct relationship between the Calobryales and Metzgeriales. These are, (*i*) anisophyllous condition of leaves in many species of the Calobryales with the third row of smaller leaves dorsal, and (*ii*) presence of thickening material in the form of longitudinally oriented median annular one or two brown bands in each elongated cell of the unistratose capsule wall. These features denote that affinities even with the Metzgeriales are remote.

(*c*) *Distinctive features of Calobryales.* The Calobryales occupy an isolated position differing from all other liverworts in (*i*) their erect leafy shoots (gametophores) central strand of conducting tissue, and with leaves radially arranged; (*ii*) arrangement of leaves in 3 rows, two lateral and one dorsal, (*iii*) leaves either isophyllous or anisophyllous, if anisophyllous, the reduced leaves are arranged in a dorsal row; (*iv*) absence of asexual reprocution; and (*v*) similarity in the early ontogeny of antheridia and archegonia, a significant primitive feature which denotes that the two kinds of sex organs are homologous structures. The only conclusion we come to from the above discussion is that the Calobryales are among the most primitive of the Hepaticae (liverworts). The wide ranging distribution with each species restricted to a small geographical region also shows that the Calobryales are an isolated, putatively primitive (ancient) order of the hepatics.

(*d*) *Relationship with the Takakiales***.** No near relatives of Calobryales were known before 1958. The intimation of the discovery of *Takakia* by *Hattori* and Inoue (1958) led Schuster to suggest an ordinal rank (Takakiales) within the Hepaticae for newly discovered genus. However, subsequent critical investigation of *Takakia* by Proskaur (1962) and Schuster (1966-67) revealed that the two genera *Haplomitrium* (Calobryales) and *Takakia* (Thakakiales) share many common significant features between them. The chief among these are : (*i*) rhizomatous gametophytes, (*ii*) erect fleshy axes of the gametophores with an ill-defined central strand, (*iii*) radially organized leafy shoots, (*iv*) lack of rhizoids, (*v*) presence of axillary slime papillae and (*vi*) isolated, scattered occurrence of massive, almost fleshy archegonia. These common features indicate close relationship between the two genera *Haplomitrium* (Calobryales) and *Takakia* (Takakiales). *Takakia*, however, differs from *Haplomitrium* in (i) the obvious unique feature of its appendages (phyllids) which the erect axis bears, (ii) nature of second type of slime papillae, (iii) low chromosome number which is $n = 4$ and (iv) archegonial neck consisting of 6 rows of neck cells (All see chapter-15).

Recently Duckett *et al* (1982) who studied spermatozoid morphology found that the spermatozoids of *Haplomitrium* have features such as accessory band of microtubules in common with the homosporous ferns. These workers thus suggest that the Calobryales is an extremely divergent group of bryophytes that represent the closest living organisms linking bryophytes to tracheophytes.

QUESTIONS

ESSAY TYPE

1. Describe the salient features of Calobryales. Discuss the affinities of the group and its distribution in India. *(Kanpur, M. Sc., 1997, 2000; Rohilkhand, 1991)*
2. Discuss the reasons for and against the separation of *Calobryum* from Jungermanniales and its inclusion in the Calobryales. *(Kanpur, M.Sc., 1998)*
3. Give an illustrated account of the distinguishing features of Calobryales. Where does *Calobryum* occur in India ?
4. Explain clearly the distinction between Acrogynae and Anacrogynae.
5. Describe the sex organs of *Calobryum.*
6. Give an illustrated account of the gametophyte and sporophyte of *Calobryum*.
7. Draw labelled sketches to show the life-cycle of *Calobryum.*
8. Discuss calobryales in detail and also mention its affinities.

   (Poorvanchal M.Sc., 1998; Allahabad, M.Sc., 2000)
9. Briefly describe *Calobryum.* Also name bryologist who worked on it

SHORT ANSWER TYPE

10. **Write short notes on :**
    (*a*) *Calobryum*
    (Kanpur, M. Sc., 1991; Rohilkhand M. Sc., 1998)
    (*b*) Distribution of Calobryales in India *(Kumar, M.Sc., 1992)*
    (*c*) Affinities between Calobryales and Takakiales *(Rohilkhand, 1993)*
    (*d*) Sexual reproduction in *Calobryum*
11. Give a brief account of capsule of *Calobryum.*
12. How would you distinguish *Calobryum* from *Takakia?(Rohilkhand, M.Sc., 1999)*
13. Give the salient features of the Gametophyte of *Calobryum.*
14. Draw labelled diagrams of the following:
    (*a*) Antheridium of *Calobryum*
    (*b*) Archegonium of *Calobryum*
    (*c*) L.S. sporophyte of *Calobryum.*
15. Give a brief account of relationship of *Calobryum* with *Takakia.*
16. Briefly describe *Calobryum* and also name the Indian bryologist who worked on this genus. *(Kanpur, 2004)*
17. Discuss about *Calobrya. (Poorvanchal M.Sc., 2002; Allahabad, M.Sc., 1999)*
18. Distinguist between *Calobryum* and *Haplomitrium* *(Lucknow, M.Sc. 2006)*

OBJECTIVE TYPE

19. **Select the correct answer :**

    (*i*) *Calobryum* has been reported from
    (*a*) Eastern Himalayas
    (*b*) Western Himalayas
    (*c*) Eastern ghats
    (*d*) Western ghats.

    (*ii*) Rhizoids are absent in
    (*a*) *Riccia* (*b*) *Marchantia*
    (*c*) *Pellia* (*d*) *Calobryum.*

    (*iii*) Asexual (vegetative) reproduction is unknown in
    (*a*) Marchantiales
    (*b*) Calobryales
    (*c*) Anthocerotales
    (*d*) Jungermanniales.

(*iv*) Plant body is differentiated into a basal branched creeping leafless rhizome like structure from which arise gametophores in

(*a*) *Calobryum* (*b*) *Riccia*
(*c*) *Funaria* (*d*) *Polytrichum.*

(*v*) Cylindrical green to yellow massive fleshy shoot calyptra is present in

(*a*) *Riccia* (*b*) *Calobryum*
(*c*) *Pellia* (*d*) *Frullania.*

(*vi*) Neck canal cells in *Haplomitrium* range from

(*a*) 1-4 (*b*) 1-8
(*c*) 20-30 (*d*) 16-40.

(*vii*) 25-30 mm long massive and solid seta is the characteristic feature of

(*a*) *Riccia* (*b*) *Pellia*
(*c*) *Funaria* (*d*) *Calobryum.*

(*viii*) Dehiscence of capsule in *Calobryum* is by

(*a*) Death and decay
(*b*) A single logitudinal slit
(*c*) One to 40 valves
(*d*) Spring board mechanism

(*ix*) The Calobryales differ from other orders of the Hepaticopsida in

(*a*) Total lack of rhizoids
(*b*) The absence of sporophyte
(*c*) The absence of gametophyte
(*d*) The absence of leaves.

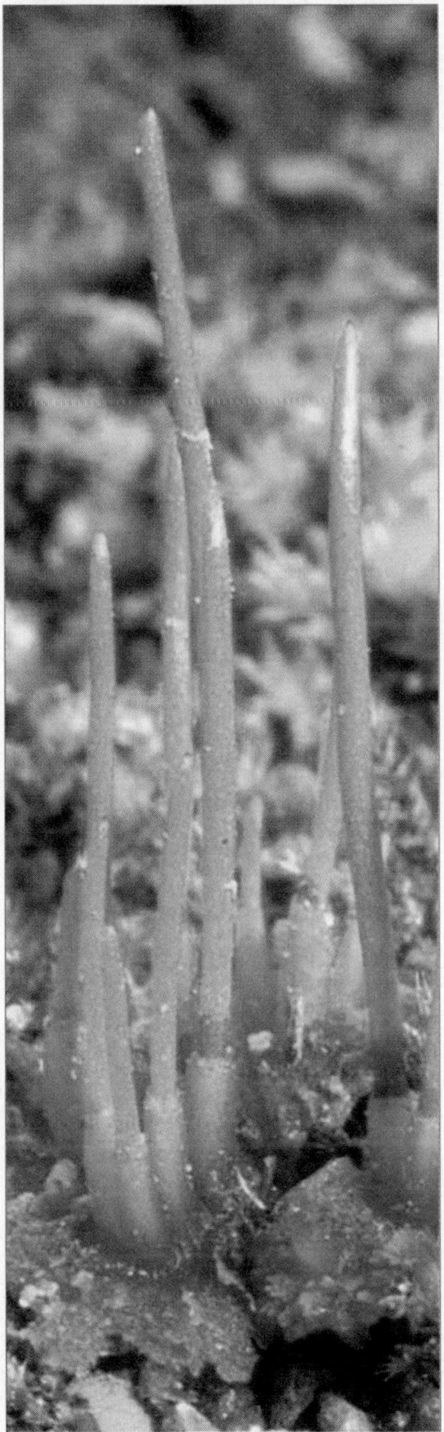

Image of *Anthoceros*

CHAPTER 13(I)

ANTHOCEROTOPSIDA (Anthocerotae) Anthocerotales (Anthoceros)

- General Characteristics
- Salient Features of the Class Anthocerotopsida
- Order Anthocerotales
- Family Anthocerotaceae
- Genus Anthouros
- Reproduction
- Sporophytic Phase

GENERAL CHARACTERISTICS

The class Anthocerotopsida (Anthocerotae) embraces a small but very clearly defined group of plants which differ in many ways, especially in its sporophyte, from the liverworts to which they are often allied. Popularly the members of this group are called the **hornworts.** They prefer to grow in moist, shady places. They are mostly found in the tropical and warm temperate regions. They all have a lobed, thallose gametophyte, simple in form and without regular dichotomous growth. The thallus is either with or without a midrib. The dorsiventral thallus shows very little internal differentiation of vegetative tissues apart from the internal cavities which contain mucilage and open by slit-like openings on the lower surface of the thallus. Occasionally these cavities contain a blue green alga *Nostoc*. There are neither any air chambers nor air pores. Most of the species have a single chloroplast in each cell. It contains a central pyrenoid—a feature unknown in other bryophytes and higher plants but common in algae. The thallus is fixed to the substratum by simple, unicellular, smooth-walled rhizoids. The tuberculate rhizoids and the ventral scales are absent. The sex organs are sunken in the thallus. The archegonium is developed from the superficial and antheridium from the hypodermal cell on the upper surface of the thallus. The antheridia are thus endogenous in origin and lie in roofed pits. The sporophyte is comparatively a long-lived object and is unique for its continued growth throughout the growing season from a basal meristem. It is differentiated into foot and capsule with a constriction-like meristematic region in between. There is no seta. The archesporium is amphithecial in origin. It is a dome-shaped cylinder parallel with the elongated axis of the sporogonium arching over the central columella at the top. The capsule dehisces basipetally from the top downwards by two valves which being hygroscopic curl back exposing the central column of spores and pseudoelaters. The class includes a single order **Anthocerotales**.

SALIENT FEATURES OF THE CLASS ANTHOCEROTOPSIDA

1. The adult plant is an independent gametophyte which is thalloid, thallus dorsiventrally flattened and lobed.

2. The thallus is attached to the substratum by means of rhizoids which are only smooth walled, where as tuberculate rhizoids and ventral scales are absent.

3. Internally, the thallus is not differentiated into photosynthetic and storage zones but has a uniform cellular organisation.

4. The cells have chloroplasts with many pyrenoids.

5. Although air chambers and air pores are absent, intercellular mucilage cavities are present. These open on the ventral surface by slit like pores.

6. Sex organs are sunken in the thallus tissues. Thallus may be monoecious or dioecious.

7. The antheridia - the male sex organ develop on the dorsal surface of the thallus. These occur singly or in groups in the antheridial chambers. The antheridium develops from the hypodermal cells.

8. The archegonia develop from dorsal epidermal cells.

9. The sporophyte is differentiated into foot, intercalary meristematic zone and capsule.

10. The intercalary zone is meristematic as a result of which the capsule is indeterminate in growth.

11. The capsule is a long cylindrical structure with 4—6 layered capsule wall having stomata in the epidermis.

12. The sporogenous tissue develops from amphithecium.

13. Pseudoelaters are present, since elaters do not have thickening bands these are called pseudoelaters.

14. The sporophyte is partially independent or dependent on the gametophyte.

Stotler, R.E. and B. Crandall Stotler (2005) have maintained the concept of (phyla) division "Anthocerotophyta" for hornworts and have proposed following classification

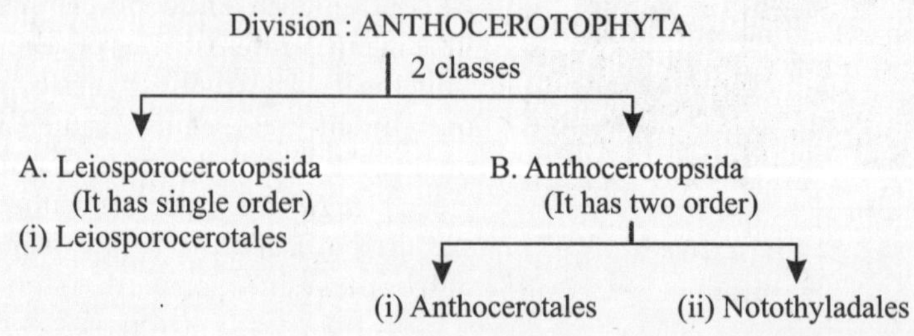

ORDER : ANTHOCEROTALES

It has the same characteristics as the class. Formerly five genera namely *Anthoceros, Notothylas, Megaceros, Aspiromitus* and *Dendroceros* with more than 300 species were included in the order Anthocerotales. Campbell in 1940 questioned the status of *Aspiromitus* as a genus based as it is on a single character which is presence of long, simple, thick-walled elaters in *Aspiromitus* and their absence in *Anthoceros*. His contention was supported by Proskauer (1948), and Mehra and Handoo (1953). The order thus is represented at present by four universally accepted genera. These are *Anthoceros, Notothylas, Megaceros* and *Dendroceros*. Of these *Anthoceros* alone comprises more than 200 species. Proskauer (1951) suggested to split the *Anthoceros* complex into two genera, *Phaeoceros* and *Anthoceros*. The former includes species which are characterised by :—

(*i*) Absence of large intercellular cavities in the gametophyte.

(*ii*) Antheridial jacket consisting of numerous small cells not regularly arranged in four tiers.

(*iii*) Spores yellow and translucent.

In *Anthoceros* are included species in which large intercellular cavities are present in the gametophyte. The antheridial jacket consists of elongated and rectangular cells regularly arranged in four vertical tiers. The spores are dark brown or black in colour.

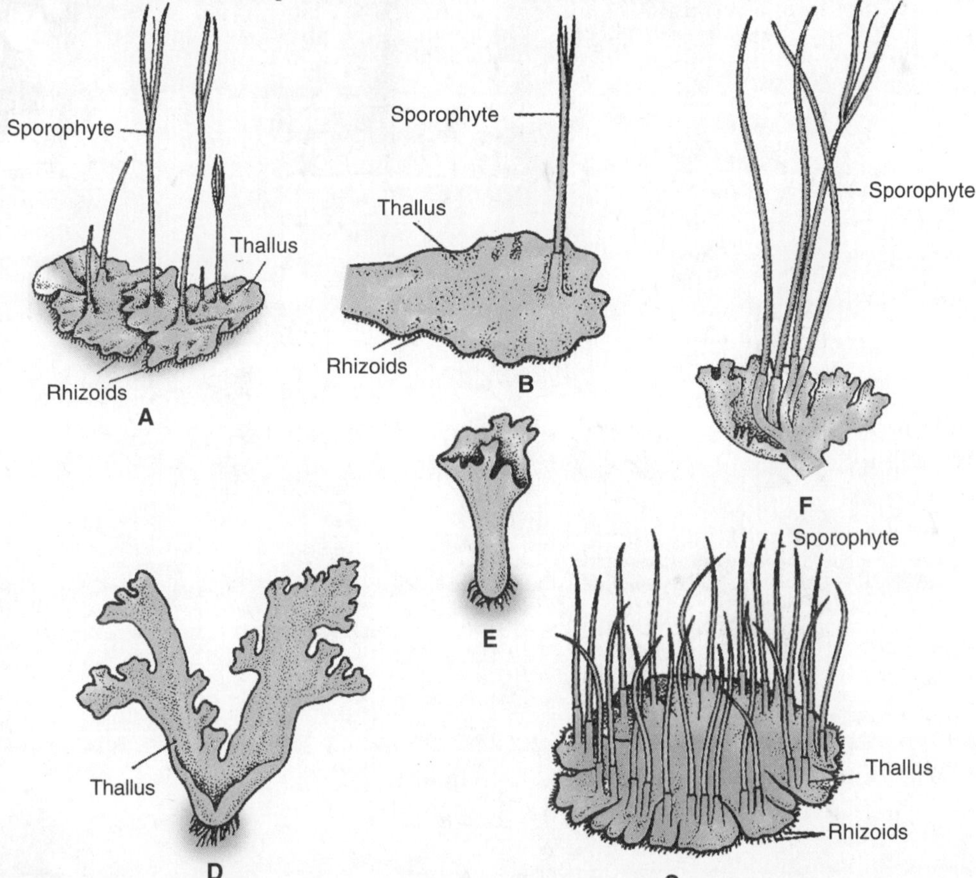

Fig. 13.1. (A—F) ***Anthoceros***. A, gametophyte of *Anthoceros* bearing three opened and three uopened, sporophytes; B, part of a thallus of *A. laevis* bearing dehiscent sporophyte; C, thallus of *A. crispulus* bearing several sporogonia; D—E, two sterile thalli of *A. erectus;* F, fertile thallus of *A. fusiformis* (C after Bharadwaj, D—E after Kashyap and F after Smith).

Distribution

According to Proskauer, the Anthocerotes popularly known as the hornworts are a small well-defined group of 5 genera namely, *Anthoceros, Phaeoceros, Notothylas, Megaceros* and *Dendroceros*. Of these *Anthoceros, Phaeoceros* and *Notothylas* are cosmopolitan in their distribution. They are ground dwellers and are found in the tropics, subtropics, and moist temperate regions. *Dendroceros* and *Megaceros* chiefly inhabit the tropics and subtropics. They grow usually as epiphytes on the bark of trees, damp litter and other suitable substrates. All the five genera are placed in a single family **Anthocerotaceae** but Modern bryologists (Muller, 1940, Preoskauer and Reimers, 1954) divide the order into two families, **Anthocerotaceae** and **Notothylaceae**. The latter includes a single genus *Notothvlas*.

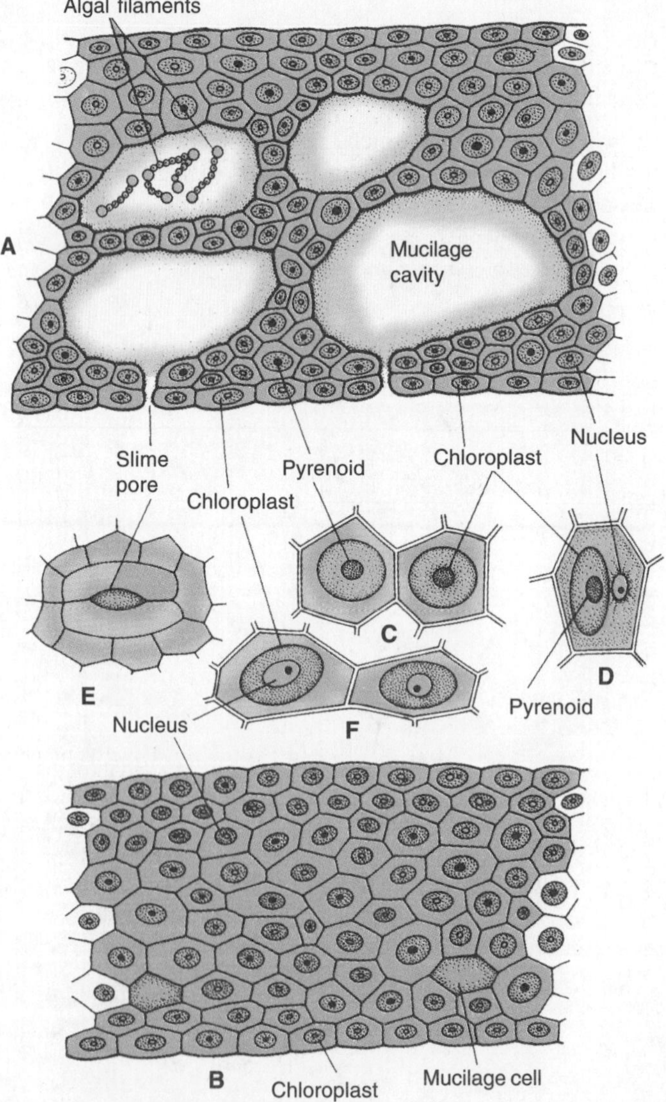

Fig. 13.2. (A—F). ***Anthoceros***. A, T.S. thallus of *Anthoceros* containing mucilage cavities; B, T.S. thallus with mucilage cells; C, two cells showing chloroplasts with a pyrenoid located in the centre; D, a single cell showing nucleus and chloroplast with pyrenoid; E, slime pore surface view; F, parenchymatous cell with a chloroplast and a nucleus.

FAMILY 1. ANTHOCEROTACEAE

GENERAL CHARACTERISTICS

The sporogonium is generally a long, upright, uniformly cylindrical structure arising from the dorsal surface of the thallus. At the base it is surrounded by a tubular sheath called the **involucre**. Mature sporogonium is differentiated into a bulbous **foot**, a median **meristematic zone** above the foot and a long **capsule**. The ripe capsule dehisces from the apex downwards. The sub-epidermal cells of the capsule wall contain chloroplasts. The central, solid core of columella is endothecial in origin. It is over-arched by the archesporium. The latter differentiates into the spores and the simple or branched **pseudo-elaters**. The family includes four genera *Anthoceros, Phaeoceros, Megaceros,* and *Dendroceros*. Of these *Anthoceros* is the best known. It is taken as a type.

ANTHOCEROS L.

Habitat and Distribution

Anthoceros is worldwide in its distribution. It commonly occurs on soil both in the tropical and temperate regions of the world. It is thus a cosmopolitan genus with over 200 species. In India alone 25 species have been reported. The three common Indian species which occur in the Himalayas are: *Anthoceros himalayensis, A. erectus* and *A. chambensis*. They usually occur at an altitude ranging from 5,000 to 8,000 ft. They have been reported by Kashyap from Mussoorie, Kulu, Manali, outer Himalayas and Kumaon, Chamba Valley, Punjab, S. India, Madras and Travancore. Mehra and Handoo collected the first two species from Simla, Nainital and Dalhousie also. All the species grow on moist, clayey soil or wet rocks in very moist, shady places, usually in dense patches. Sides of moist slopes along the hill side roads, ditches, along claybanks of streams and moist hollows among rocks are the usual habitats where they are commonly found. *A. himalayensis* is perennial but *A. erectus* is annual.

EXTERNAL FEATURES (Fig. 13.1).

The adult plant, as in the other bryophytes, is the gametophyte. It is a small, yellowish green or dark green dorsiventrally flattened, lobed thallus. The lobes with divided margins overlap. The thallus in some species is suborbicular in outline and variously lobed. The lobes are thick and fleshy generally more or less divided to form an irregularly lobed and folded margin. There is no distinct midrib. The upper surface of the thallus is smooth in some species (*A. laevis,* B) but rough in others (*A. fusiformis,* F) due to the presence of ridges. In *A. cispulus* (C) the upper surface of the thallus has flat, leaf-like lamellae, one cell thick and several cells wide (Bhardwaj, 1950). The ventral surface lacks scales, tuberculate rhizoids and mucilage hairs. However, it bears numerous, unicellular, smooth-walled rhizoids. These anchor the prostrate thallus to the substratum. In addition small, rounded bluish green thickened areas can be spotted on the ventral surface of the thallus. These thickened spots are called the **nostoc colonies**, as each is inhabited by a blue-green alga *Nostoc*.

Anthoceros erectus has generally a different habit. The thick, fleshy thallus of this species is often raised on a thick, upright or ascending, stalk-like structure (E). The latter expands above into a cup-like structure. Sometimes the thallus is prostrate and fan shaped. It is deeply lobed with a toothed margin (D).

In the months of September and October the *Anthoceros* thallus fruits. It usually bears long, cylindrical, delicate structures. These are the **sporogonia**. They arise in clusters from the dorsal surface of the thallus. Each sporogonium has a tubular sheath around it at its base. It is the **involucre** (B).

INTERNAL STRUCTURE OF THALLUS (Fig. 13.2).

Internally the thallus is several layers of cells thick but without a midrib (B). There is no tissue differentiation and little cell specialisation. Thus the assimilatory and storage regions are not recognisable. The entire thallus consists of soft parenchyma. The cells are uniform and compact. Air containing **channels** or air chambers and **air pores** are lacking. The surface cells of the thallus show more regular arrangement. They are smaller, each with a comparatively large lens-shaped chloroplast. They are, however, not cuticularized. There is thus no organised **epidermis**. In some species of *Anthoceros* there are stoma-like pores or slits on the ventral surface of the thallus. These are called the **slime pores** (A). Each slime-pore is guarded by two bean-shaped guard cells with thin walls (E). The guard cells do not function to control the size of the pore which thus remains completely open. The slime pores lead inwards often into large schizogenously formed, rounded intercellular spaces or cavities (A) which are filled with slime (mucilage), not air. The mucilage cavities open on the ventral surface of the thallus through the slime pores (A) which serve as outlets for the mucilage. Very often these mucilage cavities are inhabited by *Nostoc*—a blue green alga. Hormogones of *Nostoc* gain entry into the mucilage cavities through the slime pores. There they multiple and form colonies. The cavities containing *Nostoc* colonies are visible to the naked eye as small, deep blue-green rounded spots or specks on the under side of the thallus.

NOSTOC-ANTHOCEROS RELATIONSHIP

Ridgeway (1967) and Rodgers and Stewart (1977) reported that the presence of developing *Nostoc* colonies in cavities induces the development of branched filamentous protrusions consisting of hyaline cells on the host cavity wall opposite the slime pore. These filamentous protrusions penetrate the algal colonies and are referred to as "slime papillae" by some workers. The latter presume that the "slime papillae" produce slime which fills the cavities (Schuster, 1966). Ultrastructural observations by Ridgeway (1967) failed to find any features in the cells of the filamentous protrusions indicative of this role. The mucilage producing cells are usually characterized by the presence of golgi bodies with large vesicles and endoplasmic reticulum with distended cisternae. Both these features were absent in the neighbouring bryophytic cells. These workers, therefore, suggested that the mucilage, in fact, is secreted by the phycobiont (*Nostoc*) itself. The commonly held view is that the development of filamentous protrusions on the *Anthoceros* cavity wall increases the surface area of the *Nostoc-Anthoceros* interface. It is highly probable that this increase in the absorptive surface area in an adaptation which facilitates the exchange of metabolates between the two symbionts (*Nostoc sphaericum* and *Anthoceros*) in the association.

Nature of association. Till recently it was not definite whether *Anthoceros* in terms of thallus growth actually derived nutritional advantage from its association with *Nostoc*. Janczewski (1872) and Garjeanne (1930) observed that little or no benefit accrued to *Anthoceros* from this association. Pierce (1906) found that *Anthoceros* lacking *Nostoc* grew more vigorously than when the alga was present. Prantle (1889) and Bond and Scott (1955) concluded that association with *Nostoc* benefited *Anthoceros*. Ridgway (1967) found that *Nostoc* free *Anthoceros* on nitrogen free media was invariably chlorotic. He thus concluded that the association of *Nostoc* benefits *Anthoceros* especially when the thallus inhabiting species of *Nostoc* is capable of nitrogen fixation. Stewart (1974) showed that the alga fixes atmospheric nitrogen and reduces acetylene. He further showed that some of the products are rapidly absorbed by the host (*Anthoceros*). The algal partner received all the organic carbon it needed mainly from its host, *Anthoceros*. It showed little ability to fix carbon dioxide itself. Rodgers and Stewart (1977) demonstrated that *Nostoc-Anthoceros* association is a highly specialized form of symbiosis in which both the partners are mutually beneficial to each other. Both the components become modified morphologically, physiologically and biochemically. These modifications permit rapid interchange of metabolites between the two partners in the association. Fixed nitrogen apparently in the form of ammonia is transported out of *Nostoc* to *Anthoceros*, while living symbiotically the *Nostoc* has reduced carbon dioxide fixation capability and thus is dependent on *Anthoceros* for fixed carbon (Stewart and Rodgers, 1977).

In some species (*A. himalayensis* and *A. laevis*) the mucilage cavities are absent. Proskauer places these species of *Anthoceros* in the genus *Phaeoceros* as *P. himalayensis* and *P. laevis*. In certain species mucilage is contained in specially enlarged cells in the older portions of the thallus. They are called the *mucilage cells* (Fig. 14.2 B). The occurrence in the thallus of scizogenously formed mucilage filled cavities or chambers communicating with the outside through stoma like slime pores is a feature of singular interest. Doyle (1964) considered this pore chamber system, "a vestigial remnant of a previously extensive aerating system which functioned either in the early but now extinct hornworts or in the progenitors of hornworts".

Every thallus cell usually contains one large **chloroplast**. (Fig. 13.2 C). It is usually oval or flattened and has a large multiple **pyrenoid** in the centre. Multiple pyrenoid is a unique feature of the Anthocerotales. It is composed of numerous disc or spindle shaped structures which are aggregated into a central mass. The presence of chloroplasts with pyrenoids is a feature which *Anthoceros* shares with the green algae. In both the starch grains are synthesized at the periphery of the pyrenoid. This resemblance is apt to tempt one to speculate about the algal ancestry of Anthocerotales. Chloroplasts with pyrenoids are uncommon among the land plants. The only exceptions are *Anthoceros* thallus, *Isoetes* and *Selaginella*. Some species of *Anthoceros* have more than one chloroplast per cell, particularly in the deeper cells of the thallus. These are, however, smaller than those in the exterior. Their number varies from two (*A. pearsoni*) to four (*A. hallii*). In some species it may go up to six chloroplasts per cell. Each of these may contain a single compact pyrenoid or it occurs in 2 or 3 tiny pieces. In a few species the chloroplasts lack pyrenoids. This type of variation in the chloroplast number and structure in different species of *Anthoceros* may be of phyletic interest. According to Doyle (1970) it shows how the small pyrenoid lacking chloroplasts of land plants might have evolved from the larger, pyrenoid containing chloroplasts of algal ancestors. The single nucleus of the cell lies in the cytoplasm in close apposition to the chloroplast (Fig. 13.2 D).

The thallus of *Anthoceros* in its simple external form and little differentiation of vegetative tissues recalls that of *Pellia* as it does in the complete absence of ventral scales and tuberculate rhizoids. There is no well organised epidermis and neither any air chambers nor air pores in both. The two, however, differ in the absence of regular dichotomous growth and midrib, presence of internal cavities containing mucilage or occasionally a blue green alga *Nostoc* and a single chloroplast with a pyrenoid in each cell in the thallus of *Anthoceros*.

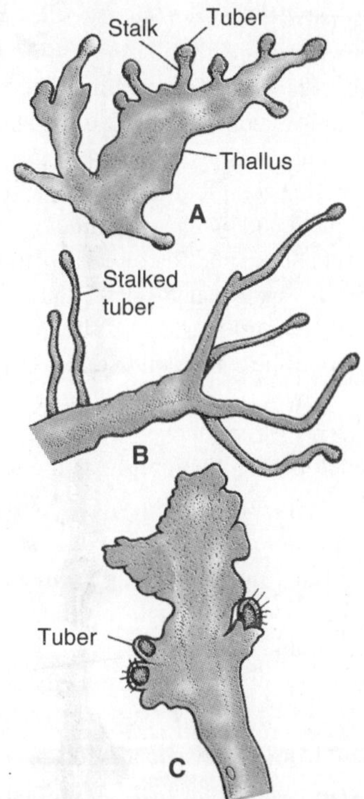

Fig. 13.3. (A—C). ***Anthoceros***. A—B, sterile thalli of *A. himalayensis* bearing stalked tubers; C, archegonia bearing thallus of *A. laevis* seen from the lower surface which bears sessile lateral tubers (A, B after Kashyap and C after Proskauer).

Apical growth. According to Campbell, Bower and Smith apical growth in *Anthoceros* takes place by means of a single **apical cell**. It is pyramidal in shape and has four cutting faces. It is located in the deeply emarginate growing point of each thallus lobe. The segments cut off right and left add to the width of the thallus. The others which are cut off parallel to the upper and lower surfaces increase its thickness. Mehra and Handoo, however, support Leitgeb who found several cells of equal rank constituting the growing point. They report that in *A. erectus* and *A. himalayensis* the growing point consists of a group of **initials.** They lie protected in a shallow depression filled with mucilage at the anterior end of each thallus lobe.

Reproduction

Anthoceros thallus is concerned with vegetative reproduction and the sexual process. Meiospore formation is the concern of the **sporogonium** or **sporophyte**.

1. Vegetative reproduction. Vegetatively the thallus of *Anthoceros* is propagated by the following methods :

(*i*) *Fragmentation.* The cells in the basal older portions of the thallus die and disorganise. When the progressive decay and death of cells reaches the branching region the thallus lobes become separated. Each separated lobe by continuous apical growth grows into a new thallus. However, propagation by this method is not so common in *Anthoceros.*

(*ii*) *Gemmae.* Some writers reported the formation of gemmae on short stalks on the upper surface and along the margin of the thallus in *A. glandulosus*, *A. formosae* and *A. propaguliferus.* The detached gemma grows into a new thallus.

(*iii*) *Tubers* (Fig. 13.3 A—C). Certain species of *Anthoceros* exposed to drought regularly develop rounded, marginal thickenings called the **tubers**. The cells of 2 or 3 surface layers of the tuber develop corky walls. The corky surface layers protect the inner cells that store starch, oil globules and protein. With the approach of dry season the thallus dies leaving behind the tubers. In this state *Anthoceros* tides over the adverse conditions. With the onset of conditions favourable for growth, each tuber develops into a new thallus. According to Mehra and Handoo (1953) the growth is apical and by a row of apical cells as in the thallus. The tubers thus primarly function as organs of perennation and secondarily serve as means of vegetative propagation. The sterile thalli of *A. himalayensis* usually bear stalked tubers (A). They are developed at the apex, along the margin and on the ventral surface of the thallus. The stalks may be long and cylindrical (B). Rhizoids develop both on the tubers and stalks. Occasionally the fertile plants of this species also bear tubers. They are, however, sessile and borne ventrally or along the margin of the thallus (C). Tuber formation has also been reported in other species such as *A. tuberosus*, *A. pearsoni* and *A. hallii* (C). They are developed on the margin of the thallus.

(*iv*) *Persistent growing apices***.** Campbell reported that the two perennial Californian species, *A. pearsoni* and *A. fusiformis* grow in regions with dry summer. With the approach of summer these plants dry up. Only the growing points of the thallus lobes with a little of adjacent tissue survive. The apices persist through the long summer drought and resume growth with the return of condition favourable for growth. Probably the growing apices become modified in some way to resist drough or the lot of mucilage in the thallus cells prevents the loss of water.

(*v*) *Apospory.* Schwarzenbach (1926) and Lang (1901) reported that *Anthoceros* thallus may arise from the unspecialised cells of the various parts of the sporogonium particullarly the intercalary meristematic zone, sub-epidermal and sporogenous regions of the capsule. In this way the life cycle is shortened by cutting the spore stage. The thallus (gametophyte) is produced directly from the vegetative cells of the sporogonium. This phenomenon is called **apospory**. Genetically the aposporously produced thalli are **diploid**. They are, however, normal in apprearance.

2. Sexual reproduction. Many species of *Anthoceros* are **monoecious**, others are **dioecious**. Examples of the former category are *A. gollani, A. longii, A. fusiformis* and *A. punctatus*. *A. crispus* and *A. himalayensis* are monoecious but reported to be markedly protandrous. The antheridia appear a good deal earlier than the archegonia. The common dioecious species are *A. erectus*, *A. chambensis*,

A. hallii, A. pearsoni and *A. laevis*. The sex organs in *Anthoceros* are immersed in the thallus tissue on the upper surface. Bensom-Evans (1964) reported that *A. laevis* is a short day plant. According to Bell and Woodcock (1968), the development of sex organs in *Anthoceros* depends upon photoperiod. Ridgway (1967) induced development of antheridia under short day conditions. He thus stated that in species of *Anthoceros, Phaeoceros* and *Notothylas* photoperiod is critical in the initiation of antheridia whereas temperature has no effect. The formation of gametes is initiated by diminishing day length. The sex organs thus develop in fall, winter and spring when water, which is essential for the dehiscence of sex organs and fetilization, is abundant.

(*a*) *Antheridia*. (*i*) *Position* (Fig. 13.4 C). The antheridia of *Anthoceros* are unique in being normally **endogenous**. They occur singly or in groups on the upper surface of the thallus within closed cavities called the **antheridial chambers**. Each antheridial cavity is roofed over by the thallus (gametophyte) tissue two cell layers in thickness. The ripe antheridia are bright orange in colour.

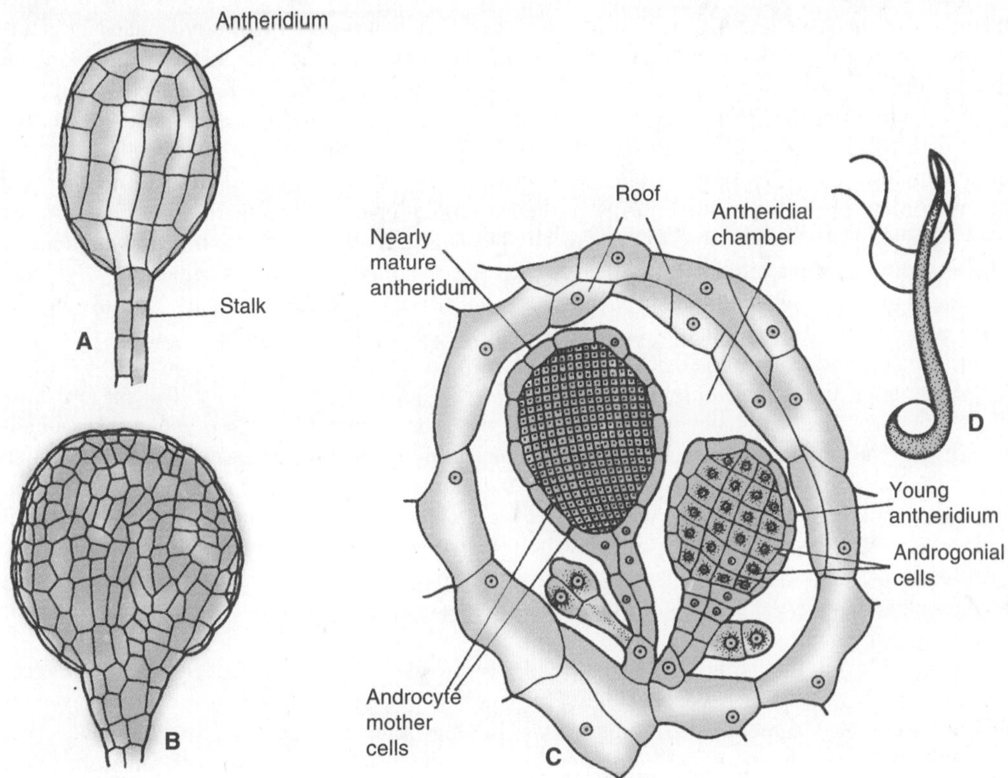

Fig. 13.4. (A—D). ***Anthoceros* sp**. A—B, entire mature antheridia of *A. crispulus* and *A. laevis*; C, L.S. through the antheridial chamber containing two primary antheridia and two young secondary antheridia formed by budding from the stalks of primary antheridia; D, sperm. (A, C, after Bhardwaj and B after Proskauer).

(*ii*) *Structure* (Fig. 13.4 C). Each antheridium has an ovoid or pouch-like **body**. It is raised on a multicellular, short or long, slender **stalk**. The later usually consists of four vertical rows of cells. In *A. laevis* it is thicker. The body of the antheridium, as in the liverworts, consists of a **jacket layer** or an **antheridial wall** enclosing a mass of **androcytes**(C). Each androcyte forms a single sperm (D). The cells of the jacket layer, in the dark spored species (*A. erectus*), are elongated and rectangular. They are regularly arranged in four superimposed tiers (A). In others (yellow spored species) the wall consists of a larger number of irregularly arranged small cells (*A. himalayensis*, B).The wall cells contain plastids one each. The plastids change colour. When the antheridia are young plastids are colourless. Later on they become green. In the mature antheridium the green plastids become bright orange or red (chromoplasts).

(*iii*) *Dehiscence* (Fig. 13.5 K). When the antheridia reach maturity, the roof of the antheridial chamber bursts open irregularly. The antheridia now lie in cup-shaped depressions or antheridial 'craters' with their orange-coloured contents obvious. The antheridia thus exposed dehisce following absorption of water presumably by the mucopolysaccharides in the matrix surrounding the sperm mass. This leads to rupture at the distal end of the swollen antheridium. Either the cells of the upper tier of the jacket layer separate (*A. punctatus*) or there is irregular separation of the distal jacket cells of the wall (*A. laevis*). An aperture is thus formed at the distal end of the antheridium, through it oozes out the matrix containing the sperm vesicles (K). Finally the sperms are discharged in the water that caused the rupture by dissolution of the walls of the sperm vesicles. Proskauer (1948) and Duckett (1973) found that in *Anthoceros laevis* following distal rupture, the jacket cells hardly separate and the sperms are thus simply squeezed out (Fig. 13.7 A).

The liberated sperm (Fig. 13.5 L) is a tiny, biflagellate structure. The two flagella are equal and almost of the same length as the body. They are inserted at the slightly broader, anterior end of the slender body which is slightly curved. The unused protion of the cytoplasm of the androcyte remains attached for some time to the swolllen posterior portion. Just behind the front end and beneath the two flagella is an elongated swelling probably a blepharoplast (Proskauer, 1948).

(*iv*) *Development of antheridium* (Fig. 13.5). The antheridia in *Anthoceros* develop **endogenously**. They lie in roofed chambers sometimes singly, sometimes in groups. In either case the antheridium or the antheridial cluster in the antheridial chamber together with the latter's two layered roof is traceable to a single **surface cell**. The surface cell lies close to the growing apex on the upper surface of the thallus. It has denser cytoplasm and a conspicuous nucleus (A). It divides periclinally into an **inner segment** and an **outer segment** (B). The former functions as an **antheridial initial** and develops into an antheridium or an antheridial cluster. The outer segment is the **roof initial**. It forms two layers of cells over roofing the chamber.

Soon after, the *antheridial* and the *roof initials* separate from each other. The space formed between them is filled with mucilage (D). The other cells surrounding the antheridial initial gradually shrink away. The mucilage space finally enlarges into a definite cavity called the **antheridial chamber**. The roof initial first divides by a periclinal wall (C). Later the two resultant daughter cells divide and redivide by anticlinal walls to form the two-layered roof of the antheridial chamber (E). The antheridial initial before segmentation nearly rounds off (D). It then either directly develops into a single antheridium (*A. pearsoni*) or it may divide vertically into two (E), four or sometimes into more daughter cells (*A. erectus*). Each of the latter functions as a antheridial initial so that there is a group of two (J), four or more antheridia in the chamber.

In either event the antheridial initial divides by two vertical divisions at right angles to each other to form four cells (F). Each of these cells again divides by a transverse wall. The young antheridium at this stage consists of eight cells (G). Only four are seen in a longitudinal section. The eight cells are arranged in two tiers (upper and lower) of four cells each. The four cells of the lower tier are the **stalk cells**(G). They divide and redivide transversely to form the stalk composed of four vertical rows of cells. The four cells of the upper tier again divide transversely (H). The octant of cells thus formed gives rise to the body of the antheridium. Each cell of the octant divides by a curved wall (periclinally). In this way eight inner **primary androgonial cells** are separated from the eight outer **primary jacket cells** (I). The latter divide only by anticlinal walls to form the single layered **antheridial wall**. Repeated divisions of the primary androgonial cells result in the formation of a central mass of fertile **androgonial cells** (J). The cells of the last cell generation of the central fertile mass are called the **androcyte mother cells**. Each androcyte mother cell divides to give rise to two **androcytes**. The protoplast of each androcyte metamorphoses into a biflagellate **sperm** (L).

Duckett (1973) with the help of electron microscope observed ingrowths of wall material directed towards the lumina on the inner wall of the jacket cells of antheridia containing mature

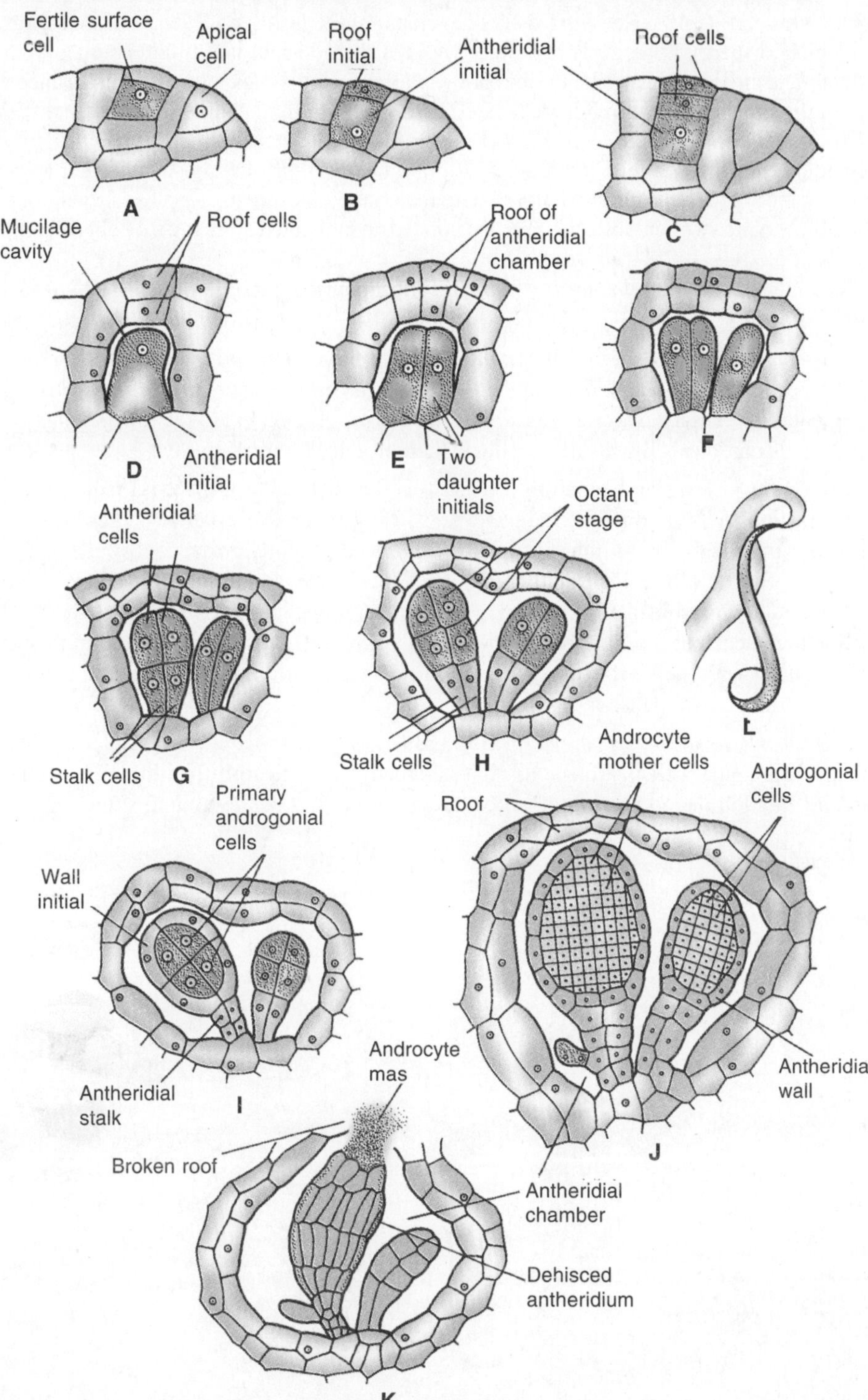

Fig. 13.5. (A—K). ***Anthoceros* sp**. Development of antheridium. A—J, stages in the development of antheridium; K, dehisced antheridium situated in the antheridial chamber with the roof broken off; L, single sperm (A—I based on Campbell, J after Bhardwaj, K, after Proskauer).

spermatocytes in *A. leavis*. These ingrowths develop rapidly during final stages of metamorphosis of androcytes into sperms. The outer and other walls of the adjacent jacket cells remain smooth. The cell membrane closely follows the outline of the wall ingrowths thus increasing its surface area as is typical of the 'transfer cells' which are located in regions where intensive short distance transport of solutes occurs. According to Bagchee (1944) the sperm in *A. laevis* has a linear body slightly broader towards the head. Two flagella are almost of the same length as the body. Praskauer (1945) found the body of the sperm to be slightly curved with the unused androcyte cytoplasm remaining attached for sometime to the swollen posterior end. He noticed an elongated swelling probably a blepharoplast just beneath the flagella bearing front end.

In some species of *Anthoceros* (*A. erectus*) secondary antheridia may arise by budding from the stalks of the older ones (Fig. 13.4 C).

(*b*)*Archegonia* (*i*) *Position* (Fig. 13.6 G, H). The archegonia of *Anthoceros* are remarkable in certain respects. They are sunk deep in the fleshy thallus on its upper surface. They lie close to the growing point in regular rows and are developed in **acropetal order**. In the monoecious species the archegonia appear later, on the same thallus which produced antheridia.

(*ii*) *Structure*. Each archegonium (Fig. 13.6 H) consists only of **an axial row** of usually four to six **neck canal cells**, a **ventral canal cell** and an **egg**. There is no sterile **jacket layer** except the distal rosette of **cover cells** forming its tip. The cover cells slightly project above the general, upper surface of the thallus where it is usually surrounded by a somewhat funnel-shaped mass of mucilage called the **mucilage mound** (Fig. 13.7 D). The surrounding vegetative cells of the thallus offer protection to the cells of the axial row. The archegonium of *Anthoceros* immersed in the thallus and in direct contact with the surrounding vegetative cells differs from that of all other bryophytes and resembles certain of the pteridophytes.

(*iii*) *Development of archegonium* (Fig. 13.6). Each archegonium originates from a dorsal segment of the apical cell just close to it. It is called the **archegonium initial** (A). According to Mehra and Handoo the archegonium initial directly functions as the **primary archegonial cell**. It

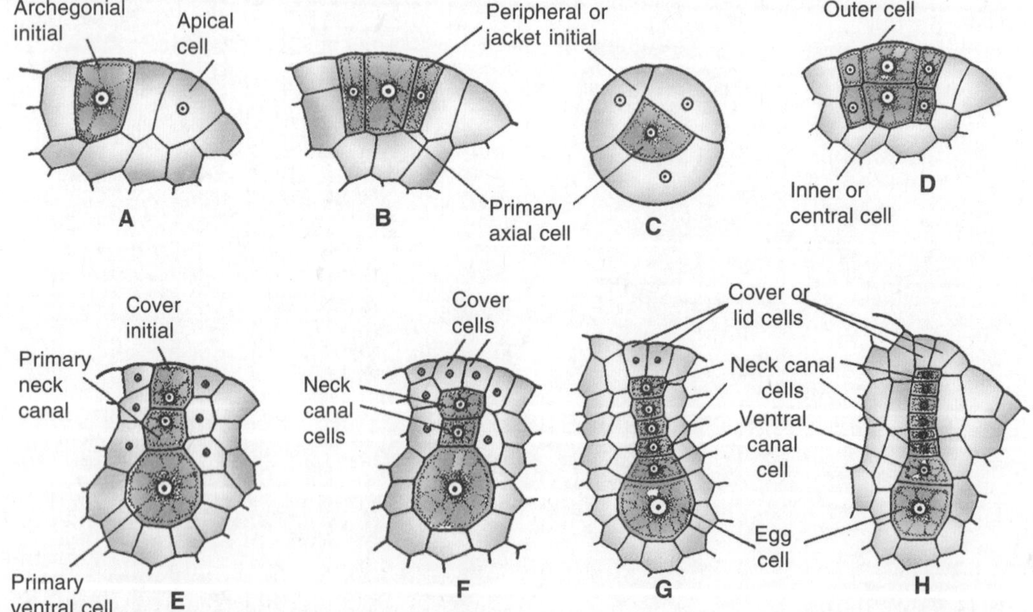

Fig. 13.6. ***Anthoceros* sp.** Development of archegonium. A—F, early stages in the development of archegonium; Explanation in the text, G and H, nearly mature archegonia, (A—F based on Campbell, G—H after Bhardwaj).

does not project above the general surface of the thallus nor does it undergo the usual horizontal division. The absence of this division accounts for the sunken nature of the archegonium and its histological continuation with the adjacent cells of the thallus tissue. Some writers such as Campbell, Bower and others, however, hold that the archegonium initial divides by a transverse or periclinal wall to form an outer **primary archegonial cell** and an inner **primary stalk cell**. The consensus of opinion favours the first view.

The primary archegonial cell (A) divides by three vertical intersecting walls (B).This separates the three **jacket initials** from the central **primary axial cell** which they enclose (C). The archegonium rudiment which now consists of four cells is completely embedded in the tissue of the thallus. The primary axial cell divides transversely into an **outer cell** and an inner **central cell** (D). The latter (central cell) functions directly as a **primary ventral cell** (E). It enlarges and fianlly divides to give rise to the **ventral canal cell** and the **oosphere** or **ovum** (G). The outer cell which corresponds to the primary cover cell of the liverworts undergoes a transverse division to separate a terminal **cover initial** from the inner **primary neck canal cell** (E). The cover initial divides by two interesecting walls to form the distal rosette of four **cover** or **lid cells** forming the apex of the archegonium (F). The primary neck canal cell undergoes a series of transverse divisions to form a chain of four to six **neck canal cells** (G-H).

Smith gives a different account. He stated that the primary **axial cell** divides transversely into a **primary cover cell** and a **central cell**. The central cell further divides into a **primary canal cell** and the **primary ventral cell** as is the case in the liverworts.

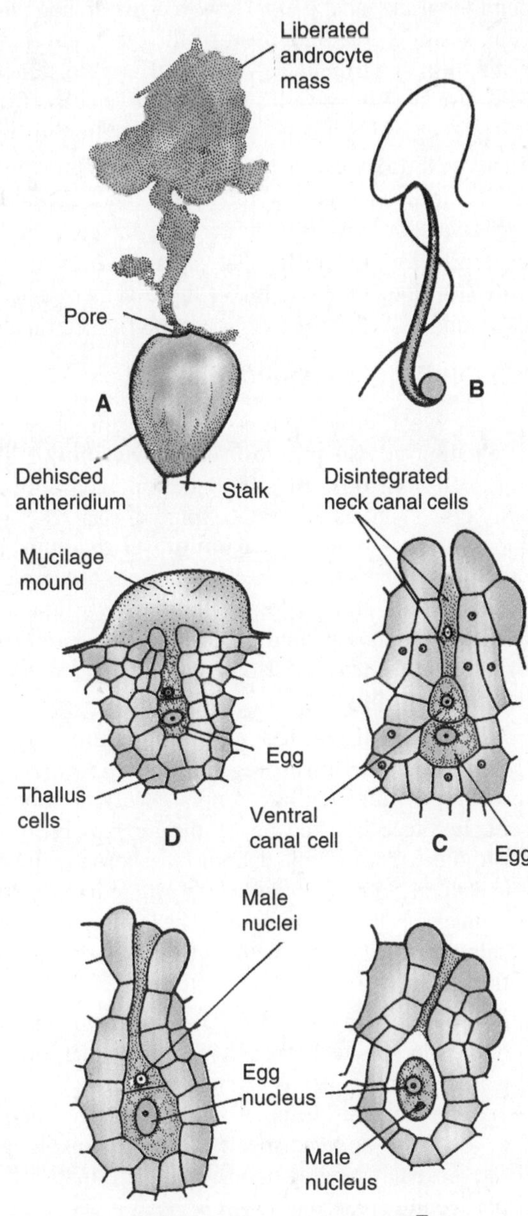

Fig. 13.7 (A—F). ***Anthoceros* sp**. Dehiscence of sex organs and fertilization. A, dehiscent antheridium of *A. laevis* extruding androcyte mass; B, single sperm; C, archegonium of *A. crispulus* showing disintegrated neck canal cells; D, mature archegonium showing disintegration of axial row of cells except the egg; E, mature archegonium with the egg ready for fertilization; F, fertilised egg in the venter with male and female nuclei side by side. (A, D after Proskauer; C, E after Bhardwaj).

Simultaneously with the differentiation of the axial row of cells, the three jacket initials have divided transversely into two tiers of 3 cells each (D). Three cells of the upper tier destined to form the sunken neck divide by vertical walls. The resultant six jacket cells divide repeatedly by transverse divisions to form the six vertical rows of **neck cells**. They form a single layered jacket of sterile cells (neck) around the neck canal cells. However, the archegonia of *Anthoceros* being completely sunk in the thallus tissue, the development of the jacket layer of the archegonium is difficult to follow. It is indistinguishable from the adjacent cells of the gametophyte. In any case the egg towards its lower face is protected by the adjacent vegetative cells of the thallus.

(*c*) *Fertilization* (Fig. 13.7 D—E). With the archegonia immersed in the thallus, fertilisation presents no difficulties. On the access of water the cells of the axial row excepting the ovum gelatinize (D). The neck canal is now filled with mucilage and the remains of the canal cells. The mucilage absorbs water and swells. Consequently the cover cells are thrown off. An open passage down to the egg is formed (E). A biflagellate sperm swims down the canal and fuses with the egg to form a **zygote** (F). The latter swells to fill the venter cavity compeltely. Thereafter the zygote secretes a wall around it. A number of zygotes are formed on a single thallus.

SPOROPHYTIC PHASE (Fig. 13.8)

The zygote is the pioneer structure of this phase. By repeated segmentation it develops into an elongated **embryo**. The latter by further cell division, cell differentiation and continued growth rapidly grows into an elongated, spindle-shaped structure with a bulbous base. It is the **sporogonium** or the **sporophyte**. The sporophytes usually grow in clusters from the upper surface of the thallus, each surrounded at its base by a tubular **involucre** (Fig. 13.8). The sporogonium produces the spores and brings about their efficient dispersal. For this reason the sporogonium is also called the **sporophyte**.

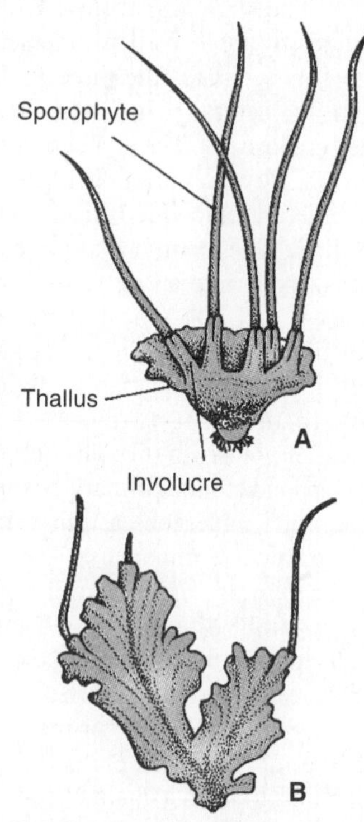

Fig. 13.8. (A—B) ***Anthoceros* sp.** A, thallus of *A. erectus* bearing sporophytes; B, gametophyte of *A. himalayensis* with sporogonia. (After Kashyap).

(*a*) **External features of sporogonium** (Fig. 13.8). It is differentiated into three regions; (*i*) the **capsule**, (*ii*) the **intercalary** or **intermediate zone** and (*iii*) the **foot**. The **seta** is absent. Its place is taken up by the intercalary zone which is **meristematic**. The unstalked, horn-like sporogonium ranges from one to several centimetres in length. At the base it is surrounded by a tubular sheath, the **involucre**. The latter is an outgrowth from the thallus and thus is a gametophytic structure. It is protective in function and also gives support to the weak intercalary zone.

(*i*) *Capsule* (Fig. 13.8). It forms the major and conspicuous part of the sporophyte. In form it is long, slender, smooth, upright and cylindrical. It is nearly of uniform thickness throughout its length except towards the apex where it slightly tapers. Usually it is 2 to 3 cms. or in some species up to 15 cms. long. It is light green at first but turns grey or brown towards maturity. Potentially the sporogonium (capsule) of *Anthoceros* is capable of unlimited growth in length because of the presence of meristematic zone at the junction of the foot and the capsule. The apex of capsule represents its oldest part. The maturation of spores in the capsule is from the apex downwards i.e. non-synchronus.

(*b*)**Internal structure of sporogonium** (Fig. 13.9). Internally the capsule shows great elaboration and complexity of structure. In the centre of the capsule is a slender solid core of sterile tissue. It is the **columella (A).** The cell constituting it are narrow, elongated with somewhat uniformly thickened walls. They are arranged in sixteen vertical rows. In a cross-section they form a solid square (B). In the young capsule, however, the columella, consists of four vertical rows of cells only. It is **endothecial** in origin. Proskauer (1960) reported the occurrence of *Anthoceros*. The columella extends from the base right through the capsule and ends a little behind its distal end

(Fig. 13.10 A). The chief function of columella is to give support to the long, delicate capsule. To some extent it helps in the dispersal of spores. Some writers look upon it as a primitive type of vascular cylinder.

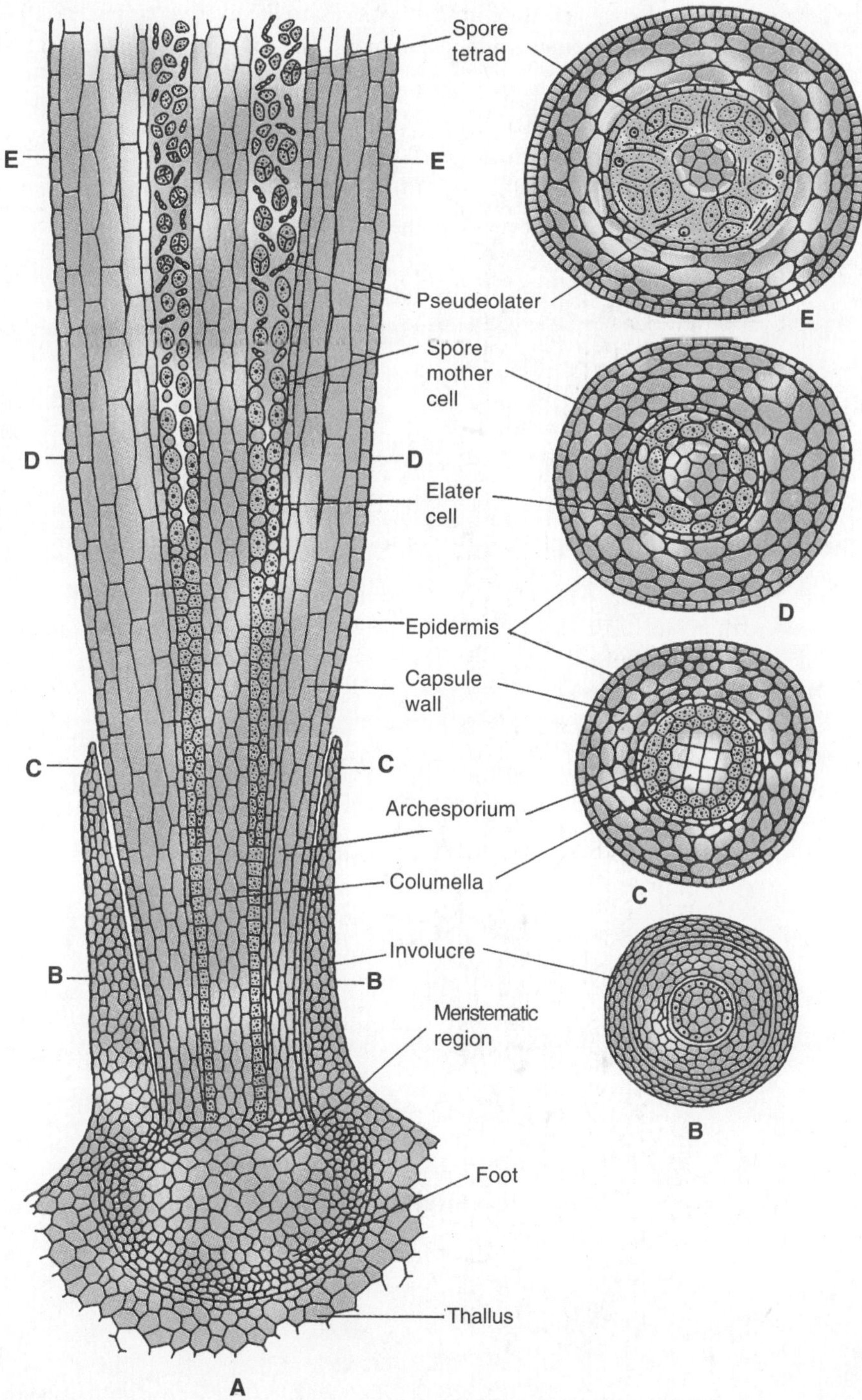

Fig. 13.9. (A—E). ***Anthoceros***. A, L.S. through the sporogonium; B, cross section of A at the level B—B; C, cross section of A at the level C—C; D, cross section of A at the level D—D; E, cross section of A at the level E—E.

Around the columella is a double layer of elongate but domed **sporogenous tissue** (A—C). It is in the form of a cylinder between the columella and the capsule wall. Sometimes it is one cell layer thick throughout. It is differentiated from the inner layer of the **amphithecium**. It extends over the top of the columella like a dome—a feature in sharp contrast to the liverworts (Fig. 13.10 A). In this respect *Anthoceros* sporophyte resembles *Sphagnum* moss. The sporogenous tissue originates in the

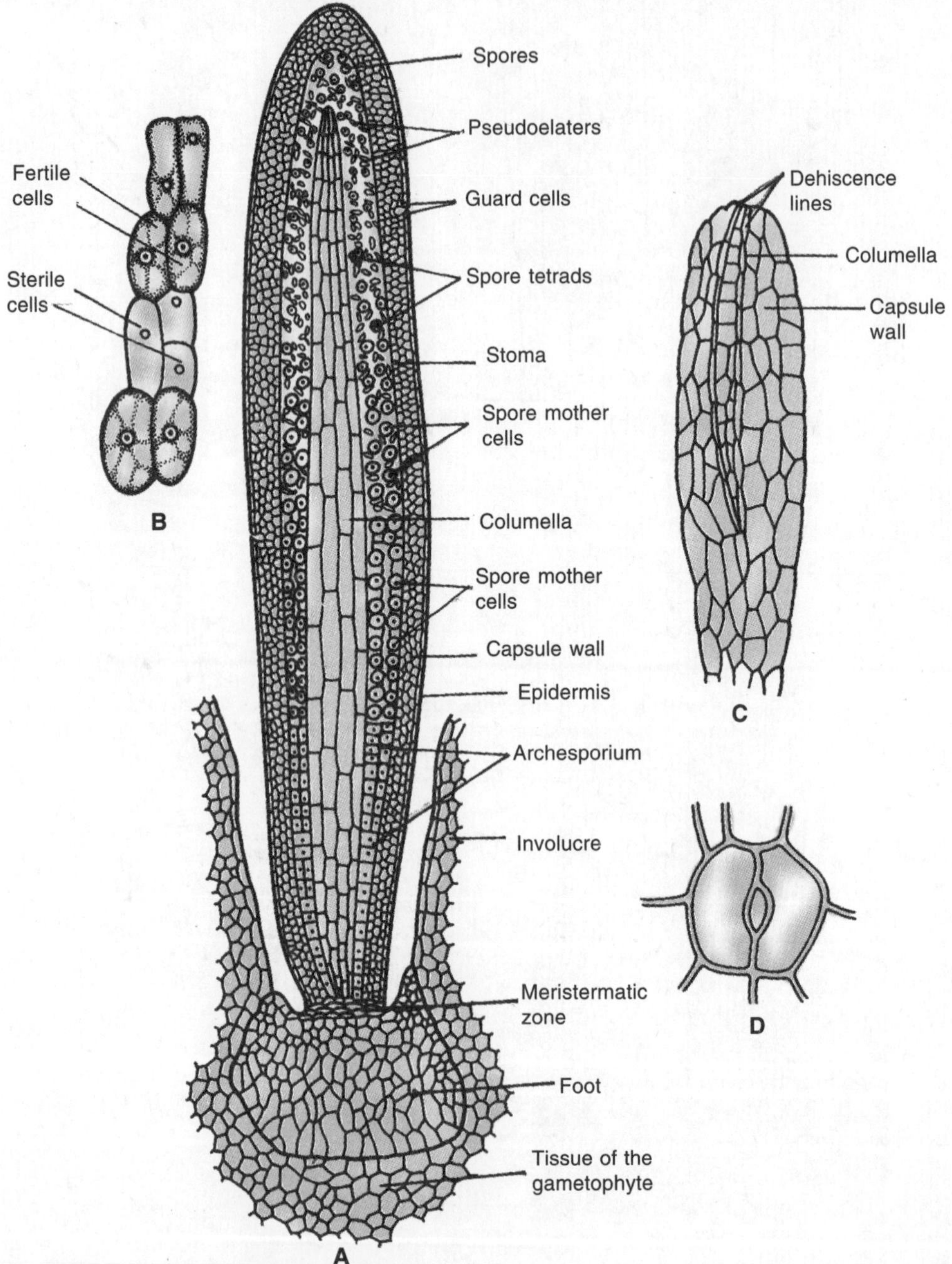

Fig. 13.10. (A—D). ***Anthoceros* sp.** A, L.S. mature but undehisced sporogonium (Diagrammatic); B, a portion of the archesporium differentiated into alternate bands of sterile (pseudoelater) cells and sporogenous (fertile) cells.; C, a portion of the capsule showing lines of dehiscence; D, a stoma from the surface of the capsule.

meristematic zone where it is single layered and is called the **archesporium** (A). Higher up it becomes a two-layered sporogenous tissue (*A. himalayensis*), rarely 3 or 4 cells in thickness. In *A. erectus* the archesporium remains single layered throughout. The archesporial cells have denser cytoplasm. In contrast to the liverworts, all parts of the *Anthoceros* capsule do not mature simultaneously. Thus at successive higher levels spore mother cells (D), spore tetrads (E) and meiospores are formed. Among the spore tetrads and mature spores are found the pseudoelaters (E). They form chains of one to four elongated thin or thick-walled, sterile cells of irregular shape (Fig. 13.11 E). The pseudoelaters are smooth-walled and are nutritive in function. They lack spiral thickenings and are pluricellular, sometimes unicellular. According to Pande, the pseudoelaters in *A. physocladus* are long and have thick walls with an extremely reduced lumen. Proskauer (1960) reported elaters with helical pattern of secondary wall thickening in some species.

External to the fertile zone is the **capsule wall** (Fig. 13.9 A). It is several layers (usually 4 to 6) of cells in thickness. The outermost layer of wall is the **epidermis**. It consists of narrow, vertically elongated cells with their outer walls cutinized. Here and there the epidermal layer is punctured by **stomata** similar to those of the higher plants. Each stoma consists of a **pore** surrounded by two **guard cells** (Fig. 13.10 D). The cells of the capsule wall within the epidermis are **chlorenchymatous**. They have intercellular spaces between them. Each cell contains double the number of chloroplasts characteristic of the gametophytic tissue. As a rule there are usually two large chloroplasts per cell. They are similar to those of the thallus. The capsule wall is thus actively **photosynthetic** in function. The intercellular spaces between the chlorenchymatous cells communicate with the exterior through the substomatal chambers and stomata to form a typically **ventilated photosynthetic tissue**.

(*ii*) **Intermediate** or **intercalary zone**. It is a narrow zone of **meristematic cells** located at the base of the capsule just above the foot. The meristem constantly adds new cells to the capsule at its base. They become progressively differntiated into columella, archesporium and capsule wall. The presence of a basal intercalary meristem enables the capsule to grow for a long period and form spores.

(*iii*) **Foot**. It is a rounded bulbous structure deeply embedded in the tissue of the thallus. By means of the foot *Anthoceros* capsule is well anchored upon and attached to the thallus. The foot mainly consists of a mass of parenchymatous cells. The surface cells of the foot, however, often grow out into short, tubular, **rhizoid-like** outgrowths. The latter serve to increase the absorptive surface of the foot and penetrate the tissue of the thallus. The foot of *Anthoceros* sporogonium is thus specialised to function as a **haustorium**. It absorbs food and water from the parent thallus for the sporophyte. The region of contact between the foot and the thallus tissue is well marked in many species. It is called the **placenta**. The cells on the gametophytic side of the placenta are "transfer cells". These cells develop long thread-like ingrowths which branch and the branches anastomose to form wall labyrinths. The plasma membrane in these cells follows the contours of the wall and the cell cytoplasm penetrates between the individual ingrowths or into the interstices of the labyrinth. The plasma membrane in the transfer cells is thus greatly increased.

It is evident from the account given above that *Anthoceros* sporophyte differs from that of the liverworts in many respects. These distinctive features of *Anthoceros* sporophyte are: (*i*) continued growth from the basal intercalary meristem located between the foot and the capsule; (*ii*) elaboration of internal tissue into a central columella; (*iii*) great reduction of fertile (sporogenous) tissue; (*iv*) archesporium amphithecial in origin and extending like a dome over the top of the columella; (*v*) green capsule wall several cell layers thick with cutinized epidermis containing stomata; (*vi*) presence of simple or branched pseudo-elaters intermixed with spores.

Nutrition of sporophyte. *Anthoceros* sporophyte has a well developed typically ventilated photosynthetic tissue. It comprises the green, several cell layers thick capsule-wall with a cuticularized epidermis possessing stomata which open into the substomatal chambers communicating with the

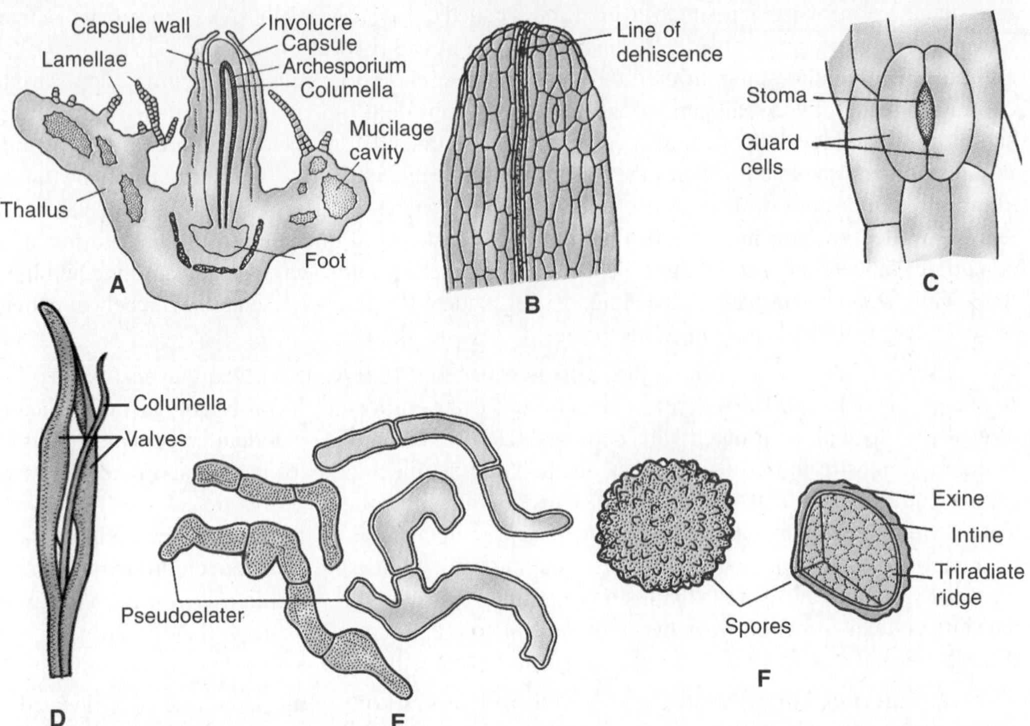

Fig. 13.11. (A—F). ***Anthoceros.*** A, L.S. thallus of *A. crispulus* showing lamellae and a young sporophyte still enclosed in the involucre; B, portion of the capsule showing lines of dehiscence; C, stoma from the surface of the capsule; D, bivalved dehiscence showing twisting of the valves; E, pseudoelaters of *A. crispulus* shaded; F, spores (A, D, E, F after Bhardwaj).

intercellular spaces between the chlorenchymatous cells of the inner layers of the capsule wall. The previous workers assumed that with such a photosynthetic power, unmatched in the liverworts sporophytes, gives the slender, green long growing *Anthoceros* sporophyte all that it needs to attain considerable nutritional independence from the gametophyte to which it is attached. They held that it has become fully self-sufficient so far as the supply of carbohydrates is concerned. For water and minerals in solution, it depends on the parent gametophyte to which it is attached by its massive foot. The sporophyte of *Anthoceros* is thus **semi-independent.** The large specimens of Californian *Anthoceros fusiformis* (Campbell, 1924) which had grown for nine months and were on the brink of achieving independence from the ageing gametophyte are frequently cited as examples of nearly independent sporophytes. There are, however, scattered observations in literature which are not compatible with the concept of nutritionally autonomous *Anthoceros* sporophyte. Campbell (1917) and Rink (1935) found that excised sporophytes in culture showed little continued growth. Rink showed that the sporophytes covered with aluminium foil caps to inhibit photosynthetic assimilation continued to grow and reached maturity so long they remained attached to the actively growing thallus. Stewart and Rodgers (1977) demonstrated net transfer of nutrients from gemetophytes to sporophytes in *Anthoceros punctatus*. It takes place by the activity of *transfer cells* at the sporophyte-gametophyte interface. Robet *et al* (1988) showed that the sprophytes of *Phaeoceros laevis* make substantial contribution to their own nutrition. It is sufficient for self-maintenance but not for sustained growth. Continued growth of hornwort sporophytes depends on the transfer of solutes from the parent thalli. At the time of higher respiratory rates there is mobilization of food reserves from the gametophyte thallus in response to the secretion of an auxin which is transported basipetally from the cells of intercalary meristem. There is increased enzymatic activity in the transfer cells located at the contact zone between the gamctophyte and sporophyte at the time of carbon transfer from the gametophyte thallus.

Development of sporophyte (Fig. 13.12). The fertilized egg enlarges until it fills the venter cavity (A). It then secretes a wall around it. After this zygote enters upon active segmentation. The first wall is vertical (B). It divides the embryo into two equal daughter cells. The next division is transverse (D). The embryo now consists of four cells. Of these the upper two cells are usually larger than the lower ones. Bhardwaj, however, reported that the first division is transverse (C) and the second vertical. In either event each of the resultant four cells divides by a vertical wall at right angles to the first. The embryo now consists of eight cells arranged in two tiers of four cells each. In a longitudinal section only four cells are seen at this stage (D). This is the **octant stage** of the embryo. The four cells of the upper tier are larger than the lower ones. According to Mehra and Handoo the upper tier (*A. erectus*) forms the capsule and the intermediate zone. The lower tier gives rise to the foot.

In the majority of the species, however, the four larger cells of the upper tier undergo another transverse division (E). The embryo now consists of three tiers of four cells each. The cells of the uppermost tier are still larger. The four cells of the lowest tier (formed from the hypobasal half of the zygote) form the foot, whole of it or at any rate a major part of it. The uppermost tier develops into the capsule. The medium tier gives rise mainly to the intermediate zone and in part to the foot (F). The cells of the intermediate zone remain **meristematic**. They establish an intercalary meristem at the base of the capsule. According to Mclean and Cook these early divisions in *A. laevis* result in an embryo composed of four cells each. The highest tier forms the capsule and the intermediate zone while the lower three cells give rise to the foot.

The cells of the foot tier divide and redivide in all directions to form a rounded mass of parenchymatous cells. It is broad, massive and shaped like an inverted cap. This structure is called the **foot** (J). The surface cells of the foot, in some species, grow out into short, tubular rhizoid-like processes. The later penetrate the tissue of the gametophyte. They are **haustorial** in function.

The four cells of the uppermost tier which are destined to form the capsule, divide by periclinal walls. This separates a central group of four cells from the surrounding peripheral ones (G). The former constitute the **endothecium** and the later **amphithecium**. Some bryologists hold that the four top cells undergo one or two transverse divisions before the periclinal walls are laid in them. From the entire endothecium originates the sterile **columella**. The later in the young capsule is made up of four vertical rows of cells (I). In the older capsule it consists of sixteen vertical rows (J). The corresponding tissue in the liverworts forms the **archesporium**. The **archesporium** in *Anthoceros* is formed from the inner cells resulting from periclinal division of the amphithecium cells (I). The outer cells of the series function as **jacket** or **wall initials**. The jacket or wall initials undergo repeated divisions by anticlinal and periclinal walls to form the **capsule wall**. It is four to six layers of cells in thickness (J). The outermost layer of the capsule wall is **epidermis**. It develops **stomata**. The epidermal cells are cutinised. The wall cells within the epidermis are photosynthetic. They, as a rule, have two large chloroplasts per cell, sometimes one, rarely as many as four. There are intercellular spaces between them. The photosynthetic tissue communicates with the exterior through the stomata.

The single-layered **archesporium** is parallel to the elongated axis of the capsule and is dome-shaped. It over-arches the rounded apex of the columella (J) and extends nearly to its base. The cells of the archesporium can easily be distinguished from the sterile cells of the columella by their denser protoplasm. In some species the archesporium remains single layered throughout (*A. erectus*) and functions as the primary sporogenous layer. In other species it becomes two-layered above the base of the capsule (*A. himalayensis*). In still others it becomes 2-4 cell layers thick by periclinal divisons and forms the sporogenous tissue. The sporogenous tissue differentiates into two kinds of

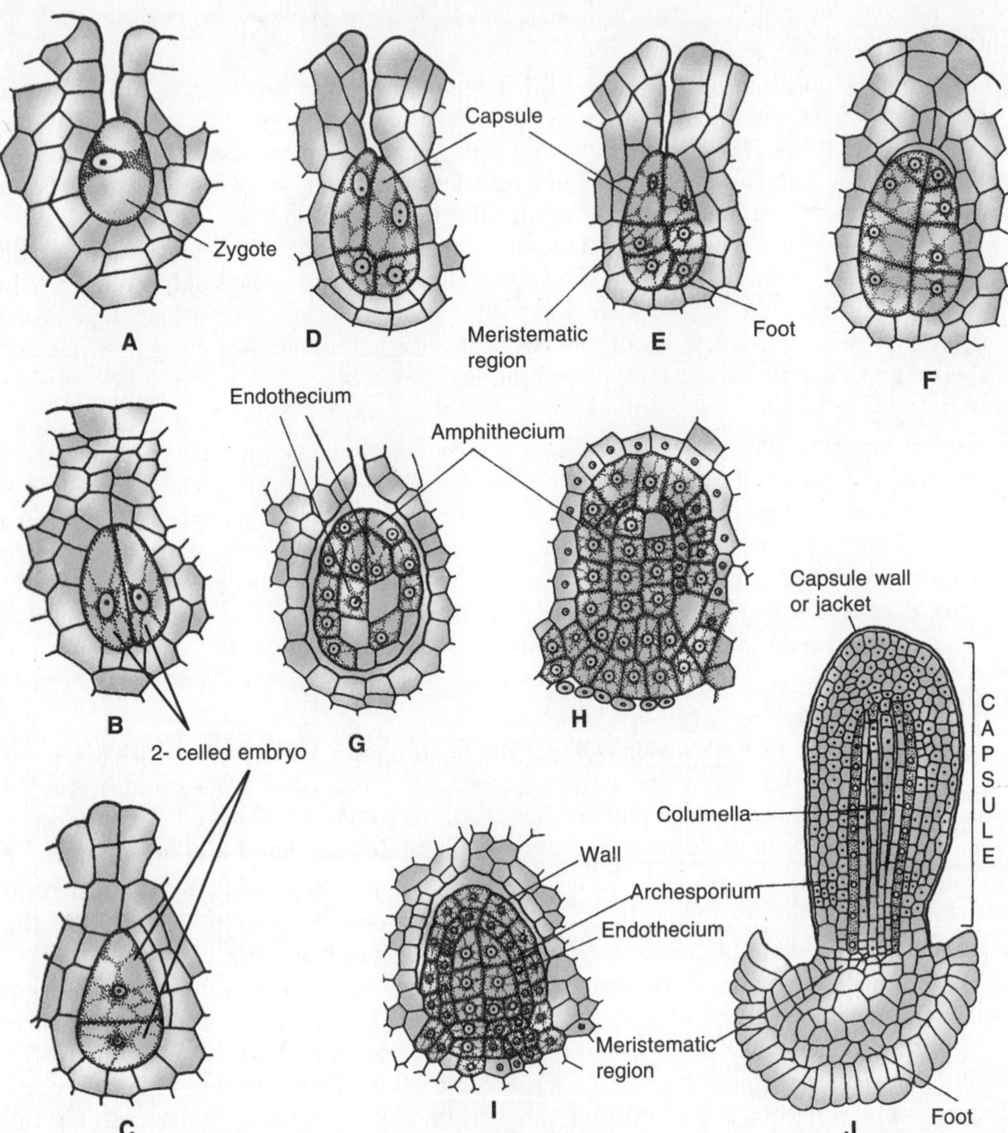

Fig. 13.12. (A—J), ***Anthoceros* sp**. Development of sporophyte (Sporogonium). A—F, early stages in the development of embryo; G—I, stages in the differentiation of amphithecium, endothecium and archesporium; J, young sporophyte differentiated into foot, meristematic zone and capsule. The capsule shows differentiation into capsule wall, archesporium and columella (B, D, E after Campbell, C, F, J after Bhardwaj).

sister cells namely, fertile cells and sterile cells (Fig. 13.10 B). The former give rise to spore mother cells and the latter to pseudoelater mother cells. These two kinds of cells may arise in regularly alternating layers or bands (Fig. 13 B).

(*i*) *Spore mother cells*. These are large cells oval to spherical in form. Each contains granular, denser cytoplasm, a distinct nucleus and a chloroplast (Fig. 13.13 A). The young spore mother cells increase in size, separate from each other and become spherical in form. Finally each of these undergoes meiosis to form the haploid spores or meiospores. This process is called sporogenesis.

Sporogenesis (Fig. 13.13). Prior to meiosis, the single chloroplast in each spore mother cell (A) divides into two (B). The two daughter chloroplasts divide again. In this way four chloroplasts are formed in each spore mother cell (C). They separate and move to the periphery of the spore mother cell and become spaced equidistantly from each other (D). The final position of 4 daughter chloroplasts in the spore mother cell indicates the location of the poles of the meiotic spindles in it. The diploid nucleus at this stage undergoes meiosis. The resultant 4 haploid nuclei move to points equidistant from each other and already occupied by the four chloroplasts. At this stage cell walls are laid simultaneously between the four haploid nuclei dividing the spore mother cell into four cells arranged tetrahedrally. These are the young spores (E). As the spores in the young spore tetrad ripen, their walls thickened. It is yellow in colour in some species and black with small tubercles in others. The chlorophyll disappears. Davis (1889), Bagchi (1924) and Wentzel (1929) reported the haploid number of chromosomes in *A. laevis* to be four (n=4). Scherrer (1915) found n=4 in *A. housnotii* and Wentzel reported the same in *A. punctatus*.

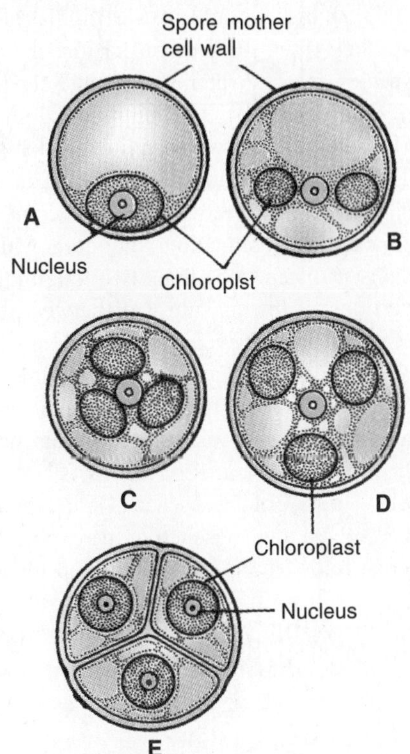

Fig. 13.13 (A—E). ***Anthoceros* sp.** Stages in sporogenesis. Explanation in the text (After Campbell).

(*ii*) *Pseudoelater mother cells*. The pseudoelater mother cells are slender, sterile cells with smaller nuclei. These increase in length but do not divide. Finally they become united to form a sort of a network. In their interstices lie the spore mother cells. Towards maturity the network breaks into simple or branched chains of 3 of 4 cells. These are the **pseudoelaters** (Fig. 13.12 E). The latter usually lack the spiral thickenings characteristic of elaters but are hygroscopic. Proskauer (1960) reported elaters with helical pattern of secondary wall thickening in some species. Bhardwaj (1950) reported that the sterile, pseudoelater mother cells divide by transverse or oblique divisions to form a network of sterile cells. At the time of capsule dehiscence, the network breaks up into 1-3 celled pseudoelaters. Later in 1958 Bhardwaj found that in *A. gemmulosus*, each sterile pseudoelater mother cell divides twice to produce a slender, four-celled pleuricellular pseudo elater which is equivalent to a spore tetrad.

The apical growth of the capsule ceases with the establishment of the archesporium, columella and the wall regions. Further growth is by activity of the basal intercalary meristem in the median zone. It continually adds new cells at the base of the capsule. They become progressively differentiated into the columella, the archesporium and the capsule wall. Consequently the growth and the dehiscence of the capsule extends over long peirods. The sporophyte of *Anthoceros* continues to live as long as thallus lives. It is a feature in sharp contrast to the short-lived sporophytes of the liverworts.

Early growth of the sporophyte is correlated with the enlargement and growth of the venter of the archegonium called the **calyptra** and equal upward growth of the surrounding thallus tissue in the form of tubular outgrowth known as the **involucre**. In the later stage, the sporophyte grows faster. Nearly mature sporophyte ruptures the calyptra pushes up through the involucre. The calyptra is carried as a small cap at the top of the sporogonium and the involucre forms a tubular sheath at the base of the mature sporogonium.

Dehiscence of capsule (Fig. 13.11 B, D). The spores ripen basipetally from the top downwards. As they ripen the mature portion of the capsule turns grey, brown or black depending upon the species. It loses water, shrinks and consequently ruptures longitudinally along with preformed lines of dehiscence (B). The longitudinal slits extend basipetally downwards. According to Mehra and Handoo there are two such lines of dehiscence of the capsule wall in *A. erectus* and *A. himalayensis*. They lie on the opposite sides each in a shallow depression extending vertically the length of the capsule. Each line of dehiscence consists of two rows of thick walled epidermal cells with their adjacent walls remaining thin along which the slit occurs. Thus the ripe *Anthoceros* capsule usually dehisces basipetally along two longitudinal slits which extend downwards from near the apex. The portions of the capsule wall between the slits are commonly called the **valves**. The two valves separate progressively downward and curl back a little bit at a time. The continuous, downward reflexing of the valves exposes the underlying mass of spores and pseudoelaters of more and more recent origin. With further drying the valves become spirally twisted owing to reversible hygroscopic reaction (D). This results in spore discharge by allowing the wind to blow away the exposed spores. The spore dispersal is further assisted by drying of the columella and the intermixed pseudo-elaters which in spite of the absence of spiral thickenings on their walls execute some hygroscopic movements. The spores thus loosened in the exposed spore mass on the central column may be scattered by the air currents. The splitting of the capsule wall does not extend into the immature region of the capsule.

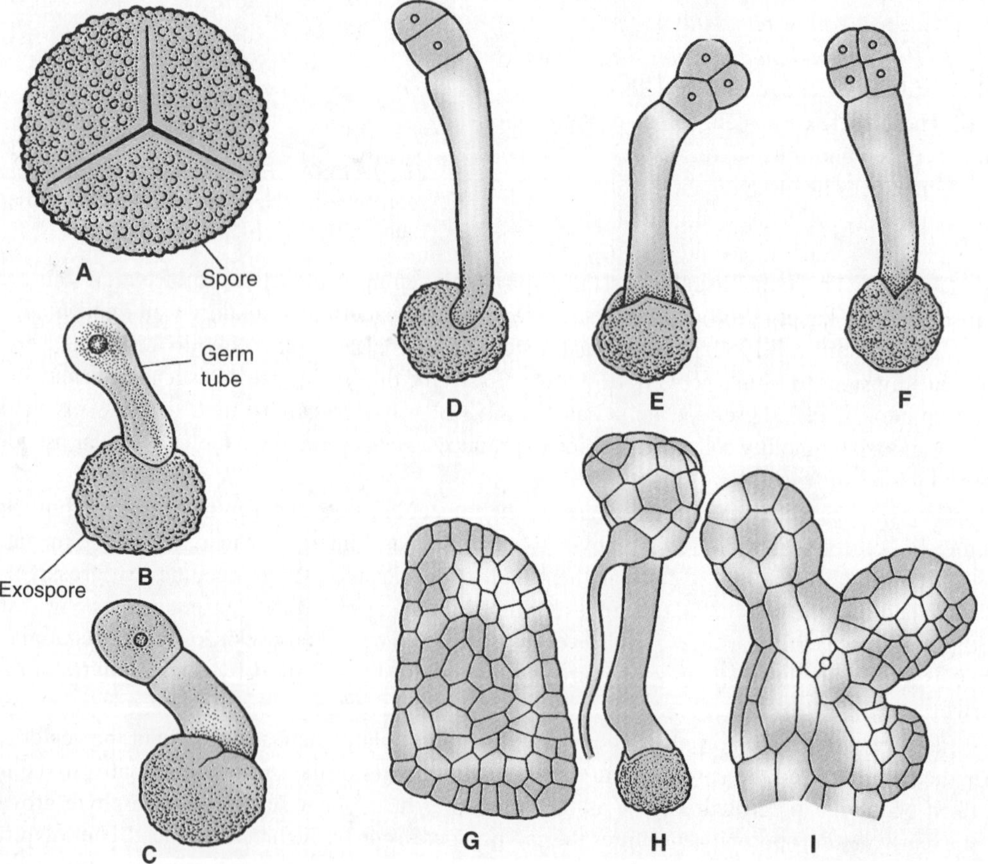

Fig. 13.14. (A—I). ***Anthoceros***. A, spore of *A. laevis* with a triradiate ridge; A—G, stages in the germination of spore of *A. erectus;* H-I, later stages in the formation of thallus. (A after Wetstein; B—G after Mehra and Kachroo, H—I after Campbell).

According to Proskauer (1948) the slit first appears at a level where the shrinking capsule wall meets resistance from the underlying solid mass of spores and pseudo-elaters. It occurs along the thin adjacent walls of the two rows of cells constituting the lines of dehiscence and extends progressively downwards and gradually widens. The underlying spore mass is exposed. The pseudo-elaters in the exposed fertile mass are hygroscopic. They exhibit twisting movements with the changes in the moisture content of the air. These movements cause active back pressure of the exposed fertile mass on the shrinking capsule wall. This results in more slits appearing along other lines of dehiscence. The *Anthoceros* capsule according to Proskauer dehisces by a varying number of slits. The number varies from 1—4 according to the species.

Spores. The mature spores are usually tetrahedral in shape and thick-walled. The thick spore wall is differentiated into two coats. The outer exospore is thick, opaque and beset with small spines or tubercles. It varies in colour from dark, brown, black or yellow according to the species. It is black and warted in *A. erectus*. In *A. himalayensis* it is yellow and beset with numerous, blunt papillae. The inner endospore is thin. Within the spore wall is the tiny protoplast. It contains a single nucleus, a colourless plastid, oil and other reserve food materials.

Germination of spore (Fig. 13. 14.) According to Campbell (1924) the liberated spores in *A. fusiformis* usually enter upon a resting period. Mehra and Kachroo (1962) who studied germination in *A. erectus* and *A. punctatus* reported that obligatory resting period is not necessary before germination. At the time of germination the spore (A) absorbs water and swells (B). The exospore ruptures along the triradite ridge. The endospore protrudes through the cleft in the form of a tube of varying lengths. It is called the **germinal tube** (C). The contents of the endospore migrate into the tube where the single plastid present turns green. Two successive transverse walls are laid at the distal end of the germinal tube. These separate two cells at its apex (D). The terminal cell divides by a vertical wall (E). A similar division takes place in the lower cell (F). A group of four cells is formed. Vertical walls at right angles to the first divide the four-celled structure into an octant (F). The four apical octants constitute the growing region of the sporeling. No apical cell with two cutting faces is established. Instead it is carried on by a group of 4 or 5 cells lying in front and constituting the apical meristem. First rhizoid appears as an elongation of any cell of the young thallus (H). On its ventral surface appears the first mucilage slit close to the growing point (I). Development of rhizoids and more mucilage slits then follows. *Nostoc* infection takes place as the growth proceeds.

SALIENT FEATURES OF *ANTHOCEROS*

GAMETOPHYTE

1. The gametophyte is simple dorsiventally flattened, usually disc-shaped lobed thallus generally without a midrib.

2. Except for smooth-walled unicellular, unbranched rhizoids the ventral surface of the thallus bears no appendages. Thus the scales, the mucilage hairs and the tuberculate rhizoids are all absent.

3. Internally the thallus is very simple in structure. It shows no differentiation into photosynthetic and storage tissues. The entire thallus consists of parenchyma composed of chlorenchymatous cells.

4. A striking feature of the gametophyte is the presence of usually a single basin-shaped chloroplast with a pyrenoid in each cell—an unusual feature not known elsewhere in the bryophytes and higher plants. In the latter the chloroplasts are discoid and occur in large numbers in each cell and have no pyrenoids.

5. Another peculiar feature is the presence of stoma-like slime pores, each surrounded by two bean-shaped guard cells with thin walls. The slime-pores occur on the lower surface of the thallus, lead inwards and open into large cavities filled with mucilage.

6. Very often the mucilage cavities are inhabited by *Nostoc*. The cavities containing *Nostoc* appear as small, dark, blue-green specks.

7. Apical growth according to Campbell takes place by means of a single, four-sided **apical cell**. It is pyramidal in shape. According to Mehra and Handoo it is initiated by a group of cells of equal rank.

8. The sex organs are not borne on any special sexual branches. The remarkable feature, however, is that they are immersed in the thallus. They actually develop within rather than above the surface of the thallus.

9. The antheridia are **endogenous** in origin. They occur singly or in a cluster on the floor of a roofed antheridial chamber.

10. The antheridium or the antheridial cluster in the closed chamber together with the later's two layered roof is traceable to a single **surface cell**. It means that the antheridial cluster in the chamber and the overlying two-layered roof are homologous to the single antheridium of liverworts.

11. The archegonia are fully immersed with their venters and necks confluent with the adjacent vegetative cells. The distal rosette of cover cells only slightly projects above the general surface of the thallus. Each young archegonium according to Proskauer and Mehra and Handoo is surrounded by a mound of mucilage.

12. The usual **archegonial jacket** of sterile cells enclosing the axial row of cells is not recognizable. Protection to them is probably afforded by the adjacent cells of the thallus.

13. Unlike the liverworts, the **archegonial initial** directly functions as the primary archegonial cell. There is no division of the former into the primary stalk cell and the primary archegonial cell by a horizontal wall. The absence of this division explains the sunken condition of the archegonium and its lateral contact with the adjacent cells of the thallus.

14. The **neck canal cells** in *Anthoceros* are derived from that segment of the primary axial cell which corresponds to the **primary cover cell** of the liverworts and not from the central cell.

SPOROPHYTE

15. The sporophyte of *Anthoceros* is a long, upright, slender, cylindrical structure surrounded at its base by a tubular sheath, the **involucre**.

16. It is differentiated into a bulbous **foot**, an **intermediate zone** composed of intercalary meristem and an unusually long, upright, cylindrical **capsule**. There is no **seta**.

17. The foot becomes specialised to function as a **haustorium**. It is furnished with rhizoid-like processes which penetrate deep down into the thallus tissue to absorb water and mineral salts in solution.

18. As soon as the apical growth of the capsule ceases the intercalary meristem of the median zone becomes active. It adds new cells at the base. These cells progressively become differentiated into the tissues of the columella, archesporium and the capsule wall. Thus the *Anthoceros* sporophyte continues to grow for a long period from a basal intercalary meristem and yields spores over a considerable period. In both these features *Anthoceros* stands alone in the bryophytes.

19. The **capsule wall** is several cell layers thick. The surface layer of the wall (epidermis) is punctured with true stomata and the component epidermal cells are cuticularised. Within the epidermis is the assimilatory tissue with intercellular spaces between the cells. The stomata lead into the air containing channels ventilating the sub-epidermal, assimilatory tissue. The sporophyte of *Anthoceros* thus carries on photosynthesis actively.

20. The archesporium which is devoted to spore formation forms only a small part of the sporophyte. The sterilisation of potentially fertile tissue in *Anthoceros*, therefore, shows further advance.

21. The archesporium is **amphithecial** in origin. The function of spore formation has thus been transferred from the central to the more superficial tissue. The sporogenous tissue forms the **spores** and the **pseudo-elaters**. The maturation of spores is from the apex downwards i.e. **non-synchronus**.

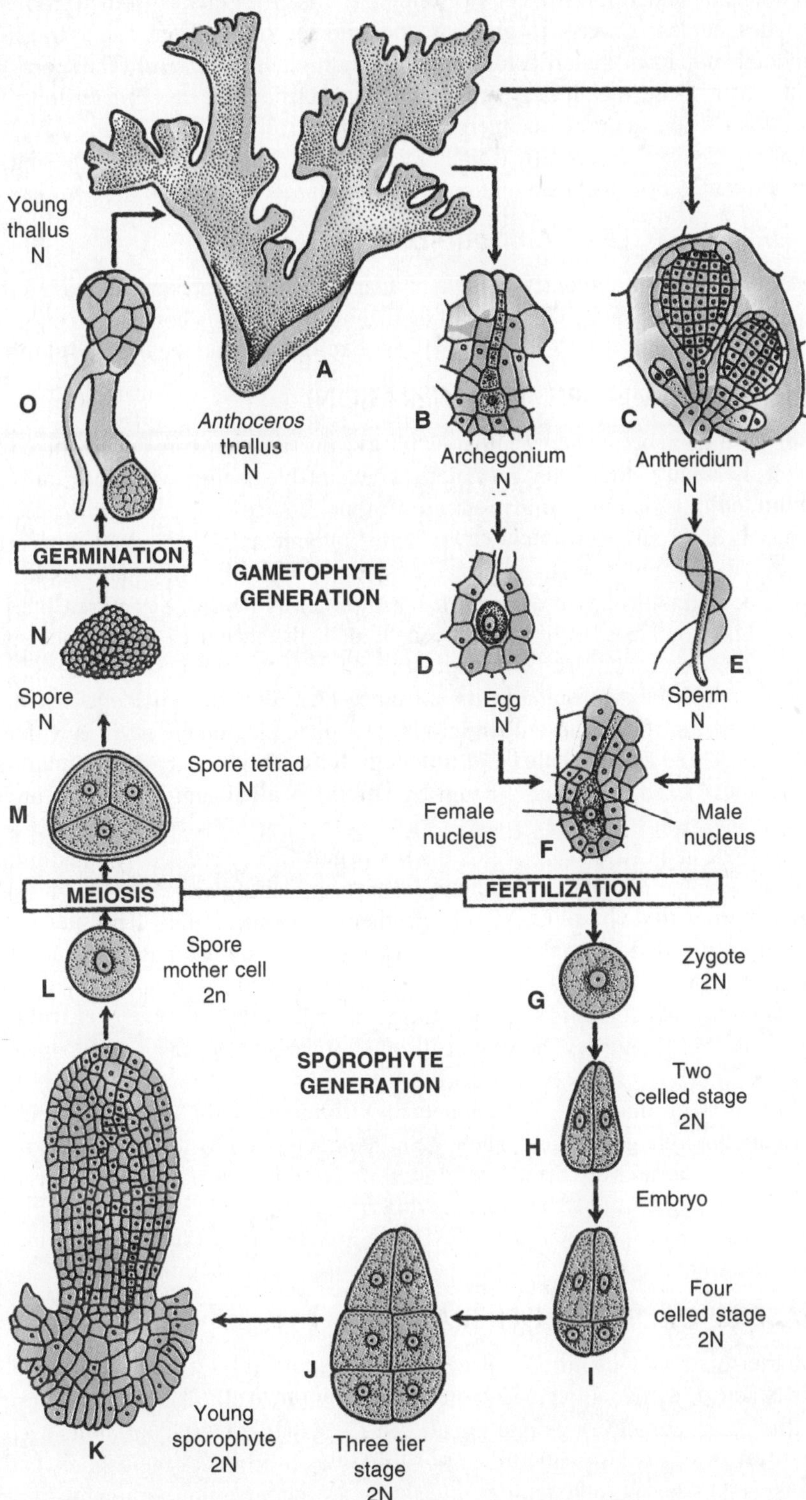

Fig. 13.15. (A—O). *Anthoceros.* Pictorial sketch of the sexual life cycle.

22. The columella, which forms a central solid core of sterile cells, is formed from the entire **endothecium**. The latter in the liverworts gives rise to the archesporium. There is thus transformation of the entire endothecium from the fertile to the sterile condition in *Anthoceros*. The sporogonium of *Anthoceros* thus has attained a high degree of complexity, elaboration and greater longevity than that of the liverworts. The elaboration is internal rather than external.

23. The capsule dehisces basipetally usually by two valves which curl back exposing the mass of spores intermixed with pseudoelaters on the central column.

SUMMARY OF LIFE CYCLE of *Anthoceros* (Fig. 13.15)

The life cycle of *Anthoceros* consists of two regularly alternating generations with fertilization and meiosis as its two critical points. With either of these the life cycle switches on from one alternating generation to the other. One of these generations is the **haplophase** and the other **diplophase**.

1. HAPLOPHASE (GAMETOPHYTE GENERATION)

The haplophase starts with the formation of **spores** (N). The spores are differentiated from the spore mother cells by **meiosis** (M). They germinate under suitable conditions each forming a simple green fleshy **gametophyte** plant (O). It loves to grow in moist, shady palces. It grows, according to Campbell, by means of a four-sides **apical cell** which is pyramidal in shape. Mehra and Handoo's contention is that the growing point is constituted by a **group of initials** of equal rank.

The thallus never attains any great size. It is simple in its internal structure. Internally the gametophyte (thallus) is made up of uniform parenchyma cells, each usually with one sometimes more chloroplasts of a large size. Each **chloroplast** encloses a **pyrenoid**. The gametophyte plant is thus green and independent throughout its existence (A). Very often it develops stoma-like slime pores on its under surface. These open into large rounded, mucilage cavities which may be inhabited by *Nostoc*.There are no **scales** and **mucilage hairs**. Nor are the **tuberculate** rhizoids present. The thallus is fixed to the substratum by **smooth-walled,** unicelluar and unbranched **rhizoids** only.

The gametophyte at a certain stage bears the **sex organs**. They are deeply sunk in the fleshy thallus. Normally the antheridia are **endogenous**. They occur singly or in a cluster inside closed cavities called the **antheridial chambers** (C). The antheridia produce biflagellate **sperms** (E). The archegonia also are embedded in the thallus (B). They are thus histologically continuous with the cells of the thallus lateral to them. Only a distal rosette of **cover cells** projects above the surface of the thallus. The axial row of cells consisting of four to six **neck canal cells** and a **ventral canal cell** except the egg gelatinize at maturity. The cover cells are thrown off to form an open passage for the sperms to reach the egg (D).

All the structures produced by and connected with the gametophyte plant constitute the **haplophase** or gametophyte generation. They are all characterized by a **haploid** (N) number of chromosomes. These structures are the *spores,* the *fleshy, dorsiventrally flattened green thallus,* the *antheridia*, the *archegonia* and the *gametes* (sperms and egg). Fertilization or syngamy is the end of this phase (F). Sperms and eggs (D, E) are therefore the last structures of the haplophase.

2. DIPLOPHASE (SPOROPHYTE GENERATION).

The diplophase starts with fertilized egg or the **zygote** (G). It has **diploid** number of chromosomes. By active segmentation the zygote forms an **embryo** (J). The later by differentiation of cell and continued growth develops into the alternate vegetative individual in the life cycle. It is the **sporogonium** (K). It is also called the **sporophyte** as it produces meiospores and aids in their efficient dispersal. The sporophyte of *Anthoceros* is a structure unique among the bryophytes in many respects. It is long, slender, upright, green more or less a cylindrical object surrounded at its base by a tubular **involucre**. It is differentiated into three regions, the **foot**, the **narrow**

intermediate zone and the **capsule**. The foot is specialized as a **haustorium**. It gives out tubular, rhizoid-like outgrowths from its surface. These pentrate deep into the tissue of the gametophyte and absorb water and minerals in solution for the sporophyte. The intermediate zone is **meristematic**. The capsule is shaped like a long spindle. It consists of several cell layers thick **capsule wall** (K). The superficial layer of the wall functions as an **epidermis**. It is punctured with ture **stomata**. The sub-epidermal tissue consists of chlorenchymatous cells with intercellular spaces between them. The chloroplasts are large in size and two in number per cell as a rule. Each chloroplast encloses a pyrenoid. The stomata communicate with the intercellular spaces to form a typical **assimilatory system**. It makes the sporophyte partially self-supporting. Within the capsule wall is the **archesporium**. It forms only a small part of the capsule and is shaped like a dome. It arches over the rounded apex of the central solid core of a sterile tissue, the **columella**. The archesporium is **amphithecial** in origin. It later differentiates into alternate bands of spore mother cells and elongated, sterile cells. The latter mature into **pseudoelaters**. The spore mother cells (L) by **meiosis** (M) produce the haploid spores which are the first structure of the next haplophase. the diplophase thus ends with the formation of meiospores (N). It comprises the *zygote,* the *embryo* and the *sporophyte*. The **spore mother cells** are the last structures of this phase (L). Another unusual feature of *Anthoceros* sporophyte is the presence of the basal intercalary **meristem** in the median zone of the sporogonium. As soon as the apical growth of the capsule ceases (with the differentiation of the capsule wall, the archesporium and the columella), the intercalary meristem becomes active. It adds new cells at the base of the capsule to the columella, the archesporium and the capsule wall. As a result, the capsule continues to grow and produces a continued succession of new spores. The sporogonium of *Anthoceros* is, therefore, a **long-lived** structure. It continues to grow as long as the thallus remains alive.

The top of the green capsule turns grey, brown or black according to the species at the time of dehiscence. The capsule wall at maturity dries and shrinks. Consequently longitudinal slits appear along the two opposite lines of dehiscence. The slits extend downwards. The two segments or valves of the capsule wall curl back and separate from the underlying spore mass. The valves thus separated diverge and twist hygroscopically. The twisting of the valves and the hygroscopic movements of the pseudo-elaters in the exposed spore mass assist in the shedding of spores. The free spores are scattered by the air currents. The dried up thread-like columella protrudes between the two valves.

The two phases or generations constituting the single life cycle of *Anthoceros* regularly occur one after the other. The life cycle of this type which is characterised by **alternation of generations** and **sporogenic meiosis** is termed **diplohaplontic.**

SYSTEMATIC position OF ANTHOCEROS

For questions on *Anthoceros* please refer to page 274

Division	:	Bryophyta
Class	:	Anthocerotopsida
Order	:	Anthocerotales
Family	:	Anthocerotaceae
Genus	:	*Anthoceros*
Species	:	*himalayensis*

Image of *Notothylas*

CHAPTER 13(II)

ANTHOCEROTALES
Notothylaceae
Notothylas

- General Characteristics
- Order Anthocerotales
- Family Notothylaceae
- Genus Notothylas
- Reproduction
- Sporophytic Phase

FAMILY 2. NOTOTHYLACEAE

GENERAL CHARACTERISTICS

The gametophyte shows strong resemblance with the Anthocerotaceae. The sporophyte, however, is slightly different. It is short, compact, marginal and grows out horizontally from the fertile lobes of the rosette-like thallus. The photosynthetic tissue, in the capsule wall, is absent and the stomata are lacking. The columella varies from species to species. It is well developed and central in position in some or entirely lacking in others. The pseudo-elaters are simple, equal in size or longer than the spores, with spiral or oblique bands. The family includes a single genus *Notothylas*.

NOTOTHYLAS

DISTRIBUTION AND HABITAT

The genus comprises a number of species which are widely distributed both in the tropics and temperate zones. Of these four namely, *N. indica, N. levieri, N. chaudhurii* and *N. javanicus* have been recorded in India. They are found on moist rocks and damp earth in humid, shady localities.

THALLUS (FIG. 13.16, A and B)

(a) **External features.** The delicate, thin thallus is dorsiventral and grows flat on the substratum. Usually it is orbicular or suborbicular in form, yellowish or light green in colour and very much lobed. Each lobe may be entire or toothed or beset with blunt, irregular processes. From the under surface of the thallus arise the unicellular, smooth-walled rhizoids which anchor it to the substratum. As in *Anthoceros,* the scales and tuberculate rhizoids are absent.

(b) **Internal structure.** A vertical section of the thallus lobe reveals that it is 6 to 8 layers of cells thick in the middle portion which forms the midrib. Gradually it thins out in the expanded portion of the thallus to a single layer at the margin. The superficial limiting layer at the upper and lower surfaces shows a more regular arrangement of cells which are smaller in size than the cells in the interior. The cells, however, are not cuticularized and thus not organised into a distinct epidermis. Within the two limiting layers the thallus consists of soft parenchyma cells of uniform pattern. Apart from the internal cavities which contain mucilage and occasionally a blue green alga *Nostoc*, there is no differentiation of vegetative cells. The mucilage cavities open by narrow slits at the ventral surface. In *N. javanicus* the mucilage cavities are absent. As in *Anthoceros* the cells contain only a single large chloroplast. The latter has a single **pyrenoid**.

SEXUAL REPRODUCTION

Notothylas normally reproduces by meiospores formed following sexual reproduction. Some species are **monoecious** and others **dioecious**. The common Indian species are reported to be monoecious but strongly **protandrous**. The sex organs (antheridia and archegonia), as in *Anthoceros,* develop within the surface tissue and not above them.

1. **Antheridia.** The antheridia occur in clusters of 2—6 on the dorsal surface of the thallus in cavities called the **antheridial chambers**. The antheridial chambers are roofed over at first. With the ripening of antheridia the roof ruptures and the orange coloured antheridia standing in a cluster at the bottom of the antheridial pit are exposed to view.

The mature antheridium is a large, oval shortly pedicellate object. The body of the antheridium consists of a jacket of sterile cells constituting the wall. The latter surrounds a mass of small, cubical cells called the **androcytes**. The protoplast of each androcyte forms a single, biflagellate sperm.

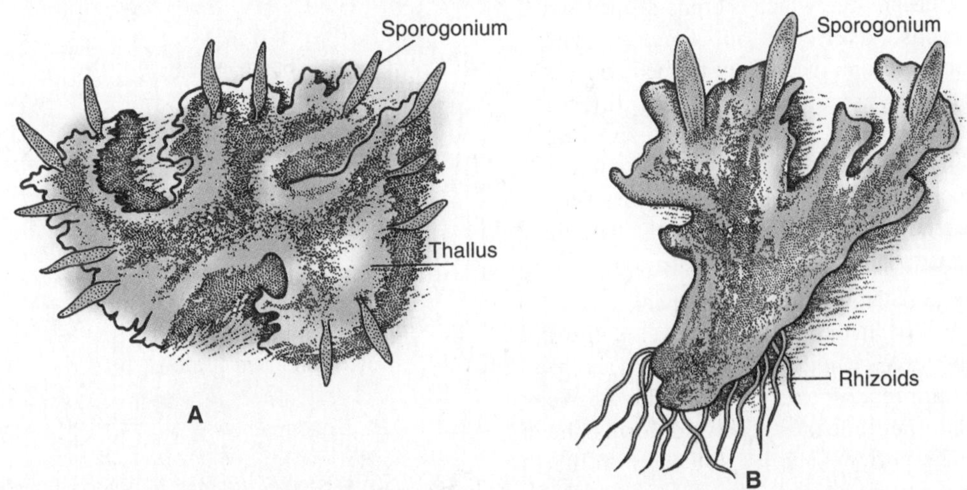

Fig. 13.16. (A—B). ***Notothylas indica***. A, thallus bearing sporogonia. B, a portion of the same slightly enlarged.

2. Archegonia. The archegonia occur immersed close to the growing tip with the necks and venters confluent with the adjacent vegetative tissue of the thallus. As in *Anthoceros* the archegonial neck is much shorter than those of the other bryophytes. The neck canal is, however, wider than that of *Anthoceros*. It contains 3—5 neck canal cells. In the monoecious protandrous species the archegonia develop on the same thallus which had earlier produced the antheridia.

The development and structure of sex organs and the method of fertilization are the same as in *Antheceros*.

SPOROPHYTE

1. DEVELOPMENT

The zygote formed as a result of fertilization, enlarges in the venter. It then secretes a wall around it and starts dividing. The first division is either transverse or vertical. To the first category belong *N. indica* and *N. orbicular* and to the second *N. levieri* and *N. javanicus*. In case the first division is vertical, the second is transverse or *vice versa*. The embryo after the second division in any case, consists of four cells. It is the quadrant stage. Each quadrant divides by a vertical wall at right angles to the first. The embryo now consists of eight cells, arranged in two tiers of four cells each. It is the **octant** stage. The cells of the upper tier undergo another transverse division. The embryo now consists of three tiers of 4 cells each. The cells of the uppermost tier by repeated divisions, differentiation and continued growth form the **capsule** and the **intermediate narrow zone**. The cells of the lower two tiers form the **foot**.

Periclinal divisions appear in the cells of the of the uppermost tier which is destined to form the capsule. This division separates the inner **endothecium** from the outer **amphithecium**. The fate of the endothecium varies in different species. Depending on the fate of the endothecium the different species of *Notothylas* are divided into two categories, namely, **columellate** species and **non-columellate species**.

(*a*)**Columellate species** (Fig. 13.17 A). In *N. indica* and *N. orbicularis* the entire endothecium forms the columella. It is central in position. The amphithecium cells divide by a periclinal wall into **outer** and **inner** cells. The cells of the outer layer form the **capsule wall** and the cells of the inner layer function as the **archesporium** which is dome-shaped and arches over the columella. The archesporium when fully formed consists of 4 layers of cells. During further development the archesporium differentiates into alternate bands of fertile spore mother cells and sterile cells. They extend from the columella to the capsule wall.

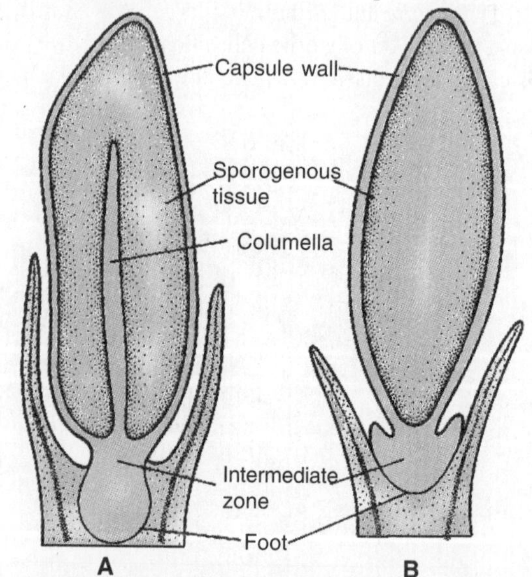

Fig. 13.17. (A—B) *Notothylas*. A, V.S. columellate sporogonium of *N. indica;* B, V.S. non-columellate sporogonium of *Notothylas levieri*.

(*b*)**Non-columellate species**. (Fig. 13.17 B). In these the columella is entirely absent. *N. chaudhurii* and *N. levieri* are the examples of this group. The entire endothecium is fertile and forms the archesporium. The amphithecium forms the capsule wall. The archesporium becomes differentiated into alternate bands

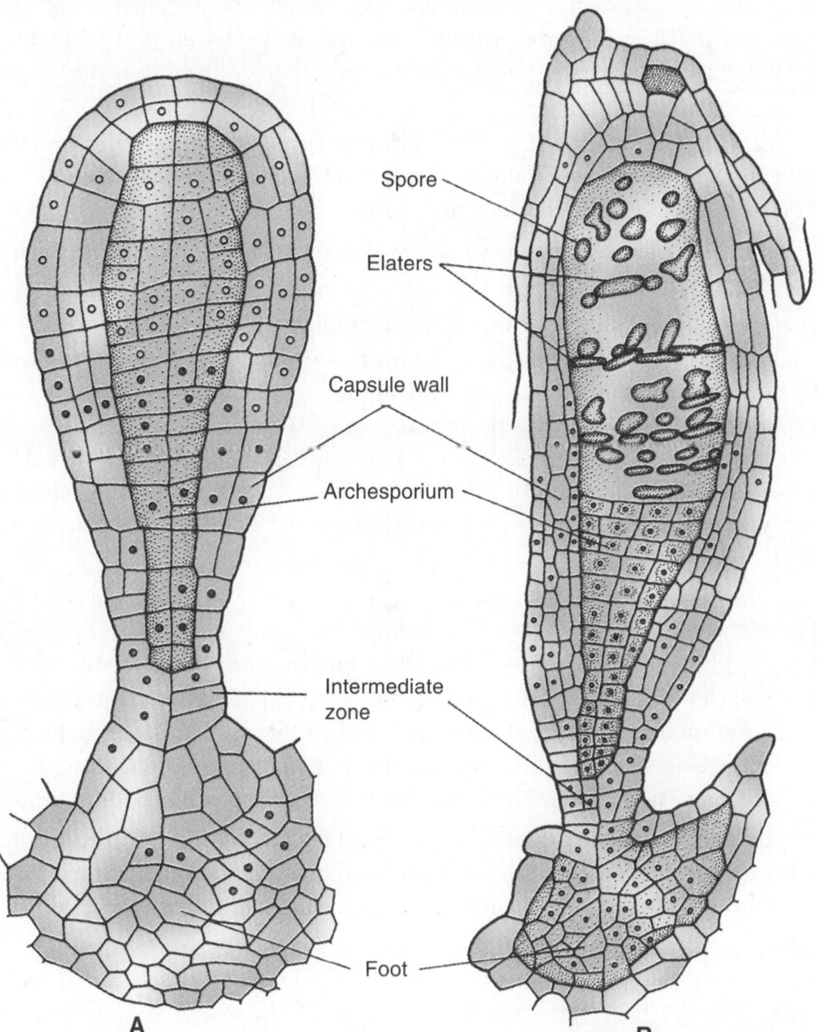

Fig. 13.18. (A—B). ***Notothylas levieri.*** A. L.S. young sporogonium; B, L.S. adult sporogonium. (After Pande).

of spore mother cell sand sterile cells. They extend across the cavity of the capsule. The spore mother cells, as usual, undergo meiosis to form the meiospores.

There are a few species of *Notothylas* which belong to neither of the above-mentioned two groups. They form a connecting link between the columellate and non-columellate species. Lang in 1907, observed that during the intercalary growth of the sporophyte in *N. breutelii* the bulk of the endothecium forms the archesporium. Towards the end of intercalary development the rest of the endothecium remains sterile and forms the columella. Campbell cited another example in 1908. He observed that in *N. javanicus* the endothecium normally develops into a well developed columella. In rare cases the columella is reduced in size and produces spores in the upper part.

Adult sporophyte. The sporogonia are marginal in position (Fig. 13.16 B) and are borne horizontally between the lobes usually in pairs. Each sporogonium is a short, compact structure about 3 mm in length and 0.5 mm in diameter. It is cylindrical in form but tapers towards both ends (Fig. 13.17 B). A thin, membranous cylindrical envelope surrounds the sporogonium. It is the

involucre. In some species such as *N. indica* and *N. levieri* the sporogonium is completely enclosed within the involucre but in *N. javanicus* and *N. breutelii* it slightly projects beyond it. The mature sporophyte is differentiated into three regions, the foot, the narrow intermediate zone and the capsule (Fig. 13.17).

The foot is large but much smaller than that of *Anthoceros*. It is triangular in shape and housed in the tissue of the gametophyte (thallus). The superficial cells of the foot are produced into small, rhizoidal outgrowths which absorb water and nutrition from the parent thallus.

The narrow intermediate zone is short and slender. It shows little meristematic activity and thus plays no significant role.

Structure of the capsule (Fig. 13.18). The capsule has a wall which is three to four layers of cells in thickness (B). The outermost layer is the **epidermis**. It consists of brown cells with thick walls. The stomata are absent. The sub-epidermal cells either lack chlorophyll or develop very little of it. Udar and Singh (1978) reported the occurrence of prominent thickened bands of wall material on the walls of the cells of the inner layer of the 3-layered capsule wall of *N. levieri*. The bands were described as incompletely annular sometimes annular, transversely rarely longitudinally oriented or even spiral. The authors attach great phylogenetical significance to this anatomical feature of the capsule wall of *N. levieri*.

Within the capsule wall is the **sporogenous tissue** (B). It surrounds the central columella in the columellate species (Fig. 13.17 A). The sporogenous tissue in a mature capsule differentiates into alternate bands of unicellular sterile cells and spore mother cells (B). The former give rise to the short, simple, unicellular elaters. They are irregular in form and have rudimentary spirals on their walls in the form of short, curved, thin or thick oblique bands. The spore mother cells undergo meiosis to form the spore tetrads. The meiospores in *N. indica* are opaque and dark brown. The spore wall is differentiated into the outer, thick **exospore** and inner thin **endospore**.

In the capsule of non-columellate species the columella is absent (B). The sporogenous tissue is formed from the entire endothecium. As usual it differentiates into alternate bands of sterile cells and spore mother cells which fill the entire cavity of the capsule within the capsule wall.

Dehiscence of the capsule. According to Muller the mature capsule dehisces by 2 to 4 valves. Kashyap, Dutt and Pande reported that it is basipetal and by the imperfect separation of two broad valves. Later Pande in 1932 reported that in *N. indica* and *N. levieri*, the dehiscence is follicular. The capsule opens by one suture, sometimes, by both sutures. The horizontal position of the capsule, the enclosing involucre, small unicellular elaters, lack or poor development of columella stand in the way of efficient dispersal of spores.

Spore germination. Under favourable conditions the spore absorbs moisture and germinates. The exospore ruptures and the contents surrounded by the endospore bulge out in the form of a short papilla. The first division in the short germ cell or papilla is variable. It may divide by a transverse or longitudinal wall. The second is in the opposite direction. A quadrant of four cells is formed. Each cell of the quadrant again divides by a vertical wall to form an octant of eight cells. According to Mehra and Handoo (1962) further growth of this cell mass or minute thallus takes place by the division of the cells lying in the front.

SYSTEMATIC POSITION OF *NOTOTHYLAS*

The older morphologists place *Notothylas* in the family Anthocerotaceae along with *Anthoceros* and its allies. The basis is the strong resemblance between their gametophytes. The modern bryologists such as Muller, Proskauer, Reimers and others favour its inclusion in a separate family Notothylaceae.

They hold that the sporophyte of *Notothylas* is unlike that of *Anthoceros* in several respects. According to the latest view the systematic position of *Notothylas* will thus be under :—

Division	:	Bryophyta
Class	:	Anthocerotopsida
Order	:	Anthocerotales
Family	:	Notothylaceae
Genus	:	*Notothylas*
Species	:	*levieri*

AFFINITIES AND EVOLUTIONARY POSITION OF *NOTOTHYLAS*

The gametophyte of *Notothylas* strongly resembles that of *Anthoceros* on one hand and liverworts (particularly the Metzgeriales) on the other. It is simple, thallus-like without any differentiation of cells and absence of appendages on the ventral side except the smooth-walled rhizoids. The sporophyte, however, is unlike that of *Anthoceros* in several respects. It grows out horizontally from the thallose lobes. The capsule is short and compact as in the liverworts. The presence of thickening bands of wall material on the cells of the innermost layer of capsule wall in *N. levieri* (Udar and Singh 1978), endothecial origin of sporogenous tissue (archesporium) and absence of columella in some species of *Notothylas*, absence of stomata and no development of photosynthetic tissue in the capsule wall and no activity in the basal meristem are the other features of *Notothylas* sporophyte which indicate closer affinity between *Notothylas* and liverworts. *Notothylas is thus regarded as a link between the liverworts and hornworts (Anthocerotales).* The evolutionary position of *Notothylas* is controversial. The bryologists hold two opposite views on this point. Lang in 1907 put forward the view that *Notothylas* is a reduced member of the Anthocerotales. It has evolved from forms like *Anthoceros* by the process of simplification. He thus considers *Anthoceros* a **primitive** genus of this group because many of the unique features of *Anthoceros* sporophyte are either absent or present in a modified form in the *Notothylas* sporophyte. It has lost its columella. There is no photosynthetic tissue in the capsule wall and the stomata in the epidermis are lacking. The basal meristem is little active. He reads genetic relationship between the Anthocerotales and the liverworts in a downward direction through forms like *Notothylas*. The supporters of Lang's hypothesis thus consider *Anthoceros* as a **primitive** genus and *Notothylas* as an **advanced** but a **reduced** genus. It has evolved from *Anthoceros* by a process of simplification.

Cavers in 1911 advanced a view diametrically opposed to that of Lang. He considers *Notothylas* as a link between the liverworts and Anthocerotales but reads genetic relationship in the upward direction. The supporters of this hypothesis consider *Notothylas* as a **primitive** genus and *Anthoceros* as a highly **evolved** or **advanced** genus which has evolved from *Notothylas* by the process of progressive evolution or natural advance.

CONCLUSION AND DISCUSSION

Affinities of Anthoceros. The life history of types like *Anthoceros* deserves special attention. The reason is that there are certain features in its life cycle which it shares with the Mosses. There are others in which it resembles the liverworts. In a few others it shows a remote resemblance with the simplest vascular plants. Some common features also exist between *Anthoceros* and the Chlorophyceae. This led the bryologists to regard *Anthoceros* as a **synthetic** type.

(*a*) **The features which Anthoceros shares with the Chlorophyceae are :**

(*i*) Smaller number per cell (one to four) but larger size and definite shape of the **chloroplasts**.

(*ii*) Presence of **pyrenoids**. The pyrenoids are characteristic of cells of green algae only.

(*iii*) The pyrenoids of *Anthoceros* and green algae function similarly and form starch grains at their periphery.

(*iv*) Simple, green dorsiventrally flattened **thallus-like** plant body and its branching.

(*v*) Biflagellate sperms with both flagella of whiplash type.

The above mentioned features of *Anthoceros* which recall those of the green algae are considered by some to indicate that *Anthoceros* stands close to the line of evolution leading from the green algae to the land plants.

This view is further supported by the fact that different species of this order can be arranged in a series which illustrates the evolutionary trend of the plastids away from an ancestral algal condition (typical anthocerote uniplastid thallus cells with a multiple pyrenoid) towards a more typical land form (cells with several small plastids without pyrenoids). The distinctive features of this evolutionary line are : (*i*) increase in plastid number and (*ii*) a concomitant decrease in plastid size coupled with (*iii*) a gradual loss of the pyrenoid (Burr, 1970). According to Burr (1970) the series starts with *Phaeoceros himalayensis* and many others in which the thallus cells are uniplastid with a single "multiple pyrenoid" per plastid. This is the typical ancestral algal condition. The next stage in the series is represented by *Megaceros mexicanis*. It often has two plastids per cell, smaller and with a less distinct multiple plastid. The series then passes through *M. flagellaris* often with 4 plastids per cell and a pyrenoid like body and ends in *M. fuegiensis* with more than 4 plastids per cell and no trace of pyrenoid or pyrenoid-like region. Burr concludes that the order Anthocerotales represents a group of extremely primitive land plants occupying a position between the green algae and the higher groups of the Archegoniatae.

Others, however, hold that these similarities are of general nature. They are so few and not so consistent as to denote any near alliance between *Anthoceros* and the *Green Algae*.

(*b*) **Features common with the Liverworts are :**

(*i*) A simple, thallus-like gametophyte without any differentiation of tissues and absence of any appendages, except the smooth-walled rhizoids, are the features which *Anthoceros* shares with the Metzgeriales such as *Pellia*.

(*ii*) Similar apical growth of the thallus lobes.

(*iii*) Sex organs differ in essential details but are constructed on the hepatic plan.

(*iv*) The biflagellate sperms similar to those of the Hepaticae.

(*v*) The construction of the deeply emarginate growing point as in the Marchantiaceae.

(*vi*) Separation of the amphithecium and endothecium by periclinal walls in the same way as in the Hepaticae.

(*vii*) Differentiation of archesporium into spore mother cells and the elongated sterile cells which develop into pseudo-elaters. In the related genus *Megaceros* the walls of the sterile cells are spirally thick-ended to form elaters as in the Hepaticae.

(*c*) **Features common with the Mosses are** :

(*i*) Development of a highly differentiated, **ventilated photosynthetic system** in the capsule wall.

(*ii*) Presence of a central solid core of sterile cells, the **columella** which is entirely endothecial in origin. In this respect *Anthoceros* resembles *Sphagnum*.

(*iii*) Archesporium greatly reduced forming a small part of the capsule.

(*iv*) Archesporium differentiated from the inner side of the amphithecium and shaped like a dome covering the top of the columella as in the *Sphagnum moss*.

(*d*) **The features in which Anthoceros resembles the Pteridophytes are :**

(*i*) General similarity in the thallus structure of *Anthoceros* and the fern prothallus.

(*ii*) Sex organs as in pteridophytes are deeply sunk in the gametophyte.

(*iii*) Similarity in the structure of the mature archegonia.

(*iv*) Campbell holds that the elaborate, semi-parasitic sporophyte of *Anthoceros* with its typically ventilated assimilatory system and continued growth denotes the nearest alliance to the independent rootless, leafless dichotomously branched sporophyte of the primitive fossil vascular plants, *Psilophytales*.

The account given above justifies the contention that *Anthoceros* is a **synthetic** type. It forms a connecting link between the Liverworts and the Mosses on one hand and links the bryophytes with the primitive pteriodphytes on the other. A remote connection with the Chlorophyceae is also indicated.

SYSTEMATIC POSITION OF *ANTHOCEROS* (Anthocerotales)

It is still a debatable question. The conventional treatment is to consider the Anthocerotales as one of the three orders of the class Hepaticae. The other two are the Marchantiales and the Jungermanniales. Many eminent scientists followed this taxon. The chief among them are Bower, Leitgeb, Kashyap, Cavers, Goebel. Maclean and Cook, etc. On the basis of this classification the systematic position of *Anthoceros* is given below :

Division	:	Bryophyta
Class	:	Hepaticae
Order	:	Anthocerotales
Family	:	Anthocerotaceae
Genus	:	*Anthoceros*
Species	:	*erectus*

Hope, Campbell, Smith and Thakhtajan are of a different opinion. They point to the following fundamental differences in which the Anthocerotales differ from the Hepticae :—

1. Presence, as rule, of a single chloroplast per cell as against numerous in the Hepaticae.
2. Nature of chloroplasts each of which contains a pyrenoid.
3. Sex organs deeply sunken in the thallus as against their superficial nature in the Hepaticae.
4. Mode of development of sex organs.
5. Mode of development of the sporogonium.
6. Presence of a narrow meristematic zone between the foot and the capsule as against its complete absence in the Hepaticae.
7. Presence of a thin, slender core of sterile tissue, the columella in the capsule as against its absence in the Hepaticae.
8. Differentiation of the domed archesporium from the amphithecium as against its endothecial nature in the Hepaticae.
9. Presence of amply ventilated photosynthetic system in the capsule wall as against its absence in the Hepaticae.
10. Basipetal dehiscence of the ripe capsule from the tip downwards along two longitudinal lines of dehiscence, which separate the capsule wall usually into two valves, is unique.
11. The long, narrow, cylindrical, upright capsule with stomata and simple or branched pseudo-elaters without spiral thickenings have no parallel in the liverworts.

12. Number of choromosomes which is usually 5 or 6 as against 8 or 9 in the other liverworts.

In view of these differences they separate the Anthocerotales from the class Hepticae and instead assign them a position parallel in rank with the latter.

Lietgeb vehemently opposes this steppointing to the several features which the Anthocerotales share with the Hepaticae, particularly the Metzgeriales. He maintains that these common features between the two indicate that the Anthocerotales are sufficiently near to the Jungermanniales (Metzgeriales). He thus advocates the retention of the Anthocerotales in a series with that order opposed to the Marchantiales.

Cavers also attaches no importance to the above-mentioned differences between the Anthocerotales and the Hepaticae. He explains them away as follows :

The number of chloroplasts per cell varies considerably in the order Anthocerotales. The endogenous origin of antheridia is a secondary character derived from the exogenous origin. The sunken archegonia are also found in the order Hepaticae as in *Aneura* though the neck is free in the latter. The meristematic zone might have arisen through the persistence of meristematic activity of repeated transverse divisions in the cells between the foot and the capsule in *Pellia*. Presence of stomata in the epidermis may be in response to the many layered capsule wall consisting of assimilatory parenchyma.

Bower considers the sunken conditions of sex organs of the Anthocerotales as probably a special and secondary condition to provide biologic protection. He considers the amphithecial origin of the archesporium of the Anthocerotales as of secondary origin due to the general tendency of decentralisation of the central tract in the Hepaticae.

Watson (1954) sound a mild note of caution saying "such a step is not necessary, although *Anthoceros* remains a remarkable plant." He further added that the long, narrow, cylindrical shape, a degree of radial symmetry and upright position of *Anthoceros capsule* with its long-lived basal meristem, well ventilated, photosynthetic tissue in the capsule wall, thin slender columella, one to three celled pseudoelaters, basipetal mode of dehiscence of the capsule and the amphithecial origin of the sporogenous tissue are features which accord *Anthoceros* a unique status but for the intermediaries like *Notothylas.* The gametophyte of the latter strongly resembles that of *Anthoceros.* The capsule, however, is short and compact. It grows out horizontally from the thallus lobes. The epidermis lacks stomata and the sub-epidermal tissue in the capsule wall has no chlorophyll. The columella, in some species, is entirely absent.

In *Notothylas levieri* (Anthocerotales), for example, the archesporium is endothecial in origin. The entire endothecium remains fertile. On the basis of this Pande favours the retention of the Anthocerotales in the Hepaticae. He holds that forms like *N. levieri* serve to link the Anthocerotales and the Hepaticae. Chopra (1983) delivering the eleventh Birbal Sahni Memorial Lecture on the "Status and Position of Hornworts" emphasised, "The diagnostic features of the three subdivisions of the Bryophyta, namely, Hepatophytina (Hepaticae), Takakiophytina and Muscophytina (Musci) indicate that the Anthocerotales belong to the Hepatophytina".

Mehra and Handoo added another point—perhaps a decisive one to the list of differences between the Anthocerotales and the other Hepaticae. It is the difference in the basic chromosome complex. The Anthocerotales have the basic number as five or six whereas the other Hepaticae (Marchantiales and Jungermanniales) have eight or nine. In the Sphaerocarpales it is ten. This difference in the basic chromosome number from the Hepaticae tempted the modern bryologists to suggest that Anthocerotales should form a third independent class alongside the Hepaticae and the Musci (mosses).

It follows from the above discussion that the Anthocerotales possess certain characteristics in common with the Hepataticae yet they cannot be grouped with the latter on account of the fundamental differences enlisted above. Similarly the Anthocerotales possess certain features which they share with the Mosses particularly *Sphagnum* differing totally from them, at the same time, in others. Consequently the growing tendency among the present day bryologists is to consider the Anthocerotales as a separate group named *Anthocerotae* or *Anthocerotopsida* equal in rank to the other two classes of the bryophytes. Since the Anthocerotae form a connecting link between the other two classes they are placed in between the Hepaticae or Hepaticopsida on one hand, and the Musci or Bryopsida on the other.

The consensus of opinion at present favours this view. So according to the latest view the systematic position of *Anthoceros* will be as under :

Division	:	Bryophyta
Class	:	Anthocerotopsida
Order	:	Anthocerotales
Family	:	Anthocerotaceae
Genus	:	*Anthoceros*
Species	:	*erectus*

BIOLOGICAL IMPORTANCE OF *ANTHOCEROS* SPOROPHYTE

Anthoceros has a remarkable sporophyte. It is distinctly different from the sporophytes of the other bryophytes and is considered a unique and an advanced type. The advanced features which also indicate evolutionary trends or the probable lines of biological progress in *Anthoceros* sporophyte are :—

1. Amply ventilated photosynthetic system in the capsule wall. The capsule wall consists of several layers of **green cells** with intercellular space between them. External to these is the protective surface layer forming the **epidermis** which is cuticularised. It is punctured with **stomata** similar to those of the higher plants. The development of the **ventilated photosynthetic tissue** is the first step towards the beginning of physiological independence of *Anthoceros* sporophyte. It makes much of its own food. However, it never becomes entirely independent of the parent gametophyte at any stage.

2. Decentralisation and complete sterilisation of the central fertile tract, the **endothecium**. This evolutionary tendency resulted in the following two events :—

(i) Development of a central core of sterile tissue forming the columella. It consists of narrow, vertically elongated, conducting cells with uniformly thickened walls. The presence of a central columella is suggestive of the demarcation of a region in *Anthoceros* sporophyte for the location and the origin of the vascular tissue. Although columella never develops any vascular elements even in exceptional cases in the entire group yet some scientists consider that its central position corresponds to the initial vascular cells of the early tracheophytes. They believe that it plays a definite role in conduction and affords mechanical support. For these reasons it is considered the forerunner of a protostele in some evolutionary concepts.

(ii) Archesporium becoming amphithecial in origin. The complete sterilisation of the central endothecium to form a columella resulted in the office of spore production being shifted from a central to a more superficial position, i.e., the inner layer of the amphithecium. This superficial origin of the generative tissue (archesporium) promotes easy dispersal of spores and its position on the surface of columella ensures easy and ready supply of nourishment.

3. Differentiation of amphithecial archesporium into alternate bands of fertile and sterile tracts. This evolutionary tendency is believed by some scientists to have great potentialities. It is considered the first step towards the origin of sporangia and sporophylls. In fact a noted British botanist Bower made the arrangement of fertile and sterile tissues into alternate bands in *Anthoceros* capsule as the basis for the origin and evolution of leaves and sporangia of the pteridophytes. It is called theory of *origin of the strobilus*. The separated sterile and fertile masses become more and more superficial on account of their amphithecial origin. Eventually the sterile, superficial tracts turn green. The green tissue develops into membranous expansions, the **sporophylls** with each of the sporogenous masses becoming enclosed by a sporangial wall to form **sporangia**. Of course all these suggested changes are hypothetical.

4. Presence of a basal intercalary meristem. It equips the capsule, at least, theoretically with unlimited power of growth. The meristem continually adds new cells at the base which get differentiated into the columella, the generative region and the photosynthetic capsule wall. This unique feature prolongs the period of spore production. The sporophyte of *Anthoceros* is thus a long-lived object as compared with the other bryophytes. It continues to live, as long as the parent gametophyte, producing and distribution spores.

5. The upright cylindrical body (Capsule) and large bulbous foot. The upright body helps in the efficient dispersal of spores and its cylindrical form is considered more suitable for a branched habit. The massive foot embedded in the thallus produces short, rhizoid-like processes.The latter penetrate the thallus tissue to absorb nutriment. The development of these rhizoidal processes from the actively growing foot was for some time a subject of interesting speculation. The probability of *Anthoceros* sporophyte becoming independent with the foot penetrating the thallus tissue to become a root in the soil was thus suggested.

The above suggestion, in fact, became a conviction with some of the bryologists. Campbell was one of them. He formulated a theory known as the *anthocerotean origin of pteridophytes*. On the basis of this theory the sporophyte of *Anthoceros* and its allies was considered to be on the line of evolution leading to the simplest and the primitive independent sporophyte of the pteridophytes. The discussion about the origin of the Pteridophytes from ancestors like *Anthoceros* entirely centred around the sporophytic generation only. It was argued that the upright, *Anthoceros* sporophyte with its amply ventilated photosynthetic system and long continued growth is nearly equipped for independent existence. It lacks only a vascular tissue and a root with its foot-hold in the soil otherwise it approaches the simplest and the most primitive, free living sporophyte of the pteridophytes. To support his contention Campbell cited the example of certain large, bulky specimens of the sporophyte of *Anthoceros fusiformis* collected in California by Pierce. They were about 6 inches tall and had been growing in unusually favourable habitats for about 9 months or more. These specimens were characterized by :—

(*i*) Suppression of sporogenous tissue near the base of the capsule.

(*ii*) Ventilated photosynthetic tissue highly developed at least twice that in the normal sporophyte.

(*iii*) Columella nearly double in diameter than that in the normal type and differentiated in its basal portion into a conducting "strand of elongated cells highly suggestive of a simple vascular bundle".

(*iv*) Foot large and bulky than usual and more or less in direct contact with the soil due to the disorganisation of the adjacent thallus tissue.

Campbell opined that these sporophytes of *Anthoceros* have "reached a condition comparable to that of the young pteridophyte after it has established its first root". This theory of Campbell received but little support from the other bryologists. They pointed out the wide gap between the rootless, leafless, non-vascular, dependent sporophyte of *Anthoceros* and the rooted leafy, vascular, independent sporophyte typical of the simplest pteridophytes.

ORIGIN OF ANTHOCEROTALES

It is difficult problem. The genetic relationship of Anthocerotae with any other existing forms of bryophytes including even the Hepaticae appears to be very remote. Campbell opined that in its thallus and sporophyte the Anthocerotae have their nearest affinities with certain pteridophytes.

Kashyap was an ardent supporter of this view. So impressed was he with the structural similarities between the radially organised prothallus of *Equisetum debile* and thallus of *Anthoceros erectus* that he suggested the possibility of the origin of the Anthocerotae by reduction from this Pteridophyte. Mehra and Handoo do not subscribe to this view. They consider it untenable for a variety of reasons. The chief among them are :

(*i*) There is nothing in common between the sporophytes of the two.

(*ii*) Absence of any relic of the lost vascular system even in exceptional and abnormal cases in the entire class Anthocerotae.

(*iii*) The difference in the basic chromosome complex of the two is very wide and thus irreconcilable. The Anthocerotae have the basic number as 5 whereas in *E. debile* it is 10.

Campbell, Smith and others, on the other hand, emphasized phylogenetic relationship between the Anthocerotae and the Psilophytales (Pteridophytes). The latter constitute a small group of the oldest and the most primitive of all the known vascular plants. All of these are the fossils of the Devonian age. The two most important of these are *Rhynia* and *Horneophyton*. They are placed in the family Rhyniaceae of the order Psilophytales. The Rhyniaceae are small, herbaceous sporophytes about 2 feet in height. They were rootless. The simplest of them were even leafless. The plant-body consisted of a rhizome bearing slender, erect, dichotomously branched shoots. The rhizome was anchored to the substratum by rhizoids. The vascular cylinder was of the nature of a protostele. There was no secondary growth. The reproductive organs were the sporangia which resembled the sporophyte of the Anthocerotae. They were borne singly and terminally. Each sporangium produced many spores. It possessed a central columella and had distal dehiscence.

Proskauer (1962) adduced further evidence in favour of the Psilophytalean ancestry of Anthocerotales. He discovered the occurrence of spiral thickenings of wall material on the lining layer of cells of the capsule wall and surface layer of columella of *Dendroceros crispus* and compared them with similar thickenings on the tapetum of *Horneophyton* and *Rhynia*. In Udar and Singh's view their recent discovery in 1978 of the occurrence of thickening bands particularly the occasional occurrence of spiral thickenings on the cells of the inner layer of the 3-layered capsule wall on *N. levieri* will give further support to Proskauer's stand.

Smith was so struck with the remarkable resemblance between the sporophytes of the Anthoceroatae and the sporangia of this ancient group (Rhyniaceae) that he suggested *affinities between them by descent in an upward direction*. The opponents of this view point out that *Anthoceros* sporophyte not only has any roots but also no vasular tissue. It exhibits no branching. To crown all, the meristem in *Anthoceros* is at the base and not at the apex.

There is, however, another school of thought. They read *genetic relationship between the Anthocerotae and the Rhyniaceae by descent in a downward direction*: According to them the Anthoceroate are a retrograde group derived from the Rhyniaceae by simplification or reduction. Mehra and Handoo find it difficult to reconcile themselves to this view. They argue, "it is difficult to visualize so complete a loss of the vascular system that it would not be present in any exceptional or abnormal cases in the entire Anthocerotales. Moreover, the structure of the columella shows no differentiation in any of the members.

Mehra and Handoo feel that the Anthocerotales and the Rhyniaceae have sprung up from the same ancestral stock in pre-Devonian. They call it the Antho-rhyniaceae. The latter evolved from a still earlier hypothetical pro-liverwort stock from which have also arisen the Marchantiales, the Jungermanniales and the Sphaerocarpales. The origin of this pro-liverwort stock according to them must be sought in some of the Chlorophyceae that migrated to land.

QUESTIONS ON *ANTHOCEROS*

ESSAY TYPE

1. Describe the sporophyte of *Anthoceros* and compare it with that of *Pellia*. *(Lucknow, 1995, 2001, 2008)*

   or

   Describe the structure of sporophyte of *Anthoceros* with neat labelled diagrams. *(Bangalore, 2001)*
2. Show that *Anthoceros* combines in itself a simple gametophyte and a highly developed gametophyte.*(Lucknow, 1997)*
3. Draw only labelled diagrams of *Anthoceros* sporogonium indicating its internal structure at various levels. *(Lucknow, 1998)*
4. With the help of labelled diagrams only compare the sporophytes of *Anthoceros, Pellia* and *Sphagnum.(Allahabad, 1993)*
5. With the help of labelled diagrams only compare the gametophytes of *Anthoceros, Porella* and *Pelia* or *Riccia*. *(Allahabad, 1994; Punjab 1999, 1998)*
6. Compare the sporophytes of *Anthoceros* and *Marchantia* on the basis of (*a*) origin of sporogenous tissues, (*b*) capsule wall and (*c*) extent of dependency on the gametophyte. *(Kanpur, 2007; Allahabad, 1998)*
7. Compare the internal structure of vegetative thallii of *Riccia*, *Marchantia* and *Anthoceros*. *(Allahabad, 1999; Rohilkhand, 1996; Kerala, 2000)*
8. Give an account of the gametophyte of *Anthoceros* with necessary diagrams. *(Lucknow, 2004)*

   or

   Describe the structure of thallus of *Anthoceros* and compare it with that of *Pogonatum*. *(Lucknow, 2004, 2006; Kanpur, 1998; Kerala, 1996, 1997)*
9. Give a comparative account of the structure of sporophytes of *Pellia* and *Anthoceros*. *(Kanpur, 1998; Rohilkhand, 1994; Gorakhpur, 1990, 1993)*
10. Justify the statement that *Anthoceros* has the simplest gametophyte and highly developed sporophyte. *(U.P. College, 1996)*
11. Give an account of salient features of the sporophyte of *Anthoceros* or Describe the structure of sporophyte of *Anthoceros* with suitable diagrams. *(U.P. College, 1997, 2000; Awadh, 1994; Vinoba Bhave, 1998)*
12. Give an illustrated account of sporophyte of *Anthoceros*. Why do you consider this sporophyte as the most advanced among liverworts. Discuss its affinities. *(Purvanchal, 1998; Gorakhpur, 1998; Punjab, 1996; Mahatma Gandhi, 1998)*
13. Give an illustrated account of sporophyte of *Anthoceros* and compare it with that of *Marchantia*. *(Purvanchal, 2000; Punjab 1999)*
14. With the help of labelled sketches only, draw the life cycle of *Anthoceros*. *(Garhwal, 2003; Rohilkhand, 1992; Awadh, 1999; Bundelkhand, 1998)*
15. Compare the sporogonium (Sporophyte) of *Riccia, Marchantia* and *Anthoceros*. *(Rohilkhand, 1995; Kerala, 1997; Punjab, 1999)*
16. With the help of suitable diagrams compare the internal and external structures of the gametophytes of *Riccia, Marchantia, Pellia* and *Anthoceros*. *(Rohilkhand, 1998, 1999, 2000; Awadh 1998, 1999; Gorakhpur, 1991, 1994, 1995, 1997)*
17. Give the comparative account of the structures of sporophytes in *Marchantia* and *Anthoceros*. *(Meerut, 1997; Bundelkhand, 1995)*

18. With the help of suitable diagrams, describe the development of sporophyte of *Anthoceros*. *(Meerut, 2000)*
19. Describe in brief the life cycle of *Anthoceros* with the help of suitable diagrams.
(Kanpur, 1992; Devi Ahilya, 2001; Bundelkhand, 1996)
20. Give an account of the life history of *Anthoceros* and mention its phylogenetic importance. *(Nagarjuna, 1990, 1992)*
21. Describe the structure of sporophyte of *Anthoceros* with neat labelled diagrams.
(Bangalore, 2001; Kerala, 1999; Vinoba Bhave, 1998; Trichy, 1995)
22. What are the features of the sporophyte of *Anthoceros* which give evolutionary link to higher plants?
(Calicut, M.Sc. 2001; Kerala, 1996)
23. With the help of suitable diagrams describe the structure of sporophyte of *Anthoceros* and comment on its nutrition.
(Calicut, 1998; Mahatma Gandhi, 1998)
24. Describe the structure of sporophyte of *Anthoceros*. What is its evolutionary significance? Discuss.
(Nagpur, 1996; Magadh, 1993)
25. Give an account of development and structure of sporogonium in *Anthoceros*.
(Gurananak Dev, 1991)
26. Draw and explain the structure of sporogonium in *Anthoceros*.
(Gurunanak Dev, 1992)
27. Give an illustrated account of the external morphology of plant body of *Anthoceros* and *Riccia*. Place them in their systematic position. *(Punjab 1992)*
28. (*a*) Draw diagrams antheridia and archegonia of *Marchantia* and *Anthoceros* and give structural differences in the sex organs of the two plants.
(*b*) Compare the internal structure of thallus of *Marchantia* and *Anthoceros*.
(Himachal Pradesh, 1992)
29. Draw the L.S. of mature sporophyte of *Anthoceros*, label the parts and briefly describe its structure. Mention the evolutionary features noticed in this genus.
(Mahatma Gandhi, 1998)
30. Give an account of the sporophyte of *Anthoceros*. Discuss its evolutionary significance.
(Vir Kumar Singh 1991; Magadh, 1996)
31. Describe the structure and development of sporophyte of *Anthoceros*. Mention its advanced characters.
(Vir Kumar Singh 1991, 1998; Magadh, 1994)
32. "*Anthoceros* is the progenitor of higher plants" Discuss this statement.
(Vir Kumar Singh, 1992)
33. Write about the salient features of *Anthoceros* and mention the evolutionary significance of its sporogonium.
(Magadh, 1996, 1997)
34. With the help of suitable diagrams describe the external and internal morphology of the gametophyte of *Anthoceros*. *(Kanpur, 2003)*
35. Describe the structure and development of sex organs in *Anthoceros*.
36. Briefly describe the development of the sporophytic phase right from the zygote. Mention the peculiarities.
37. 'Anthoceros is a synthetic type', with the help of suitable sketches justify the truth or falsity of this statement.
38. Compare the thallus of *Anthoceros* with those of *Riccia* and *Marchantia*.
(Rohilkhand, 2002)
39. Describe in detail the significance of intercalary meristem, stomata and chloroplast in the sporogonium of *Anthoceros*. *(Lucknow, 2002)*
40. Describe the mature sporogonium of *Anthoceros*. *(Lucknow, 2003)*
41. Give a concise account of Anthocerotales. Discuss the possible Contribution of the group in the evolution of land plants.
(Gauhati M.Sc. 2002)

42. Describe in detail the characteristic features of *Anthocerotopsida.* Discuss its affinities. *(Poorvanchal M.Sc. 1998)*

43. Explain the external features and internal structure of the thallus of *Anthoceros.* *(Punjab 2001)*

SHORT ANSWER TYPE

44. Give a comparature account of the gametophytes of *Marchantia* and *Anthoceros* *(Lucknow, 2008)*

45. Describe in detail the life cycle of *Anthoceros* or *Marchantia* *(Kanpur, 2008)*

46. Compare the structure of sporophytes of *Marchanti*a and *Anthocero*s (Give diagrams only) *(Kanpur, M.Sc. 2009)*

47. Describe the structure of sporophytes following :

(*a*) *Reccia*

(*b*) *Marchantia*

(*c*) *Anthoceros*

(*d*) *Funaria*

48. Differentiate between thallus structure of *Anthoceros* and *Pellia.(Allahabad, 2002)*

49. Give a brief account of amphithecium in *Anthoceros.* *(Allahabad, 2004)*

50. Draw well labelled diagrams of the following :

(*a*) V.L.S. sporophyte of *Anthoceros.* *(Lucknow, 1994, 1996, 1999, 2001, 2005; Allahabad, 1991, 2002, 2005; Kanpur, M.Sc. 2002. Rohilkhand 2000; Awadh, 1992, 1996, 1998; Gorakhpur, 1996, 1999; Meerut, 1998; Poorvanchal, 2002 Vikram, 1990; Himachal Pradesh 1992, 93; Bundelkhand, 1993, 1999)*

(*b*) Structure of antheridial chamber of *Anthoceros.* *(Lucknow, 1993)*

(*c*) T.S. capsule of *Anthoceros* (middle region). *(Lucknow, 1993; Allahabad, 1996)*

(*d*) V.T.S. thallus of *Anthoceros* through antheridium. *(Lucknow, 1997, 2002; Purvanchal, 1996, 2000, 2003; Gorakhpur, 1993, 1999)*

(*e*) Male thalli of *Anthoceros* and *Pellia.* *(Allahabad, 1992, 1993)*

(*f*) L.S. sporogonium of *Anthoceros.* *(Allahabad 2004; Punjab, 2001; U.P. College, 1998)*

(*g*) T.S. of *Anthoceros* thallus (Cellular) *(U.P. College, 1999; Purvanchal 1997; Awadh, 1995; Kumaon 1995; S.K. Univ. 1991; Meerut, 2002)*

(*h*) T.S./L.S. of *Anthoceros* capsule. *(Kanpur, 2002; Purvanchal 1996)*

(*i*) Pseudoelaters. *(Purvanchal, 1999)*

(*j*) Sporophyte of *Anthoceros.* *(Rohilkhand, 1998)*

(*k*) T.S. thallus of *Riccia, Marchantia, Pellia* and *Anthoceros.* *(Awadh, 1992)*

(*l*) T.S. *Anthoceros* sporophyte passing through spore zone. *(Gorakhpur, 1994, 1998; Kumaon, 2000)*

(*m*) Antheridia of *Anthoceros(Meerut, 1999)*

(*n*) T.S. Sporophyte of *Anthoceros* at the top. *(Allahabad, 2006)*

(*o*) Sporophyte of *Anthoceros* *(Lucknow, 2008, Kanpur, 2009)*

51. Write notes on the following :

(*a*) Significance of intercalary meristem, stomata and chloroplast in the sporogonium of *Anthoceros.* *(Lucknow, 1993, 1996)*

(*b*) Sporophyte of *Anthoceros.* *(Allahabad, 1999; Kumaon, 1996)*

(*c*) Sex organs of *Anthoceros.* *(Purvanchal, 1999)*

(*d*) Dehiscence of capsule in *Anthoceros.* *(Rohilkhand, 1993, 1996)*

(*e*) Special features of sporophyte in *Anthoceros. (Awadh, 1995, Nagpur, 1995)*

(*f*) Pseudoelaters. *(Awadh, 1996; Kerala, 1996)*

(*g*) Thallus structure in *Anthoceros* *(Gorakhpur, 1996; Meerut, 1997; Osmania, 1992; Virkumar Singh, 1999)*

(*h*) Important features of the class Anthocerotopsida. *(Kumaon, 1997)*

(*i*) Internal structure of *Anthoceros* thallus. *(Kumaon, 1998, 1999; Kerala, 2000; Himachal Pradesh, 1990)*

(*j*) Primitive and advanced features of *Anthoceros.* *(Meerut, 1998)*

(*k*) Differences between elaters and pseudoelaters. *(Lucknow, 2005 Himachal Pradesh, 1993; M .D. Saraswati, 1998; Bundelkhand, 1998)*

(*l*) Elaters and pseudoelaters. *(Vinoba Bhave, 1997; Mahatma Gandhi, 1997)*

(*m*) Capsule of *Anthoceros.* *(Mahatma Gandhi, 1997)*

(*n*) *Anthoceros.* *(Lucknow, 2002)*

(*o*) Male reproductive structure of *Anthoceros.* *(Rohilkhand, 2001)*

(*p*) Outline of the lifecycle of *Anthoceros.* *(Rohilkhand, 2002)*

(*q*) Structure and development of Archegonium in *Anthoceros.* *(Andhra Pradesh, 2002)*

(*r*) Systematic position of Anthocerotales. *(Awadh M.Sc. 2001)*

(*s*) Hornworts *(Poorvanchal, 2001)*

(*t*) Characteristic features of Anthoceratales *(Kanpur, M.Sc., 2006)*

52. Name the bryophyte in which

(*i*) Simple rhizoids are present.

(*ii*) Growth of sporophyte is indeterminate.

(*iii*) Stomata are present on the wall of sporophyte.

(*iv*) Thallus is not differentiated into assimilatory and storage zones.

(*v*) Pseudoelaters are present in the capsule.

(*vi*) Chloroplast and pyrenoids are present in each cell.

(Kanpur, 1996, 1999; Allahabad, 1991, 1994, 1999; Awadh, 1993)

53. Explain the structure of the sporophyte of *Anthoceros* only with their diagrams. *(Kottayan, 2004, Ravishankar, 1992)*

54. Describe two important differences between liverworts and hornworts. *(Purvanchal, 1997, 2000)*

55. Name two monoecious species of *Anthoceros.* *(Purvanchal, 1999)*

56. Name a bryophyte in which cellular differentiation in the thallus like *Riccia* and *Marchantia* is absent. *(Rohilkhand, 1993)*

57. Hornworts is the other name of which plant group? *(Rohilkhand, 1995)*

58. What are pseudoelaters? *(Gorakhpur, 1990)*

59. What is the difference between elaters and pseudoelaters? *(Gorakhpur, 1991, 1994, 1998)*

60. Bring out the internal structure of *Anthoceros.* *(Kerala, 2000)*

61. Give important points of sporophyte of *Anthoceros.* *(Kerala, 1998)*

62. What are the algal characters of *Anthoceros*? *(Kerala,* 1996)

63. Name a bryophyte which has pyrenoids in the cells of its thallus. State the class to which it belongs. *(Himachal Pradesh, 1993)*

64. Describe the mechanism of spore dispersal in the capsule of *Anthoceros* and *Riccia.* *(Punjab, 1992)*

65. Describe the internal structure of the thallus of *Anthoceros.* *(Himachal Pradesh, 1990)*

66. How are the capsules of *Anthoceros* nourished? *(Mahatma Gandhi, 1998)*

67. Trace the development of antheridia and archegonia in *Anthoceros.* *(Madras, 1997)*

68. How would you justify the separation of *Anthoceros* from the Hepaticae.

69. Discuss the biological importance of the sporogonium of *Anthoceros.*

70. With the help of labelled sketches only describe the structure of :
(*a*) Sporogonium
(*b*) Antheridium
(*c*) Archegonium
(*d*) Thallus.

71. Write a note on dehiscence of capsule of *Anthoceros* and dispersal of spores.

72. Explain the longitudinal section of *Anthoceros* sporophyte. *(Bangalore, 2002)*

73. Describe vegetative reproduction in *Anthoceros.*

74. Give a brief account of T.S. thallus of *Anthoceros.* *(Poorvanchal, 2002)*

75. What do you mean by pseudoelaters. *(Poorvanchal, 2002)*

76. How many layers are found in the roof of antheridial chamber in *Anthoceros.* *(Meerut, 2004)*

77. Mention common features between Anthocerotales and Chlorophyceae. *(Kanpur, 2002)*

78. How do the sex organs of hepaticopsia and antheropsida differ from those of algae ? Are there exceptions ? *(Poorvanchal, M.Sc. 1998)*

89. Compare archegonium in *Anthoceros* and *Riccia.* *(Punjab, 2001)*

80. What is the fate of endothecium in *Anthoceros* *(Kanpur, M.Sc. 2003)*

81. Describe the thallus structure and habitat of *Anthoceros* *(Kanpur, 2005)*

82. Among the Sporangia of *Riccia* and *Anthoceros* which is more primutive and why ? *(Kanpur, 2006)*

83. Name of bryophyte which shows pyrenoids in the chloroplast *(Allahabad, 2006)*

84. Differentiate between (a) Liverwert and Hornwort *(Lucknow, 2007)*
(b) Elaters and pseudoelaters *(Lucknow, 2008)*

85. Describe *Anthoceros* has endosymbiosis. *(Lucknow, 2007)*

86. Enumate the characteristics of *Anthoceros*. Which defy its placement in class Hepatecae. *(Lucknow, M.Sc., 2007)*

OBJECTIVE TYPE

87. **Fill in the blanks**
(*i*) In *Anthoceros* columella develops from ____________.
(*ii*) In *Anthoceros* the sporogenous tissue is ____________ in origin.
(*iii*) Pseudoelaters occur in ____________.
(*iv*) In *Anthoceros*, the elaterophore is ____________ in origin.
(*v*) The bryophyte in which the sporophyte has an intercalary meristematic zone is ____________.
(*vi*) The stalk of the sporogonium that connects with capsule is called ____________.
(*vii*) Thallus cells have chloroplasts with pyrenoids in ____________.
(*viii*) The thalli of *Anthoceros* are dark green because of the presence of ____________ colonies.
(*ix*) Vegetative reproduction in *Anthoceros* takes place by ____________.
(*x*) Elongated cylindrical sporogonium is characteristic of ____________.
(*xi*) In the genus ____________ stomata are present on the capsule walls.
(*xii*) *Nostoc* colonies are present in the thallus of ____________.
(*xiii*) The entire ____________ gives rise to columella in *Anthoceros.*
(*xiv*) Pseudoelaters are found in the capsule of ____________.

88. Select the correct answer :
(*i*) In *Anthoceros*, the archesporium is formed from
(*a*) Outer layer of amphithecium
(*b*) Inner layer of amphithecium,
(*c*) Endothecium
(*d*) Amphithecium and endothecium.

(*ii*) *Anthoceros* is commonly known as

(*a*) Stoneworts

(*b*) Liverworts

(*c*) Hornworts

(*d*) Bladderworts.

(*iii*) Meristematic tissue is present in the sporophyte of

(*a*) *Riccia*

(*b*) *Marchantia*

(*c*) *Anthoceros*

(*d*) *Polytrichum*.

(*iv*) Which of the following has elongated cylindrical sporogonium?

(*a*) *Funaria* (*b*) *Polytrichum*
(*c*) *Marchantia* (*d*) *Anthoceros*.

(*v*) In *Anthoceros* the meristematic tissue is

(*a*) Present at the apex of sporogonium

(*b*) Present in the middle of sporogonium

(*c*) Present at the base of sporogonium

(*d*) Absent.

(*vi*) Sporogenous tissue in *Anthoceros* is derived from

(*a*) Endothecium

(*b*) Amphithecium

(*c*) Gametophyte

(*d*) Tissues of columella.

(*vii*) In which of the following the sporophyte grows continuously due to the activity of basal meristem?

(*a*) *Riccia* (*b*) *Marchantia*
(*c*) *Anthoceros* (*d*) *Funaria*.

(*viii*) In *Anthoceros*, cells of the thallus contain colonies of an alga belonging to the genus

(*a*) *Chlamydomonas*

(*b*) *Chlorella*

(*c*) *Nostoc*

(*d*) *Hydrodictyon*.

(*ix*) Pseudoelaters are characteristic of the sporophyte of

(*a*) *Funaria* (*b*) *Anthoceros*
(*c*) *Marchantia* (*d*) *Riccia*.

(*x*) An endophytic alga is present in the thallus of

(*a*) *Riccia* (*b*) *Marchantia*
(*c*) *Anthoceros* (*d*) *Pellia*.

(*xi*) Hornwort is the name given to the members of the class

(*a*) Hepaticopsida

(*b*) Anthocerotopsida

(*c*) Bryopsida

(*d*) Chlorophyceae.

(*xii*) Stomata are present on the capsule wall of the genus

(*a*) *Riccia* (*b*) *Marchantia*
(*c*) *Anthoceros* (*d*) *Porella*.

(*xiii*) The sporophyte of *Anthoceros* is

(*a*) Dependent on the gametophyte

(*b*) Semi-independent on the gametophyte

(*c*) Independent of the gametophyte

(*d*) A saprophyte.

(*xiv*) Name a bryophyte in which the cells of the thallus have chloroplast with pyrenoid.

(*a*) *Pellia* (*b*) *Anthoceros*
(*c*) *Porella* (*d*) *Funaria*.

(*xv*) The member of pyrenoids in the thallus cells of *Anthoceros* is usually

(*a*) One in each cell

(*b*) Two in each cell

(*c*) Numerous in each cell

(*d*) Absent.

(*xvi*) Which of the following species of *Anthoceros* is annual ?

(*a*) *A. himalayensis*(*b*) *A. erectus*

(*d*) *A. chambensis* (*d*) *A. laevis*.

(*xvii*) Mucilage cavities are characteristic feature of

(*a*) *Riccia* (*b*) *Marchantia*
(*c*) *Funaria* (*d*) *Anthoceros*.

(*xviii*) Air pores are absent in

(*a*) *Riccia* (*b*) *Marchantia*
(*c*) *Lunularia* (*d*) *Anthoceros*.

(*xix*) Which of the following species of *Anthoceros* is monoecious.

(*a*) *A. himalayensis*(*b*) *A. erectus*
(*c*) *A. chambensis* (*d*) *A. laevis.*

(*xx*) The entire endothecium gives rise to columella in

(*a*) *Riccia* (*b*) *Marchantia*
(*c*) *Anthoceros* (*d*) *Funaria.*

(*xxi*) Cyanobacteria are found in the thallus of

(*a*) *Riccia* (*b*) *Anthoceros*
(*c*) *Funaria* (*d*) *Pellia.*

(*xxii*) In *Anthoceros* spore producing layer originates from

(*a*) *Endothecium*
(*b*) Amphithecum
(*c*) Columella
(*d*) Foot.

(*xxiii*) Development of Antheridia in *Anthoceros* is of__________type.

(*a*) Endogenous (*b*) Exogenous
(*c*) Endoscopic (*d*) Exoscopic.

QUESTIONS ON NOTOTHYLAS

ESSAY TYPE

1. Compare and contrast the structure of gametophytes of *Notothylas* and *Marchantia* and mention the simplicity and complexity of the two types.
(Vir Kumar Singh, 1995)

2. Describe the development of the sporophyte of *Notothylas* and present a well labelled longitudinal section diagram of its sporogonium.
(Vir Kumar Singh, 1997)

3. Give a comparative account of the sporophytes of *Anthoceros* and *Notothylas.* *(Vir Kumar Singh, 1998)*

4. Discuss the life history of *Notothylas.*
(Bhagalpur, 1991; Vinoba Bhave, 1999)

5. Class Anthocerotopsida is a synthetic group in Bryophytes. Discuss
(Vinoba Bhave, 1997)

6. Describe the external and internal features of the gametophyte of *Notothylas.*

7. With the help of labelled diagrams describe the structure of sporophyte of *Notothylas.*

8. Describe structure of Chloroplast in Notothylas and Megaeeros
(Lucknow, M.Sc., 2006)

9. Discuss the following statement : Notothylas as a conneting link between Hepaticae and Anthocerotales.
(Lucknow, M.Sc., 2007)

10. Give an account of differenting features of Anthrocerotae and Hepaticae.

11. Discuss evolutrorary tendency of sporophytic organisation in Anthocerotae.

SHORT ANSWER TYPE

12. Write short notes on :

(*a*) Sporophyte of *Notothylas.*
(Vir Kumar Singh, 1992; Viboba Bhave, 1998)

(*b*) Differences between sporophytes of *Anthoceros* and *Notothylas.*
(Vir Kumar Singh, 1993; Magadh, 1993)

(*c*) *Notothylas.*
(Vir Kumar Singh, 1997; Bihar, 1991)

(*d*) Labelled diagram of L.S. sporophyte of *Notothylas.* *(Bhagalpur, 1990)*

(*e*) Features of special interest in the sporophyte of *Notothylas.*

(*f*) Archesporium in Anthocerotae.
(Allahabad, M.Sc. 2000)

13. Which of the two is primitive, *Anthocerous* or *Notothylas*? Why?
14. Describe the similarities of Anthocerotales with Bryopsida.
15. Comment on the features of Anthocerotales common with pteridophytes.
16. Compare *Anthoceros* with *Notothylas*
17. Describe the development of sporophyte of *Notothylus.*
18. Distinguish between antheridia of *Takakia* and *Nolothylus(Rohilkhand M.Sc. 2003)*
19. Write explanatory notes on taxonomic status of *Anthoceros* complex.
20. Give a comparative account of Sporophytes of *Takakia, Targonia* and *Notothylus.* *(Awadh M.Sc. 2002)*

OBJECTIVE TYPE

21. **Select the correct answer :**

(*i*) Which of the following is a common columellate species of *Notothylas.*

(*a*) *N. indica* (*b*) *N. javanicus*
(*c*) *N. chaudhurii* (*d*) *N. breutelii.*

(*ii*) In the presence of pyrenoids in the cells of the thallus, *Notothylas* resembles

(*a*) Algae
(*b*) Fungi
(*c*) Bryophytes
(*d*) Pteridophytes.

(*iii*) Which of the following statement is correct.

(*a*) All the species of *Anthoceros* are non columellate.
(*b*) All the species of *Notothylas* are columellate.
(*c*) A few species of *Notothylas* are columellate while a few species are non-columellate.
(*d*) All the species of *Notothylas* are non-columellate

(*iv*) Which of the following is primitive.

(*a*) *Notothylas*
(*b*) *Anthoceros*
(*c*) Both a & b
(*d*) Neither a nor b.

(*v*) Like *Anthoceros, Notothylas* thallus also contains

(*a*) Fungi
(*b*) Green algae
(*c*) Red algae
(*d*) Blue green algae.

Image of *Sphagnum*

CHAPTER 14

BRYOPSIDA (Musci or Mosses)

- Distribution and Habitat
- Habit
- Asexual Reproduction
- Gametic Reproduction
- Sporophyte
- Comparison Between Liverworts and Mosses
- Classification

DISTRIBUTION AND HABITAT

The mosses are the higher bryophytes. They are worldwide in their distribution and occur in almost all situations where life is possible. The only exception is the sea. They occur both in the plains and at altitudes ranging from 4000 to 8000 ft. above sea level. Some species have been reported from altitudes as high as 18,000 to 20,000 ft. A moss known as *Aongstroemia julacea* has been collected from a height of 19,800 ft. above sea level. The leafy plant body of a moss plant is better adapted for a life on land than the thallus of liverworts. Different species grow in diverse habitats. However, they flourish the most in the wet and humid regions such as the moist mountain, forests of tropics and subtropics. A few are aquatic (*Fontinalis antipyretica*). A few such as *Sphagnum* grow in bogs. The species which can withstand periodic drought are quite at home in the temperate and the arctic tundras. Some drought enduring species grow in exposed situations such as soil, fence posts, rocks, old stone buildings (*Tortula muralis*), tree trunks (*Hypnum cupressiforme*) and in dry heaths (*Polytrichum juniperinum*). Some grow on the leaves of perennial plants. Even the dried mosses in these regions quickly revive upon wetting. Majority, however, grow in damp situations forming extensive mats. Some mosses can withstand more arid climates. One species *Tortula desertorum* has been reported from the deserts of Transcapsia.

HABIT

The mosses, which number about 15,000 species, are placed under 660 genera. Mostly they are gregarious in their habit. The predominate stage in the life cycle is the *gametophyte*. It is green and independent. In several species, such as *Funaria* and *Mnium,* the moss gametophyte grows erect with little branching. These illustrate *acrocarp habit*. Some such as *Hypnum cupressiforme* which illustrate *plurocarp habit* are prostrate and freely branched. Because of problem of attachment acrocarps are often absent from substrates such as steeply sloping rock faces and tree trunks. Rhizoids of acrocarps are usually longer than those of prostrate mosses (pleurocarps) which are shorter and repeatedly branched. The moss gametophyte phase comprises two growth stages namely, the *juvenile stage* called the **protonema** and the *adult leafy stage,* the so-called *moss plant* (Fig. 14.2).

1. Protonema stage (Fig. 14.1). It is creeping, green, branched and frequently filamentous. In rare cases it is plate-like (*Sphagnum, Andreaea* and a few others). It develops directly from a spore. The chief role of this juvenile stage is vegetative. It bears no sex organs.

2. Leafy stage (Fig. 14.2). It consists of an upright, slender axis bearing spirally arranged leaves. This stage finally produces sex organs. It is the so-called **moss plant** comparable to the gametophores of *Marchantia*. It arises as a lateral bud from the protonema. Usually several moss plants may arise from a protonema derived from a single spore. *Sphagnum* is an exception.

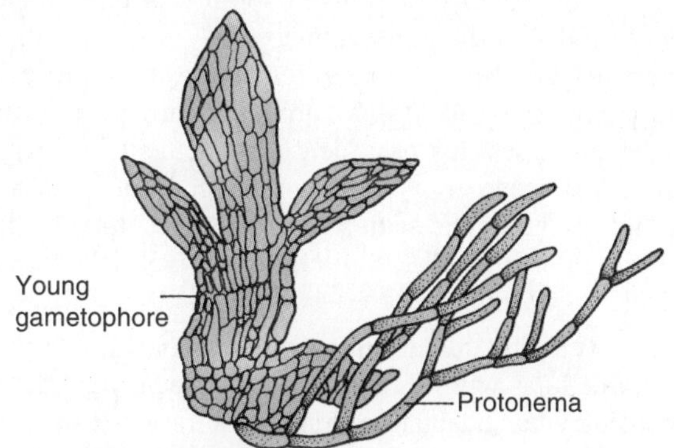

Fig. 14.1. Bryopsida. Moss protonema bearing the young leafy gametophyte.

The protonema in the majority of mosses dies and disappears. This makes the leafy gametophore independent and the sole representative of the gametophyte stage. In a few mosses (*Ephemeropsis* and *Buxbaumia aphylla*), the protonema persists as long as the gametophyte phase lasts (Phascaceae). It may turn brown and contribute to the mass of rhizoids. In such cases the leafy gametophore (moss plant) is undoubtedly a secondary structure comparable to the gametophore of *Marchantia*. It is developed for a special purpose which is the production of sex organs. In the overwhelming majority of the mosses, the leafy gametophore is the conspicuous, long-lived form of the moss plant.

Moss gametophore (Fig. 14.2). In form the gametophore apparently resembles a low growing flowering plant. It is differentiated into a stem-like central axis bearing green leaf-like expansion. Although Koch (1956) suggested the term **cauloid** for the former and **phylloid** for the latter yet the bryologists still prefer to call them **stem** and **leaves** respectively. The upright moss gametophore is usually attached to the substratum by a well developed rhizoid system. It consists of a number of brown or dark brown attaching filaments known as the **rhizoids**. Thus the three fundamental organs of the moss plant are the **stem, leaves** and **rhizoids**.

(*a*) *Stem.* It may be branched or unbranched. All the branches may be erect or some of them may be erect and others prostrate. The branching in mosses is usually later. Dichotomous branching is unknown in them. The branch always arises from below a leaf and is never axillary.

(b) Leaves. The delicate moss leaves which are the main photosynthetic organs of the gametophore are sessile. They are usually attached by a broad base to the stem. In form they present a great variety usually ranging from narrowly linear to oblong ovate or broadly suborbicular. The leaf cells contain large and prominent chloroplasts. In some mosses such as *Sphagnum* and *Hypnum cupressiforme*, the leaf has no midrib. In majority of mosses however, the leaf has a single, distinct midrib which transverse the lamina one cell in thickness. The midrib may not reach the leaf tip in some species (*Tetraphis pellucida*) or may extend to the leaf apex (*Fissidens bryoides*) or extends beyond the leaf tip (*Phascum cuspidatum*). In rare cases the moss leaf is traversed by two midribs as in *Lepidopilum*.

The leaves are arranged spirally in three ranks on the stem and thus the moss gametophore in general has a radial symmetry. *Fontanalis* and *Tetraphis pellucida* are typical *examples* of 3-ranked spiral arrangement with 1/3 divergence. In many cases this basic leaf arrangement in three ranks is soon lost due to growth torsions and consequent displacement of leaves during the maturation of stem resulting in divergence of 2/5 in *Sphagnum*, 3/8 in *Funaria*, 5/13 in *Polytrichum* and 4/11 in *Dicranium*.

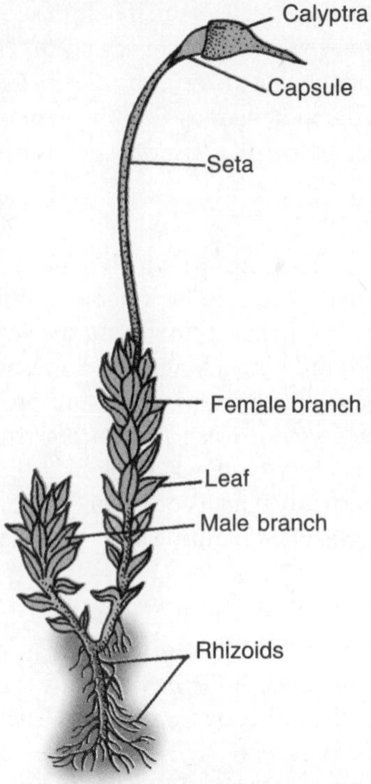

Calyptra
Capsule
Seta
Female branch
Leaf
Male branch
Rhizoids

Fig. 14.2. Bryopsida. A leafy moss gametophore bearing a nearly mature sporogonium at the apex of the female branch.

(c) Rhizoids. In mosses the rhizoids are branched and multicellular with oblique septa between the cells which is considered an adaptation to facilitate faster conduction (Goebal, 1905). The main rhizoidal strands are conducting and anchoring in function. They grow vertically downwards from the base of the stem and are brown or dark brown in colour. From these arise finer branches of second order which grow obliquely. The secondary laterals in turn bear still finer tertiary branches which are colourless and have exceedingly delicate cell walls. In pleurocarp mosses which grow on hard substrates, the rhizoids develop in tufts. According to Odu (1978) it is probably a specialization for stronger anchorage. Rhizoids of acrocarps are usually longer and the rhizoid cells also longer than those of the pleurocarps which possess shorter and repeatedly branched rhizoids.

ASEXUAL (VEGETATIVE) REPRODUCTION (Fig. 14.3)

The capacity for vegetative reproduction is widespread in the mosses. To achieve this they have developed several methods of vegetatively propagating the leafy gametophore and thus enabling the individual plant to form dense mats extending over considerable areas. Besides, any part of the gametophyte namely, leaf, stem, rhizoid or any portion there of and short specialized branches, in fact any undamaged living cell of the plant or protonema may act as a vegetative reproductive structure and regenerates a new gametophore. In fact asexual reproduction has become obligatory in some mosses like the gemmaeferous species of *Bryum* which remain sterile in many parts of the world. Excepting a few, in most of these methods, there is first the development of the juvenile growth phase (protonema) and from it the development of adult gametophores. Only a few important examples of these methods are described here.

1. Progressive growth and death. Some genera of mosses (*Polytrichum*) have a creeping main stem. It bears upright branches. The older portions of the creeping stem which are more or less cut off from light and air, die and decay. This leads eventually to the separation of the upright branches as separate entities. The result is the rapid increase in the number of leafy individuals.

2. Branching of the leafy stem. In many mosses the leafy axis develops buds at its base. The buds grow into branches which finally get detached by the decay of their basal connecting parts. Each detached branch develops into an independent plant.

3. Formation of stolons. Some mosses develop stoloniferous branches from the base of the stem. The stolons may be naked or bear small scaly leaves and creep on or just beneath the surface of soil. Eventually the tip of each stolon grows upward as upright, leafy axis.

4. Separation of a specially modified branch of bud-like form. In some species of *Bryum* and *Pohlia*, the detached structure which functions as an organ of vegetative propagation is a modified branch of bud-like form.

5. Preliminary protonemal stage. Moss plants arise as lateral buds from the extensively branched **primary protonema**. The protonema originating from a single spore may bear several such buds. The latter develop into leafy shoots. This is accompanied by the decay of the connecting portions of the protonema. This results in the separation of the leafy shoots as separate individuals.

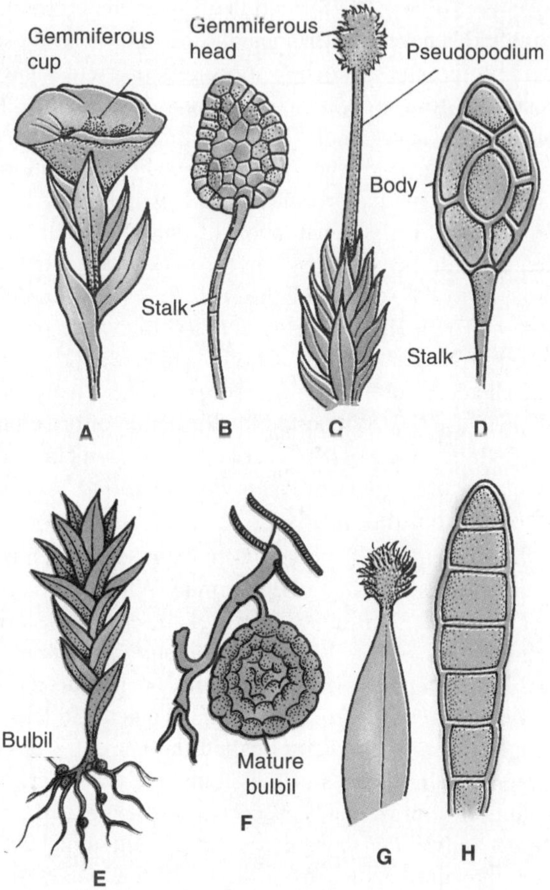

Fig. 14.3. (A—H). Bryopsida. Vegetative reproduction in mosses. A, *Tetraphis pellucida* with a terminal gemmiferous cup; B, Gemma with a stalk; C, *Aulacommium androgynum* with a pseudopodium ending in a gemmiferous head; D, a stalked gemma of the same; E, *Bryum erythrocarpum* bearing bulbils or tubers on the rhizoids; F, a mature globose tuber or bulbil; G,*Ulota phyllantha*, upper part of the leaf with an apical cluster of gemma; H, a single gemmae.

6. Multiplication of the protonemal stage. The primary protonema by death and decay of cells here and there may break into short, detachable segments (*Funaria*). Each segment grows into a protonema. The latter produces a fresh crop of leafy gametophores. The multiplication of the protonema stage thus provides a very efficient method of increase in numbers of the moss plants.

7. Secondary protonema (Plural—protonemata). The mosses have a great power of regeneration. Any undamaged cell of a detached or injured portion of almost any part of the moss plant (such as stem, leaf or protonema) under suitable conditions (when surrounded by moist air) develops into a green, branched, alga-like filament. It is called the **secondary protonema.** A crop of moss plants will spring from the secondary protonema as small buds. The latter grow into independent individuals by the decay of the connecting threads. Secondary protonemata may also spring from the rhizoids when the latter grow in light and are surrounded by moist air. The formation of secondary protonemata is an important and more effective method of vegetative propagation than the original protonema. In *Sphagnum* secondary protonema may be formed from the marginal cell of the primary protonema.

8. Tubers. The formation of small, underground resting, bud-like structures called the **tubers** has also been reported in some mosses. Formerly these underground bud-like structures were called the **bulbils**. The tubers develop singly on stems, leaves and rhizoids (Egunnyomi, 1980) as small, spherical storage organs containing starch. These serve as means of **perennation** and enable the plant to tide over periods unfavourable for vegetative growth. They are found in *Bryum nitens, Funaria* (Fig. 14.6) and *Trematodon*. On germination in the growing season each tuber produces a protonema. The latter bears the buds which grow up into a new crop of leafy aerial shoots. Direct formation of leafy gametophores from tubers without the formation of protonemata is rare. Tubers generally do not germinate in the dark or when attached to the stem. They germinate only when brought to the surface of the soil. *Bryum erythrocarpum* bears spherical tubers on the rhizoidal system (E, F). They are bright red in colour when mature. *Leptobryum pyriforme* is another example. It bears ovoid tubers. R.N. Chopra and Rawat (1973) reported that *Bryum klingyraeffii*, a local moss in Delhi does not fruit. It reproduces exclusively by means of gemmae (tubers) borne on the rhizoids. Whitehouse (1978) reported the formation of brown tubers on the rhizoids in *Bryum cruegeri*. Hart and Whitehouse (1978) described rhizoids tubers in *Pohlia lutescens*. Risse (1985) reported the formation of rhizoidal tubers in *Pottia intermedia*. The tubers are borne terminally on the primary or secondary brown rhizoids.

9. Gemmae. Frequently small, green, oval, multicellular buds are produced on short stalks in many mosses. They are the **gemmae**. Whitehouse (1980) listed about 28 moss species which bear **protonemal gemmae**. The chief among these are *Barbula, Leptobryum pyriforme, Torula standfordensis, Eucladium verticillatum, Bryum coronatum, B. klingyraeffii, Trematodon brevicalyx* and *Didymaton recurvus*. The gemmae are produced in groups in the axils of leaves in *Webra prolifera*. In *Tetrophis pellucida* they are long stalked and lens shaped (B). These gemmae are produced in a peculiar, cup-like structure called the **gemmiferous receptacle** (A), which is constituted by the large spreading leaves at the summit of the erect shoot. The gemmae are easily detachable. On falling on a moist soil any cell of the gemma may produce a green protonema. The gemmae in *Aulacomnium androgynum* are borne in a terminal cluster or gemmiferous head on a leafless stalk or pseudopodium arising from the tip of the leafy shoot (C). Another interesting example is that of *Ulota phyllantha* in which the gemmae are produced in a cluster at the tip of the leaf (G). *Grimmia* bears gemmae on the leaves at the tips or along the midrib. Each gemma is a mass of embryonic cells. It invariably produces a protonemal stage. The formation of gemmae on primary protonema in *Schistostega plunata*. The gemmae are obclavate and 3 or 4 cells long including a tapering distal cell which is sticky. The cells are green. Each gemma also has proximal abscission cell which is short and well marked. Eguneyomi (1980) describing propagules of *Bryumnitens* reported that the moss produces *deciduous shoot* tips and tubers. Tubers are formed on the stems, leaves and rhizoids. He further added that the shoot tips and fragments serve for immediate vegetative spread but tubers serve as a means of perennation.

Schofield (1981) observed that gemma production is generally vigorous while gametophore remains vegetative. With the initiation of sexual cycle gemma production decreases or ceases.

10. Persistent apices. In some mosses with the creeping stems the entire plant dries up in the dry season except the growing apices. The cells of the surviving apices secrete a mucilage sheath around them and persist. With the return of favourable conditions the surviving apices resume growth.

11. Apospory. The mosses have an extraordinary power of regeneration. Any undamaged cell of the sporophyte besides the gametophyte, can grow out into a protonema. The wounding of the unspecialised cells of the various parts of the sporophyte, induces the production of the green protonemal filament. The latter bears a new crop of leafy gametophytes. The formation of the gametophytes directly from the cells of the sporophyte other than a spore is called **apospory**. The phenomenon of apospory cuts out the spore stage in the life cycle. In other words the moss plant is produced directly from the sporophyte without the intervention of spores. The aposporously produced moss plants have a **diploid** chromosome number. They tend to be larger but otherwise normal in appearance. They bear diploid fertile gametes. Fusion between two diploid gametes or between a diploid and a normal gamete results in **tetraploid** (having four sets of chromosomes) or **triploid** sporophyte.

GAMETIC REPRODUCTION

(a) Position of sex organs (Fig. 14.4 A). The sex organs containing the gametes are borne in clusters in the mosses in general. *Sphagnum* in which the long-stalked antheridia occur singly in the axil of perigonial leaves, is an exception. Generally the cluster is developed at the apex of the main stem or the lateral branches. Intermixed with the sex organs in the cluster are the sterile green filaments. They are called the **paraphysis**. Some mosses are **monoecious** (*Mnium medium*) and some others are **dioecious** (*Polytrichum commune* and *Buxbaumia*). On the basis of the distribution of the **sex organs**, the **monoecious mosses** are placed under the following three categories.

(i) Paroicous mosses. In some of the monoecious mosses, the two kinds of sex organs are borne in the same head in separate groups. The antheridial and archegonial groups in the same head are demarcated from one another by one or two **perichaetial** bracts. Such monoecious mosses are called *paroicous.*

(ii) Autoicous mosses. The monoecious mosses in which the two kinds of sex organs are borne on separate branches of the same plant are termed *autoicous* (*Funaria hygrometrica* Fig. 14.6 A).

(iii) Synoicous mosses. The antheridia and archegonia occur in the same head intermingled with each other (*Mnium medium*). The leaves below the sex organs usually lie close to one another forming a distinct sheath or a rosette-like structure.

All the four conditions occur in different species of *Pohlia.* Similarly in *Bryum* all except the paroicous condition are found. *Buxbaumia aphylla* exhibits *sexual dimorphism.* The male and the female plants differ in size and appearance. The male plants of *Buxbaumia* are perhaps the simplest so far known among the mosses. Each consists of a protonema with some of its branches bearing a minute hood-like leaf protecting the antheridium. In some dimorphic tropical species, the male plants have been found growing on the leaves of the larger female plants.

(b) Form, structure and development of antheridia (Fig. 14.4 B, C) Except *Sphagnum,* the moss antheridia are longer and narrower than those of the hepaticae. The elongate body is usually club-shaped in form. It is supported by a stalk which remains short but is distinctly multicellular. All

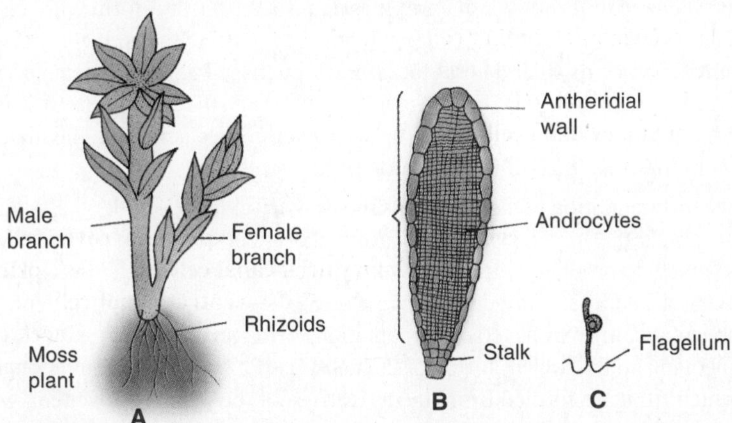

Fig. 14.4. (A—C) **Bryopsida.** A, gametophyte plant (Monoecious and autoecious); B, antheridium in section; C, sperm.

moss antheridia have the same structure but vary greatly in size. In many mosses the antheridia are smaller in size than those of *Funaria hygrometrica* which grow to a height of 0.25 mm. The mature antheridium of *Polytrichum juniperinum* ranges in length from 1.2 mm to 1.8 mm rarely 1.95mm (Hausmann and Paolillo, 1977). The average length, however, is 1.5mm. *Mnium hornum* has antheridia intermediate in size between *F. hygrometrica* and *P. junipernium*. When mature, the orange-coloured club-shaped body of the antheridium consists of a jacket layer enclosing a mass of androcytes or mature male gametes, the **sperms**. The jacket layer or antheridial wall is always one layer of cells in thickness. The jacket layer at the apex of the antheridium is differentiated into a lid-like structure consisting of one, two or rarely more cells of large size (sometimes small as in *Polytrichum*) with thicker walls and hyaline contents. In the mature antheridium of *Polytrichum* and sperm mass lies in the upper half whereas the lower half has a fluid filled space. The liberated male gamete is a motile, biflagellate spirally coiled structure (C).

Development (Fig. 14.5). The moss antheridium invariably originates from a single cell and continues to grow for a considerable time by the activity of a wedge-shaped apical cell with two segmenting faces. This is in marked contrast to that of the antheridium of liverworts in which the growth is intercalary. The moss antheridial initial is a superficial cell at the tip of the stem or the branch (A). It becomes papillate and then divides transversely to form a short filament of a few cells (C). The terminal cell of the filament; henceforth functions as an apical cell with two cutting faces (D). It cuts off a series of segments (about 12 to 15 E). Each young segment divides by a vertically diagonal wall into a jacket initial and a larger sister cell (G.H.). The latter again divides by a similar division to cut off a second jacket initial and an inner fertile cell termed *primary androgonial cell* (I). All the upper segments cut off by the apical cell divide in this fashion. The primary androgonial cells divide and redivide periclinally and anticlinally. The cells of the last cell generation of androgones are termed the *androcyte mother cells*. The jacket initials, meanwhile divide by anticlinally to complete the antheridial wall. Each androcyte mother cell divides to form two androcytes. This division in mosses is not diagonal. The androcytes are transformed into biflagellate sperms (O,P).

(c) **Archegonia** (Fig. 14.6). The moss archegonia are similar to those of the liverworts except that the moss archegonium has a longer stalk, a massive venter and a long neck about 40 to 50 cells in height.

Development of moss archegonium, in general. (Fig. 14.7). In Bryidae, in general, the archegonium initial (A) directly functions as an **apical cell** with two cutting faces. It cuts off two rows of 4 to 8 segments by alternate cleavages (D—F). The segments get bisected and in the course of time form the columnar stalk of the archegonium. Distally the apical cell is still there are active (F). However, it changes abruptly in nature. It assumes a tetrahedral form with a truncated base and functions as the **archegonial mother cell** (F). It has three cutting faces. It cuts off three segments by walls parallel to each of its three lateral faces. Each of these lateral segments divides by a vertical wall to form six **jacket initials (G)**. The jacket initials surround the apical cell (F). The latter henceforth functions as the **primary axial cell**. From the six jacket initials is formed the major part of the wall of the archegonium. It is doubled in the region of the venter.

With the differentiation of jacket initials the primary axial cell undergoes a transverse cleavage (H) which separates the lower **central cell** from the upper **primary cover cell**. The central cell divides transversely to produce an upper **primary neck canal cell** and a lower **primary ventral cell** (I). The latter at a later stage divides to give rise to the **ventral canal cell** and the **egg** (L). The primary neck canal cell by transverse segmentation forms an axial row of **neck canal cells** which occupy the median and the lower portion of the neck (J). The upper portion of the neck and the neck canal cells which fill it are formed from the derivatives of the primary cover cell which functions as an **apical cell** for some time (L, M). The segments cut off parallel to its three lateral faces from the upper part of the wall of the neck. The canal cells in this region are formed from the segments cut off from the truncated base of the apical cell.

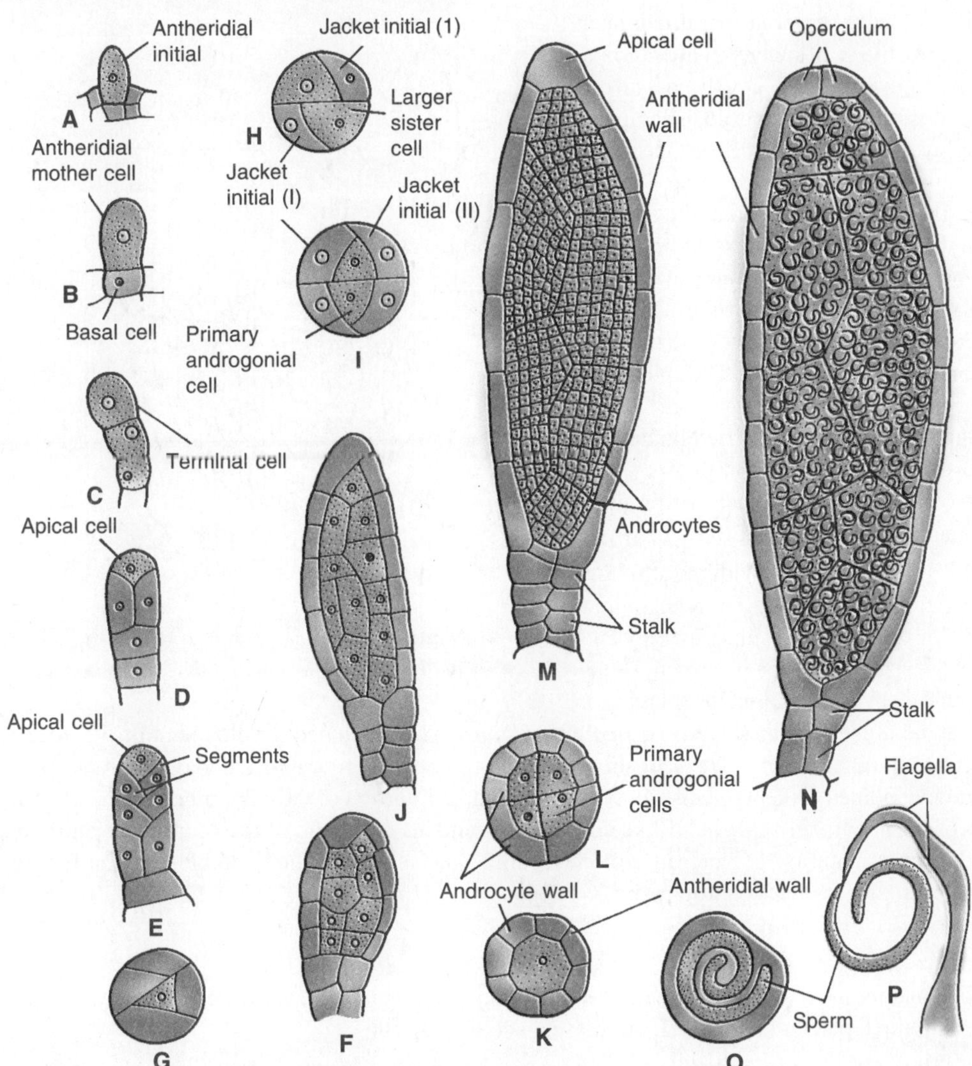

Fig.14.5 (A—P). ***Funaria***. Successive stages in the development of antheridium (A—L). G-L, are transverse sections; M, nearly mature antheridium; N, mature antheridium ready for dehiscence; O, sperm enclosed in a vesicle; P, free sperm. (Adapted from Campbell).

(*d*) **Fertilization**. Water is needed for fertilization. In the mature archegonium, the neck canal and the ventral canal cells disorganise to form a swelling slimy mass which exerts pressure to separate the cover cells. A small amount of mucilage emanates through the open archegonial neck. It contains a chemical substance which serves as a sperm attractant. In many mosses it is said to be sucrose. Attracted by the chemical substance the sperms swim towards and collect at the open mouth of the archegonium. Eventually they find their way down the archegonial neck to the egg. Water as a surface film is just sufficient for the movement of sperms to the egg. The sperm carries the paternal genes to the egg which contains maternal genes. Fusion of the sperm with the egg completes fertilization. Fertilization and subsequent development of embryo (embryogenesis from the fertilized egg occurs in the venter of the archegonium.

Embryo development. The fertilized egg secretes a wall around it. The zygote thus formed increases in size and undergoes segmentation. Except *Sphagnum* the first division wall is transverse or oblique. The upper or epibasal daughter cell divides by two successive diagonal divisions to establish an apical cell at the upper end of the young embryo. The apical cell has two segmenting faces. In the same way an apical cell with two cutting faces is differentiated at the lower end of the embryo in the hypobasal cell. The moss embryo thus grows by the activity of two apical cells in opposite directions for a long time. This is in sharp contrast to the intercalary growth of the liverwort embryo sporophyte. The apical cell at the upper end is, however, more active. The segments cut off by it differentiate into the capsule and greater part of the seta. The derivatives of the lower apical cell produce the foot and lower portion of the seta.

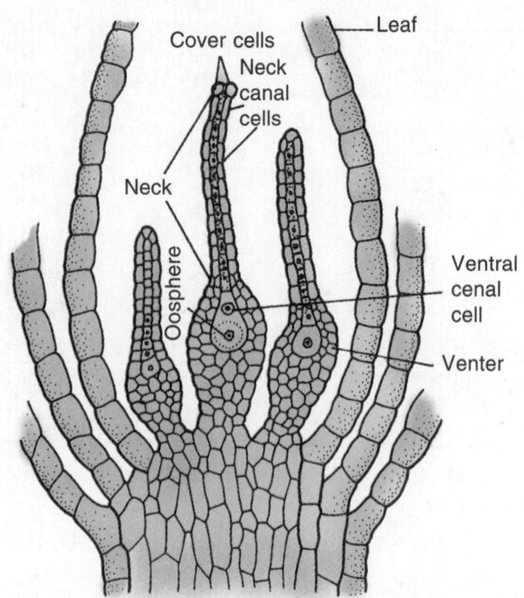

Fig. 14.6. **Bryopsida.** Longitudinal section through the tip of the female branch of a moss gametophore.

Calyptra formation. With the stimulus of fertilization, the venter of the archegonium surrounding the embryo resumes activity and increases in size. For a time its growth keeps pace with the growth of the enclosed embryo. The enlarged archegonium venter is called the *calyptra*. The continued development of the young sporophyte and elongation of the seta soon causes a transverse rupture of the clayptra at an early stage of development except *Sphagnum*. The severed upper portion of the calyptra is carried aloft at the top of the sporophyte as a hood-like covering. It remains at the top of the sporophyte until the capsule reaches maturity. The presence of calyptra has recently been shown to be essential for the normal development of the sporophyte.

SPOROPHYTE (Fig. 14.2)

The mature moss sporophyte with the exception of *Sphagnum* and *Andreaea* is differentiated usually into three parts namely, the foot, the seta and the capsule.

1. The foot. It forms the basal region of the moss sporophyte and functions both as an attaching and absorbing organ. It remains embedded in the tissues of the tip of the leafy gametophyte. In certain mosses cells with wall ingrowths occur at the junction between the sporophyte foot and the gametophyte. This region is referred to as the **placentary zone**. The cells with wall ingrowths in this zone are termed the **transfer cells**. The plasma membrane of these cells is greatly increased through the development of ingrowths of wall material of these cells. The wall ingrowths in some cases are long, fillform and branched. The branches anastomose to form veritable labyrinths of wall material. The labyrinth fills up a large part of the cellular volume. The plasma membrane follows the contours of the wall and cytoplasm penetrates between the individual ingrowths or into the interstices of the labyrinths. Ingrowths are located on the external and radial walls of the epidermal cells of the foot which are more swollen than those of the seta cells. Plasmodesmata occur in areas lacking wall ingrowths. In some moss genera such as *Funaria* and *Mnium* transfer cells occur both in the foot region and in the adjacent gametophyte tissues. Transfer cells in sporophytes of the Polytrichales have been reported to be present in the peripheral cells only in the sporophyte foot. The transfer cells are claimed to play an important role in efficient and rapid short distance transport of solutes by enhancing exchanges between the sporophyte and the gametophyte.

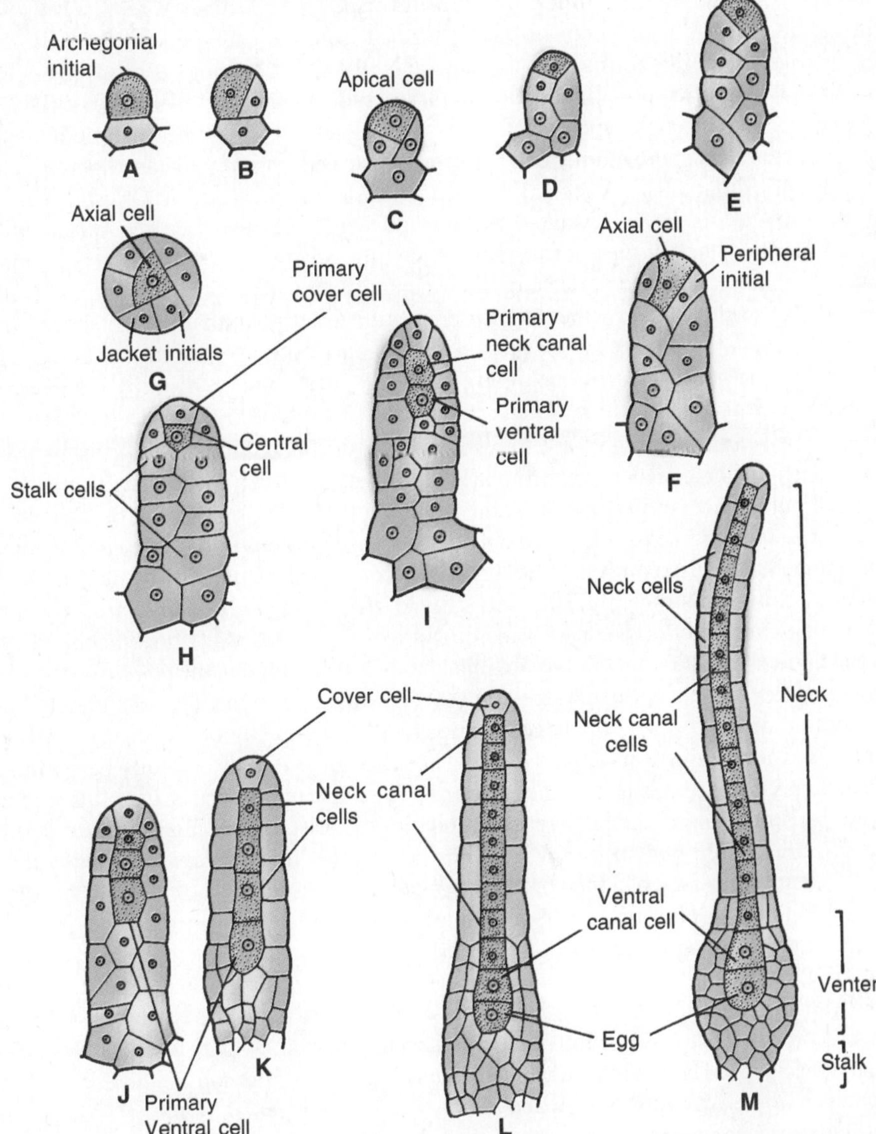

Fig. 14.7. (A—M). Bryidae. Successive stages in the development of moss archegonium other than *Funaria*.

2. The seta. It raises the capsule far above the level of the gametophore enabling ready dispersal of spores by the wind.

3. The capsule. In the true mosses it is complex in structure and reaches a high degree of specialisation. Externally it is differentiated into three regions, the basal **apophysis region**, the **middle theca region**, and the **apical lid** or **operculum region**. Each region performs a distinctive function.

Apophysis region is specialized for photosynthesis. Usually stomata and abundant chlorenchyma occur in this region. Theca is specialized for spore production. It consists of **epidermis, capsule** wall several layer of cells in thickness, an **air space** transversed by short filaments of narrow, green cells known as the **trabeculae, outer spore sac** or **tapetum, archesporium, inner spore sac** or **tapetum** and a central pillar of sterile cells, the **columella**. In more advanced mosses such as

Polytrichum there is, in addition, an **inner air space** traversed by trabeculae. It separates the spore sac from the columella. The sporogenous tissue is formed from the endothecium. It is not dome-shaped. The sporogenous tissue forms the spore mother cells which by meiosis produce numerous meiospores. Several workers reported reduction in plastid number from several in the archesporial cells to just one elongate or cup-shaped plastid per sporogenous cell. The last mitotic division of sporogenous cells results in spore mother cells or sporocytes. The single cup-shaped plastid in each sporocyte divides prior to meiosis. A second division results in the presence of 4 plastids per spore mother cell. Prior to meiosis the four daughter plastids move and become spaced equidistantly from each other near the periphery of the sporocyte indicating the positions of the poles of the meiotic spindles. As each spore is delimited after meiosis it contains a single plastid. Jensen and Hulbury (1978) reported that each plastid in the spore produces distinct lobes that are "blebbed" off as *proplastids*. Elaters are not formed in any moss species. The apical portion of the capsule is specialized to regulate spore discharge. It matures into **operculum** and **peristome**. At maturity the operculum falls exposing the underlying peristome which surrounds the mouth of the dehisced capsule.

The peristome is a fringe of teeth-like projections that surround the mouth of capsule in most of the Bryidae. The peristome teeth spring from the rim or diaphragm. Their number is variable. The least number is 4 but may occur in some other mosses in multiple of 4 such as 8, 16, 32 or 64. The teeth may be solid cellular tissue or composed only of thickened portions of the cell walls of adjacent cells. When the teeth of peristome are solid structures composed of bundles of dead cells, it is termed **nematodontous peristome** (Fig. 20.15). It is found in *Polytrichum, Pogonatum* and *Tetraphis*. The solid teeth of the nematodontous peristome do not exhibit hygroscopic movements. They are arranged in a single series. Their upper ends are joined to a thin membrane, the *epiphragm* stretched over the mouth of the capsule. In peristome composed of thin, membranous, transversely barred teeth, each tooth is made up of the thickened portions of the cell walls of adjacent cells. Such a peristome is called **orthodontous** (Fig. 18.15). The teeth of the orthodontous peristome are hygroscopic and may be arranged in a single series or two series. In the former case it is said to be **haplolepidous** peristome and in the later case **diplolepidous** peristome (*Funaria* and *Bryum*). The teeth comprising the haplolepidous peristome and outer series of diplolepidous peristome are hygroscopic. They are composed of a kind of two-ply material furnished by the cell walls of adjacent cells. Each tooth thus consists of two layers joined together. One layer forms the outer face of the tooth and the second forms the inner layer of the tooth. The outer layer lengthens when wet and shortens when dry. The inner face of the tooth remains unaffected by changes in the moisture content of the air. The teeth of the inner series of the diplolepidous peristome are not hygroscopic. The presence of peristome in the apical portion of the moss capsule regulates spore discharge by slowing the rate of spore discharge. The Bryidae in which the apical portion of the capsule differentiates into operculum and peristome are called **stegocarpous** mosses. In a few genera of the true mosses, both the operculum and peristome are absent. They are said to be **cleistocarpous**. In them the capsule wall at the time of dehiscence ruptures by splitting transversely, longitudinally or irregularly.

Structure of moss spore It consists of a tiny mass of protoplast surrounded by a thin spore wall. It has a single nucleus. The reserve food is stored in the cytoplasm in the form of lipid of some sort. There is very little starch. There are many proplastids in the mature spore. A photosynthetic membrane system is poorly established within many proplastids as the spore matures. The other cell organelles the spore cytoplasm contains are mitochondria and endoplasmic reticulum as highly convoluted tubules near the plasma membrane. The Golgi apparatus is sparse. The vacuoles are absent. The studies on spore wall development with electron microscope have revealed that it typically shows differentiation into 3 wall layers. These are from within outwards, *intine, exine* and *perine*. The fourth *separating opaque layer* which is a subunit of the exine may or may not be present (McClaymount and Larson, 1964). The intine is generally of spore (endogenous) origin and perine probably of exogenous origin (Niedhart, 1979). There is difference of opinion as regards the origin of exine. Both exogenous and endogenous origin have been suggested.

(*i*) *Intine.* It is the innermost layer of the spore wall and is fibrillar in nature. It is electron translucent and contains carbohydrate material including cellulose.

(*ii*) *Separating layer.* It is external to the intine, and is very thin, electron opaque, dense layer of uniform thickness. This spore wall layer is considered a subunit of the exine. In some mosses it is absent.

(*iii*) *Exine.* This third layer of the spore wall is external to the second. It is non-stratified (non-lamellate) in contrast to the typically lamellate nature of the exine of the spore wall of liverworts. It shows electron opacity similar to that of pollen exines. It is resistant to acetolysis and thus termed the**exine** . It is more or less of uniform thickness. It may or may not take part in ornamentation of the spore wall. In the former case it either forms only the base of the sculpture element (*Polytrichum* and *Astomum*) or the entire element.

(*iv*) *Perine.* It is the outermost spore wall layer which is fourth in number when the separating layer is present. It is extremely opaque, homogenous and yellowish in colour. In some genera the perine forms the entire structural element whereas, in others in which the exine forms the entire structural element, the perine forms a thin surface layer covering the exine.

(*v*) *Aperture region.* Mc Claymount and Larson (164) reported that the moss spores do not externally exhibit a distinguishable aperture area but many of them including *Funaria* and *Polytrichum* show a marked thickening of intine on one side of the spore wall. There is a corresponding reduction in exine thickening in this region. This spot is interpreted as a defined region for protonemal emergence when the spore germinates.

Germination of moss spore. The spore has a thin wall. Falling on a suitable soil it germinates. Germination is light dependent. Moss spores do not germinate in the dark in nature. Germination involves two steps. The first step involves uptake of water by the spore, increase in size, cracking of exine and reappearance of green pigment in the plastids. The second stage which depends on photosynthesis is characterized by emergence of a germ papilla which turns green, grows in length and divides by septa to form a short filament of green cells. Except *Sphagnum* and *Andreaea* in which the green filament forms a thalloid protonema, most commonly the filament grows apically and branches freely to form a green, branched alga-like filament called the *primary protonema.* It represents the juvenile stage of moss gametophyte. The leafy gametophore which represents the adult stage and bears the sex organs arises as a lateral outgrowth from the protonema. A number of leafy gametophores arise from the protonema of one spore in contradistinction to the liverworts in which one spore produces a single sporeling that passes into an adult plant. It is a continuous process.

COMPARISON BETWEEN LIVERWORTS AND MOSSES

It may be discussed under two heads, resemblances and differences as follows. The differences between the two groups are many and pronounced. The resemblances are very few and of a general nature.

(a) Resemblances. The points in which the liverworts resemble the mosses are :

1. The pattern of life history in both is *diplohaplontic*. It is characterized by heterologous type of alternation of generations and sporogenic meiosis.

2. Early segmentation of archegonial mother cell is essentially similar.

3. Meristematic tissue is absent in the sporogonium of both but it is present in the horn worts.

4. The conspicuous phase in the life cycle is the gametophyte. It is long lived and independent as compared with the sporophyte.

5. The sperms are biflagellate and the flagella are of whiplash type.

6. Calyptra is present in both.

(*b*) **Differences**

Liverworts	Mosses
1. *Protonema*: The development of gametophyte from a spore is a continuous process.	1. The development of gametophyte from a spore is not a continuous process. It passes through two distinct stages namely, (*i*) spore to protonema constituting the *juvenile stage*, and (*ii*) development of a leafy shoot representing the *adult stage* as a lateral outfgrowth from the protonema.
2. The spore, on germination, produces a single sporeling which passes into an adult gametophyte plant.	2. The spore, on germination, produces an extensively branched green filamentous protonema. A number of leafy gametophyte plants arise from it. *Sphagnum* in which a single gametophyte palnt arises from a thallose protonema is an exception.
3. The protonema, when present, is small, inconspicuous and transitory.	3. It is conspicuous and relatively persistent or long-lived.
4. *Gametophyte plant* : The plant body is typically dorsiventral, thalloid or foliose.	4. It is typically radial and always leafy.
5. Internally there is no differentiation of the central conducting strand. Takakia and Haplomitrium are the only exceptions.	5. There is differentiation of a central conducting strand.
6. Leaves, when present, lack a midrib. The leaf growth is by and large intercalary.	6. Except *Sphagnum*, the leaf, as a rule, has a midrib. Leaf growth is by the activity of an apical cell.
7. The rhizoids are unicellular and unbranched.	7. The rhizoids are multicellular and branched.
8. *Sex organs* : The development of sex organs is intocalary and not apical.	8. The early development of sex organs is by the activity of a clearly defined apical cell.
9. The antheridia vary in form from subglobose through ovoid to ellipsoid.	9. Except *Sphagnum* the antheridia are much longer, narrow and club-shaped in form.
10. *Sporophyte* : The early growth of embryo sporophyte is by successive transverse cleavage and thus intercalary.	10. Except *Sphagnum*, the early development of embryo sporophyte is biapical.
11. The hepatic seta is soft, pellucid and without any internal differentiation.	11. Except *Sphagnum* and *Andreaea,* the moss seta is fairly long and tough with a well developed hypodermis and a central strand.
12. Sporophyte breaks through the calyptra at a late stage (only when the spores are ripe) by the lengthening of the seta.	12. Except *Sphagnum* sporophyte breaks through the calyptra at an early stage by the lengthening of the seta.
13. The hepatic capsule is simple in organisation. It lacks the basal apophysis region and terminal operculum region of moss capsule and represents only the middle spore-producing theca region.	13. The moss capsule is highly organised both externally as well as internally. Externally it is differentiated into, (*i*) the basal photosynthetic *apophysis region*, (*ii*) middle fertile *theca region* and (*iii*) terminal *operculum region*.
14. The capsule lacks stomata on the capsule wall. There is no air space within.	14. Except *Sphagnum* and *Andreaea*, the moss capsule has stomata on the capsule wall. There are one or two air spaces as well.
15. There is no annulus.	15. Annulus is present in most of the moss capsules. It assists in the detachment of lid.
16. The hepatic capsule lacks columella.	16. Columella is, as a rule, present in moss capsules.
17. Elaters are generally present to facilitate spore dispersal.	17. The elaters, as a rule, are absent. The dispersal of spores is controlled by the peristome.
18. The entire endothecium is devoted to the formation of spores and elaters.	18. Except *Sphagnum*, the outermost layer of endothecium is devoted to the formation of spores and the rest produces the columella.

DISTINCTIVE FEATURES OF MOSSES

1. The moss plant is **radially** symmetrical and differentiated into **stem** and **leaves.**
2. Internally the stem shows a certain amount of tissue differentiation into the **cortex** and the **conducting strand**. There is however no true vascular system.
3. The gametophyte invariably consists of two growth stages. These are the **protonema stage** and the **leafy gametophore stage.**
4. The upright leafy gametophore (moss plant) is not dichotomously branched. The branching is invariably **monopodial.** The lateral branches are never **axillary.** Each arises from below a leaf.
5. The gemtophore usually grows by means of a single **apical cell** which is pyramidal in shape.
6. With the exception of *Sphagnum*, the moss leaf usually has a **midrib.**
7. The cell walls are reported to consist mainly of **hemicelluloses** and **pentosanes.** Cellulose is rarely found.
8. The rhizoids which anchor the moss plant to the substratum are **multicellular** and **branched.** The septa between the cells are **oblique.**
9. The sex organs are **stalked** and the stalks are longer than those of other bryophytes.
10. Early growth of the sex organs is by means of an **apical cell.**
11. The venter of the archegonium is much more **massive** than in the liverworts.
12. The sporophyte is more elaborate and complex and shows high degree of **specialisation** and **sterilisation.**
13. With the exception of *Sphagnum* early growth of the sporophyte is by means of an **apical cell.**
14. Except *Sphagnum* the **archesporium** is differentiated from the outer layer of the endothecium and differentiates into spores. There are no **elaters.**
15. Except *Andreaea* the capsule usually dehisces by the separation of a **lid.**
16. Except *Sphagnum, Andreaea* and some reduced forms of true mosses, peristome is present in all.

CLASSIFICATION

Smith divides the class Bryopsida or Musci into three groups giving each the status of a sub-class. These are the (*i*) Sphagnobrya, (*ii*) Andreaeobrya and (*iii*) Eubrya.

The older bryologists such as Bower, Campbell, Wattestien, and others divide the class into three groups but they give each of these groups the rank of an order as follows :

(*i*) Sphagnales.

(*ii*) Andreales.

(*iii*) Bryales.

Reimers (1954) recognized five sub-classes as follows :

1. Sub-class Sphagnidae comprising a single order *Sphagnales* explanations have been advanced for.
2. Sub-class Andreaeidae. It includes one order *Andreales* with a single family.
3. Sub-class Bryidae. It comprise twelve orders.
4. Sub-class Buxbaumidae with a single order *Buxbaumiales* with two families.

5. Sub-class Polytrichidae comprising two orders (*Polytrichales* and *Dawsoniales*) each with a single family.

Some bryologists including Parihar divide the class Bryopsida into the following three sub-classes:

Sub-class I. Sphagnidae. It is characterized by thallose protonema, globular sporogonium elevated on a stalk-like, leafless gametophytic structure, the pseudopodium, seta absent, columella roofed over by the dome-shaped spore sac, opening of the capsule by the separation of a lid, calyptra present, no peristome.

Sub-class II. Andreaeidae. The diagnostic features are ribbon-shaped protonema, elongate sporogonium elevated on a pseudopodium, columella roofed over by the spore sac, calyptra massive, capsule dehisces by longitudinal slits but the valves remain united at the tip, no peristome.

Sub-class III. Bryidae. It is equivalent to Bryales of the older bryologists and Eubrya of Smith. The distinguishing features are the filamentous protonema, sporogonium elevated on a seta, spore sac in the form of hollow cylinder around the columella, capsule opens by a lid, calyptra well developed, except some of the reduced forms, peristome is present in all.

Buck and Goffinet (2000) have excluded liverworts and hornworts under division Marchantiophyta and Anthocerotophyta respectively. Thus, for remaing mosses, they have assigned to division Bryophyta. In comparison to division Marchantophyta (all liverworts) and Division Anthocecerotophyta (all hornworts), the last division Bryophyta (all mosses) is biggest one. It has been divided in five classes; (A) Takakiopsida, (B) Sphagnopsida, (C) Andreaeopsida, (D) Andreaeobryopsida, (E) Polytrychopsida. Among five aforesaid classes of division Bryophyta, the class Andreaeopsida has been divided in four subclasses : (i) Diphysciidae, (ii) Funariidae, (iii) Dicranidae, (iv) Bryidae.

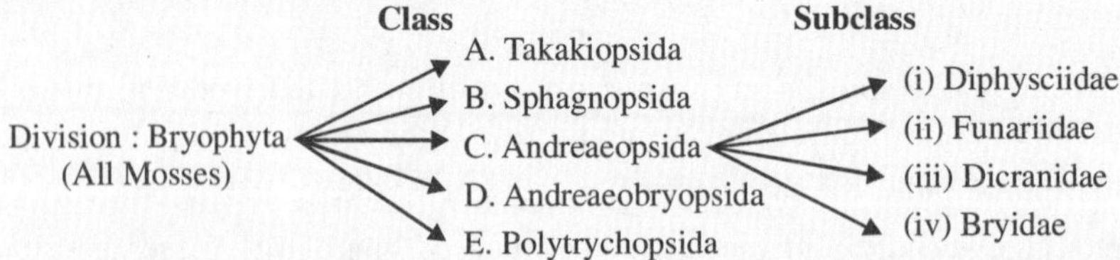

QUESTIONS

ESSAY TYPE

1. List the distinctive features of the class Bryopsida (Musci or the Mosses).
2. Give a concise account of the various vegetative methods of multiplication met with in the Mosses.
3. What is apospory? Does this phenomenon throw any light on the nature of the two generations in the life cycle of a moss plant?
4. In what respects do the Mosses differ from the other Bryophytes?
5. Write an essay on vegetative reproduction in the Bryophytes.
6. Describe different types of peristome structures met within mosses. Discuss taxonomic importance of peristome. *(Kanpur, M.Sc. 1993)*
7. What is peristome? Discuss the structural variations of peristome in mosses with suitable examples and diagrams. *(Kanpur, M.Sc. 1995)*
8. Enumerate the taxonomic features of Mosses and attempt to evolve a simple system of classification based on a dichotomous key. *(Rohilkhand, M.Sc. 1998)*

9. Write an account of the mechanism of spore dispersal in mosses. *(Punjab, 1992)*
10. Give an account of Protonema differentiation in Mosses and factors influencing induction of buds *(Lucknow, M.Sc., 2007)*
11. Briefly discuss imporatnce of Peristone in systematics of Musce *(Lucknow, M.Sc., 2007)*

SHORT ANSWER TYPE

12. **Comment upon the following :**
    (*i*) Moss protonema and induction of buds on Moss protonema. *(Awadh, M.Sc. 2000)*
    (*ii*) Distribution of mosses
    (*iii*) Classification of Bryopsida upto order level. *(Poorvanchal, M.Sc. 2002)*
13. Draw well labelled diagrams of peristomial teeth. *(Lucknow, 1995, 1997)*
14. Write short notes on
    (*a*) Spore discharge mechanism in Mosses *(Kumaon, 1997)*
    (a_1) Taxonomic importance of Peristone. *(Allahabad, M.Sc. 1999)*
    (*b*) Peristome/Peristomial teeth *(Kanpur, 1999, 2001; Purvanchal, 1996; Gorakhpur 1991, 1992, 1993, 1999; Lucknow 1997, 1998, 2000, 2001; Kerala 1998, 2000; Bundelkhand, 1993, Punjab, 1993, Himachal Pradesh, 1997)*
    (*c*) Spore dispersal in mosses *(Rohilkhand, M.Sc. 1990; Awadh, 1991)*
    (*d*) Protonema in Bryidae *(Rohilkhand, M.Sc. 1995)*
    (*e*) Protonema *(Rohilkhand, M.Sc. 2003; Kanpur, 1997, 1999; Awadh, 1993; Gorakhpur, 1991, 1995; Lucknow, 1999, 1997;Purvanchal, 1997; Kerala, 1998, 2000; Bangalore, 2000; Himachal Pradesh, 1996, 1999)*
    (*f*) Mode of conduction of water in Mosses. *(Kanpur, M.Sc. 2004)*
    (*g*) General characters of Bryopsida
    (*h*) Structure of Protonema *(Kerala, 1996)*
    (*i*) Dispersal mechanism of seeds in Moss *(Poorvanchal, 2005)*
15. Give structure and function of peristome. *(Lucknow, 1993, 1994)*
16. Define Protonema. What does it represent? *(Calicut, 2001)*
17. What is the role of protonema in the life history of Moss plant? *(Kerala, 1996)*
18. What are peristomial teeth? *(Ajmer, 1998)*
19. With the help of diagrams write the characteristics of rhizoids in liverworts and mosses. *(Lucknow, 2004)*
20. Which genus has largest spore among hepaticopsida and bryopsida ? *(Poorvanchal, M.Sc. 1998)*
21. Autherozoids of Moss always enter archegonia. Explain. *(Kanpur, 2009)*

OBJECTIVE TYPE

22. **Fill in the blanks :**
    (*i*) Moss protonema differs from the filament of alga by ________ .
    (*ii*) The gametophyte in mosses have ________ stages.
    (*iii*) The rhizoids in mosses are ________ and ________ .
    (*iv*) When two kinds of sex organs are borne on separate branches of the same plant, such mosses are called ________ .
    (*v*) Conducting strands in mosses are called ________ .
    (*vi*) The teeth like structures in capsule of mosses are termed ________ .
    (*vii*) The sporophyte in mosses are partially ________ .

(*viii*) Elaters are absent in ________________ .

(*ix*) Juvenile stage in mosses is called ___________ .

(*x*) ______________is called juvenile stage of gametophyte in__________.

23. Select the correct answer :

(*i*) The conducting strand in mosses is

(*a*) Cortex (*b*) Medulla

(*c*) Xylem (*d*) Epidermis.

(*ii*) The juvenile stage in mosses is known as

(*a*) Filament (*b*) Spore

(*c*) Hypha (*d*) Protonema.

(*iii*) The sperms in mosses are

(*a*) Uniflagellate

(*b*) Biflagellate with tinsel and whiplash flagella

(*c*) Biflagellate with whiplash flagella

(*d*) A flagellate.

(*iv*) The sporophyte in mosses is

(*a*) Independent completely

(*b*) Independent partially

(*c*) Dependent completely

(*d*) Absent.

(*v*) Rhizoids in Mosses are

(*a*) Branched but unicellular

(*b*) Unbranched unicellular

(*c*) Branched and unicellular

(*d*) Simple and tuberculate

(*vi*) Gametophyte in Mosses is

(*a*) Thalloid

(*b*) Leafy

(*c*) Protonemal and leafy

(*d*) Filamentous only.

(*vii*) Mosses are

(*a*) Monoecious

(*b*) Dioecious

(*c*) Monoecious and dioceious

(*d*) Neither monoecious nor dioecious.

(*viii*) The rhizoids, gemmae, protonema and sex organs are produced on

(*a*) Gametophyte

(*b*) Sporophyte

(*c*) Capsule

(*d*) None of the above.

(*ix*) The stem of mosses differs from that of mustard in the absence of

(*a*) Epidermis

(*b*) Cortex

(*c*) Vascular system

(*d*) All of the above.

(*x*) Which one of the following is a saprophytic moss ?

(*a*) *Cryptothallus* (*b*) *Sphagnum*

(*c*) *Buxbaumia* (*d*) *Pogonatum*

Image of *Takakia*

CHAPTER 15

TAKAKIIDAE : Takakiales : Takakia

- Characteristic Features
- Distribution and Habitat
- Gametophyte
- Reproduction
- Sporophyte
- Phylogenetic Importance

Udar (1976) believed that *Takakia* is held to be nearest to the ancestors of Hepaticopsida because at that time the genus was known and recognised only by the female gametophyte. The structure, development and dehiscence of antheridia and sporophyte were unknown. After the discovery of antheridia and sporophyte, *Takakia* is held to be the ancestors of class Bryopsida (Musci) and occupies a separate rank of sub-class Takakiidae, having single order Takakilaes and single family Takakiaceae which is monogeneric (Higuchi and Zhang 1998). The characteristic features of Takakiaceae has been described below :

CHARACTERISTIC FEATURES

The small bright, green radially and freely branched symmetrical gametophytes are rhizomatous like the Calobryales (Also see chapter-12). From the creeping pale yellow, leafless rhizome arise negatively geotropic, erect, green leafy shoots 1—1.5 cm tall.

These are known as the **gametophores**. Sometimes a newly formed stoloniferous branch from the rhizome may creep over the substratum for sometime and then suddenly turn upwards giving rise to a solitary erect leafy axis. Both the rhizome and the leafy shoots are destitute of rhizoids. The thick, fleshy, terete soft textured gametophore axis bears green leaf-like appendages in a 3-ranked phyllotaxy. The spirally arranged leaf-like appendages are thick, fleshy, terete and isophyllous. They are small and remote below but larger and contiguous above. These are either undivided but more frequently 2—or 3—4 fid to the very base. These leaf segments usually called the **phyllids** are fleshy, straight to arcuate and incurved. The gametophyte bears slime papillae of two types. One type are non-beaked and axillary in position 1-2 per leaf (Fig. 15.2 C). The second type are beaked and occur on the stolons only. The gametophytes are heterothallic. The strongly elongated antheridial form and the very short stalks are similar to mosses. The development of an ill-defined "cap" or lid is also similar to mosses. The archegonia on the female plants occur singly, occasionally 2 or 3 juxtaposed, scattered and not in 'inflorescences'. The archegonium is intra-axillary in position with respect to a so-called leaf, sometimes lateral. The greenish archegonia are plump with a massive neck which is not very long. It consists of 6 rows of neck cells. The venter is fleshy. The haploid number of chromosomes is $n = 4$ or $n = 5$

The young developing sporophyte, which has distinct tapered **foot** (penetrating in gametophytic tissue), erect stout **seta** and elliptical **capsule**, is protected by **vaginula** at base and reminant part of Calyptra at apex. The peripheral cells of young **seta** and epidermal layer of capsule wall possess chlorophyll. Thus sporophyte in early stage of development is autotrophic. The mature sporophyte is stout and persistant. The seta elongates by mitotic cell division (not by cell-elongation as in liverworts) before the maturity of capsule. The capsule has no operculum, apophysis, theca, peristome teeth. The capsule is thick in middle region and tapered at anterior and posterior side. The presence of columella, which is short, 3/4 of capsular cavity, and overarched by sporogenous tissue is moss like. The elaters or pseudoelaters are absent (strictly moss like feature). The stomata are absent on the surface of capsule wall. The dehiscence of capsule is by a longitudinal slit appearing in middle region and gradually extending at upper and lower regions. The slit is formed by the weaker suture cells at (surface) epidermal wall of capsule where thickening is poorly developed. The spores are dispersed passively (very slowly) as seta and capsule both show twisting at maturity.

FAMILY TAKAKIACEAE

The family Takakiaceae is represented by a single genus *Takakia* which includes two species. *T. lepidozioides* and *T. ceratophylla*. The former was discovered by Hattori and Inoue (1958) and the latter by Grolle (1963), Smith and Davison (1993) and Higuchi and Zhang (1994).

TAKAKIA

Distribution and Habitat

T. lepidozioides was first dicovered by Hattori and Inoue (1958) from the alpine zone of Japanese Alps at an altitude of 2400—2800 m growing on rocks, crevices and humus 1—2 cm thick over androcyte rocks which were kept cool and wet by melting snow. In Northern Borneo it was collected at an altitude of 3000 m from the moist shady habitats. Besides, it was reported from Aleutian island and Hyperoceanic portions of British Columbia. The second species *T. ceratophylla* was reported from the pools in Sikkim in Eastern Himalayas (India) at an altitude of 3800 m and from Yuman Province of China at 3750 m alt.. It has also been recorded from the Aleutian islands growing on moist soil, in ditches and on the banks of streams. Both the species thus grow in cool, moist or wet shady places at higher altitudes. They are hygrophytes. However *T. ceratophylla* grows under less wet conditions than *T. lepidozioides*.

GAMETOPHYTE (FIG.15.1)

It is bright green and is differentiated into a cylindrical, branched, creeping, leafless rhizome-like structure from which arise the aerial, erect, negatively geotropic radially symmetrical leafy shoots, the *gametophores* about 1—1.5 cm tall. Sometimes a newly formed branch from the rhizome grows horizontally for a short distance and then turns up giving rise to a solitary, erect leafy axis, the **gametophore** (A). Both the rhizome and the leafy axes are completely devoid of rhizoids. Instead from the base of erect gametophore (*T. lepidozioides*) may arise one or more vertically descending leafless branches which grow downward into the substratum. These positively geotropic, leafless axes are variously termed as "flagella" or "stolons". Crubs (1970) thought it fit to call them "roots". The gametophore axis is terete, rather thick, fleshy and soft-textured. Thus it cannot withstand drought. The leaf-like appendages borne on the erect gametophore axis are unique in form. In earlier accounts they were termed "**phyllids**". Schuster (1967) used the term "polymorphous leaves" for them. They are isophyllous and are produced in a spiral manner from the shoot tip which grows by the activity of a 3 sided apical cell. The leaves are arranged in 3-ranked phyllotaxy. Lower down on the gametophore axis they are small and remote but higher up they become larger and contiguous (A). The leaves are, at first, transversely inserted on the axis but with maturity become obliquely displaced.

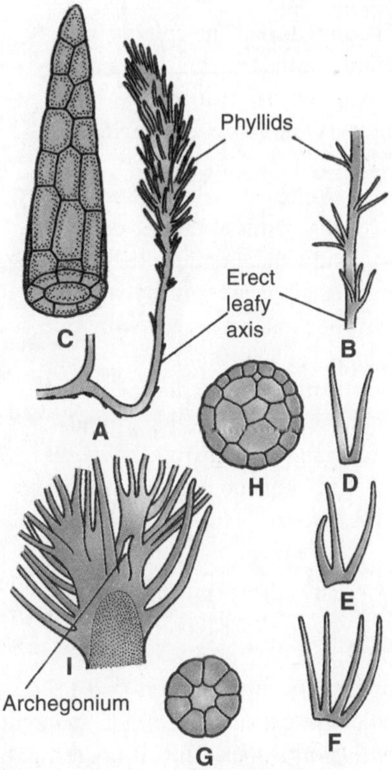

Phyllids
Erect leafy axis
Archegonium
A B C D E F G H I

Fig. 15.1. (A—I) ***Takakia*** sp. A, rhizomatous gametophore of *T. ceratophylla*; B, portion of gametophore of *T. lepidoziodies* with phyllids; C, a single undivided phyllid; D, E, F, bifid, trifid and quadrified phyllids respectively; G, T.S. simple phyllid; H, T.S. phyllid of complex construction; I, archegonial shoot (A, C based on Grolle; B, D—E, after Hattori and Mizuttani; F, H, I, after Schuster).

According to Schuster (1967) each leaf (Fig. 15.1) is forked right to the base into two (D) three (E) or four (F) segments which often are so nearly independent and apparently arise at some distance apart that Hattori and Mizutani (1958) considered each leaf segment to be a simple or undivided leaf which they termed a **phyllid** (C). The terete segments are multistratose, solid and fleshy. Each gradually tapers towards the apex ending in a short, bluntly conical cell (C).

Anatomy of leaf (Fig. 15.1 G—H). Excepting the tip region the segments are 3—5 cells thick. They gradually taper towards the apex ending in a short bluntly conical cell (C). The cells are parenchymatous and contain chloroplasts. In a cross section above and near the middle the leaf segments of *T. lepidozioides* have only one big medullary cell much larger than the surrounding single layered cortical cells (G). In the lower half of the leaf segment the number of medullary or axillary cell row varies from 2 to several (usually 5 rows). The central strand of medullary cells is always surrounded by a single layered cortex of cells smaller in size (H).

Stem anatomy (Fig. 15.2 E). A cross section of *Takakia* stem revealed that it consists of two zones; outer cortical region surrounding the inner medullary region. The cortical region is chlorophyllose. It is 1—2 stratose thick and consists of slightly to strongly thick-walled cortical cells with brownish walls. The medullary region shows differentiation into a small central core of small-celled tissue constituting an ill-defined or feebly defined vestigial **central strand** surrounded by thick-walled, somewhat larger celled **medulla**. The cells of the central strand, having lost their protoplasmic contents, are empty. They are colourless, elongated and have delicate walls. With electron microscope, the walls of these empty cells, especially their end wall have been seen to possess many small plasmodesmata derived pores. Hebant (1975) remarked, "the occurrence of a specialized central water conducting strand in the gametophytes of *Takakia* is significant because most contemporary Hepaticae lack such a strand".

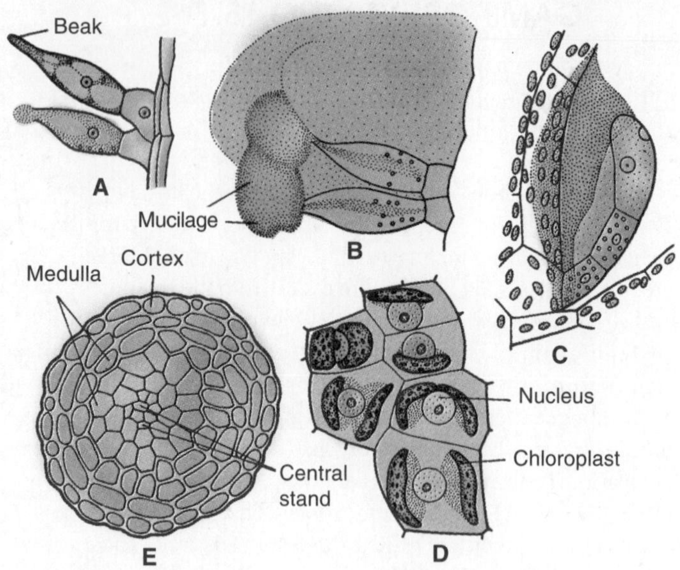

Fig. 15.2. (A—E). ***Takakia*** sp. A, beaked 'open' slime papillae (immature); B, mature beaked 'open' slime papillae; C, stalked "closed" slime papillae; D, cells from the leaf primordia showing chloroplasts & nuclei; E, T.S. aerial stem (A—D after Proskauer).

Oil bodies (Fig. 15.3 H). In *T. lepidozioides* several minute (1-5 μm in diameters) spherical, apparently homogenous oil bodies are present in leaf and stem cortical cells. In *T. ceratophylla* only epidermal leaf cells have few 2-5 oil bodies. The oil-bodies, in both species, are smaller than chloroplasts. Some Bryologists believe them as "lipid droplets". However, Asakawa *et.al.* (1979) found the presence of sesquiterpenes in oil-bodies of *Takakia* which is a normal component of liverworts (Hepatics).

Slime papillae. Proskauer (1962) reported the occurrence of slime papillae on the axes of *Takakia*. These are of two types, (*i*) non-beaked and (ii) beaked slime papillae.

(*i*) *Non-beaked slime papillae* (Fig. 15.2 C). These occur singly on the erect shoots in or near the leaf axils. The non-beaked slime papillae in *T. ceratophylla* consist of a 2 celled short filament (C). The lower cell functions as the **stalk cell**. The upper or distal cell is the mucilage secreting cell. The mucilage is secreted through its wall. It is not perforated. For this reason they are also called the "closed" slime papillae. The non-beaked slime papillae in *T. lepidozioides* consist of a short filament of usually 2—4 occasionally 5—6 cells. The mucilage is secreted through the wall of the distal cell.

(*ii*) *Beaked slime papillae* (15.2 A—B). These occur both on the leafy and leafless axes in small to large clusters. Each beaked slime papilla in the cluster consists of a slender, flask-shaped distal cell supported on a 2 or more-celled stalk. At maturity the distal, flask-shaped cell becomes beaked. The beak has an opening or aperture at its tip through which mucilage is secreted.

Reproduction

It takes place by two methods.

1. Vegetative reproduction. In *T. lepidozioides* the freely eadicpis leaves and very brittle shoots in *T. Ceratophylla* the upper portion of shorts help in vegetative reproduction. These parts are taken away to new locality either by wind or water where they propagate and form new populations.

2. Sexual reproduction. It is rather rare sexually it is dioecious or heterothallic. In external morphology, there is no differences among starile, male or female plants.

(*a*) *Antheridia.* (Fig. 15.3, A-G) They are found in axil of (3) —4 lobed leaves (The axillary position of antheridium is same as in Calobryales and Jungermonniales). They are obelavate to ellipsoidal in shape and bright orange in colour. The stalk of antheridium is ill-demarkated and is made up of 3—4 ties of 4 cells each. The dehiscence of antheridium is via an ill defined cap or lid. The development of antheridium is in centrifugal pattern, where apical cell is not utilized or consumed in its formation, leading to further growth of male shoot subsequently the formation of another crop of antheridia.

(*b*) *Archegonia.* The female plant produces a single archegonium (Fig. 15.1, I), occasionally 2—3 irregularly scattered archegonia. Neither the archegonia have any clear relationship to the insertion of leaves nor do they involve the apical cell in their formation. The archegonium is naked (without any protective structures around it), plump, large; green when young and stalked. The archegonial neck is not unduly long. It consists of six rows of neck cells (Inoue, 1961) and not four as reported by Hattori and Mizutani 1958). The venter is fleshy. It becomes 2 stratose prior to fertilization. The sporophyte is unknown.

(*c*) *Fertilization.* In requires water for the movement of antherozoids. As in *Takakia* the archegonia are naked and neither protected by perianthal bracts (female bracts) nor by perianth that also fasalitating in movement of antherozoids to reach in vicinily of archegonium and finally leading to fertilization (as in Calbryales, Jungermanniales and leafy Metzgeriales). The fertilization in rather rare. It has been observed that sporophyte formation antheria. It is estimated that this ratio (Sporophyte : antheridial shoots) is 1 : 100.

Sporophyte

The sporophyte (Fig. 15.3, I–M; Fig. 15.4, A–I) has distinct three parts, (i) Foot (ii) Seta and (iii) Capsule. The young developing sporophyte needs protection which is provided by two gametophytic coverings that develop after the fertilization. These protective coverings are:

(i) Vaginula (as found in **Andreaea** sp.);

(ii) Calyptra

The lower part of young sporophyte (foot and major portion of seta) is protected by vaginula whereas upper part of capsule and some part–c of seta is protected by calyptra. The calyptra is 1-3 stratose, cucullate, smooth, transparent and evanescent that torns loose from the gametophytic plant and borne upward on the elongating sporophyte. This delicate calyptra, in early stage, closely invests the enlarging capsule and frequently sheds off before the maturation of capsule. In this feature it resembles with *Sphagnum* and *Andreaea*. The pseudopodium is absent in *Takakia*.

The development of sporophyte is sub-synchronous (Smith and Davison, 1993) or not synchronous (Higuchi and Zhang, 1998). In liverworts the development of sporophyte is strictly synchronous (the development and maturation of whole sporophyte in a fixed period) and in hornworts it is strictly non-synchronous (the development of capsule continues from Meristematic zone where as maturation of capsule strats from its tip. It results that developing young spores and mature spores are found within in same capsule).

Foot is well developed, tapered into the apex, penetrating into the gametophytic mineral nutrients. The food consists of terminal quadrate cells with dense protoplasm and upper elongated thin-walled cells.

Seta is erect, straight and stout, well developed and becoming slightly twisted at maturity that helps in dispersal of spores in all directions. In anatomy, seta is massive *i.e.*, several cells across the diametre. The peripheral 1-2(3) strata have thick-walled cells enclosing cells of seta contain chlorophyll which help in photosynthesis (a feature similar to mosses) the development of seta is clearly mosslike *i.e.*, it elongates by cell division (not by cell elongation as reported in liver worts). The other remarkable feature is that the sporogenesis takes place after seta elongation (in *Calobryum*, *Haplomitrium* and *Monoclea*, sporogenesis takes place prior to sets elongation).

Capsule is schizocarpous erect, elliptical, green in early stage of development due to presence of chlorophyll in surface wall-cells. Thus, sporophyte is autotrophic in nature. The capsule is thick in middle region and symmetrically tapered at base and apex. There is no operculum, theca and apophysis. The peristome teeth are absent. The stomata, on the surface of capsule, are also absent. Within the cavity of capsule, there is present short, rather less developed, cylindric, consisting or 3-4 layers of thin walled cells columella (moss like character) the columella, which extends upto 3/4 inner space of capsule) is over arched by sporogenous tissue. The elaters are absent (moss like character). The spores are arranged all around the columella. The spores are brown, papillose on distal face, slightly roughened tetrahedral and have a triradiate mark on proximal surfaces which is rather smooth in comparison to distal face. The capsule wall is multistratose and consists of an epidermal layer of cells (which are pigmented and thick-walled) and 4-5 layers of thin walled cells (which are not pigmented).

PHYLOGENETIC IMPORTANCE OF *TAKAKIA*

Before the discovery of antheridia and sporophyte, it was generally held that *Takakia* is an exceedingly primitive genus and thus is considered nearest the ancestors of Hepaticae. Such a viewpoint is supported by a number of primitive features which *Takakia* possesses. These are : (*i*) its disjunct distribution; (*ii*) simple radial organziation with no differentiation yet into typical leaves; (*iii*) exogenous and intercalary mode of branching, (*iv*) polymorphous leaves with a unique leaf form; (*v*) lack of drought resistance; (*vi*) presence of slime papillae; (*vii*) total absence of rhizoids; (*viii*) primitive type of structure of the sex organ (archegonium); and (*ix*) lowest haploid chromosome number which is n=4 in *T. lepidozioides* or n =5 in *T. Ceratophylla.* All the features enumerated above denote that *Takakia* is an exceedingly primitive genus and leads one to the conclusion that it is nearest to the ancestral stock of liverworts. Tatuno (1958) postulated that n=4 is the original base number of the Hepaticae and the common number 9 characteristic of other groups of liverworts (rarely 10 and 11) is derivative and at the diploid level. Some investigators thus consider *Takakia* truly at the haploid level. It represents relics of a race that seems to have died out. Mehra (1969) remarked "*Takakia* is a living fossil in the Hepaticae. The Calobryales and foliose Jungermanniales are off shoots from ancestors like *Takakia* but at the diploid level."

After the discovery of sporophyte of *Takakia*, which shows affinities with mosses *(Andreaeobryum microsporum)*, suggest its better placement in class Bryopsida. The affinities of *Takakia* with class Bryopsida (mosses) are (i) The presence of columella, (ii) The young developing sporophyte is protected at basal region by vaginula and at upper region by calyptra, (iii) The presence of chlorophyll in young seta and capsule. (iv) The elongation of seta by mitotic cell division before the maturity of capsule, (v) The twisting of seta consisting of thick-walled cells at peripheral region, (iv) the tapered foot, (vii) The long term of the release of spores, (viii) The stoutness and persistence of sporophyte, (ix) The absence of elaters.

Based on the above mentioned affinities, Smith and Division (1993) have grouped three genera viz. *Andreaea*, *Andreaobryum* and *Takakia* in a separate class "Andreaeopsida. This class has been divided in two subclasses: (i) Sub class- Andreaeidae for the genus Andreaea, (ii) Sub class-Takakiidae for '*Andreaeobryum* and *Takakia.* Where as Higuchi and Zhang (1998) are of the same opinion to place *Takakia* with in mosses but with a little modication. They recognised the old rank of mosses as class Musci under division Bryophyta. The class Musci has been divided in four Sub classes : (i) Sub class - Takakiidae, (ii) Subclass - Andreaeiedae, (iii) Subclass - Sphagnidae, (iv) Subclass -Bryidae. On the other hand Schuster (1997), based on the affinities of *Takakia* with liverworts and mosses, gave different openion to place the genus in a system of classification. He has discussed the plesiomorphic (old, primitive and archaic characters) and apomorphic advanced

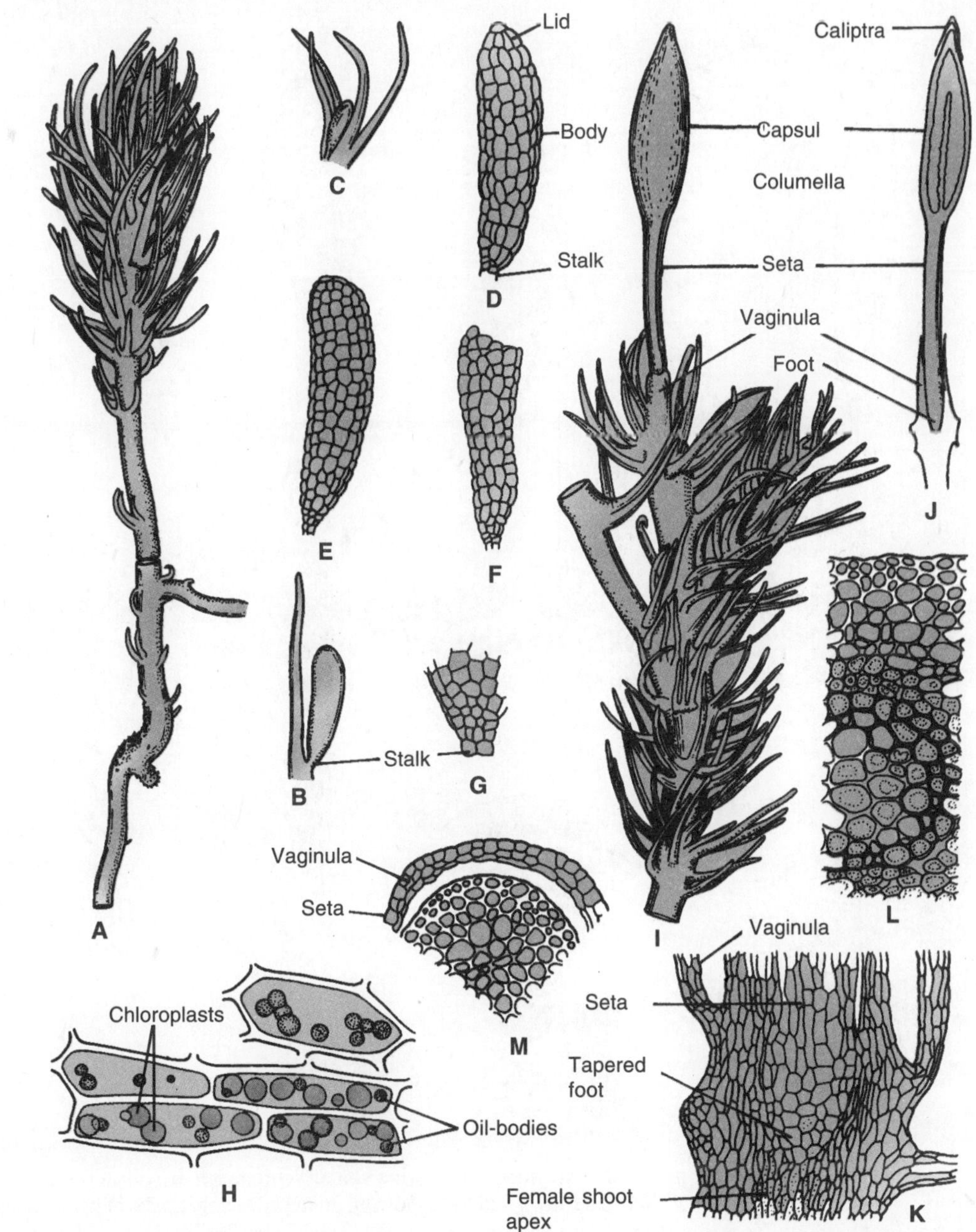

Fig. 15.3 (A-M). *Takakia sp.* A, Male plant showing antheridia; B,C, Antheridium in axil of leaf; D, A mature antheridium, ; E, F, Dehisced antheridium; G, Babal part of antheridium; H, Leaf cells with oil-bodies; I, Female plant with young sporophyte; J, L.S. of sporophyte; K, L.S. of female shoot apex showing tapered embedded foot; L,T.S. of foot surrounded by gametophytic tissue of female shoot apex; M, T.S. of upper region of vaginula with seta.

and acquired characters) features of *Takakia*. He wrote," ultimately, consideration of all the available evidence suggests that Takakia is a "basal" genus in the bryophytes; and its diffuse affinities to *Haplomitrium* on one hand, *Andreaeobryum* on the other, prohibit placing it in either Hepaticopsida or Bryopsida *s. lat*". He supported to the concept to create a new separate, autonomous class Takakiopssida. Moreover, he is not of the openion to divide bryophytes into two or more divisions

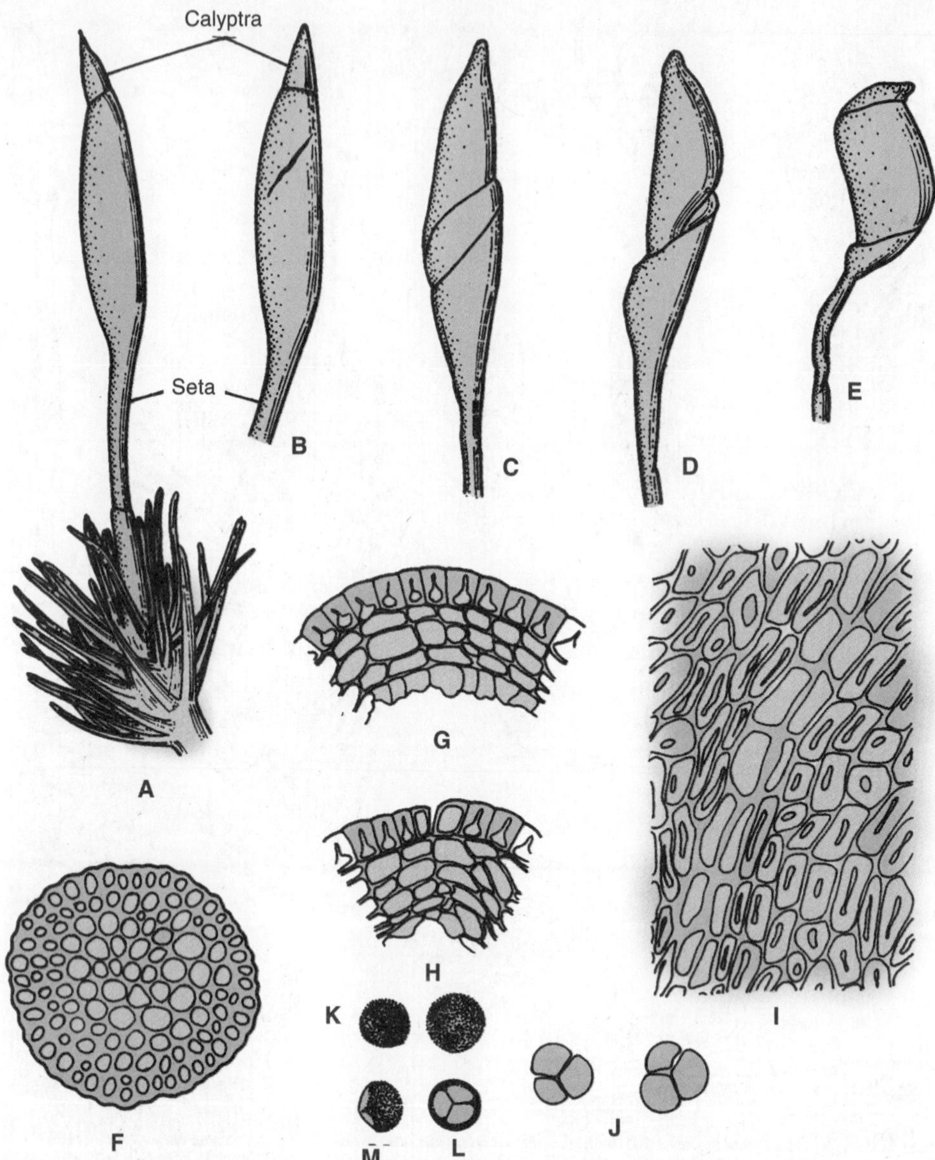

Fig. 15.4 (A-M) *Takakia sp.* A, part of female shoot apex with young sporophyte; B, capsule showing longitudinal slit below calptra; C, D, E, capsule along with seta showing gradual different stages of dehiscence; F, T.S. of seta; G, T.S. of Capsule wall showing thickening only in cells of epidermal (surface) layer; H, T.S. of capsule wall showing suture cells (weaker point without thickenings) of epidermal (surfaces) layer; S, surface view of capsule well showing two rows of suture cells, from where it forms longitudinal slit : J, young tertrahedral spoes; K, two spores from distal surface showing papillose exine; L, Spore from proximal surface showing triradiate mark; M, spore in lateral view.

as Marchantiophyta (liverworts), Anthocerotophyta (hornworts) and Bryophyta (mosses). He believes that in real sense, *Takakia* is just like "glue" that binds the bryophytes together. However in the present text book the authors believe that sporophytic characters of bryophytes are more reliable than gametophytic characters, where as among gametophytic characters, the reproductive characters are more reliable than simple vegetative characters. Hence, the placement of *Takakia* with in class Bryopsida is more suitable and tenable.

Systematic Position of Takakia

In old system of classification (Before the discovery of antheridia and sporophyte)

Division	:	Bryophyta
Class	:	Hepaticopsida (Hepaticae)
Order	:	Takakiles
Family	:	Takakiaceae
Genus	:	Takakia
Species	:	Lepidozioides

In recent system of classification (After the discovery of antheridia & sporophyte) Higuchi and Zhang 1998).

Division	:	Bryophyta
Class	:	Bryopsida (Musci)
Subclass	:	Takakiidae
Order	:	Takakiales
Family	:	Takakiaceae
Genus	:	Takakia
Species	:	Lipidozioides

QUESTIONS

ESSAY TYPE

1. Give an illustrated account of *Takakia.*
2. Describe the gametophyte of *Takakia.*
3. Describe the characteristic features, distribution and habitat of Takakiales.
4. With the help of suitable diagrams describe the sex organs of *Takakia.*
5. Write explanatory notes on systematic position of *Takakia* in the light of recent researches. *(Allahabad M.Sc., 2000)*
6. Discuss the systematic position of *Takakia.*

SHORT ANSWER TYPE

7. **Write short notes on :**
   (*a*) *Takakia*
   (Poorvanchal, Msc., 1998; Rohilkhand, M.Sc. 1995, 1997)
   (*b*) Affinities between Calobryales and Takakiales *(Rohilkhand M.Sc., 1993)*
   (*c*) Characteristic features of *Takakia*
   (*d*) Sex organs of *Takakia*
8. How will you distinguish *Calobryum* from *Takakia.*
9. Describe briefly the mechanism of dehiscence of capsule in *Takakia, Andreaea* and *sphagum*
   (Lucknow, M.Sc., 2006)
10. Answer briefly the mechanism of dehiscence of capsule of *Takakia* and *Andreae*
    (Lucknow, M.Sc., 2007)
11. Complete the mechanism of dehiscence of capsule in *Takakia* and *Calobryum*
    (Lucknow, M.Sc., 2004)
12. Distinguish between *Takakia* and
    (i) *Calobryum*
    (ii) *Andreae*
    (iii) *Sphagnum*

OBJECTIVE TYPE

13. **Select the correct answer :**

(*i*) To which family would you place *Takakia*?

(*a*) Ricciaceae
(*b*) Marchantiaceae
(*c*) Pelliaceae
(*d*) Takakiaceae

(*ii*) In Takakiales, the phyllotaxy is

(*a*) 1-ranked (*b*) 2-ranked
(*c*) 3-ranked (*d*) 4-ranked.

(*iii*) The gametophytes of Takakiales resemble those of

(*a*) Metzgeriales
(*b*) Jungermanniales
(*c*) Anthocerotales
(*d*) Calobryales.

(*iv*) *Takakia lepidozioides* was discovered by

(*a*) S.K. Pande
(*b*) Ram Udar
(*c*) Hattorri and Inoue
(*d*) R.M. Schuster.

(*v*) Sexually *Takakia* is

(*a*) Monoecious and homothalliic
(*b*) Monoecious and heterothalliic
(*c*) Dioecious and homothalliic
(*d*) Deoceious and heterothallic.

Image of *Sphagnum*

CHAPTER 16

SPHAGNIDAE
Sphagnales
Sphagnum

- General Characteristics
- Habitat
- Distribution
- Gemetophyte Phase
- Reproduction
- Sporophyte Phase
- Economic Importance
- Affinities or Relationships

GENERAL CHARACTERISTICS

The subclass-Sphagnidae includes the mosses which are often very important constituents of peat bog vegetation. Hence the name *peat* or the *bog* mosses. They grow in extensive masses on boggy and peaty soils and also as submerged aquatics in peaty pools. The subclass Sphagnidae is characterised by the following distinctive features:—

1. The simple, flat, plate-like thallose **protonema** is fixed to the substratum by numerous **rhizoids**.

2. The rhizoids are multicellular. The septa between the cells are oblique.

3. The upright, **leafy branch** originates from a single protonemal cell. It grows by means of a three-sided **apical cell** into the adult or mature plant, also called the **gametophore**.

4. Usually a single gametophore develops from one protonema.

5. The leaf of adult bog moss has a unique structure. It consists of two kinds of cells, the narrow, living, green **assimilatory cells** and the large, colourless, dead **capillary cells**.

6. The leaf has no **midrib**.

7. The antheridia occur singly and are **axillary** in position.

8. They develop on special **side branches**. The antheridial branches are relatively stronger than the vegetative shoots.

9. The archegonia are **terminal** in position. They occur in clusters of three usually at the apices of short **female branches** from among a crown at the top of the plant.

10. The mature sporogonium is differentiated into an enlarged **foot**, a rudimentary **constriction-like seta** and a large, rounded **capsule** which is globular in form.

11. The young capsule is invested by the calyptra.

12. The leafless, stalk-like **pseudopodium** carries the ripe sporogonium at its top.

13. The columella develops from the entire **endothecium**. It occupies the major part of the cavity of the capsule.

14. The **sporogenous tissue** develops from the inner layer of the **amphithecium**.

15. The central, hemispherical columella is capped by the domeshaped spore sac.

16. The ripe capsule dehisces by the separation of a disc-shaped **lid** or **operculum** at its top.

17. The peristome is absent.

18. The basic chromosome number in *Sphagnum* is n=19, with of course, a varying number of tiny bodies, the so-called *m* chromosomes.

The sub-class Sphagnidae includes a single order Sphagnales with a single family Sphagnacea represented by a single genus *Sphagnum*.

SPHAGNUM (DILL) Hedw.

HABITAT

Sphagnum is an interesting genus of the mosses. No other group of mosses is as ecologically dominant or economically important as the *Sphagnum* species are as a group. The genus includes more than 336 species. Of these ten (Bruhl, 1931) to seventeen (Sharma, 1948) have been reported from India. All love to grow in wet or very wet places as semiaquatics and also as submerged aquatics confined to acidic water logged sites that are poorly mineralised as well. As a group these water loving *Sphagnum* species (hydrophytes) possess some adaptations for dealing with periodic drought conditions. For this reason some workers term them Xerophytic hydrophytes.

They thrive best in cold bogs and marshes of higher latitudes. The individual *Sphagnum* plants grow closely matted together forming extensive masses. The latter form a continuous and complete vegetative spongy cover over the surface of water in acid pools, ponds and lakes converting them to quaking bogs of peat lands. It is dangerous to traverse the quaking bog. *Sphagnum* is intolerant of lime. The growth of *Sphagnum* increases the acidity of its fluid environment. Skene (1915) attributed it to the process of selective ionic absorption. Rose (1953) reported that the pH in the interior of tufts is usually lower as compared with the surrounding water. The bog water is antiseptic. Owing to its germicidal properties and deficiency of oxygen it acts as a preservative. Plants, animals, logs of wood and even human bodies entrapped beneath the surface in the quaking bogs have been recovered well preserved after centuries.

DISTRIBUTION

Sphagnum has a world-wide distribution. It occurs in all parts of the world except the Arctic region. It thrives in the tropics and extends through the temperate zone to the sub-arctic and the subantarctic region. Normally it grows on peat and in oligotrophic waters. In India it occurs in the Himalayas on the wet dripping rocks and on the sides of furrows cut by the fast flowing streams.

HABIT (Fig. 16.1)

Sphagnum plant generally is an erect **perennial** with various shades of green, pale green or yellow. Some species are of bright colours such as deep red (*S. rubellum*), orange brown, salmon to rose-pink (*S. plumulosum*), orangepink, etc. *Sphagnum* is counted among the largest mosses in point of size. As the plant grows its basal older parts die. The dead portions, accumulate from year to year as partially decomposed material which gradually fills the pond or the lake. These deposits may as well contain the remains of other plants growing there such as the sledges, heathers, cotton, grass etc. The water in which *Sphagnum* grows is often so acidic, that the decay of the accumulated plant tissue is very slow. These deposits of dead, partially decomposed tissues are slowly compressed and hardened by the weight of fresh deposit above it. The compacted, partially decomposed and hardened dead plant deposit is called the **peat**. The peat is a brown or dark-coloured spongy substance. It is rich in carbon. When air dried it is used as fuel.

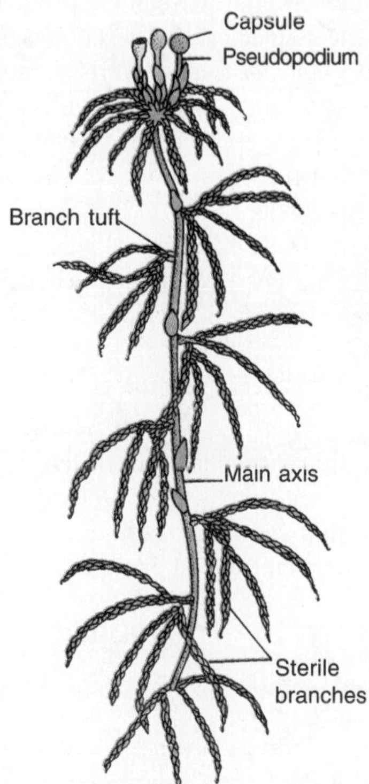

Fig. 16.1. ***Sphagnum*** sp. An adult leafy gametophore with a terminal cluster of sporogonia, each at the end of pseudopodium (based on Schimper).

Since *Sphagnum* is the chief component of peat it is often called the peat moss. It implies that it is not exclusively decomposed under the conditions which occur in the surface layers of peat bogs. Several explanations have been advanced for the apparent resistance to decomposition shown by *Sphagnum* tissues. Czapek (1899) reported that the moss contains a phenolic compound termed *sphagnol* which inhibits microbial activity. Rumjantzewa (1939) suggested that *Sphagnum* cellulose is less easily broken down due to the presence of higher lignins. Lindberg and Theander (1952), and Farmer and Morrison (1964) confirmed the presence of unusual lignin containing p-hygroxyphenyl units in various species. Other workers have suggested that the physical environment is largely responsible for the tardy decomposition of dead *Sphagnum* tissues. The question whether chemical characteristics are responsible for tardy decomposition or the physical environment of the habitat is still undecided.

The life cycle of *Sphagnum* includes two distinct, alternating phases or generations, the *gametophyte* and the *sporophyte*.

GAMETOPHYTE PHASE

It starts with the spore and consists of two stages, the **juvenile** stage and the **leafy gametophyte stage**.

1. Juvenile stage (Fig. 16.2).

It is also called the **protonema** and is formed by the germination of the spore. When young, the protonema is a short filament of a few cells (A). By further growth and cell division the filament becomes a flat, green plate of cells. It is an irregularly lobed **thallus-like** structure one cell in thickness (B). It is fixed to the substratum by multicellular rhizoids. The thallus-like protonema of *Sphagnum* moss recalls the thallose protonema of the leafy Jungermanniales and thus points out the relationship of *Sphagnum* to a liverwort ancestor. From the margin of the lobed protonema arises the erect, leafy gametophyte called the *Sphagnum* plant (B). It is also called the **gametophore**. The stem of the young gametophore bears a few colourless rhizoids at its base. The rhizoids are delicate, multicellular, hair-like processes. The septa between the cells are oblique. As the gametophore grows, the rhizoids soon disappear. The mature gametophytes of *Sphagnum* thus do not possess rhizoids.

Iwatsuki (1986) found specimens of *Sphagnum novo*—Caladonae with fascicles of brown, thick-walled, almost smooth, obliquely cross walled rhizoids at the tips of gametophore branches that often attach to soil or rocks.

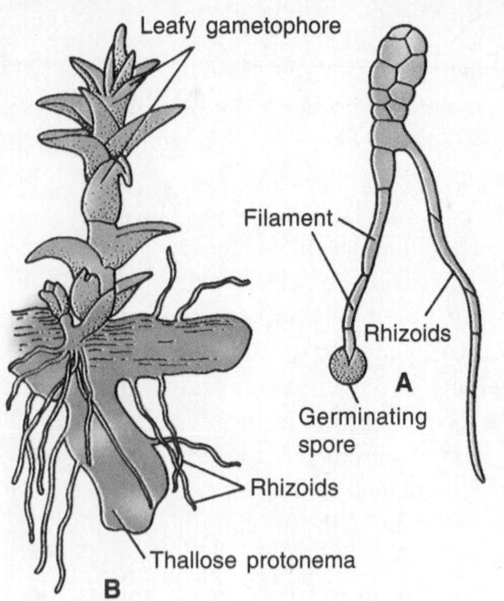

Fig. 16.2. (A—B). ***Sphagnum* sp**. Juvenile stage: A, filamentous protonema arising from the germinating spore and forming terminally a few-celled thallus by the activity of an apical cell; B, older thallose protonema bearing rhizoids and producing a leafy gametophore (After Schimper).

2. Leafy Gametophyte

(a) **External characters** (Fig. 16.1). The leafy gametophyte is a perennial plant. It has an upright stem. Individually the erect stem is weak and fragile. It gets support to grow upright from the neighbouring dense clumps of stems. The stem often grows to a considerable length—a foot or more with a diameter up to 1.2 mm only. The mature gametophyte lacks rhizoids but branches freely. The branching is lateral and the branches arise in fascicles. Both the stem and the branches are clothed with small leaves. At the apex of the stem is a dense cluster of short, stout branches. These are of limited growth. This terminal cluster of closely set branches protects the apical bud and forms a conspicuous compact head of the plant. It is called the **coma** or **comal tuft**. As the apical bud grows, these branches become displaced downwards.

Lower down on the stem are borne additional elongated branches. They usually occur in tufts or fascicles of 3 to 8 commonly five in the axil of every fourth leaf on the main stem (Fig. 16.1). In the species which grow out of water, the following two types of branches can be distinguished in the cluster :

(*i*) *Divergent branches* (Fig. 16.3). These are usually short and stout branches which grow out laterally from the main axis. They extend outward in a horizontal position and sometimes slightly upward but usually become arched at the middle with their distal portions carving downward.

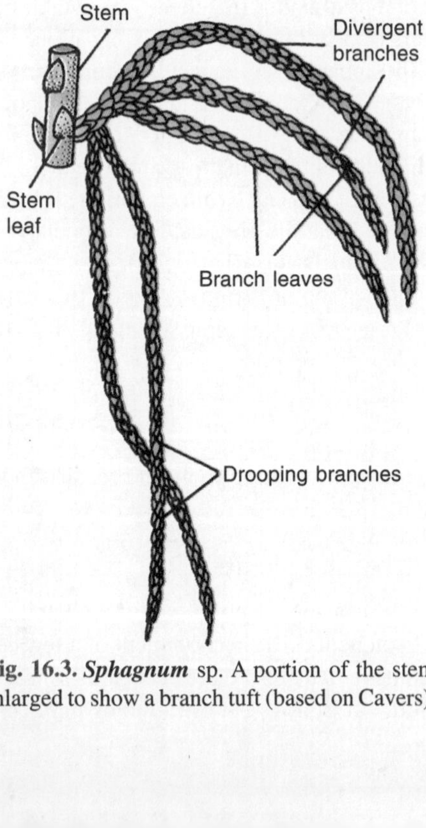

Fig. 16.3. ***Sphagnum*** sp. A portion of the stem enlarged to show a branch tuft (based on Cavers).

(*ii*) *Flagelliform or drooping branches* (Fig. 16.3). These are long, slender, descending branches which droop or hang down, often very close to and around the main stem. These pendent or decurrent branches act as water conductors. In the submerged species of *Sphagnum* (*S. obesum*) the drooping branches in the cluster are rare. They are all of the divergent type.

(b) Anatomy

(*i*) *Stem* (Fig. 16.4). Internally the stem shows well marked differentiation of tissues into three zones. These are the **cortex** or the **hyalodermis**, the **hadrome** (prosenchymatous region) and the **medulla** (axial cylinder).

The **cortex** or **hyalodermis** forms the outermost region of the stem. It varies in thickness. In young stems and branches it is only one cell thick (Fig. 16.5 A). It consists of small compactly arranged cells. In older stems the cortex becomes 3 to 6 layers of cells thick (Fig. 16.4). Gradually the cortical cells lose their protoplasmic contents and increase in size. In the mature stems they are thus dead, empty, colourless and large in size. In many species (*S. palustre*), the cortical cells develop large oval pores on their walls and sometimes spiral thickenings also (Fig. 16.5 D). The cortex of older stems consequently becomes spongy or porous in **nature**. The cortical cells store water. Like velamen in the Orchid roots, the cortex of *Sphagnum* stem absorbs water by capillary action. It thus compensates for the absence of rhizoids in the adult gametophyte plant.

The cortex of the side branches remains one cell thick. The cortical cells of the side branches in certain species such as *S. tenellum* and *S. molluscum* develop peculiar absorptive cells at the points of insertion of leaves. These are elongated and flask-shaped. Some people call them the **retort** cells (Fig. 16.5 C). The neck of each retort cell is turned outward away from the axis. It opens at its distal end by an aperture. The retort cells are inhabited by small microscope animals.

The prosenchymatous region or **hadrome** lies next to the cortex. It surrounds the medulla and consists of elongated thick-walled, prosenchymatous cells. The hadrome functions as a supporting tissue.

The axial cylinder or **medulla** forms the core of the stem. It is composed of colourless collenchymatous cells with thin walls. The cells are somewhat elongated. The medulla thus forms a tissue corresponding, somewhat, to the pith of the higher plants and functions as storage region.

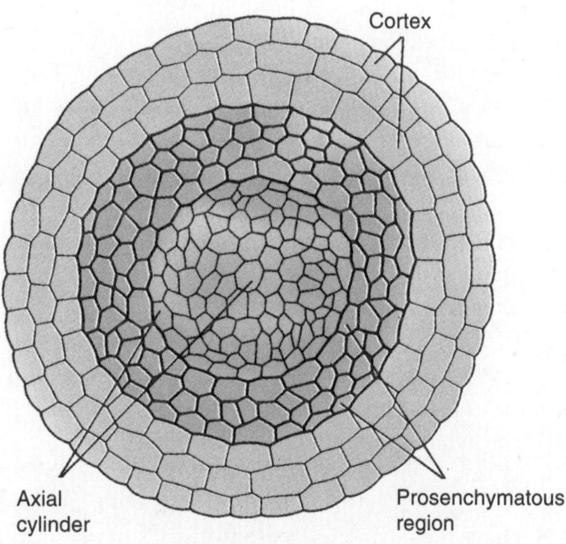

Fig. 16.4. *Sphagnum* sp. Cross section of an old stem showing the three regions (After Campbell).

(*ii*) *Leaves* (Fig. 16.6). The leaves occur on the main stem as well as the branches (Fig. 16.1). On the branches they are closely set and thus overlapping. On the main stem they are a little apart. Besides, the leaves on the stem differ in size, shape and details of cells structure from those on the branches. In general the leaves are small, thin and scale like. They are sessile and are arranged spirally on the stem. The midrib is lacking. The margin is entire and the apex acute (A).

Structure of leaf (Fig. 16.6). *Sphagnum* has a unique type of leaf. It is single layer of cells in thickness (A). The cells constituting the leaf are much elongated. They are of two kinds, the **ordinary type capillary cells** and the green **photosynthetic** or the **assimilatory cells**. Two kinds of cells alternate with each other to form a net-like pattern (B). When viewed under the microscope the narrow, elongate assimilatory cells are seen to form the network with large and wide capillary cells occupying the meshes (A).

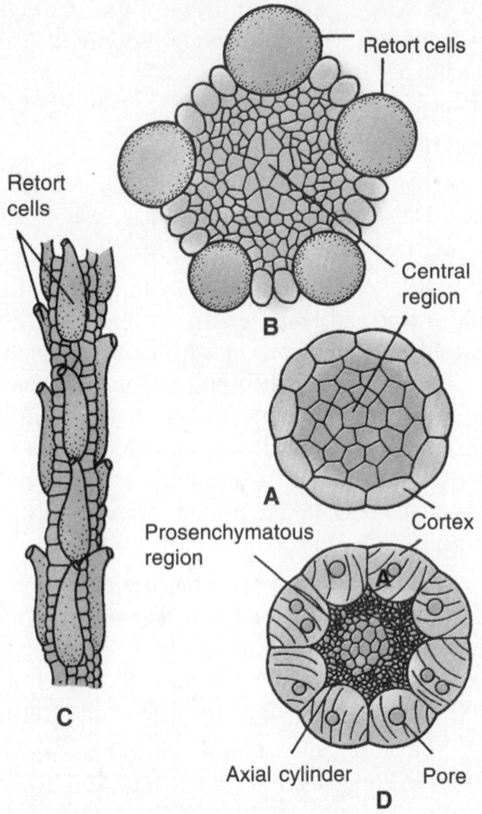

Fig. 16.5. (A—D). ***Sphagnum***. Anatomy of stem. A, T.S. young branch of *S. palustre*; B. T.S. stem of *S. molluscum* with retort cells; C, portion of a branch of *S. acutifolium* with leaves removed to show retort cells; D, T.S. of old branch of *S. palustre*. (A, after Campbell; B, D after Cavors, C after Schimper).

The hyaline capillary cells have no protoplasmic contents and thus are dead and somewhat rhomboidal in shape (B). They are colourless, wide and filled with water. They frequently have circular or oval pores on either the upper or lower surface of their walls. The inner surface of the walls of the hyaline cells is frequently strengthened by spiral or ring-shaped thickening bands of wall material. The strengthening bands help the empty dead cells from collapsing. The pores enable the leaf to absorb water readily and retain it much like a sponge. Because of this property the hyaline cells are also called the **capillary cells**.

The assimilatory cells are alive and photosynthetic in function. They contain chloroplasts and are thus green in colour. They are very narrow and lie between the dead hyaline cells forming a network (B). The meshes are thus occupied by the dead hyaline cells—one dead cells per mesh. Owing to the presence of dead capillary cells the *Sphagnum* leaves play an important role in the absorption and retention of water.

The cross-section of a mature leaf has bead-like appearance. The bead consists of two kinds of cells. They are the large **capillary cells** and the small, green, **assimilatory cells**. The two kinds of cells alternate with each other. The assimilatory cells are variable in from and position according to the species. In *S. acutifolium* the assimilatory cells have their bases directed towards the upper surface of the leaf and the apices towards the lower surface (C). They are in flush with the upper surface of the leaf. The large bead-like capillary cells bulge towards the lower surface (C). The leaves of *S. tenellum* have the position of these two kinds of cells reversed. The large capillary cells bulge towards the upper surface. The basis of triangular assimilatory cells face the lower surface

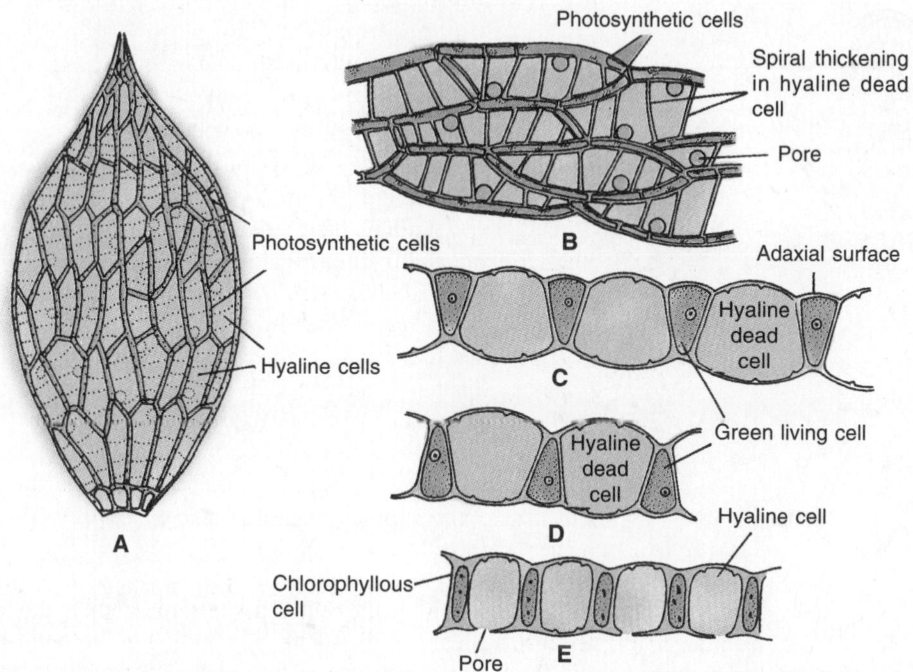

Fig. 16.6. (A—E). ***Sphagnum* sp**. Structure of leaf. A, entire leaf showing arrangement of two kinds of cells, surface view; B, portion of A under higher magnification; C—E, portions of cross-section of the leaf of different species.

(D). *S. squarrosum* has fusiform assimilatory cells. They are hemmed in between the capillary cells. Their ends reach neither the upper nor the lower surface of the leaf (E).

It is obvious from the account given above that *Sphagnum* stands apart from other mosses in many of the structural features of its gametophyte.

Physiology of water absorption, retention and conduction. The adult *Sphagnum* plant lacks rhizoids. Their function of water absorption is taken up by :—

(*i*) The **spongy cortex** of the stem and branches which consists of dead, water filled cells with porous walls.

(*ii*) The large hyaline **capillary cells** of leaves with entrance pores. These cells have no protoplasmic contents. Instead they are filled with water.

The capillary cells of both the stem and the leaves account for the remarkable water absorbing and water retaining capacity possessed by *Sphagnum*. It absorbs water directly through its leaves and stem by the capillary action of these cells. The latter as well hold a large amount of water like a sponge. These porous elements of the cortex of the stem also serve as a capillary apparatus for raising the water to the top of the plant and to other places where needed.

In species which lack the porous elements in the cortex of the stem the upward movement of water is facilitated by the **drooping branches**. They hang down and around the main stem clothing it thickly and acting as water conductors. The spaces in the thick loose covering of the pendent branches serve as a **capillary apparatus**. They draw up water by capillary action.

Apical growth. (Fig. 16.7). The main stem and the branches grow by means of a three sided **apical cells** (A). It has three cutting faces. Each segment, cut off parallel to its flat face, divides by a periclinal wall into an outer cell (O) and inner cell (*i*). The outer cell undergoes divisions to form

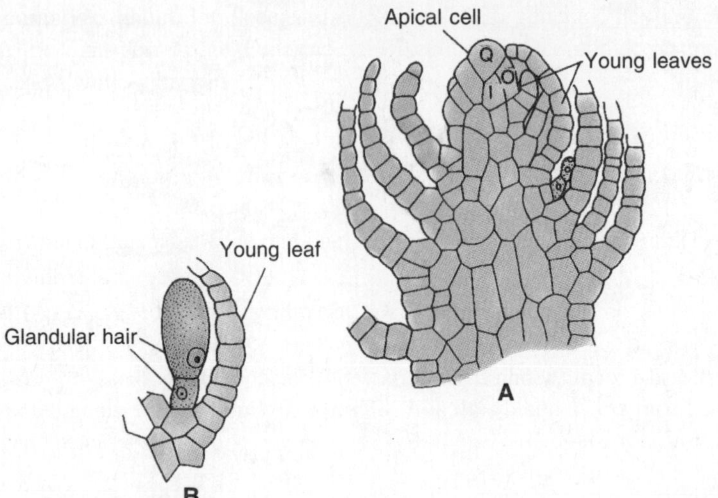

Fig. 16.7. (A—B) ***Sphagnum***. Apical growth of stem. A, median longitudinal section of the apex of stem of *S. cymbifolium*; B, glandular hair (After Campbell).

the stem cortex and a single leaf. The inner cell gives rise to the central tissue of the stem. In this way each segment derived from the apical cell forms a leaf and the subtending portion of the stem. This explains the three ranked arrangement in the younger portions of the stem. This arrangement is, however, soon replaced by more complex phyllotaxy.

Development of leaf (Fig. 16.8). The leaf when young grows by means of an **apical cell** (A). It has two cutting faces. Segments are cut off alternately right and left parallel to its flat faces. This results in a young leaf consisting of a single layer of diamond shaped cells (B). They are all green and contain protoplasm and chloroplasts. Later the apical growth ceases. The further growth of the leaf is entirely **basal**. Each diamond-shaped green cell divides asymmetrically. It cuts off narrow daughter cells but on two sides only either right and tip side (E) or left and tip side of the leaf (C). The narrow daughter cells develop chloroplasts and remain green and alive. The larger mother cells lose chloroplasts and protoplasmic contents to become hyaline and empty. These empty cells develop entrance pores on their walls and spiral thickenings on the inner surface of the walls only.

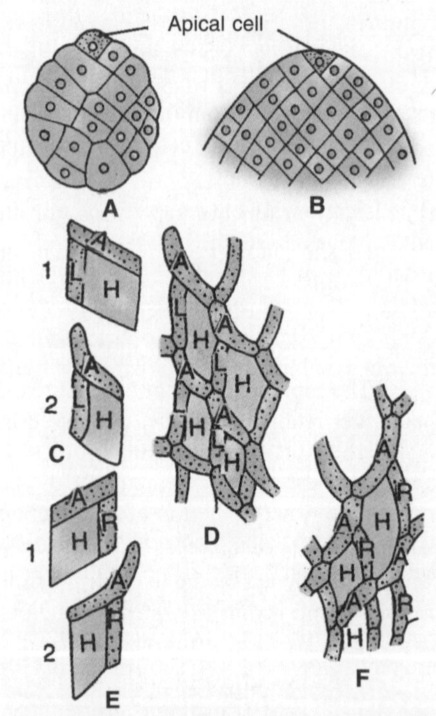

Fig. 16.8. (A—F) ***Sphagnum.*** Development of leaf (After Muller-Berol).

REPRODUCTION

Sphagnum gametophyte reproduces by two methods usual for all the bryophytes. These are **vegetative** and **sexual reproduction**.

1. Vegetative Reproduction

Reproduction in *Sphagnum* is principally vegetative. However, it lacks special structures for vegetative propagation. The stem progressively disintegrates from the basal older parts upwards causing the branches to separate and develop into independent plants.

Innovation. The common vegetative method is by the formation of innovations. Occasionally one of the branches in the axillary cluster may turn upward. It grows more vigorously than the others and continues its upward growth. This long, upright branch takes on all the characteristics of the main axis. It is called an **innovation**. Sooner or later the innovations become separated from the main stem by progressive dying of their basal, older parts. The detached innovation establishes itself as an independent individual. Vegetative propagation by this method is a very effective means of multiplication in *Sphagnum*. It is mainly responsible for its occurrence in extensive masses.

According to Woesler (1934) the leafy gametophyte of *S. palustre* reproduces vegetatively by several methods. Buds and even plates of cells from the young growing apices of stems and young leaves grow into new leafy individuals. Even old **leaves** and short branches under exceptionally humid conditions and moderate light function as vegetative reproductive structures.

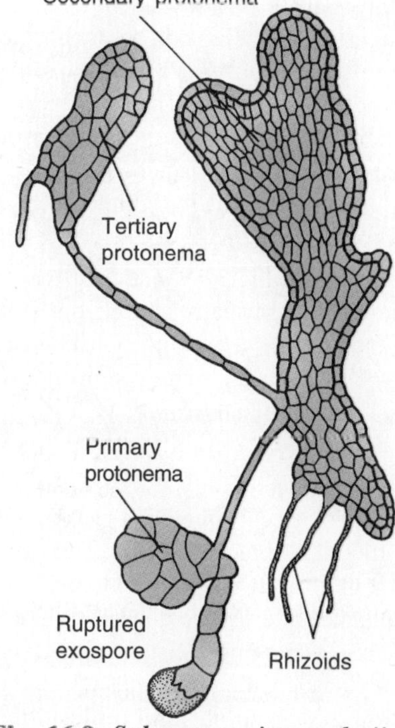

Fig. 16.9. ***Sphagnum girgensohnii.*** Vegetative reproduction by multiplication of protonemal stage (Based on Noguchi).

Multiplication of protonemal stage (Fig. 16.9). Vegetative reproduction also takes place by the multiplication of the protonemal stage. Any marginal cell of the thallose, primary protonema may become **meristematic**. By division and growth it forms a green cellular **filament**. The apical portion of the filament grows into a flat, thallus-like green **secondary protonema**. From one of its marginal cells arises the erect leafy gametophore.

Regeneration. *Sphagnum* like other bryophytes has great power of regeneration. It is attributed to the physiological adaptations which allow suspension of metabolism during periods of desiccation and its resumption when water is once more available. In these plants which Buch (1947) called **pollacuophytes**, water is lost rapidly to dry air and the cytoplasm itself shows a high degree of resistance to desiccation. It is suggested that one possible cause of suspension of metabolism (photosynthetic and respiratory activities) may be the inactivation of photosynthetic and respiratory enzymes.

Sobotka (1976) reported that fragments of *S. palustra* placed on agar in laboratory situations do regenerate successfully. There is no regeneration from leaves alone.

Gemmae. These structures were previously unknown for sphagnales. Redhead (1981) discovered gemmae in *S. capillaceum*. The gemmae are subglobose and double-walled. Usually they occur in pairs, sometimes in clusters or even singly. On germination the gemma produces a small, uniseriate filamentous protonema prior to prothallus development.

2. Sexual Reproduction (Fig. 16.10)

Mature *Sphagnum* plants produce sex organs in favourable situations. They are formed in autumn on special, short, densely leafy and slightly modified branches. The **sexual branches** either occur in the terminal branch cluster, the **coma** (Fig. 16.1) or lower down on the stem. In some species the antheridial and archegonial branches are borne on the same plant and in others on separate plants. The former are called **monoecious** (Fig. 16.10) and the latter **dioecious**. Even in the monoecious species the two kinds of sex organs never occur on the same branch. The antheridial branches appear first. The sex organs are formed in abundance. Paraphyses are always absent. Benson-Evans (1964) reported that *S. plumulosum* is perhaps the only moss studied in which initiation of sexuality is induced by short days. In all others temperature seems to be the critical factor.

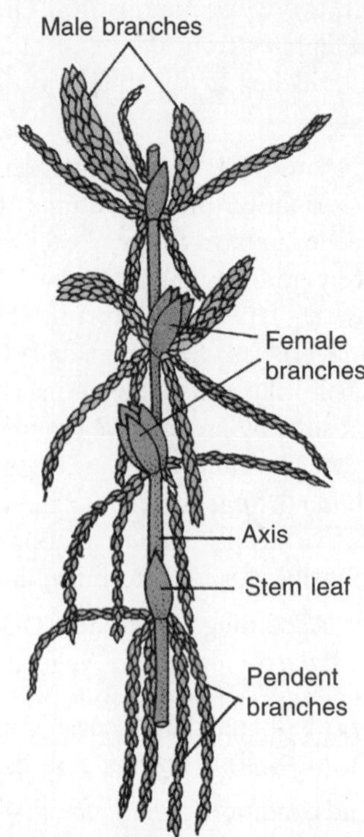

Fig. 16.10. ***Sphagnum*** sp. Portion of a gametophore of a monoecious species bearing both the male and the female branches (after Schimper).

(a) Antheridial branches (Fig. 16.11). The antheridial branches are usually shorter but stouter than the vegetative branches. They are spindle-shaped and resemble small catkins (A, B). They are strongly pigmented and often densely clothed with red, purple, brown or yellow leaves generally small than the foliage leaves.

Antheridia. (*i*) *Position and structure* (Fig. 16.11). The antheridia occur singly in the axils of leaves towards the tip on antheridial branches (A, B). The mature antheridium consists of a **globular body** elevated on a long, slender **stalk** (D). The stalk may be as long as the body of the antheridium. It is usually 2 cells broad and consists of 2-4 vertical rows of cells. The body of the antheridium has a jacket layer of sterile cells. It is known as the **antheridial wall**. Hofmeister (1862) reported the presence of a glossy transparent tough cuticle layer on the living antheridium of *Sphagnum*. Manton (1954) confirmed it with the help of electron microscope. He reported that the cuticle forms a very conspicuous layer on the outer side. The one cell

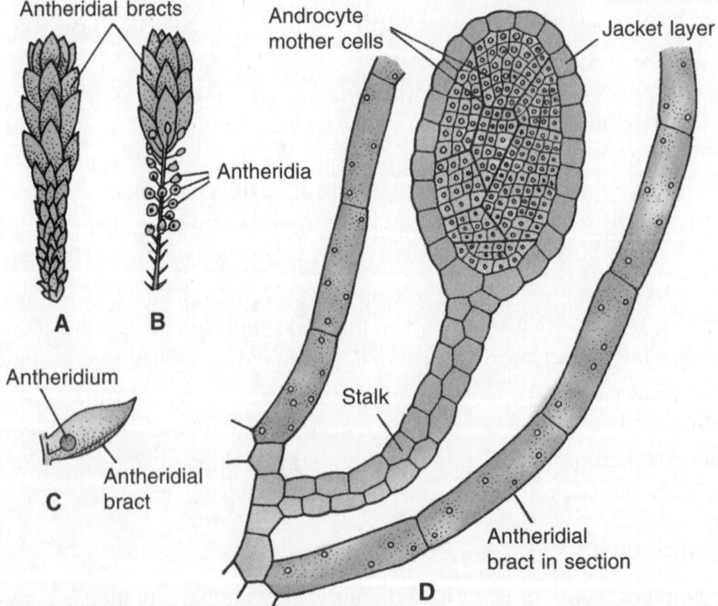

Fig. 16.11. (A—D) ***Sphagnum*** sp. A, antheridial branch; B, male branch with the antheridial bracts removed from the lower portion to expose the antheridia arising from the branch axis; C, antheridium with the protective antheridial bract; D, nearly mature antheridium arising between two leaves (C after Waston and D after Smith).

thick antheridial wall encloses a mass of *androcyte mother cells*. Each androcyte mother cell divides into two androcytes. The division is not diagonal. The androcytes metamorphose into **sperms.** Each sperm is an elongated, spirally coiled structure furnished with two **flagella** (Fig. 16.12 C). The number of coils is 2 to 3. The flagella are inserted at the end which is cytoplasmic in origin and called the **flagellophore**. The greater part of the body of the sperm is nuclear in origin. To its posterior end is attached a vesicle-like structure consisting of a cytoplasmic matrix.

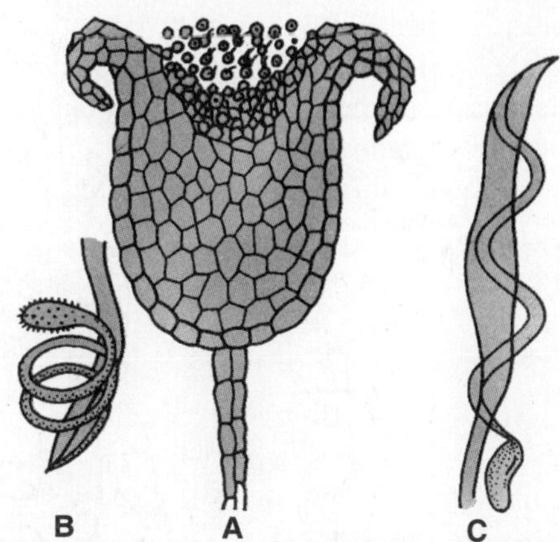

Fig. 16.12. (A—C). ***Sphagnum*** sp. A, opened mature antheridium; B—C, sperm (A—B after Schimper, C, after Campbell).

(ii) Dehiscence (Fig. 16.12). The mature antheridium dehisces following absorption of water. The jacket cells of the swollen antheridium undergo irregular separation at its distal end. The antheridium thus opens at its apex by a number of irregular lobes. The ejection of sperms is further facilitated by swelling of the jacket cells which cause the lobes to bend outwards away from the aperture. The formerly convex outer surfaces of these cells become concave and the inner surfaces previously concave due to internal pressure of spermatocytes become convex. With the dissolution of the androcyte vesicles, the sperms are liberated. They swim about actively in the water that caused the rupture of the antheridium.

(iii) Development of antheridia (Fig. 16.13). Each antheridium develops from a single superficial cell of the stem. It is the modified initial cell of the axillary bud. It grows into a papilla-like outgrowth (A). The papilla is then cut off by a transverse wall at the base (B). The protruding papillate cell now functions as an **antheridial initial** (B). It divides a number of times by transverse walls to produce a row of few cells (C). The terminal cell of the row functions as an **apical cell** (C). It has two cutting forces. The segments are cut off alternately right and left parallel to its two faces (E). When the young antheridium is 12-15 cells in height each of the last 2 to 5 segments derived from the apical cell undergoes two successive vertical divisions (H). These divisions are best seen in cross sections of the antheridium at this stage (G and I). The first division (1-1) is asymmetrical (G). It cuts off a small **jacket initial** from a larger **sister cell** (G). The second vertical division (2-2) divides the sister cell into a **second jacket initial** and a **primary androgonial cell** (G). The young antheridium at this stage has 2 to 5 primary androgonial cells (I). They are surrounded by a wall of a few jacket initials. The old apical cell of the antheridium also contributes to one of the jacket cells. The jacket initials divide by anticlinal walls to form the single layered wall of the antheridium (J). The primary androgonial cells undergo repeated divisions. The cells of the last cell generation are called the **androcytes.**

Meanwhile the lower cells of the row which do not take part in the formation of the body of the antheridium undergo divisions. They divide by vertical and transverse walls to form the stalk of the antheridium.

(b) Archegonial branches (Fig. 16.10). The female branches are very short and more or less globular in form. They are green and bud-like aggregates of bracts and archegonia. In many species the archegonial branch occurs just below the apex of the stem within the terminal branch cluster (Fig. 16.1). It bears leaves larger than the normal. These leaves are rich in chloroplasts and have fewer fibres in the hyaline cells. The archegonial branches are thus more deeply pigmented than the vegetative branches in the cluster. The leaves increase in size towards the apex where a number of them form the **perichaetium.** The perichaetium surrounds and protects the archegonia.

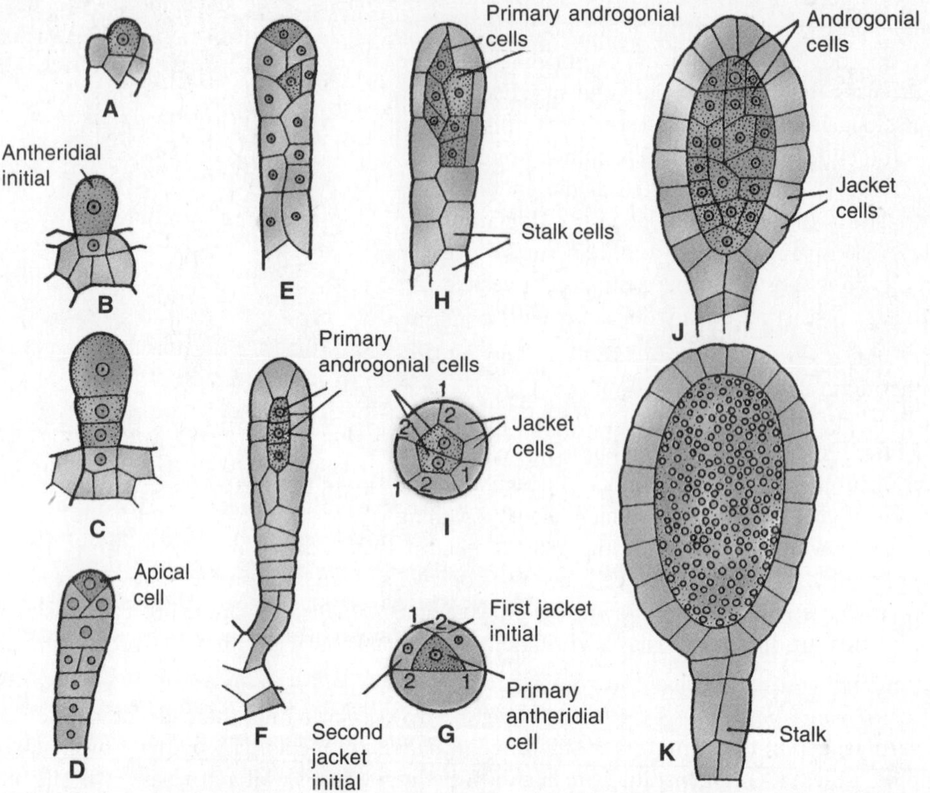

Fig. 16.13. (A—K). ***Sphagnum*** sp. Development of antheridium. A—F, H, J, early stages in the development of antheridium in longitudinal section; G and I, in transverse section; K, mature antheridium. Explanation in the text, (D after Campbell, and F—J after Smith *et al*

Archegonia. (*i*) *Position and structure* (Fig. 16.14). The archegonia are terminal on the specialized archegonial branches. They usually occur in small groups (Fig. 16.14). Typically there are three archegonia in the group. The number, however, varies from 2 to 5. The central or the middle archegonium in the cluster grows directly from the **apical cell** of the branch. It is called the **primary archegonium** and is the first to be formed. The others in the cluster are called the **secondary archegonia**. They are developed from the last segments cut off by the apical cell. The secondary archegonia are thus formed about the base of the primary archegonium.

The mature archegonium (Fig. 16.15 J) is relatively a large structure. It is stalked. The stalk is fairly long. The body of the archegonium consists of a long twisted **neck** and a massive **venter**. The neck consists of six vertical rows of **neck cells**. The neck canal contains numerous (usually 8 or 9) **neck canal cells**. The venter and the lower portion of the neck is 2 to 3 layers of cells in thickness. The venter cavity contains a small ovoid **egg**. It is about the same size as the **ventral canal cell** which lies above it.

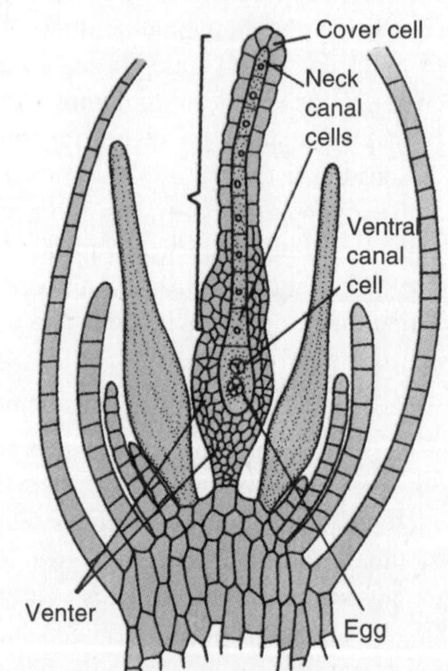

Fig. 16.14. ***Sphagnum*** sp. Vertical section through the tip of a female branch showing a cluster of archegonia.

(*ii*) *Development* (Fig. 16.15). The development of the archegonium is the same as in the Jungermanniales (liverworts). The apical cell of the female branch directly functions as an **archegonial initial** (A). It forms the primary archegonium of the cluster and is reported to undergo a succession of transverse divisions. In some cases it functions as an **apical cell** of the archegonium with two cutting faces. There is thus some irregularity in the early segmentation. However in either case a short filament of cells is formed (B).

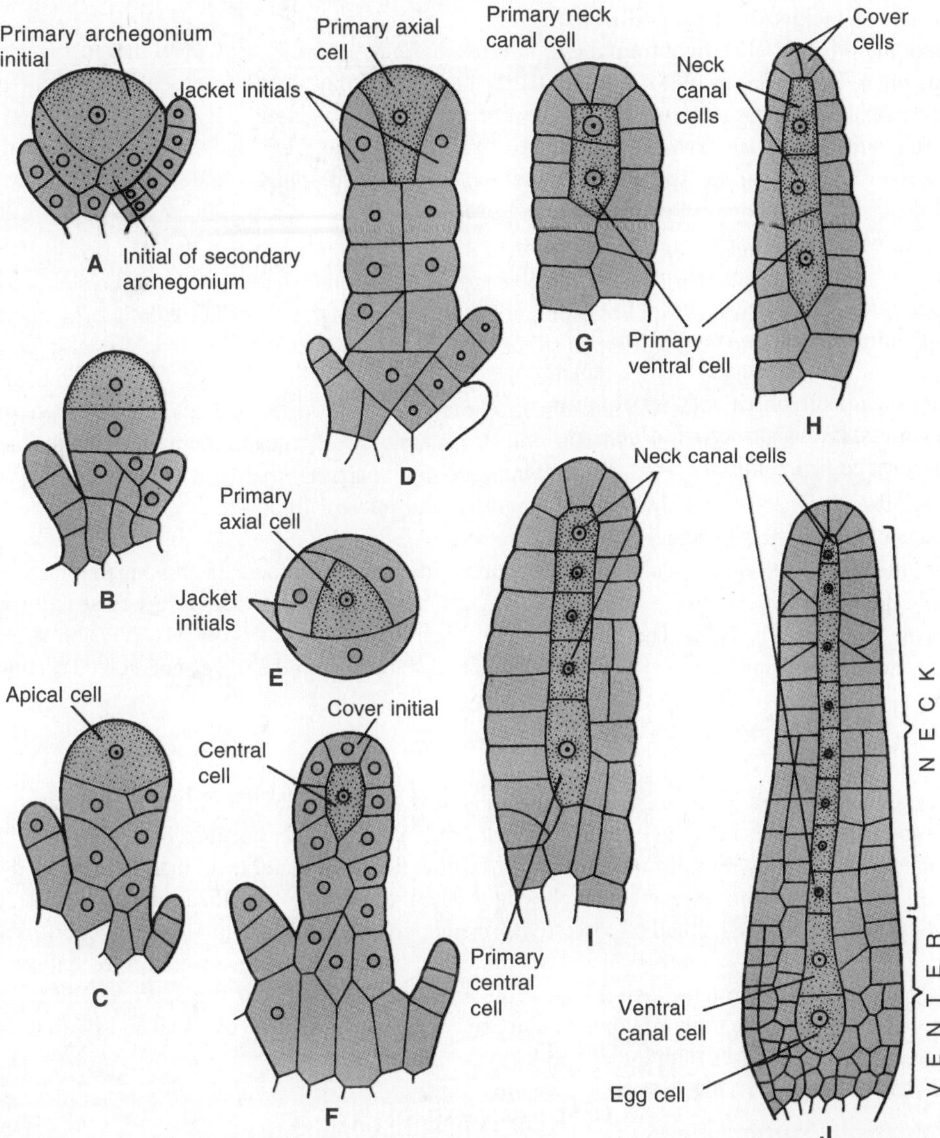

Fig. 16.15. (A—J). ***Sphagnum*** sp. Development of archegonium. A—D, and F—J are longitudinal sections and E is a transverse section of stage D; J, a nearly mature archegonium (D—J after Bryan)

The development of the secondary archegonia of the cluster is brought about by the segments of the apical cell functioning as archegonium initials. The initial of the secondary archegonium invariably undergoes a series of transverse divisions to form a short filament of 4 to 5 cells. The first step in the development of the archegonium in both cases is the formation of filament of a few cells.

During further development the terminal cell of the filament increases in size (C). It then divides by three oblique vertical walls (D). This results in the separation of three peripheral cells, **jacket initials**. They surround a single central cell called the **primary axial cell** (D). It has the form of an inverted pyramid. The primary axial cell divides by a transverse wall into an **outer** and an **inner cell** (F). The former is called the **cover initial** and the latter **central cell** (F). The cover initial divides by a series of vertical walls to form a group of cells. These by further divisions in other directions form the terminal portion of the jacket of the neck of the archegonium. The three jacket initials in the meantime divide and redivide to form the lower portion of the neck and the venter wall. The jacket portion (wall) of the archegonium is thus formed from the cover initial and the jacket initials. The cells of the basal portion of the neck and the venter undergo periclinal divisions so that these portions become 2 to 3 cell layers thick (I, J).

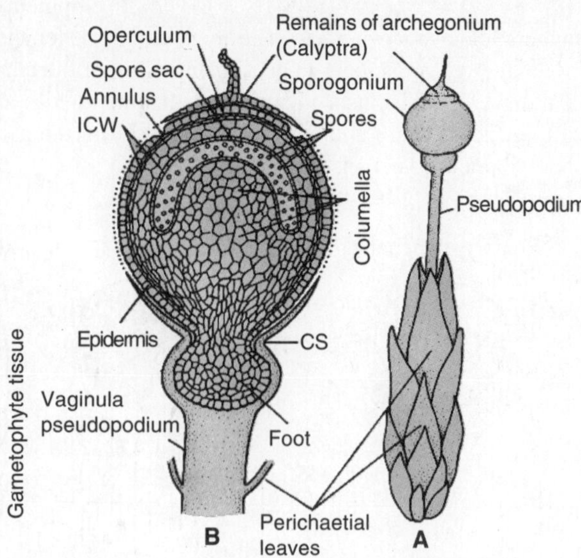

Fig. 16.16. (A—B). ***Sphagnum*** sp. A, Female branch with a terminal sporogonium of *S. acutifolium*; B, M.L.S. of a nearly mature sporogonium; CS constriction like seta, ICW, inner layers of the capsule wall (A after Schimper; B, Adapted from Waldner).

The central cell in the meantime has divided transversely to produce an upper **primary canal cell** and the lower **primary ventral cell** (G). The primary canal cell divides to give rise to a row of 8 to 9 **neck canal cell** (H, I). The primary ventral cell divides transversely. The division is nearly symmetrical. As a result an upper **ventral canal cell**is cut off from the lower **egg cell** (J). They are nearly of the same size and lie in the venter cavity.

FERTILIZATION

As mentioned above the sex organs are produced in abundance but the sporogonia are rarely found in large numbers. On the contrary they are regarded as of rare occurrence. This scarcity of sporophytes may be the result of infrequency of fertilization. The water level may be either too high or two low for the sperms to reach the archegonia. The uncertainty of fertilization may also account for the rapid and effective method of vegetative propagation by *innovations* in *Sphagnum*. Fertilisation, however, occurs in the same manner as in the other bryophytes. The axial row of cells in the archegonium, except the egg, disintegrates to form a passage way for the sperms. The released sperms swim to the archegonium. Some of them find their way into the neck canal and swim down to the egg. One of them fuses with the egg to form the diploid zygote.

SPOROPHYTE PHASE

This phase in the life cycle ushers with the act of fertilization. The diploid zygote is thus the pioneer structure of this generation. The zygote encased in the venter, increase in size, secretes a wall around it and starts dividing. By repeated division it develops into an embryo which by further division, differentiation and growth forms the young sporogonium or sporophyte. Usually the zygote on one archegonium in the cluster develops into the sporogonium. The others persist for sometime and finally abort. One wet moors and peat bogs fruiting species of *Sphagnum* in June can be seen bearing pale greenish young sporogonia (sporophytes) amongst the leaves of the terminal clusters of branches. By the middle of July they mature and each is seen elevated on a short, cylindrical and leafless stalk, the **pseudopodium** which is of gametophyte origin. The mature sporogonia are brown or dark brown in colour and ready for spore dispersal.

MATURE SPOROPHYTE (Fig. 16.16)

The ripe sporogonium or sporophyte consists of a **foot** and a **capsule** (B). The two are linked by a small, narrow, neck-like constriction which represents the suppressed **seta**.

(*i*) **Foot**. It is an enlarged, bulbous structure which absorbs nutrition for the developing sporophyte from the gametophyte. It is embedded in the tissue of the dilated apex of the **pseudopodium** which develops as a prolongation of the tip of the archegonial branch after fertilisation when the spores are ripe for dispersal. It is short, leafless about 12 mm or a little more in length. The pseudopodium elevates the capsule far above the perichaetial leaves and the terminal branch cluster. It thus compensates for the suppression of seta and assists in spore dispersal. The pseudopodium is liable to be mistaken as seta. In fact it is a prolongation of the axis of the archegonial branch and thus a part of the parent gametophyte.

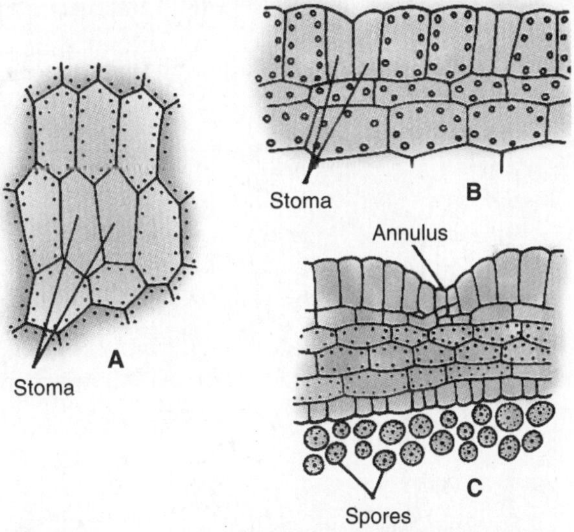

Fig. 16.17. (A—C). ***Sphagnum* sp.** A, stoma in surface view; B, portion of L.S. of capsule wall showing two stomata; C, portion of L.S. capsule showing the capsule wall, annulus, and the spore sac with meiospores (After Cavers).

(*ii*) **Capsule.** The capsule is a small nearly globose structure. It is dark brown or black in colour when mature. It mainly consists of a massive hemispherical central column of sterile cells termed the **columella**. Overarching the columella is a relatively thin dome-shaped spore sac which contains the spores. There are no **elaters**. Surrounding the columella and the **spore sac** is the capsule wall which is 4-6 layers of cells thick. The superficial or outermost layer of the cell wall is called the **epidermis**. It consists of cuticularized cells arranged compactly.

Interspersed here and there between the epidermal cells are the stomata which are rudimentary and thus nonfunctional (Fig. 16.17 B). Each stoma consists of two guard cells. There is no stomatal aperture (Fig. 16.17 A). The capsule wall cells contain chloroplasts but have no intercellular spaces between them (B). At the top of the capsule is the convex disc-shaped **operculum** or **lid** (Fig. 16.16 B). The operculum is sharply marked off from the rest of the capsule region by a ring-like (circular) groove of thin-walled cells, the **annulus** (Fig. 16.17 C).

Development of sporophyte (Fig. 16.18). The fertilized egg enlarges and secretes a wall around it to become the zygote (A). The zygote divides by a transverse wall. The division is nearly symmetrical (A). The account of segmentation of the basal cell varies. According to Waldner, it undergoes a few irregular divisions to form the **foot**. Byran holds that it functions as a **boring organ** (H). However, it is evident that there is some irregularity in the segmentation of the basal cell. Hence its fate is difficult to follow.

The upper cell divides by a series of horizontal walls. Consequently a filament of 6-12 cells is formed (B and C). The early growth of the embryo (young sporogonium) is thus by a succession of

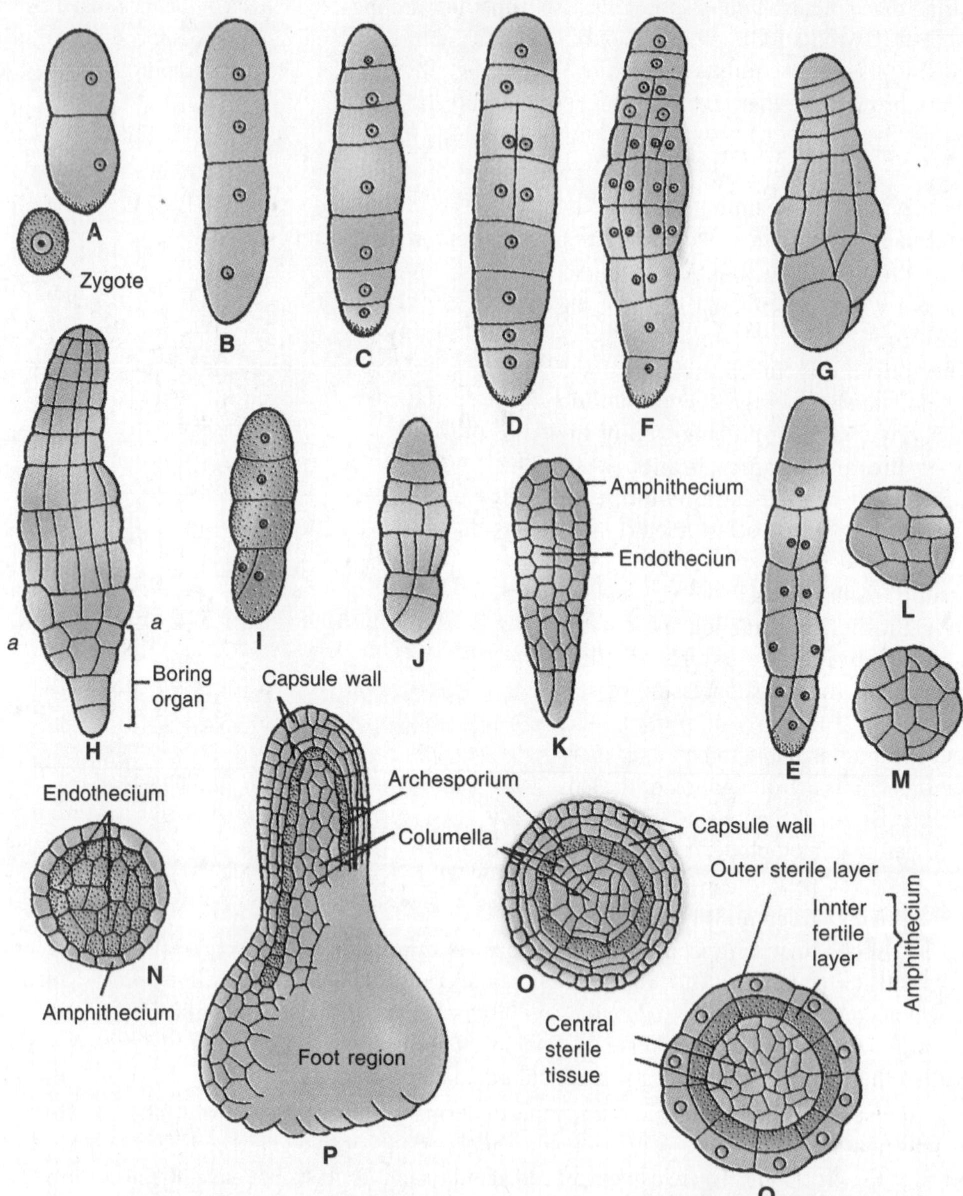

Fig. 16.18. (A—Q). ***Sphagnum*** sp. A—H, stages in the development of embryo and young sporogonium of *S. subsecundum*. A, zygote and a 2-celled embryo; B, 4-celled embryo; C, 7-celled embryo; D—E, appearance of vertical walls in embryo with 8 primary segments (D) and six primary segments (E); F, vertical walls in the central segments of an embryo with 10 primary segments; G, embryo with a bulbous basal portion; H, young sporogonium with a boring organ, the foot will develop above wall a—a; I—Q, stages in the development of embryo and young sporophyte of *S. acutifolium*; I, embryo with 4 primary segments; J, embryo with 5 primary segments; K, embryo at a late stage showing differentiation into regions; L—N, cross sections of the embryo at different stages showing differentiation of amphithecium and endothecium; O, cross section of the embryo showing division of the amphithecium into the outer sterile and inner fertile layer; P, M.L.S. of young sporogonium showing 3 layered capsule wall and the bell-shaped archesporium layer arching over the columella; Q, cross section of the sporogonium at the same stage as P. (A—H alter Bryon, I—N P—Q after Waldner).

transverse walls. The upper three to four cells of the filamentous embryo by further divisions and differentiation form the **capsule** (K). The lower portion forms the **bulbous foot** and the constriction-like **seta**. The foot acts as a **haustorium**. It bores its way down through the stalk of the archegonium into the apex of the female branch. Each segment of the upper part of the embryo undergoes two successive vertical divisions at right angles to each other to form four cells (F and G).

Periclinal divisions appear in all the cells of each tier. This results in the separation of an outer layer of the cells called the **amphithecium**. The amphithecium encloses a central mass of cells called the **endothecium** (K). The cells of the endothecium undergo repeated divisions to form a massive, central dome of sterile cells. It is the **columella** (P). The capsule portion of the sporogonium at this stage become spherical in shape.

As in *Anthoceros* periclinal divisions appear in the amphithecium dividing it into two layers, the **outer** and the **inner** (O). The inner layer of cells is **fertile**. It constitutes the **archesporium** (P, Q.). The archesporium cells divide by periclinal walls to form a **sporogenous tissue** 2 to 4 cell layers thick. The sporogenous tissue form a dome-shaped zone in the upper part of the capsule. It over arches the columella (P). The sporogenous cells of the last cell generation are all fertile. They function as **spore mother cells**. Each spore mother cell (Fig. 16.19 B—C) undergoes the usual tetrad division (meiosis) to form four haploid spore which are the first structures of the young gametophyte. *Sphagnum* like other mosses of the class Bryopsida differ from the liverworts in that no special wall is formed around the spore-tetrad membrane following meiosis.

The cells of the outer layer of the amphithecium by periclinal divisions give rise to the **capsule rise** (P,Q). It is 4 to 6 layer of cells in thickness. The surface layer of the capsule wall forms an **epidermis**. It has rudimentary **non-functional** stomata. The inner layers of the capsule wall consist of thin-walled cells without intercellular spaces between them. They, however, contain **chloroplasts.** The photosynthetic tissues in the capsule wall is thus not ventilated.

As the spores in the spore sac advance towards maturity a transverse ring of epidermal cells in the upper portion of the capsule grows less actively than their neighbours. These cells remain small. They form a sort of circular groove of thin-walled cells called the **annulus** (Fig. 16.17 C). It delimits the convex lid or operculum at the top of the capsule.

The young sporogonium remains enveloped and thus protected in the venter now called the **calyptra**. The later in the early stages of development of the young sporogonium keeps pace with its growth. The neck of the archegonium however dries up. As the capsule enlarges and advances towards maturity, the delicate calyptra ruptures irregularly. A cup-like sheath remains at the base surrounding the foot. This cup-like, basal portion of the calyptra together with the dilated tip of the pseudopodium into which is embedded the sporophyte foot, constitute **vaginula**. The seta in the sporogonium of *Sphagnum* remains suppressed. It is very short and constriction-like. Its function is taken up by a peculiar leafless stalk called the **pseudopodium**.

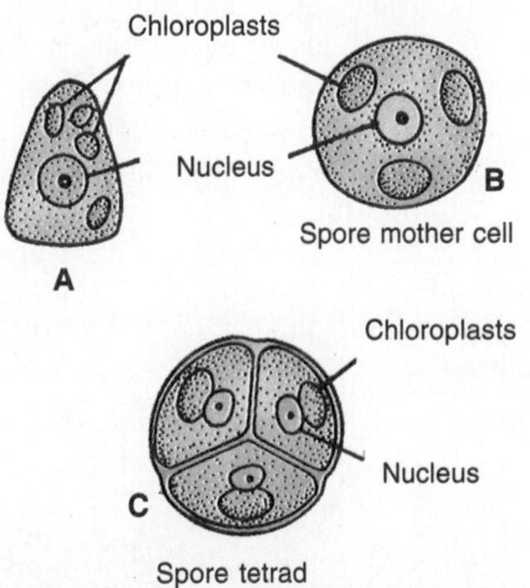

Fig. 16.19. (A—C). ***Sphagnum*** sp. A, archesporial cell; B, spore mother cell; C, spore tetrad (A, C after Melin).

The **pseudopodium** (Fig. 16.16) is an overgrowth of the apex of the archegonial branch. It develops by the elongation of the tip of the archegonial branch when the capsule is ripe. It is thus a gametophytic structure. As it elongates it carries the ripe sporogonium at its top beyond the perichaetial leaves.

Mechanism of dehiscence (Fig. 16.20) and **dispersal of spores**. The dehiscence of the capsule is by an **explosive** mechanism. It takes place on sunny days. With the formation of spore tetrads in the spore sac, cells of the columella break down. This results in the formation of a large **air cavity** below the spore sac (A). Under the influence of the sun the wall of the exposed, mature, dark brown capsule dries and shrinks. The spherical capsule gradually becomes cylindrical (B). The imprisoned air in the lower half of the capsule is compressed and thus held under considerable pressure. It cannot escape. As the capsule wall shrinks the thickened lid cells resist shrinkage. A difference in tension is thus set up. This puts a strain on the thin-walled annulus cells which finally rupture under the mounting pressure of air within. Eventually the lossened small, convex lid is blown off with explosive force (E). The imprisoned air is suddenly released and with it the spores in a cloud. Ingold (1939) described this method of spore discharge in *Sphagnum* as 'air gun' mechanism. The spores discharged upward into the air (D) are readily taken up by the wind and dispersed.

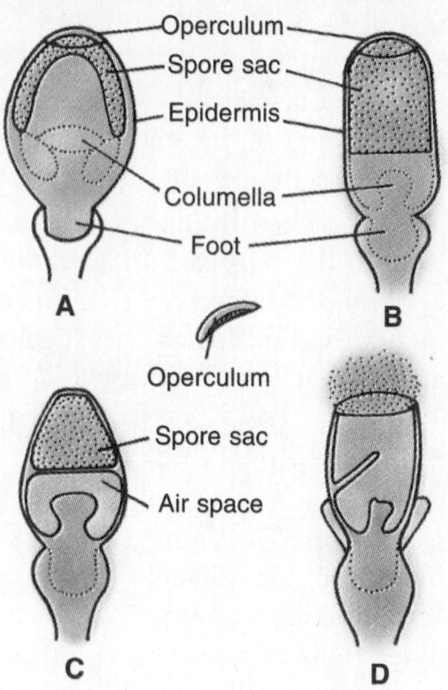

Fig. 16.20. (A—D). ***Sphagnum*** sp. Stages in the dehiscence of sporogonium. A, an outline sketch of undehisced capsule at the onset of drying; B—C, the same after drying just before dehiscence; D, capsule with a lid blown off releasing spores forcibly; E, blown off lid.

From the account given above it is evident that the chief peculiarities of the *Sphagnum* sporophyte are : (*i*) absence of seta, (*ii*) absence of peristome teeth, (*iii*) air gun mechanism of spore discharge, (*iv*) dome-shaped spore sac, and (*v*) development of sporogneous tissue from the amphithecium.

Spore structure. The released spores are the pioneer structures of the future young gametophyte. They are tetrahedral in form and yellow to brown in colour. Each spore is a uninucleated tiny mass of protoplast protected by the surrounding spore wall. Spore cytoplasm contains one to several large oil droplets (*S. palustre*). The spore wall is differentiated into two layers, **outer exine** (exosporium) and **inner intine** (endosporium). The exine is brown smooth or roughened with punctae. The triradiate mark is prominent.

Brown *et al* (1982) using electron microscope discovered that the spore exine in *S. lescurii* is differentiated into two layers (*i*) an inner lamellate layer termed *A layer* and outer thick homogeneous layer called *B layer*. The spore exine of *Sphagnum* thus differs from the exine of other mosses which consists of only the outermost homogeneous layer and at the most a thin ill-defined opaque *separating layer*. The *B layer* of exine in *Sphagnum* is responsible for the primary sculpturing of the spore surface. In a mature spore external to the exine is the perine. It forms the secondary surface ornamentation. A trilaesirate pore occurs on the proximal surface of each spore. It does not penetrate the *A layer* of the exine. The lamellate *A layer* of exine is in direct contact with the inner intine layer of spore wall. The intine is fibrillar. It is composed of thin closely spaced lamellae.

Germination of spores (Fig. 16.21). The spores remain viable for six months under dry conditions. Under suitable conditions the spore (A) germinates within a weak's time. It absorbs water and swells up slightly (A). The exosporium ruptures (B). The endosporium grows through the split as a short protuberance, the *germ tube* which turns green. The green tube grows and divides by transverse septa to form a short, green filament of 2 to 4 usually 3 cells (C). At this stage the terminal cell of the filament begins to function as an apical cell (C). It has two cutting faces (D). Segments are cut off parallel to these alternately right and left (D). Eventually a flat green protonema is formed (E).

The protonema. It consists of photosynthetic cells. They are arranged in the form of a plate, one cell thick. During further growth the apical cell becomes inactive and indistinguishable. Certain marginal cells of the plate-like protonema undergo anticlinal and periclinal divisions. As a result the primary protonema becomes an irregularly lobed, green plate, one cell in thickness (F). It is fixed to the substratum by colourless, multicellular rhizoids with oblique septa. The rhizoids are unbranched. The ruptured exospore persists at the base of the protonema for a long time. From one of the marginal cells near the base of the primary protonema arises the erect, leafy gametophore. The cell in question by growth and segmentation form a tiny bud (F). Soon a tetrahedral apical cell becomes established in the bud (G). It cuts off segments like the apical cell of the adult gametophore. As a result an upright, apically growing shoot of *Sphagnum* is formed. Normally one leafy shoot is developed from a single protonema (Fig. 16.2 B). According to Bold (1948), the first 3 leaves are homogeneous in cell structure. The 4th or 5th leaf on the young gametophore shows typical cellular dimorphism. The protonema becomes moribund and soon disappears after the establishment of the leafy gametophore.

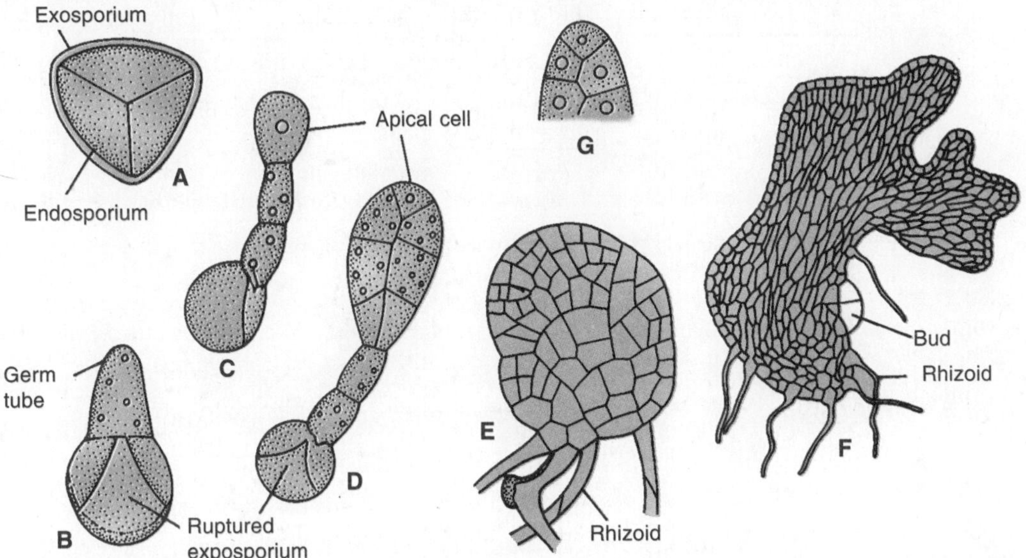

Fig. 16.21. (A—G). ***Sphagnum*** sp. Germination of spore and stages in the development of primary protonema (Based on Muller).

Boatman and Lark (1971) reported that the large, thallus-like protonema of *Sphagnum* as described in text books develops only when the culture medium contains mineral salts at concentrations considerably in excess of those which the plants are likely to encounter in nature. In a solution with reduced concentration, the filamentous system becomes more extensive and thallus is reduced in size. Goebel (1889) reported that the spores always produce a flat prothallium on a solid substrate if light is sufficiently intense. Bold (1948) observed that the factors which govern the initial form of the young protonema are light and available mineral nutrients. Diffuse light in cultures promotes filamentous growth of the germlings and intense light initiates flat thallose form. Anderson and Crosby (1965) reported that in cultures of *S. meridense* many germinating spores develop directly into the prothallia condition.

The protonema stage may be propagated vegetatively. Any marginal cell of the thallose primary protonema may become meristematic. By growth and segmentation it grows into a green cellular filament. The apical portion of the filament in turn may grow into a new green, flat thallus-like structure. It is called the **secondary protonema** (Fig. 16.9). Goebel (1889) reported that prothallia could proliferate from the tips of rhizoids and form protonemal branches.

ECONOMIC IMPORTANCE

It is only genus of the bryophytes which is of real worth. The peat deposits are cut into blocks, dried and used as fuel. Because of its superior absorptive powers and antiseptic properties, carefully dried, cleaned and sterilized *Sphagnum* has been employed for gauze to dress wounds and is used for other surgical dressings in hospitals. For its ability to hold water tenaciously, dried *Sphagnum* is remoistened and used for packing live plants and cut flowers which are to be shipped and thus are to be protected from drying. Peat is also of great use in horticulture. It is added to heavy (clayey) soils to improve their texture as it keeps them porous and prevents caking. When added to dry, sandy soils or other humus poor soils, it improves their water holding capacity. It is employed by gardeners as a substratum in which seeds are germinated and other plants are grown. It is as well used as a packing for grafting scions to protect them against drying influence of the surrounding air.

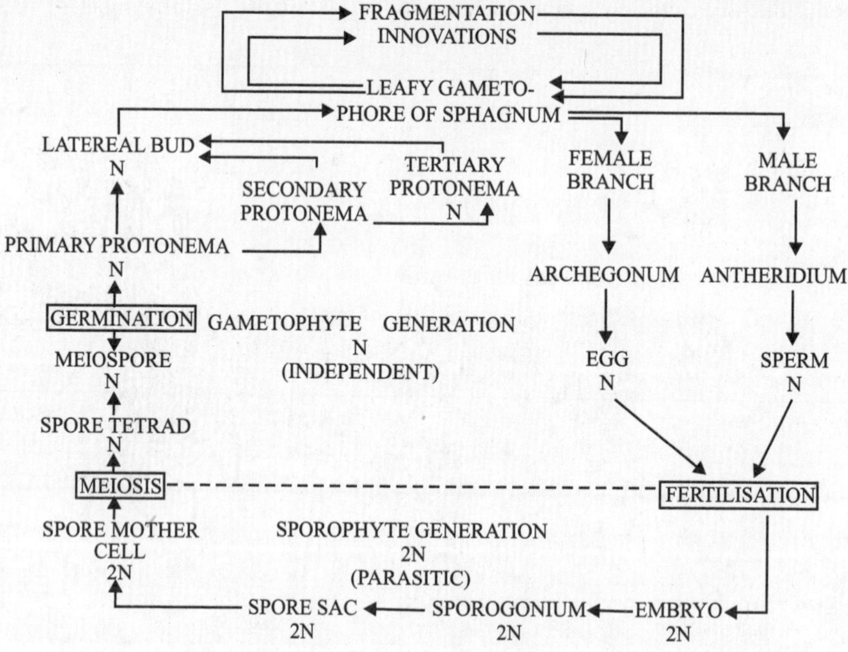

Fig. 16.22. Sphagnum sp. Word diagram of the life cycle.

Some of the by-products of peat such as peat tar, ammonia, and paraffin are of industrial use. By filling ponds, pools and lakes with its extensive growth and debris these areas are converted into solid earth. Hence this moss is considered a great soil builder. *Sphagnum* is also employed as a stuffing material in upholstery and also as bedding for domesticated animals.

Species of *Sphagnum* both alive and air-dried have been widely used as indicators of both atmospheric and aquatic pollution. Ferguson *et al* (1928) established the sensitivity of *Sphagnum* species to sulphur pollution. More recently Ferguson *et al* (1984) investigated element concentration in five species of *Sphagnum* in relation to atmospheric pollution. The *Sphagna* accumulate elements in three ways, (*i*) By net influx of solutes into the assimilatory cells, (*ii*) By ion uptake at the exchange sites of cell walls of assimilatory and capillary cell walls, and (*iii*) By accumulation of particles of pollutants on the surface of the stem, leaves and within the capillary cells.

Ecological Importance

Sphagnum is of great ecological importance. As it establishes itself on the shore of a lake it gradually extends inwards and grows over water. The surface of water in the lake is finally completely covered. The *Sphagnum* plants are intertwined so as to give the appearance of solid soil from the surface. Such areas are called the **quacking bogs**. Sometimes seed plants (hydrophytic) grow on the bog. The moss plants gradually die and settle to the bottom. In the course of long periods of time these swamps, ponds, and lakes, which were sterile sheets of water, become filled with partially decomposed, old parts of this moss and other hydrophytic plants. Finally these areas are converted into solid soil. The constantly accumulated debris raises the surface level. The moss and the other hydrophytic angiosperms gradually disappear. They are replaced by forest growth of mesophytic type. In this way *Sphagnum* moss modifies the landscape in regions with small lakes and ponds.

AFFINITIES OR RELATIONSHIPS

Sphagnum is a unique genus of the Mosses. One is struck by the remarkable mixture of liverwort, anthocerote and moss characters it possesses. In addition it possesses certain characters in which it stands apart from all the three.

Sphagnum **resembles** the **true mosses** in the following features :

1. Radial, leafy, upright gametophore.
2. Multicellular rhizoids with oblique septa.
3. Apical growth of stem, leaves and antheridia as in the mosses. The development of the antheridium is after the manner of the mosses.
4. Structure of the archegonium.
5. Absence of elaters.
6. Dehiscence of the capsule by the separation of a lid.
7. Rupturing of the calyptra.

In view of the above-mentioned characteristics which *Sphagnum* shares with the true mosses it is rightly placed in the class Musci or Bryopsida.

Sphagnum **differs** *from the* **higher mosses** in its peculiar gross morphology, leaf anatomy and certain features of the sporophyte. These are enumerated as follows :—

1. Broadly thallose protonema.
2. Absence of rhizoids in the adult gametophyte.
3. Origin of branches in clusters in the axils of leaves.
4. The spongy cortex of the mature stem consisting of dead, empty cells with pores on their walls.
5. Presence of two kinds of cells in the leaves; larger, dead, **hyaline** perforate cells and living **green** cells.
6. Development of archesporium from the amphithecium.
7. Archesporium over-arching the columella.
8. Origin of the columella from the entire endothecium.
9. Early development of the embryo by a succession of transverse walls.
10. Presence of pseudopodium and absence of seta.
11. Absence of peristome teeth.

From among the **Liverworts** *Sphagnum resembles* the **Jungermanniales** in the following respects:—

1. Flat, disc-like protonema resembles the juvenile stage of some Jungermanniales.
2. Axillary position of antheridia, and their dehiscence like Jungermanniales.

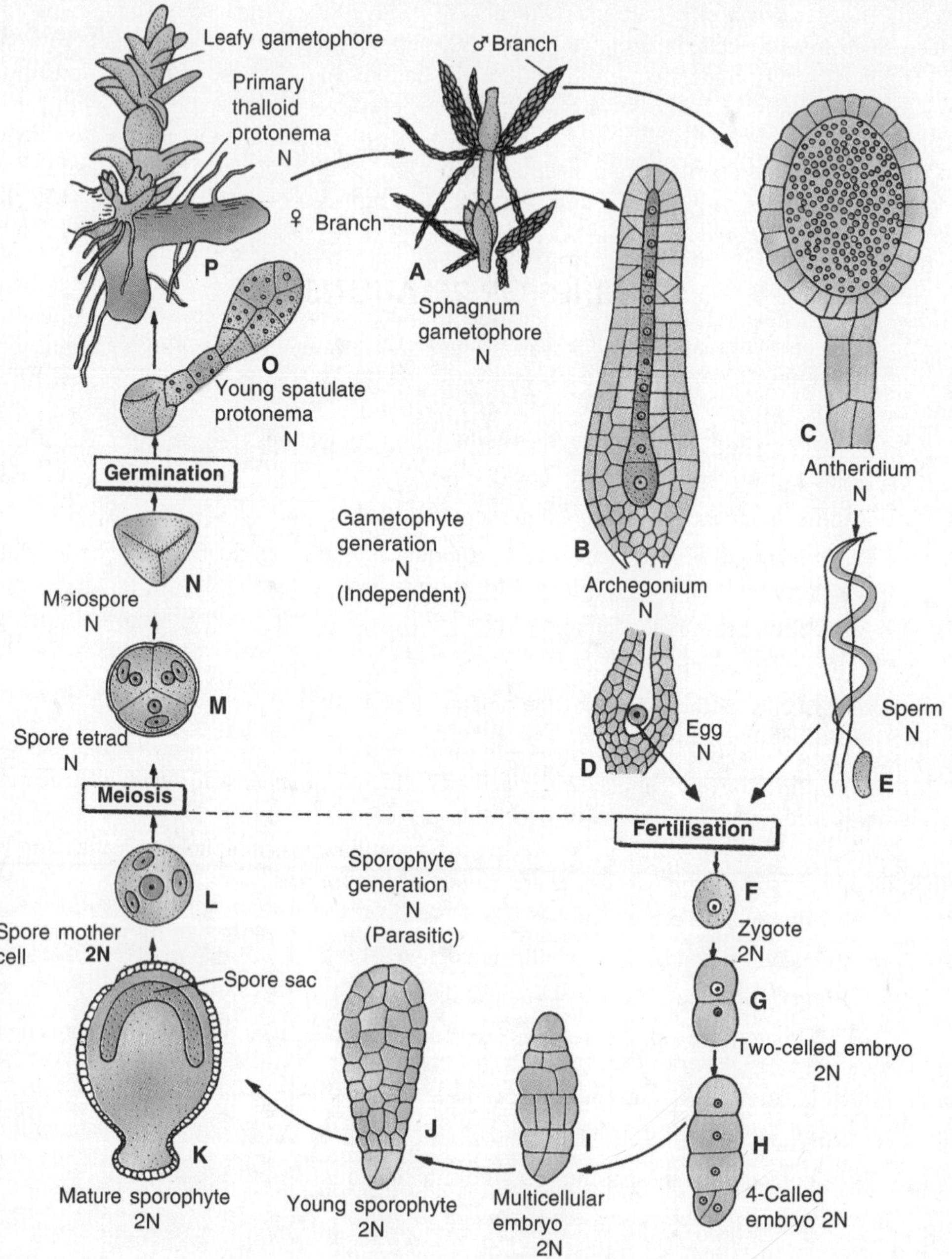

Fig. 16.23. ***Sphagnum.*** Pictorial sketch of the sexual life cycle.

3. Position and development of archegonia like Jungermanniales.

4. Presence of rudimentary stomata scattered over the capsule wall is another feature in which it resembles the Jungermanniales.

These similarities between the Jungermanniales and *Sphagnum* point to the intermediate position which the latter occupies between the **Liverworts** and the **Mosses**.

Features **common** with the **Anthocerotae** (**Anthocerotopsida**) are :—

1. Absence of apical growth in the embryo sporophyte.

2. Origin of the archesporium from the amphithecium.

3. Dome-shaped amphithecium over-arching the columella.

4. Entire endothecium forming the columella.

5. Presence of assimilatory tissue in the capsule wall which of course is not ventilated.

6. Presence of massive foot and constriction-like seta.

These features serve to link *Sphagnum* to the **Anthocerotae** rather than to the true Mosses. However, in its spherical form, absence of basal meristem, absence of any type of elaters and dehiscence of the capsule by the separation of a lid, the sporophyte of *Sphagnum* differs from that of *Anthoceros*.

From the foregoing account it is evident that *Sphagnum* combines the characters of all the three classes of the bryophytes. It serves to link them together. Such forms are called the **synthetic types.**

Characters peculiar to Sphagnum are:—

1. Absence of **rhizoids** in the adult gametophore.

2. Origin of branches in **tufts** from the axil of every fourth leaf.

3. Absence of a **midrib** in the leaves.

4. Unique structure of the stem and the leaves. The cortex of the old stems is **spongy** or **porous** in nature. It consists of **hyaline cells** with large, oval pores and sometimes with spiral thickenings also. The leaf consists of a single layer of two kinds of cells : the large dead, **hyaline cells** with pores and the narrow, elongated green **assimilatory cells.**

5. Peculiar physiology of water absorption, retention and conduction.

6. Presence of some organic substance of a colloidal nature in the cell walls. It absorbs the base and releases the acid. For this reason the water in which *Sphagnum* grows is highly acidic.

SYSTEMATIC POSITION OF *SPHAGNUM*

Division	:	Bryophyta
Class	:	Bryopsida or Musci
Sub-class	:	Sphagnidae
Order	:	Sphagnales
Family	:	Sphagnaceae
Genus	:	*Sphagnum*
Species	:	*palustre*

QUESTIONS

ESSAY TYPE

1. " *Sphagnum* is a connecting link between liverworts and mosses". Discuss. *(Awadh, 1992)*

2. Describe the structure of the gametophyte of *Sphagnum* with the help of suitable diagrams. *(Awadh, 1994)*

3. (*a*) Give an illustrated account of the sporophyte of *Sphagnum* and the mechanism of dehiscence of its capsule. *(U.P. College, 1998; Bihar, 1990; Ranchi 1991; Vinoba Bhave, 1999)* (*b*) Illustrate diagrammatic description of sporophyte of moss (*Poorvanchal, 2006*)

4. Describe the life cycle of *Sphagnum* with suitable diagrams. (*Gorakhpur, 1997*)
5. Give a comparative account of gametophytes of *Sphagnum* and *Pogonatum*. (*Gorakhpur, 1998*)
6. What is the difference between sporogonium and sporangium? Write a comparative account of sporogonium of *Porella* and *Sphagnum*. (*Allahabad, 1992, 1999*)
7. With the help of labelled diagrams only compare the sporophytes of *Anthoceros, Pellia* and *Sphagnum*. (*Allahabad, 1993*)
8. Describe the structure of Sporophyte of *Sphagnum*. (*Allahabad, 1997; Vinoba Bhave, 1997*)
9. Give a brief account of the development and structure of archegonia in *Sphagnum*. (*Allahabad, 2000*)
10. Give a comparative account of the sporophytes of *Sphagnum* and *Pogonatum*. (*Poorvanchal, 1999*)
11. Write the morphology, life history, phylogeny and affinities of Sphagnales. Support your answer with suitable diagrams.
12. What are characteristic features of Sphagnales? Give their affinities. (*Rohilkhand M.Sc., 1990*)
13. Give an illustrated account of the structure and development of antheridium in *Sphagnum*. (*Gurunanak Dev, 1992*)
14. Give a brief account of the structure and development of sporophyte in *Sphagnum*. (*Vir Kumar Singh, 1990; Bhagalpur, 1991*)
15. Mention the salient features in the life history of *Sphagnum*. (*Magadh, 1996, 1999*)
16. Describe the morphology and anatomy of *Sphagnum* plant. (*Himachal Pradesh, 1993*)
17. Give an illustrated account of the external and internal features of the gametophyte of *Sphagnum*. (*Himachal Pradesh, 1995*)
18. Discuss the gametophytic generations of *Sphagnum* and *Pogonatum* (*Bihar, 1992*)
19. What is an archesporium? What does it contribute to in *Marchantia, Anthoceros* and *Sphagnum*. (*Bhagalpur, 1990*)
20. Discuss how sporophyte of *Sphagnum* is formed? What is the economic importance of this moss? (*Ranchi, 1992*)
21. "*Sphagnum* is a unique member of Bryophytes" Discuss (*Vinoba Bhave, 1997*)
22. Describe the sporophyte of *Sphagnum*. Discuss its affinities with Hepaticae, Anthocerotae and mosses. (*Vinoba Bhave, 1998*)
23. List the salient features met within the life cycle of *Sphagnum*
24. Describe the strucutre and development of sex organs in *Sphagnum*.
25. Describe the external and internal morphology of the sporophyte of *Sphagnum*. Of what advantage is the seta to the Moss sporophyte? How does *Sphagnum* compensate for its absence?
26. Describe briefly the salient features of the genus *Sphagnum* Justify the view for considering *Sphagnum* as a synthetic type of between Hepaticae and musci. (*Gauhati M.Sc. 2002*)
27. (*a*) With the help of suitable diagrams, describe the position and structure of sex organs in *Sphagnam*. (*Poorvanchal, 2005*)

    (*b*) Illustrate diagrammatic description of gametophytic of moss. (*Poorvanchal, 2005*)
28. Give an illustrated account of *Riccia Porella* and *Sphagnum* (*Allahabad, 2006*)
29. Classify the following genera :
    (*a*) *Notothylas*
    (*b*) *Targionia*
    (*c*) *Polytrichum*
    (*d*) *Sphagnum* (*Kanpur, M.Sc., 2006*)
30. Briefly discuss structure and development of *Sporogonium* in *Sphagnum*. (*Lucknow, M.Sc., 2007*)

SHORT ANSWER TYPE

31. What are retort cells? *(Awadh, 1993)*

32. Draw labelled diagrams only of the life cycle of *Sphagnum*.

33. Give reasons to explain the following :

(*a*) Dried and Dead remains of *Sphagnum* plants serve as an excellent absorbent.

(*b*) Sex organs are produced in abundance in *Sphagnum* but sporophytes are only rarely found.

34. Discuss the affinities of *Sphagnum*.

35. Draw labelled diagrams of the following :

(*i*) V.L.S. sprophyte of *Sphagnum* *(Awadh, 1993, 1995, 1997, 1998; U.P. College 1999, 2000; Gorakhpur, 1998; Allahabad, 2000, 2005, 2006; Poorvanchal, 1996, 2000, 2001, 2002)*

(*ii*) Leaf of *Sphagnum*. *(Awadh, 2000; Poorvanchal, 1999)*

(*iii*) L.S. of the mature sporogonium *(Poorvanchal, 2004, 2006; Gorakhpur, 1990)*

(*iv*) Leaf and leaf cells of *Sphagnum* (*Gorakhpur*, 1992)

(*v*) L.S. Capsule of *Sphagnum* (*Allahabad, 2004; Gorakhpur*, 1993)

(*vi*) Different types of cells in the leaf of *Sphagnum* (*Gorakhpur*, 1994)

(*vii*) V.L.S. antheridial head of *Sphagnum* *(Gorakhpur, 1996)*

(*viii*) T.S. capsule of *Sphagnum* *(Allahabad, 1996)*

(*ix*) L.S. sporophyte of Moss *(Poorvanchal, 2005)*

36. Write short notes on :

(*i*) *Sphagnum* leaf *(Awadh, 1997; Gorakhpur, 1999; Allahabad, 1993, 1999, 2002; Poorvanchal 1996, 1998; Kanpur M.Sc. 1994; Vir Kumar Singh, 1992; Magadh, 1994, 1996; Himachal Pradesh, 1994, 1995; Vinoba Bhave, 1999)*

(*ii*) Structure of leaf in *Sphagnum* *(Gorakhpur, 1990)*

(*iii*) Retort cells *(Gorakhpur, 1991; Himachal Pradesh 1999)*

(*iv*) Dehiscence of capsule in *Sphagnum* *(Gorakhpur, 1993, 1998)*

(*v*) Compare the external morphology of thalli of *Porella, Sphagnum* and *Pogonatum* *(Gorakhpur, 1994)*

(*vi*) Economic importance of *Sphagnum* *(Allahabad, 2005; Poorvanchal; M.Sc. 1998; Gorakhpur, 1995; Vinoba Bhave, 1997)*

(*vii*) Sporophyte of *Sphagnum* *(Gorakhpur, 1999)*

(*viii*) *Pseudopodium* *(Allahabad, 1992, 1996, 1997)*

(*ix*) Antheridial head in *Sphagnum* *(Allahabad, 1994)*

(*x*) Details of leaf cells of *Sphagnum* *(Allahabad, 1998)*

(*xi*) *Sphagnum* *(Awadh, M.Sc. 1997; Kanpur, M.Sc. 1996, 1997)*

(*xii*) Capsule of *Sphagnum* *(Magadh, 1990, 1994, 1995)*

(*xiii*) Economic and ecological significance of *Sphagnum* *(Himachal Pradesh, 1992, 1994, 1999)*

(*xiv*) Structure of sporophyte of *Sphagnum* *(Rohilkhand, 2003)*

(*xv*) Structure and mechanism of dehiscence of capsule in *Sphagnum.* *(Allahabad M.Sc. 1999)*

(*xvi*) Antheridial branch of *Sphagnum* *(Allahabad, 2005)*

37. Draw annotated sketches only to bring about the distinguishing features of the following :

(*i*) Protonema of *Funaria* and *Sphagnum* *(Allahabad, 1992)* (*ii*) Archegonia of *Porella* and *Sphagnum* *(Allahabad, 1992)*

(*iii*) *Protonema* of *Sphagnum* *(Allahabad, 1997)*

(*iv*) L.S. Sporogonium of *Anthoceros* and *Sphagnum* *(Himachal Pradesh, 1997)*

(*v*) Surface view of leaf of *Sphagnum* under microscope. *(Bhagalpur, 1991)*

38. Comment upon the following :

(*i*) Mechanism of dehiscence of Capsule in *Andreaea* and *Sphagnum* *(Awadh M.Sc., 2000; Rohilkhand M.Sc., 1991)*

(*ii*) Affinities between Sphagnales and Andreales *(Rohilkhand M.Sc., 1993)*

(*iii*) Identification of *Sphagnum* *(Rohilkhand M.Sc., 1997)*

(*iv*) Sporophytes of *Marchantia* and *Sphagnum* *(Magadh, 1995)*

(*v*) *Antheridia* of *Sphagnum* and *Riccia*. *(Allahabad, 2002)*

(*vi*) Peat Moss *(Kanpur, 2004)*

39. How will you distinguish between :

(*i*) *Sphagnum* and *Pogonatum*? *(Kanpur M.Sc., 1998)*

(*ii*) *Sphagnum* and *Polytrichum* *(Kanpur M.Sc., 1999)*

(*iii*) Sporogonium of *Madotheca* and *Sphagnum* *(Himachal Pradesh, 2000)*

(*iv*) Gametophyte of *Sphagnum* and *Pogonatum* *(Vir Kumar Singh, 1993)*

(*v*) *Antheridia* of *Sphagnum* and *Riccia*. *(Allahabad, 2002)*

40. Describe the salient features of gametophyte of *Sphagnum* . *(Magadh, 1996)*

41. Give the systematic position of *Sphagnum*. *(Punjab, 1993)*

42. Describe the sporogonium of *Sphagnum*. *(Himachal Pradesh, 1990)*

43. Describe the internal structure of the stem of *Sphagnum*. *(Himachal Pradesh, 1995)*

44. Draw the structure of sporogonium of *Sphagnum* and write its mechanism of dehiscence. *(Himachal Pradesh, 1995)*

45. Explain what prevents the collapsing of chlorophyllous cells in *Sphagnum*. *(Himachal Pradesh, 1997)*

46. Why *Sphagnum* plant is used in surgical dressing in hospitals? *(Himachal Pradesh, 1997)*

47. (*a*) Describe the dehiscence mechanisms of the sporophytes of *Sphagnum* and *Funaria*.

(*b*) Compare the archegonia of *Marchantia*, *Anthoceros, Sphagnum* and *Funaria*. *(Himachal Pradesh, 1998)*

48. Briefly describe the biological importance of *Sphagnum*.

49. Which moss capsule is devoid of peristome teeth? *(U.P. College, 1997)*

50. (*a*) Give the botanical name of bog moss or peat moss. *(Poorvanchal, 2002; U.P. College, 1998)*

(*b*) Write botanical name of peat moss *(Allahabad, 2006)*

(*c*) Describe peat moss *(Kanpur, M.Sc., 2007)*

51. Name the embryonic layer in *Sphagnum* from which archesporium originates. *(U.P. College,* 2000)

52. Name the bryophyte that has a remarkable power to absorb and hold water like a sponge is used as antiseptic and is a potential source of coal. *(Gorakhpur, 1990)*

53. Name a bryophyte which has the capacity to store water. *(Gorakhpur, 1993)*

54. Name a bryophyte which lacks rhizoids in mature gametophyte. *(Gorakhpur, 1996)*

55. What is the function of pseudopodium in *Sphagnum*? *(Gorakhpur, 1999)*

56. Name a bryophyte which has pseudopodium. *(Allahabad, 1992, 1999, 2001)*

57. What is the ecological importance of *Sphagnum* ? *(Allahabad, 1992)*

58. Name a bryophyte which is commonly called as the "peat moss". *(Allahabad 1992; Poorvanchal, 2000)*

59. Name the moss in which the capsule lacks the peristome teeth. *(Allahabad, 1996, 1997)*

60. What is the name given to the conducting column of centrally located cells of certain bryophytes? *(Allahabad, 1998)*

61. Name a bryophyte which has a pseudopodium. *(Allahabad, 2004)*

62. Give a brief account of development and structure of archegonia in *Sphagnum.* *(Allahabad, 2004)*

63. Sex organs are produced in abundance in *Sphagnum* but sporophytes are only rarely found. Give reasons. *(Poorvanchal, 2003)*

64. Describe the mechanism of spore discharge in *Sphagnum.* *(Poorvanchal, 2003)*

65. How many kinds of component cells are seen in the leaf anatomy of *Sphagnum.* *(Poorvanchal, 2003)*

66. Give the name of an antibiotic obtained from peat moss. *(Poorvanchal, 2003)*

67. Give the differences between *Sporogonium* of *Madotheca* and *Sphagnum.* *(Himachal Pradesh, 2000)*

68. How many types of cells are present in the leaves of *Sphagnum.* *(Kanpur M.Sc. 2003)*

69. Name the bryophyte in which retort cells are found. *(Allahabad, 1998, 2001)*

70. Write botanical name of the bryophyte which is called "Cotton moss". *(Poorvanchal, 1997)*

71. Describe the habitat of *Sphagnum.* *(Ajmer; 1998)*

72. Describe leaf arrangement in *Sphagnum.* *(Punjab, 1993)*

73. Describe vegetative reproduction in *Sphagnum* very briefly.

74. Write the salient features of Sphagnales.

75. How many types of cells are present in leaves of *Sphagnum* ? *(Kanpur, 2003)*

76. Write a note or identifycation of sphagnum *(Kanpur, M.Sc., 2009)*

77. Name Peat Moss. Describe *(Kanpur, M.Sc., 2006)*

OBJECTIVE TYPE

78. **Select the correct answer :**

(*i*) Which of the following has only foot and capsule in its sporophytes?
(*a*) *Riccia* (*b*) *Marchantia*
(*c*) *Anthoceros* (*d*) *Sphagnum.*

(*ii*) Retort cells are present in
(*a*) *Porella* (*b*) *Sphagnum*
(*c*) *Anthoceros* (*d*) *Pogonatum.*

(*iii*) The bryophyte responsible for forming "creeping bogs" and "blanket bogs" is
(*a*) *Riccia* (*b*) *Pellia*
(*c*) *Anthoceros* (*d*) *Sphagnum.*

(*iv*) Sporogenous tissue is of amphithecial origin in
(*a*) *Riccia* (*b*) *Pellia*
(*c*) *Marchantia* (*d*) *Sphagnum.*

(*v*) Peristome is absent in
(*a*) *Funaria* (*b*) *Sphagnum*
(*c*) *Polytrichum* (*d*) *Pogonatum.*

(*vi*) Spore mother cell in *Sphagnum* is
(*a*) Haploid (*b*) Diploid
(*c*) Triploid (*d*) Tetraploid.

(*vii*) The pseudopodium present at the base of sporophyte in *Sphagnum* is
(*a*) elongated part of archegonial axis
(*b*) basal part of the foot of the sporophyte
(*c*) part of the seta of the sporophyte
(*d*) part of the seta and foot.

(*viii*) In *Sphagnum* the spore sac is
(*a*) Spindle shaped
(*b*) Arc shaped
(*c*) Dome shaped
(*d*) Disc shaped.

(*ix*) In *Sphagnum* the zygote first divides
(*a*) Transversely
(*b*) Longitudinally
(*c*) Obliquely
(*d*) Irregularly.

(*x*) Pseudopodium is present in
(*a*) *Sphagnum* (*b*) *Pellia*
(*c*) *Porella* (*d*) *Marchantia.*

(*xi*) Vaginula is present in the sporophyte of
(*a*) *Porella* (*b*) *Funaria*
(*c*) *Sphagnum* (*d*) *Anthoceros.*

(*xii*) Peat moss is the common name for
(*a*) *Funaria* (*b*) *Andreaea*
(*c*) *Pogonatum* (*d*) *Sphagnum.*

(*xiii*) The rhizoids are absent in mature gametophytes of
(*a*) *Funaria* (*b*) *Andreaea*
(*c*) *Sphagnum* (*d*) *Pogonatum.*

(*xiv*) *Sphagnum* belongs to the order
(*a*) *Marchantiales* (*b*) Andreales
(*c*) Polytrichales (*d*) Sphagnales.

(*xv*) Young leaves in *Sphagnum* gametophyte are arranged
(*a*) Spirally
(*b*) Alternately
(*c*) Opposite to each
(*d*) Without any specific phyllotaxy.

(*xvi*) Hyaline and retort cells are found in the leaves of
(*a*) *Sphagnum* (*b*) *Pogonatum*
(*c*) *Pogonatum* (*d*) *Andreaea.*

79. Fill in the blanks:

(*i*) Young leaves are spirally arranged in three vertical rows with a divergence of ____________ in *Sphagnum.*

(*ii*) Vaginula is present in the sporophytes of ______________.

(*iii*) Retort cells are found in the ______________ of *Sphagnum.*

(*iv*) In *Sphagnum* pseudopodium is ______________.

(*v*) Peat moss is the common name for ______________.

(*vi*) The lone representative of the order Sphagnales is ____________.

(*vii*) Spore sac in *Sphagnum* Capsule is ____________ shaped.

(*viii*) *Rhizoids* are absent in mature gametophytes in ____________.

(*ix*) Peristome is ____________ in *Sphagnum.*

(*x*) Although sex organs are present in plenty in *Sphagnum*, the sporophytes are ______________.

Image of *Andreaea*

CHAPTER 17

ANDREAEIDAE – Andreaeales – Andreaea

- General Characteristics
- Order Andreaeales
- Affinities of Andreaeidae
- Systematic position of Andreaea

GENERAL CHARACTERISTICS

The subclass Andreaeidae is a small group of low growing, brittle dark brown or reddish-coloured, rock inhabiting mosses. These share some features with Sphagnidae and some with Bryidae and thus form a connecting link between the two subclasses. There is nothing remarkable about the leafy shoots of these mosses. They exhibit vegetative structure generally similar to that of the Bryidae but are distinguishable by the strikingly peculiar capsule, sex organs and protonema on the basis of which these mosses are placed in a separate subclass Andreaeidae. The chief characteristics of this subclass are : (1) the protonema, as in *Sphagnum*, is thalloid and the forerunner of the leafy shoot is either a plate of cells or a cylindrical cell mass; (2) the stem lacks the central conducting strand; (3) the leaves are with or without a midrib; (4) the cells of both the stem and the leaf are notably thick-walled; (5) there is a tendency to replace initial rhizoids by cylindrical or plate like masses of cells—an unusual feature; (6) the perichaetial leaves are erect, convolute and enlarged; (7) the apical cell is involved in the formation of sex organs; (8) the seta remains undeveloped and the ripe capsule is raised on a post fertilization leafless gametophore stalk termed the **pseudopodium**—a feature in common with *Sphagnum*; (9) the sporogenous tissue and columella are endothecial in origin as in the Bryidae; (10) the spore sac extends like a dome over the central columella as in *Sphagnum*; (11) the minute ovoid mature capsule tapers a little both at the base and tip; (12) measuring only 0.5 mm in length, it is perhaps amongst the smallest known; (13) another peculiarity of the mature capsule is its hygroscopic wall and mode of dehiscence by four to eight longitudinal slits which do not meet at the tip.

It is obvious that the capsule of Andreaeidae agrees with that of the Bryidae only in the endothecial origin of spore producing tissue and columella but in all other counts it is just as unusual as *Sphagnum*. This subclass includes a single order Andreaeales.

ORDER ANDREAEALES

It is a small order with one family Andreaceae and with two genera, *Andreaea* and *Androbryum*. We study *Andreaea* as a type.

ANDREAEA (Hedw.)

Distribution. This genus includes about 125 species. They are widely distributed all over the globe. Most of them grow in regions with a cold climate. They are thus abundant in the arctic, antarctic and the temperate region. In the warmer regions they occur at higher altitude at the top of very high mountains. In Britain *Andreaea* is represented by many species. Four have been recorded from Sikkim (Eastern Himalayas) in India. These are *A. pterophyla*, *A. densifolia*, *A rigida and A. indica*.

Habitat. Majority of the species occur in alpine or subalpine habitats in extremely Xeric substrates inhabiting exposed siliceous mountain rocks. For this reason *Andreaea* is popularly called the "granite moss". A few species such as *A. navalis* grow on endocyte rocks submerged in the water of streams.

Habit. Small in size and dark-brown to almost black or bluish green in colour and quite brittle *Andreaea* grows in dense tufts upon siliceous mountain rocks or in crevices with its prostrate stem firmly anchored by curiously modified plate-like or cylindrical cell masses. The leafy gametophore is hardly 1 cm in height. This moss is distinguished by its strikingly peculiar capsule.

Gametophyte (Fig. 17.1. A). The forerunner of the leafy gametophore is the juvenile protonema base, which like that of *Sphagnum*, is thallose. The short, slender stem of the leafy shoot is prostrate. It grows horizontally over the surface of rocks and branches freely. The branching is sympodial with apparent dichotomies in which one branch grows much more vigorously than the other. Numerous rhizoids originate in tufts from the basal part of the creeping stem. These are not uniseriate multicellular, branched filaments with oblique cross walls as in the mosses in general but are strikingly peculiar in structure. These are either cylindrical masses of cells or flattened cell plates which function as anchoring organs. The former are useful in penetrating the crevices of the hard rock and the latter make firm anchorage on is surface. Scott and Redhead (1973) who studied the rhizoids of five species of *Andreaea* reported that

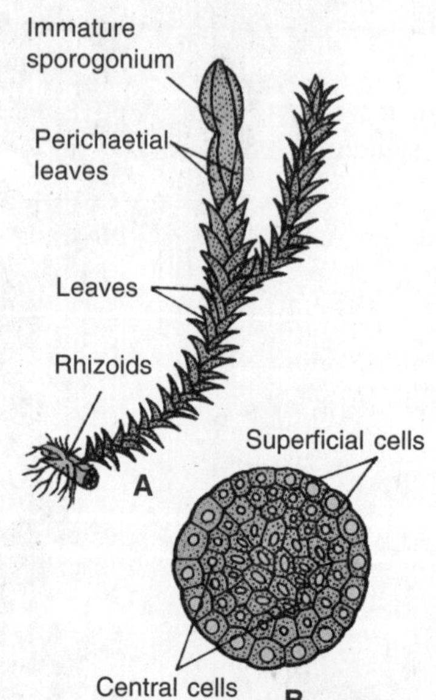

Fig. 17.1. (A—D) ***Andreaea*** sp. A, median longitudinal section of a mature antheridium; B-D, early stages in the developemnt of antheridium.

these are of four morphological types, namely, uniseriate and biseriate filamentous forms and cylindric cell mass plus cell plate forms. The rhizoids which originates in tufts from the basal part of the leafy shoot are biseriate. The oblique cross walls of two series of cells are almost continuous with each other in the same plane. The initial biseriate rhizoids branch. The branches are either uniseriate or biseriate. The biseriate rhizoids of plants growing on hard rock surfaces are shorter and repeatedly branched forming cell plate masses and connecting cylindric cell masses. He further stated that a thick layer of some unknown substance occurs on the tips of rhizoids of plants growing on hard substrate. Possibly this layer assists in anchoring the plant to the bare rocky surface. Odu (1978) reported that the development of rhizoids in tufts in prostrate (pleurocarp) mosses (*Andreaea*) on hard substrates is probably a specialization for stronger anchorage. The rhizoid bases on the stem may also become fused thus increasing mechanical strength.

The leaves clotting the stem are small, smooth, olive to brown in colour and brittle. They are closely set on the slender stem and on the branch axes and are arranged specially in three rows. In shape they vary with the species ranging from ovate to subulate with a distinct nerve in some species (*A. rothii* and *A. blyttii*) and nerveless in most other species (*A. obovata* and *A. rupestris*). In the species lacking the midrib, the leaf is one cell in thickness throughout, whereas in others only the region of the midrib is more than one cell in thickness. The leaf cells have notably thick walls and are more or less rounded in shape.

The stem in cross section shows no distinction into outer cortex and the central strand (Fig. 17.1 B). It shows uniform structure consisting of uniformly thick-walled cells. The outer cells, however, may have somewhat thicker with darker-coloured walls than the inner ones.

Apical growth. It takes place by the activity of a tetrahedral apical cell in the stem. Each segment cut off parallel to its segmenting face produces a leaf and a portion of the stem subtending it. In this way the leaves are produced from the stem tip in a spiral manner arranged in three rows with 3/8 divergence.

Sexual reproduction. Generally *Andreaea* is homothallic (monoecious). The antheridia and archegonia are borne in terminal groups on the separate branches of the same plant. A few species for instance, *A. nivalis* and *A. blyttii* are heterothallic (dioecious). The apical cell of the leafy gametophore is involved in the formation of sex organs.

Antheridia (*a*) *Position and structure*. The antheridia occur in a terminal cluster on the male branch. The antheridial cluster is surrounded by a number of male (perigonial) bracts. Interspersed among the antherida in the cluster are numerous filamentous paraphyses.

The mature antheridium (Fig. 17.2 A) has an ellipsoidal or nearly globular body raised on a long stalk composed of one or two longitudinal rows of cells. The body of the antheridium, as usual, consists of a jacket layer of sterile cells enclosing a mass of sperm cells. The protoplast of each sperm cell metamorphoses into a biflagellate sperm.

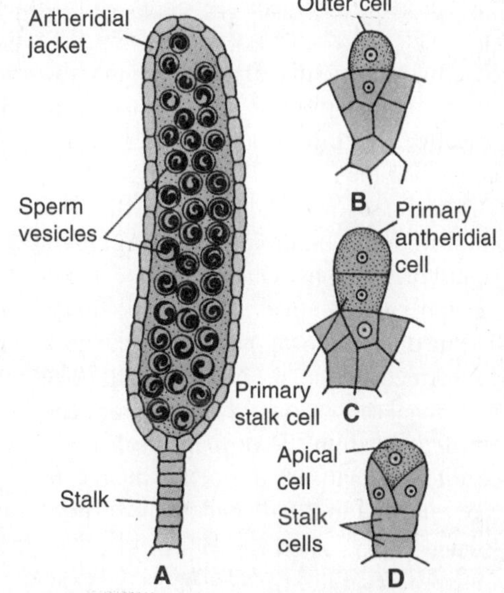

Fig. 17.2. (A—D) ***Andreaea*** sp. A, median longitudinal section of a mature antheridium; B-D, early stages in the developemnt of antheridium.

(*b*) *Development* (Fig. 17.2 B-D). The apical cell of the male branch is directly involved in the development of the first-formed antheridium in the cluster. It functions as the *antheridial initial* and projects above the thallus surface. A transverse wall appears in it separating an outer cell from the inner (B). The outer cell undergoes another transverse division. A short filament of three cells is formed (C). The terminal cell of the filament functions as the **primary antheridial cell**. The middle one constitutes the **primary stalk cell**. The lower one which is embedded takes no part in the further development of the antheridium.

The primary antheridial cell divides by two inclined walls to differentiate a two-sided apical cell (D). The subsequent development of antheridium is by the activity of the apical cell and the stages of development are very closely similar to those of the other mosses. The primary stalk cell undergoes repeated division either by transverse walls only or by alternating transverse and longitudinal walls to form the stalk consisting of a single row or two rows of cells. Thus in its origin and development the antheridium of *Andreaea* very closely resembles that of the higher mosses (Bryidae) but in its long stalk it approaches the antheridium of *Sphagnum.*

Archegonia. *(a) Position and structure.* The archegonia occur in a terminal cluster on the female branch in the monoecious species. The perichaetial bracts surrounding the cluster are erect, convolute and enlarged.

Typical of the true mosses the archegonia in *Andreaea* are massive, each with a comparatively long neck with many neck canal cells and a short stalk (Fig. 17.3. A).

(b) Development (Fig. 17.3. B-E). The apical cell of the female branch is involved in the formation of the first archegonium in the cluster. The first divisions in the **archegonial initial** (apical cell) are similar to those of the antheridium. A short filament of three cells results (B). The terminal cell of the filament functions as the **archegonial mother cell**. It divides by three characteristically eccentric vertical walls which separate the **primary axial cell** from the three peripheral cells or **jacket initials** (C). Each of the three jacket initials divides by a vertical wall to form six jacket cells which divide and redivide to form the major part of the jacket (wall) of the archegonium. It is doubled in the region of the venter. With the differentiation of the jacket initials, the primary axial cell undergoes a transverse division to separate an outer **primary cover cell** from the inner fertile **central cell** (D). The central cell immediately divides by a transverse wall to give rise to an upper **primary neck canal cell** and a lower **primary ventral cell** (E). Thus the development of the archegonium of *Andreaea* is exactly similar to that of the higher mosses. The primary cover cell functions as an apical cell with four cutting faces—three lateral and the fourth truncated basal face. The lateral segments contribute to the neck cells and the inner or basal segments contribute to the neck canal cells located in the upper portion of the archegonial neck. The median and lower portions of the neck are formed by the six jacket initials. The neck canal cells in these regions of the neck are derived from the primary neck canal cell. The primary ventral cell gives rise to the ventral canal cell and the egg both located in the venter.

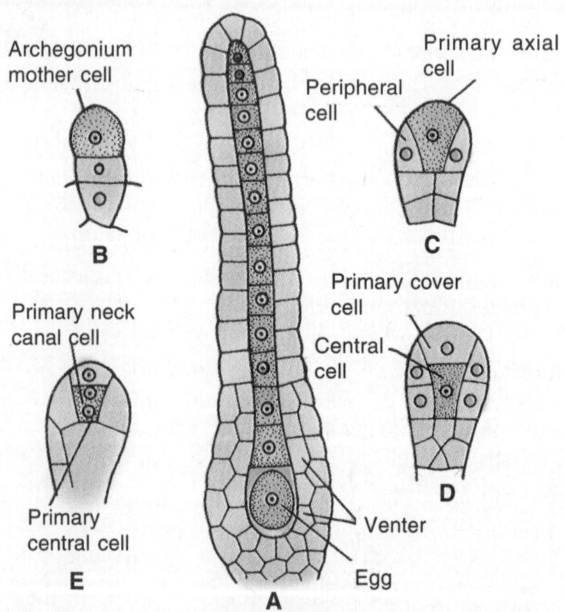

Fig. 17.3. (A—E). ***Andreaea*** sp. A, median longitudinal section of nearly mature archegonium; B-E, early stages in the development of archegonium.

Sporophyte. *(a) Development* (Fig. 17.4). Following fertilization, the zygote divides by a transverse wall into two nearly equal parts, the outer **epibasal cell** and the inner **hypobasal cell** (A). The hypobasal cell divides much more slowly than the epibasal cell and the divisions are in an irregular sequence. The resultant mass of irregularly arranged cells, which are haustorial in nature, constitute the foot. The foot makes its way through the base of the venter into the tip of the female branch. The hypobasal region of the zygote thus forms the foot region of the sporophyte.

The first division in the epibasal cell is by a curved oblique wall (B) followed by a second curved intersecting wall. As a result an apical cell (with two cutting faces) is organized in the epibasal half of the zygote (C). The apical cell in the epibasal half of the embryo cuts off about a dozen six on either side (E). In a cross-section the two alternating segments are nearly spherical, each being semi-circular in outline. Each of these segments divides by a vertical median wall into two equal parts. A cross-section of the embryo at this stage consists of four equal quadrant cells (G). The next division in each quadrant cell is by a periclinal wall resulting in the separation of a central group of **endothecium cells** from an outer layer of cells, the **amphithecium** (H). The amphithecium forms the **capsule wall** which is 3-8 cells in thickness. The cells of the outer-most layer become thick-walled except along four vertical strips of cells equidistant from each other, that remain small and thin-walled. These constitute the **lines of dehiscence**. Periclinal division of the endothecium cells separates an outer fertile layer from an inner sterile region (I). The former constitutes an **archesporium** and the latter **columella.** The archesporium eventually develops into a **sporogenous layer** two cells in thickness. It extends over the columella like a dome (Fig. 17.5). The cells of the sporogenous tissue develop into **spore mother cells**, each of which undergoes meiosis to form four spores. With the development of the sporophyte within the venter, the latter increases in thickness and develops into a thick **calyptra** which along with the perichaetial leaves encloses the developing sporophyte until it is nearly mature. As the spores mature within the capsule, there is an elongation of the tip of the female branch into a slender, leafless, stalk-like axis, the **pseudopodium** (Fig. 17.6 A). The latter elevates the mature sporophyte above the enveloping perichaetial bracts. The tip of the pseudopodium is slightly swollen to accommodate the foot embedded in it.

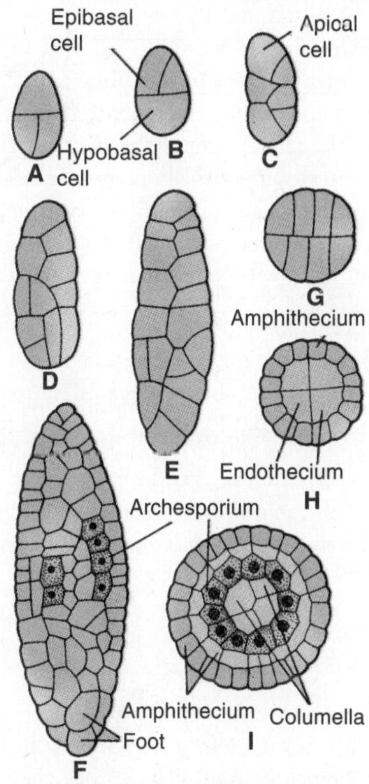

Fig. 17.4. (A—I). ***Andreaea*** sp. Stages in the development of sporogonium. A-B, two views of a very young stage of embryo; C-E, older embryos in longitudinal section; F, still older embryo in L.S. showing differentiation of archegonium; G-I are transverse sections of embryo (A-D, F-I after Waldner, E after Muller Beral).

Structure of adult sporophyte (Fig. 17.6 A). The mature sporophyte is small and dark brown or black in colour. It is differentiated into two regions, the minute **capsule** about 0.5 mm in length and swollen **foot**. The seta which connects the two regions remains undeveloped. It remains very short and neck-like. The tapering foot is embedded in the tip of the female branch. In an adult sporophyte this tip elongates into a leafless stalk, the **pseudopodium** which functions in place of the seta and lifts the sporophyte above the perichaetial leaves. The minute ovoid capsule tapers a little both towards the base and the apex. The capsule wall is about six layers of cells in thickness (Fig. 17.5). The surface layer is called the **epidermis**. It consists of thick-walled cells except along usually 4, sometimes 6—8 longitudinal lines of thin-walled, weaker cells equidistant from each other. These are the **lines of dehiscence**. They later extend neither to the base nor to the apex of the capsule. Within the capsule wall in the spore sac or cavity filled with spores only (Fig. 17.6 B). It extends like a dome over the central club-shaped columella which extends nearly to the top of the spore cavity but does not penetrate it. The capsule, therefore, lacks any differentiation of annuals and peristome. The operculum is also absent.

Dehiscence of capsule (Fig. 17.6 A). With the ripening of spores, the pseudopodium elongates lifting the mature sporophyte at its tip above the surrounding perichaetial leaves. The enlarging capsule breaks through the overlapping calyptra carrying its upper part at its top. Later it is brushed aside. The cup-like basal part of the calyptra together with the slightly swollen apex of the pseudopodium forms the **vaginula**. The ripe capsule is thus exposed. It loses water and dries. Under the strain the capsule wall splits along the four lines of dehiscence which do not meet at the top. The ends of the resulting 4 valves thus remain united. The hygroscopic properties of the capsule wall cause the slits to close in damp conditions and to open and gape apart in dry weather allowing the spores to disperse (Fig. 17.6 C). Erdtman (1957, 1965) reported that the spores in *Andreaea* are shed as tetrads but Brown and Lemmon (1982) could not confirm it.

Spores (Fig. 17.7 A). The spore-coat is differentiated into two layers, outer **exospore** and inner **endospore**. The exospore is thick, dark-brown with a smooth or slightly roughened surface. The endospore is thin. The spore cytoplasm has a single nucleus and contains chloroplasts and oil globules. Brown and Lemmon (1984) studied the ultrastructure of spore and development of spore wall. According to them the mature spore of *Andreaea* is weakly trilete and inapertulate. The single nucleus is centrally located. There are two sometimes more plastids and numerous lipid droplets which are frequently arranged in a ring beneath the plasmalemma. The spore wall is differentiated into three

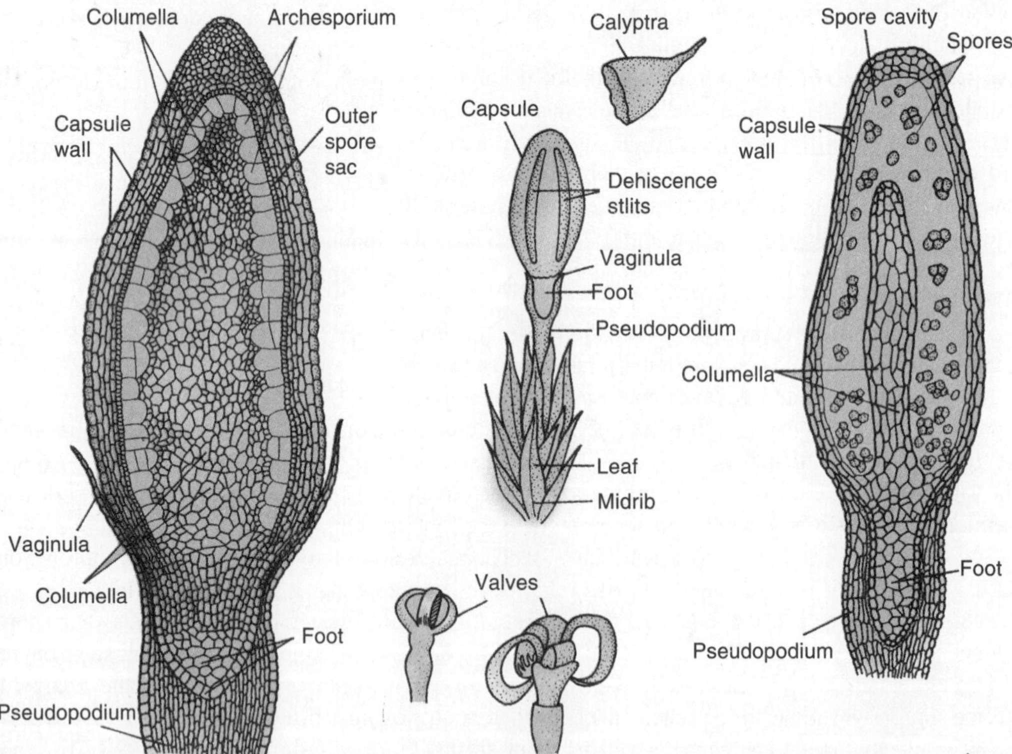

Fig. 17.5. ***Andreaea* sp.** M.L.S. of an immature sporogonium showing division of the archesporium (After Kuhn).

Fig. 17.6. (A—D). ***Andreaea* sp.** A, portion of a gametophore of *A. rothii* with a mature terminal sporophyte; B, median longitudinal section of nearly mature sporophyte of *A. rupestris* with the mature capsule having dehisced 4 valves when dry; C—D, dehisced capsule showing curvature of valves in dry condition (A—D partly diagrammatic).

layers namely, (*i*) the innermost fibrillar **intine**. (*ii*) external to the intine is the spongy **exine** composed of loosely compacted globules of sporopollenin and the outermost **perine** the latter shows greater degree of capacity than the exine.

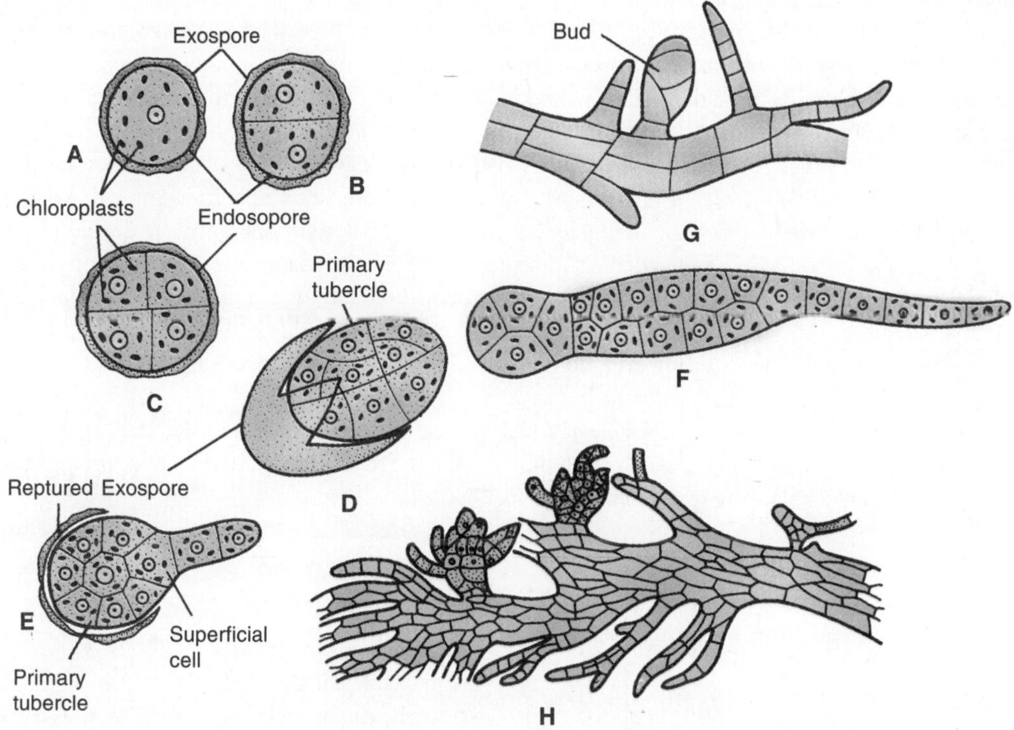

Fig. 17.7. (A—H). ***Andreaea* sp.** Spore germination and development of thallose protonema. A, spore; B—C, spore protoplast dividing to form primary tubercle; D, rupturing of exospore; E, one of the superficial cells of primary tubercle growing into a short filament; F, showing further growth of the filament; G—H, portions of the old thalloid protonema (After Kuhn and Berggran).

Germination of spores (17.7 B—F). The spore, on falling on the substratum, may germinate immediately within a week. Sometimes they remain dormant for a few months. On germination the spore imbibes moisture. The spore protoplast becomes activated. It divides several times (B—C) and may be in three planes within the exospore to form a globular cell mass termed the "primary tubercle" (D). This is comparable to sporegermination in *Pellia* except that in the latter these divisions take place before the spore is shed. Due to pressure from within the exospore cracks (D). One or more of the surface cells of the exposed primary tubercle grow out separately into short filaments, each consisting of 3—5 cells (E). Thereafter the terminal cell of each filament starts functioning as an apical cell with a single posterior segmenting face (F). Due to the activity of the apical cell, the filaments become much branched, strap-like and ramify extensively (H). Some of the branches grow erect and turn green, others creep over the substratum and still others grow into the crevices in the rock and remain colourless. The erect green branches may become transformed into cylindrical cell masses or leaf-like plates much like the protonema of *Sphagnum*. The protonema of *Andreaea* thus shows great diversity in form. Buds, each of which becomes a globular cell mass of 20—30 cells, develop on any portion of the protonema (G). One of the cells in the globular cell mass functions as an apical cell with three cutting faces. Further growth is apical and similar to that at the apex of the adult plant. It results in the development of the leafy axis.

AFFINITIES OF ANDREAEIDAE

The Andreaeidae are considered a synthetic group because in some respects its sporophyte resembles the Sphagnidae in others it approaches the Bryidae (true mosses) and in a few others the Jungermanniales. The features in which it approaches the Sphagnidae are: (1) apical growth by a pyramidal apical cell; (2) absence of conducting strand in the stem; (3) long, stalked antheridium with a globular body; (4) inconspicuous seta; (5) development of pseudopodium; (6) archesporium overcharging the columella in a dome-like manner; (7) thallus-like protonema; (8) nerveless leaves in some species as in *Sphagnum*.

The features which Andreaeidae shares with the Bryidae are : (1) the leafy shoot similar in habit to that of the Bryidae; (2) nerved leaves in some species; (3) presence of numerous rhizoids arising from the basal part of the stem; (4) antheridia in a terminal cluster on the male branch; (5) development of sex organs (antheridia and archegonia) similar to that of the Bryidae; (6) endothecial origin of archesporium; (7) divisions of zygote as in the Bryidae. To the Jungermanniales the Andreaeidae resembles firstly in the dehiscence of the ripe capsule by means of four valves and secondly in the absence of operculum. The slits, however, do not extend to apex of the capsule and thus dehiscence by valves is not complete in the Andreaidae.

The account given above shows clearly that the affinities between the three subclasses are undeniable but to assume a single line of evolution in the upward or downward direction through the three groups in untenable. It requires more evidence.

Systematic Position of Andreaea

Division	:	Bryophyta
Class	:	Bryopsida (Musci)
Subclass	:	Andreaeidae
Order	:	Andreaeales
Family	:	Andreaeaceae
Genus	:	*Andreaea*
Species	:	*pterophyla*

QUESTIONS

ESSAY TYPE

1. Discuss the statement, "the Andreaeidae are considered a synthetic group".
2. Describe the structure of the mature capsule of *Andreaea*.
3. Give an account of the habit, habitat and distribution of the moss genus *Andreaea*.
4. With the help of labelled diagrams, describe the life cycle of *Andreaea*
5. Give an account of external and internal morphology of the gametophyte of *Andreaea*
6. Describe the structure and development of sporophyte in *Andreaea*.
7. Describe the structure and germination of spores of *Andreaea*.
8. Give an illustrated account of the development and structure of sex organs in *Andreaea*.
9. Discuss Andreales and mention its affinities. *(Poorvanchal, M.Sc. 1998)*
10. Why *Andrea* is not placed with true mosses the Bryales ? Discuss. *(Allahabad, M.Sc. 1999)*

SHORT ANSWER TYPE

11. *Andreaea* generally defies its placement in Brayales or true mosses why ? Discuss *(Lucknow, M.Sc., 2006)*
12. List the chief characteristics of sub-class Andreaeidae.
13. Write systematic position and important features of *Andreaea*.
14. Write short notes on the following :
    (*i*) Mechanism of capsule dehiscence and dispersal of spores in *Andreaea* and *Sphagnum* *(Rohilkhand M.Sc., 1991; Awadh, 2000)*
    (*ii*) Affinities between sphagnales and Andreaea. *(Rohilkhand M.Sc., 1993)*
    (*iii*) Affinities between Andreales and Polytrichales. *(Rohilkhand M.Sc., 1994)*
    (*iv*) *Andreaea* *(Allahabad, M.Sc. 2000; Kanpur M.Sc., 1991, 1992)*
    (*v*) Capsule of *Andreaea*
    (*vi*) Sporophyte of *Andreaea*
    (*vii*) Distribution of *Andreaea*
15. Draw a well labelled diagram of a mature antheridium and archegonium of *Andreaea*.
16. Distinguish between
    (*i*) Sporophyte of *Polytrichum* and *Andreaea* *(Rohilkhand M.Sc., 1995)*
    (*ii*) *Andreaea* and *Polytrichum* *(Rohilkhand M.Sc., 1999)*
    (*iii*) *Andreaea* and *Pogonatum* *(Kanpur M.Sc., 1993)*
    (*iv*) Capsule of *Andreaea* and *Sphagnum.*
    (*v*) Capsule of *Andreaea* and *Takakia.*
17. Briefly describe the mechanism of dehiscence of capsule in *Andreaea*

OBJECTIVE TYPE

18. **Select the correct answer :**
    (*i*) The leaf divergence of *Andreaea* is
    (*a*) 1/2 (*b*) 2/4
    (*c*) 3/6 (*d*) 3/8.
    (*ii*) Vaginula is present in the sporophyte of
    (*a*) *Riccia* (*b*) *Marchantia*
    (*c*) *Andreaea* (*d*) *Anthoceros.*
    (*iii*) Operculum is absent in
    (*a*) *Andreaea* (*b*) *Funaria*
    (*c*) *Polytrichum* (*d*) *Pogonatum.*
    (*iv*) Which of the following features is present in mature gametophytes of *Andreaea* but is absent in mature gametophytes of *sphagnum*?
    (*a*) Spores (*b*) Capsule
    (*c*) Operculum (*d*) *Rhizoids.*
    (*v*) Four types of Rhizoids are found in the gametophytes of
    (*a*) *Funaria* (*b*) Andreaea
    (*c*) *Polytrichum* (*d*) *Sphagnum*

Image of *Funaria sp.*

CHAPTER 18

BRYIDAE

Funariales

Funaria

- General Characteristics
- Classification
- Order Funariales
- Summary of the Life History of Funaria
- The Chife Difierences Between Funaria and The Liverworts

GENERAL CHARACTERISTICS

The sub-class Bryidae include a great majority of the common mosses called the **true** or the **higher mosses**. They number about 14,000 species allotted to nearly 650 genera. The Bryidae comprise about 90 percent of all the species of mosses. These are characterized by :—

1. Leaf one to several cells in thickness and often with a distinct **midrib** more than one cell in thickness.

2. Early growth of the embryo by means of a two-sided **apical cell** situated both at the anterior and the posterior ends.

3. Archesporium differentiated from the **outer layer** of the **endothecium**.

4. Archesporium not arching over the columella.

5. Presence of a large **intercellular space** around the spore sac transversed by **trabeculae**.

6. Absence of **pseudopodium**.

7. Presence of a well-developed **seta** which serves to elevate the capsule far above the surrounding leaves of the gametophore.

8. Columella extending right up to the lid and is surrounded by the spore sac.

9. Presence of **peristome** teeth around the mouth of the spore cavity.

10. Dehiscence of the capsule by the separation of a lid.

11. Calyptra well developed.

12. Greater elaboration and complexity in the structure of the **capsule**.

13. Filamentous **protonema**.

CLASSIFICATION

The sub-class Bryidae includes about 80 families (Brotherus, 1924-25). There is some difference of opinion when it comes to grouping families into orders. The majority of the bryologists at present follow Fleischer (1920) with slight modifications. He divides the sub-class into 15 orders as follows:

Orders: Fissidentales ⟵ with one family.

Dicranales ⟵ with eight families. Reimers (1954) makes seven.

Pottiales ⟵ with five families. Reimers (1954) recognises three.

Grimmiales ⟵ with one family.

Funariales ⟵ with five families. Reimers (1954) makes six.

Schistostegales ⟵ with one family.

Tetraphidales ⟵ with one family.

Eubryales ⟵ with sixteen families.

Isobryales ⟵ with twenty one families. Reimers (1954) makes 23.

Hookeriales ⟵ with six families

Hypnobryales ⟵ with eleven or twelve (Reimers 1954) families.

Buxbaumiales ⟵ with one or two families (Reimers, 1954).

Diphysciales ⟵ with one family.

Polytrichales ⟵ with one family.

Dawsoniales ⟵ with one family.

Of this long list, the two important orders are the Funariales and the Polytrichales. Both have been considered in this text.

ORDER FUNARIALES

The members included in this order are small, annual or biennial land mosses. They are characterised by the following features :—

1. The leaves are sessile usually ovate in form with a drawn out broad base and generally arranged in a terminal rosette.

2. The broad capsule has a lid without a long beak.

3. The peristome teeth are arranged in two rings, the teeth of the inner ring (**endostome**) are usually opposite the outer peristome (**exostome**).

The order comprises about 356 species grouped under 26 genera. They are allotted to five families which are the Gigaspermaceae, Funariaceae, Disceliaceae, Oedipodiaceae and Splachaceae. Of these Funariaceae is widely known.

FAMILY FUNARIACEAE

The members of this family (Funariaceae) grow in large dense patches. The other characteristic features of the family are :—

1. Leaves prominent, usually wide and one cell in thickness except the midrib.
2. Calyptra with a long, slender beak.
3. The pyriform capsule usually nodding at maturity, immersed or borne on a long, twisted seta.

The family comprises about 200 species. They are placed under nine genera. The best known and widely distributed genus of this family is *Funaria*. It is thus taken as the type genus.

FUNARIA (HEDW.)

Habit and habitat. *Funaria* is a common terrestrial moss which grows in dense patches of bright, green colour. It usually grows in moist shady situations such as damp soil, shady banks, sometimes on the trunks of trees and on the walls. *Funaria* comprises more then 117 species including 15 species reported from India (Bruhl, 1931). Of these *F. hygrometrica* (n=14, 28, 56) has a worldwide (cosmopolitan) distribution, being common and abundant from the tropics to the arctic. According to Nakosteen and Hughes (1978) it completes its sexual life cycle (from spore to spore) in culture in 4 months' time whereas Dieter (1980) reported that the growing season for *Funaria* varies from 148 to 244 days depending on the location. It usually grows in close tufts on the moist ground in shady places, sometimes on walls, rocks and crevices. Frequently it occurs in disturbed environments as well as on recently burnt sites.

Southern (1976) reported that *F. hygrometrica, Marchantia polymorpha* and *Ceratoten purpurea* are the characteristic bryophytes of the initial phase recolonisation of burnt areas. Steer (1969) opined that there is increase in the level of soil nutrients due to burning. It results in high concentration of soluble organic matter and inorganic nutrients. Hoffman (1966) however, questioned the correlation between abundance of *F. hygrometrica* and high pH and high nutrient contents of the soil following fire. Watson (1971) reaffirmed that there is strong association between the soil conditions following fire and the colonizing species. This is the widely accepted view at present. It has been supported by the recent work of Southern (1976, 77) who experimentally showed that the nutrient status of the post burnt soil is primarily important for the establishment of these pioneer species. He found that the concentration of calcium, potassium, nitrogen and phosphorus must all be high for rapid growth of *Funaria* although nitrogen and phosphorus seem particularly important. The other view is that the effect of heating and burning the soil provides a greater stimulus to growth than the presence of these nutrients.

Gametophyte phase. This phase in the life cycle of *Funaria*, as in other mosses, consists of two growth stages namely, (*i*) **juvenile stage** represented by *primary protonema* (Fig. 18.1) and (*ii*) the **leafy stage** represented by the *leafy gametophore* (Fig. 18.2 B).

(*i*) *Juvenile stage* (Fig. 18.1). It results from the germinating meiospore. When fully grown it consists of a slender, green, branching system of filaments called the **protonema**. The filamentous protonema branches freely. It forms a brilliant green, felt-like coating on the damp soil resembling algal growth. Many of the branches grow and spread over the moist soil. These are the green **chloronemal branches**. The cells comprising them contain numerous, discoid chloroplasts and are separated by transverse cross walls. The other branches penetrate the soil. They are colourless or brown. The cells of these **rhizoidal branches** lack chloroplasts. They have oblique septa between them. The protonema stage in *Funaria* is only vegetative and transitory.

(*ii*) *Leafy stage* (Fig. (18.1 b). It starts as a lateral bud (*a*) on the protonema. Several buds may develop on a single protonema. Each of these develops into an erect leafy stem (*b*). The latter bears numerous rhizoids at its base which anchor it to the substratum. Thus in many cases several leafy stems or shoots will be seen arising from the same protonema. At first they are all parts of the same individual (protonema). However, the protonema soon degenerates and disappears. The upright leafy stems or shoots are left behind as separate, independent representatives of the gametophyte stage. Each of these is usually called the moss plant. It bears the sex organs. This feature and the fact that the leafy stem or shoot arises from the prostrate protonema suggests that each leafy stem or the so-called moss plant, in fact is a **gametophore** homologous to the erect gametophores growing on the thalli of *Marchantia*.

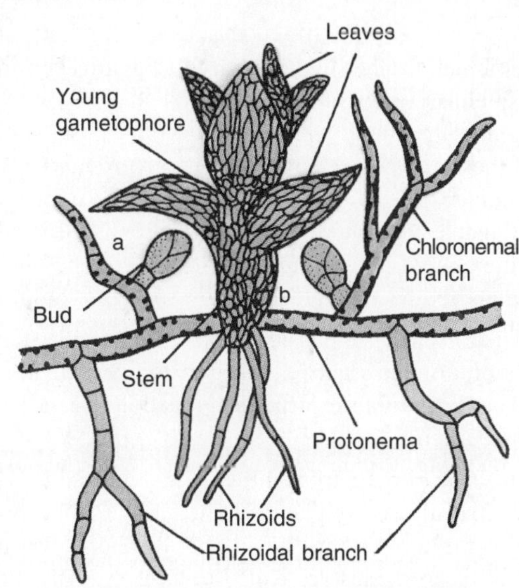

Fig. 18.1. Bryidae. Moss protonema representing the juvenile growth stage bearing buds (*a*) and a young gametophore (*b*).

Adult gametophore (Fig. 18.2). (*a*) *External features*. The mature *Funaria* plant has a slender, upright, central axis (A). It is about 13mm or a little more in height. It bears flat, green, lateral expansions inserted spirally. For convenience we call the central axis as **stem** and the green expansions as **leaves**. We cannot consider them as such for taxonomic purposes. Koch (1956) would call stems as **caulodids** and leaves **phylloids**. Besides these two principal organs of the moss gametophore, the

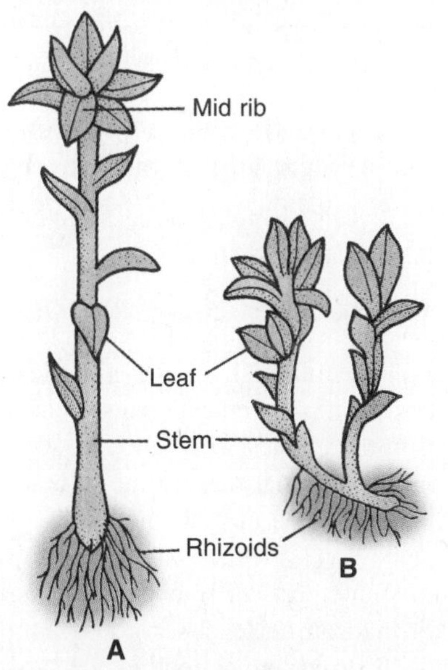

Fig. 18.2. (A—B), ***Funaria*** sp.. A, plant with an unbranched stem; B, a plant with a branched stem (B after Janzen).

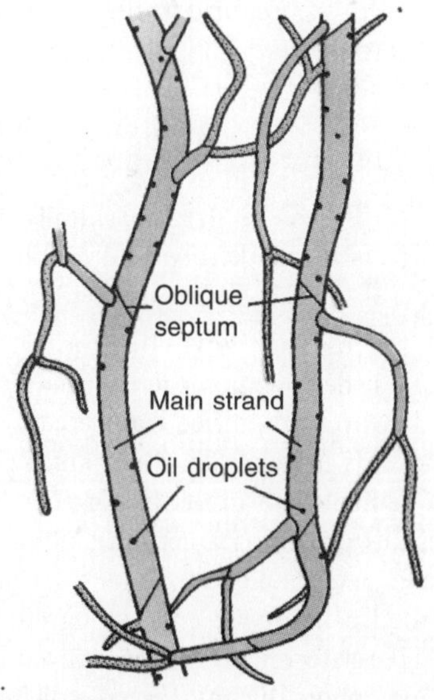

Fig. 18.3. ***Funaria*** sp. Branched, multicellular rhizoids.

third is the **rhizoid system**. It consists of numerous attaching filaments, the **rhizoids** which arise from the basal, naked, brown part of the stem. The rhizoids penetrate the substratum to a depth, at least, equal to the height of the leafy stem if not more. They are multicellular and branched (Fig. 18.3). The main strands which arise from the basal part of the moss stem are brown and stout. From each of these arise branches of the second order which are colourless and thin. The branches of the third order are of still finer calibre. The septa between the cells are oblique and occur at long intervals. According to Goebel (1905), the oblique septa are an adaptation to promote rapid conduction. When young the rhizoids are colourless. The mature ones are coloured red or brown. The rhizoids contain oil droplets and become green when exposed to light.

The rhizoid system is analogous to the root system but more so to the root hairs. Like the latter the finer or ultimate branches of the rhizoid system are slender and colourless and have delicate cell walls. They are mainly absorptive in function like the root hairs. The older ones function in anchorage and conduction.

Because of their apparent **leaves, stem** and root-like **rhizoids** the *mosses* might be mistaken for any small flowering plant. These structures, however, are neither homologous nor structurally similar to the roots, stems and leaves of the flowering plants. No doubt they perform the same functions. Such organs are called **analogous**. The moss rhizoids, stem and leaves belong to the gametophyte stage. Their cells have nuclei with a **haploid** number of chromosomes. True roots, leaves and stems, as those of angiosperms, are sporophytic structures. The cells constituting them have 2*n* (**diploid**) number of chromosomes. These sporophytic organs are more complex. They show greater differentiation of tissues as compared with those of the *mosses*. They have a well developed *epidermis* with stomata and guard cells (in the leaves and stems) and the vascular system. All these structures are absent in the stems and leaves of *Mosses*.

The so-called stem in *Funaria* is sparingly branched (Fig. 18.2 B). The branching is lateral. Dichotomous branching which is characteristic of the liverworts, is entirely absent in the mosses. The branch always arises from below a leaf and is never axillary. It originates from the surface layer of the stem and shares origin with a common segment cell. The leaves are the main photosynthetic organs of the *Funaria* plant. The leaf size increases upwards on the stem. Thus they are more crowded and large towards the apex (A). Those surrounding the terminal sex organs are the largest. The spiral phyllotoxy is 3/8. The leaves are sessile and oblong-ovate in form with an entire margin and pointed apex. Each leaf has a distinct midrib and is inserted on the stem by a drawn out, fairly broad base (Fig. 18.4 B).

(*b*) *Anatomy.* (*i*) *Stem* (Fig. 18.4 A) A cross-section of the stem reveals a simple internal structure. There is no marked specialization of cells. The cells are arranged in three distinct zones; (*i*) the **central cylinder** or **strand**, (*ii*) the **cortex**, and (*iii*) the **epidermis** (A).

The **central cylinder** forms the core of the stem (A). It consists of vertically elongated, thin-walled, narrow, compactly arranged cells without protoplasm. These thin walled, elongate, dead cells with nonlignified walls are now commonly called the **hydroids**. They are considered similar to tracheids in being dead at maturity. In cells devoid of protoplasm, there is less resistance to water movement than in the living cells. On this basis many bryologists hold that the central cylinder, besides providing a certain amount of mechanical support, functions in the upward movement of water and solutes even though it has no tracheids and vessels. Doyle (1970) considered the thin walled cells of the conducting strand (hydroids) as functional counterparts of tracheids. Hebant (1970) referred to the central strand as a strand of hydroids (hadrom). He observed that the gametophore of *Funaria* has a well-developed strand of hydroids (hadrom) but no leptoids. He also recorded the occurrence of wall ingrowths on the contact wall between the parenchymatous cells constituting the **hadrom sheath** and hadrom. Hebant considered these cells with wall ingrowths similar to the 'transfer cells' of Gunning and Pate (1969). These 'transfer cells' are considered specialized for short distance transport of solutes. Bop and Stehle (1957) studied the flow of water in the stem of *F. hygrometrica*. They used water-soluble fluorescent dyes to trace the path of internal conduction in this species. They found that water is rapidly conducted in the cells of the central strand called the hadrom. In general they came to the conclusion that in *Funaria* water conduction is partly external and partly internal. Thus they considered *Funaria* as typical example of a *myxohydric* moss. Internal conduction is slow in the rhizoids. The water reaches the base of stem more rapidly by external capillary channels. Within the stem central cylinder plays the major role. The leaves also receive water supply by external channels.

The **cortex** is of relatively greater thickness. It surrounds the central cylinder and is composed of undifferentiated, large, thin-walled, parenchymatous cells. In young stems the cortical cells contain chloroplasts (A). The mature portion of the stem has the cortex usually differentiated into an outer **thick-walled**, brown cortex and an inner, **thin-walled** cortex. The latter lies next to the central cylinder. According to Hebant (1970) the thin-walled cortical cells abutting the central hydroid strand constitute the hadrom sheath. Near the periphery of the cortex may be seen small, isolated patches of thin-walled parenchyma cells constituting the 'false leaf traces'. They end blindly in the cortex and do not join the central strand of the stem.

The **epidermis** usually consists of a single surface layer of cells external to the cortex. The cells are small and contain chloroplasts in the younger portions of the stem. In the mature portions of the stem the epidermal cells become thick-walled and lack **chloroplasts**. The stomata characteristic of the true stems are absent.

(*ii*) *Leaf* (Fig. 18.4 C). Excepting the midrib, the leaf consists of a single layer of undifferentiated parenchymatous cells. They are large and rectangular or hexagonal rectangular in surface view. The leaf cells are rich in chloroplasts which are comparatively large and prominent (C). The marginal cells are specialized. They are narrow and thick-walled in contrast to the rest and afford strength to the frail moss leaves. The midrib is several cells thick. It has an upper and lower epidermis. Below the upper epidermis is a small group of thin-walled, large cells followed by a group of small, thick-walled cells with a narrow lumen. The structures characteristic of the leaves of the vascular plants such as the tracheids and the sieve tubes or the fibre vascular bundle are absent. There is no trace of the mesophyll tissue or the stomata.

The root in the *mosses* is lacking. The rhizoids may perform some of the functions of roots such as anchorage and absorption of water and solutes from the soil.

Apical growth. The stem grows by means of single **apical cell**. It is located at the stem tip. The apical cell is pyramidal in shape. It cuts off segments parallel to its three sides. Each segment divides into an inner and outer part. The inner part divides to give rise to the major part of the stem. The outer part forms the leaves, buds and the outer part of the stem.

The growth of the leaf is carried on by means of a three

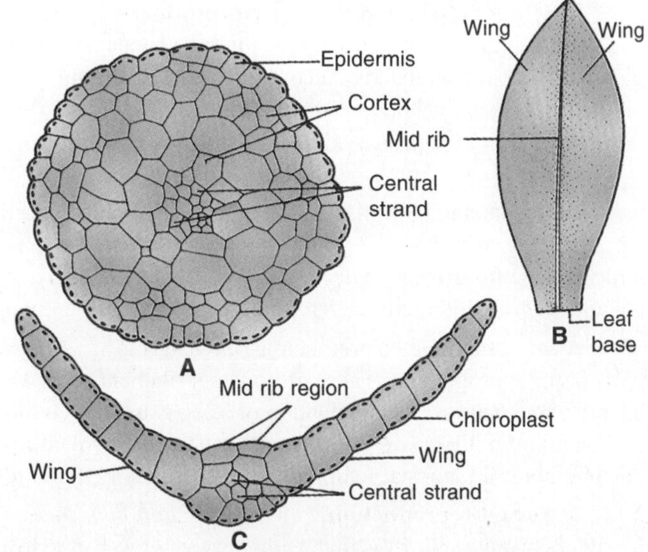

Fig. 18.4. (A—C). *Funaria hygrometrica.* A, cross section of stem; B, outline sketch of leaf; C, cross section of leaf.

sided apical cell. The rhizoids grow in length by means of an apical cell at the free end of each filament.

Reproduction. The leafy gametophore of *Funaria* reproduces by two methods: (*i*) Vegetative and (*ii*) Sexual.

1. Vegetative reproduction. The gametophyte stage of *Funaria* is frequently propagated vegetatively by the following methods:-

(*i*) *Multiplication of the protonemal stage.* The primary protonema breaks into short fragments of living, green cells by the death of cells at intervals. Each detached fragment which may consist of a single green cell or several cells grows into a new protonema which bears a fresh crop of leafy gametophores. Formation of cells with colourless contents has been reported to be formed by intercalary divisions at certain places in the protonema. These serve as separation cells breaking up the primary protonema into fragments.

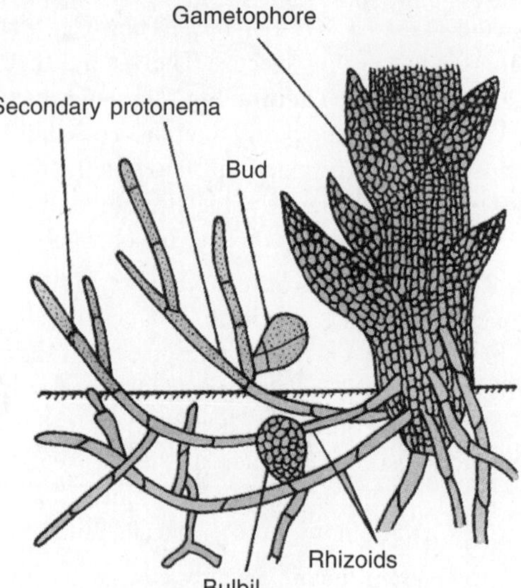

Fig. 18.5. *Funaria hygrometrica*. Lower part of the gametophore with some of the rhizoids coming above the surface of the substratum to form secondary protonema which bears buds. Note also the formation of a bulbil (tuber) on the rhizoid. (After Luerssen).

(*ii*) *Secondary protonema* (Fig. 18.5). Filamentous protonema may also be formed from any cell of a detached injured portion of the stem, leaf and rhizoid when surrounded by moist air. It is known as the **secondary protonema**. From it arise the leafy gametophores as lateral buds in the same way as from the primary protonema. Sometimes in *F. hygrometrica*, some of the rhizoids of the gametophore grow up and come above the surface of the substratum, turn green and branch to form the **secondary protonema** (Fig. 18.5). The latter bear buds which grow into leafy gametophores.

(*iii*) *Bulbils.* These are small **resting buds** developed on the rhizoids. With the onset of conditions suitable for growth the bulbil produces a protonema which bears a crop of moss gametophores as lateral buds. According to the latest terminology the perennating structures produced on the rhizoids are called the **tubers** (Fig. 18.5).

(*iv*) *Gemmae.* Berkley (1941) reported the formation of small bud-like structures, the **gemmae** from the terminal cells of the protonemal branches. The cells constituting the gemmae are thin-walled and contain chloroplasts. The detached gemmae germinates to produce the protonema. The gemmae may also develop on the stem and leaves of the gametophore at the onset of condition unfavourable for growth or during injury. These detached gemmae under conditions favourable for vegetative growth directly develop into new leafy gametophores.

(*v*) *Apospory.* Green protonemal filaments may arise from the unspecialised cells of the various parts of the sporogonium. These protonemal filaments bear lateral buds each of which develops into a leafy gametophore. The production of leafy gametophytes directly from the vegetative cells of the sporogonium without the intervention of spores is called **apospory**. The aposporously produced gametophores are normal in appearance. Genetically they are diploid.

2. Sexual reproduction. (*a*) *Position and distribution of sex organs* (Fig. 18.6 A). Sexual reproduction takes place, as in the other bryophytes, by the formation of **antheridia** and **archegonia** which are multicellular. They are borne on the leafy gametophores and are never sunken. On the other hand, they project freely from the surface of the plant. The sex organs are developed in **terminal**

clusters. The formation of sex organs thus limits the growth of the vegetative axis. Apparently *Funaria* looks **dioecious**. In reality it is **monoecious** (A). The antheridia are formed at the summit of a relatively small, main leafy shoot which develops first. It is in fact the parent plant (A). The female branch arises later as a lateral outgrowth from the base of the parent male shoot. When the two kinds of sex organs are borne in separate clusters on two distinct branches of the same plant the arrangement is said to be **autoicous** and species **monoecious**. *Funaria* is protandrous. This ensures cross fertilization.

(b) Factors influencing development of sex organ. Benson-Evans and Brough (1966) reported that the sex organs of *F. hygrometrica* mature in autumn or winter. Monroe (1965) reported that low temperature was the critical factor in the induction of gametangia in *F. hygrometrica*. The day length has no effect as long as certain minimum period of illumination is provided. Nakosteen and Hughes (1978) showed that cooler temperature is the critical factor for induction and maturation of gametangia in *F. hygrometrica*. Photoperiod has no effect. *Funaria* requires an inductive temperature of 7°C.

Male branch or **antheridiophore** (Fig. 18.6 A—B). Its tip is expanded to form a slightly convex male receptacle with the antheridia closely packed on it to form a cluster which to the naked eye appears as a tiny red spot (A). Unlike the antheridiophore of *Marchantia*, the antheridiophore of *Funaria* is leafy. It has no grooves and bears no scales. The antheridia are not sunk in pits and are not arranged in rows but project form the surface of the receptacle and are aggregated to form a cluster. The leaves surrounding the antheridial cluster are known as the perigonial leaves. They are closely set and spread out in the form of a rosette to form a shallow cup-like structure which affords protection to the antheridial cluster with the surrounding perigonal leaves is called the **perigonium**. The orange coloured mature antheridia and the rosette-like arrangement of the perigonial leaves make the male shoot conspicuous and easily recognisable. Antheridia at various stages of development occur in a single male receptacle which is thus capable of releasing sperms in succession over a long period extending over several weeks.

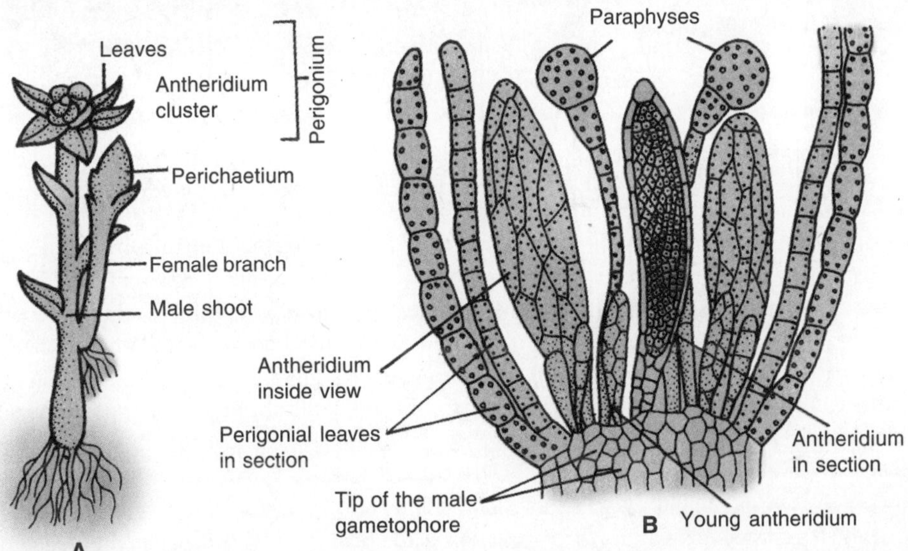

Fig. 18.6 (A—B). ***Funaria*** sp. A, plant with male and female branches; B, L.S. through the apex of the male shoot showing antheridia, paraphyses and the surrounding perigonial leaves. (B, Adapted from Sachs).

Associated with the antheridia in the cluster are numerous, green, sterile, hair-like filaments (B). They are multicellular and upright with large capitate heads and are called the **paraphysis**. Each paraphysis is usually 4 to 6 cells in height. It consists of a single row of cells. The top cell is large and nearly sub-spherical in outline. The cells below it are elongated and narrow. All the cells are rich in chloroplasts. The top cells of the paraphysis meet over the antheridia. Thus the paraphyses afford protection and help to a limited extent in photosynthesis. Lorch (1931) suggested that they help to conserve moisture around the antheridia either by holding or secreting water. The water is held between them by capillarity. The other suggestion is the paraphyses secrete mucilage which protects the young antheridia from undue water-loss and also assists in the efficient discharge of sperms by building up pressure. To sum up, the paraphysis are considered to be of value in protection, moisture conservation, photosynthesis, and discharge of sperms by building up pressure.

(*i*) *Structure* (Fig. 18.7 M). The mature **antheridium** of *Funaria hygrometrica* may be 0.25 mm in length. It has an elongate, club-shaped, orange-coloured body raised on a short, multicellular stalk (N). The body has a jacket layer of polyhedral, flattened cells. The cells of the single layered wall contain chloroplasts when the antheridium is young. As it ripens the chloroplasts change into

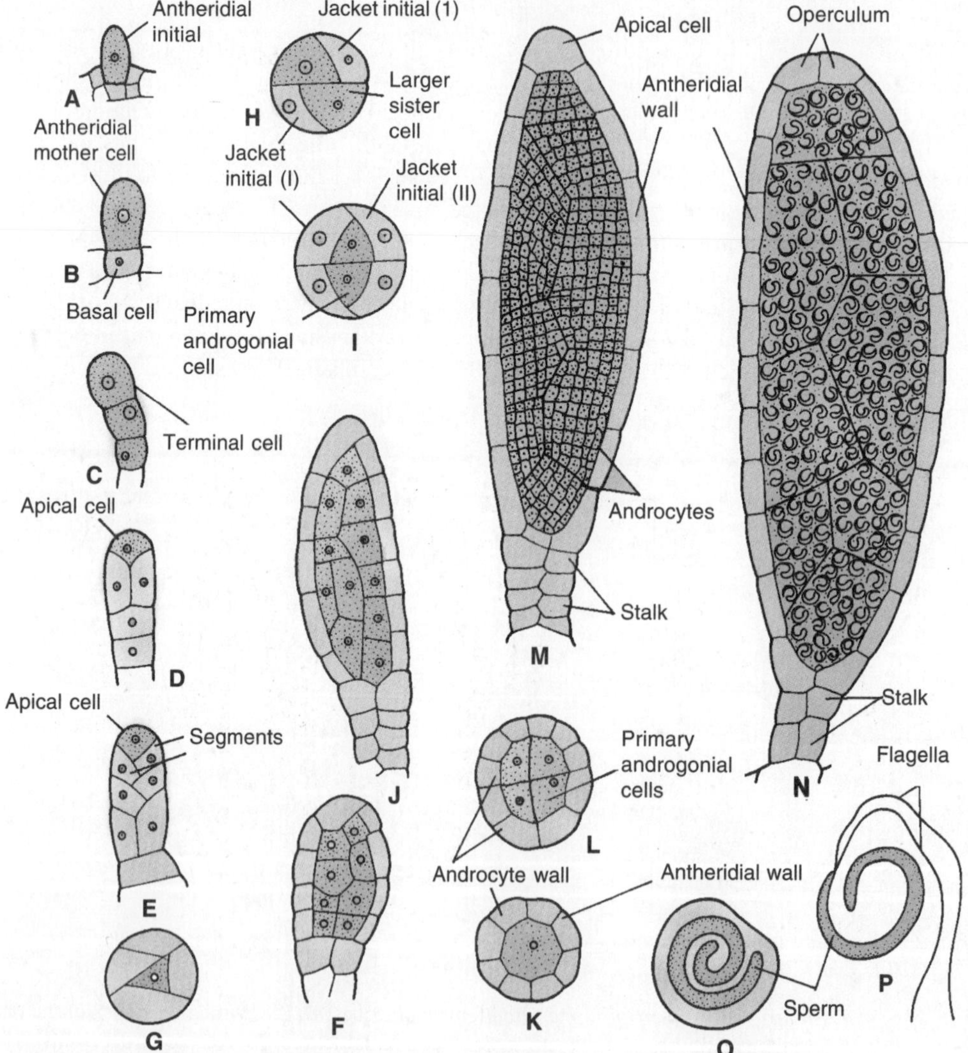

Fig. 18.7. (A—P). ***Funaria*** sp. Successive stages in the early development of antheridium (A—L). G—L, are transverse sections; M, nearly mature antheridium; N, mature antheridium ready for dehiscence; O, sperm enclosed in a vesicle; P, free sperm. (Adapted from Campbell).

orange-coloured chromoplasts. With an antheridial wall is a dense mass of small cells. They are known as the **androcytes** (M). Each androcyte produces a single, biflagellate **sperm** (N). At maturity the free distal end of the antheridium is differentiated into a **cap-like** structure. It is the **operculum** (N). It consists of one or two cells and is formed from the apical cell itself of the antheridium. The cells of the operculum are comparatively large in size. They have thicker walls and colourless contents.

(*ii*) *Development of antheridia* (Fig. 18.7, A—P). The antheridia develop from the superficial embryonic cells including even the apical cell at the expanded tip of the male shoot. Each antheridium originates from a single such cell. It is called the **antheridium initial** (A). The antheridium initial grows into a **papillate** outgrowth. The latter projects above its neighbours. The papillate initial divides by a transverse wall into two cells (B). Of these the inner or basal cell forms the embedded portion of the antheridial stalk. The outer or distal cell forms the entire antheridium and is known as the **antheridial mother cell.**

The antheridial mother cell undergoes transverse segmentation to form a short filament of 2 or 3 cells (C). The terminal cell of the filament divides by intersecting walls to establish a wedge-shaped apical cell with two segmenting faces (D). It cuts off two series of segments alternately right and left by successive walls parallel to its cutting faces (E). In this way 5-7 or even more segments are cut off. They are regularly arranged in two rows. One of these segments which is 3 or 4 cells away from the apical cell divides by a periclinal wall. Thereafter the segments above it (towards the apex) begin to divide in the same way. All these segments have denser contents. The lowermost segments of the young antheridium derived from the apical cell do not undergo periclinal divisions. They form the exposed portion of the stalk of the antheridium. The periclinal divisions in each

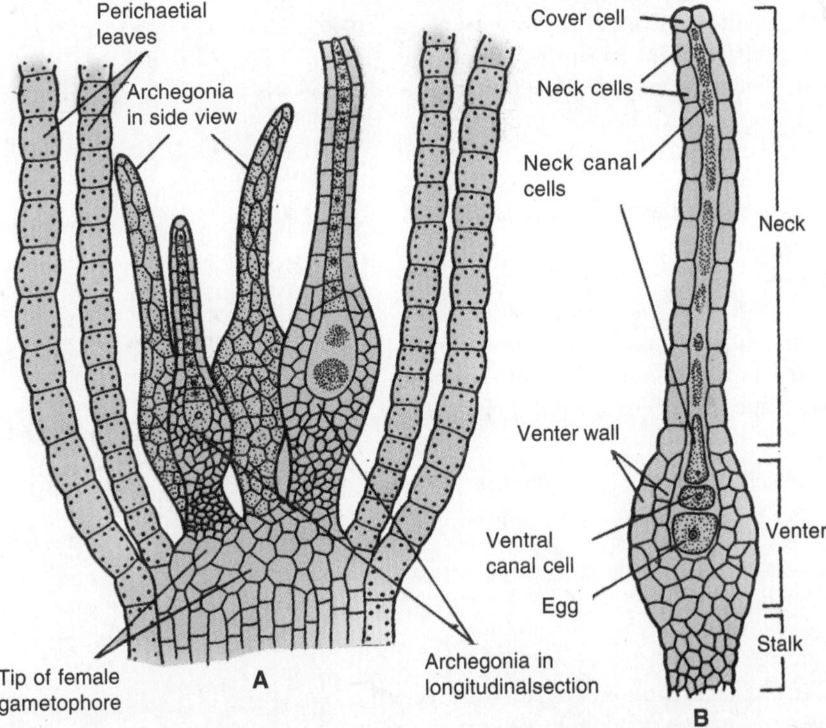

Fig. 18.8. (A—B). ***Funaria* sp.** A, L.S. through the tip of the female branch showing some archegonia in side view, some in section and the surrounding perichaetial leaves in section; B, a nearly mature archegonium in section showing structure (After Sachs).

segment with denser contents are asymmetrical and best seen in cross-sections G, H and I. The smaller daughter cell functions as the first **jacket initial** (H). The larger sister cell undergoes another similar division (I). It separates a second **jacket initial** on the outer side and a **primary androgonial cell** on the inner side (I). All the jacket initials divide only by anticlinal divisions to form a single layered wall of the antheridium (J). The apical cell forms the operculum or cap region of the antheridial wall (M). The antheridial wall encloses the primary androgonial cells (K). The latter divide and redivide. The cells of the last cell generation are called the **androcyte mother cells** (M). Each androcyte mother cell divides to form two **androcytes**. The division, however, is not diagonal. The protoplast of each androcyte gives rise to a single biflagellate sperm (O). In the mature, unopened antheridium, the sperms lie still enclosed in their respective vesicles forming a sperms mass. The development of antheridia in the cluster is not simultaneous. Consequently antheridia at all stages of development may be found in the same cluster.

Female branch or **archegoniophore** (Fig. 18.8 A). The archegonial branch (archegoniophore) springs from the base of the male shoot (Fig. 18.6 A). Unlike that of *Marchantia* it is leafy and has no grooves. The archegonia are not arranged in rows and do not hang down from the under surface of the female receptacle formed by the flattening of the tip of the female branch (Fig. 18.8 A). Instead they are aggregated into a terminal cluster, stand erect and project from the surface of the female receptacle. The leaves surrounding the archegonial cluster are called the perichaetial leaves. They overlap and close over to the top to protect the archegonia. The archegonial cluster with the surrounding perichaetial leaves constitutes the **perichaetium**. Intermingled with the archegonia in the cluster are the paraphyses (Fig. 18.9 D).

(i) Structure of archegonium (Fig. 18.9 C). The **archegonia** are typically flask-shaped, each consisting of the two usual parts, the **venter** and the **neck** (C). It is borne on a distinct, multicellular stalk which is long and massive. The venter consists of a double layer of sterile cells enclosing a cavity known as the **venter cavity**. In it lies the **egg cell** below and the **ventral canal cell** above it. The long, tubular slightly twisted neck consists of six rows of neck cells which enclose an axial row of ten or more intensely protoplasmic **neck canal cells**. Owing to the tortion of the archegonial neck, the neck cells do not stand in vertical rows in older archegonia. The archegonium is thus similar in strucutre to that of the liverworts differing only in the following respects :

(*a*) A long, massive, well developed stalk.

(*b*) Somewhat enlarged venter with two cell layers thick venter wall.

(*c*) A long, twisted neck with a larger number of neck canal cells.

(ii) Development of archegonium of Funaria (Fig. 18.10). The archegonia arise from the embryonic cells at the tip of the archegonial branch including even the apical cell. Each archegonium develops from the single such cell. It is called the **archegonium initial** (A). According to Campbell,

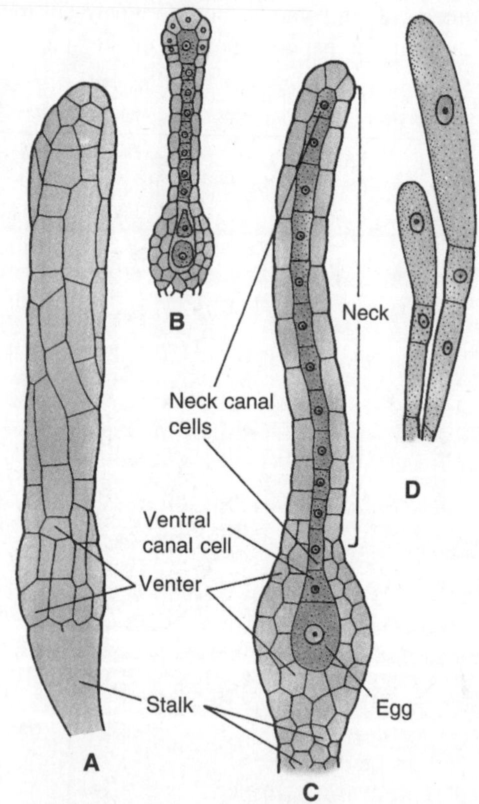

Fig. 18.9. (A—D). ***Funaria*** sp. A, surface view of mature archegonium, B, L.S. young archegonium; C, L.S. nearly mature archegonium; D, paraphysis (A, D after Campbell).

the archegonium initial in *Funaria* divides by a transverse wall. It separates a basal from a terminal cell (B). The former divides and redivides to form the stalk of archegonium. The terminal cell functions as the **archegonium mother cells.** It divides by three oblique walls intersecting each other at some distance from above the first transverse septum. In this way three **peripheral cells** surrounding the central **axial cell** are formed (C and D). The axial cell is tetrahedral in form and is pointed below. The three peripheral cells undergo segmentation to form the single layered jacket or wall in the venter portion of the archegonium (F). During further growth it is doubled. The axial cell divides transversely to separate an inner cell from an outer cell (F). The former functions as the **central cell** and divides to give rise to the **primary neck canal cell**, and the **primary ventral cell** (G). The outer cell which corresponds to the **primary cover cell** of the liverworts behaves in a different way. It functions as an **apical cell** with four cutting faces, three lateral and one basal (G). The apical cell thus cuts four rows of segments. Three of these are lateral and one basal. The three lateral rows of segments function as **neck cells**. Each of these divides by a vertical wall to form six rows. The number of cells in each row increases by transverse cleavage. The archegonial neck thus finally consists of a jacket layer made up of six rows of cells. At maturity it is irregularly twisted. The segments of the basal row undergo no further division. They contribute to the axial row of **neck canal cells** (H and I). Thus the cover cell in Funaria contributes to the formation of the archegonial neck and the axial row of neck canal cells (J). The primary ventral cell eventually divides to form the **egg cell** and the **ventral** canal cell which are lodged in the cavity of the venter (I).

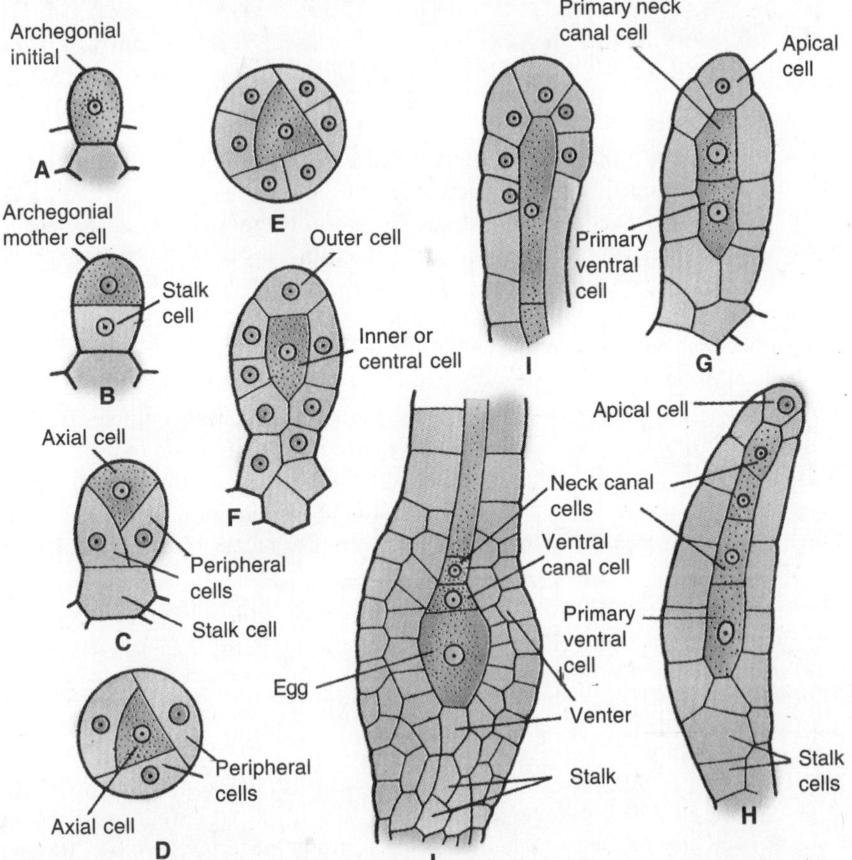

Fig. 18.10. (A—J). ***Funaria hygrometrica***. Development of archegonium. A—C and F—H, longitudinal sections of early stages of development; D—E, T.S. of the same; I—J, longitudinal sections of the lower and upper part of mature archegonium (F—I after Campbell).

Dehiscence of sex organs (Fig. 18.11). The sex organs dehisce in the presence of moisture.

(*a*) *Dehiscence of antheridium* (Fig. 18.11 A—B). The mature antheridia dehiscence only in the presence of water that collects in the surrounding perigonial cup. It may be provided by rain or dew.

(*i*) *Formation of a distal pore.* On the access of water, the inner surface of the outer wall of the distal opercular cell or cells becomes mucilaginous and swells (Muggoch and Walton, 1942).

The wall swelling fills the cell lumen and proceeds to a point when the inner wall of the opercular cell bursts and the cell contents are extruded into the sperm chamber at the tip of the sperm mass. Thereafter the outer wall of the opercular cell also ruptures or breaks its connection with the adjacent cells. This distal rupture forms an open pore to the exterior. The pore, of course, is a small or narrow one at the distal end of the dehisced antheridium. Through this orifice oozes a small stream of a viscous fluid containing the sperms still enclosed within their vesicles (B).

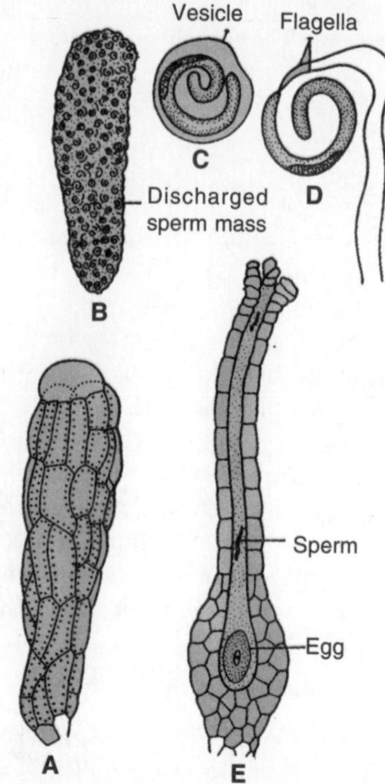

Fig. 18.11. (A—E). ***Funaria*** sp. Showing dehiscence of sex organs and fertilisation. A, antheridium after the discharge of sperm mass; B, discharged sperm mass; C, sperm enclosed within the vesicle; D, free sperm after dissolution of the vesicle; E, mature archegonium showing the passage of

(*ii*) *Release of sperm mass*. Paolillo (1977) reported that the antheridia of *Funaria* empty their contents in two stages. In the first stage, the release of sperm mass is rapid and forceful. It is known as the **rapid phase** of sperm release. As the tip of the antheridium opens, there is contraction of the antheridial jacket that rapidly reduces the size of the sperm chamber. Consequently there is powerful ejection of, at least, a part of the sperm mass which remains coherent through its egress from the antheridium. This rapid phase of sperm release, which is powered by the contraction of the antheridial jacket, is usually completed in less than a minute (Paolillo, 1977). Thereafter immediately follows the **slow phase** and the emptying process continues. The slow phase of sperm release is powered by the swelling of the sperm mass still within the sperm chamber. In spite of the fact that an appreciable quantity of the sperm mass is ejected in the rapid phase of the sperm release, the sperm chamber remains full owing to the swelling of the sperm mass still within the antheridium. The sperm vesicles are now pulled from the chamber by the cohesiveness of the sperm mass.

The presence of fatty materials (lipids) in the matrix containing the sperm mass permits rapid spread of sperm vesicles into a thin film on the surface of water in the perigonial cup. Eventually the vesicles dissolve to set free the sperms which swim freely in the surrounding medium. The liberated sperm is an elongated, spirally coiled, biflagellate structure (D). The empty antheridia wither and die.

(*b*) *Dehiscence of archegonium* (Fig. 18.11 E). In the mature archegonium ready for fertilization, the axial row of cells (neck canal cells and the ventral canal cell) except the egg, degenerates to form a slimy fluid. The latter absorbs moisture and swells. As a result the terminal cells of the archegonial neck are forced apart into a trumpet shape (E). During the process some of the neck cells may become detached and thrown off. A passage way down to the egg is thus formed.

Fertilization (Fig. 18.11 A—E). In *Funaria* fertilization occurs, as in other bryophytes when the plants are wet with rain or dew. The sperms may reach the archegonial cluster in autoecious mosses like *Funaria* in any of the following ways :—

1. *Splash cup mechanism*. The overlapping perigonial bracts surrounding the terminal antheridial cluster in *Funaria* form a small, cup-like structure which acts as a *splash cup*. Muggoch and Walton (1942) suggested that the spreading of sperm vesicles in a thin film on the water surface in the cup presents an excellent opportunity for antherozoid dispersal by *rain drop splash*. Falling rain drops from a height would result in splashes travelling up to and falling on the archegonial cluster situated at a lower level. Since all the rain drops would be coated with a layer of sperms, the splash cup mechanism is considered adequate to effect fertilizations. The air currents present in nature would add to the range of splash downward. The splash drops strike the archegonial cluster.

2. The possibility that the water containing sperms may trickle down from the perigonial cup to the archegonial cluster situated at a lower level, is not ruled out.

3. The antherozoids dispersal by water currents or by swimming in thin films of water connecting the antheridial and archegonial cluster after rain is a remote possibility.

4. The fact that small insects such as mites, spring tails and midges (Diptera), which are attracted by and subsequently feed on the mucilage exuded by the paraphyses surrounding the sex organs, serve as agents of antherozoid dispersal. It has been demonstrated in another moss, *Polytrichum* by Harvey-Gibson and Miller Brown (1927).

Reaching the archegonial cluster the sperms swim to the archegonia (D). The source of attraction is the cane sugar present in the slimy mass given out from the open archegonial necks. Thus guided the sperms arch the archegonia. Eventually they enter the open necks and swim down their neck canals to reach the egg in the venter. Only one sperm unites with the egg to accomplish fertilization. More than one archegonia may be fertilized. Normally only one zygote develops into a sporophyte.

Post-fertilization changes (Fig. 18.12). The fertilised egg located in the venter secretes a wall around it and is called the **zygote**. (18.16 A). It increases in size and enters upon active segmentation (18.16, B—D). The segments are cut off alternately by two growing points, each located at the opposite end. The early development of the embryo in *Funaria* is thus **biapical**. A mass of cells is soon formed within the venter. It is the **embryo** (18.16 F—H). The cells constituting the embryo divide, redivide and grow with little tissue differentiation. It becomes a long, slender structure (18.16, I). The growth of the embryo is accompanied by resumption of growth by the venter. The latter for a time keeps pace with the developing embryo and forms a protective covering around it. The enlarged venter is called the **calyptra** (Fig. 18.12 A,B). The lower end of the embryo makes its way through the base of the venter and the stalk of the archegonium into the top of the female branch. This part of the young sporophyte is called the **foot**. It absorbs food and water for the growing sporophyte from the female branch. The young sprophyte is thus surrounded by the tissues of the parent gametophyte. It takes its nourishment from these tissues. The upper part of the embryo undergoes a high degree of differentiation and specialization to grow into the **capsule**. The middle portion of the embryo elongates to form the stalk-like seta. The continued and gradual elongation of seta ruptures the calyptra at its base. The upper part of the ruptured calyptra is carried aloft as a hood-like covering over the developing capsule (Fig. 18.12 C).

Functions of calyptra. It functions as a transpiration shield around the immature capsule. Besides affording protection to the young capsule, the calyptra is considered essential for its normal development. Bopp (1954) reported that premature removal of calyptra (i.e. when the sporophyte is very young) induces rapid increase in the number of cell divisions or in the volume of new cells formed or in both resulting in precocious swelling of the apex of the sporophyte. There is thus abnormal seta thickening and lack of capsule development. He concluded that the presence of calyptra exercises a physical mechanical restraint on the growth of the sporophyte. The sporophytes which are capable of forming a capsule, despite the removal of calyptra, must have attained the required "physiological age" before the calyptra is removed. According to French and Paolillo (1975) who largely confirmed Bopp's findings, this stage coincides with a length 10 mm in *Funaria* sporophyte.

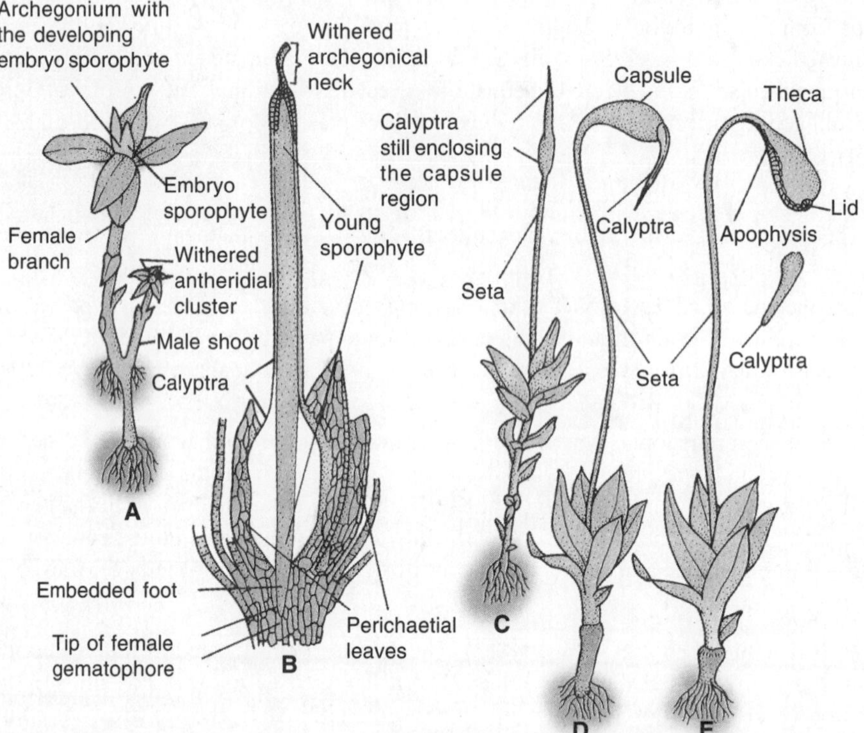

Fig. 18.12. (A—E). ***Funaria*** sp. Post-fertilization changes. A, plant with the female branch having overgrown and outstripped the dwindling male shoot shifted to one side. Note the embryo sporophyte has started to develop within the archegonium; B, section through the tip of the female gametophore showing the young sporophyte still enclosed within the calyptra with the foot having made its way through the archegonial stalk and penetrated the tip of the female gametophore; C, young sporophyte with elongated seta carrying the torn calyptra upwards around the capsule; D, mature sporophytes with a hood-like calyptra still covering the tip of the capsule arising from the distal end of the parent gametophore; E, moss gametophore with a pendent mature capsule with the calyptra fallen off and lid exposed.

Sporophyte. The sporophyte is formed from the zygote. It is the diploid, asexual individual which is usually called the **sporogonium**. The formation of meiospores and their efficient dispersal are its sole functions.

(*a*) *External morphology of sporogonium* (Fig. 18.12 E). *Funaria* is an **acrocarpous** moss with the fruit or sporogonium located at the distal end of the erect female branch. The latter has by now outgrown and replaced the main shoot (Fig. 18.12 A). The sporogonium is a complex and highly elaborate structure. It is differentiated into the **foot**, the **seta** and the **capsule**.

Foot. The foot forms the basal portion of the sporogonium. It is a small, dagger-like conical structure which is embedded in the tissues of the tip of the leafy female branch and functions both as an anchorage and an absorbing organ. Its removal results in less vigorous growth of the sporophyte. The special role of foot in the absorption of nutrients can be deduced from the presence of wall ingrowths of foot cells (Wiencke and Schulz, 1975). The outer walls of the epidermal cells of the foot at the sporophyte-gametophyte interface develop finger-like ingrowths of secondary wall material. The ingrowths extend inwards and often fuse at their extremities to form a complex labyrinth containing pockets of cytoplasm. The wall ingrowths in which surface area amplification is brought by wall ingrowths are termed **transfer cells** (Gunning and Pate, 1969; Pate and Gunning, 1972). The lining layer of the sporophyte foot in *F. hygrometrica* consists almost entirely of transfer cells. The opposed cells in the neighbouring gametophyte tissue as well develop extensive labyrinths. These cells located in the placentary zone are considered to enhance exchanges between the sporophyte and the gametophyte (Browning and Gunning 1979 A). The latter postulated a role for the transfer cells of the sporophyte foot in the uptake of assimilates and found experimentally that the movement of label from the foot along the seta occurs at a velocity of 1—3mm h^{-1}. Bopp and Stehle (1957) stated that the haustorial (sucker-like) base of the foot plunges deep in the tissue of the central strand of the parent gametophore. It absorbs water and nutrient from the parent plant for the sporophyte. The foot thus is similar in function to the root of the ferm plant. Both the organs are sporophytic structures. However, they are not homologous to each other. The two are quite different in their origin, in structure and to some extent in their nature of absorption.

Seta. The seta is a long, slender but tough, reddish brown, stalk-like structure. It carries the capsule at its top and raises it more than an inch above the apex of the leafy gametophore. The leafless seta is homologous to the stem of Pteridophytes. The two are quite similar in origin and function. They differ only in the complexity of structure. The seta has a simple strucutre but shows more tissue differentiation than in the liverworts. It is differentiated into a central strand of small, thin-walled cells surrounded by a region of thick-walled cortex and epidermis with a cuticle (Fig. 18.13 A). The central straws functions as a primitive type of vascular system. The thick-walled cortex gives strength to the slender seta. It enables the seta to bear the weight of the capsule. Conduction and support thus are the two functions of seta. There is a suggestion that seta in *Funaria* plays an important role in the photosynthesis of the sporophyte. Bopp (1954) found that surgically shortened explants of *Funaria* sporophytes gave smaller capsules. He proposed that light limits capsule expansion in *Funaria* by its effect on photosynthesis in the seta which is green in the developing sporophytes. Krupa (1969); on the other hand, argued that the seta contributes a little to the photosynthetic capacity of *Funaria* sporophyte. In his view, the *Funaria* sporophyte depends on the gametophyte to supplement its supply of photosynthates. French and Paolillo (1976) showed experimentally that the length of the seta controls the dry weight of the capsules. They found that shortening of the seta reduced the weights of the capsule. However, they suggested that seta is not an evident source of reserve dry matter. The possibility is that the photoreceptors for capsule expansion are located in seta as well as in the precapsular region. The latter may be more directly concerned with the response at low light intensities. The dry seta in the mature sporogonium is wavy and twisted. It is hygroscopic. In the humid atmosphere it becomes untwisted. As it does so the capsule at its summit swings round and round. When the air dries up its movements are reverse. The capsule now swings in the opposite direction. The swinging round of the opened capsule on the hygroscopic seta assists in sifting spores gradually through the slits between the adjacent peristome teeth, a few at a time.

Capsule (Fig. 18.12 D—E). The capsule is a highly organized structure. It is pear-shaped and green at first but later turns yellow, then orange. Its upper portion is covered by a conical hood or a cap, the **calyptra** (D). At first the capsule is upright on the seta. Eventually it turns dark brown. The calyptra falls off laying bare its apex (E). The capsule is concerned with the production and dispersal of meiospores. Externally it shows three well marked regions, each specialized to perform a definite function. These regions are the (*i*) **apophysis**, (*ii*) **operculum**, and (*iii*) **theca**.

The **apophysis** is the solid, somewhat swollen, basal, green portion of the capsule. It is the **photosynthetic** region of the capsule. It also helps in the conduction of water and food materials.

The apophysis is continuous above with a more swollen, urn-shaped, fertile region of the capsule called the **theca**. The theca forms the major and middle part of the body of the capsule. It is primarily a **spore producing region** of the capsule. Above the theca, forming the apical portion of the capsule, is an obliquely placed cap-like structure. It is the **lid** or the **operculum**. It becomes visible when the calyptra falls off. The operculum regulates spore discharge. There is a well marked line of junction that delimits the operculum from the rest of the capsule. It is the **annulus**. The high gloss seen on the moss seta and the capsule is due to a cuticular covering.

(b) Internal structure of sporogonium. (i) Apophysis. (Fig. 17.13 B—E). On the outside the apophysis is covered by an **epidermal layer** (B). Stomata occur in the epidermis. According to Schimper (1848) and Haberlandt (1886), individually the stomata are two celled and similar in structure to those of the angiosperms. Each stoma has a stomatal aperture bounded by two guard cells (D). The mature stomata, however, has the stomatal aperture surrounded by only a one ring-shaped guard cell with two nuclei (E). How it happens has been explained differently by both. Haberlandt believed that towards maturity the ends of the separating walls are resorbed. Consequently the cytoplasm of the two guard cells comes in contact during development covering the initially two-celled stoma into one-celled.

Schimper and others hold that the growth of the separating wall in the young two-celled stoma cannot keep pace with the overall growth of the stoma. This gives rise to the one-celled condition.

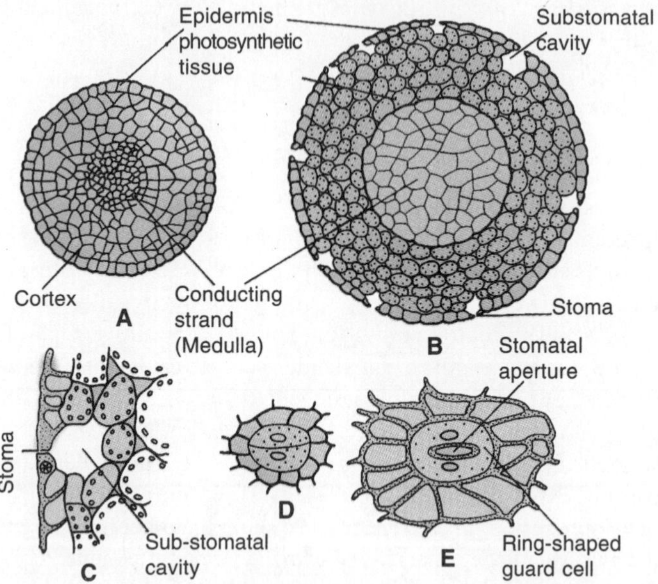

Fig. 18.13. (A—E). ***Funaria hygrometrica***. A, transverse section of seta; B, transverse section through apophysis; C, a portion of B magnified, to show stoma, substomatal cavity and photosynthetic tissue; D, young stoma in surface view; E, mature stoma in surface view.

Sack and Paolillo Jr (1985), on the contrary claim that at no stage does the stoma in *Funaria* becomes two-celled. Using Normarski differential interference contrast optics and transmission electron microscopy they found that the parental cell of the guard cell undergoes mitosis but incomplete cytokinesis. The cell plate in the *Funaria* guard cell never joins the end walls. The resultant young stoma is binucleate no doubt but one-celled. The incomplete septum thickens and separates to form the pore.

Garner and Paolillo, Jr (1973) studied the functioning of stomata in *F. hygrometrica*. They found that the stomata open on the 4th day of capsule expansion in green house conditions. From the 5th to the 10th day of capsule expansion these respond to the environmental conditions like the stomata of the flowering plants opening by light and closing by darkness. Later on as the capsule ripens they lose their responsiveness to environmental changes. In the late stages of ripening they remain open in the light and in the dark. Each stoma leads into an **air** space below called the **substomatal cavity** (C). Within the epidermis is a broad **spongy zone** of sterile cells rich in chloroplasts (B). There are distinct intercellular spaces between these cells. The spongy zone surrounds the central conducting strand composed of thin-walled, narrow, vertically elongated cells devoid of chloroplasts. The central strand is continuous below with the central strand of the seta. Above it is linked with the columella by means of a bundle of filaments. Each filament consists of a few thin-walled, vertically elongated cells (Fig. 18.14 B). The presence of abundant chlorenchyma with air spaces and stomata shows that apophysis region is specialized for photosynthesis.

(*ii*) *Theca* (Fig. 18.14 B). It forms the middle major portion of the capsule. The capsule wall in this region is highly differentiated and several cells in thickness. The outermost layer is the **epidermis**. It is continuous with the epidermis of the apophysis but contains fewer stomata. The cells within the epidermis are colourless. These colourless parenchymatous cells are compactly arranged in two hypodermal layers and constitute the **hypodermis**. Within the hypodermis is the spongy layer. It is one or, at the most, two cells in thickness. The cells constituting the spongy layer contain chloroplasts and are loosely arranged. The spongy layer is continuous with that of the apophysis where it becomes broader.

Within the capsule wall is a wide, cylindrical **air space**. It is traversed by strands of narrow, elongated, green cells. The strands of green cells are called the **trabeculae**. The trabeculae connect the innermost layer of the capsule wall with the outer wall of the **spore sac**. In the centre of the theca region is a solid cylinder of pitch-like (delicate, colourless, compact parenchyma) cells. It is referred to as the **columella**. The columella is narrow below and expanded above. Below it is connected with the central strand of the apophysis. Just outside or surrounding the columella is the **spore sac**. It is a barrel-shaped structure open above and below. It surrounds the columella. The inner wall of the spore sac, often referred to as **inner spore sac**, is one cell in thickness. The outer wall or **outer spore sac** is three or four cells in thickness. These cells are colourless. Between the inner and the outer walls is the cavity of the spore sac. It contains numerous **spores** at maturity but no **elaters**. The spores are formed from the spore mother cells in tertrads. In their formation the diploid nucleus of the spore mother cell undergoes the usual meiotic division. The spores are thus **haploid**. They are the first cells of the next gametophyte generation.

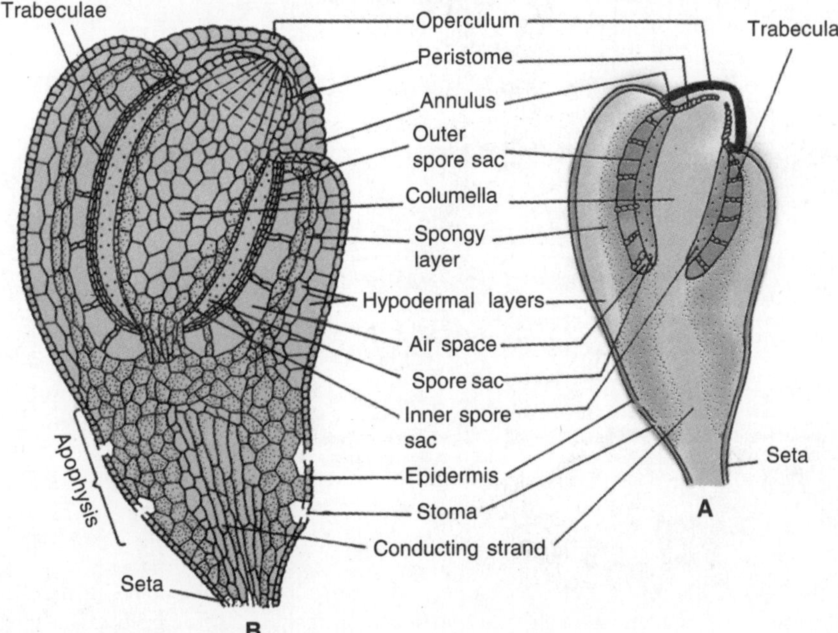

Fig. 18.14. (A—B). ***Funaria hygrometrica***. A, L.S. capsule, outline sketch; B, L.S. capsule showing structural details.

(*iii*) *Operculum or lid.* The terminal, obliquely placed, conical, cap-like portion of the capsule is the **operculum** (Fig. 18.14 B). It is 4 or 5 layers of cells in thickness. The inner 3-4 layers of cells are composed of small, thin-walled parenchyma cells. This thin-walled tissue forms the major portion of the operculum. It is bounded by a surface layer which consists of cells with greatly thickened walls. It is the **epidermis**. The operculum at first, is continuous with the theca region. Eventually it becomes delimited by the appearance of a narrow, circular constriction. Below the constriction are 2-3 layers of special, radially elongated, thick-walled cells. These form a circular rim or diaphragm. The latter constitutes the upper end of the open theca. It joins the epidermis to the peristome within and is perforated in the centre by the thin-walled tissue in continuation with the columella.

Immediately underneath the operculum lies the **peristome** (Fig. 18.15 A, B). It is orthodontous type and consists of two sets of long, conical teeth, one within the other. There are sixteen teeth in each set (D) the total being 32. The teeth of both the sets are on the same radii and thus opposite to each other. The tapering distal ends of the teeth of the outer set converge towards each other and are united terminally in a small central disc of tissue (B, C). The peristome teeth close the opening of the spore sac. They are attached at the base to the rim or the diaphragm (A). The peristome teeth are elaborately sculptured. Those of the outer set respond to changes in humidity and thus are said to be **hygroscopic**. The inner peristome teeth do not show hygroscopic movements. The presence of peristome teeth guarding the mouth of the theca region slows the rate of spore discharge.

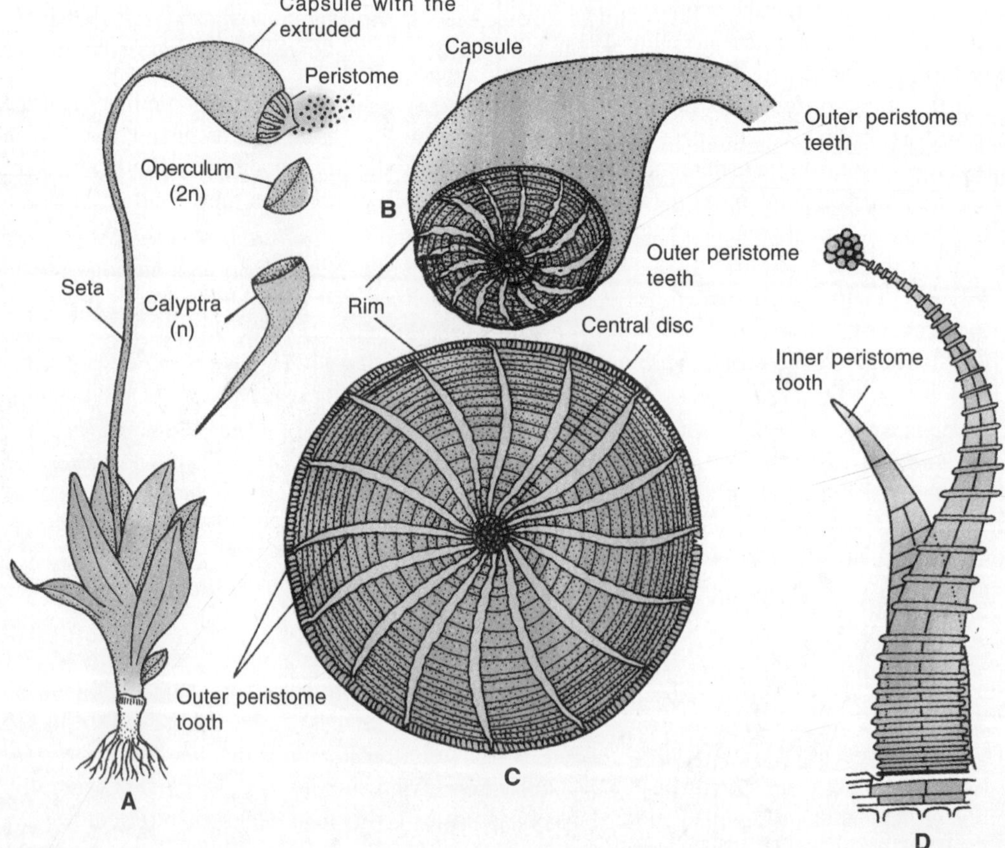

Fig. 18.15. (A—D). ***Funaria*** sp. Dehiscence of capsule and structure of peristome. A, moss gametophore bearing the mature sporophyte in which the calyptra and operculum have dropped exposing the extruded peristome; B, mature capsule in which the operculum has dropped exposing the peristome; C, outer peristome seen from above; D, two peristome teeth, outer and inner showing structure (A, diagrammatic, B—C based on Cavers).

Above the rim of the theca forming the broadest lower part of the operculum is the **annulus** (Fig. 18.14 B). It consists of 4 or 5 layers of cells. The upper two or three layers form a special ring of modified cells constituting the edge of the detached operculum. The lower two layers constitute the annulus proper. It consists of thin-walled cells with distended form. By the destruction of thin-walled annulus cells the operculum is, at first, loosened and later dropped off.

The remarkable feature of the moss capsule is its extremely reduced archesporium or fertile tissue as compared with its sterile tissue. The **sterile tissue** composing the capsule can be divided into the following four regions :—

(*i*) The sterile cells constituting the apophysis.

(*ii*) The sterile cells forming the several cell layers thick capsule wall.

(*iii*) The sterile cells forming the columella.

(*iv*) The sterile cells constituting the operculum and the peristome.

There is a suggestion that the **capsule** bears a rough resemblance to a **true leaf** of the pteridophytes. It is eminently fitted to carry on photosynthesis. In case we take the homology to be correct the **spore sac** will then correspond to the **sporangium**.

(*c*) *Dehiscence of capsule* (Fig. 18.15 A, B). The mature capsule begins to dry up. Consequently the thin-walled cells of the operculum within the epidermis and the thin-walled cells of the annulus proper which hold the operculum in place, shrink and shrivel. This causes strain and eventual break-down of the thin-walled cells. As a result the operculum is loosened from the underlying tissue. Soon it drops off exposing the peristome which forms a fringe around the mouth of the opened capsule (A). Dropping off the operculum is said to be assisted by the upward hygroscopic movement of the underlying peristome teeth. By this time the columella and the adjoining thin-walled tissues except the capsule wall have shrivelled leaving a central cavity. It is filled with spores, which are ready for dispersal.

(*d*) *Dispersal of spores.* The exposed peristome plays an important role in the dispersal of spores. The peristome teeth by their hygroscopic movements assist in the gradual discharge of spores which lie free in the otherwise hollow capsule. The teeth are united at their tips of a small central disc of tissue (A, B). Slight rotation of the teeth with changes in the moisture content of air may permit spores to sift out gradually through the slits between the adjacent teeth (A). The bowing movements of the peristome, however, play a more important role in regulating spore discharge. The teeth bend inward and outward with changes in humidity. In high humidity the hygroscopic teeth of the outer peristome (exostome) absorb water and bend together inwards with their tips inserted into the gaps between the inner peristome (endostome). The dome thus reconstituted completely closes the mouth of the cavity containing the spores. This prevents the escape of spores in wet weather. In dry weather, the arched outer peristome teeth lose water and bend outward with jerky movements. As they do so, the slits between them widen allowing the spores to filter out. The inner peristome simply functions as a sieve. At this time assisted by the swinging round of the open capsule on the twisting hygroscopic seta, the spores sift out gradually though these slits, a few at a time. The spores are thus liberated in the dry weather when they are most likely to be carried by the air currents. The spores also escape through the slits between the adjacent teeth when the wind shakes the capsule.

Development of sporophyte (Fig. 18.16). The sporophyte (sporogonium) originates from the diploid zygote (A). Its early development consists in the segmentation of the zygote. The details of segmentation of the zygote have been studied by many observers. These are as follows :—

1. **Development of embryo**. The first division in the zygote is transverse (B). It separates the upper **epibasal** half from the lower **hypobasal** half. Each of these regions undergoes two successive diagonal divisions (C—D). As a result an **apical cell** with two cutting faces is differentiated at each end (E—F). The embryo thus grows from two growing points—a feature in sharp contrast to the

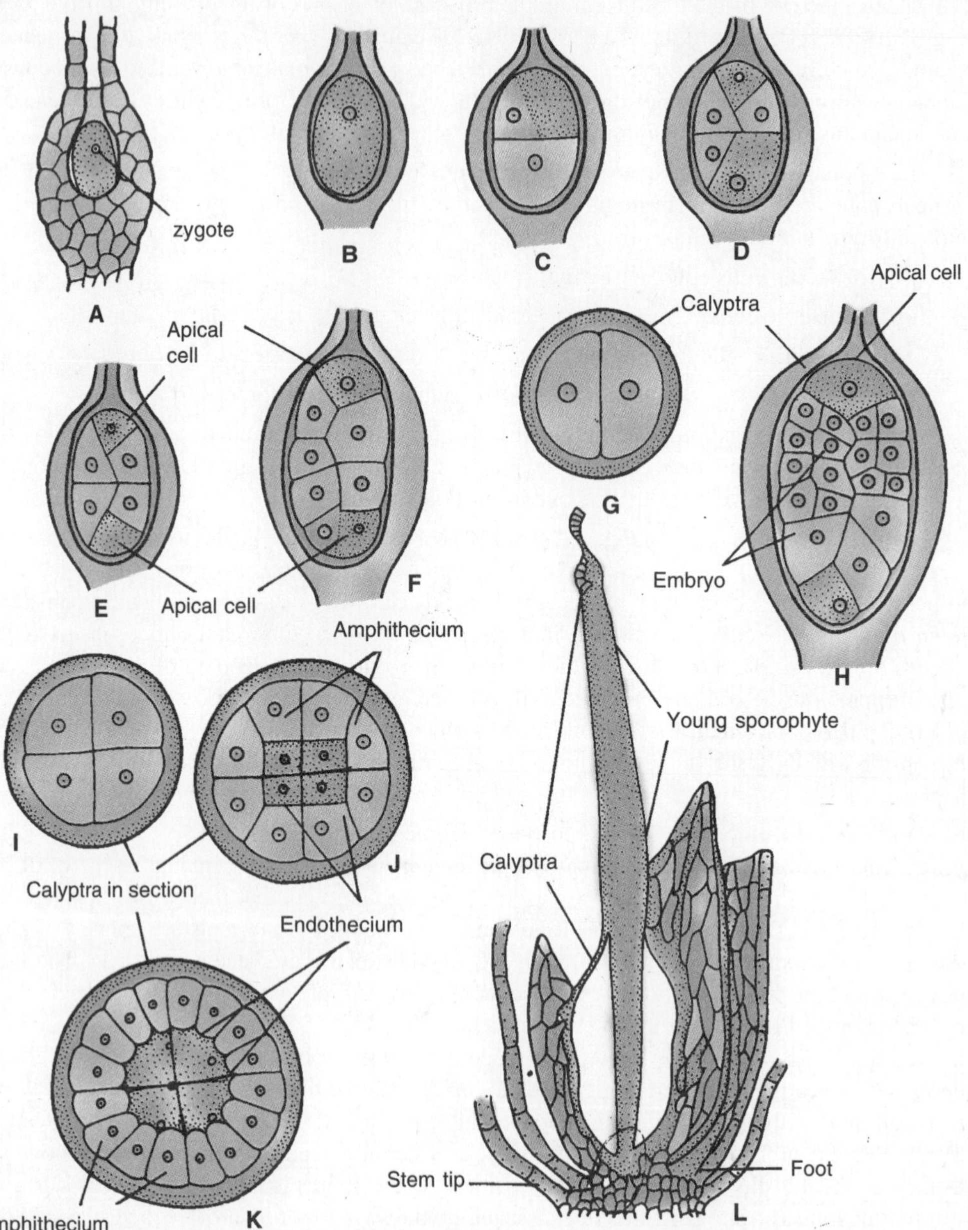

Fig. 18.16. (A—L). ***Funaria*** sp. Successive stages in the development of young sporophyte. A—F, H and L are longitudinal sections; G, I, J and K are transverse sections.

other bryophytes. The two apical cells cut off segments right and left (F). These alternate cleavages from the two apical cells produce a spindle-shaped **embryo** (H). The latter grows rapidly at the upper end. Here the segments are cut off in quick succession alternately right and left. The segments divide and re-divide. The apical cell at the lower end of the embryo is not so active. The divisions at his end are thus much less and irregular. The biapical growth of the embryo goes on till it assumes an extremely elongated, cylindrical form (I). According to French and Paolillo (1975) before the embryo is 8 mm. long, its apical growth ceases. The distal or apical region of the embryo becomes earmarked to form the operculum, spore sac and a part of the apophysis. It does into contribute to seta growth. The subapical region of the embryo contains an intercalary meristem which is organized during embryogeny. This intercalary meristem accounts for the development of the seta and lower part of apophysis. The lower end of the embryo burrows through the base of the venter and the archegonial stalk into the tip of the stem upon which the archegonium is seated. Eventually it enlarges to form the **foot**. The latter obtains water, nutrients and food for the developing sporophyte from the parent plant. Subsequent to the formation of the foot the seta develops from the derivatives of the intercalary meristem. During the growth of the seta, the region of the embryo distal to the intercalary meristem expands into the capsule region. Krupa (1969) reported that the sporophyte of *F. hygrometrica* takes about 96 days to mature. Garner and Paolillo, Jr. (1973) who studied the time course of sporophyte development in this moss put it at about 65-70 days. They divided sporophyte development in *F. hygrometrica* into three stages namely, (*i*) elongation stage, (*ii*) capsule expansion stage which also includes other premeiotic developments and (*iii*) capsule ripening stage. The elongation phase extends over 2 to 2.5 weeks. It is followed by the capsule expansion stage which takes 9 days. The peristome teeth redden when the capsule is in its 12th day. Chlorosis of capsule begins in the 4th week after the commencement of capsule expansion. It is followed by reddening of the capsule and complete ripening which is complete in 45 days after the

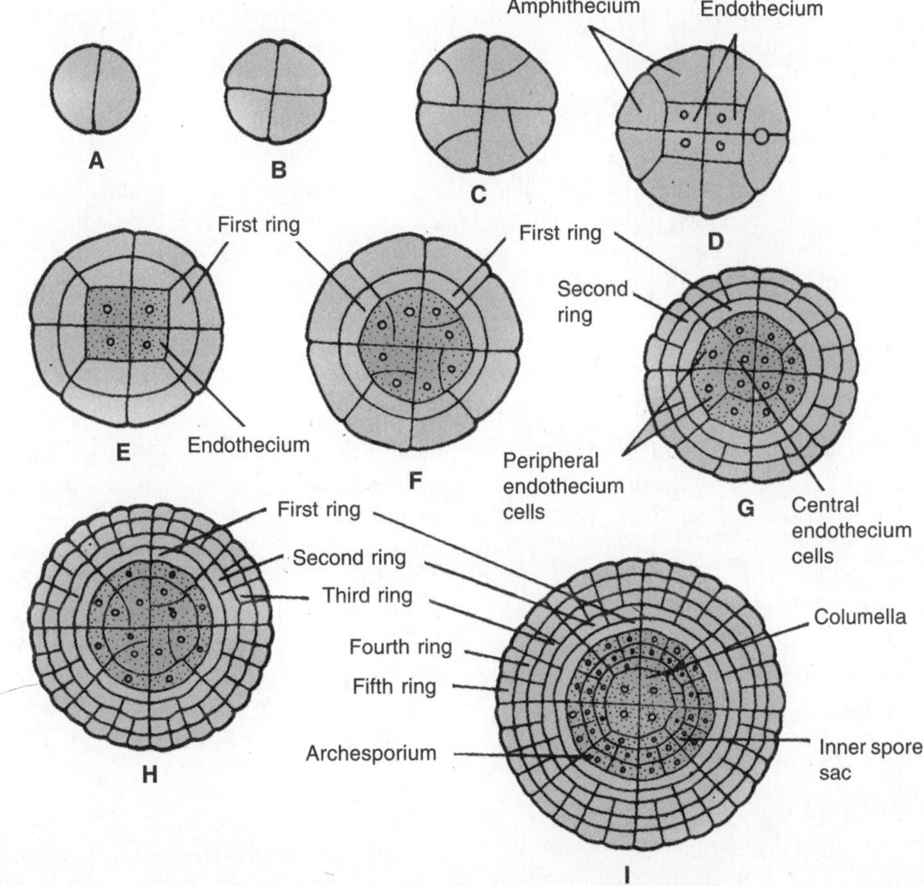

Fig. 18.17 (A—I). ***Funaria hygrometrica***. Diagrams of transverse sections of young capsule showing stages of development at successive levels below its apex. A—D, differentiation of amphithecium and endothecium; E—I, Differentiation of five rings of cells from the amphithecium. (Diagrammatic).

start of capsule expansion. The calyptra splits on the 5th day and sheds between 11th and 16th day after the capsule expansion begins.

2. **Development of capsule** (Fig. 18.17). The alternating segments cut off by the apical cell of the epibasal half subdivide with great regularity. In a cross-section the two alternating segments are nearly spherical (A) each being semi-circular in outline. Each of these segments divides by a radial vertical wall. The resultant four cells are arranged quadrately (B). Each cell of the quadrant then undergoes an anticlinal division. The division wall is curved. Since it is in a plane perpendicular to an internal wall, one of the daughter cells in a cross-section is nearly rectangular and the other more or less triangular (C). The third set of walls are periclinal. They appear only in the rectangular daughter cells. With the formation of the periclinal walls, the embryo in the capsule portion is divided into two regions the outer and the inner. The former is called the amphithecium and the latter endothecium (D). The endothecium, at this stage, forms a central column of four clearly defined rows. They extend throughout that part of the embryo which is destined to form the capsule. In a cross section the endothecium forms a central rectangular tract of four quadrately arranged cells (D). It is surrounded by a single-layered, eight-celled amphithecium.

These two regions (the amphitecium and the endothecium) are the primary or the **fundamental embryonic** layers of the sporogonium. They are recognisable though to a lesser extent in the epibasal segments of the seta region as well. The inner region corresponding to the endothecium forms the central strand in the region of seta. The outer corresponding to the amphithecium forms the cortex. For the sake of the convenience and clarity we consider the differentiation of tissues in the three well defined regions of the capsule separately as follows :

(a) Differentiation of tissues in the middle or the theca region

(*i*) *Fate of the primary endothecium* (Fig. 18.17, C—I). The next divisions appear in the amphithecium but we first trace the destiny of the endothecium. The four central quadrately arranged cells of the endothecium undergo cleavage in the same way as the four cells of the quadrants at the apex of the embryo. The first walls are curved and anticlinal. The following ones are periclinal (G). This results in the separation of a central group of four endothecial cells surrounded by a layer of eight peripheral endothecium. These eventually differentiate into the **columella**. The columella forms the core of theca region of the capsule. It consists of large colourless cells.

The eight peripheral endothecial cells undergo cleavage by radial walls. The daughter cells divide periclinally. In this way two concentric layers, **outer** and **inner**, of endothecial cells are formed (I). The cells of the outer layer constitute the **primary archesporium**. They divide at first by radial walls only. The cells of the inner layer remain small and are transformed into the **inner space sac**. The latter remains one cell thick. The archesporium in *Funaria* is thus endothecial in origin. It is formed from the outermost layer of the endothecium. Originally it consists of a single layer of cells. It is thus extremely reduced forming but a small and narrow part of the theca region of the capsule. It extends neither to the base nor to the apex of the capsule. It is a barrel-shaped tract open at both ends. The archesporium cells may undergo sub-division to form two cell layers thick **sporogenous tissue**. All the sporogenous cells are functional. They mature into spore mother cells. The elaters are lacking. Each spore mother cell undergoes the usual tetrad division to produce four haploid spores. The four-celled embryonic or primary endothecium in the theca region thus gives rise to :

A. The columella.

B. The single-layered inner spore sac.

C. The sporogenous tissue with all the cells fertile and functional. No elaters are formed.

(*ii*) *Fate of the primary amphithecium* (Fig. 18.17 E-I). Meanwhile the eight cells of the primary amphithecium have undergone rapid segmentation. They divide both periclinally and anticlinally in a definite pattern and regular sequence to produce five concentric layers or ring of cells. The first division in the 8 primary amphithecium cells is periclinal. Two concentric layers of 8 cells each are formed (E). The 8 cells of the *inner layer* constitute the **first ring**. The latter is in contact with the archesporium. It consists of cells smaller in size. The cells of the first ring divide by radial walls to increase in number. The derivative undergo periclinal divisions to form three to four layers of cells. These mature into the **outer spore sac**. The cells of the outer spore sac lack chloroplasts.

The *outer layer* external to the first ring consists of 8 larger cells. These undergo two successive divisions. The first is anticlinal and next periclinal. Two concentric layers of 16 cells each is the result (G). The inner of these two layers is known as the **second ring**. The outer layer of 16 cells again undergoes segmentation. The 16 cells of the second ring undergo a radical change. They develop chloroplasts and elongate radially. Owing to the increase in diameter of the theca region intercellular spaces appear between the radially stretched cells of the second ring. They thus become separated from each other laterally by these intercellular spaces. The air spaces become wider and extend to the top of the theca-region. Finally these radially elongated cells divide by transverse wall to become short filaments of three or four chlorophyll containing cells. These are called the **trabeculae**. The latter extend across the air space and link the outer spore sac with several layers thick capsule wall.

The 16 cells of the layer external to the second ring undergo the anticlinal division followed by the periclinal one (Fig. 18.17 H). Two concentric layers of 32 cells each are produced. Of these the inner layer of 32 cells constitutes the **third ring**. The cells of the third ring develop chloroplasts. They mature into the inner layer of the capsule wall. It is called the **spongy layer**. It usually remains one or at the most becomes two cells thick in the theca region of the capsule.

The 32 cells of the layer external to the third ring divide only by periclinal walls. They do not undergo the anticlinal division. Two concentric layers of 32 cells each are formed (I). The inner layer of 32 cells is known as the **fourth ring** and the outer **fifth ring**. The cells of the fourth ring later undergo periclinal divisions producing 2 to 3 layers of cells. These mature into the **hypodermis** region of the capsule wall. The cells of the hypodermis are colourless as they lack chloroplasts. They are, however, larger in size and are thin-walled and parenchymatous.

The cells of the fifth ring divide by anticlinal walls only. They eventually mature into the single-layered surface layer of the capsule wall. It is called the **epidermis**. The epidermal cells have greatly thickened walls. Here and there the epidermis is punctured with functional **stomata**. They are, however, more numerous in the apophysis region.

To sum up the various tissues derived from the primary or embryonic amphithecium in the theca region from without inwards are :—

A. Single layered **epidermis**.

B. Two or three layers thick **hypodermis**.

C. One cell or at the most two cells thick **spongy layer**.

D. Short filaments of green cells or the **trabeculae** extending across the air space.

(*b*) **Differentiation of tissues in the apical** or **operculum region** (Fig. 18.18). With the development of the theca region the apical portion of the capsule differentiates into a cone of tissues. It constitutes the **operculum** region. In this tissue originates the **peristome**. The surface layers of the operculum region cover the peristome.

(*i*) *Fate of endothecium.* The operculum region originally consists of the same two embryonic layers. There is the central tract of four **primary endothecium cells** surrounded by a peripheral layer of the 8 **primary amphithecium cells**. The former undergo repeated cleavage. A central mass of thin-walled parenchymatous cells in continuation with the columella is produced. The endothecium thus differentiates into that portion of the columella which lies in this region of the capsule.

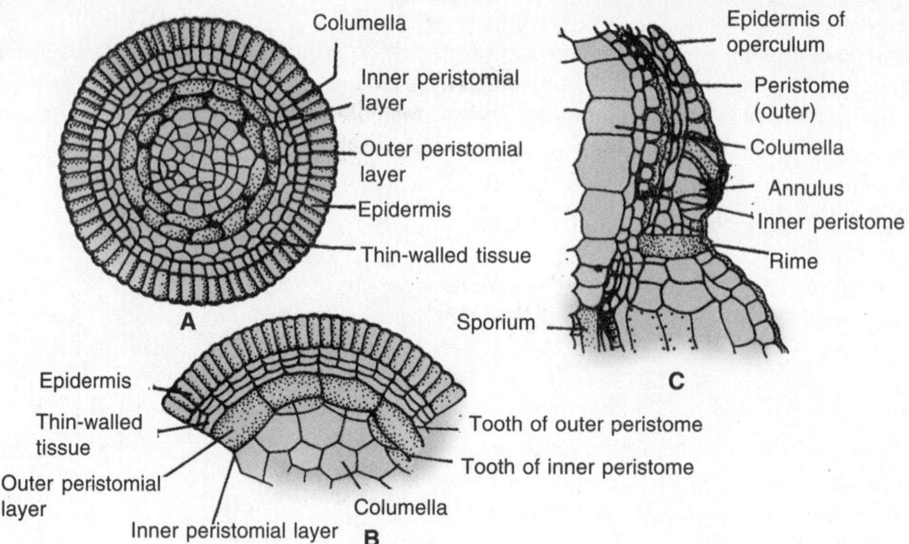

Fig. 18.18 (A—C). ***Funaria hygrometrica***. A, transverse section through the operculum at a lower level; B, a portion of the same from a still older capsule showing development of peristome teeth from the opposite walls of peristome cells; C, a portion of a longitudinal section through the operculum and upper part of the theca showing the relationship of peristome and rim.

(ii) Fate of amphithecium. The eight primary amphithecium cells undergo the usual anticlinal and periclinal divisions (as in the theca region) to produce six concentric rings of amphithecium cells. It is from these rings that the **operculum** and the **peristome** tissues are differentiated as follows :—

Formation of peristome. The account of the development of the peristome is mainly based on Proskauer's investigations (1958). The peristome in *Funaria* is developed from the **three inner rings** of the amphithecium in the opercular region. The eight cells of the **first ring** undergo anticlinal divisions till this ring becomes 32 cells in perimeter. It is a now called the **inner peristomial layer** (A). The second ring which consists of 16 cells form the **middle peristomial layer**. The cells in this layer undergo no division and thus determine the number of peristome teeth in each ring of the peristome of the mature capsule. The third ring which consists of 32 cells functions as the **outer peristomial layer**. The cells of the three peristomial layers are so disposed of with respect to one another that one cell of the middle layer is opposite two cells of outer and inner peristomial layers. These peristomial layers form a dome-shaped structure external to the columella in this region. From it are differentiated the **outer peristome (exostome)** and the **inner peristome (endostome)**. The former originates at the juncture of the outer and middle peristomial layers. The **inner peristome** is formed at the juncture of the middle and inner peristomial layers. The next step is the deposition of additional wall material (cutin). It is laid on the tangential walls contiguous to the outer and middle peristomial layers in the case of outer peristome. In the case of the inner peristome the thickenin wall material is deposited only on the outer wall of the inner peristomial layer. The vertical anticlinal (radial) walls of the peristomial cells of the three layers undergo no noticeable thickening. It is along these unthickened anticlinal walls of the peristomial cells that splitting takes place. The unthickened radial cellulose walls and the contents of these cells disappear. Only the two thickened cutinized walls are left behind. These split longitudinally into two (outer and inner) rings of peristomial teeth with 16 teeth in each ring. These peristome-teeth are built up of strips of specially thickened and cutinized cell walls. They are curved, narrow, triangular plates with thick, transverse bars on the brownish red, conical teeth of the outer series. The teeth of the inner series or endostome are comparatively smaller, more delicate and colourless. The outer peristome teeth converge towards their tapering distal ends to meet a small central disc.

Formation of operculum (Fig. 18.18 A). The three rings (4th to 6th) of the amphithecium which are on the outer side of the peristome form the **lid** or **operculum**. The cells of the fourth and fifth rings jointly produce a tissue. It consists of thin-walled parenchymatous cells and is arranged in three layers. This thin-walled tissue forms the inner and major portion of the operculum. The cells of the 6th ring mature into the protective surface layer called the **epidermis**. The epidermal cells have greatly thickened outer walls.

Differentiation of annulus (Fig. 18.18 C). Very early in the development of the capsule there appears a narrow, shallow, circular depression at the junction of the operculum and the theca region (C). It delimits the former from the latter. In this depression lies a narrow zone of thin walled, narrow cells. It serves as an **abscission layer**. It is there that the ripe operculum becomes detached. The epidermal cells above and below the narrow zone show active growth and elongate radially. Two distinct rings of cells are formed one above the other below the narrow zone. The former is called the **annulus** and the latter **rim** or **diaphragm** of theca. The epidermal cells of these regions project beyond those of the narrow zone.

The annulus forms the periphery of the broadest part of the operculum. It consists of about 5 or 6 years of epidermal cells layer one above the other. The cells of the upper three or four layers become specially modified. They are narrow and radially elongated. They have thicker walls and form the rim of the mature detached operculum. The cells of the two lower layers of the annulus, which constitute the **annulus proper,** remain thin-walled. They are reported to be filled with mucilage. The mucilaginous contents of these cells absorb water and swell as the capsule matures. Subsequently they are destroyed and the operculum is detached. To sum up the **amphithecium** in the region of the operculum gives rise to :—

(*i*) Surface layers of the operculum consisting of the epidermis and the three layers of thin-walled, parenchymatous cells internal to it. They cover the peristome.

(*ii*) The two rings of peristome teeth.

(*iii*) The annulus.

(*c*) **Differentiation of tissues in the basal or apophysis region** (Fig. 18.14B). A broad zone of cells between the theca and seta regions in the young capsule enlarges considerably. It forms the basal, swollen, sterile regions of capsule. It is called the **apophysis** (B). The four primary endothecium cells in this region divide and re-divide to form the **conducting strand**. It is continuous with the conducting strand of the seta. The archesporium and the inner spore sac characteristic of the theca region are not differentiated. The eight primary amphithecium cells divide and re-divide in the usual manner to form five concentric rings of cells. The latter get differentiated into the various tissues external to the conducting strand. The order of cell succession and differentiation is practically the same as in the theca region. The cells of the first, second, third and fourth rings form the broad spongy zone with cells rich in chloroplasts and intercellular spaces between them. The cells of the fifth ring mature into the single-layered **epidermis** punctured here and there with stomata. There is neither any hypodermis nor any air space traversed by trabeculae. Apophysis is, therefore, the solid photosynthetic region of the capsule.

As these developmental changes have taken place the young sporogonium grows faster than the surrounding calyptra. The neck of the archegonium has by now dried up. It is, however, persistent. The seta elongates rapidly. Consequently the calyptra is ruptured around its base. The ruptured portion of the calyptra tipped by the persistent, dark brown, archegonial neck is carried up as a **conical hood** at the top of the elongating sporogonium (Fig. 18.12 C). It surrounds and protects the developing theca. For a while the capsule is upright on the seta. Later it becomes pendent or nodding (Fig. 18.12 D). The calyptra is stripped off and lost (Fig. 18.12 E).

Comparison between the *sporophytes* of *Sphagnum* **and** *Funaria.* Having discussed the structure and the development of the sporogonium of *Funaria*, we are in a position to compare it with that of *Sphagnum*. The two may be contrasted as follows :—

Sphagnum	Funaria
(a) Development	
1. The early growth of the embryo is by transverse cleavage followed by intercalary enlargement of the segments. There is no apical growth.	**1.** The early growth of the embryo is **biapical**. The segments are cut off alternately from the two apical cells each located at the opposite end. The apical growth later gives place to intercalary activity.
2. The entire endothecium gives rise to the **columella** which is a bulky mass of parenchyma cells. It has rounded apex.	**2.** Only the inner part of the endothecium forms the **columella**.
3. The **archesporium** is derived from the inner layer of the **amphithecium**.	**3.** The **archesporium** arises fromt he outer-most layer of the **endothecium**.
4. The archesporium forms a **dome** arching over the columella.	**4.** The archesporium is a **barrel-shaped** structure open both at the top and the base. It does not arch over the columella but surrounds it instead.
(b) Structure	
5. The mature sporophyte consists of a **foot** and a spherical **capsule**. There is no seta. Its place is taken up by a **constriction**. The function of the seta is taken up by the **pseudopodium**. The foot is massive and functions as an **haustorium**.	**5.** It consists of a **foot**, a long, slender **seta** and a pear-shaped **capsule**. The **pseudopodium** is absent. The foot is poorly developed.
6. The capsule of *Sphagnum* is comparatively a simpler structure representing only the **theca** portion concerned with spore production and the **opercular** portion concerned with dehiscence. The **apophysis** is absent. So is the peristome from the opercular region. The theca region is also comparatively simple in structure.	**6.** The capsule shows complex strucutre with considerable differentiation of tissues. It shows three well marked regions :— (*a*) **Apophysis**—a solid, somewhat swollen, sterile, basal portion mainly concerned with photosynthesis and conduction. (*b*) **Theca**—a middle urn-shaped portion concerned with spore production. (*c*) **Operculum**—apical region closely related to dehiscence. Beneath the operculum is an elaborate mechanism of dispersal of spores in the form of **peristome** teeth.
7. The capsule is bounded by **epidermis** bearing functionless **stomata**. They have no **pores**. There are no substantial air spaces. Thus the many layered capsule wall lacks ventilated photosynthetic tissue.	**7.** The capsule has a well developed **edipermis** punctured with functional **stomata**, particularly numerous, in the apophysis region. They open into sub-stomatal **air spaces** which communicate with a system of intercellular spaces aerating the green, photosynthetic **spongy tissue** in the capsule wall. The capsule wall in *Funaria* has thus a well ventilated, photosynthetic system. In the theca region there is the two cell layers thick hypodermis, in addition, beneath the epidermis.

Sphagnum	Funaria
8. Within the several layers thick capsule wall there is no intercellular space so that the capsule is a compact solid structure.	**8.** Within the several layers thick capsule wall is the wide air space. It is, in fact, a highly distended cavity in the spongy zone of the capsule wall. In the centre of this wide air space remains suspended by filaments of green cells (**trabeculae**), the **columella** surrounded by the **spore sac.**
9. The **spore sac** is a wide dome-shaped structure over-arching the rounded tip of the massive central columella.	**9.** The **spore sac** is narrow and barrel-shaped. It is open at the top and the base. It does not over-arch but surrounds the columella which forms the central core of the capsule in the theca region.

The points of resemblance between the two are (*i*) absence of elaters; (*ii*) dehiscence of the capsule by the detachment of a lid; (*iii*) rupturing of the calyptra; and (*iv*) presence of a well defined columella in both.

Nutrition of sporophyte. Some earlier morphologists like Goebal (1930), Bower (1935) and others held that the young moss sporophyte lacks chlorophyll and thus is incapable of self nutrition. In their view the moss sporophyte becomes photosynthetic relatively late and at the time when the foot and the seta are advanced in development, the photosynthetic tissue in the apophysis and theca regions is established and sporogenesis is in progress. Bold (1940) pointed out that these statements are incompatible with the familiar bright green appearance of the young needle-like sporophyte in which the theca and the apophysis regions are far from being differentiated. In his study of the ontogeny of *Funaria* sporophyte he found that the egg before and after fertilization and the embryo sporophyte till it reaches in size the green colour (chlorophyll) appears and the embryo sporophyte till it reaches the 16-called stage are nongreen. After the 16-called stage as the embryo increases in size the green colour (chlorophyll) appears and the embryo sporophyte becomes photosynthetic. Photosynthesis in *Funaria* sporophyte thus begins early and continues throughout further development of the sporophyte. It starts long before the apophysis and these regions are differentiated. Garner and Paolillo (1973) reported that during the phase of capsule expansion and other premeiotic developments, the *Funaria* sporophyte is essentially self-sufficient so far its carbohydrate food is concerned.

The question arises whether or not the presence of chlorophyll throughout the early stages of sporophyte development, and the development of well ventilated photosynthetic tissue and its persistence for a considerably period in the capsule, enable *Funaria* sporophyte to synthesize by photosynthesis the whole of the carbohydrate food it needs. The photosynthetic capacity of *Funaria* capsule has been estimated by certain bryologists. It is considered equivalent to that of the fourteen leaves of the leafy gametophore. This study shows net photosynthesis capacity for *Funaria* sporophyte. It has been confirmed by Paolillo and Bazaz (1968) by infra-red gas analysis for the detecting of photosynthesis. However, Krupa (1969) reported that the photosynthesis in *Funaria* sporophyte is significant but falls short of net photosynthesis. It may be sufficient for self-maintenance but not for sustained growth. It does not account for the sporophyte's carbohydrate requirements including respiration. To meet the deficit the sporophyte must rely on translocation from the gametophyte.

It is evident from the account given above that for the greater part of its organic nutrition, *Funaria* sporophyte (capsule) is autonomous and in part it is supplied through the seta by the gametophyte. For inorganic nutrients and water the sporophyte has to depend entirely on the gametophyte because it is separated from the ground. However, Chvallier *et al* (1977) showed that the capsule of *Funaria* can utilize salts dissolved in water which fall on to it or flow over it. A supply of water is essential to obtain normal spores. The sporophyte of *Funaria* thus is a *semi* or *partial parasite*.

Funaria spores : (*a*) *Stucture*. With light microscope the mature spore is seen as a tiny more or less spherical structure with a smooth surface ranging in diameter from 0.012 to 0.020 mm in diameter. It consists of a tiny mass of protoplast surrounded by a spore wall (18.20 A). The latter shows differentiation into two distinct layers. The inner layer which is adjacent to the protoplast is even and hyaline. It is known as the **intine** or **endospore**. The outer layer which is smooth and coloured is termed the **exine** or **exospore**. The spore protoplast comprises a plasma membrane investing the spore cytoplasm containing a single nucleus, oil globules and plastids.

The study of fine structure of *Funaria spores* (Fig. 18.19 B) revealed that the spore wall consists of 4 layers (Afzelius, 1957) as in most other mosses. The innermost of these is fibrillar and transparent. It contains carbohydrate material including cellulose. This layer is termed the **intine**. External to the intine is the second layer which is very thin and electron dense or opaque. It is of uniform thickness. It is a subunit of the exine and demarcates the intine layer from the exine proper. It is often called the **separating layer**. On the outer side of separating layer is a non-stratified third

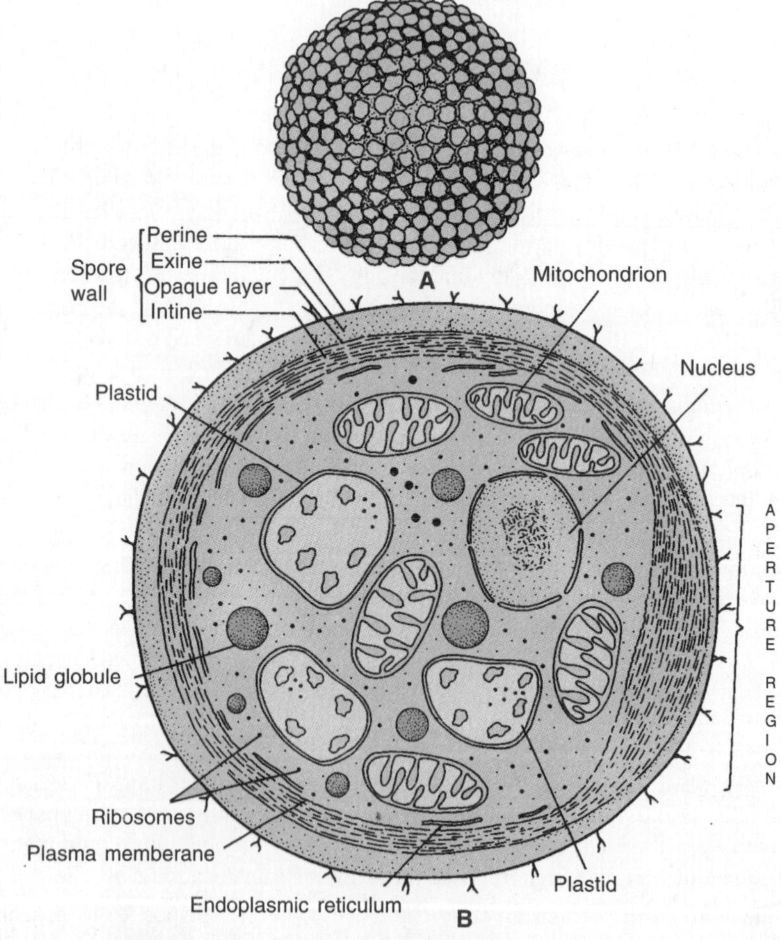

Fig. 18.19. (A—B). ***Funaria hygrometrica***. Diagrammatic representation of surface sculpturing (A) and fine structure (B) of a slightly dehydrated spore as seen with SEM (Based on Nakosteen and Hughes).

layer of the spore wall which is prominent, non-striped and more or less of uniform thickness. It is the **exine**. The exine does not exhibit fibrillar structure. Exine is resistant to acetolysis. It may or may not be involved in ornamentation of the spore wall. The outermost fourth layer of the spore wall is referred to as the **perine** (Erdtman, 1952). It is yellowish in colour, homogeneous and extremely opaque in election micrographs. The perine forms a thin covering on the outer surface of exine and forms the entire sculpture element in the form of truncate projections (Nakosteen and Hughes, 1978).

Within the spore wall is the plasma membrane which is distinct. It forms a tight investment around the cytoplasm which besides the nucleus contains food reserve in the form of a large lipid droplet sometimes 2 or more in number. There is very little starch. Of cell organelles, it has small regular mitochondria, numerous chloroplasts with poorly developed lamellae, small sparsely present dictyasomes and endoplasmic reticulum in the form of highly convoluted tubules near the plasma membrane. The cytoplasm lacks vacuoles (Kofler, 1959) but has abundant ribosomes.

Aperture region. Mcclymont and Larson (1964) reported that despite the absence of an externally differentiated aperture region on the spore wall some mosses including *Funaria hygrometrica* possess a well-defined region for protonemal emergence which is termed the **aperture region**. The latter exhibits four characteristics, namely (*i*) 2 or 3 times disc-shaped thickening of intine, (*ii*) pronounced decrease in exine thickening, (*iii*) more conspicuous thin electron-dense separating layer between the intine and exine, and (*iv*) presence of a lamellate structure in the intine adjacent to the exine. Despite all this there is no external sign of the existence of the aperture region. The germtube usually emerges through the centre of the aperture region. When two germ tubes arise from a single spore each emerges through the sporewall at the periphery of the aperture region.

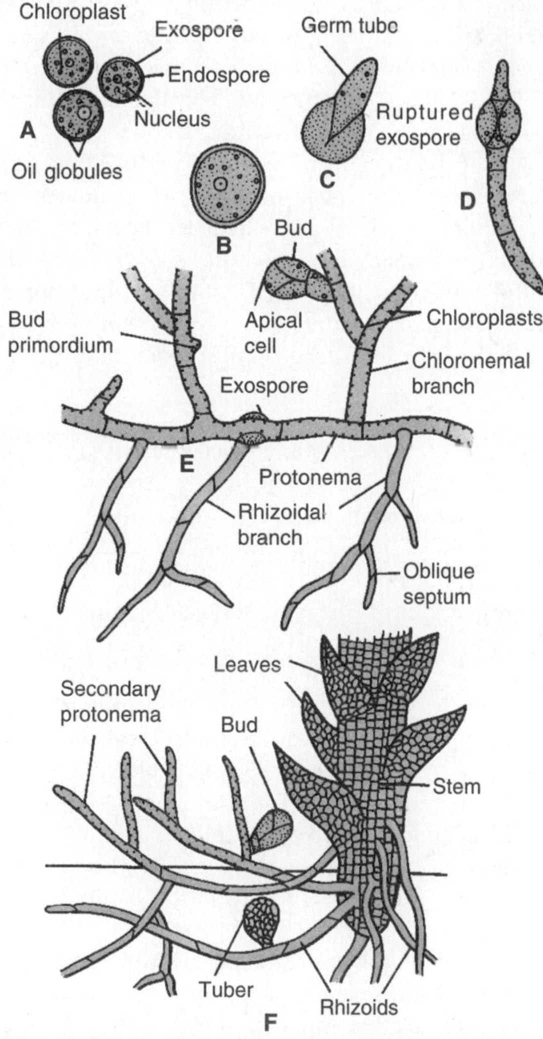

Fig. 18.20. (A—F). ***Funaria hygrometrica***. A, spores showing structure; B—E, successive stages in the germination of spore to form primary protonema; F, gametophore with some of the rhizoids coming above ground to form secondary protonema (A, based on Muller Berol; C—E after Muller Thurgau and F after Luerssen).

(*b*) *Functions*. The moss spores (meiospores) are haploid reproductive units with genetic potential for the production of moss gametophyte. They are usually dispersed by wind and perform several functions. The chief among these are, (*i*) assist in the dispersal of the species to new habitats, (*ii*) carry new gene combinations with potential for better adaptation of the new gametophyte to the environment, and (*iii*) are resistant to degradation and thus enable the species to tide over conditions unfavourable for growth.

(*c*) *Vitality of spores.* Under suitable conditions spores of *F. hygrometrica* germinate promptly and in most cases to nearly 100%. However the vitality decreases with time. Heitz (1942) reported that the spores of *Funaria* remain viable for 2 years but Meyer (1941) reported that they remain viable up to 9 years. Hofmann (1970) found that the viability of spores of *F. hygrometrica* extends to nearly 11 years.

Germination of spores (Fig. 18.20). Falling on moist soil and under favourable conditions of light and temperature, the spores germinate immediately. Baver (1959) and Mohar (1963) showed that germination of *Funaria* is light dependent. Light provides energy for the emergence of the germ tubes. The optimum temperature for spore germination is 30°C with 100% germination at 12-24 hr photo-period (Dietert, 1980). The first step in germination is the imbibition of water which mainly enters through the aperture region of the spore. The subsequent sequence of germinations stages is: (*i*) *swelling phase*, (*ii*) *spore wall rupture phase*, (*iii*) *protrusion phase* and (*vi*) *spore distension phase*.

(*i*) *Swelling phase.* Imbibion of water by the spore ushers the swelling phase. The swelling is of two different types, symmetrical and asymmetrical. The symmetrical swelling consists in the general swelling of the major unthickened part of the intine. It is negligible and not of much consequence in germination as it affects the whole spore. Germination, in fact, is initiated by 2-3 fold swelling of the disc-shaped intine thickening in the aperture region of the spore wall.

(*ii*) *Spore wall rupture phase.* The drastic asymmetrical swelling of the local intine thickening ruptures the exine at the centre of the aperture region where the exine is the thinnest. The rupture is apparently a mechanical fracture. Besides exine rupture, the separating layer also disappears in this phase of spore germination and the plastids turn green.

(*iii*) *Protrusion phase.* Through the rupture in the aperture region protrudes the disc-shaped thickened part of the intine.

(*iv*) *Distension phase.* Following protrusion of the aperture region intine, the spore protoplast adjacent to it follows suit. The protruding protoplast is covered and thus protected by the thickened protruded intine of the aperture region. This tubular outgrowth is called the *germ tube* (C). It emerges through the centre of the aperture region. Sometimes two divergent germ tubes originate from a single spore. They emerge through the spore wall at the periphery of the aperture region in two opposite directions (D).

Development of protonema. A cross wall soon form at the point of emergence of each germ tube. One of these may remain colourless and grows into a first rhizoid and the other turns green. The emergence of the rhizoid and plastid rich green germ tube is dependent on photosynthesis. The green tube grows in length and divides by septa to form a filament of green cells (D). The green filament grows over the soil and branches freely. The growth is apical. The branched green alga-like filament thus formed is the *primary protonema* (E). It forms a thin green web-like net over the substratum. Most of the branches of the primary protonema grow prostrate on the moist soil surface or grow upright or horizontal in the air for a short distance. They are green and thus known as the **chloronemal branches**. They are positively phototrophic and consist of elongate cells rich in chloroplasts. Some of the branches, however, penetrate the substratum and function as absorbing and anchoring organs. These *rhizoidal branches* are non-green, thin and possess oblique septa between the cells. The moss protonema with its chloronemal and rhizoidal branches very much resembles the heterotrichous thallus of a green alga. It can however, be distinguished from the latter by the presence of oblique septa in the rhizoidal branches.

Sironwal (1947) recognized two distinct growth phases in the development of primary protonema. These are the **chloronema** and **caulonema** stages. Bopp (1959-61) and many other workers strongly supported this view point.

(*i*) *Chloronemal stage.* It represents the early growth of the primary protonema following spore germination. It consists of a system of green, positively phototrophic filaments with transverse septa between the component cells. Other characteristic features of this protonemal growth phase are (*i*) sparse and irregular branching, (*ii*) colourless cell walls, (*iii*) cells with numerous, evenly distributed discoid chloroplasts. This first formed chloronemal growth stage of primary protonema continues for several (about 20) days according to Sironwal.

(*ii*) *Caulonemal stage*. The chloronemal stage is late followed by the caulonema growth stage under favourable conditions which are low temperature, submersion and low light intensity (Bopp, 1961). Each of these conditions may independently delay or check the growth of caulonema. After about 20 days most of the cells of the initial stage degenerate. A few apical cells that persist give rise to another type of filaments, the *caulonema* upon which develop the buds that give rise to leafy gametophores. The caulonema filaments are negatively phototrophic. They grow rapidly along the surface of the substratum. The individual cells have oblique cross walls, brown cell wall and fewer, spindle-shaped, less evenly distributed chloroplasts. Caulonema filaments branch regularly and grow exclusively by tip growth at a rather high rate. The side branches are small, erect or horizontal and chloronematic. They grow at a slow rate and exhibit other characters of a chloronema cell. Erichsen *et al* (1977) reported that caulonema contains a special pattern of caulonema specific proteins (CSP) lacking in chloronema. The CSP disappear when caulonema is isolated and its cells regenerate to chloronema. Buds which develop into leafy gametophores are formed only on the branches of the caulonema.

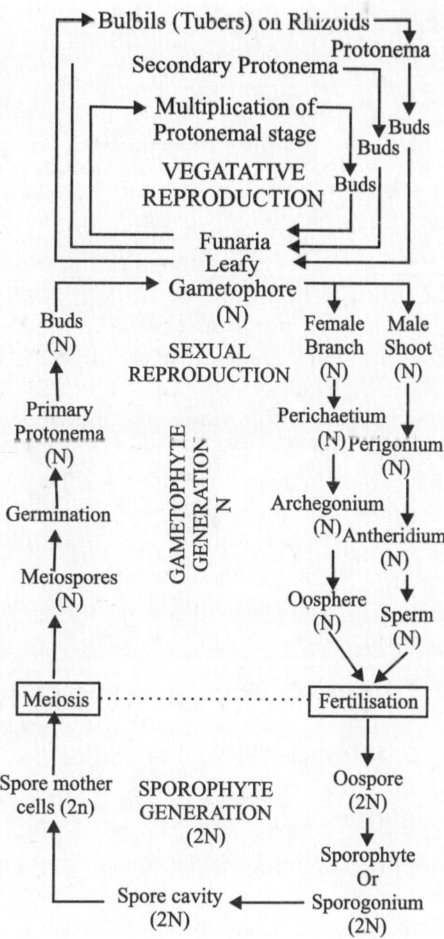

Fig. 18.21. ***Funaria.*** Graphic representation of the life cycle.

Bud formation. Buds which give rise to leafy gametophores arise on the chloronemal branches of the caulonema when protonema attains a critical size or age. According to Nakosteen and Hughes they appear on the protonema approximately 9-11 days after sowing. The formation of buds is said to be induced by the presence of a naturally occurring growth factor known as **bryokenin**. Bopp and Kleen (1963) reported that protonema produces a heat stable factor 'H' which inhibits growth of caulonema but promotes bud formation. Normally the bud arises as a lateral protrusion from a cell of the chloronemal branch just below a septum near the base. Cross wall appear in the bud initial to separate one or two stalk cells at the base. These after three successive oblique walls appear in the bulging terminal cell of the bud to establish a tetrahedral apical cell with three segmenting faces. By the activity of its apical cell each bud grows into a leafy gametophore. Normally the buds are not initiated in weak light or in the dark (Mitra *et al*, 1959). Low temperature also inhibits bud induction (Bopp, 1959) Of the growth promoting substances cytokinins are well known for their bud inducing activities on moss protonemata (Bopp, 1968, Chopra and Rashid, 1973)

Van Andel (1952), Allsopp and Mitra (1958) and Kofler (1959) do not subscribe to Sironwal's viewpoint of the existence of two clear cut growth stages in the protonemal life of *F. hygrometrica.* They failed to find the caulonema stage.

Alternation of generations (Fig. 18.21). In the life cycle of *Funaria*, there occur two distinct individuals. They are unlike each other. One of these is **haploid**. It is the independent **leafy moss plant.** The other is **diploid.** The diploid individual is the leafless **sporogonium**. It is partially dependent on the leafy gametophyte for its nutrition. The nuclei in the cells of the leafy plant contain *n* chromosomes and in the sporogonium 2 *n* chromosomes. The haploid leafy plant reproduces by **gametes**. The diploid plant reproduces by **spores**. Because of its characteristic method of reproduction by gametes the haploid leafy plant is often called the **gametophyte**. The diploid plant because of its reproduction by spores is known as the **sporophyte**. The leafy gametophyte represents the **sexual generation** and the sporophyte or sporogonium **asexual generation**. The gametophyte is developed from the spore. The sporophyte is formed from the zygote. The latter is the result of the union of two gametes (male and female). The two kinds of individuals (sporophyte and gametophyte) alternate with each other in the life cycle. In fact one of them is the parent of the other. This phenomenon is expressed by the phrase **Alternation of Generations**. It means the alternation in a single life cycle of two vegetative individuals with different functions and different genetic constitution. The structures developed during the gametophyte phase are the *spores*, the *protonema*, the *leafy gametophore*, the *sex organs* (antheridia and archegonia) and the *gametes* (sperms and the eggs). The structures developed during the sporophyte stage in order of their appearance are the *zygote*, the *embryo*, the mature *sporogonium* consisting of a *foot*, a *seta* and a *capsule*, and the *spore mother cells*. The spore mother cells are the last structures of the sporophyte generation. They differentiate by meiosis into spores which are haploid. The meiospores are, therefore, the first structures of the next gametophyte generation.

SUMMARY OF THE LIFE HISTORY OF *FUNARIA* (FIG. 18.22)

GAMETOPHYTE

There occur two distinct individuals in the life cycle of *Funaria*. They are the leafy **gametophore** (A) and the **sporophyte** (G, H). Leafy gametophyte is far more conspicuous of the two. It is developed from a germinating spore (K—M). The spore germinates as it falls on the moist soil and produces a freely branched, green filament of cells called the **protonema** (M). The protonema is the juvenile stage in the life cycle. It is purely vegetative. It has two kinds of branches, the **chloronema** and the **rhizoidal** branches. The former grow horizontally on the moist soil and the latter penetrate the substratum. The chloronemal branches manufacture food and the rhizoidal function as anchoring and absorbing organs. Sooner or later certain of the older cells of the chloronemal branches grow into buds. Each bud has an apical cell with three cutting faces. With the activity of its apical cell each bud finally grows into a leafy shoot anchored to the substratum by the rhizoids. With the development of leafy shoots the protonema dies leaving each leafy axis as the sole, independent representative of the gametophyte phase. It is the so-called moss plant (A). The protonema and the leafy shoot are the two stages of the gametophyte generation. The former is purely vegetative in function. The leafy gametophore is reproductive. It bears the sex organs.

The adult *Funaria plant* (A) is an upright, leafy axis about 12-20 mm. in height. It has a slender, central axis, the so-called stem. The latter bears multicelluar, branched **rhizoids** at its base and leaf-like expansions throughout its length. The leaves are arranged spirally and are more crowded towards the apex. They are sessile and oblong-ovate with entire margin and pointed apex. Each leaf is traversed by a distinct midrib. Internally the stem is differentiated into an **epidermis, a cortex** and a **central strand**. Excepting the midrib the leaf is composed of a single layer of parenchymatous, rectangular cells rich in chloroplasts. The few layers thick midrib has a small conducting strand.

Sex organs. The leafy gemetophore is concerned with sexual reproduction by the formation of antheridia and archegonia. They are borne in separate terminal clusters on distinct branches of the same plane. The antheridia are borne at the tip of the main shoot and the archegonia on a lateral branch, that arises from the base of the male shoot (A).

The perigonial leaves surrounding the antheridial cluster are crowded together and spread out to form a rosette-like structure. The leaves on the inner side of the rosette are reddish in colour. Intermingled with the antheridia are the **paraphyses**. Each mature **antheridium** (B) is more or less a club-shaped, orange coloured structure. It consists of a short, multicellular **stalk** and a **body**. The body of the antheridium has a jacket or wall one cell in thickness. At the free, distal end of the antheridium the antheridial wall is differentiated into a lid-like structure. It is the **operculum**. It consists of one or two large cells derived from the apical cell by the activity of which the antheridium grows in its early stages of development. Within the wall is a dense mass of small, closely packed cells, the **androcytes**. Each of the latter gives rise to a biflagellate, spirally coiled **sperm**. On the access of water the opercular cells at the apex of the mature antheridium disintegrate or separate by hydrolysis. A viscous fluid containing the adrocytes oozes out. With the dissolution of the walls of the androcytes the sperms escape and swim about in the water surrounding the antheridial cluster.

The archegonia (C) are typically flask-shaped structures each borne on a short multicellular stalk. The long, slightly twisted neck has one cell thick jacket layer of cells enclosing the neck canal cells. The jacket is double in the enlarged basal portion or the venter of the archegonium. The venter cavity contains an ovum with a ventral canal cell above it. On the access of water, the axial row of cells in the archegonium, excepting the ovum, gets disintegrated to form a mass of mucilage. The mucilage in the canal absorbs water and swells. Consequently the end cells of the archegonial neck are forced apart.

Fertilization. The antheridia and the archegonia are borne in separate clusters of different branches. Naturally they are always some distance apart. The sperms from the perigonial rosette must be transported by some external agency to the archegonia. How it takes place is all a guess? There is a suggestion that the sperms may be splashed out of perigonial rosette by rain drops on to the archegonial cluster at a lower level. The other possibility is that water containing sperms may trickle down from the perigonial cup at a higher level to the archegonial cluster at a lower level. Small insects such as mites which visit the antheridial and the archegonial clusters in search of mucilage secreted by the paraphysis, have also been suspected to carry the sperms to the archegonia. Any how fertilization is frequently accomplished. Once the sperms reach the archegonial cluster they swim to the open necks of the archegonia which they eventually enter and swim down the canal to reach the egg in the venter. As a rule only one sperm unites with the egg to effect fertilization (C). The others perish.

SPOROPHYTE

The zygote thus formed is the pioneer structure of the sporophyte phase (D). It is diploid. It secretes a wall around it and divides by a transverse wall. Each half again undergoes two successive diagonal divisions (E). An actively dividing apical cell is established at each end (F). The apical cells cut off segments alternately right and left. Soon the embryo develops into a long, slender structure (G). The lower end of the embryo makes its way through the archegonial stalk into the tissues at the apex of the female branch. The upper part develops into the slender, cylindrical sporogonium. Differentiation into the stalk-like seta and the terminal capsule takes place late. The early growth of the sporophyte within the venter is accompanied by the resumption of growth by the latter. The two grow at about equal pace. Later the young sporophyte grows at a faster rate. The seta elongates rapidly. Consequently the calyptra is ruptured. A greater part of it is carried as a conical cap at the top of the elongating sporogonium enclosing and protecting the young theca. At first the green capsule is upright on the seta. As it advances towards maturity it becomes pendent (H). The calyptra falls off and the capsule finally turns dark brown in colour.

The mature sporophyte is differentiated into three regions, the **foot,** the **seta** and the **capsule** (H). The foot functions as an anchoring and an absorbing organ. It is embedded in the tissues at gametophyte throughout its life. The long, slender, reddish brown seta elevates the capsule more

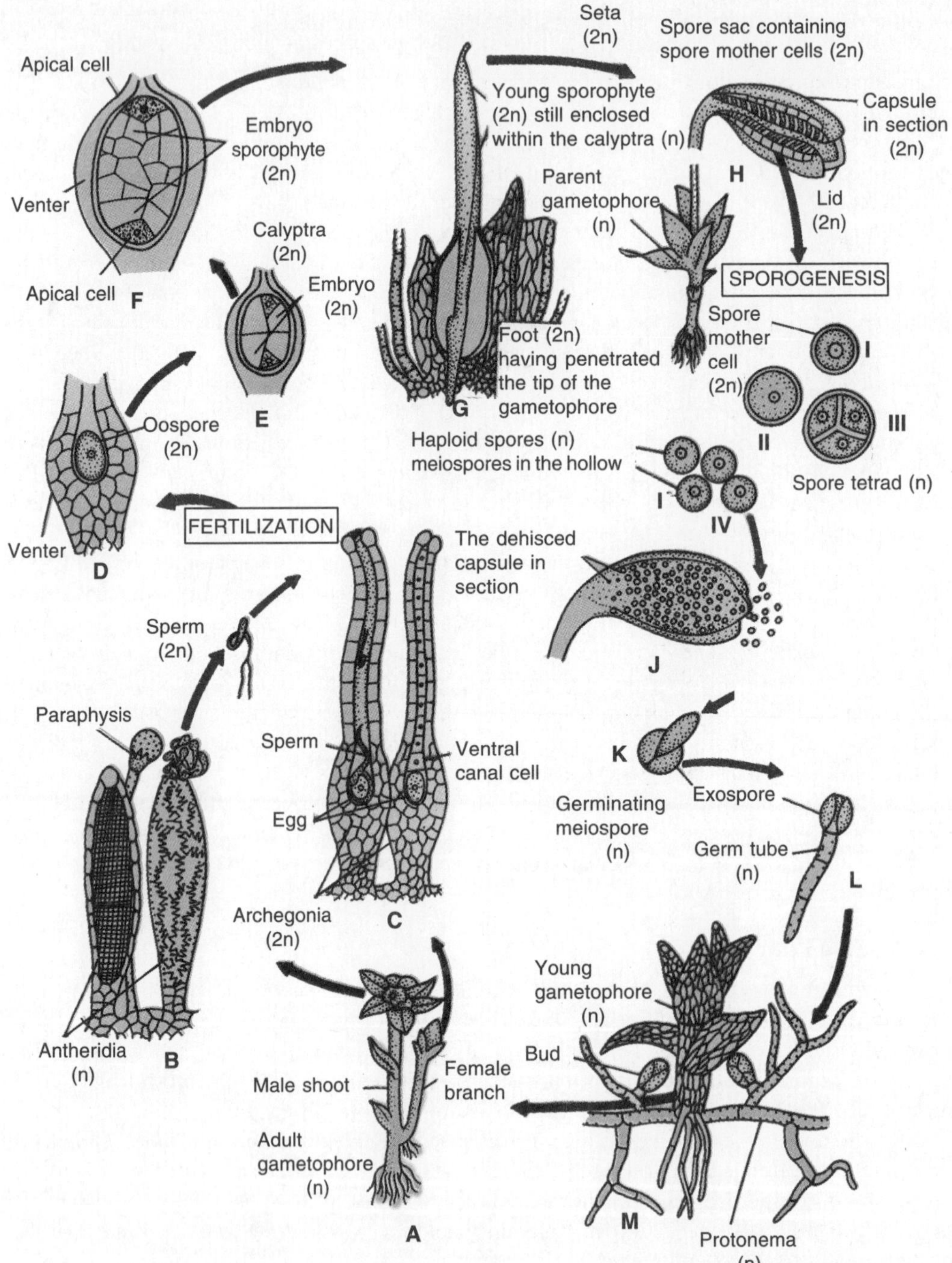

Fig. 18.22. (A—M). ***Funaria***. Diagrammatic representation of the sexual life cycle.

than 25 mm. above the surrounding leaves of the gametophyte. It consists of a central strand of thin-walled, elongated cells surrounded by the thick-walled cortex. The pear-shaped capsule is a highly organised and elaborate structure. The elaboration is more internal than external. Externally the capsule is well marked into three regions : the **apophysis**, the **theca** and the **operculum**.

The **apophysis** is bounded by a well-defined, protective surface layer, the **epidermis**. It bears numerous functional **stomata** each leading into a sub-stomatal air space. Within the epidermis is the nutritive or the **spongy parenchyma**. The sub-stomatal air spaces communicate with a system of intercellular spaces ventilating the green, spongy parenchyma. The capsule of *Funaria* is therefore self-supporting so far as its carbohydrate food is concerned. For water and mineral salts it is parasitic on the parent gametophyte to which it is organically attached throughout its life. Within-the photosynthetic tissue is the conducting strand continuous above with the columella and below with the conducting strand of the seta.

The **theca** has a centrally located column of thin-walled, sterile parenchyma cells. It is the **columella**. Surrounding the latter is the barrel-shaped **spore sac** with its top and bottom knocked out. The spore sac therefore does not extend into the basal and the apical portions of the capsule. It is bounded by an inner wall one cell thick and an outer 3 or 4 cell layers thick. Outside the spore sac is a wide **air-space** traversed by green filaments, the **trabeculae**. The columella and the spore sac thus lie suspended in the air space by the **trabeculae**. The spore contains the spore mother cells (I) which undergo the tetrad divisions (III) to form the haploid spores (IV). All the spore mother cells are functional. No elaters are formed in the mosses. External to the air space is the wall of the theca. It consists of the inner **spongy layer** one or two cells thick. It is continuous below with the spongy tissue of the apophysis. Then comes the **hypodermis** consisting of two layers of colourless cells. The hypodermis is bounded by the single layered **epidermis** with fewer stomata.

Above the theca constituting the apical portion of the capsule is the **operculum** or **lid**. A transverse ring of modified epidermal cells delimits the operculum from the theca. It is the **annulus**. Beneath the operculum are two rings of conical teeth constituting the **peristome**. Together the peristome teeth form a cone-like structure which obstructs the mouth of the spore sac. The teeth are hygroscopic.

The mature capsule dries up. The thin-walled cells of the annulus proper, which hold the operculum in place, shrink and shrivel. Finally they rupture. The lid or the operculum drops off exposing the dome-like hygroscopic peristome teeth (J). The latter close over the central cavity formed by the drying up and shrivelling of the columella and the adjoining tissue. This cavity is now filled with spores. The escape of these spores is prevented in the wet weather as the peristome teeth close together. In dry weather the teeth bend outward. In doing so they separate from each other. The slits between them open. Through these slits the spores escape a few at a time when they are likely to be carried and thus dispersed by air currents. Falling on a suitable substratum and under favourable conditions the spores germinate (K—L), each producing a protonema (M), the juvenile stage of *Funaria*. According to Nakosteen and Hughes (1978) *F. hygrometrica* completes its sexual life cycle (spore to spore) in culture in 4 months time.

SIGNIFICANT STEPS IN THE LIFE HISTORY OF *FUNARIA*

A. GAMETOPHYTE

1. It consists of (*a*) a branched, green, alga-like filament, the **protonema** and (*b*) a leafy gametophore the so-called **moss plant**. The protonema is short-lived.

2. The leafy gametophore consists of a slender, stem-like central axis bearing rhizoids at its base and leaf-like expansions throughout its length. It is independent.

3. The so-called **leaf** is traversed by a definite midrib more than one cell in the thickness.

4. The **rhizoids** are branched and multicellular. The septa between the cells are oblique.

5. The **sex organs** (antheridia and archegonia) are borne in terminal clusters, at the tips of separate branches of the leafy gametophyte.

6. Early development of the sex organs is by means of the activity of an **apical cell**.

B. SPOROPHYTE

7. The embryo sporophyte grows from two growing points, each located at the opposite end. The growth of the embryo is thus **apical**.

8. The mature sporogonium is differentiated into the **foot**, the **seta** and the pear-shaped **capsule** of great complexity. The seta is long and carries the capsule far above the leafy gametophore.

9. The mature capsule is differentiated externally into **apophysis**, **theca** and **operculum** regions. Internally it consists of several tissues. There is a well developed **ventilated photosynthetic tissue** and a large **air space** in which lies suspended the **spore sac** by filaments of green cells and the **columella**. The capsule has a complex organisation in the form of a **operculum** and **peristome** for the dehiscence and dispersal of spores at its apical portion.

10. The archesporium does not arch over the columella, and is derived from the exterior portion of the **endothecium**. It is reduced to a single layer. The progressive sterilisation of the potentially fertile tissue has thus reached its extreme in *Funaria*.

THE CHIEF DIFFERENCES BETWEEN *FUNARIA* AND THE LIVERWORTS

A. GAMETOPYTE

1. Presence of protonema in the mosses and its usual absence in the liverworts.

2. Radial symmetry of the upright moss plant as compared with the dorsiventral symmetry of the liverworts.

3. More elaborate external appearance and greater differentiation of tissues of moss gametophyte as compared with the liverworts.

4. The branched and multicellular rhizoids as compared with the unbranched, unicellular rhizoids of liverworts.

5. Early apical growth of the sex organs.

B. SPOROPHYTE

6. Development of the embryo sporophyte is **bi-apical**. It takes place by two growing points as against by successive transverse cleavage in the liverworts.

7. The foot is usually dagger-shaped and the seta longer, stronger, hygroscopic and much longer-lived than in the liverworts.

8. The seta lengthens earlier than that of the liverworts and shows greater tissue differentiation.

9. Highly organised mature capsule externally differentiated into the basal, photosynthetic **apophysis region,** middle fertile **theca region** and the terminal **lid** or **operculum region** as compared with the simple capsule of liverworts represented by the theca region only.

10. Presence of a well developed, **ventilated photosynthetic system** in the several cell layers thick capsule wall of *Funaria* and its absence in the liverworts.

11. The characteristic wide **air spore** in which lies suspended the spore sac and the columella by green filaments in the capsule of *Funaria*, is absent in the liverworts.

12. Single-layered **archesporium** derived from the external layer of the endothecium in *Funaria* as against the massive archesporium derived from the entire endothecium in the liverworts.

13. Presence in *Funaria* of a central column of sterile tissue, the **columella** which is absent in the liverworts.

14. The mechanism of dehiscence and dispersal of spores in the form of **operculum** and **peristome** is much more elaborate and efficient in *Funaria* than in the liverworts in which capsule usually dehisces by valves or by the separation of a lid only. The peristome is absent in the liverworts and the lid when present is very simple in structure.

systematic Position of Funaria

Division	:	Bryophyta
Class	:	Bryopsida (Musci)
Subclass	:	Bryidae
Order	:	Funariales
Family	:	Funariaceae
Genus	:	*Funaria*
Species	:	*hygrometrica*

QUESTIONS

ESSAY TYPE

1. Draw a series of labelled diagrams of the life-cycle of *Funaria* (Description not required). *(Kanpur, 1995)*
2. Describe the life cycle of *Funaria* with the help of labelled sketches. *(Kanpur, 1989, 1996; Agra, 1989)*
3. Give a well illustrated account of the life-cycle of *Funaria* *(Kanpur, 1998; Rohilkhand, 1987)*
4. With the help of labelled sketches only compare the sporophytes of *Pellia*, *Anthoceros* and *Funaria*. *(Allahabad, 1997)*
5. Explain the method of fertlization in Moss and describe the post fertilisation changes in Moss plant with the help of suitable diagrams. *(Kanpur, 2000)*
6. Write a comparative account of the organisation of sporophyte in *Riccia*, *Anthoceros* and *Funaria*. *(Punjab, 1999)*
7. With the help of neat and labelled sketches, give structural details of sporogonium of *Funaria*. *(Punjab, 1998)*
8. Draw well labelled diagram of sporogonium of *Funaria*. Comment whether it is advanced or primitive. *(Himachal Pradesh, 1999)*
9. With the help of labelled diagrams describe the structure of Moss sporophyte. *(Madras, 1995; Kerala, 1994)*
10. Give the structure and development of sporophyte in *Funaria* *(Kerala, 1999)*
11. Describe the gametophyte of *Funaria*. *(Kerala, 1995)*
12. Give an account of vegetative and sexual reproduction in *Funaria*.
13. What is meant by alternation of generation? Explain it with the life-cycle of *Funaria*.
14. Describe the external and internal structure of the gametophyte of *Funaria*.
15. Enumerate significant steps in the life-cycle of *Funaria*.
16. Give an account of the phenomenon of alternation of generations in *Funaria*.
17. Describe in detail the external and internal structure of capsule of *Funaria*.
18. Describe the structure and development of sex organs in *Funaria*. How does fertilization take place in this plant?
19. Describe briefly the development of sporophyte in *Funaria* and compare with that of liverworts.
20. With the help of suitable diagram, explain the structure of capsule in *Funaria*. Discuss its dehiscence also. *(Punjab, 2001)*
21. Describe the identifying characters of *Pellia, Anthoceros* and *Funaria*. *(Kanpur, 2007)*
22. Give a comparative account of sporophyte of *Anthoceros* and *Funaria*. *(Kanpur, 2006)*

SHORT ANSWER TYPE

23. By mistake the material of the following got mixed up:

(*a*) *Lunularia* (*b*) *Targionia*

(*c*) *Noththylas* (*d*) *Funaria*

What are the criteria which you use do separate the components? Give suitable diagrams also. *(Kanpur, M.Sc., 2005)*

24. Write short notes on :

(*i*) Gametophyte of *Funaria* or *Moss*. *(Bombay, 1990; Karnataka, 1990)*

(*ii*) T.S. of Moss stem *(Kanpur, 1987)*

(*iii*) V.S. leaf of *Funaria* *(Rohilkhand, 1985)*

(*iv*) Spore dispersal in *Funaria* *(Kanpur, 1994, 1997; Punjab, 1992)*

(*v*) Protonema *(Kanpur, 1995, 1999; Lucknow, 1997, 1999, 2002, 2007; Bangalore, 2001; Kerala 2001; Himachal Pradesh, 1993, 1997; Kerala, 1995; Rajasthan, 1988; Allahabad, 2003, 2004; Poorvanchal, M.Sc., 1998)*

(*vi*) Peristomial teeth *(Kanpur, 1999; Lucknow, 1996, 1997, 2001; Himachal Pradesh 1997)*

(*vii*) Moss Protonema *(Lucknow, 1998)*

(*viii*) Peristome *(Lucknow, 1998, 2000, 2003; Allahabad, 1991, 1995, 1998, 1999, 2004; Himachal Pradesh, 1993; Kerala, 1995; Poorvanchal M.Sc. 1998; Garhwal, 2001)*

(*ix*) Mechanism of dehiscence of capsule in *Funaria.* *(Allahabad, 1993)*

(*x*) Sporophyte of *Funaria* *(Kumaon, 1996, 1997)*

(*xi*) Development of protonema in *Funaria* *(Himachal Pradesh, 1992)*

(*xii*) Peristome and its mechanism in dispersal *(Himachal Pradesh, 1996)*

(*xiii*) Role of Protonema in the life cycle of Moss plant

(*xiv*) Function of columella in *Funaria* *(Kerala, 1996)*

(*xv*) Columella *(Lucknow, 2002)*

25. Draw neat and labelled diagrams of the following:

(*a*) L.S. of capsule of *Funaria* *(Kanpur, 2004; 2009 Garhwal, 2004; Allahabad, 1998)*

(*b*) V.L.S. sporophyte of *Funaria* *(Allahabad, 2005, Kanpur, 1994)*

(*c*) Peristome teeth in Moss *(Kanpur 2000)*

(*d*) L.S. of the tip of male branch in *Funaria* and label its parts. *(Kerala, 1998)*

(*e*) T.S. capsule of *Funaria.*

(*f*) L.S. of the tip of female branch of *Funaria*. *(Allahabad, 2002)*

(*g*) T.S. stem

(*h*) T.S. Leaf.

(*i*) L.S. Archegonia of *Funaria.* *(Garhwal, 2000)*

(*j*) Life cycle of *Funaria.* *(Kanpur, 2008)*

26. Give very brief answers of the following:

(*a*) What is calyptra? Describe. *(Punjab, 2001; Lucknow, 1993)*

(*b*) Give structure and function of peristome. *(Lucknow, 1993, 2001)*

(*c*) Name a bryophyte in which rhizoids are branched and multicellular. *(Allahabad, 1991)*

(*d*) Define protonema. What does it represent? *(Calicut, 2001; Kerala, 2000)*

(*e*) Why is Seta short in *Marchantia* and long in *Funaria*?

(*f*) How do rhizoids of Mosses differ from those of liverworts?

(*g*) In what respects archegonia of *Funaria* differ from those of *Sphagnum*?

(*h*) In which plant would you find peristome?

(*i*) Give two important points of Moss archegonia *(Kerala, 1999)*

(*j*) What is protonema?

(*k*) What is the role of protonema in the life cycle of moss plant? *(Kerala, 1995, 1996)*

(*l*) What is the function of peristome teeth in *Funaria*. *(Kerala, 1995, 1996)*

(*m*) Name two distinct phases of gametophyte of *Funaria*. *(Kerala, 1998)*

27. Describe the internal structure of aerial stem of *Funaria*.
28. Make a comparative study of the male shoot of *Madotheca* (*Porella*) and *Funaria* *(Himachal Pradesh, 1990)*
29. Draw the vegetative structure of *Porella*, *Sphagnum* and *Funaria* plants and compare them. *(Himachal Pradesh, 1992)*
30. (*a*) Compare the rhizoids of *Marchantia*, *Funaria* and ferns. *(Himachal Pradesh, 1994)*

    (*b*) Compare the strucutre and position of archegonia in *Riccia*, *Marchantia* and *Funaria*.

    (*c*) Compare the structure and position of antheridia in *Riccia*, *Marchantia* and *Funaria*.
31. Explain the structure and position of sex organs in *Funaria*. *(Himachal Pradesh, 1996)*
32. How do liverworts differ from Mosses?
33. Explain the differences between archegonia of *Porella* and *Funaria*. *(Himachal Pradesh, 1996)*
34. How does the capsule of *Funaria* look in L.S. ? *(Kerala, 2000)*
35. (*a*) Describe the dehiscence mechanism of sporophyte of the following :

    (*i*) *Funaria* (*ii*) *Sphagnum* *(Himachal Pradesh, 1997)*

    (*b*) Give a brief account of spore dispersal in *Funaria*. *(Punjab, 2001)*

    (*c*) Describe the amphithecium in *Funaria* *(Himachal Pradesh, 1997)*
36. Explain the anatomy of the capsule of *Funaria* *(Trichy, 1995; Kerala, 1995)*
37. Why do plants of *Funaria* not grow beyond 10 cms in length?
38. What is the term applied to conducting strand in *Funaria*.
39. Explain the structure and significance of elaterphore and protonema. *(Kanpur, 2004)*
40. Differentiate with the help of diagrams only between

    (*a*) Sporophytes of *Funaria* and *Riccia*. *(Kanpur, 2003)*

    (*b*) Antheridial branches of *Funaria* and *Anthoceros*. *(Allahabad, 2003)*

    (*c*) *Funaria* and *Riccia*.

    (*d*) Peristome of Funaria of Polynuhum *(Lucknow, 1996)*
41. Draw graphic life cycle of *Funaria*. *(Punjab, 2001)*
42. Describe the following :

    (*a*) Anatomy of Gametophyte axis of *Sphagnum* and *Funaria* *(Allahabad, 2002)*

    (*b*) Development of sporophyte in *Riccia* and *Funaria*. *(Allahabad, 2002)*
43. Write one word for filamentous stage produced after germination of asexual spore in bryophytes.
44. What is protonema ? What does it represent. *(Kerala, 2001)*
45. Differentiate between caulonema and chloronema *(Allabahad 2006)*

OBJECTIVE TYPE

46. **Fill in the blanks :**

    (*a*) Moss protonema differs from algal filament by ____________.

    (*b*) The early filamentous stage produced on germination of asexual spore in some bryophytes is called ____________.

    (*c*) The stalk of sporogonium in mosses which connects the foot with capsule is known as ____________.

    (*d*) Spores on germination produce ____________ from which the gametophyte develops.

(*e*) Paraphyses and leaves protect antheridia in ____________.

(*f*) Calyptra is seen in ____________.

(*g*) Spore mother cell in *Funaria* is ____________ in nature.

(*h*) Nourishing tissue surrounding the spore producing tissue in sporangium is ____________.

(*i*) In *Funaria* spores germinate to form ____________.

(*j*) In *Funaria* the reduction division takes place in ____________.

(*k*) The number of peristome teeth in *Funaria* is ____________.

(*l*) The conducting strand in *Funaria* is called ____________.

(*m*) The terminal cap like portion of capsule in *Funaria* is called____________.

43. Select the correct answer :

(*i*) In Archegonium of *Funaria* the cell above the egg cell is
(*a*) Neck canal cell
(*b*) Neck-cell
(*c*) Cover cell
(*d*) ventral canal cell.

(*ii*) Calyptra is seen in
(*a*) Gametophyte
(*b*) Sporophyte
(*c*) Archegoniophore
(*d*) Antheridiophore.

(*iii*) Spore mother cell in *Funaria* is
(*a*) haploid (*b*) diploid
(*c*) triploid (*d*) tetraploid.

(*iv*) Chloroplasts are present in the spores of
(*a*) *Funaria* (*b*) *Bryopteris*
(*c*) *Riccia* (*d*) *Anthoceros.*

(*v*) When spores of *Funaria* germinate, they form
(*a*) Capsule directly
(*b*) Leafy gametophyte directly
(*c*) Protonema which bears antheridia and archegonia
(*d*) First protonema then bud and then leafy gametophyte.

(*vi*) In *Funaria* reduction diversion takes place in the
(*a*) Archegonium (*b*) Capsule
(*c*) At the tips of rhizoids
(*d*) Antheridium.

(*vii*) The leafy gametophyte develops from protonema in
(*a*) *Riccial* (*b*) *Anthoceros*
(*c*) *Funaria* (*d*) *Marchnatia.*

(*viii*) Antheridia intermixed with paraphyses are observed in
(*a*) *Riccia* (*b*) *Marchantia*
(*c*) *Funaria* (*d*) *Anthoceros.*

(*ix*) Formation of elaters is completely absent in
(*a*) *Marchantia* (*b*) *Anthoceros*
(*c*) *Notothylus* (*d*) *Funaria.*

(*x*) Outer and inner spore sac is present in
(*a*) *Funaria* (*b*) *Riccia*
(*c*) *Anthoceros* (*d*) *Marchantia.*

(*xi*) The arrangement of leaves on the axis of *Funaria* is in the pattern of
(*a*) 3/8 (*b*) 5/8
(*c*) 2/2 (*d*) 6/8.

(*xii*) *Funaria* differs from *Pteris* in having
(*a*) An independent gametophyte
(*b*) An independent sporophyte
(*c*) Swimming antherozoids
(*d*) Archegonia.

(*xiii*) Multicellular jacketed sex organs are present in
(*a*) *Funaria* (*b*) *Spirogyra*
(*c*) *Saccharomyces*(*d*) *Hibiscus.*

(*xiv*) In *Funaria* the rhizoids are
(*a*) Unicellular and pigmented
(*b*) Multicellular and pigmented
(*c*) Unicellular and non pigmented
(*d*) Multicellular and non-pigmented.

(*xv*) What is the relationship of the sporophyte to the gametophyte in *Funaria* plant?
(*a*) The sporophyte is dominant phase
(*b*) The sporophyte produces gametes which give rise to gametophyte

(c) The sporophyte arises from a spore produced by the gametophyte

(d) The sporophyte is partially parasitic on the gametophyte.

(xvi) The middle sterile part of *Funaria* capsule is known as

(a) Columella (b) Apophysis

(c) Operculum (d) Spore sac.

(xvii) Which of the following statements in correct?

(a) Adult plant of *Funaria* is sporophytic

(b) Archegonium of *Funaria* is formed on the sporophyte

(c) The antheridium of *Funaria* has egg cells

(d) The zygote formed after fertlisation in *Funaria* gives rise to sporogonium— the sporophytic phase.

(xviii) The growth of *Funaria* plants is generally restricted after a height of 10cms because of the absence of

(a) Vascular tissues

(b) Roots

(c) Semipermeable membrane

(d) Water in the habitat.

(xix) *Funaria* generally grows

(a) On water

(b) On damp ground

(c) As epiphytes

(d) In sea.

(xx) Plants of *Funaria* generally grow

(a) In pairs (b) Solitary

(c) In aggregates

(d) As saprophytes.

(xxi) *Funaria*

(a) Monoecious (b) Dioecious

(c) Both of the above

(d) None of the above.

(xxii) In *Funaria* the leaves are arranged on the stem

(a) Oppositely (b) Spirally

(c) Alternately

(d) All of the above.

(xxiii) The leaves of *Funaria* are

(a) Green but without stomata

(b) With very few stomata

(c) With numerous stomata

(d) Colour less without stomata.

(xxiv) The teeth of the peristome of *Funaria* are

(a) Sensitive (b) Hygroscopic

(c) Hydrophobic

(d) Sentitive and hydrophobia.

(xxv) Which of the following plays an active role in the dispersal of spores in *Funaria*?

(a) Operculum (b) Capsule

(c) Peristome and annulus

(d) Sporogonium.

(xxvi) *Funaria* is a bryophyte because

(a) It lacks vasular tissue

(b) It lacks seeds

(c) It has multicellular and jacketed sex organs

(d) All of the above.

(xxvii) In *Funaria* sporogenous tissue arise from

(a) Outer endothecium

(b) Inner endothecium

(c) Total endothecium

(d) total amphithecium.

(xxviii) In *Funaria* stomata are found in

(a) Capsule (b) Foot

(c) Seta (d) Nowhere

(xxix) Which part of the *Funaria* capsule is haploid ?

(a) Annulus (b) Columella

(c) Opsculum (d) Calyptra.

(xxx) In *Funaria* the calyptra is formed by

(a) Antheridium (b) Archegonium

(c) Columella (d) Capsule.

(xxxi) In *Funaria* the reduction division takes place in the

(a) Antheridium (b) Archegonium

(c) Capsule (d) Zygote.

(xxxii) Largest gametophyte is found in which of the following ?

(a) *Funaria* (b) Cycas

(c) *Selaginella* (d) *Pinus*.

Image of *Buxbaumia*

CHAPTER 19

BRYIDAE
Buxbaumiales
Buxbaumia

- Order Buxbaumiales
- Buxbaumia Hedw.
- Sporophyte

ORDER BUXBAUMIALES

GENERAL CHARACTERISTICS

The order Buxbaumiales is a specialized group and characterized by the following features :

1. The gametophytic plant body is partialy saprophytic whereas sporophytic phase is fully developed.

2. The plants grow sporadically on rotten wood.

3. The branched filamentous protonema forms dense mat from which arises male and female plants.

4. The sporophyte is fully developed.

5. The peristome is made up of three layers or rings-the outer layer is papillose, filamentous and arthrodontous type, the middle peristome ring is membranous while the inner peristome ring is cone like and consists of 16 nematodontous type of teeth.

The order includes a single family *Buxbaumiaceae* which is represented by *Diphyscium* and *Buxbaumia,* of which the later is briefly discussed here.

Buxbaumia Hedw.

Distribution

The genus *Buxbaumia* was reported from India for the first time by Udar, Srivastava and Kumar in 1970 from western Himalayas (Deoban-alt. ca 10,500 ft.) as-a new species *B. himalayensis* Udar *et. al.*

Habit and Habitat

Buxbaumia is a strange moss because it occurs sporadically, not in huge population. The genus is remarkable in being a partial saprophyte. The plants grow on rotten wood. The protonemal phase of the plant shows dominance over gametophores. The branched filamentous protonema forms an extensive mat over decaying wood surface from where they absorb nutrients.

Gametophyte

The gametophytic plants which arise on protonema are partial saprophytes and are very small. The plants are dioecious (heterothallic) therefore, male and female plants are produced separately.

Male plant. (Fig. 19.1A). The whole male plant is represented by a single mussel-shell-shaped male bract (leaf) which contains a single globular antheridium. The stem is absent.

Female plant (Fig. 19. 1B). The female plant is relatively larger than the male plant. It consists of two to four rows of very small lanceolate leaves which are without midrib. The stem, in the female plant, is present but it is extremely reduced. A single archegonium is present at the apex of the female shoot. There is no differentiation in between leaves and female bracts. In *B. aphylla* there is no leaves in the gametophores.

Sporophyte

After the fertilization, the stem of female shoot develops into a tuberous out growth in which foot of the sporophyte remains embedded (Fig. 19.1). After some time numerous rhizoids are produced from tuberous out growth and help the sporophyte in fixing with the substratum of rotten and decaying wood. In *Buxbaumia* the sporophytic phase is very prominent and dominant. The sporophyte is differentiated into foot, seta and capsule.

Foot (Fig. 19.C, D). It is embedded up to the base of the tuberous out growth of the stem.

Seta (Fig. 19.G). It is elongated, straight or arcuate with the outer surface being roughly papillose throughout. In cross section, the seta is massive (several celled thick across the diameter). The outer cells of seta are slightly pigmented and form cortex whereas the inner cells are relatively thin walled and without pigmentation and form medulla.

Capsule (Fig. 19.1 E, 19.2). It is oblique to horizontal, flat or concave on upper side and swollen at the base. The annulus is absent. The capsule has three parts : (*a*) Operculum, (*b*) Theca and (*c*) Apophysis

(*a*) *Operculum.* It is the uppermost part of the capsule and present at the mouth (peristomial teeth) which it covers and protects. It is conical in shape and obtuse at the apex. At maturity the operculum is thrown off by air and the peristome teeth are seen at the mouth of the capsule.

(*b*) *Theca.* It is the middle part of the capsule which is slightly narrow at the apex and broad at the base. The mouth of the theca is covered by three rings of peristomial teeth (Fig. 19.1 I) Viz.

(*i*) *Outer peristome.* These are papillose, filamentous and arthrodontous type.

(*ii*) *Middle peristome.* The middle peristomial teeth are membranous.

(*iii*) *Inner peristome.* It is cone like and made up of 16 prominent nematodontous type of teeth.

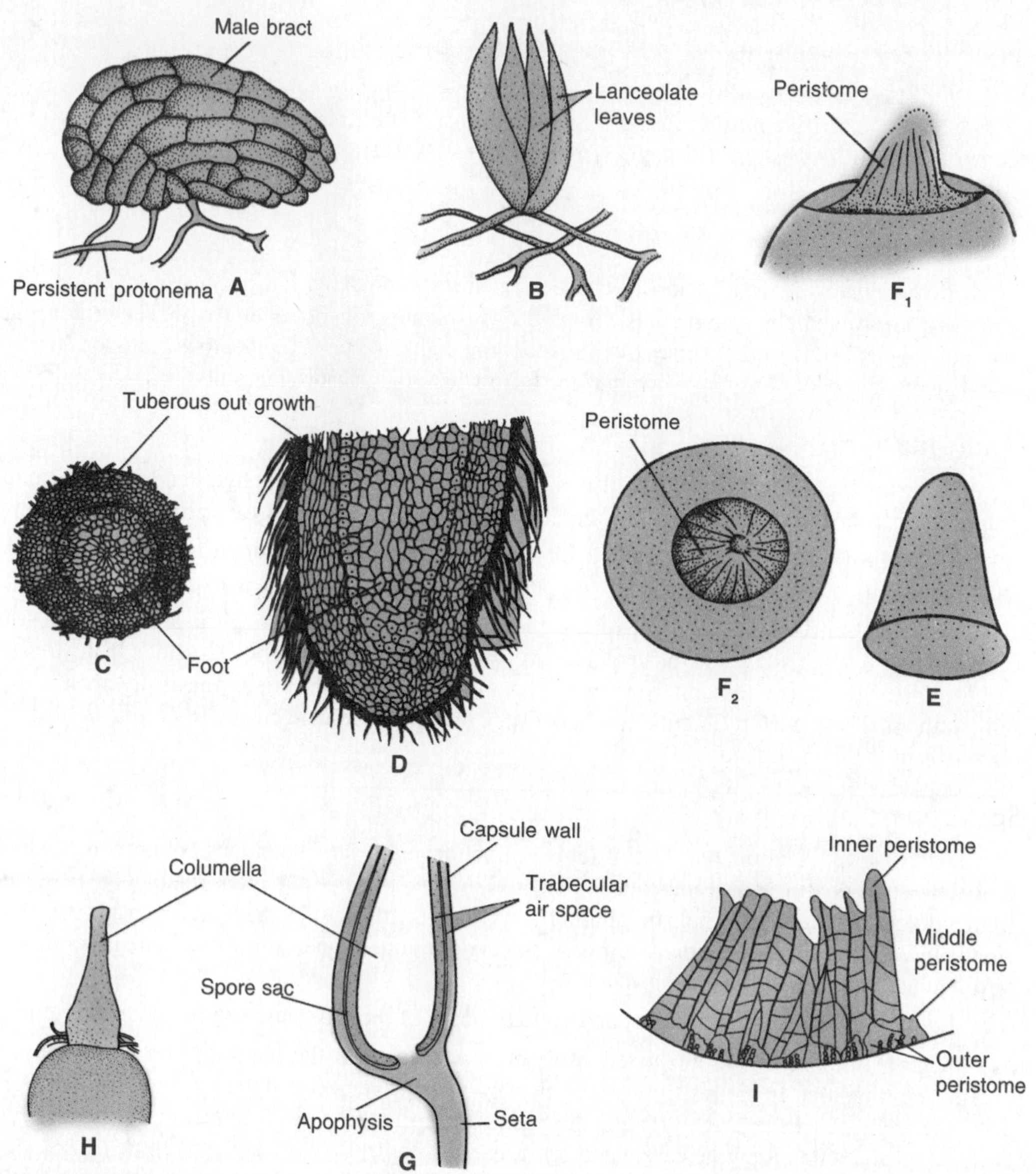

Fig. 19.1. (A—I). ***Buxbaumia* sp.** A, male plant with a single male bract on persistent protonema; B, female plant with lanceolate leaves; C, T.S. of tuberous out growth enclosing foot of sporophyte; D, L.S. of tuberous out growth; E, operculum; F, mouth of theca showing peristome; G, top view of mouth of theca, H, columella; I. peristome.

In longitudinal section of the theca, there are four parts:— (*i*) capsule wall, (*ii*) trabecular air space, (*iii*) spore sac and (iv) columella.

(*i*) *Capsule wall* (Fig. 19.1 G). It is the outer most surface layer of the theca which is multistratose and bears rudimentary stomata on its surface. The stomata are very small opening present on the surface of the capsule wall and formed by four small surface cells.

(*ii*) *Trabecular air space* (Fig. 20.1 G). It is present on all the sides of the spore sac. On the outer side it is attached with capsule wall and on the inner side with columella.

(*iii*) *Spore sac* (Fig. 19.1 G, 19.2). It is cylindrical structure filled with spores and surrounded on all sides by trabecular air space.

(*iv*) *Columella* (Fig. 19.1 G,H). It is the inner most region of the theca

(*c*) *Apophysis.* This is the sterile lower part of the capsule and is connected with the seta.

The spores : The spores are yellowish to reddish brown in colour, small, 9-12 mm in diameter with smooth exine and filled in the spore sac just like dust particles. At maturity of the capsule, the operculum is shed off and peristome teeth, which initially covers the opening of the spore sac, become dry and straight providing the space to spores to come out in air from where they settle down on rotten wood. The spores germinate under favourable conditions and form persistent protonema of *Buxbaumia*.

Protonemal phase : The protonemal phase, formed after the germination of spores on the wood surface, is persistent. The protonemal branches ramify on decaying logs or wood in the same manner as the fungal hypae. The male and female gametophores are produced sporadically on persistent protonemal mat.

Systematic position of buxbaumia

Division	:	Bryophyta
Class	:	Bryopsida (Musci or Mosses)
Sub-class	:	Bryidae
Order	:	Buxbaumiales
Family	:	Buxbaumiaceae
Genus	:	*Buxbaumia*
Species	:	*himalayensis*

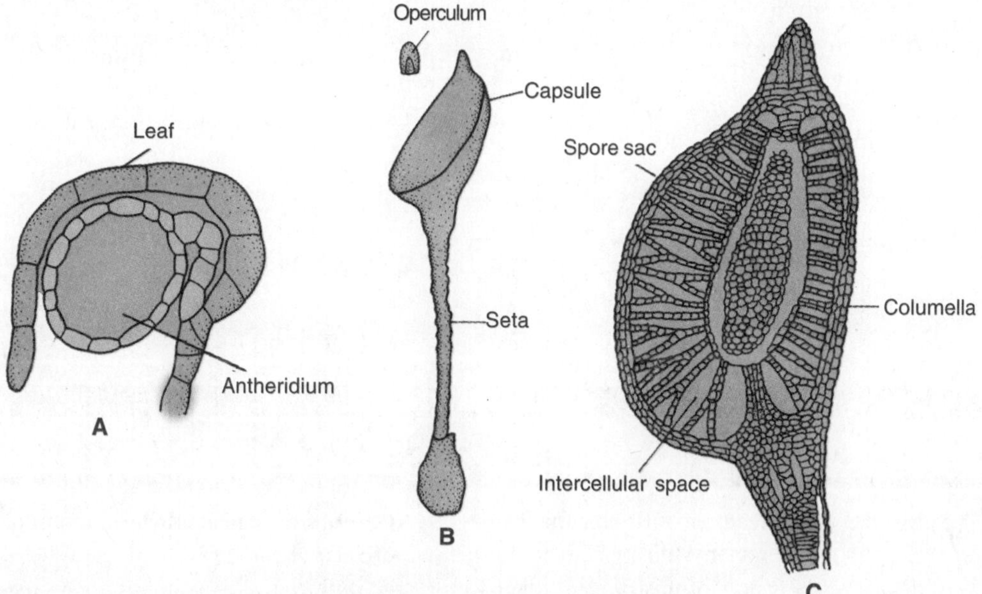

Fig. 19.2. (A–C) ***Buxbaumia*,sp.** A, vertical section of male gametophyte showing a single antheridium; B, a fruiting plant showing operculum, capsule and seta; C, L.S. capsule.

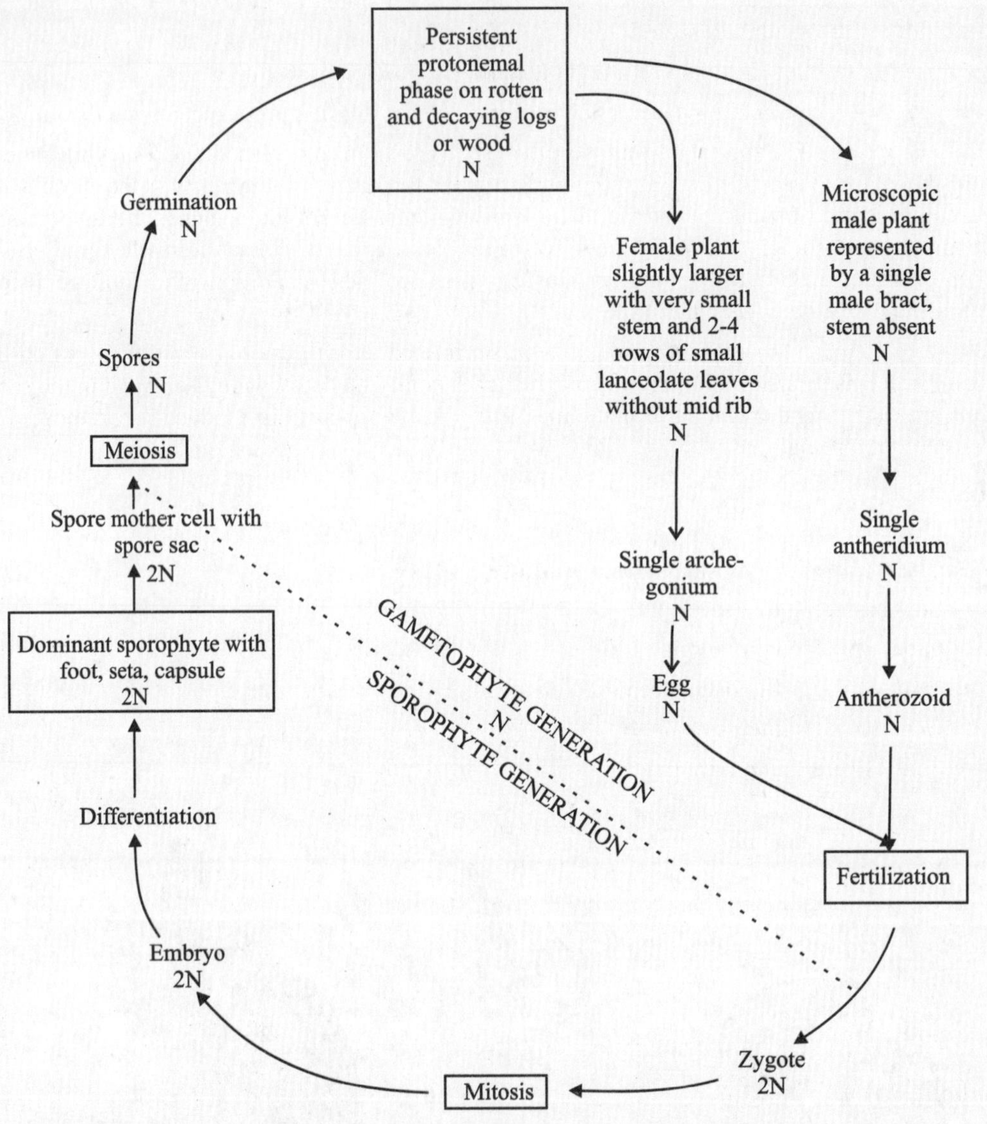

Fig. 19.3. *Buxbaumia.* Word diagram of the life cycle.

QUESTIONS

ESSAY TYPE

1. List the salient features of Buxbaumiales. Explain the characters with the help of the details of the genus of this order studied by you.
2. How will you distinguish Funariales, Buxbaumiales and Polytrichales on the basis of sporophytic characters. *(Kanpur M.Sc., 1999)*
3. Describe the gametophyte and sporophyte of *Buxbaumia*.
4. Describe the gametophyte, sex organs and the sporophyte of *Buxbaumia*
5. Describe the important characters of *Buxbaumia* with special reference to its distribution in India.*(Kanpur M.Sc. 2004)*

SHORT ANSWER TYPE

6. Describe in brief the genus *Buxbaumia* mentioning features and their significance. *(Kanpur M.Sc. 1990, 1992)*
7. **Write short notes on :**
   (*a*) *Buxbaumia* *(Allahabad, M.Sc. 2000; Kanpur M.Sc. 1991, 1997, 2000)*
   (*b*) Male plant of *Buxbaumia* *(Lucknow M.Sc. 2004)*
   (*c*) Sporophyte of *Buxbaumia*
   (*d*) Peristome in *Buxbaumia*
8. Draw a labelled diagram of L.S. capsule of *Buxbaumia*.
9. What are the peculiar features of *Buxbaumia*?
10. (*a*) Write the name of any saprophytic bryophyte. *(Kanpur, M.Sc. 2003)*
    (*b*) Name atleast two saprophytic bryophyte and assign them to their systematic position. *(Lucknow M.Sc. 2007)*

OBJECTIVE TYPE

11. **Select the correct answer:**
    (*i*) Protonema is persistent in
    (*a*) *Andreaea* (*b*) *Sphagnum*
    (*c*) *Funaria* (*d*) *Polytrichum.*
    (*ii*) The male plant in *Buxbaumia* has
    (*a*) A single antheridium
    (*b*) Two antheridia
    (*c*) A cluster of antheridia
    (*d*) No antheridium.
    (*iii*) In which of the following peristome is 3-layered?
    (*a*) *Riccia* (*b*) *Anthoceros*
    (*c*) *Buxbaumia* (*d*) *Polytrichum.*
    (*iv*) *Buxbaumia* is a
    (*a*) Total saprophyte
    (*b*) Partial saprophyte
    (*c*) Total parasite
    (*d*) Total hydrophyte.
    (*v*) The capsule is obliquely egg shaped and borne on a stout seta in
    (*a*) *Funaria* (*b*) *Andreaea*
    (*c*) *Buxbaumia* (*d*) *Pogonatum.*
    (*vi*) Which one of the following is a saprophytic moss ?
    (*a*) *Cryptothallus* (*b*) *Sphagnum*
    (*c*) *Buxbaumia* (*d*) *Pogonatum.*

Image of *Polytrichum*

CHAPTER 20

BRYIDAE

Polytrichales : Polytrichum, Pogonatum

- Order Polytrichales
- Polytrichum
- Pogonatum

ORDER POLYTRICHALES

General Features of the Order

1. The gametophores are highly organised, tall and perennial almost comparable in size of the low growing vascular plants.

2. The leaf consists of a distal green narrow part, the **limb** and a proximal broad almost colourless **sheathing base**.

3. From the upper or adaxial surface of the limb arise close set, thin plates of green cells called the **lamellae**. In fact the members of this order can be recognised by the presence of leaf lamellae. The sheathing leaf base is devoid of lamellae.

4. The capsule is erect to horizontal covered by the hood-shaped or cucullate calyptra which may be smooth, hairy or spinulose depending on the species.

5. The operculum has a distinct beak.

6. The archesporium is usually bounded by a double air space system.

7. The peristome is of **nematodontous** type. It consists of a ring of 32 or 64 short, pyramidal, solid teeth with their tips joined above to a thin, pale membrane (epiphragm) stretching across the mouth of the capsule.

The order includes a single family **Polytrichaceae** comprising about 15 genera with 350 species. The family Polytrichacae is well represented in India by 5 genera namely, *Polytrichum*, *Pogonatum*, *Atrichium*, *Oligotrichum* and *Lyellia*. Of these the life histories of *Polytrichum* and *Pogonatum* are discussed here in some detail.

POLYTRICHUM Hedw. (Hairy cap moss)

Distribution

Polytrichum is one of the largest mosses. It is commonly called the hairy cap moss because of the luzzy calyptra enclosing the mature capsule. The genus comprises over 100 species found all over the world. These are chiefly confined to the tropical and temperate countries. Bruhl (1931) listed four species from India namely, *P. juniperinum*, *P. densifolium*, *P. xanthopilum*, and *P. alpinum*. These occur in the Himalayas at high altitude. *P. commune* which is considered cosmopolitan in its distribution has not so far been recorded from India.

Habit

Polytrichum commune is a cosmopolitan perennial woodland moss which occurs in clonal groupings. Many aerial leafy stems are interconnected by underground rhizomes. The erect aerial shoots may attain a length up to 45 cm and the rhizomes may reach a depth of about 30 cm (Grum, 1976).

Habitat

Polytrichum occurs in diverse habitats. Some species grow on clayey soil liable to desiccation, on dry stony places, dry woods and dry forest bogs, others on sandy banks, heaths, swamps, open peat bogs and still others on wet soil along the margin of lakes and ponds. *P. juniperinum* grows in extremely dry sites but closely related *P. strictum* grows in peat lands. *P. sexangulare* grows in late-snow areas and thus is subjected to relatively short periods of desiccation.

Gametophyte (Fig. 20.1).

The conspicuous part of the plant body is an erect leafy shoot (A) but it is not the entire gametophyte. In fact the leafy shoots arise from the haploid branched, alga-like, green filamentous structure called the **protonema** which is the product of germination of a haploid spore (meiospore), the first cell of the gametophyte generation. The protonema represents the

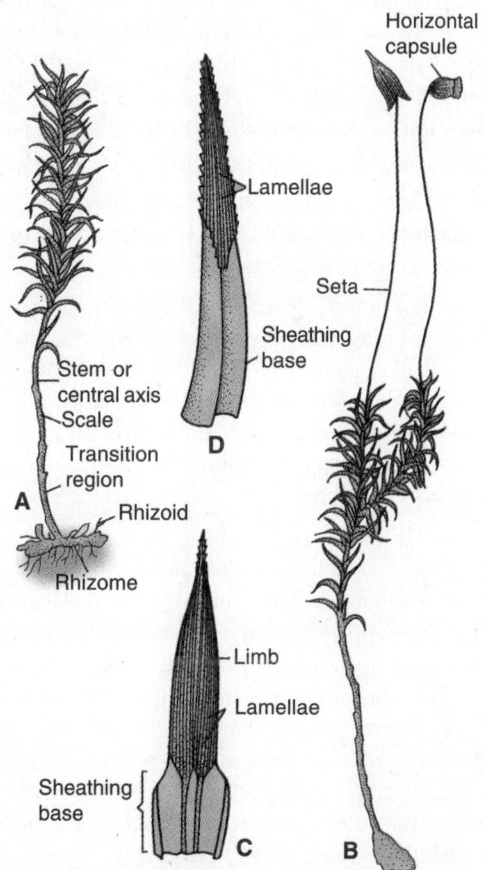

Fig. 20.1. (A—D). ***Polytrichum***. A, leafy gametophore with an unbranched stem; B, leafy gametophore with a branched stem, each branch bearing terminally a sporophyte; C, leaf of *P. juniperium*. D. leaf of *P. commune* (B after Sehenck).

juvenile stage and the erect leafy shoot represents the leafy stage of the moss gametophyte. The fact that the erect leafy shoots bear the sex organs containing the gametes and arise from the prostrate protonema suggest that they (leafy shoots) are gametophores equivalent to or homologous with the erect, stalk-like, leafless gametophores growing on the thalli of *Marchantia*.

The adult gametophores in *Polytrichum* are rhizomatous and thus consists of two parts, the **rhizome** and the upright **leafy** shoot (A).

(a) **Rhizome**. It is the horizontally growing underground portion of the gametophore. It bears only small, brown or colourless scale leaves in three rows and numerous rhizoids which tend to be massed together.

(b) **Leafy shoot**. It is the most conspicuous, erect, leafy axis arising from the rhizome. In *P. commune* it may be 45 cm. tall (Grum, 1976). Externally it is differentiated into a stem-like central axis which bears two kinds of leaves, (*i*) small scale-like in the lower portion or transition zone and (*ii*) comparatively larger firm, dark green foliage leaves in a spiral arrangement in the upper portion. Typically the erect, leafy axis is unbranched (A). Rarely it is branched (B). The branch arises from a primordium below the young leaf and not axillary to it. The branch primordia occur at intervals both on the rhizome and erect axis roughly at the base of every 12th leaf. Normally they remain dormant on the aerial shoot and become active only if the growing tip of the axis is decapitated and the damaged shoot is kept in a moist atmosphere. The stem grows by means of a three-side apical cell. It cuts off segments in such a way that the position of the apical cell is shifted in a spiral manner.

Leaves. The leaves in *Polytrichum* as mentioned in the previous paragraph are of two morphological types, the small *scale leaves* and the comparatively larger *foliage leaves*.

(*i*) *Scale leaves*. These are small, brown or almost colourless leaves with a rudimentary blade which is triangular in outline and non-photosynthetic in function. The scale leaves occur in a spiral manner with a divergence of 1/3 on the rhizome and transition zone (lower portion) of the aerial branches both of which are brown.

(*ii*) *Foliage leaves* (Fig. 20.1 C—D). The foliage leaves occur only in the upper portion of the upright branches. They are comparatively large and green. Each foliage leaf which is 6—10 mm long in *P. commune* (D) is differentiated into two parts, the proximal **sheathing base** and the distal diverging narrow **limb** or **blade**. The sheathing base is well developed, broad, colourless membranous and unistratose. It is traversed by a relatively narrow midrib and is generally devoid of lamellae. The growth is intercalary. The sheathing leaf bases closely clasp the stem so as to provide capillary channels for water.

The green limb is lanceolate or linear lanceolate in outline and has a accuminate apex. It grows by the activity of a broad multistratose midrib (nerve of costa) which makes up most of the width of the leaf blade, runs through it flanked by a thin, unistratose, narrow wing constituting the *true lamina*. The lamina region in *Polytrichum* leaf is thus poorly developed. The margin of the leaf may be entire (*P. juniperinum*, C) or coarsely toothed (*P. commune*, D). Smith (1971) and Vauzanlen (1974) reported the presence of a short celled *hinge tissue* where the leaf blade joins its sheathing base. The most significant and the unique feature of *Polytrichum* leaf is the occurrence of a highly photosynthetic tissue in the form of thin, closely set and longitudinally oriented one cell layer thick vertical plates of green cells known as the *photosynthetic lamellae*. They arise from the upper (adaxial) or ventral surface of the leaf and run longitudinally along the midrib with very narrow spaces between them. Their number varies from 21—55 rows per leaf depending upon the width of the blade. The presence of lamellae makes the narrow limb firm, opaque and dark green. The leaf lamellae are usually restricted to the costa (midrib) region only. Occasionally they are distributed all over the blade. They compensate for the poor development of the lamina region.

Rhizoids (Fig. 20.2). The rhizoids may arise from the base of the erect gametophore. They serve a mechanical function by providing support in species in which the gametophore grows to a considerable height. The rhizoids, however are more numerous on the rhizome and tend to be massed together and spirally twisted. As in other mosses, the rhizoids in *Polytrichum* are long, branched and multicellular. The cells are long with oblique septa. The rhizome with its dense rhizoidal covering is well equipped for external capillary conduction. The twisted rhizoidal strings function like a wick (A) and thus assist in external conduction enabling *Polytrichum* to grow in habitats liable to desiccation. The rhizoids absorb water and minerals in solution which move upwards not only through the lamina but also externally through the wick-like rhizoidal strands. The conduction in rhizoids is thus both internal and external. Wriglesworth reported the development of vegetative structures on the rhizoidal strands. These were called the **gemmae** (B). It is more appropriate to call them tubers. These serve as means of perennation and vegetative propagation.

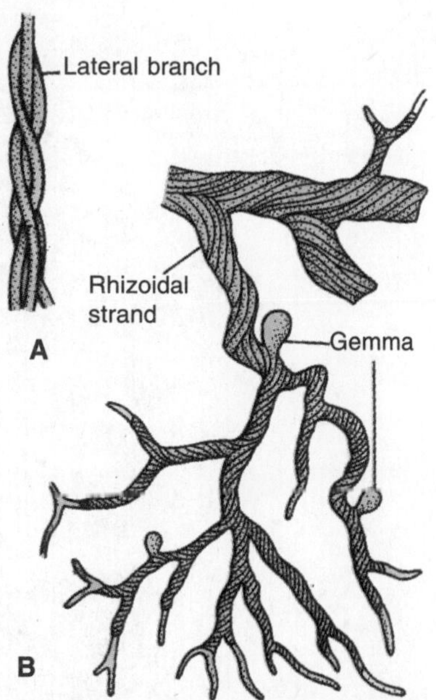

Fig. 20.2. (A—B). ***Polytrichum***. A, rhizoidal strand; B, rope-like rhizoids bearing gemmae (After Schimper).

Anatomy of stem. The anatomy of stem in *Polytrichum* is complex. It shows a highly differentiated, structural organisation with radially symmetrical zonation and complex tissue differentiation in the two inner zones. There is the outer **epidermis** followed by **cortex** and **central strand**. As the internal structure of the two parts of the gametophore, the rhizome and the upright leafy stem, differs they are discussed below separately :—

(*a*) *Internal structure of rhizome* (Fig. 20.3). In a cross section the rhizome is circular in outline in some species (*P. commune* and *P. formusum*) and triangular with rounded ends in many others. From without inwards it shows the following details :—

Epidermis. It forms the outermost zone consisting of a single layer of thin or thick-walled cells. The stomata are absent. The rhizoids which are the direct outgrowths of the epidermal cells form a dense tangle.

Cortex. Within the epidermis and surrounding the central strand is the cortical region. It consists of a few (3 or 4) layers of living thin-walled parenchyma cells. Lying embedded in the cortical region next to the epidermis are the three **hypodermal strands**, one opposite each ridge. Each hypodermal strand consists of a group of living prosenchymatous cells with pointed ends. Extending radially inwards from each hypodermal strand is a group of cells of greater diameter with comparatively thin lignified walls. The latter together with the hypodermal strand form a wedge-shaped mass of cells constituting the **radial strand**. It tapers inwards. Together the three radial strands break up the cortical region into three **arcs**. The cortex is delimited internally by a layer of large radially elongated cells with suberized thickening on the radial and horizontal walls. This layer is likened to the **endodermis**. The so-called endodermal layer is not continuous. Its continuity is broken opposite the ridges by the three radial strands.

Pericycle. In some species pericycle consisting of 2 or 3 layers of thin-walled cells is recognisable at the periphery of the 3 lobed central cylinder. It is not continuous and is absent in the region of furrows, where the centre of the bay is occupied by the leptoids.

Leptoids. In the centre of the bay, in each furrow of the 3-lobed central cylinder, is present a group of polygonal cells with their granular contents of protein nature. These large, elongated sieve tube-like cells are termed the **leptoids**. The end walls of the leptoids are more or less oblique and in some cases show plasmodesmata. Collectively the three groups of leptoids, which more or less

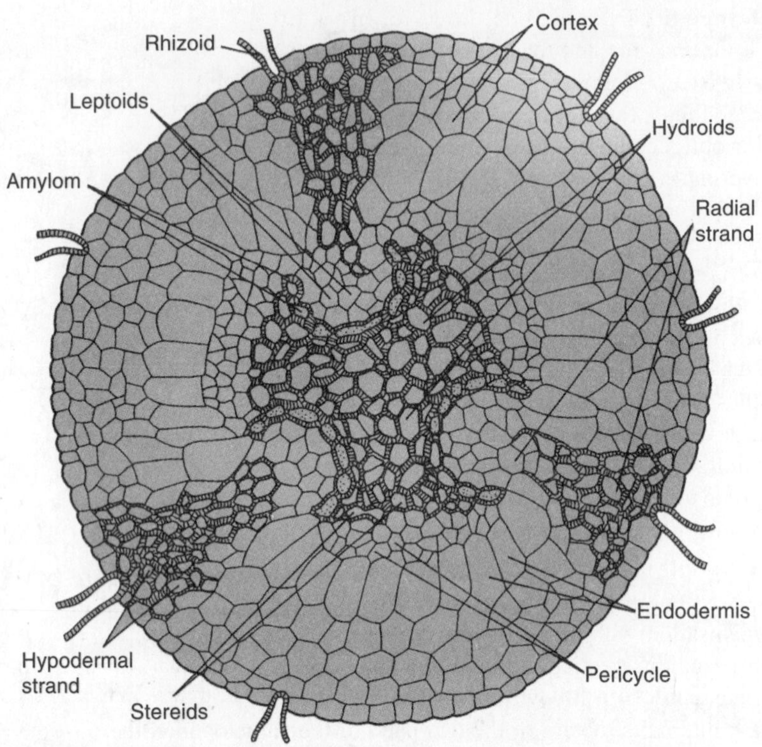

Fig. 20.3. ***Polytrichum.*** T.S. Rhizome showing detailed structure (Based on Tansley and Chick).

resemble the sieve cells of the vascular plants, constitute the leptom. It is the food (photoassimilate) conducting system. It consists of the leptoids and associated parenchyma.

Amylom. On the side away from the radial strand each group of leptoids is surrounded by a single layered sheath of starchy parenchyma. It is the **amylom**. The amylom thus separates the leptom from the central trilobed hydrom.

Central cylinder. It is the central, compact, 3-lobe mass of tissue forming the core of the rhizome. It consists of two kinds of elements, the **stereids** (or sclereids) and **hydroids**. The central mass mainly consists of the stereids. These are thick-walled, elongated cells with oblique end walls. Here and there they contain a little starch. Collectively the stereids constitute **stereom**. The latter functions as the supporting tissue. In addition it provides an alternative route for the conduction of water (Trachtenberg and Zamski, 1979). Interspersed among the stereids are the empty elements in groups of 2 or 3. These are termed the **hydroids**. The cells in each group are separated by fine delicate cellulose walls. Collectively the hydroids, which are considered to function as the water conducting tissue, constitute the **hydrom**. The stereom and the hydrom together constitute the **hydrom cylinder**.

(b) Structure of aerial stem (Fig. 20.4). A cross-section of the erect stem is more or less circular in outline (A). Sometimes it is irregular due to the attachment of leaves. Internally it is differentiated into **epidermis** followed by the wide **cortex** and central **cylinder** (A).

Epidermis. The single layered epidermis is usually not well defined.

Cortex. Within the epidermis is the wide cortex. It is differentiated into outer thick-walled cortex and inner thin-walled cortex. In the young stem the cortical cells contain chloroplasts. Leaf traces are present in the cortical region. Each leaf trace consists of a central patch of colourless, thin-

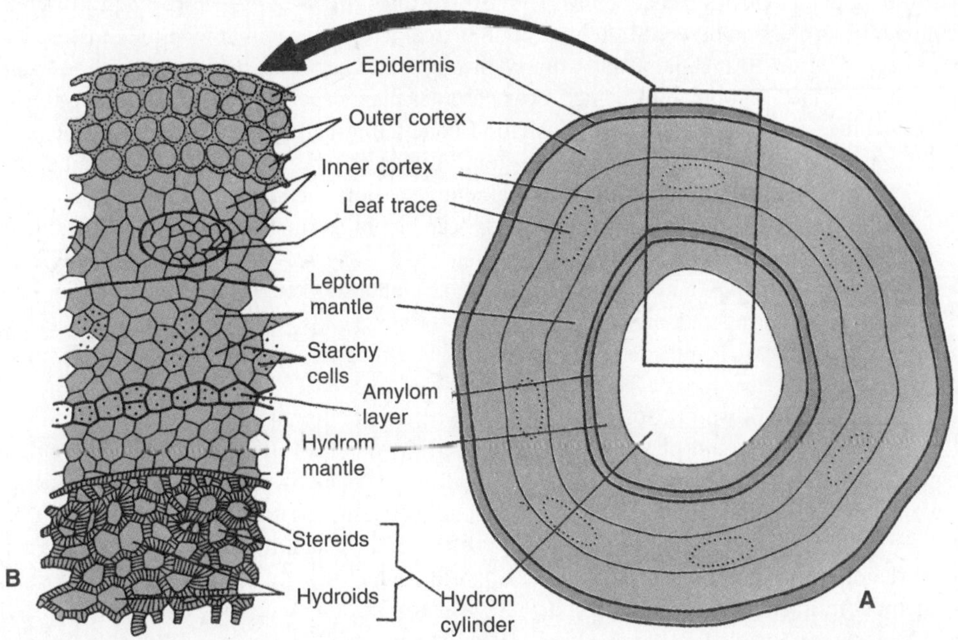

Fig. 20.4. (A—B). ***Polytrichum***. A, T.S. aerial stem (outline sketch); B, portion of A showing details (Based on Tansley and Chick).

walled, water conducting hydroid cells which are surrounded by parenchymatous cells, the **socii** on the abaxial side and **deuter** on the adaxial side (Eschrich and Steiner, 1968). The leaf trace entering the stem has 11 rows of central cells. In its course through the ground tissue it loses all the central cells except the middle most one. The latter finally merges with the hydroids. The parenchymatous cells are either eliminated or successively taken off by the ground tissue. It is thus evident that there exists only a loose connection between the axial conducting strand (central cylinder) and the leaf traces (Eschrich and Steiner, 1968). The leaf trace extends across the cortex to form a loose connection with the central cylinder.

Central cylinder (B). Next to the inner cortex is the central cylinder. It occupies the core of the stem and consists of tissues showing symmetrical zonation. In the centre is a compact mass of thick-walled cells constituting the **hydrom cylinder**. It comprises two kinds of cell elements, the **stereids** and **hydroids**. The former are thick-walled supporting cells constituting the major part of the hydrom cylinder. Interspersed among the stereids are the thin-walled elongated empty cells in groups of 2 or 3. These are the **hydroids** concerned with water conduction. Surrounding the **hydrom cylinder** is a zone consisting of two or three layers of thin-walled cells devoid of contents. It is the **hydrom mantle.** External to the hydrom mantle is a narrow zone consisting of a single layer, sometimes of two layers, of cells containing starch. These cells have dark-brown suberized walls. This zone is called the **hydrom sheath** or **amylom layer**. Situated at the periphery of the central cylinder, just external to the amylom layer is a broad irregular zone composed of thin-walled, sieve tube-like cells. It is known as the **leptom mantle**. Situated here and there in the leptom mantle are a few starchy cells with protoplasmic contents but no starch. A layer of parenchymatous cells delimits cortex from the central cylinder. Since the cells of this layer bordering the central cylinder contain starch, it has been termed the **starchy sheath**. Kawai and Ikeda (1970) defined this layer between the leptom and cortex as **endodermis**. Trachtenberg and Zamski (1978) suggested that since functional aspect of this tissue has not yet been examined it would be more appropriate to term this layer as central strand sheath instead of endodermis.

It is evident from the account given above that *Polytrichum* has reached a high level of complexity in cell and tissue differentiation in the gametophore stem among the mosses. It exhibits an internal tissue arrangement particularly in the central cylinder which approaches that of the protostele of the sporophyte of some lower vascular plants such as *Rhynia* and *Psilotum*. Stereids (thick-walled supporting cells), leptoids (food conducting cells) and hydroids (water conducting cells) all occur in the central region of the stem. A layer of parenchymatous cells containing starch (the starch sheath) delimits cortex from the central region. Hebant (1964, 1966, 1969, 1970 and 1974) who studied the ultra structure of hydroids and leptoids considers them to be conducting cells comparable to the xylem and phloem of vascular plants. The only difference he noted between the hydroids of *Polytrichum* and tracheids of vascular plants was the absence of lignin in the former. The leptoids, he considered, are comparable with the sieve cells. These are elongated elements with enlarged extremities. Their terminal walls are oblique and perforated with great many plasmodesmata pores.

Conduction of water. Bowen (1931, 1933) held that internal path way of conduction of water through the central strand plays little or no role in *Polytrichum*. It is mainly by external capillary channels. Blaikley (1932) and Magdefrau (1935) observed that upward movement of water is internal and through the central strand. Hebant (1970) studied the ultrastructure of hydroids and considered them functionally comparable to the tracheids of vascular plants. He confirmed earlier findings of Haberlandt (1886) and Vaisey (1888) that hydroids, which constitute the axial strand in the leafy gametophore and the seta, are concerned with water conduction. According to Hebant (1970), Hebant and Johnson (1976) and Scheirer (1973, 1975) the hydroids consist of two morphologically distinct cell walls namely, (*i*) polyphenolic encrusted lateral walls and (*ii*) hydrolysed end walls. Scheirer and Gold Klang (1977) investigated the pathway of water movement through the hydroid walls with electron microscope using an electron dense crystal (Prussian blue). Based on their observations they arrived at the following conclusions:—

(*i*) Water moves preferentially across the hydrolised end walls of the hydroids.

(*ii*) Water movement through the encrusted lateral walls is negligible.

Translocation of assimilates. Haberlandt (1886) suggested leptom, which is an ensemble of leptoids and associated parenchyma cells, as the pathway for the conduction of elaborated organic substances. This view was supported by Strassburger (1891). Eschrich and Steiner (1967, 1968) demonstrated by autoradiography the presence of assimilates in the leptom. They described that in *P. commune* the hydroid cylinder is surrounded by the leptom cylinder. Embedded in the cylinder of parenchymatous cells are eight longitudinal strands of leptoids. The latter are supposed to be concerned with the transport of assimilates to long distances. They calculated that C^{14}- labelled assimilates move in the leptom at a velocity up to 32 cm per hour. Later Robert *et al* (1988) conducted an experiment in which isolated stems in the clonal grouping of *P. commune* were pulse labelled with $^{14}CO_2$. They found that labelled sugar mostly sucrose, glucose and fructose appeared in the pulse-labelled stems 30 minutes after treatment. A small amount of labelled sugar (3.3%) was

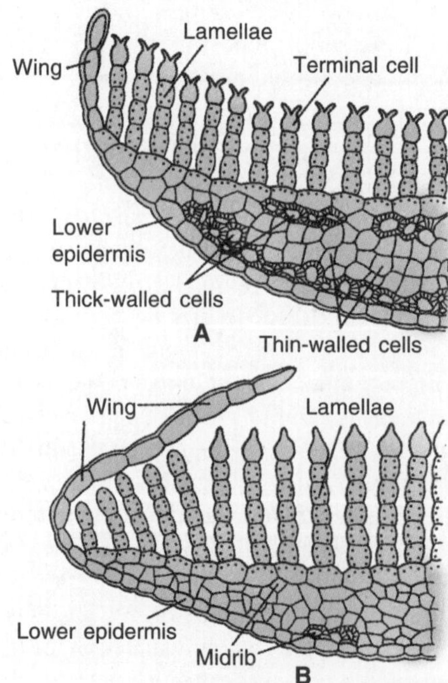

Fig. 20.5. (A—B). ***Polytrichum.*** Anatomy of leaf. A, T.S. leaf of *P. commune*; B, T.S. leaf of *P. juniperinum*.

transported to the neighbouring stems. This shows that transport of photoassimilates occurs through the leptom of perennating rhizomes.

Trachtenberg and Zamski (1978) investigated the conduction of ionic solutes and assimilates in the leptom of *P. juniperinum*. They concluded that leptom is concerned with the conduction of assimilates, exogenously applied surcrose and ionic solutes such as sulphate and lead.

Anatomy of leaf (Fig. 20.5). Structurally *Polytrichum* leaf is the most complex of all the mosses and provides a good example of structure related to function.

Structure (A, B). A cross section of the leaf shows that a major portion of it consists of a *broad nerve* or **midrib** flanked by a narrow wing (A) constituting the *lamina*. The wing of lamina is composed of a single layer of hyaline cells (unistratose). In species growing comparatively in dry or exposed habitats, the wing bends over the midrib in dry weather leaving only a small space for gaseous exchange (*P. juniperinum* and *P. filiferum*).

The wide midrib which makes up most of the width of the leaf is multistratose (several cells thick) in the centre. Gradually it thins towards the margins and finally merges into the wing or lamina on either sides. The lower epidermis is well marked. It consists of a single layer of regularly arranged large cells with their outer walls strongly thickened. Within the lower epidermis, the midrib generally shows one to two, rarely more layers of thick band of small elements (sclereids) with extremely thickened walls and narrow lumina. There is a narrow and interrupted band of similar elements (sclereids) on the upper (adaxial) side. Between these two bands of sclereids, the midrib tissue consists of thin-walled parenchyma cells differentiated into (*i*) a band of large thin-walled parenchyma cells immediately beneath the upper band of sclereids and (*ii*) the much narrow empty central parenchyma cells. The former are termed the *deuters* and the latter water conducting *hydroids* (Hebant, 1971). Eschrich and Steiner (1968) speculated that the deuters are concerned with the translocation of assimilates out of the leaf.

The midrib lacks the upper epidermis. It is replaced by a layer of large, thin-walled cells similar in diameter to the deuters. These cells bear the **lamellae** which in a cross section appear as close set, one cell thick rows of green or dark green cells 4-7 or 8 cells high, standing vertically parallel to each other with extremely narrow *interlamellar spaces* between them, each not more than few microns wide. The distal or terminal cells of the lamellae, often referred to as the *marginal cells*, are slightly larger and hyaline. All others are green or dark green and contain chloroplasts. Paolilla and Reighard (1967) reported that these green cells exhibit an infrastructure characteristic of chlorenchyma. Hebant and Marty (1972) reported that cytoplasmic organelles similar to microbodies and termed *peroxisoiner* occur amongst the plastids and mitochondria and were abundant in the vicinity of chloroplads. The leaf lamellae function as a *pseudomesophyll* (Smith, 1971).

The marginal or terminal cells are often more or less differentiated, variously shaped and ornamented. In *P. juniperinum* they are wider and papillose, whereas in *P. commune* they are bifid. The notch provides a convenient taxonomic character as well as suitable niche for micro-organisms (Schecter and Dolan, 1983). When wetted the marginal cells contact laterally with those of the adjacent lamellae, thus providing a functional equivalent of the upper epidermis. It is therefore termed the upper or ventral *pseudo-epidermis*.

Function of lamellae. Goebel (1893) remarked that the primary function of the lamellae was capillary conduction of water. Stolz (1902) supporting Goebel further added that the lamellae are in contact with the sheathing leaf bases and formed a part of a continuous external capillary conducting system which extends from the base of the plant to the leaf apices. Buch (1945) experimentally demonstrated that all parts of the leaf of *P. commune* including the lamellae except the hinge tissue, are water repellent. He thus concluded that the narrow spaces between the lamellae are normally filled with air. Paolillo and Reighard (1967) using fluorescent dye tracers showed water movement in the hydroids of the leaf midrib in *Polytrichum. They* confirmed that *Polytrichum* is chiefly a endohydric moss. In view of these observations, the consensus of opinion, at present, favour the view that the upper pseudo-epdermis which consists of the marginal cells, enclosing the green lamellae with air-filled narrow interlameller spaces, constitutes a well ventilated photosynthetic tissue. The marginal cells are densely covered with epicuticular wax in the form of platelets which provide an effective barrier to the penetration of the underlying photosynthetic tissue (lamellae) by water droplets. Watson (1974) remarked that the photosynthetic tissue in *Polytrichum* leaf is equivalent to the phtosynthetic tissue on the upper surface of the thallus of *Riccia*.

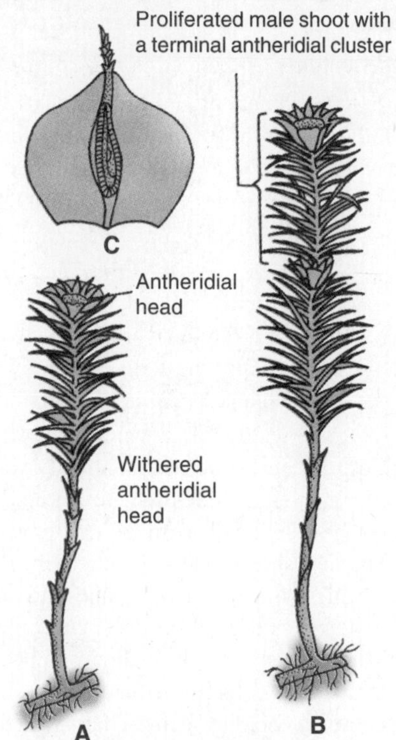

Fig. 20.6. (A—C). ***Polytrichum.*** A, male plant; B, male plant with a proliferated male shoot; C, perigonial leaf of *P. juniperinum* (C after Watson).

Vegetative reproduction. It takes place by vegetative buds (bulbils) developed on the rhizoids and also by the multiplication of the protonemal stage. The gametophore of *Polytrichum* is rhizomatous. From the horizontally growing rhizome arise upright leafy stems at intervals. Death or breakage of the intervening rhizome pieces results in the establishment of separate free living plants.

Secondary protonemata. Wilmot-Dear (1980) showed that at 20°C in 12 hr. days detached leaves of *P. commune*, *P. formosum*, and *P. juniperinum* produced long, branched secondary protonemata filaments bearing vegetative buds at intervals in cultures. The buds develop into new leafy gametophores. The regenerates (secondary protonemata) in all cases developed either from the large cells on the adaxial surface of the leaf at the bases of lamellae or basal cells of the lamellae themselves.

Sexual reproduction. The sex organs are borne in groups at the tip of the main axis of the gametophore which is unbranched. All species of *Polytrichum* are **dioecious**. The antheridia (Fig. 20.6 A) and archegonia (Fig. 20.11 A) are thus borne on different gemetophores.

Initiation of gametangia. Benson-Evans (1961) reported *Polytrichum* spp. to be day neutral. Photoperiod thus has no effect on gametangia initiation. *Polytrichum* showed optimum gametangial formation at 21°C with 30°C proving inhibitory. Hughes (1962) remarked that temperature seems to be the critical factor in the initiation of sexual cycle in *Polytrichum*, although day length may play some role in the development after induction of sex organs.

Antheridial head (Fig. 20.6 A). The leaves surrounding the antheridia are called the **perigonial leaves**. They are widely different from the vegetative leaves in form and colour and are modified to form a perianth-like structure. The perigonial leaf is comparatively shorter. It usually consists of a broadly expanded sheathing leaf base terminating in a short bristle point (C). In colour the perigonial leaves may be red-brown or olive in some species (*P. juniperinum*) and dull red in others (*P. piliferum*). They lie close together forming a rosette around the antheridia. The male gametophore can thus be easily recognised from its female counterpart by its perigonial cup looking very much like an open floral envelope superficially resembling a miniature flower (A). The antheridia in the perigonial cup occur in small groups under the perigonial leaves occupying the same position as the lateral buds lower down in the vegetative portion. Leitgeb thus considered each antheridial group homologous to a lateral branch. According to this view the entire antheridial head in *Polytrichum* is a compound structure in contrast to that of *Funaria*. The apical cell of the male gametophore is not used up in the formation of antheridia. Consequently the vegetative axis may resume growth in the following year through the withered antheridial head to produce a new male shoot terminating in a perigonial cup. This process of proliferation of the vegetative shoot through the antheridial head may be repeated successively several times (B).

A longitudinal section through the antheridial head (Fig. 20.7) shows a conspicuous apical dome surrounded by a number of well developed antheridia. The central dome represents the apical bud containing the growing point (apical cell) which is not used up in the formation of antheridia. Associated with the antheridia in the cluster are two kinds of paraphyses, filamentous (1) and with a spathulate tip (2).

Antheridium (Fig. 20.8). Hausmann and Paolillo, Jr. (1977) investigated the development and maturation of antheridia of *P. juniperinum*. The account given here is based on their findings. The mature antheridium ranges in length from 1.2 mm to 1.8 mm, rarely 1.95mm. The average length is 1.5 mm. According to Paolillo, Jr. and Kossa (1977) when the antheridium is young and half the normal size, its jacket layer contains almost the same number of cells as the jacket layer of the mature antheridium. Within the jacket layer are the actively dividing, close packed **androgones** (20.9 K). The final doubling in the length of the antheridium is chiefly a process of cell enlargement of the cells of the jakcet layer. Cell elongation is accompanied by increase in the number of plastids which are of the nature of chloroplasts. The green jacket cells lack a large central vacuole but contain rough endoplasmic reticulum, dictyosomes and vesicles of modest size. The distal 4 or 5 tiers of cells of the antheridial jacket show a lesser tendency for cell enlargement but are marked by the thickening of their cell walls. There is no space within the antheridium when young.

The mature antheridium of *Polytrichum* (Fig. 20.8) consists of an elongated, club-shaped body raised on a short multicellular stalk consisting of a few cells. It is characterized by: (*i*) the presence of a large fluid filled space in the sperm chamber below the spermatogenous mass, (*ii*) differentiated tip, termed **operculum** consisting of 4 or 5 distal tiers of small cells with markedly thickened walls and (*iii*) the presence of a tough, glossy transparent, cuticle-like layer on the antheridium cutting at the base across the stalk. All these are absent in the young antheridium. With

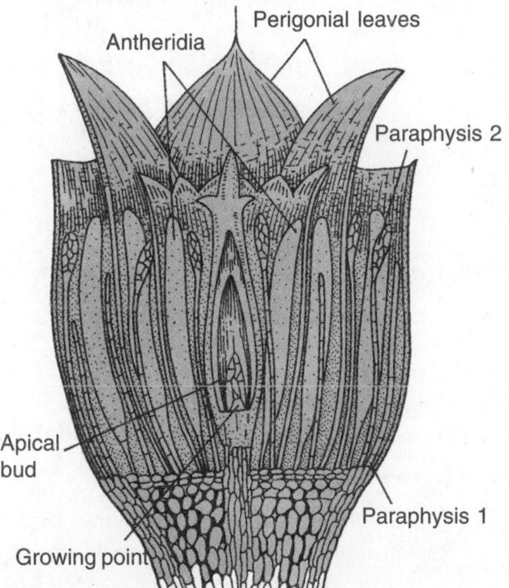

Fig. 20.7. *Polytrichum* sp. Longitudinal section of the tip of the male gametophore passing through the antheridial cluster.

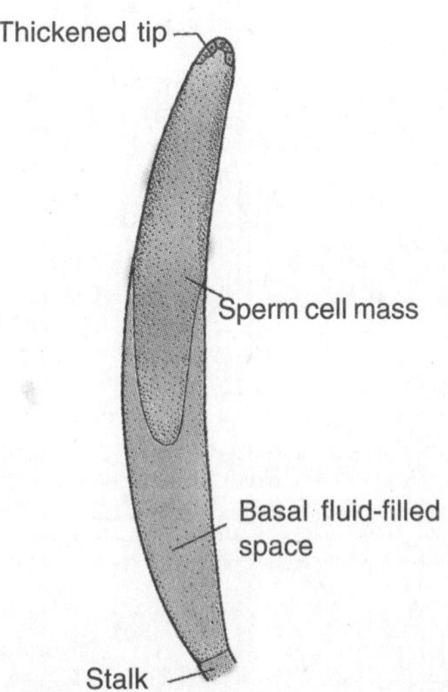

Fig. 20.8. *Polytrichum juniperinum*. A mature antheridium.

the maturation of the boundary of the half grown antheridium, the last mitosis of spermatogenous cells in the antheridium is completed. As a result it is maintained at a small size but the antheridium as it ages doubles its length by elongation and enlargement of the jacket cells. Consequently a fluid-filled space develops in the sperm chamber. It accounts for nearly half the volume enclosed by the jacket. During the accumulation of the fluid, the antheridium increases in size, the androcytes metamorphose into sperms and the jacket cells at the distal end of the antheridium continue to thicken their walls. The maturation of these tip cells determines when the antheridium is ripe. Intermingled with the antheridia in the antheridial head are multicellular hair-like structures called the **paraphysis**. Majority of them are simple, filamentous structures consisting of a single row of uniform cells. Some, however, are more elaborate having several cells wide spathulate tips (Fig. 20.9 K).

Development of antheridia (Fig. 20.9) The development of antheridium is similar to that of *Funaria*. The antheridia develop from the embryonic cells at the tip of the male gametophore. The apical cell is, however, not used up in their developemnt. Each antheridium arises from a single embryonic segment of the apical cell. It is known as the **antheridial initial**. It grows into a papilla-

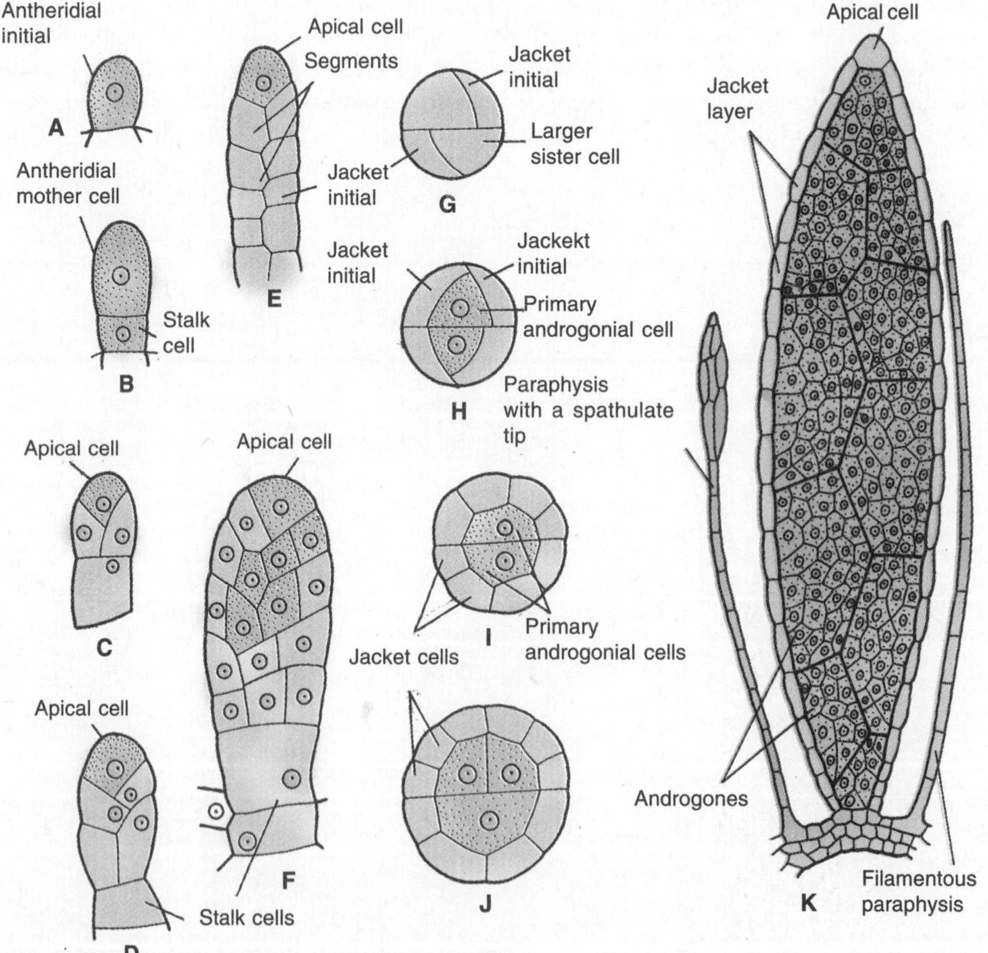

Fig. 20.9. (A—K). ***Polytrichum*** sp. A—F, early stages of antheridial development as seen in longitudinal sections; G—J, cross sections of young antheridia at various stages of development; K, L.S. young antheridium showing androgones arranged in blocks.

like structure projecting well above the neighbouring cells (A). The papillate antheridial initial divides by a transverse wall into two cells, the lower **stalk cell** and the upper **antheridial mother' cell** (B). The former at a very late stage of antheridium development undergoes a few divisions to form a few-celled stalk. The antheridial mother cell divides by two oblique intersecting walls to establish a three-sides apical cell with two cutting faces (C). The young antheridium from now onwards grows by the activity of the apical cell for a considerable time. The development of moss antheridium by an apical cell is in marked contrast to that of the hepatics where it is intercalary.

The apical cell regularly cuts off two series of segments alternately right and left by a succession of walls parallel to its two cutting faces (D) till 13-15 segments are cut off (E). It then ceases to be active and contributes to the opercular region of the wall of the antheridium. Periclinal divisions appear in the young antheridium when 3 or 4 segments have been cut off by the apical cell on either side (F). Thereafter the segments above, cut off by the apical cell, divide in the same way. The segments in which the periclinal walls appear have denser contents. In a cross section the two alternating segments are nearly spherical, each being hemispherical in outline. The periclinal division in each of the two segments is in a diagonal vertical plane and thus is asymmetrical.

It is best seen in a cross section (G). The smaller daughter cell thus separated is the **first jacket initial**. The larger sister cell undergoes another similar division which separates a **second jacket initial** towards the periphery from the primary **androgonial cell** on the inner side (H). The jacket or wall initials, hence onwards divide only by anticlinal and transverse divisions (I). Consequently the antheridial wall increases in circumference and height only but remains one cell-layer in thickness. Each primary androgonial cell then divides by a median vertical wall to form two spermatogenic or androgonial cells (J). In a cross section of the antheridium at this stage, they are seen surrounded by the jacket layer. Now ushers in the **androgonial phase**. It is the growth phase of the sperm mass. During this phase the androgonial cells or the androgones multiply. They divide and redivide in all planes resulting in a large number of androgones arranged in blocks by walls that are thicker than the walls around the individual androgones (K). The androgonial cells thus have the attributes of meristematic cells, each containing copious quantity of rough endoplasmic reticulum, flattened biconcave plastids, small vacuoles, dictyosomes, mitochondria and vesicles of modest size. These cells are close packed within the jacket layer. With the approach of last mitosis there is thickening of their thin wall particularly at the angles to facilitate rounding up of the protoplast. Two centrosomes appear *de novo* in each cell in the centre in a perinuclear location. Subsequently they migrate to the opposite poles, each positioning itself between the nucleus and the plastids. These cells of the penultimate generation of the androgones are called the *androcyte mother cells*. Each androcyte mother cell undergoes the last mitosis to produce two androcytes which metamorphose into sperms.

When all these changes have taken place, the antheridium is half its final length. The jacket layer, which is suberized contains almost the same number of cells as the jacket of the mature antheridium. The cells of 4 or 5 distal tiers have started thickening their walls. The androcyte mother cells have divided into androcytes. With the cessation of division in the spermatogenous cells, the space begins to form at the base. Simultaneously the water and solutes move from protoplast to protoplast to accumulate in it. During accumulation of fluid the antheridium increases in size by the process of cell enlargement of the jacket cells, the sperms mature and the thickening of cell wall at the distal end of the antheridium continues till the latter achieves its final length. Thus the fluid-filled space below the sperm mass in the mature antheridium accounts for nearly half the volume enclosed by the jacket layer.

Spermatogenesis (Fig. 20.10). The events leading to the transformation of androcytes into sperms constitute **spermatogenesis**. The freshly formed androcyte contains a small, darkly staining, rounded dense granule besides the nucleus (A). The granule which behaved like a centrosome in the

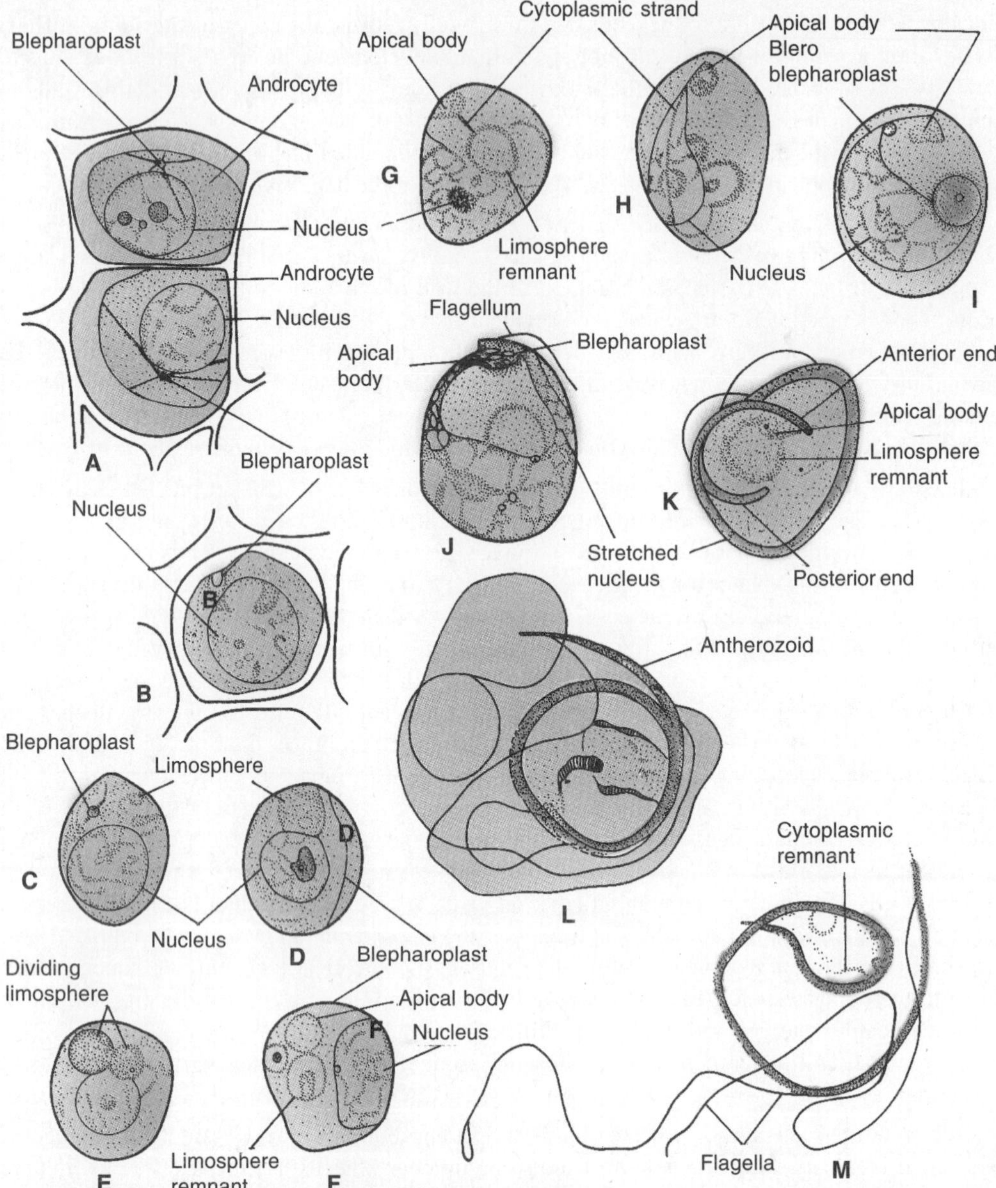

Fig. 20.10. (A—M). ***Polytrichum juniperinum***. Spermatogenesis. A, androcyte mother cell having divided into two androcytes, each with a blepharoplast; B, androcyte with the blepharoplast move to the periphery and grown somewhat; C, androcyte with the blepharoplast grown into a short rod and limosphere appearing; D, androcyte with a peripheral blepharoplast in the form of curved rod with one end near the limosphere; E, androcyte with the limosphere diving unequally; F, apical body separated from the limosphere remnant; G, apical body and limosphere remnant connected by a cytoplasmic strand and beak-like projection of the nucleus showing beginning of nucleus elongation; H, apical body attached to the anterior end of the blepharoplast and limosphere remnant in contact with the posterior end of the more stretched nucleus; I, further stage showing elongation of the nucleus; J, showing still further elongation of the nucleus into two beaks anterior and posterior; K, apical body still attached to the anterior end of the blepharoplast and nucleus stretched to its final length; L, antherozoid escaping from its vesicle; M, liberated sperm with the cytoplasmic remnant still attached to its posterior end (After Allen).

division of the androcyte mother cell is now termed the **blepharoplast** in view of the function it performs in the androcyte. The other important cell organelles which the androcyte contains are the mitochnondria, dictyosomes and the plastids. Paolillo (1965) reported that the mitochondrial files in the androcyte cluster and coalesce about the plastid to form a spherical structure called the **limosphere**.

Allen (1917) who studied spermatogenesis in *P. juniperinum* with light microscope observed that blepharoplast which is originally very small begins to increase in size (B) and becomes somewhat elongated. It usually moves to the periphery of the cell and comes to lie in contact with the plasma membrane of the adrocyte (B). Gradually it enlarges and becomes considerably elongated to form a curved rod of uniform thickness placed in contact with the plasma membrane (F). The nucleus, which is located in the centre of the cell, now moves to the periphery, comes in contact with blepharoplast, presses against it and the plasma membrane (F) and gradually begins to draw out into a point by the side of the latter (G, H). As the nucleus stretches out along the blepharoplast and the transformation continues, the boundary between the two gradually becomes indistinguishable (I, J, K). The nucleus continues to elongate and condense becoming an increasingly long, slender, coiled structure of about one and one-half turns (L). The blepharoplast, at this stage, can be traced along the entire length of the slender body of the nucleus except for its anterior end which projects a short distance beyond the tip of the nucleus. From this portion which seems to have been formed by the blepharoplast alone arise two flagella near the tip. One of these is located somewhat more anteriorly than the other (M). Allen concluded that the nuleus and the blepharoplast constitute the entire body of the mature sperm.

While the blepharoplast is still small and has just started to elongate, a large, spherical body, the **limosphere** appears in the cytoplasm (C). Soon it moves close to the anterior end of the blepharoplast (D) and divides into two unequal parts. The smaller part which is termed the **apical body** becomes attached to the anterior end of the blepharoplast (E, F) and remains so until a very late stage. Eventually it is lost as the sperm matures. According to Allen it takes no part in the formation of the body of the sperm. The larger part called the **limosphere remnant** moves away and comes to lie in contact with the nucleus usually its posterior part (H). It persists until the time of maturity of the sperm (M).

Paolillo *et al* (1968 a) studied the ultrastructure of spermatogenesis of *P. juniperinum*. According to them the so called centrosome consists of a pair of minute, coaxial rod-shaped bodies, the **centrioles**. A complex 3-parted, multilayered structure (MLS) arises *de novo* in the cytoplasm below the centrioles at an early stage of androcyte development. It is thus associated with the centrioles and consists of 3 layers of microtubules in *Polytrichum*. The two centrioles eventually become the basal bodies from which emerge the two flagella and the multilayered structure (MLS) serves as a supporting framework (cytoskeleton) for nuclear elongation. The two move as an integral unit called the **blepharoplast** and become positioned at the periphery of the androcyte in contact with the plasma membranes.

Thereafter the androcyte nucleus, as well, moves, comes in contact with the blepharoplast and presses against it and the plasma membrane. Positioned as such, the shape of the nucleus begins to change. A well-defined anterior beak-like prolongation is formed. At this stage a portion of the mitochondrial sheath, the apical body separates from the limosphere and becomes attached to the lower elements of the MLS at the anterior beak-like end and grows rearward along the side of the elongating nucleus. The coiling and elongation of the nucleus occurs as the microtubules of the uppermost layer of the cytoskeleton, which adhere to its surface, extend and grow rearward along the membranous envelope. Their number gradually decreases as they extend rearward over it and finally persist as a tailpiece which Sato (1956) called 'filamentous appendage' and Manton (1957) referred to as a "fibrous band".

During the process of transformation of androcytes into spermatozoids, bulk of the androcyte cytoplasm is used up. Finally a small portion of it including the limosphere remnant remains within the posterior curve of the mature sperm. The walls of the androcytes dissolve as the sperms mature. Each mature sperm, ready to escape from the antheridium, lies in a vesicle bounded by a distinct membrane. The separate vesicles lie embedded in a viscous substance formed by the degeneration of the walls of the androcytes. The sperm mass lies in the distal half of the mature antheridium.

The body of the biflagellate mature sperm ready for liberation consists of one and one half coils. A major part of it is nuclear in origin. Besides, it contains a part of the apical body and two basal bodies with their flagella. The unused cytoplasm containing the plastid and the portion of the mitochondrial sheath, that did not take part in the formation of the apical body, remain attached to the posterior end of sperm body as a cytoplasmic remnant or posterior vesicle.

Archegonial head (Fig. 20.11). The archegonia occur in a cluster at the tip of female gametophore (A). The leaves surrounding the archegonia are called the **perichaetial leaves**. The perichaetial leaves overlap close over at the top of the archegonial cluster to form a bud-like structure called the **perichaetium**. Intermingled with the archegonia in the cluster are the **paraphysis**. Each paraphysis is a filamentous structure consisting of a row of uniform cells (C). The apical cell of the female gametophore itself sooner or later functions as the archegonial initial. Consequently further growth of the female gametophyte ceases.

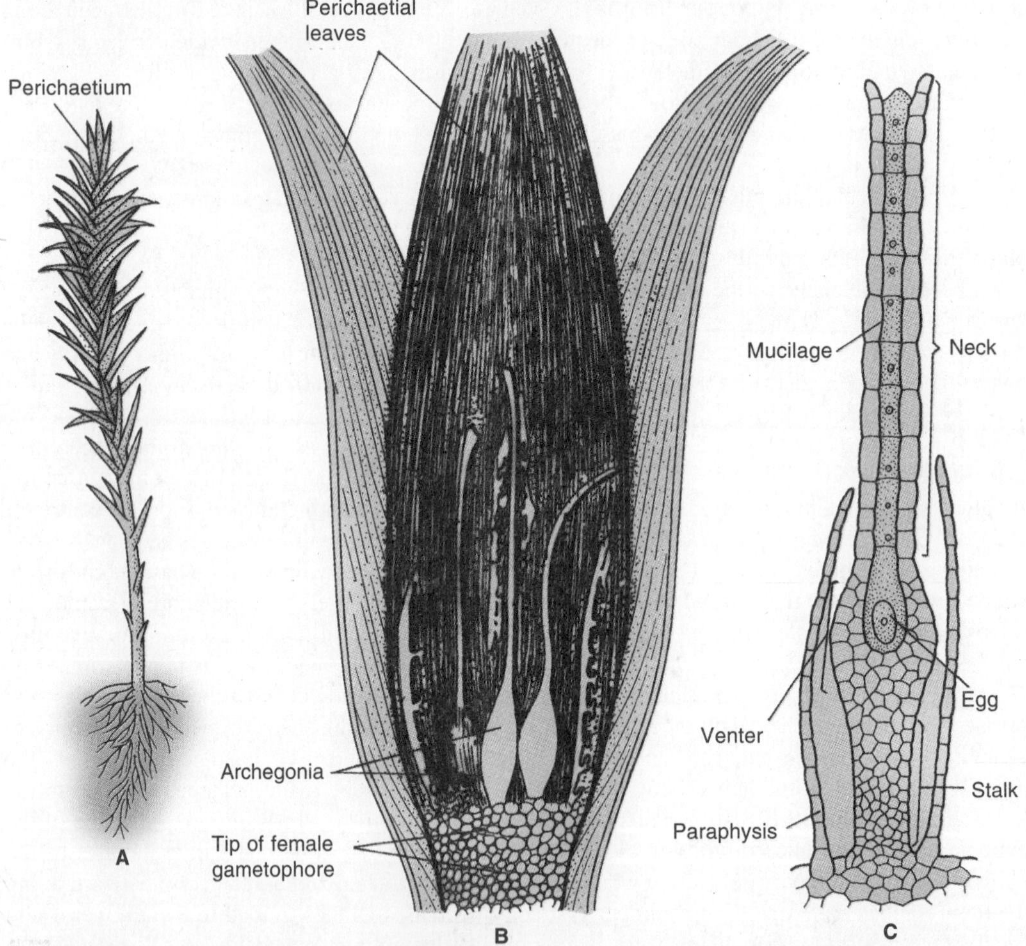

Fig. 20.11. (A—D). *Polytrichum*. A, female plant; B, L.S. through the tip of the female gametophore; C, mature archegonium ready for fertilization.

Structure of archegonium (Fig. 20.12 H). The mature archegonium is typically a flask shaped structure consisting of a very long **neck, venter** and massive **stalk**. The venter wall is two cell-layers thick. The venter cavity contains a single spherical **egg** and a **vertical canal cell** just above it. The long, narrow neck consists of six vertical rows of neck cells enclosing a narrow **neck canal** which houses a row of a considerable number (about 13 or more) of **neck canal cells**.

Development of archegonium. (Fig. 20.12). The archegonium develops from any embryonic cell in the growing region of the female gametophore. It grows and protrudes above the neighbouring cells (A) and then divides by a transverse wall at the surface to function as the **archegonial initial** (A). Sooner or later the apical cell of the female gametophore itself, functions as the archegonial initial. The protuberant archegonial initial divides by a transverse wall separating a basal **primary stalk cell** and an upper **archegonial mother cell** (B). The former divides to form the massive stalk. The archegonium mother cell divides by three oblique walls intersecting each other at some distance above the first transverse septum. In this way three **peripheral cells** surrounding an **axial cell** are carved from the archegonial mother cell (C). The axial cell is tetrahedral in form and is pointed below. The three peripheral cells divide transversely, radially and tangentially to form 2 to 3 cells thick wall in the venter portion of the archegonium.

The axial cell divides transversely into an inner **central cell** and an outer cell (D). Occasionally it may cut off one or two segments at the sides before undergoing transverse divisions. The central cell divides to give rise to the **egg** and the **ventral canal cell**. The outer cell which corresponds to

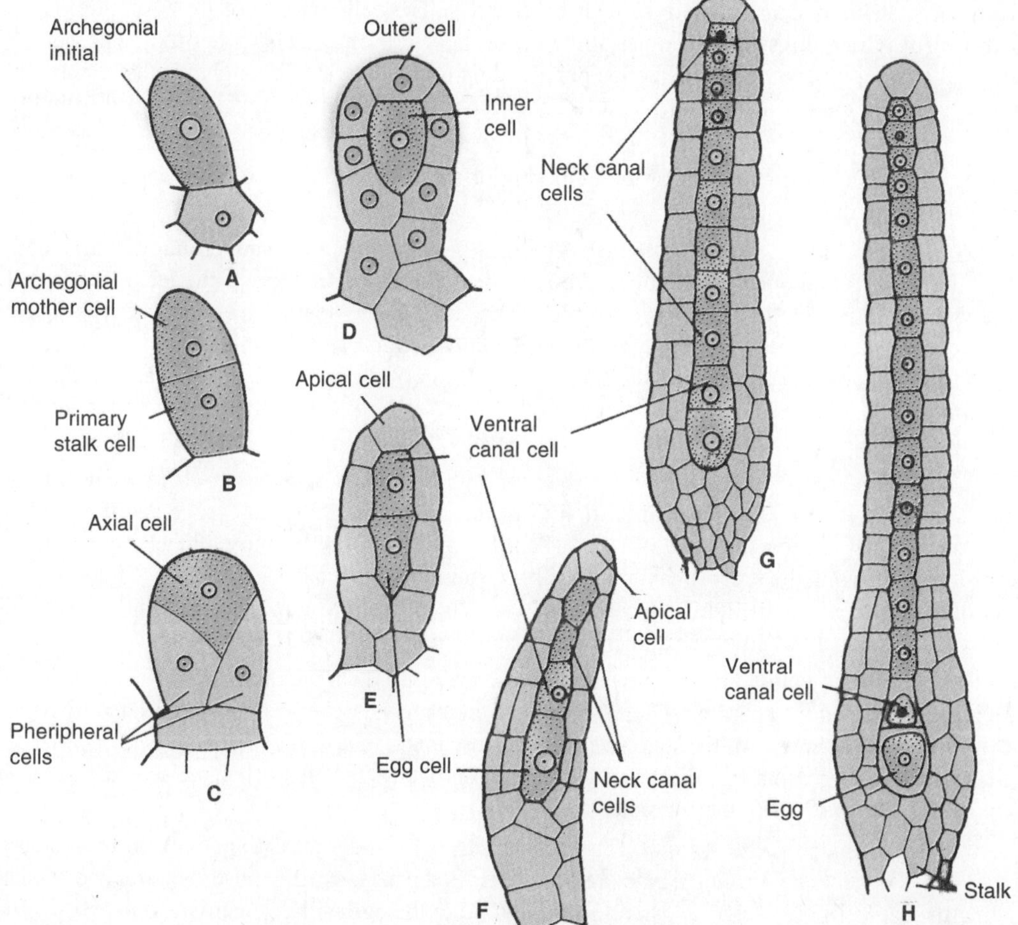

Fig. 20.12. (A—H). ***Polytrichum*** sp. A—F, early stages in the development of archegonium; G, young archegonium, H, nearly mature archegonium.

primary cover cell of the hepatics functions as the apical cell (E). It is five sided with four cutting faces and fifth side free. It cuts off 4 rows of segments, three lateral and one basal. The three rows of lateral or peripheral segments function as one basal segment. The three rows of lateral or peripheral segments function as **neck initials**. Each neck initial divides by a vertical wall. The 6 rows of neck cells thus formed constitute the neck of the archegonium. The neck cells in each row increase in number by transverse division. The archegonial neck which consists of 6 longitudinal rows of neck cells is one cell thick. The segments of the fourth basal row do not divide further. They form an axial row of **neck canal cells**.

Dehiscence of sex organs. The mature sex organs of *Polytrichum* dehisce like those of other bryophytes in the presence of moisture provided by rain or dew.

(a) Dehiscence of antheridium. The spermatogenous mass in the upper half of the mature antheridium contains sperms capable of swimming still coiled and enclosed within their respective vesicles. The lower half contains a sufficient charge of fluid under pressure to function in sperm release (Fig. 20.8). The antheridium opens only at its distal end. The distal opening is caused by alternations of the cell walls of the cells which occur at the tip of the antheridium. On the access of water present in the perigonial cup, the inner surface of the outer wall of certain cells at antheridial tip becomes mucilaginous and swells (Muggoch and Walton, 1942). The wall swellings fill the cell lumen and eventually cause rupture of their inner walls. The cell contents of these ruptured cells make their way into the sperm chamber at the tip of the sperm mass. Thereafter the outer wall of these cell also rupture resulting in an open pore leading to the exterior. Through this distal pore the antheridia empty their contents somewhat like the shaving cream being forcibly extruded from the tube.

Paolillo, Jr (1975) showed that the emptying of the antheridium (release of sperm vesicles) occurs in two phases, **rapid** and **slow**.

(i) Rapid phase of the sperm release. The jacket of the unopened antheridium is stretched. When the antheridium opens at the tip, there is sudden elastic contraction of the jacket layer that rapidly reduces the size of the sperm chamber. The fluid in the sperm chamber which is under pressure acts as a hydraulic ram. It causes the jacket contraction to expel rapidly and forcibly all or some of the viscous fluid containing the sperm vesicles out of the sperm chamber. The rapid phase of sperm release, which is the first to occur, is thus powered by elastic contraction of the jacket-layer. It is completed within a few seconds.

(ii) Slow phase of sperm release. The second phase of sperm release, which immediately follows the first, is slow. The residual portion of the sperm mass (if any) left at the anterior end, is discharged slowly during the next 1-5 mts. (Paolillo, Jr., 1975). After the rapid phase of sperm expulsion, the fluid in the sperm chamber acts as an osmotic sink. It takes up water by osmosis. The entry of more water into the fluid in the chamber would increase its volume causing expulsion of the residual mass of sperms out of the antheridium at a low rate (Paolillo, Jr. 1975, 1977).

Muggoch and Walton (1942) showed the presence of lipids in the discharged viscous fluid in which are embedded the sperm vesicles. Because of their physico-chemical properties, the lipids in the matrix cause the spread of the sperm vesicles rapidly into a thin film over the surface of water in the perigonial splash cup as the discharged sperm mass touches the air water interface. The sperms swim within the confines of their vesicles.

(b) Dehiscence of archegonium. The neck canal cells and ventral canal cell in the mature archegonium degenerate forming a mucilaginous mass in the neck canal. It absorbs water and swells forcing the cap cells to diverge. A passage way leading to the egg in the venter is formed.

Fertilization. *Polytrichum* is a dioecious moss. Fertilization is facilitated when the male and the female plants occur intertwined or occur within the range of maximum splash distance.

1. Harvey-Gibson and Miller Brown (1927) suggested that small insects such as mites, spring tails and midges which feed on mucilage secreted by the paraphyses transport sperms to a considerable distance from the perigonal cup to the archegonial cluster.

2. Splash cup mechanism. The perigonial bracts surrounding the terminal antheridial cluster lie close together and overlap thus forming a shallow cup-like structure. It serves as a **splash cup**. The presence of lipids in the released matrix containing the sperm vesicles causes rapid spread of the latter in a thin film over the surface of water that collects in the perigonial cup. Falling rain drops from a height would result in splashes coated with sperms travelling considerable distances. Brodie (1951) could experimentally disperse sperms from the splash cup of *P. ohioeuse* up to 2 ft.

Splashing drops or other agents of dispersal bring vesicles containing sperms to the archegonial cluster (female plants) where the vesicles dissolve. The sperms are released to swim into archegonia. The source of attraction is the cane sugar present in the slimy mass which oozes from the open archegonial necks. Only one sperm unites with the egg to accomplish fertilization. The fertilized egg secretes a wall around it to become an **oospore**.

Post fertilization changes. The diploid zygote-oospore is the first structure of the sporophyte generation. Located in the venter cavity, it increases in size and divides by a transverse wall into an upper and a lower cell. Each of these further divides by two successive intersecting walls establishing a wedge-shaped apical cell with two cutting faces at each end of the embryo. Henceforth the latter grows by the activity of two apical cells in opposite directions. They cut off segments alternately right and left.

The apical cell at the upper end is, however, more active. It cuts off segment in regular order and quick succession. The segments divide and redivide to form a spindle-shaped embryo. The division products of the lower apical cell form the slender foot which penetrates the archegonial stalk and the tip of the female gametophore. The derivatives of the apical cell at the upper end of the embryo form the seta and capsule. About one-fourth of the top region of the embryo derived from the apical cell forms the capsule and the rest three-fourth contributes to the formation of the seta.

With the stimulus of fertilization and increase in the size of the contained embryo, the lower part of the archegonium (venter) is stimulated to resume growth. The venter wall increases in circumference and becomes 4-6 cells in thickness. The expanding venter is now called the *calyptra*. It completely encloses the developing embryo. With the elongation of seta, the calyptra is ruptured at the base and is carried upwards as a cap or hood over the young capsule which it completely covers. The brown calyptra in *Polytrichum* is hairy. It is a haploid tissue. The capsule covered by calyptra is erect in position.

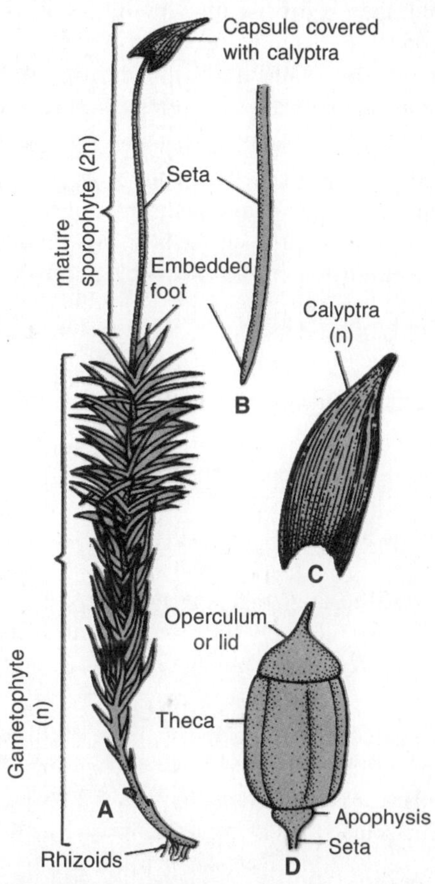

Fig. 20.13. (A—D). *Polytrichum*. A, female gametophore bearing terminally a nearly mature sporophyte; B, lower portion of seta ending in a dagger-shaped foot; C, calyptra, removed from the capsule; D, mature capsule.

Adult sporophyte (Fig. 20.13). The mature sporophyte (sporogonium) of *Polytrichum*, as in other mosses, is differentiated into foot, seta and capsule (A).

1. *Foot* (B). It is a dagger-shaped structure with more or less parallel sides and tapering tip. It is buried deep in the tip of the female gametophore (A). The foot consists of parenchyma cells rich in contents somewhat swollen than the seta cells. It functions as an anchoring and absorbing organ. "Transfer cells" are reported to occur only in the peripheral cells of the foot of *Polytrichum* sporophyte (Maier, 1967). The ingrowths in the peripheral cells of the foot of this moss are long and thread-like. They branch and even anastomose to form extensive veritable labyrinths of wall material. Causin *et al* (1983) reported that both the epidermal and subepidermal cells in the foot are characterized by very dense cytoplasm and internal cell wall ingrowths. These transfer cells are considered to enhance exchanges between the gametophyte and sporophyte. They facilitate absorption of not only carbohydrates and ions but also that of aminoacids.

2. *Seta*. The seta is a long, slender, stalk-like structure which carries the capsule at its distal end and is continuous at its proximal (lower) end with the foot. In *P. commune*, the seta is seldom more than 5 cm long and is nearly 0.5 mm in diameter. Support and conduction are its two functions. Structurally it consists of an outer layer of thick-walled cells constituting the **epidermis**. Within the epidermis is a band of **hypoderma** consisting of brown sclerenchymatous cells. Next to the hypodermis is the **cortex** consisting of green, thin-walled parenchymatous cells with intercellular spaces between them. Forming the core of the seta is a well-developed central strand of compactly arranged, thin-walled hydroid cells similar to but much simpler in structure than those of the stem.

Apophysis (D). Just below the capsule, the seta is considerably swollen to form a bulbous, sterile structure called the **apophysis**. The apophysis is thus situated at the base of the capsule but is demarcated from it by a distinct groove. It is specialized for photosynthesis. Structurally (Fig. 20.14 A) it consists of a single layer of well-defined epidermis continuous with the epidermis of seta below. It has stomata which are confined to the region of the groove only. The stomatal aperture is guarded usually by two and occasionally by one ring-shaped guard cell. Next to the epidermis is the chlorenchyma consisting of a mass of loosely arranged thin-walled parenchymatous cells containing chloroplasts. The hypodermis is absent in the apophysis region. In the centre is the conducting strand continuous with the columella above (Fig. 20. 14 A).

3. *Capsule* (Fig. 20.13 A). Perched at the distal end of the seta above the apophysis is the capsule. It is erect in position and almost completely covered by the brown, coccullate **calyptra** with a hairy surface even when nearly mature. In form the capsule is angular and almost squarish in outline in a cross section (Fig. 2014 B). It functions in the production of haploid spores (meiospores or gonospores) and their dispersal. The capsule in *Polytrichum* is differentiated into two regions (Fig. 20.13 D), (*i*) the lower, larger spore bearing angular portion forming the body of the capsule called the **theca** and (*ii*) a sterile, conical portion forming the **lid** or **operculum** as its free distal end. The operculum has a long beak or rostrum. It becomes visible only when calyptra (C) falls off.

Structure of theca (Fig. 20.14). There is several cell layers thick *theca* or **capsule wall** (A). The outermost layer of the wall consists of compactly arranged cells with their outer walls appreciably thickened. It is the **epidermis**. The epidermis in the capsule region lacks stomata. Next to the epidermis is the **chlorophyll tissue** typically 2-celled in thickness. It consists of thin-walled parenchymatous cells containing chloroplasts. Within the theca wall is the **outer air space**. It is traversed by short filaments of green cells called the **trabeculae**. The trabeculae connect the theca wall with the two cell-layer thick **outer wall of the spore sac**. Internal to the spore sac is **inner air space**. It is also traversed by trabeculae which connect the two cell layer thick **inner wall of the spore sac** to the central column of sterile cells constituting the **columella**. The spore sac is thus bounded by a double wall both at its outer and inner face and is surrounded by a double air space system. The archesporium originates in the young capsule as a single layer from the outer layer of the endothecium and extends to the base of the capsule. Later it divides to form 4-6 layers of **sporogenous tissue.** All the cells of the sporogenous tissue are fertile. They separate and round off to form the **spore mother cells** which are diploid. The diploid protoplast of each spore mother cell undergoes **meiosis** to form 4 **haploid spores** or **meiospores**. In the centre of the theca region is a solid core of sterile tissue forming the columella. It is continuous below with the central strand of seta and extends above into the opercular region to form a shield-shaped membrane, the **epiphragm** at the base of the operculum. The columella is squarish in outline in a cross section (Fig. 20.14 B). The cells at the periphery of the columella may become photosynthetic in function.

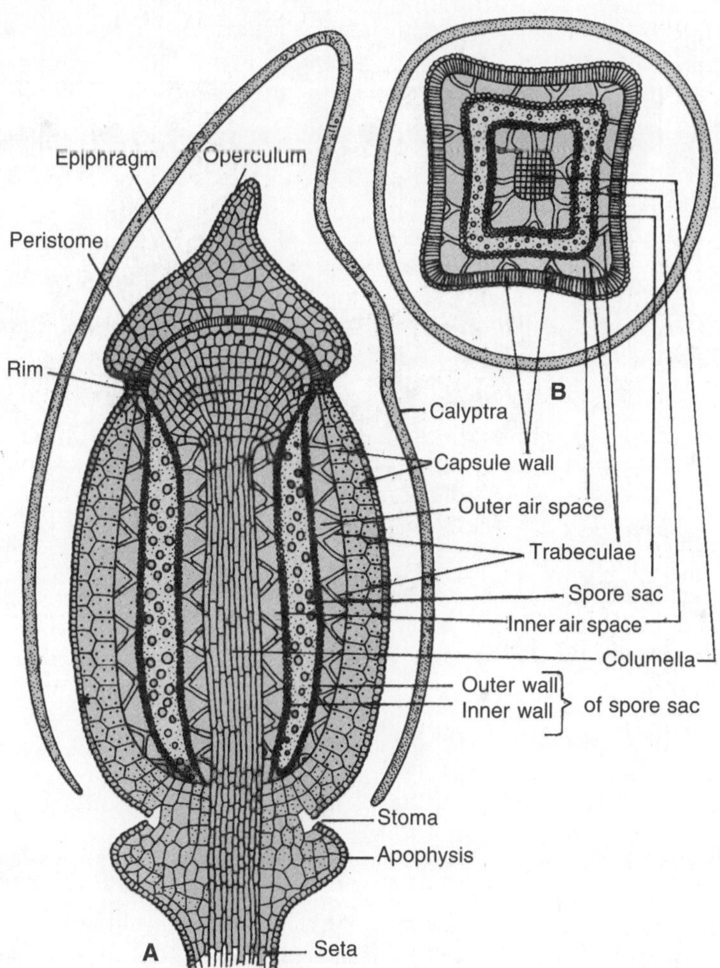

Fig. 20.14 (A—B). *Polytrichum*. A, L.S. capsule showing structure; B, T.S. capsule through the theca region.

Structure of operculum or lid (Fig. 20.14 A). It is the terminal, conical portion of the capsule which fits like a cap or lid at the mouth of the theca region. In *Polytrichum*, the operculum is produced into a long beak or rostrum at its free, distal end. It is delimited from the theca region by a narrow circular constriction in the nearly mature capsule. At the base of the constriction there are 2-3 layers of radially elongated thick-walled cells forming the **rim** or **diaphragm**. The latter constitutes the upper end of the theca. The annulus is absent. At the base of the operculum stretching like the tympanum of a drum across the mouth of the theca and thus closing it is a thin, shield-shaped pale membranous structure known as the **epiphragm**. It is a fan-shaped expansion of the columella in the opercular region.

Peristome (Fig. 20.15 F—G). (*a*) *Structure*. The peristome in the moss capsule regulates and slows the rate of spore discharge. In *Polytrichum* it is nematodontous type and consists of a ring of 64 short, stout pyramidal teeth which are solid structures (F). Each peristome tooth (G) is composed of curved crescent-shaped, thickened, fibre-like cells, several layers in thickness and thus differs markedly from that of *Funaria* which consists merely of strips of cuticle. In a mature peristome, each tooth often has a coloured longitudinal axis or a central pillar-like structure (G). At their tips, the teeth are joined to the margin of the epiphragm and arise from the rim or diaphragm (F). They do not exhibit hygroscopic movements.

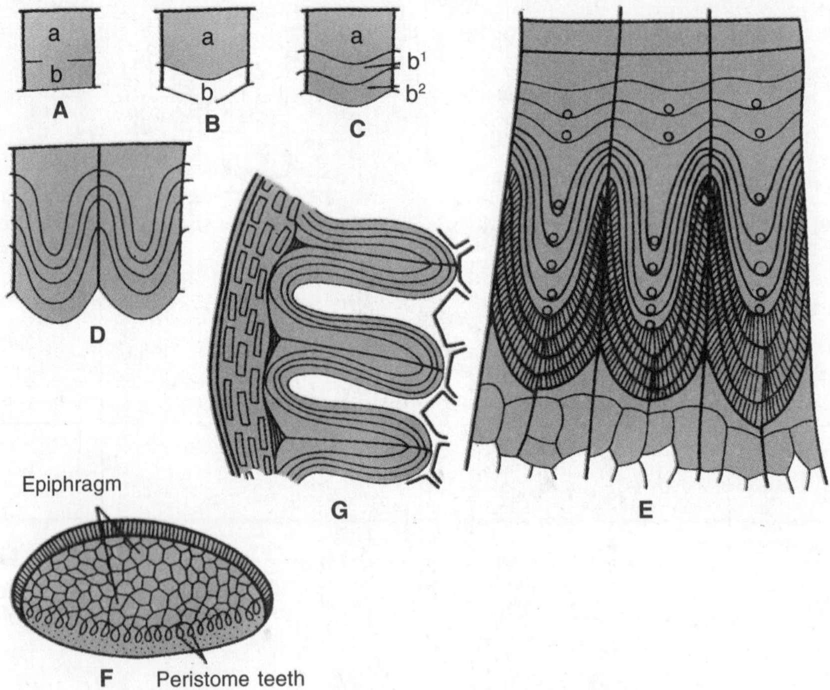

Fig. 20.15. (A—G). ***Polytrichum***. A—E, successive stages in the development of peristome; F, peristome teeth and epiphragm; G, enlarged view of peristome teeth.

(*b*) *Development* (Fig. 20.15). The peristome primordium originates in the inner zone of amphithecium. According to Cavers (1911), the initials which produce the peristome in *Polytrichum* are one cell high and are arranged in the form of a ring. Each initial divides by curved walls several times so as to form bundles of curved, crescent-shaped cells (A—E). The ends of crescents are directed upwards and are joined with the ends of the adjacent horse-shoe shaped bundles to constitute a ring of 64 short, solid, pyramidal teeth which are not hygroscopic. Each tooth is thus formed by the union of a number of the opposite arms of the adjacent U-shaped cells.

According to Chopra and Sharma (1958) and Chopra and Bhandare (1959), who studied the development of peristome in *Pogonatum* (Fig. 20.16), the peristome develops from several concentric rings of cells of the amphithecium except the outermost just below the operculum. The peristome initials are several (5-7) cells high, from the very beginning. They have dense contents and upward oblique orientation. The initial rows of cells appear in 32 radially arranged sectors in *Pogonatum*. Each initial divides by a vertical wall to cut off a small cell on either side. The smaller cells on either side of the larger central cells increase in number by repeated division. So do the larger cells. At this stage alternating groups of smaller and larger rectangular cells are recognisable (A). During further development the smaller and the larger cells elongate. The latter become U-shaped with their ends joined and glued with the free ends of similar cells on the right and left to form the teeth. The smaller cells elongate to form the supporting central pillar consisting of thick-walled narrow cells in each mature peristome tooth (B).

Dispersal of spores. (Fig. 20.17). In a mature capsule, the central, non-sporogenous tissue, (excepting the spores) degenerates. The spores come to lie in the hollow capsule and are ready for dispersal. The calyptra falls off. The exposed mature capsule begins to dry. Subsequently the lid also drops off exposing the peristome (A). At this stage the capsule becomes horizontal in position due to the curvature of the seta below the apophysis. Minute holes appear between the successive peristome teeth in the margin of the epiphragm by the drying up of thin-walled cells between them. The minute spores are dispersed, a few at a time through these pores by a censer mechanism (as the capsule sways in the wind). The spore discharge is also regulated by the up and down movements of the epiphragm which stretches like a drum head-like covering over the mouth of the theca.

Spores. The small yellow spores have a smooth surface and attain a diameter of 10-11 μm which is roughly equal to that of the spore mother cell. The spore wall is differentiated into two layers, the outer **exospore** and the inner **endospore**. The reserve food is in the form of globules in the spore cytoplasm. The number of plastids varies from 2-4.

Fine structure of spore (Fig. 20.11). (*a*) *Spore wall*. The study of fine structure of the spore wall of mature spore of *Polytrichum* (by McClymont and Larsen, 1964 and Olesan and Magensen, 1978), revealed that it consists of four layers. Three of these namely, intine, exine and perine are distinct. Whether the fourth electron opaque "separating layer", which is normally present between the intine and the exine, is present all over the spore wall or not could not be determined.

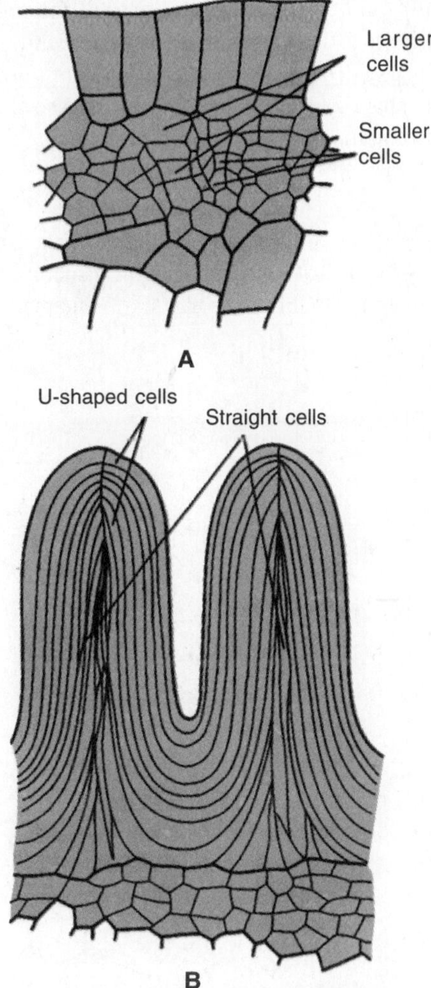

Fig. 20.16. (A—B). ***Pogonatum***. Two stages in the development of peristome (After Chopra & Sharma).

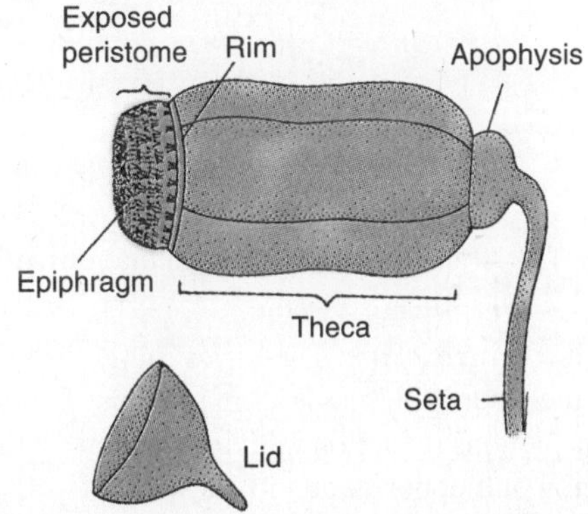

Fig. 20.17. *Polytrichum*. Dehiscence of capsule and dispersal of spores.

Intine. The innermost layer of the spore wall which encloses the protoplast is termed as the **intine**. It is fibrillar in texture and electron-translucent. It includes the carbohydrate materials including cellulose. The intine is not of uniform thickness all over the spore wall but shows a conspicuous disc-shaped local thickening towards the slightly flattened area of the sub-spherical spore. Situated between the disc-shaped intine thickening and the plasma membrane is a knob-like structure of wall material.

Exine. It is a conspicuous, non-stratified layer of medium electron density resistant to acetolysis. Just outside the disc shaped intine thickening, the exine is markedly thinner than in the rest of the spore wall. In *Polytrichum* exine structurally enters into the formation of ornamentation. It forms the bases of "Christmas tree like" ornamentation of the perine.

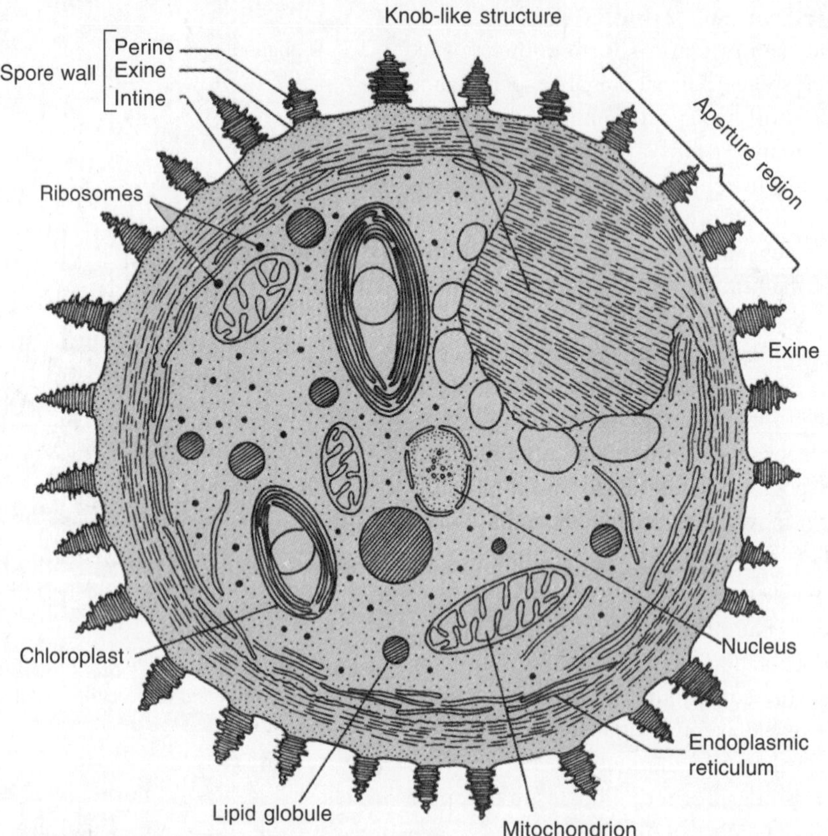

Fig. 20.18. *Polytrichum*. Diagrammatic representation of fine structure of the spore.

Perine. It is the outermost extremely opaque layer of the spore wall. It forms the major part of the "Christmas tree-like" ornamentation with exine forming the bases.

Aperture region of the spore. There is no externally differentiated aperture region on the spore wall of *Polytrichum*. The ultrastructural study of the spore wall, however, revealed that on one side of the spore there is a conspicuous disc-shaped local thickening of intine accompanied by a conspicuous reduction in exine thickening than in the rest of the spore wall. This specially modified region of the spore wall indicates the position where the spore germinates and the germ tube emerges. Despite the absence of any external evidence, this well-defined region in the spore wall has been termed the **aperture region**. Olesen and Magensen (1978) reported that the aperture region of *Polytrichum* spore exhibits five characteristic features. These are : (*i*) pronounced reduction in exine thickness, (*ii*) presence of a lamellate structure in the intine subjacent to thin part of exine, (*iii*) a very thin electron dense "separating" layer of wall material present between the exine and intine, (*iv*) drastic thickening of the intine into a disc-shaped structure more pronounced than in *Funaria hygrometrica* and (*v*) presence of a peculiar knoblike structure of wall material between the disc-shaped intine thickening and the plasma membrane.

(*b*) *Spore protoplast.* Besides the centrally located nucleus, the cytoplasm contains mitochondria and granular endoplasmic reticulum. It is rich in ribosomes. The reserve food is in the form of a large number of lipid droplets, sometimes coalesced into a single large lipid body. The cytoplasm lacks vacuoles. The number of plastids varies from 2-4. On remoistening the yellow, unruptured spores turn bright green in colour. The green plastids or chloroplasts have well developed grana lamellae (Paolillo, 1969 and Karunen 1972) and are rich in chlorophylls and carotenoids (Karunen, 1971). Karunen and Ihantola (1977) reported that the chief caroteinoids are carotenes, violaxanthin, lutein, antheraxanthin, neoxanthin and zeaxanthin.

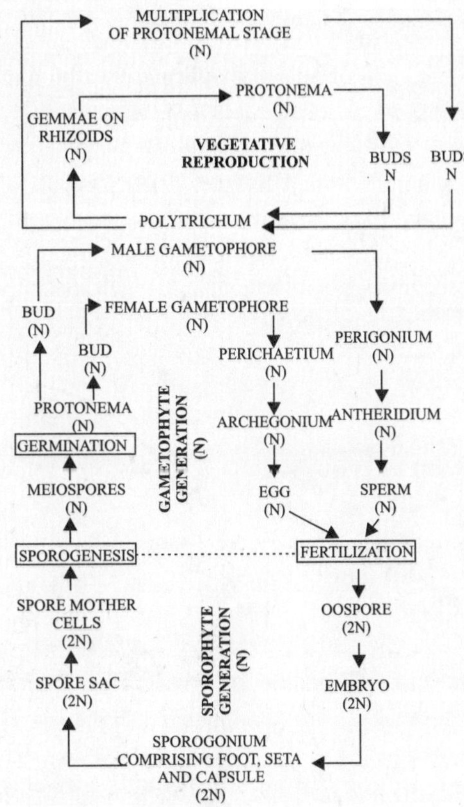

Fig. 20.19. ***Polytrichum***. Graphic representation of the life cycle.

Germination of spores. On landing on a suitable substratum, the spore takes up water. It mainly enters through the aperture region. Consequently the spore increases in size considerably. Olesen and Magensen (1978) reported that besides, some general swelling of the unthickened part of the intine, there is drastic swelling of the disc-shaped intine thickening of the aperture region. It is about two to three fold and thus causes the exine rupture at the centre of the aperture region where it is the thinnest. The rupture is considered to be a mechanical fracture (Olesen and Magensen, 1978). Following exine rupture, the lamellate structure and the separating layer disappear and the disc-shaped intine thickening protrudes. The knob-like structure located between the plasma membrane and the thickened intine also gradually diminishes. After the protrusion of the intine (protrusion phase) the distension phase begins during which the spore protoplast surrounded by the intine emerges through the rupture in the form of a small germ tube.

Formation of protonema. The germ tube grows actively and soon produces a richly branched, septate, filamentous *protonema*. The growth of the filament is apical. The branch may arise from any cell of the filament near the anterior end. The protonema forms a green mat-like dense growth on the substratum. Some of the branches of the protonema are **rhizoidal**. They are comparatively narrow, have no chloroplasts and show little contents. The colourless rhizoidal branches grow down into the soil and have oblique cross walls between the cells. Other branches of the filament are green. They are known as the **chloronemal branches**. They spread over the surface of the substratum. The cells of the chloronemal branches contain chloroplasts and have straight transverse septa between them. Several buds may grow on a fully developed protonema formed from a single spore. Each bud by the activity of its pyramidal apical cell (with three cutting faces at the sides) grows into a future erect, leafy gametophore. The first formed leaves are different from the typical leaves. The latter appear in the third year on the young gametophore.

SYSTEMATIC POSITION OF *POLYTRICHUM*

Division	:	Bryophyta
Class	:	Bryopsida (Musci or Mosses)
Sub-class	:	Bryidae
Order	:	Polytrichales
Family	:	Polytrichaceae
Genus	:	*Polytrichum*
Species	:	*commune*

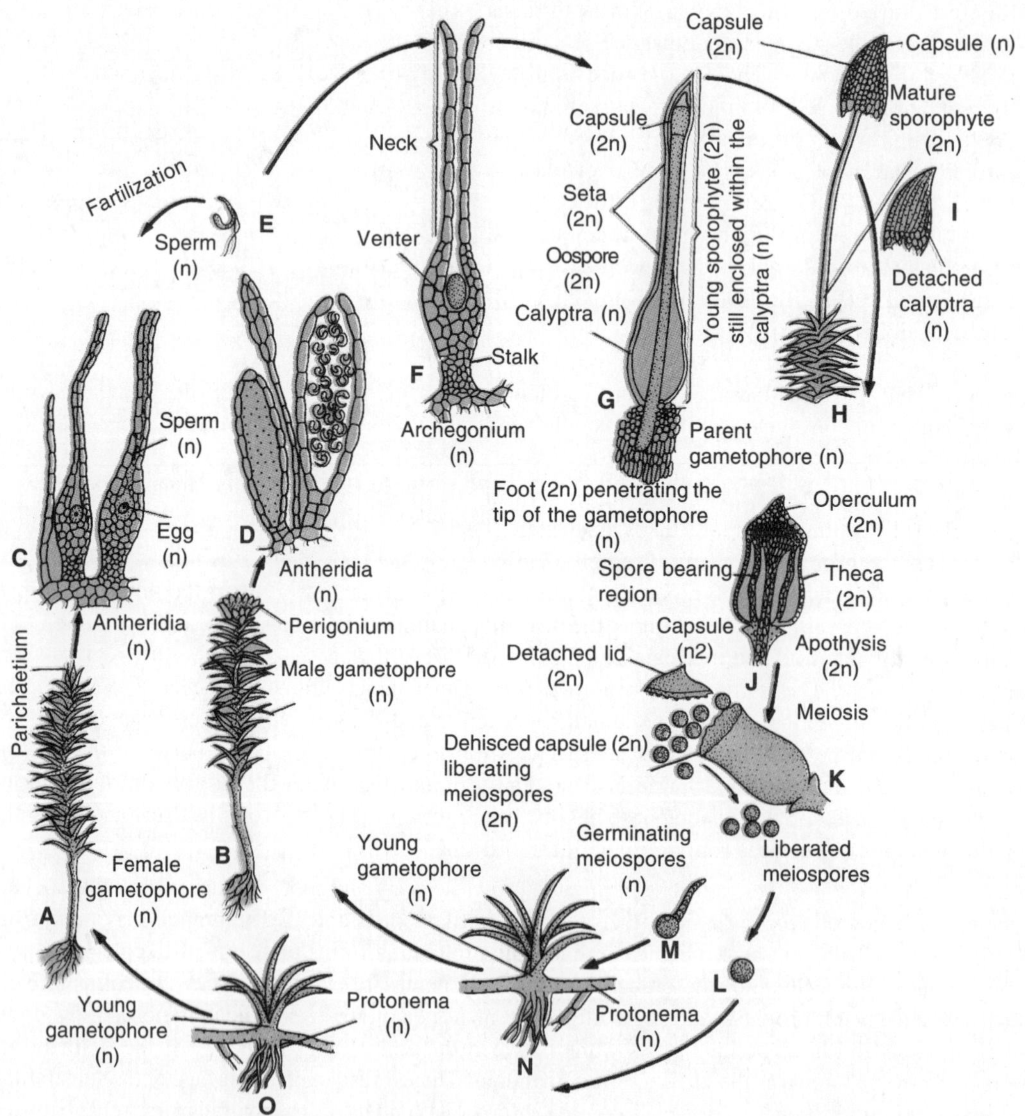

Fig. 20.20. (A—O). ***Polytrichum***. Diagrammatic representation of the sexual life cycle.

Economic Importance

Rogue (1941) reported that tea made of *Polytrichum commune* helps to dissolve stones of kidney and gall bladder. The ancients used decoction of this moss to strengthen and beautify ladies' tresses. The Laplanders used bed and bedding of this moss. The moss bed could be rolled and carried from place to place. The hair-cap mosses were also used for stuffing mattresses and upholstery (Welch, 1949). The central core of the long stems (about 1`2 to 18 inches or even more) of this moss, when cleansed, forms a flexible tough strand. These strands were used to make brooms, and brushes. Plaited articles such as baskets, mats and rugs were also made out of them. The broom made out of the well combed stems divested of their outer skin is soft and flexible. It is called the **besom**. The besoms were well suited for dusting beds, carpets, and curtains.

POGONATUM

Polytrichum and *Pogonatum* are more close to each other in gametophytic characters than in sporophytic characters. Probably due to these similarities some bryologists like Dixon 1932 and Watson 1955 have described all the species of *Pogonatum* under the composite genus *Polytrichum*. Later some morpho-taxonomic investigations exclusively made on the sporophyte have strengthened the concept to create a separate genus *Pogonatum* from several previously known species of *Polytrichum*. At present, the status of the genus *Pogonatum* has been universally accepted as an independent and separate genus. Hence the genus *Poganatum* is briefly discussed here.

The genus *Pogonatum* is the largest genus of the family Polytrichaceae and is represented by 158 species which are distributed all over the world. From India about 23 species have been reported most of them growing on hills. The species show dominance in eastern and western himalayas. Some important species of the genus *Pogonatum* are :—

(*i*) *Pogonatum aloides*, (*ii*) *P. junghuhnianum* (*iii*) *P. microstomium*, (*iv*) *P. perichaetiale* (*v*) *P. stevensii*.

Comparison of *Pogonatum* and *Polytrichum*

A comparative account of *Pogonatum* and *Polytrichum* is as follows :—

Resemblances :

A. The *gametophyte*.

1. The general habit of both the genera is similar.

2. Rhizome is perennial and well developed from which arises upwardly growing erect stems which are less branched. They altogether form a thick mat like cushions mostly on hills.

3. The leaves have sheathing leaf base and are spirally arranged on the stem. The leaves have distinct thick midrib which bears lamina (wings) on its sides

4. The rhizoids are similar.

5. In anatomy, rhizome and stem are similar.

6. The vegetative reproduction in both the genera is by gemmae produced on the rhizoids, by secondary protonema and by fragmentation of the rhizome.

7. The structure and development of sex organs (both antheridia and archegonia) is same.

8. The process of fertilization is also same in both the genera

B. The *Sporophyte* :

1. In both the genera the sporophyte has foot, seta and capsule.

2. The development of sporophyte is more or less similar in both.

3. The peristome teeth are nematodontous type in both.

4. The spore-sac is surrounded from all the sides (outer and inner) by outer air space (outer lacuna) and by inner air space (inner lacuna) which are traversed by trabeculae.

5. The columella is present in both.

6. The upper part of columella is in contact with drum-shaped epiphragm (Tympanum).

7. At the maturity of the capsule, the calyptra becomes brown and forms a dry fibrous hairy hood or cap covering the capsule. Due to presence of hairy cap both the genera are also known as hairy mosses.

8. In both the genera the spores are liberated through the minute holes in the epiphragm which is present in between the peristomial teeth.

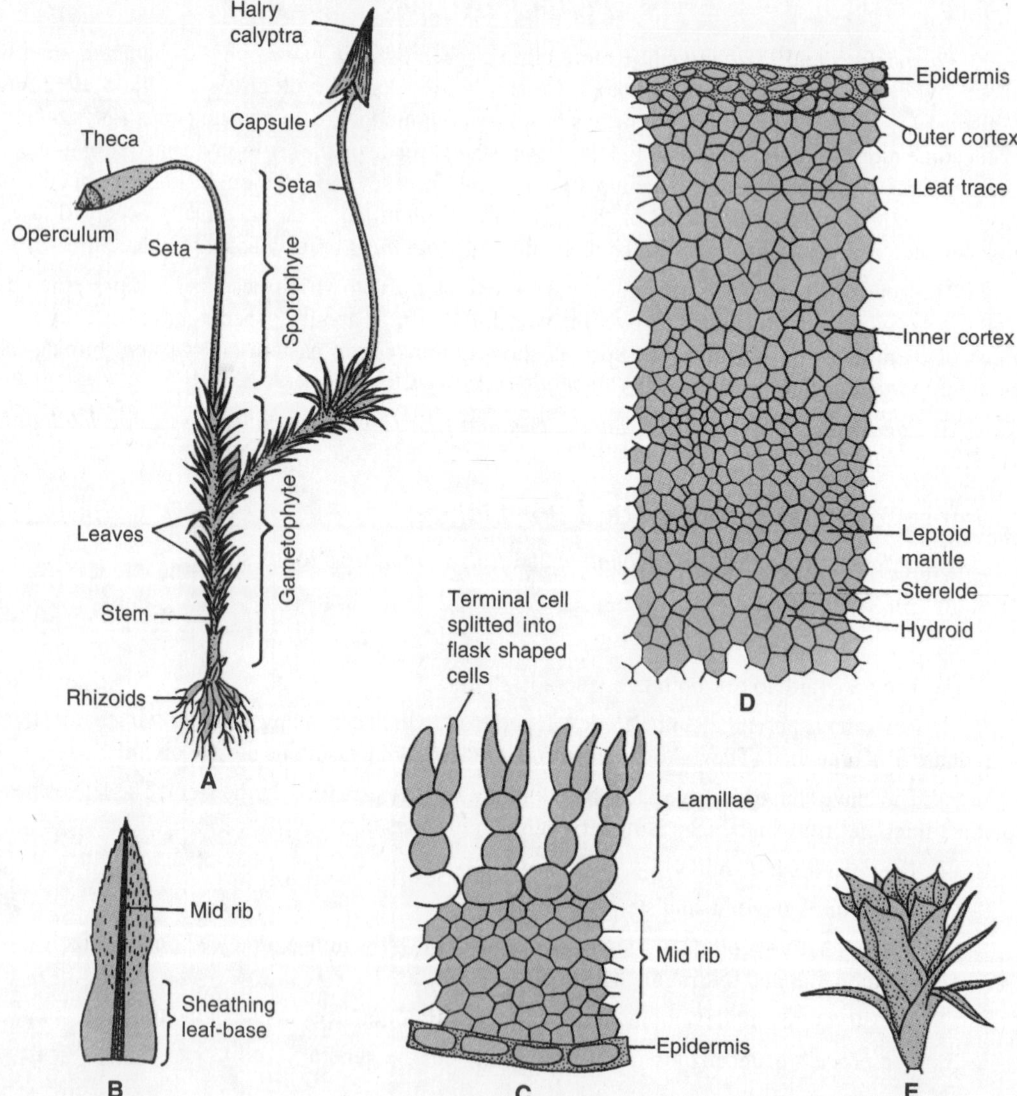

Fig. 20.21. (A-E). ***Pogonatum***. A, female plant with sporophyte; B, a leaf; C, T.S. of leaf in part; D, T.S. of stem; E, antheridial head.

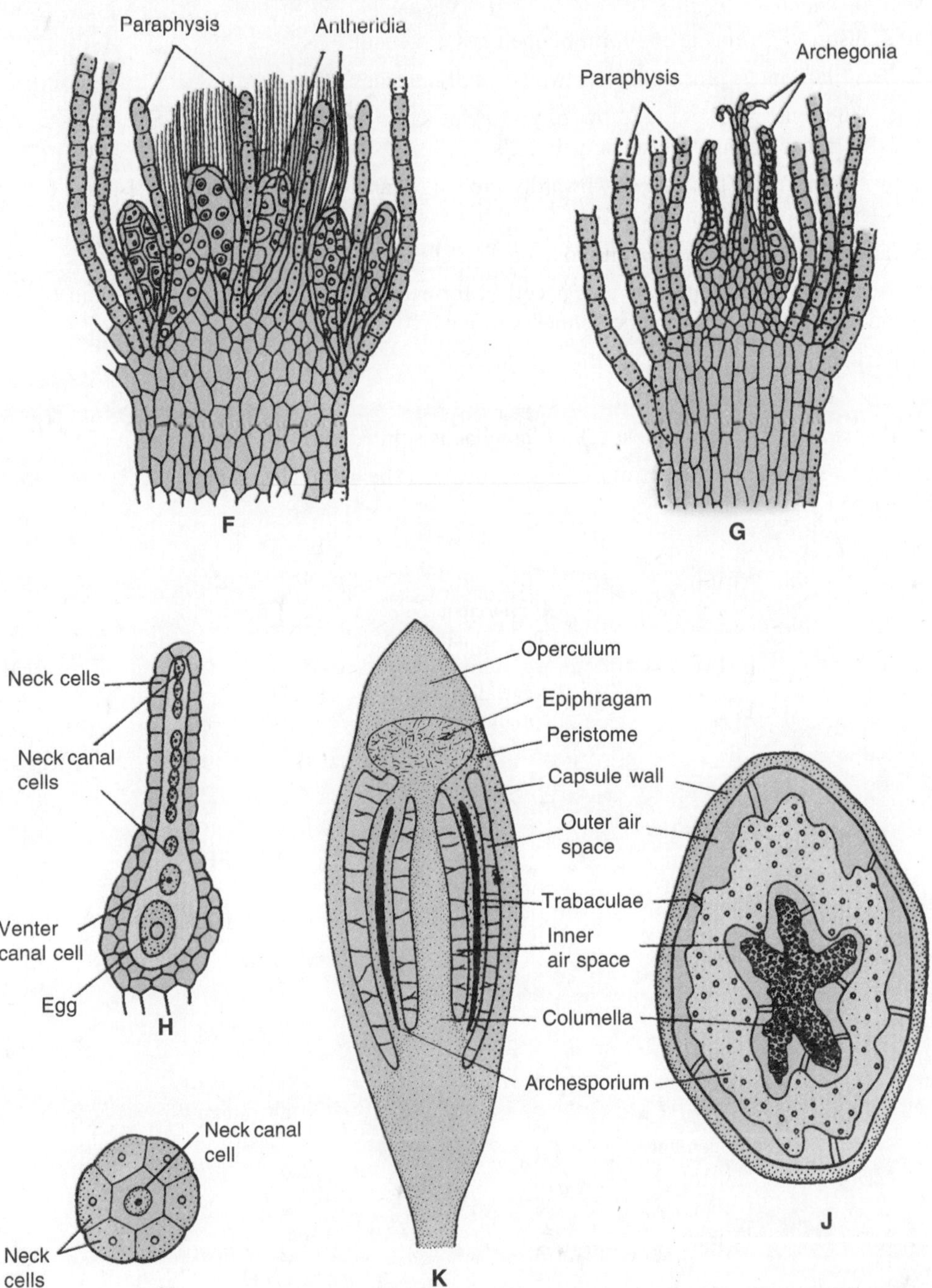

Fig. 20.21. (F-K). ***Pogonatum***. F, L.S. antheridial head; G, L.S. archegonial head; H, an archegonium; I, T.S. neck of archegonium; J, T.S. capsule; K, L.S. capsule

C. The *Protonema* :

1. The spores germinate and form filamentous protonema
2. The filamentous protonema has two types of branches.
   (*a*) Chloronema. These are upwardly growing erect branches which are green due to the presence of chloroplasts in their cells.
   (*b*) Caulonema. These are downwardly growing branches which are colourless and act as hizods.
3. The buds are produced on chloronema.

4. A pyramidal (tetrahedral) apical cell is formed. It has three cutting faces and by its meristematic activity the whole gametophore is formed.

Differences

A. The *Gametophyte*

In *Pogonatum*. The upper most cell of lamellae is splitted into two flask-shaped cells

but in *Polytrichum* the upper most cell of lamellae is being notched due to which it becomes crescent shaped.

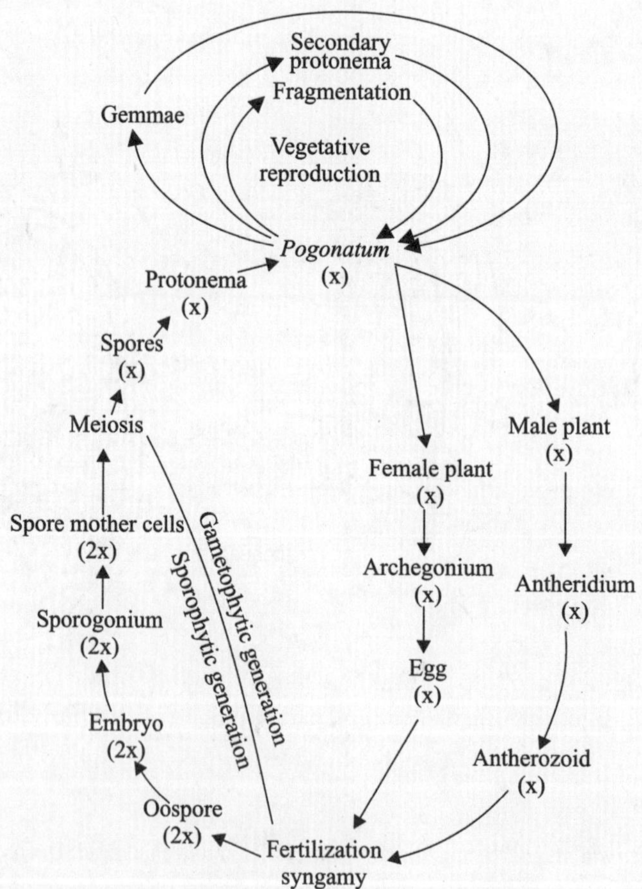

Fig. 20.22. ***Pogonatum***. Word diagram of Life-cycle.

B. The Sporophyte.

Pogonatum	*Polytrichum*
1. In transverse section, the capsule appears move or less round.	1. In transverse section the capsule appears angular (mostly quadrangular).
2. The stomata are absent in the capsule.	2. The stomata are present on the capsule.
3. The apophysis is not well-marked.	3. Apophysis is well marked.
4. In T.S., the columella forms wing-like out growths.	4. In T.S. the columella is cylindrical and wings are not formed.
5. The peristome teeth are up to 32	5. Peristome teeth are up to 64.

SYSTEMATIC POSITION OF *POGONATUM*

Division	:	Bryophyta
Class	:	Bryopsida
Sub-class	:	Bryidae
Order	:	Polytrichales
Family	:	Polytrichaceae
Genus	:	*Pogonatum*
Species	:	*aloides*

QUESTIONS

ESSAY TYPE

1. Give a comparative account of sporophyte of *Sphagnum* and *Pogonatum.* *(Poorvanchal, 1999; Gorakhpur, 1998)*
2. Give an account of external and internal structure of gametophyte of *Pogonatum.* *(Lucknow, 1993)*
3. Describe the adult gametophyte of *Pogonatum*. In what respects does it differ from the adult gametophyte of *Frullania*? *(Lucknow, 1996)*
4. Give a comparative account of the adult gametophytes of *Pogonatum* and *Frullania.* *(Lucknow, 2001)*
5. Give an illustrated account of the external morphology and anatomy of gametophytic thallus of *Marchantia* and *Pogonatum.* *(Kumaon, 2000)*
6. Give a comparative and illustrated account of the adult gametophyte of *Pogonatum* and *Porella*. *(Gorakhpur, 1996)*
7. Give a comparative account of the gametophytes of *Sphagnum* and *Pogonatum* *(Gorakhpur, 1998)*
8. With the help of diagrams, describe
   (*i*) the spore dispersal mechanism in *Pogonatum.* *(Rohilkhand, 1992)*
   (*ii*) antheridium of *Pogonatum.* *(Rohilkhand, 1993, 1994)*
   (*iii*) sporophyte of *Pogonatum.* *(Rohilkhand, 1997)*
   (*iv*) adult plant of *Pogonatum.* *(Lucknow, 2003)*
   (*v*) capsule in *Polytrichum.* *(Andhra Pradesh, 2002)*
   (*vi*) development of sporophyte in Pogonatum. *(Kanpur, M.Sc. 2003)*
9. Give a comparative account of the sex organs of *Pellia*, *Anthoceros* and *Pogonatum.* *(Rohilkhand, 1997)*

10. What do you understand by alternation of generation? Explain it on the basis of life-cycle of *Pogonatum*. *(Rohilkhand, 2000)*

11. Describe in brief :
    (*a*) *Pogonatum* *(Kanpur M.Sc., 1990, 1995)*
    (*b*) *Polytrichum*

12. Describe different types of peristome structure met within mosses. Discuss taxonomic importance of peristome. *(Kanpur M.Sc., 1993)*

13. What is Peristome? Discuss the structural variations of peristomes in mosses with suitable examples and diagrams. *(Kanpur M.Sc., 1995)*

14. How will you distinguish Funariales, Buxbaumiales and Polytrichales on the basis of sporophytic characters? *(Kanpur M.Sc., 1999)*

15. Mention salient features of gametophyte of *Pogonatum*. *(Magadh, 1996; Vir Kumar Singh, 1998)*

16. Compare the sporophyte of *Anthoceros* with that of *Polytrichum*. *(Bharathidasan, 1995)*

17. Describe the internal structure of aerial stem in *Polytrichum*. *(Punjab, 1992)*

18. Describe giving suitable diagrams the various vegetative methods of reproduction in *Riccia*, *Pellia* and *Polytrichum*. *(Ravi Shankar, 1996)*

19. Draw labelled diagrams of sporophyte of *Polytrichum* and *Marchantia* and give a comparative account of these structures. *(Ravi Shankar, 1995)*

20. Explain the structure of the sporophyte of *Anthoceros* and *Polytrichum* only with their diagrams *(Ravi Shankar, 1993)*

21. Describe in detail the structure of sporophyte of *Polytrichum*. *(Calicat, 2004; Nagpur, 1996)*

22. Give an account of the life history of *Polytrichum*.

23. Write an illustrated account of sporophyte of *Polytrichum*. *(Osmania, 1991)*

24. With the help of labelled diagrams only describe life cycle of *Polytrichum*.

25. Give an illustrated account of the capsule of *Polytrichum*.

26. Give an account of the external features of gametophyte of *Polytrichum*.

27. Describe the anatomy of rhizome and aerial stem of *Polytrichum* and state the functions of various tissues comprising it.

28. Draw labelled diagrams of Sporophytes of *Riccia* and *Pogonatum*. *(Rohilkhand, 2003)*

29. Describe in detail the external and internal structure of adult gametophyte of Pogonatum. *(Lucknow, 2002)*

SHORT ANSWER TYPE

30. **Write notes on the following :**
    (*a*) Sex organs of *Pogonatum* *(Poorvanchal, 1997)*
    (*b*) Thallus of *Pogonatum* *(Vir Kumar Singh, 1992)*
    (*c*) Dispersal of spores in *Pogonatum* *(Poorvanchal, 1999; Mahatma Gandhi, 1998; Kerala, 1996)*
    (*d*) *Pogonatum* leaf *(Lucknow, 1998; Kanpur M.Sc., 1995)*
    (*e*) *Sporophyte* of *Pogonatum* *(Kumaon, 1998; Gorakhpur 1994; Rohilkhand, 1995)*
    (*f*) Peristome of *Pogonatum* *(Lucknow, 2006 Gorakhpur, 1990)*
    (*g*) Sporogenous tissue in *Pogonatum* *(Gorakhpur, 1997)*
    (*h*) Protonemal stage of *Pogonatum* *(Gorakhpur, 1993; Rohilkhand, 1996)*
    (*i*) Mode of conduction of water in mosses. *(Kanpur M.Sc., 1997, 2000)*
    (*j*) Affinities between Andreales and Polytrichales *(Rohilkhand M.Sc., 1994)*
    (*k*) *Sporophyte* of *Polytrichum* *(Rohilkhand M.Sc., 1997)*

(*l*) Function of apophysis in the sporophyte of *Pogonatum*

(*m*) Gametophyte of *Polytrichum* *(Guru Nanak Dev, 1991)*

(*n*) Sporogonium of *Polytrichum* *(Nagpur, 1995)*

(*o*) T.S. of stem axis of *Pogonatum* *(Vinoba Bhave, 1997)*

(*p*) Rhizome of *Polytrichum* *(Osmania, 1992)*

(*q*) Capsule of *Polytrichum* *(Kakatiya, 1991)*

(*r*) Calyptra

(*s*) Physiology of Bud formation on the Protonema of mosses *(Rohilkhand M.Sc., 1993)*

(*t*) Capsule of pogonatum *(Lucknow, 2006)*

(*u*) Protonema *(Lucknow, 2006)*

31. Compare the external morphology of the thalli of *Porella*, *Sphagnum* and *Pogonatum.* *(Gorakhpur 1994)*

32. Write a brief note on the sporophyte of *Polytrichum.* *(Mahatma Gandhi, 1998)*

33. Name the genus known as "spike moss" .

34. Describe dehiscence of capsule in *Polytrichum.* *(Maharshi Dayanand Saraswati Ajmer, 1998)*

35. Discuss the gametophytic generations of *Sphagnum* and *Pogonatum*.*(Bihar, 1991)*

36. Name a moss in which the gemmae are produced on rhizoids.

37. Write a brief account of the internal structure of stem of *Polytrichum*.

38. List the characteristic features of the order Polytrichales.

39. Name at least five species of *Polytrichum* found in Himalayas.

40. The stem of *Pogonatum* is said to be comparable to that of vascular plant in function but not in structure, why?

41. Which organ in the sporogonium of *Pogonatum* regulates the spore dispersal?

42. Draw well labelled diagrams of the following :

(*i*) L.S. Sporophyte of *Pogonatum.* *(Poorvanchal 1998; Gorakhpur, 1992, 1995, 1998; Bhagalpur, 1990)*

(*ii*) T.S. of axis rhizome of *Pogonatum* *(Lucknow, 2006, Poorvanchal, 1999)*

(*iii*) T.S. Sporophyte of *Pogonatum* *(Lucknow, 1994)*

(*iv*) T.S. leaf of *Pogonatum* *(Lucknow, 1995, 1997; Gorakhpur, 1999)*

(*v*) Apical notch L.S. of *Pogonatum* thallus showing reproductive organs. *(Kumaon, 2001)*

(*vi*) Mature archegonium of *Polytrichum* *(Maharshi Dayanand Saraswati, Ajmer, 1998)*

(*vii*) T.S. of leaf of *Polytrichum.* *(Osmania, 1990; Shri Venkateshwara, 1991)*

(*viii*) L.S. Sporophyte of *Polytrichum.* *(Osmania, 1993)*

(*ix*) L.S. Capsule of Pogonatum. *(Lucknow, 2002)*

(*x*) Peristome of Pogonatum *(Lucknow, 2005)*

(*xi*) Gametophyte of Pogonatum *(Lucknow, 2008)*

43. Write systematic position of *Pogonatum.* *(Lucknow, 2006; Gorakhpur 1994, 1997, 1998, Poorvanchal, 1999)*

44. What are leptoids? *(Awadh, 1993)*

45. Name a bryophyte which has a cluster of archegonia at its female plant.

46. Name a bryophyte whose sporophyte is cylindrical and partially independent. *(Gorakhpur, 1990)*

47. Name the bryophyte having its sporophyte partially parasitic on its gametophyte. *(Gorakhpur, 1994)*

48. Give an illustrated account of adult plant of pogonatum *(Lucknow, 2005)*

49. How would you distinguish the protonema of moss from a filamentous green alga?

50. What is the difference between rhizoids of liverworts and mosses?

51. Name the bryophyte in which epiphragm is present.

52. Give the number of layers found in the spore wall of *Pogonatum*. *(Rohilkhand, 1994)*

53. How will you distinguish *Sphagnum* from *Polytrichum*. *(Kanpur M.Sc., 2000)*

54. Write systematic position and important features of *Pogonatum*.

55. Distinguish between :

(*a*) Peristome of *Pogonatum* and *Funaria*. *(Rohilkhand M.Sc., 2003)*

(*b*) Sporophyte of *Polytrichum* and *Andreaea* *(Kanpur M.Sc., 200; Rohilkhand, M.Sc., 1995)*

(*c*) *Andreaea* and *Polytrichum* *(Rohilkhand M.Sc., 1999)*

(*d*) Gametophyte of *Sphagnum* and *Pogonatum* *(Vir Kumar Singh, 1993; Kanpur M.Sc., 1998)*

(*e*) *Andreaea* and *Pogonatum* *(Kanpur M.Sc., 1993)*

(*f*) *Sphagnum* and *Polytrichum* *(Lucknow, 2001)*

(*g*) Rhizoids of *Marchantia* and *Pogonatum*. *(Poorvanchal, 2001)*

56. What are hydroids?

57. What is the function of columella in *Pogonatum*.

58. What are the functions of calyptra and operculum.

59. Describe the functions of various tissues of aerial stem in *Pogonatum*.

OBJECTIVE TYPE

60. Fill in the blanks:

(*i*) The shape of mature capsule is spherical in ___________ and cylindrical in ___________.

(*ii*) The rhizoids in *Pogonatum* are ___________.

(*iii*) Paraphyses and leaves protect the antheridium in ___________.

(*iv*) In *Polytrichum*, rhizoids are ___________.

(*v*) Leptoids are found in the ___________ of *Polytrichum*.

(*vi*) In *Polytrichum*, scale leaves and ___________ leaves are present.

(*vii*) In *Polytrichum*, ___________ are borne on rhizoids.

(*viii*) Hydroids, are present as water conducting tissue in the ___________ of ___________.

(*ix*) Lamina in *Polytrichum* is composed of _________ cells.

(*x*) Hair cap moss is the name given to ___________.

(*xi*) In *Polytrichum* the number of peristome teeth is ___________.

(*xii*) Epiphragm develops in___________.

(*xiii*) In *Polytrichum* the ___________ is dagger shaped.

(*xiv*) The archegonial neck in *Pogonatum* is made up of__________ tier of cells.

(*xv*) The peristome in *Pogonatum* is made up of __________ cells.

(*xvi*) The spores in *Pogonatum* are discharged and regulated by the movements of ___________.

(*xvii*) Columella is present in the capsule of ___________.

(*xviii*) The capsule wall contains ___________ cells.

(*xix*) On germination the spores form ___________.

(*xx*) The spores in _________ are ___________.

61. Select the correct answer :

(*i*) Columella in *Pogonatum* is

(*a*) Fertile tissue

(*b*) Nutritive tissue

(*c*) Conducting tissue

(*d*) Protective tissue.

(*ii*) In moss sporophyte which of the following is absent ?

(*a*) Foot (*b*) Seta

(*c*) Capsule (*d*) elaters.

(*iii*) In *Pogonatum*, the archesporium is formed from
(*a*) Outer layer of amphithecium
(*b*) inner layer of amphithecium
(*c*) peripheral layer of endothecium
(*d*) inner most layer of endothecium.

(*iv*) Elongated cylindrical sporogonium is seen in
(*a*) *Anthoceros* (*b*) *Polytrichum*
(*c*) *Marchantia* (*d*) *Porella.*

(*v*) In *Polytrichum* the spore liberation is regulated by
(*a*) Operculum (*b*) Columella
(*c*) Peristome (*d*) *Annulus.*

(*vi*) Peristomes are present in
(*a*) *Marchantia* (*b*) *Polytrichum*
(*c*) *Sphagnum* (*d*) *Porella.*

(*vii*) Leptoids are present in
(*a*) *Sphagnum* (*b*) *Polytrichum*
(*c*) *Anthoceros* (*d*) *Marchantia.*

(*viii*) Hydroids in *Polytrichum* function as
(*a*) Water conducting tissue
(*b*) Water storing tissue
(*c*) Food transporting tissue
(*d*) Food storage tissue.

(*ix*) In which of the following gemmae are produced on rhizoids?
(*a*) *Sphagnum* (*b*) *Funaria*
(*c*) *Marchantia* (*d*) *Polytrichum.*

(*x*) *Polytrichum* is also known as
(*a*) Peat moss (*b*) Spike moss
(*c*) Hair-cap moss
(*d*) Reinder moss.

(*xi*) The number of Peristome teeth in *Pogonatum* is
(*a*) 8 (*b*) 16
(*c*) 32 (*d*) 64.

(*xii*) Spores in *Polytrichum* and *Pogonatum* are
(*a*) Haploid (*b*) Diploid
(*c*) Triploid (*d*) Tetraploid.

(*xiii*) Chlorophyllose cells are present in
(*a*) Columella (*b*) Theca
(*c*) Foot
(*d*) Capsule wall.

(*xiv*) In *Pogonatum* the discharge of spores is regulated by the movements of
(*a*) Peristome (*b*) Columella
(*c*) epiphragm (*d*) Seta.

(*xv*) The number of peristome teeth is 64 in
(*a*) *Funaria* (*b*) *Sphagnum*
(*c*) *Pogonatum* (*d*) *Polytrichum.*

(*xvi*) Neck of archegonium in *Pogonatum* is made up of
(*a*) 2 tiers of cells (*b*)4 tiers of cells
(*c*) 6 tiers of cells (*d*)8 tiers of cells.

(*xvii*) Columella is a part of
(*a*) Capsule (*b*) Seta
(*c*) Foot (*d*) Rhizome.

(*xviii*) First division of the zygote is always
(*a*) Transverse (*b*) Vertical
(*c*) Oblique (*d*) Periclinal.

(*xix*) Gemmae are usually produced on
(*a*) Rhizoids (*b*) Stem
(*c*) Leaves (*d*) Capsule

(*xx*) When spores in *Polytrichum* and *Pogonatum* germinate, they form
(*a*) Capsule directly
(*b*) Leafy gametophytes directly
(*c*) protonema which bears archegonia and antheridia
(*d*) First protonema, then bud and leafy gametophytes

(*xxi*) Leptome mantle in *Polytrichum* represents
(*a*) Rudimentary pericycle
(*b*) Starchy layer
(*c*) Physiological phloem
(*d*) Physiological xylem.

(*xxii*) The columella in *Polytrichum* and *Pogonatum* is
(*a*) Fertile tissue
(*b*) Sterile tissue
(*c*) Nourishing tissue
(*d*) Conducting tissue.

(*xxiii*) In *Polytrichum* the leaves are arranged in
(*a*) Five rows (*b*) Four rows
(*c*) Three rows (*d*) Two rows.

(*xxiv*) How many peristome teeth are found in *Pogonatum* ?
(*a*) 16 (*b*) 32
(*c*) 64 (*d*) 128.

Image of *Fossils Mosses*

CHAPTER 21

GENERAL CONCLUSION

● Fossil Bryophytes ● Origin of Bryophyta ● Systematic Position ● Biological Importance Origin and fate of the Archesporium ● Evolution of the Sporophyte ● Ecology of Bryophytes ● Oil-bodies ● Morphogenesis ● Bryophytes -as Bioindicaters of water pollution ● Bryophytes -as Bioindicators of air pollution ● Vegetative reproduction in Bryophytes ● Economic importance of Bryophyta ● Comparison between gametophytes Table-1 ● Comparison between sex organs : Table-2 ● Comparison between sporophytes : Table-3

1. FOSSIL BRYOPHYTES

Fossil history of Bryophyte is not perfectly known. The reasons, which are responsible, are as follows :

(i) Plant body is simple and small in size,

(ii) Plants are delicate and gametophytic,

(iii) The surface of thallus or leaf is not properly cuticularised,

(iv) Lignified cells are not present,

(v) Vascular bundles are also absent.

Inspite of the above weaknesses, there are a few bryophytes known in fossil state from different era/ periods. These are listed below :

1. Palaeozoic Era

(a) **Devonian period** (330,000,000)

(*i*) *Sporogonitis exuberans*

(*ii*) *Hepaticites devonicum*

(b) **Carboniferous period** (285,000,000)

(*i*) *Hepaticites willsii*

(*ii*) *Hepaticites kidstonii*

(*iii*) *Hepaticites lobatus*
(*iv*) *Hepaticites metzgerioides*
(*v*) *Muscites polytrichaceous*
(*vi*) *Muscites burtrandi*
(c) **Permian Period** (205,000,000)
(*i*) *Intia vermicularis*

2. Mesozoic Era

(a) **Triassic period** (180,000,000)
(*i*) *Naiadita lanceolata*
(b) **Jurassic period** (140,000,000)
(*i*) *Ricciopsis florinii*
(*ii*) *Hepaticites laevis*
(c) **Cretaceous period** (1,00,000,000)
(*i*) *Marchantites yukonensis*
(*ii*) *Jungermannites cretaceus*
(*iii*) *Muscites lesguereuxi*

3. Cenozoic Era

(a) **Eocene period** (60,000,000)
(*i*) *Marchantites stephensoni*
(*ii*) *Jungermannites bryopteroides*
(b) **Miocene period** (20,000,000)
(*i*) *Marchantites coloradensis*
(*ii*) *Jungermannites cockerelii*

The description of some important fossil bryophytes along with locality and age, as reported by palaeobotanists, is given below :

(*i*) *Sporogonites exuberans* (Fig. 21.1) : The fossil was described by Halle (1916) from lower devonian of Norway and was later worked out by Andrews (1960) from the fossils collected from lower devonian of Belgium. The plant body of this fossil consists of an irregular thalloid base over which a parallel crop of sporangiophores bearing sporangia at apices is observed. There is no evidence of lignified tissues either in stalk of sporangiophore or in the thallus. The sporagium consists of multilayered wall having a dome shaped spore sac filled with spores. Since the preservation is not perfect, there is no indication of a clear cut columella. This fossil may be compared with the fossil *Horneophyton* and also with living *Sphagnum*.

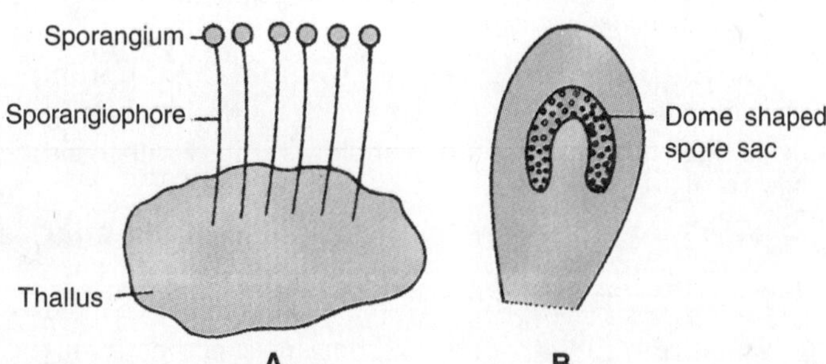

Fig. 21.1 (A—B) ***Sporogonites exuberans.*** A, thalloid plant body; B, L.S. sporangium.

(*ii*) *Hepaticites devonicum* (Fig. 21.2) : Huber in 1961 reported this fossil from upper devonian of New York. This is the earliest fossil record of hepaticae found associated with other fossil remains of psilophytales, ferns, lycopods and gymnosperms. *H. devonicum* has a prostrate rhizomatous base and an erect thallus. The rhizomatic region of this fossil contains numerous simple rhizoids. Internally it has elongated parenchymatous cells similar to the axis of a leafy plant or midrib region of a

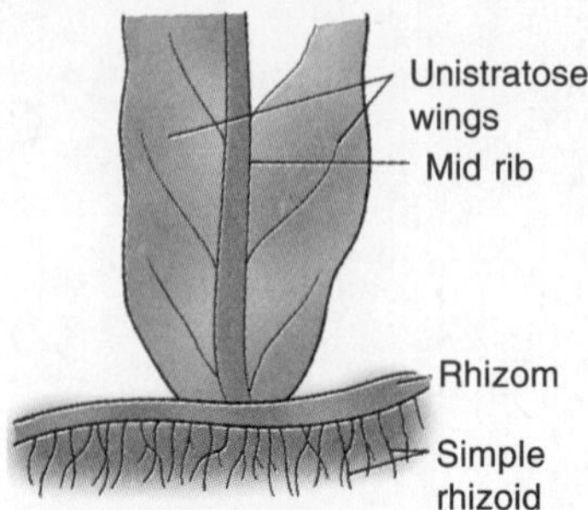

Fig. 21.2. *Hepaticites devonicum.*

thalloid plant. Rest of the thallus is unistratose. No reproductive structures are seen. This fossil very much resembles with the living *Pallavicinia* and hence it is now named as *Pallavicinites*.

Fig. 21.3. ***Hepaticites willsii***

(*iii*) *Hepaticites willsii* (Fig. 21.3) : Walton (1925) reported this fossil from upper carboniferous. The fossil is made up of ribbon shaped dichotomously branched thallus which is several cell layer thick in the middle. In habit it resembles *Riccia fluitans* but in overall features it shows affinity with *Riccardia*. Schuster (1966) believed that *Hepaticites langi*, another fossil reported by Walton, is congeneric with *H. willsii*.

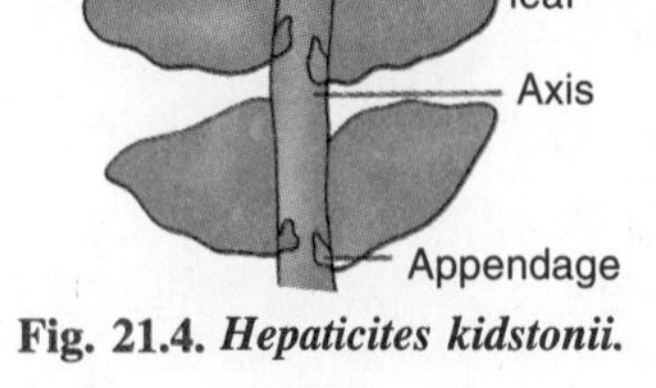

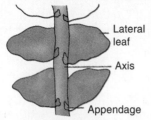

Fig. 21.4. *Hepaticites kidstonii.*

(*iv*) *Hepaticites kidstonii* : (Fig. 21.4) Walton (1925) discovered this fossil from upper carboniferous. This fossil has well marked axis and two rows of lateral leaves on its dorsal surface. There is a small scale like appendage associated with each leaf. The rhizoids are not visible. It resembles externally with the genus *Treubia.* Schuster (1966) proposed a new name for this fossil as *Treubiites.*

(*v*) *Hepaticites lobatus* (Fig. 21.5) : Walton (1925) described this fossil from the upper carboniferous. The plant body has a broad midrib or axis like structure associated with lateral alternate lobes. The appendages are absent. Harris beleived that this fossil shows affinity with the living leafy genus *Fossombronia* where as Muller established its resemblance with thalloid genus *Blasia*.

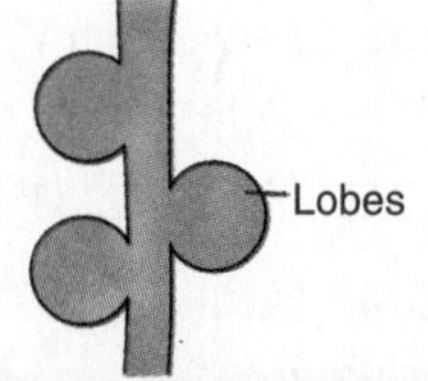

Fig. 21.5. ***Hepaticites lobatus***

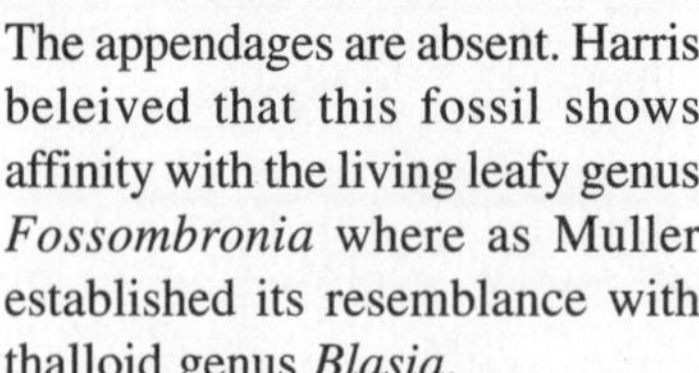
Fig. 21.6. *Hepaticites metzgeroides.*

(*vi*) *Hepaticites metzgeroides* (Fig. 21.6) : The fossil was reported by Walton (1925) from upper carboniferous. The fossil has a simple ribbon like thalloid body. In external appearance this fossil shows affinity with living genus *Metzgeria*.

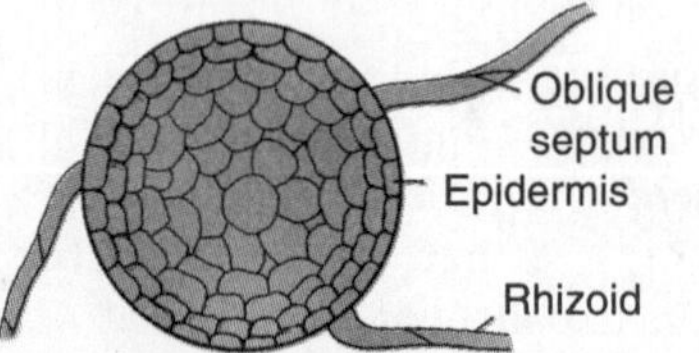

Fig. 21.7. ***Muscites bertrandi.*** T.S. stem.

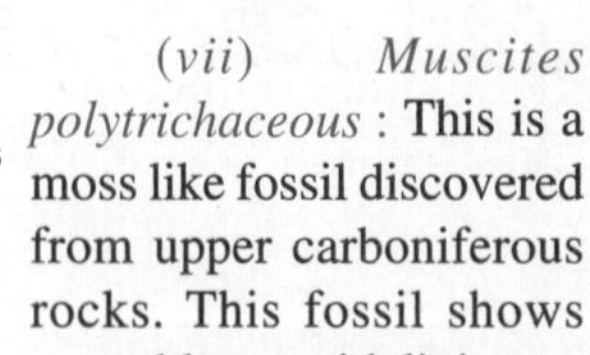

(*vii*) *Muscites polytrichaceous* : This is a moss like fossil discovered from upper carboniferous rocks. This fossil shows resemblance with living moss *Polytrichum.* Dixon (1927) found that *M. polytrichaceous* is not closely related with *Polytrichum.* The fossil has only stem and leaves.

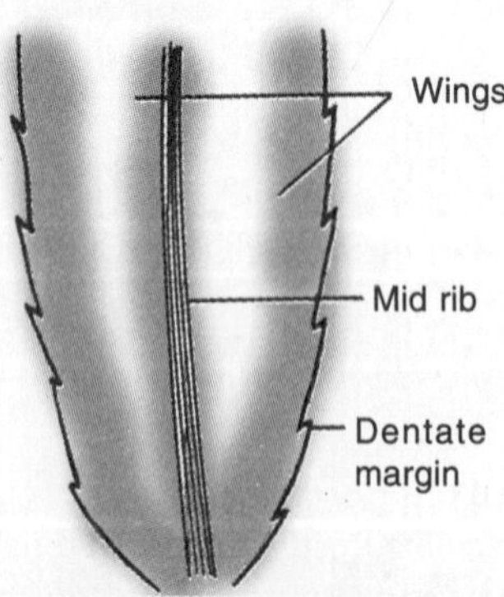

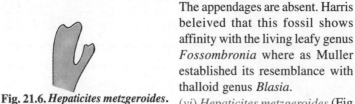

Fig. 21.8. ***Intia vermicularis.*** Apart of leaf impression.

(*viii*) *Muscites bertrandi* (Fig. 21.7) : It is also an oldest record of moss fossil reported from upper carboniferous. The fossil represents a cross section of the stem with rhizoids having oblique septa (a diognostic feature of mosses). On outer surface the epidermis is present. The vascular bundles are absent.

(*ix*) *Intia vermicularis* (Fig. 21.8) : The fossil is a form genus reported from permian rocks of USSR. It consists of a thallus/leaf impression with distinct midirib and wings with dentate margin.

(*x*) *Naiadita lanceolata* (Fig. 21.9) : Harris (1938) reported this complete fossil from upper triassic of England. The plant body consists of a small, erect and cylindrical axis bearing spirally arranged lanceolate leaves all over. The rhizoids are simple and found only at the base there is no differentiation into conducting strand in the internal structure of the axis. The leaves lack midrib and are unistratose. At the apex of the stem there is a cup like structure called gemma cup which is found covered with lanceolate leaves. It contains discoid multicellular gemmae (B).

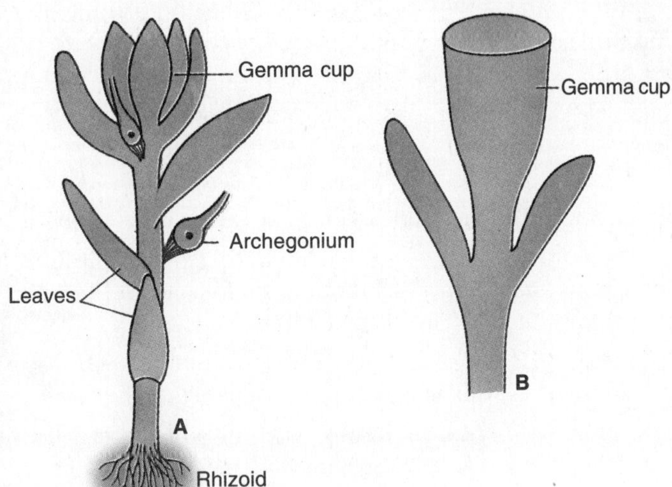

Fig. 21.9. (A–B) ***Naiadita lanceolata.*** A, thallus; B, a part with gemma cup.

The archegonia are present on the surface of the axis in extra axillary position (A). The archegonia have stalk and a long neck. Some of the fragments of fossil showed perianth like structure which indicate that some of the archegonia might have been associated with perianth like structures (C). The sporophytes were also present at the apex of main axis. It consists of a small foot and more or less spherical capsule (D). Seta is absent. The capsule wall is one cell layer thick. The dehiscence of capsule seems to be irregular.The spores were not associated with elaters.

In general habit, particularly in leaf arrangement, the plant is moss like. But the lack of midrib indicates a liverwort character. The other liverwort like characters are simple rhizoids, archegonia with one cell layer thick venter and lack of tissue differentiation in the axis. The sporophyte is also liverwort type and shows resemblance with the sporophyte of order Marchantiales having capsule wall of one cell layer thick. However, the absence of elaters within the capsule brings *Naiadita* nearer to Sphaerocarpales. On the other hand the erect habit, spirally arranged leaves and extra axillary position of archegonia suggest its affinity with order Calobryales. However, the presence of rhizoids rule out the possibility of its affinity with Calobryales. Harris considered *Naiadita* closely related to genus *Riella.*

(*xi*) *Ricciopsis florinii* : Lundbland (1954) discovered this fossil from the Jurassic (Lias) of Scania, Sweden. The plant shows resemblance with *Riccia.*

(*xii*) *Hepaticites laevis* : Harris (1931) reported this fossil from the Jurassic (Lias) of Green land. The fossil shows affinity with order Metzgeriales.

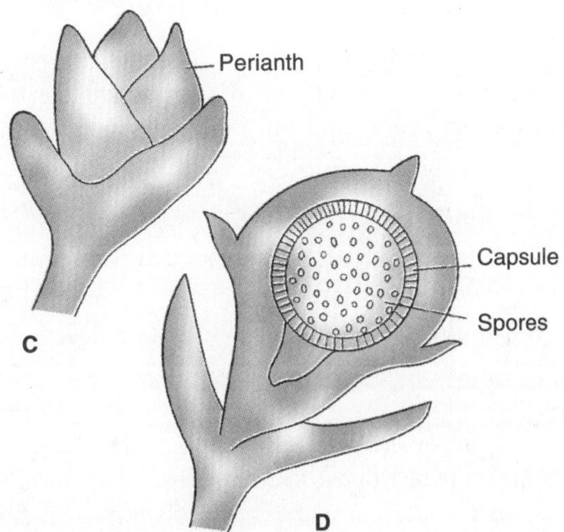

Fig. 21.9. (C—D). ***Naiadita lanceolata.*** C, part of sporophyte; D, V.S. sporophyte.

(*xiii*) *Marchantites yukonensis* : Hollick (1930) discovered this fossil from Cretaceous of Yukon. The fossil resembles with *Marchantia*.

(*xiv*) *Jungermannites cretaceous* : This fossil was reported by Berry in 1919 from Cretaceous rocks of Alabama. The fossil is over all similar to living leafy liverwort *Jungermannia* in which leaves are arranged in two lateral rows and archegonia are acrogunous in position.

(*xv*) *Muscites lesguereuxi* : Berry (1928) discovered this rare mesozoic moss fossil from Cretaceous of North America.This fossil seems to be a moss in appearance.

(*xvi*) *Marchantites stephensoni* : Berry reported this fossil from eocene of Texas. The name of the species "*stephensoni*" has been given in honour of the great bryologist F. Stephani. The fossil resembles with the living plant of *Marchantia*.

(*xvii*) *Jungermannites bryopteroides* : Ball in 1931 discovered it from eocene of Texas. The fossil resembles with modern Jungermanniales.

(*xviii*) *Marchantites coloradensis* : Knowlton in 1930 found this fossil from Miocene of Colorado. It seems to be close to modern member of Marchantiales.

(*xix*) *Jungermannites cockerelli* : This fossil was discovered and reported by Howe & Hollick in 1922 from Miocene of Colorado. It shows affinity with living member of order Jungermannials.

Some fossil bryophytes from India

1. *Capsularis gondwanensis* : Saksena in 1947 discovered a fossil capsule of a probable bryophyte from Permo-carboniferous of Ganjra Mala. The fossil represents only a dark capsule with operculum, short seta and foot.

2. *Shuklanites deccanii* : Singhai in 1964 discovered a fossil sporophyte from Deccan Intertrappean beds of Chhindwara (M.P.). The fossil has foot, seta — which is represented only by a constriction, and capsule. The latter has only spores and pseudoelaters but columella is absent. This fossil shows some affinity with Marchantiales and some with Anthocerotales.

3. *Sphagnum papillosum* : Vishnu-Mittre & Gupta in 1971 discovered a sub-fossil from the sediments of Bhimtal, Nainital.

2. ORIGIN OF BRYOPHYTA

Nothing definite is known about this subject. The little geologic record that we have is of little help. In fact no fossil forms more primitive than the present day bryophytes have been found. All the views about their origin must therefore be based on the evidence under the following three heads :—

(*i*) Evidence from comparative morphology of the living plants.

(*ii*) Evidence from ontogony of the living plants.

(*iii*) Evidence based on analogies with the living plants of other groups.

Bryologists are divided into two camps on the origin of bryophytes. The followers of one camp hold that the bryophytes have descended from the Pteridophytes. This is called the **Pteridophytean hypothesis** of the origin of bryophytes. The ardent supporters of this view are Scot, Lang and Kidston, Haskall, Kashyap and others.

The adherents of the second school believe in the aquatic ancestry of the bryophytes. They hold that the bryophytes have evolved from the Algae. This viewpoint has come to be known as the **Algael Hypothesis** of the origin of bryophytes. Bower, Cavers, Smith, Campbell and Fritsch are the eminent supporters of this hypothesis. These two hypotheses which attempt to explain the origin of the bryophytes are thus diametrically opposed to each other.

(a) Pterophytean Hypothesis

The supporters of this view formulated their argument on the basis of the following two features :—

(*i*) Close similarity between the sex organs of the two groups.

(*ii*) Resemblance between the sporogonium of *Anthoceros* and the terminal *sporogonium* of the fossil pteridophytes such as *Sporogonites* and *Horoneophyton.*

The kinship between the two groups is further strengthened by the similarity in their pigments, structure of cell walls, food reserves, reproductive methods and life cycle. These similarities between the bryophytes and the pteridophytes encouraged the followers of this school of thought to presume that the former have evolved from the latter by **progressive simplification** or **reduction**.

Scott (1911) was the first to moot this idea on the basis of the presence of chlorophyll and plastids in the sporogonium of mosses, liverworts and *Anthoceros* and also the presence of stomata of the type met within the primitive vascular plants on the sporogonium of *Anthoceros* and the apophysis region of the capsule of mosses. He interpreted these features as ancestral characters retained from the time when the sporophyte was an independent plant (as in the pteridophytes). The sporogonium of *Anthoceros* which is to a great extent independent of the parent thallus plant (gametophyte) was believed to be the immediate descendant in all the bryophytes.

Kashyap (1919), another ardent supporter of this hypothesis, considered the liverworts to have evolved from the Equisetales along three independent lines namely the Marchantiales, Jungermanniales and Anthocerotales. It may be worthwhile to note that uptill then the Psilophytales had not yet been known.

Haskell (1949) advanced the origin of the bryophytes from the algae through the Psilophytes by simplification. The resemblance between the *Anthoceros* sporogonium and terminal sporangium of *Horneophyton* and the presence of stomata typical of the vascular plants on the *Anthoceros* sporogonium and apophysis region of the capsule of mosses were the two chief features on which he based his viewpoint. The subsequent disappearance of stomata in other members of the Anthoceratales was linked with the parasitic habit of their sporogonia.

To sum up, the supporters of Pteridophytean hypothesis believe that the bryophytes represent a degenerate evolutionary line of the pteridophytes. In their view it is difficult to explain these similarities between the two groups otherwise. However this hypothesis now stands discarded. The opponents of this hypothesis point out to the complete absence of any relic of the lost vascular system in the sporophyte of all the bryophytes including the sturdy mosses. Mehra (1967) writes, "We know of many vascular plants including the water ferns that have taken to aquatic modes of life since the ages or have assumed parastitic mode of life but even then retain the vascular system."

(b) Algal Hypothesis

The occurrence of flagellated sperms in the bryophytes which necessitates the presence of free water, at least, at the time of the fertilisation is a clear sign of their aquatic ancestry. The development of a green filamentous, alga-like protonema as a **juvenile stage** in the life cycle of some of the bryophytes shows beyond doubt that the bryophytes had their origin in some algal form. It is a biological principle that the juvenile stage of an organism resembles its ancestral form.

The consensus of opinion, at present, favours the view that the bryophytes have evolved from the green algae rather than the brown. This view is supported by the several similarities that exist between the two. These are, identical photosynthetic pigments (chlorophyll and xanthophyll), essentially thallus-like plant body lacking vascular tissues, starch as a food reserve, cellulose as the main component of cell wall and the type (whiplash) and number of flagella.

The above-mentioned similarities between the green algae and the bryophytes serve to denote that the latter have arisen from the former. This is the *Chlorophycean Hypothesis* of the origin of the bryophytes.

The bryophytes, on the other hand are more advanced and highly organized than the green algae in their land habit, more complex and elaborate thallus, multicellular and protected sex organs, retention of the zygote within the venter and its germination in *situ*, production of wind disseminated spores and heteromorphic type of alternation of generations. How these changes actually occurred during the evolution of bryophytes from the green algae still remains an unsolved problem. The species which constituted the links between the two have long since disappeared. These transitional species must have been small, delicate, thallose organisms. They could not be handed down to us in fossil form. We are therefore left with no alternative but to speculate what these bridging species might have looked like. It is suggested that the transitional species probably were heterotrichous in habit. The presence of a small, flat, plate-like protonema in *Sphagnum* suggested the possibility of a green alga with a small, simple *Sphaerocarpos*-like thallus having become adapted to a life on land.

Smith, an ardent supporter of this hypothesis, has suggested *Fritschiella* as the probable nearer approach to the primitive ancestral form which evolved the bryophytes. It is an amphibious green alga of the family Chaetophoraceae. It appears on the moist silt of the drying pools. Bower writes, "This amphibial plant possesses the essentials of a three dimensional, photosynthetic, subaerial thallus originating from a simple filament."

The occurrence in the bryophytes of multicellular sex organs with their sterile jackets is, however, difficult to explain. There are no known parallels among the living or fossil Chlorophycease. The presence of a protective sterile jacket around the sex organs, it seems, is an adaptation to a land habit.The jacketed sex organs have a better chance of survival when exposed to the drying effects of the air. Bower writes, "in the amphibial green algae this is distantly adumbrated by the nucule of the *Characeae* or still less perfectly by the protective filaments surrounding the zygote of *Coleochaete*."

The algal ancestry of the bryophytes is now acknowledged by all the botanists. The older view advocated by Smith (1955) that the bryophytes arose from the algae and then gave rise to the simple pteridophytes (primitive vascular plants) is no longer considered tenable. On the contrary the modern bryologists hold that the bryophytes represent a blind alley in evolution. Their viewpoint is that to avoid increased competition in water a group of remote ancestors of the green algae migrated to a subaerial habitat. These primitive amphibious plants developed multicellular sex organs as an adaptation to a life on land. From this hypothetical group arose both the bryophytes and the primitive vascular plants (pteridophytes) along two parallel lines.

The supporters of the algal origin differ among themselves as regards the origin of the two main groups of bryophytes. According to one school which supports the polyphylletic origin, the three groups of the bryophytes namely liverworts, hornworts (*Anthoceros*) and mosses represent three independent evolutionary lines, each having an independent origin from the transitional archegoniate forms which evolved from still earlier, different, hypothetical green algal stocks that migrated to the land. The supporters of monophylletic origin advocate that the mosses are more primitive than the other bryophytes. The latter have evolved from the moss-like ancestors by simplification or reduction. According to this view the mosses are nearer to the supposed algal ancestors than the other bryophytes.

3. SYSTEMATIC POSITION

The bryophytes are a group of interesting plants. They resemble the green algae in certain respects and differ from them in others. The features in which they agree with the green algae are :

(*i*) The simple, green, thalloid plant body.

(*ii*) Lack of vascular tissue and absence of roots.

(*iii*) Predominant plant in the life cycle being the gametophyte.

(*iv*) Autotrophic mode of nutrition

They differ from the green algae in the following respects :

(*i*) Terrestrail habit

(*ii*) Multicellular sex organs each with a jacket layer of sterile cells.

(*iii*) Embryo formation

(*iv*) Constant occurrence in the life cycle of a heterologous type of alternation of generations

(*v*) Development of a remarkable female sex organ, the **archegonium**. It corresponds no doubt to the oogonium of the green algae but has no exact counterpart among them.

(*vi*) Origin and early development of the future sporophyte within the archegonium

(*vii*) Sporophyte attached throughout life to and dependent for nutrition upon the parent gametophyte.

Because of the above-mentioned differences these thallus-bearing plants (bryophytes) are not included among the other thallus bearing plants such as the green algae to which they resemble in certain other respects. They are thus separated from the division *Thallophyta*.

The features in which the bryophytes differ from the green algae they share with the primitive vascular plants pteridophytes except point (*vii*). But they cannot be included among the pteriodophytes as they are very unlike them in the following important respects besides others:

(*i*) Absence of vascular tissue.

(*ii*) The dominant phase in the life cycle being the gametophyte and not the sporophyte.

It is for this reason that the bryophytes are placed in a separate division Bryophyta occupying a position intermediate between the Thallophyta and the Pteridophyta.

4. BIOLOGICAL IMPORTANCE

This group of lowly organisms illustrates that plants may be successful (widespread and numerous) despite their small size.

(a) Origin of Land Habit among Plants

To the botanist the group is of a singular interest. It throws light on the origin of land habit among plants. This event of change in habit from a life in water to a life on land must have been a red letter day in the history of plant life. It is so because it made possible all subsequent progress in the plant world. The group bryophyta includes the most primitive land plants which illustrate some of the steps this change in habit from water to land involved. Their structure, physiology and reproductive habits provide a striking evidence of their having evolved from the aquatic ancestors such as the Algae. The retention of swimming habit by the male gametes of the group is clear sign of their ancestry. The important structural adaptations of a terrestrial existence shown by the bryophytes are:

(*i*) Their compact plant bodies usually protected by epidermis containing air pores.

(*ii*) Primitive type of conducting strand.

(*iii*) To facilitate absorption of water and salts from the soil the plant body is provided with rhizoids. The latter in addition function as organs of attachment.

(*iv*) Jacketed, multicellular sex organs.

(*v*) Retention of the zygote within the archegonium. It serves a double purpose namely ensures food and water from the parent plant as it develops into a multicellular embryo and affords protection from drying.

(*vi*) Thick-walled, wind disseminated spores.

It seems the nature in its quest for a suitable plant body for a life on land tried two schemes. One of these is the upright leafy body habit of the mosses. It favours photosynthesis as it presents greater photosynthetic surface to light. It, however, presents difficulties in the way of fertilisation as the sex organs are elevated. The elevated position of the moss sporophyte is, no doubt, ideal for spore dispersal but how can there be a sporophyte without fertilisation. The two physiological processes, fertilization and photosynthesis have opposite requirements. The former is facilitated by flat, thalloid body and the latter is favoured by a tall, upright body. Hence the scheme of combining photosynthesis with fertilisation as the functions of the gametophyte failed. It proved an unprogressive evolutionary trend. This is the main reason why the Mosses end blindly in the evolutionary line. They have given rise to no new plants. Nor have they progressed beyond this stage. The gametophyte plant in the mosses both morphologically and anatomically shows highest development of the vegetative body in the bryophytes. But there can be no progress beyond this stage. The two main factors which check further growth are :—

(*i*) Absence of root and vascular tissue. The rhizoids as absorbing organs proved inefficient.

(*ii*) Dependence upon water for fertilisation. It also hinders further growth.

Hence the plan of combining photosynthesis with fertilisation as functions of the gametophyte failed. It permitted no further progress.

In the second scheme nature tried the combination of photosynthesis with spore dispersal as functions of the sporophyte. Both the processes have the same requirements. They are favoured by a upright, tall body. It thus proved an ideal combination as it permits further progress. On the other hand, fertilization is favoured by a flat, thalloid body. This combination we find in *Anthoceros*. It has a flat, thalloid gametophyte ideal for fertilisation. The gametophyte bears an erect, tall cylindrical sporophyte with a well ventilated green tissue in the capsule wall for photosynthesis. From such a sporophyte, some botanists believe, may have arisen the sporophyte of the simplest and the primitive vascular plants (pteridophytes).

(b) Stabilisation of Alternation of Generations

This important biological phenomenon is found in the life cycles of a few of the thallophytes but is far from being fixed. The two generations in their life cycles are either quite similar or somewhat different. In the bryophytes, however, this phenomenon is stabilised. It becomes a constant feature of their life cycles. Besides, the vegetative individuals of the two generations differ markedly in their physiological and anatomical details.

5. ORIGIN AND FATE OF THE ARCHESPORIUM

In the bryophytes archesporium originates as a continuous tract of primary cells. These divide and redivide to give rise to a mass of cells forming, at first, a solid tissue. The cells of the last cell generation of this solid tissue separate from each tissue derived from the archesporium comes to be called as the **sporogenous tissue**. On this basis archesporium is defined as the first generation of the sporogenous tissue. The origin and consequently the position of this tissue varies in different classes of the bryophytes. The fate may vary in different genera of the same order :—

Classes and Orders	Origin	Position	Fate
1. **Hepaticopsida** (*a*) *Marchantiales*: *Riccia*	The entire endothecium becomes the archesporium, and forms the sporogenous tissue.	It is central in position and forms the bulk of the sporophyte except the single layered wall. It fills the cavity of the capsule within the single layered capsule wall.	Practically all the sporogenous cells function as **spore mother cells** and form the spores. A few at the periphery degenerate to form a nutritive fluid. These are called the **nurse cells**.
Marchantia	The whole mass of endothecium forms the archesporium which divides and redivides to form the sporogenous tissue.	It fills the cavity of the capsule within the single layered capsule wall.	Half the sporogenous tissue yields the **spore mother cells** and the other half gives rise to the **elaters**. A few towards the top may remain sterile and form the **apical cap**.
(*b*) *Metzgeriales* *Pellia*	The entire endothecium forms the archesporium. The archesporium gives rise to the sporogenous tissue.	It fills the entire cavity of the capsule within the two or more cell layers thick capsule wall.	A central mass of sporogenous cells forms the **basal elaterophore**. The rest form the **spore mother cells** and the **elaters**.
(*d*) *Jungermanniales*: *Porella*	As in *Pellia*	As in *Pellia*	There is no elaterophore. The entire sporogenous tissue forms the **spore mother cells** and the **elaters**.
2. **Anthocerotopsida** (*a*) *Anthocerotales:* *Anthoceros*	Archesporium arises from the innermost layer of the amphithecium. It divides to form 2-4 layers thick sporogenous tissue.	It is more superficial in position than the Hepaticopsida. It overarches the tip of the columella and lies between the central columella and the several layers thick capsule wall.	It differentiates into the **spore mother cells** and the **pseudoelaters**.
3. **Bryopsida (Musci)** (*a*) *Sphagnidae—Sphagnales* *Sphagnum*	Archesporium as in *Anthoceros* originates from the inner layer of the amphithecium. By division it forms 4 layers thick sporogenous tissue.	As in *Anthoceros* it is superficial in position. It is dome-shaped and lies in the upper part of a capsule overarching the top of the massive central columella within the capsule wall.	The entire sporogenous tissue is devoted to the formation of **spores**. The sporogenous tissue thus forms a coherent tract of fertile cells in the capsule.
(*b*) *Bryidae—Funariales* *Funaria*	The archesporium originates from the outermost layer of the endothecium. It gives rise to the sporogenous tissue, 2 cellsin thickness.	It is superficial and surrounds the columella like a barrel.	All the sporogenous cells are fertile and form the **spores**. The sporogenous tissue thus forms a coherent tract of fertile cells as in *Sphagnum*.

6. EVOLUTION OF THE SPOROPHYTE

The sporophyte of the bryophytes is, at first, a solid object radial in construction. It lacks lateral appendages and is incapable of self-nutrition wholly or partially from the parent gemtophyte to which it remains organically attached throughout its life. Its chief function is the production and dispersal of spores. In form it varies from only a spherical spore producing case as in *Ricia* to an elaborate object differentiated into foot and capsule (*Corsinia*) or more usually into the foot, seta and the capsule. The foot functions as an anchoring and absorbing organ. The seta may either be small and constriction like or a long slender stalk. It helps in conduction and aids in spore dispersal. The capsule also varies in form. It may be spherical, oval, cylindrical or pear-shaped, etc. It varies in its elaboration.The elaboration, however, is internal rather than external.

According to the complexity of structure the sporophytes of bryophytes may be arranged in a series between the simplest and the most elaborate. The series starts with the simple sporophyte of *Riccia* runs through that of *Sphaerocarpos, Targionia, Marchantia, Pellia*, *Anthoceros* and finally ends in the highly complex sporophyte of *Funaria* and *Pogonatum*. So seriated the sporophytes of the bryophytes suggest a possible line of evolution.

(a) Theory of Sterilisation

Bower holds that the series runs in an upward direction. It illustrates a natural advance in the progressive elaboration and complexity of the sporophyte. The fundamental principle upon which he formulated his argument is the "*progressive sterilisation of the potentially fertile cells* (*sporogenous tissue*)." Instead of forming spores and serving a propagative function they remain sterile. These sterile cells are put to other uses such as nutrition, support, dehiscence, dispersal, etc. This hypothesis of Bower is called the **theory of sterilisation**. It attempts to explain the evolution of the sporophyte in the bryophytes on the basis of progressive elaboration. The ardent supporters of this theory are Cavers, Campbell and Smith. Let us apply Bower's theory of sterilisation to the individual sporophytes f this group and see if it stands the test.

(*i*) **Riccia sporophyte**. The zygote enters upon active segmentation to form a spherical mass of 20—30 undifferentiated cells. Periclinal segmentation at this stage defines an inner mass of **endothecium** from an outer single layer **amphithecium**. The amphithecium forms the single layered capsule wall. The endothecium which occupies the central position as a rule, in whole becomes the archesporium. The latter divides and redivides to form the sporogenous tissue. Practically all the sporogenous cells are fertile. However, a few at the periphery undergo degeneration to form a nutritive fluid. These are the **nurse cells**. There is a large output of spores and no or very little sterilisation of the potentially fertile cells.

The sporophyte of Riccia is thus the simplest among the bryophytes and has the least amount of sterile tissue. The entire embryo forms the spore producing capsule. There is no foot and no seta. It is simply a spore producing organ without any distributing function. It does not dehisce to allow the spores to escape.

(*ii*) **Sphaerocarpos sporophyte.** Sterilisation of fertile cells is more advanced in genus *Sphaerocarpos*. The lower part of young sporophyte becomes sterile and forms small bulbous foot and a very short seta. Infact, in between *Riccia* sporophyte and *Sphaerocarpos* sporophyte, there is an intermediate sporophyte called *Corsinia* sporophyte which has only capsule and a few celled small sterile foot. Thus, due to development of foot or both foot and seta, the sporophyte develops a clear polarity which is absent in case of *Riccia* sporophyte. The other sterile structures such as capsule wall and nurse cells are more or less similar among the three genera.

(*iii*) **Targionia sporophyte.** In this plant, the foot is large and bulbous, the seta is comparatively more long than *Sphaerocarpos* and, instead of nurse cells, half of sporogenous cells form elaters.

(*iv*) **Marchantia sporophyte**. Half of the embryo derived from the **hypobasal region** remains sterile. It forms the **foot** and the **seta**. It is only the upper **epibasal half** of the embryo which forms the spore producing capsule. The amphithecium forms the single layered capsule wall. Towards maturity ring-like thickenings appear on the walls of these cells. The entire mass of endothecium becomes the archesporium as in *Riccia*. The archesporium cells divide and re-divide to form the sporogenous tissue. Unlike *Riccia* only half of the sporogenous cells differentiate into spore mother cells. The other half remain sterile. These sterile cells elongate, develop spirally thickened bands on their walls and become the **elaters**. The elaters are **hygroscopic**. They help in the scattering of spores. A few of the sporogenous cells at the top may differentiate into the sterile, apical cap. The capsule of *Marchantia* has specialised both as a spore producing and spore distributing body. It illustrates a step further in the progressive sterilisation of the sporogenous tissue and consequent elaboration of its sporophyte.

(*v*) **Pellia sporophyte**. **Hypobasal half** of the zygote takes no part in the development of the embryo sporophyte. The entire sporophyte including the **foot** and the **seta** is developed from the **epibasal half**. The shape of capsule is globose and periclinal divisions in the embryonic capsule differentiate into an outer amphithecium surrounding the inner endothecium. The amphithecium forms the capsule wall 2 or more cell layers thick. The cells of the outer layer develop radial thickening bands. The endothecium in whole becomes the archesporium as in *Riccia* and *Marchantia*. The archesporial cells divide and redivide to form sporogenous tissue. Unlike *Riccia* and *Marchantia* a central mass of sporogenous cells, at the base of the capsule, remains sterile. These sterile cells elongate considerably and develop spiral thickenings on their walls to become elater-like. The central solid mass of elater-like cells attached at their lower ends to the cavity of the capsule is called the **basal elaterophore**. It is the result of progressive sterilisation of the potentially fertile cells of the sporogenous tissue. In addition some other widely dispersed cells in the rest of the sporogenous tissue form **elaters** which remain unattached. In *Riccardia* similar type of central solid mass of elaters found fixed at apical end of capsular cavity is called apical elaterophore. The shape of capsule is oblong. It is thought that basal elaterophore and apical elaterophore unite and form columella in *Anthoceros*. The remaining sporogenous cells form the **spore mother cells**. The attached basal elaterophore and apical elaterophore are mechanically more effective in the dispersal of spores. The advancing sterilisation of the sporogenous tissue is thus associated with mroe efficient mechanism for spore dispersal. The other evolutionary trend has been the **decentralisation** of the remaining fertile tissue. This is achieved by sterilisation at the centre.

(*vi*) **Anthoceros sporophyte**. It illustrates a step further than *Pellia* and *Riccardia* in the progressive sterilisation of the potentially fertile tissue. There is complete sterilisation at the centre. The entire endothecium remains sterile. It forms a central column of sterile cells with a rounded apex. It is the **columella**. Consequently the office of spore formation is transferred to a more superficial tissue. The archesporium thus arises from the innermost layer of the amphithecium. It over-arches the free tip of the columella and surrounds it. The sporogenous cells become differentiated into **spore mother cells** and **pseudoelaters**. The archesporium in *Anthoceros* is thus extremely reduced. It forms only a small narrow part of the capsule. The outer amphithecium gives rise to the several cell layers thick capsule wall. The capsule wall develops a well-ventilated photosynthetic tissue protected by the epidermis containing perfect stomata like those of the vascular plants. The capsule is cylindrical (never globose).

(*vii*) **Funaria sporophyte**. Major portion of the embryo sporophyte remains sterile to form the **foot** and the **seta**. The embryonic capsule region becomes differentiated into an inner central column of endothecium surrounded by many layered amphithecium. The amphithecium becomes differentiated into the epidermis, the photosynthetic tissue of the capsule wall and the outer spore sac. Excepting the superficial layer there is complete sterilisation of the endothecium to form the central columella which is continuous right up to the top of the capsule. The archesporium arises

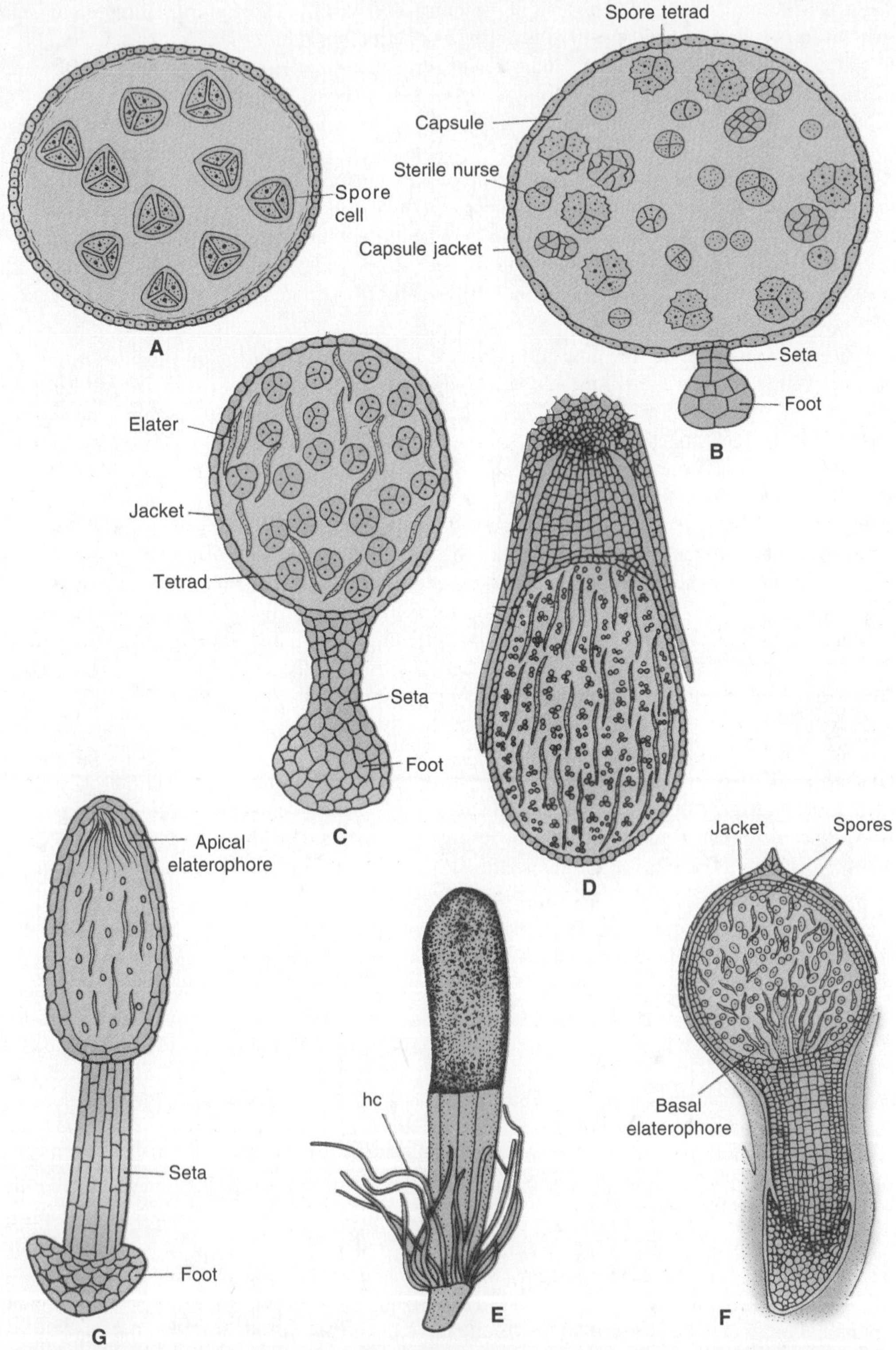

Fig. 21.10. (A—G). Evolution of sporophytes in Bryophyta. A. *Riccia*; B, *Sphaerocarpos*; C, *Targiona;* D, *Marchantia*; E.Jackiella hc-haustorial collar; F. *Pellia*; G. *Riccardia.*

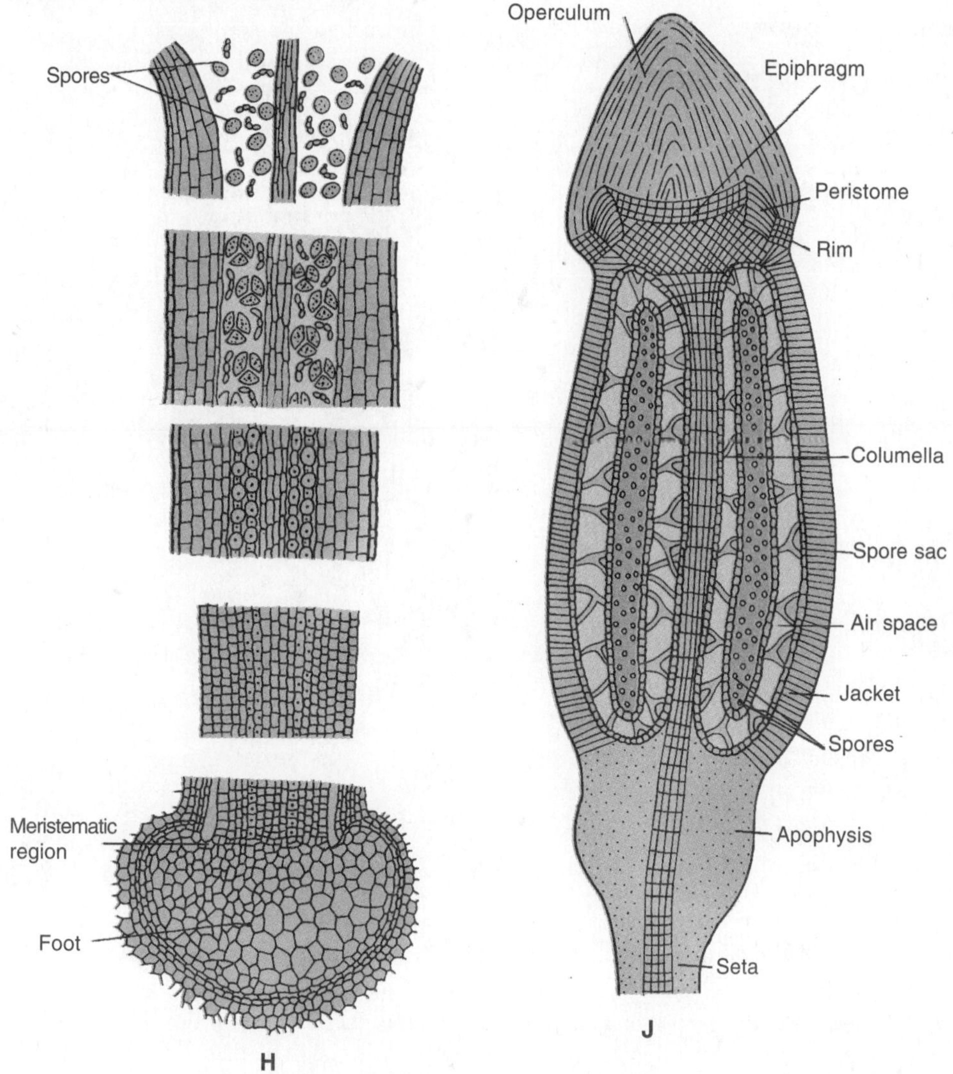

Fig. 21.10 (H, J) Evolution of sporophytes in Bryophyta; H, *Anthoceros*; J, *Polytrichum.*

from the outermost layer of the enodthecium. It is thus extremely reduced and consists of a single layer of cells. Besides its fertility is limited above in the operculum region and below in the apophysis region. Consequently the archesporium becomes barrel-shaped. It is confined to the theca region only. The barrel is open at both the ends. The sterilisation of archesporium towards the base results in the increase in size of the photosynthetic tissue in the apophysis region. The arrest of fertility towards the top according to Bower may be correlated with the specialisation of this region for spore distribution. This view is supported by the presence of peristome, operculum and annulus in this region. In fact the archesporium stops short just at the base of the annulus and the peristome. The accessory dehiscing apparatus of the Moss capsule is mechanically more efficient in scattering the spores. Consequently the reduced archesporium with all its fertile and no elaters suffices for all the needs.

Bower's theory of sterilisation offers a plausible explanation of the evolution of the sporophyte in this group in the upward direction. It is appealing.

(b) Reduction Theory

There is, however, an opposite school of thought led by Kashyap, Church, Goebel and Evans. They hold that so seriated the evolution of the sporophyte has been in the downward direction. The series they believe furnishes an example of retrogressive evolution. There is ample evidence of reduction rather than progressive elaboration of the sporophytes of this group. The reduction is accompanied by simplification of the structure of the sporophyte in the series. On the basis of this view of simplest sporophyte of *Ricia* will be considered as highly evolved or advanced though reduced as a result of progressive simplification. The significant steps in the reduction series are :—

(*i*) Simplification of the dehiscence apparatus.

(*ii*) Reduction of the green photosynthetic tissue in the capsule wall.

(*iii*) Associated with the above is the disappearance of stomata and intercellular spaces.

(*iv*) Decrease in the thickness of the capsule wall along with the disappearance of the thickening of all types of wall material from the walls of the cells.

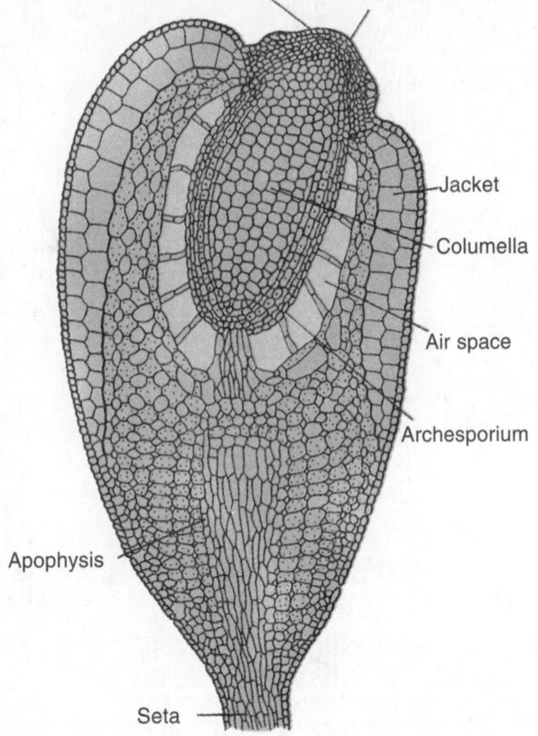

Fig. 21.10 (I) Evolution of sporophytes in Bryophyta; *Funaria.*

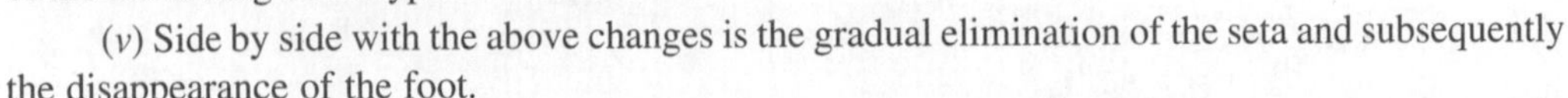

(*v*) Side by side with the above changes is the gradual elimination of the seta and subsequently the disappearance of the foot.

(*vi*) All these changes are accompanied by the progressive increase in the fertility of the sporogenous cells. This change eliminates the presence of sterile cells and elaters in the capsule.

Evidence from comparative morphology and experimental genetics support the view that the simple sporophyte of *Riccia* is an advanced but a reduced structure.

7. ECOLOGY OF BRYOPHYTES

Ecology — The term was first proposed by a zoologist Reiter. It is derived from Greek. *OIKOS* — meaning home and *logos* — meaning study. Thus, ecology of bryophytes means the study of the relation of individual bryophyte plant and plant communities to complex environment.

The place, where a bryophyte or community of bryophytes lives, is called its habitat. The bryophytes grow in different habitats which are as follows :—

1. Terrestrial. The bryophytes which grow on soil surface are called terrestrial bryophytes.

e.g. *Riccia discolor, R. billardieri.*

2. Aquatic. Those bryophytes which grow in water are called aquatic bryophytes. These are of two types:-

(*a*)*Fresh water* : Those bryophytes which grow in fresh-water of ponds, pools or lakes either in free floating or in submerged conditions.

e.g. *Riccia fluitans* – a free floating liverwort

Riella affinis – a submerged liverwort.

(*b*) *Marine water*. Those bryophytes which grow in marine sea water where salinity is very high.

e.g. *Scapania undulata* - a leafy liverwort found submerged in sea water.

3. Epiphytic or **Corticolous.** Those bryophytes which grow on the bark of living trees and shrubs are called epiphytic or corticolous. These are of two types :—

(*a*)*Obligate epiphytic or Corticolous* - These are usually restricted to bark and never grow on other substrate e.g. *Tortula laevipila, Zygodon conoidens*

(*b*)*Facultative epiphytic or Corticolous* - They may grow and survive on other substrate too

e.g. *Bryum capillare, Metzgeria* sp. and *Frullania* sp.

4. Lignicolous. Those bryophytes which grow on fallen old logs are called *lignicolous*. The bryophytes which appear first on these logs are members of family Lepidoziaceae, Lophocoleaceae, Lejeuneaceae and genera like *Nowillia, Odontoschisma, Zoopsis* and *Cephalozia*.

5. Epilithic or Saxicolous. Those bryophytes which grow directly on rock surface (either alkaline or acidic) are called epilithic or saxicolous. These are of two types :—

(*a*)*Obligate epilithic or Saxicolous* - These bryophytes are only restricted to specific rock surface e.g. almost all the members of family Grimmiaceae, *Porella thuja* and *Frullania microphylla*.

(*b*)*Facultative epilithic or Saxicolous* - They may grow and survive on other substrate too. e.g. *Bryum capillare, Conocephalum conicum* and *Porella platyphylla*.

6. Epiphyllous or Foliicolous. Such bryophytes are mostly found in wet tropical rain forests. The bryophytes grow and survive on the surface of living leaves of higher plants. Epiphyllous bryophytes are never found on the leaves of decidous higher plants. The rhizoids of these bryophytes are modified. They develop rhizoidal plates to fix the bryophyte on leaf surface. Epiphyllous bryophytes are of two types.

(*a*) *Obligate epiphyllous or Foliicolous*. Those bryophytes which grow only on leaf surface of higher plants and never grow on other substrate e.g. *Cololejeunea* and *Leucolejeunea* are the examples of leafy liverworts. Some obligate epiphyllous mosses are *Ephemeropsis* and *Crossomitrium*.

(*b*) *Facultative epiphyllous or Foliicolous*. They may grow and survive on other substrate too. Pocs (1978) have reported several liverworts and mosses as facultative epiphyllous bryophytes which grow on leaf surface as well as epiphyte on the bark of same living tree.

7. Desert bryophytes. Those bryophytes which have the capability to tolerate great heat and great drought are called desert bryophytes. Moore and Scott (1979) have reported *Barbula torquata* and *Tortula princes* on sand dunes to a depth of 4cm in the fields.

Distribution of Bryophytes

Regarding the distribution of bryophytes in India, Pande (1958) divided the Indian subcontinent into four major bryogeographical units or regions which are as follows :

1. *The Himalayan Regions.*

   It has two territories which are

   (A) *The Western Himalayan Territory.* It extends from the western boundary of Nepal to Kashmir.

   (B) *The Eastern Himalayan Territory.* It includes eastern part of mountains of Indian territory separating India from neighbouring countries like Burma, Bangladesh and China.

2. *The Punjab and the West Rajasthan Plains.* It represents the area of Western India which receives comparatively low rain fall.

3. *Central India and the Gangetic Plains.* It includes Uttar Pradesh, Bihar, Bengal, Orissa, Madhya Pradesh and some parts of Gujrat and Maharashtra .
4. *Sourthern Zone.* It represents the total peninsular India which can be divided into two parts which are :
   (A) *The West Coast Region.* It represents the total area of Western Ghats.
   (B) *The East Coast region and Deccan Plateau.* It represents the eastern Ghats, Nilgiris and the Deccan Plateau.

Singh (1992) has rightly proposed and recommended to include Andaman and Nicobar Islands as a major bryogeographical unit or region. In fact, its climatic conditions and biodiversity is different from those regions as proposed by Pande 1958.

8. PHYSIOLOGY OF BRYOPHYTES

It was assumed that the physiology of bryophytes may be different from those of the higher plants as the two groups are widely different from each other. The plant body of bryophyte is gemetophytic and those of higher plants is sporophytic. However, investigations have shown that the various physiological processes in bryophytes are on the same lines as in Pteridophytes, Gymnosperms and Angiosperms. A brief account of some important physiological processes in bryophyte is being discussed here.

1. Water Relations

Bryophytes differ fundamentally from higher plants so far as the water relations are concerned. In bryophytes, being member of Atracheophyta, water absorption takes place either from the plant surface or through the rhizoids. Bryophytes have been grouped into three main catagories on the basis of their water relations. These are as follows :—

(a) Ectohydric. It includes those species which are capable of absorbing water or solutes by surface absorption only. Such species usually do not possess a well developed conducting strands, *e.g.* majority of leafy liverworts.

(b) Endohydric. It includes those species which are able to absorb water or solute mainly through their rhizoids which are internally conducted through well defined conducting strands. Such species also possess a waxy delicate layer on the leaf surface which partially or wholly checks the surface absorption. Examples are highly developed mosses or majority of thalloid liverworts.

(c) Mixohydric. It includes those species in which water and solute are absorbed by both the ways that is by ectohydric and endohydric methods. The best example of mixohydric bryophyte is *Funaria* plant.

The movement of water within the plant of a bryophyte takes place by following methods :

(*i*) External capillary space,

(*ii*) Cell to cell through cell membrane and walls,

(*iii*) Through the free space of the cell wall,

(*iv*) In higher mosses water moves within the plant from one part to another through the specialized conducting cells called Hydroids.

2. Mineral Nutrition

Mineral nutritional studies have been carried out on several species of bryophytes such as *Marchantia, Barbula, Jungermannia* and *Hyaloeonium* in which characteristic symptoms of N, P, K, Mg, and Ca deficiency have been reported. In *M. polymorpha*, the absence of Ca results in immediate death of growing point. Deficiency of N & P results in the deterioration of scales, rhizoids and the lower epidermis. Plants lacking NO_3 also become light green. In fact each species of bryophyte has its specific requirements for a particular element. Its deficiency or excess amount in substratum develops specific symptoms.

On the other hand some bryophytes are very specific for a particular element. Such bryophytes grow on those rocks which are rich in specific element. *Scopelophila lingulata* [Copper moss] prefers to grow on those rocks which are rich in copper element. Brooks (1972) recommended bryophytes as best guide to mineralization. This distinction is so pronounced that the bryoflora can be "*read like an instrument*" to give an idea of the nature of the underlying substrate. *Rhacomitrium himalayanum* grows on hard granites of Himalayas along with *Grimia* sp. Sometimes, admixture of bryoflora prefer to grow on polymetelic substrate. Pant and Tiwari (1989) have reported that *Marchantia - Barbula - Mielichhoferia* (admixture) grow on rock which is rich in copper, lead, and zinc at Askot (a well known locality in Pithoragarh). *Hyophila involuta, Tortella tortuosa* and *Zygodon viridissimus* grow on iron- haematite (Fe_2O_3) substrate which is alkaline in nature. *Jungermannia confertissima, Campylopus involutus* and *Pogonatum junghuhnianum* grow on limonitic substrate ($Fe_2O_3N'H_2O$) which is acidic in nature. *Hymenostylium recurvirostrum* var. *cylindricum* prefers its growth on magnesite deposits.

3. Translocation

The synthesized food materials i.e. carbohydrates are translocated through cell to cell diffusion along the concentration gradient. By using radioactive $C^{14}O_2$, it has been experimentally demonstrated that in *Dawsonia* the food is translocated from cell to cell along concentration gradient.

It has also been reported that in higher mosses where leptome (which is made up of leptoids and parenchyma cells) is present, the translocation of food takes place through longitudinal strands of leptoids.

Haberlandt (1886), Strassburger (1891), Eschrich and Steiner (1967) and Robert *et al* (1988) have supported this view.

4. Metabolism

The metabolic processes like photosynthesis, respiration and protein synthesis in bryophytes correspond to the heigher plants. The metabolites are classified in three main catagories.

(a)Primary metabolites. They are parts of vital metabolic pathway and most of them are of common occurrence. For example presence of Ribulose diphosphate (RuDP) in Calvin cycle is present in all C_3 plants or presence of Citric Acid (which participate in Krebs cycle) is present in all aerobic organisms.

(b) Secondary metabolites. They are mostly food storage. In bryophytes the food storage takes place in two forms:— Starch and oil.

(c) Semantides. These are information carrying molecules which are of three types :

(1) Primary semantide - D.N.A.

(2) Secondary semantide - R.N.A.

(3) Tertiary semantide - Proteins

The secondary metabolites and semantides (in which the data in term of sequences, ratio or percentages are studied) help in solving of taxonomic problems.

Chemotaxonomy. It is also known as chemosystematics or phytochemistry. Under chemotaxonomy one seeks to utilize chemical information to improve the classification of plants. Regarding the chemotaxonomy of bryophytes, Asakawa *et al* (1980 a, b) using several new techniques have reported several chemical compounds of liverworts, hornworts and mosses.

They analysed the plant extract by T.L.C., G.L.C. and GC-MS techniques. The chemical nature of the compounds isolated from bryophyte plant extract were established by chemical reactions.

The liverworts (Hepaticae) mostly possess terpenoids and/or aromatic compounds. The most important terpenoids of Hepaticae are :— (1) sesquiterpenoids and (ii) diterpenoids. The structure of these are as follows :—

Sesquiterpenoid

CHO
CHO
R

Diterpenoids

The hornworts (Anthocerotae) possess sesquiterpene hydrocarbon and sesquiterpene phenol which are more or less similar to liverworts.

The mosses possess triterpene hydrocarbons which are neither found in liverworts nor in hornworts. Therefore, hornworts are very close to liverworts in gametophytic plant body than mosses (musci). Asakaw *et. al* (1979) reported that mosses and ferns both possess hopane-type triterpenoids in common. Therefore, mosses are close to pteridophytes.

Enzymes. The enzymes are functional proteins which are very specific to temperature and pH. Udar and Chandra (1960) were the first to have reported several enzymes from liverworts. These are:

(*i*) Lipase, (*ii*) Amylase, (*iii*) Ribonuclease, (*iv*) Butyrase (*v*) Invertase (*vi*) Catalase, (*vii*) Acid phosphatase (*viii*) Maltase (*ix*) Urease (*x*) Phosphorylase and (*xi*) Proteolytic enzyme. Rao *et. al.* (1969) reported the activity of four oxidizing enzymes viz. (*i*) Polyphenol oxidase, (*ii*) Peroxidase (*iii*) Catalase and (*iv*) Ascorbic acid oxidase in *Riccia plana* when thalli of this species were kept under light and darkness. Taylor *et. al.* (1970) reported formic, glutamic, lactic and malic dehydrogenases from several genera of bryophytes.

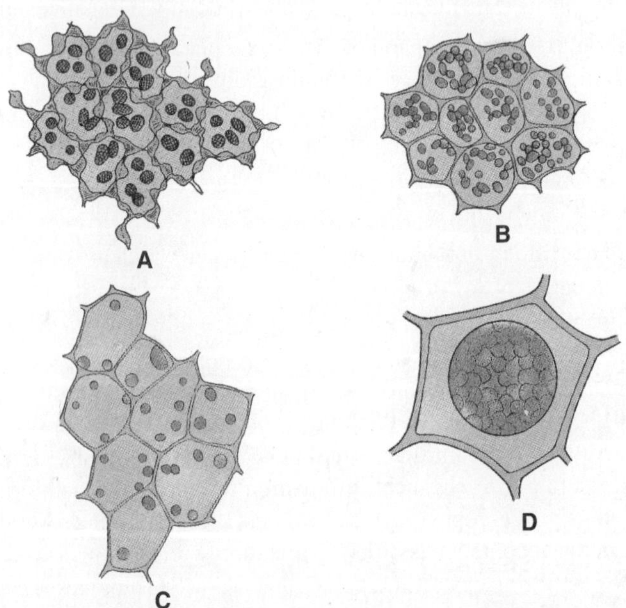

Fig. 21.11. Oil-bodies in liverworts. A, *Frullania* sp.; B, *Porella* sp.; C, *Sprucianthus* sp.; D, *Marchantia* sp.

9. OIL BODIES

The oil-bodies are distinctive and characteristic features of only liverworts. They are absent in hornworts and mosses. Most interesting feature is this that such type of oil-bodies are not found elsewhere in the whole of plant kingdom. Oil bodies are cytoplasmic inclusions made up of different types of volatile etherial oils. Their number, size, shape, surface structure and refractive index are also very unique and specific. The function of oil-bodies in liverworts has been a matter of controversy. A few of the function of these oil bodies are as follows:

1. Oil-bodies protect the plant body from bright light.
2. They provide a mechanism to protect the plant against dessication.
3. Some bryologists believe that oil-bodies help the plant to survive under extreme cold environments. Hence, they are also known as "cold protection bodies".
4. Only due to presence of oil-bodies, the liverworts are not attacked by snails and insects.
5. Liverworts are first primitive archegoniate land plants therefore, oil-bodies might have lost their original function.
6. They help in taxonomy of liverworts.
7. They emit different types of odours.
8. Their presence may be correlated with overwintering.

Schuster (1966) recognised two basic type of oil bodies which are :

(*i*) Those occuring in Jungermanniales are two or more per cell.

(*ii*) Those occuring in Marchantiales are one oil body per cell.

Muller studied 210 species of liverworts out of which 187 (89%) had oil bodies. Schuster studied 345 holarctic species out of which 307 (90%) had oil bodies. They found that annual or biennial forms of liverworts generally lack oil bodies, while perennial forms possess them. This suggests that their presence help in overwintering. Udar and his associates have studied the morpho-taxonomical values of oil-bodies in more than 100 taxa. The size, shape and number of oil bodies vary from species to species. Some oil-bodies are homogeneous and some are provided with droplets or granules. Miiller also studied the optical properties, specific gravity and saponifecation values of these oil-bodies of hepaticae which possess a very distinctive odour such as:

1. *Leptolejeunea* sp : Odour of Licoriel, odour similar to angiosperm *Osmorhiza*
2. *Conocephalum conicum* : Strong mushroom like smell.
3. *Lophozia bicrinata* : Odour similar to Cedar oil.
4. *Geocalyx graveolans* : Turpentine like odour.

The oil-bodies are usually colourless except with few exceptions such as in *Calypogeia trichomanis*, *C. peruviana* and *Lophocolea echinellus* where bright blue oil bodies are found.

10. MORPHOGENESIS

The term morphogenesis is made up of two words:—

Morpho-means form and *Genesis* - means origin of. Thus, morphogenesis can be defined as a branch of biology which deals with the origin or genesis or initiation of form of an organism. The morphogenesis aims to identify all metabolic processes which take place in the organism starting from the single celled stage; the spore-which is haploid and forms gametophyte and the zygote-which is diploid and forms sporophyte.

The bryophytes, which occupy unique position in plant kingdom (Cryptogams) in between thallophyta and pteridophyta, have gametophytic plant body on which sporophytic phase depends for support and for nutrition. The morphogenesis in bryophytes involves the entire bio-chemistry right from germination of spore to formation of spore within the capsule.

Phenomenon of Morphogenesis

The phenomenon of morphogenesis may thus include two primary functions

(*i*) Growth and (*ii*) Differentiation

Growth is a synthesis of protoplasm. Growth can be distinguished at the level of cells, tissues, organ and the organism in order of complexities. The growth follows the principles of the kinetics of open system in which both matter and energy enter and leave the system.

The process of differentiation leads from simplicity to complexity in the structure of an organism.

The scientists who are engaged in morphogenetic work of bryophytes have following advantages:

(*i*) The plants are simple, small in size and gametophytic.

(*ii*) Being non-vascular, the cellular complexity is not so much as found in higher plants.

(*iii*) The zygote, which is diploid and also called as first cell of the sporophyte, develops with in fertilized archegonium and forms embryo.

(*iv*) As embryo formation starts within the bryophytes, it is primitive and most simple.

(*v*) Embryo forms foot, seta and capsule. (In *Riccia* only capsule is present, in *Corsinia* only capsule and small few celled foot are present and in *Sphaerocarpos* capsule, small seta and small foot are present).

(*vi*) Embryo never forms root, stem and leaves as in higher plants.

(*vii*) Vegetative propagation is common.

(*viii*) Both the generations can be studied on the same plant.

(*ix*) Life span is short, therefore within a very short duration the experimental work can be completed.

(*x*) Bryophytes also provide apical cell with one cutting face as in protonema, with two cutting faces as in the development of sporophyte and with three cuting faces in gametophore.

(*xi*) It is easy to induce callus from gametophyte and sporophyte.

Edmund W. Sinnott (1960) has divided the subject of morphogenesis into three parts:

(*a*) Growth

(*b*) The phenomenon of morphogenesis : This part includes following aspects such as

(*i*) Correlation — Genetic correlation,Physiological correlation.

(*ii*) Polarity

(*iii*) Symmetry

(*iv*) Differentiation

(*v*) Regeneration

(*vi*) Tissue mixtures

(*vii*) Abnormal growth

(*c*) Morphogenetic factors : These factors are

(*i*) Light, (*ii*) Water, (*iii*) Temperature (*iv*) Gravity (*v*) Chemical factors, (*vi*) Growth substances, (*vii*) Genetic factors including cytoplasmic and (*viii*) nuclear organization.

Techniques for the Culture of Bryophytes

The techniques used for the culture of bryophytes as proposed by Bopp and Knoop (1984) is basically more or less similar as applied for other plants. Chopra (1987) has proposed following ten steps for the culture of bryophytes:—

(*i*) Suitability and selection of bryophyte for culture studies,
(*ii*) Starting the cultures,
(*iii*) Glasswares and instruments used,
(*iv*) Gadgets used,
(*v*) Composition of culture media and then preparation,
(*vi*) Culture room conditions,
(*vii*) Sterilization of plant materials, galssware, culture media, instruments and inoculation chamber,
(*viii*) Inoculation procedures,
(*ix*) Special culture techniques and
(*x*) Observations and presentation of data.

Callus formation. For the development of a callus it is necessary to suppress the polarity — an important phenomenon of morphogenesis. It is achieved by nutrilization of internal gradients of nutrients and/or growth substances. The factors, the bryophyte and the name of the investigator (s) are summarised below :

Factors	System	Investigators
1. Increase in Sugar Concentration	*Calypogeia granulate*	Takeda and Kotch (1981)
2. X-Rays	*Polytrichum commune*	Ward (1960)
3. UV-Rays	*Asterella wallichiana*	Chopra and Kumar (1986)
4. Auxins	*Riccia frostii*	Vashistha (1985)
5. Cytokinins	*Tetraphis pellucida*	Demkiv *et. al* (1981)
6. Auxin + Cytokinin	*Athalamia pusilla*	Mehra and Pental (1976)
7. High Sugar Concentration + Coconut milk	*Fossombronia himalayensis*	Mehra and Pahwa (1976)
8. Vitamin B_1	*Funaria hygrometrica*	Bumning and Wettstein (1953)
9. Peptone	*Riccia crystallina*	Sood (1974)
10. Yeast extract	*Riccia crystallina*	Sood (1974)
11. Casein hydrolysate	*Riccia frostii*	Vashistha, 1985.

Differentiation in callus. In some bryophytes such as *Riccia* and *Funaria* the differentiation in callus usually takes place on the same medium in which they were induced. In other bryophytes, the differentiation is influenced by several morphogenetic factors as reported by Sinnott (1960). The cultures grown in light develop both gametophyte and sporophyte but when grown in dark, they develop only sporophyte as reported in a moss *Physcomitrium coorgense*. Kumra (1981) has reported that low temperature enhances the sporophytic differentiation in *Funaria hygrometrica,* The coconut milk, when added in the medium, also enhances the sporophytic differentiation.

In morphogenesis, the growth is followed by differentiation. The differentiation is controlled in three ways :—

(*i*) Exogenous control
(*ii*) Cytoplasmic control
(*iii*) Nuclear control.

All the three controls are inter-dependent and work in intimate co-ordination. The exogenous controls include, light, temperature, gravity and mineral nutrients etc. The cytoplasmic controls mediate between the exogenous control and nuclear control. In fact, cytoplasmic control is very important as it acts as buffer. The third control also called nuclear control is the most important control amongst the three. It is exerted by the genes of the organism. It can be better explained by Mehra's gene block hypothesis which states that there is no fundamental difference in gametophytic and sporophytic generations. In these two generations, it is the different gene systems that are in the activated state.

Apogamy in Bryophytes

Apogamy means the development of a sporophyte (embryo) out of any gametophytic cell without the union of male and female gametes.

In bryophytes the sporophyte, which is most simple amongst all the members of embryophyta and consists of foot, seta and capsule, may be produced apogamously from haploid gametophytic tissues which may be protonema buds, rhizoids, or any part of the plant body.

Rashid and Chopra (1969) got success to produce apogamous sporophytes in *Funaria hygrometrica* on the axis of the gametophyte plant. Lal (1963) produced numerous apogamous sporophytes of *Physcomitrium coorgense* on culture medium containing sugar and coconut milk. The gametophytic tissue was taken out from stem and venter wall of the archegonium.

Apospory in Byrophytes

Apospory means the development of a gametophyte from any part of thc sporophytc without any reduction division.

In bryophytes the gametophyte, which is thalloid or leafy in liverworts but only leafy in mosses, is produced aposporously from diploid sporophytic tissues of either foot or seta or capsule. In mosses, the protenema and buds are produced before the formation of the plant, therefore, both of them can also be produced aposporously from sporophytic tissues.

Rautzens and Matzke (1963) have reported the apospory in *Blasia pusilla* - a leafy liverwort of order Metzgeriales. Ulychna (1971) has successfully produced aposporous protonema in *Dicrancella schreberi.*

Pringshein (1876) and Stahl (1876) reported the development of protonema from the small fragment of seta. The diploid protonema, later on, produces the axis of the plant.

11. BRYOPHYTES — AS BIOINDICATORS OF WATER POLLUTION

The life form of bryophytes is very simple so they are comparatively more affected by polluted waters than other groups. The polluted water also affects the benthic and marginal soils thus it directly affects the aquatic bryoflora and directly or indirectly affects those bryophytes which grow on its banks.

More often the terms contamination and pollution are confused. While contamination means addition of unwanted organisms or nutrients pollution to widely used for both addition and deletion of important elements and organisms. Therefore, the water is called polluted when water pollutants are found in water. The water pollutants are any foreign particles in water (which is living or non living or both) present beyond permissible limits and become injurious to living organism. These pollutants change the quality of water which is determined on the basis of several physico-chemical and biological parameters. It has been reported that physico-chemical parameters generally affect the plant life.

Because of their simple plant body, the bryophytes appear to be sensitive to polluted waters due to following reasons :—

(*i*) The plant body is gametophytic, very small, soft and delicate. Thus bryophytes mostly prefer moist places to grow.

(*ii*) The plants lack well developed vascular system comprising of xylem and phloem.

(*iii*) The plants lack well developed root system but develop rhizoids which help in absorption of water.

(*iv*) The water is essential for fertilization.

The bryophytes absorb the water either by rhizoids or by entire surface of plant or by both ways. The movement of water within plant body of a bryophyte takes place either by central strand or by free space of cell or cell to cell or external capillary space. Therefore, if water is polluted it certainly affects the life forms of bryophytes including external morphology, anatomy, fertilization, spore germination and physiology. Therefore, the bryophytes have been reported to be more sensitive to water pollution than air pollution (Kumar and Sinha, 1989).

Saxena and Glime (1991) have proposed several arguments for the use of aquatic bryophytes to monitor pollution. Empain (1967) and Trollope and Evans (1976) believed that bryophytes can provide an integrated information of pollution within a system. Some aquatic bryophytes which are pollution tolerant species have been recommended to monitor the levels of pollution in water. These species are :—

1. *Amblystegium riparium.* It is a moss which is cosmopolitan in distribution and found in running and stagnant water or sewage rich in nutrition.

2. *Eurhynechium riparioides.* It is a moss which is found only in northern region of world. It grows in ponds and rivers rich in nutrition. Empain (1976) and Empain *et. al.* (1980) have reported pollutant contents and heavy metals of these waters.

3. *Fontinalis antipyretica.* A moss which is also restricted in northern part and grows in both stagnant and running water. Welsh and Dinny (1980) have analysed Cu and Pb and the moss.

4. *Fontinalis squamosa.* It is also restricted in distribution. McLean and Jones (1975) have reported the details of pollutants and heavy metals.

Pandey *et. al.* (1986), Sinha (1988) and Kumar and Sinha (1989), during a comprehensive study of River Ganga, have reported some specific bryophytes which appear on its banks and are affected by river water quality. These bryophytes are

1. *Riccia gangetica.* A pollution tolerant species. The tuberculate rhizoids and marginal scales are more developed in highly polluted sites. It is a monoecious species.

2. *Riccia frostii.* A pollution sensitive species which grows in lesser polluted sites. The sensitivity towards polluted water is due to presence of only smooth-walled rhizoids, absence of scales and separate male and female plants.

3. *Funaria hygrometrica.* Found only on those sites where cremation takes place and benthic and marginal soil is rich in P & Ca.

4. *Physcomitrium indicum.* It is a moss which absorbs the heavy metals.

Pandey *et.al.* (2001) have reported that bryophytes growing on the river banks of Ganga absorb very high levels of heavy metals like Cr, Zn and Ni.

12. BRYOPHYTES — AS BIOINDICATORS OF AIR POLLUTION

The bryophytes have been reported to be good indicators of air pollution. A lot of work has been done on this aspect by serveral workers such as Le Blanc *et. al.* (1971), Le Blanc and Rao (1971). Le Blanc and Rao (1973) and Rao *et. al.* (1977).

The bryophytes are very sensitive to air pollution. The air becomes polluted when air pollutants, which are beyond permissible limits and injurious to living organism, are found mixed within it. According to World Health Organisation (WHO), air pollution may be defined as limited to situations in which the out door ambient atmosphere contains materials in concentrations which are harmful to man and his environment. Zutshi (1970) of Bhabha Atomic Research Centre (BARC) classified sources of air pollution as follows :—

(*i*) Combusion :— From fuel burning, transportation and open burning dumps.

(*ii*) Manufacturing process :— Chemical plants, Metallurgical plants and waste recovery.

(*iii*) Agricultural activities :— Crop spraying as weed and pest control, Gases evolved from the fields.

(*iv*) Solvent usage :— Spray painting, solvent extraction inks, solvent cleaning.

(*v*) Nuclear energy :— Fuel fabrication, Ore preparation, Nuclear device testing, spent fuel processing.

The air pollutants are mainly of three types :— (1) In the form of gases — as (*i*) Sulphur dioxide, (*ii*) Fluoride, (*iii*) Hydrogen sulphide, (*iv*) Ozone, (*v*) Nitrogen dioxide, (*vi*) Ammonia (*vii*) Methane, (*viii*) Petrolium vapours and (*ix*) Hydrogen Fluoride; (2) In the form of particulate matters - as solid and liquid aerosols and (3) Micro organism and spores/pollens of plants.

The bryophytes, being very sensitive to gaseous and particulate matters, are being used as bio indicators. Some species of bryophytes are pollution tolerant and some are pollution sensitive. Regarding the pollution sensitivity of bryophytes a review article on bryophytes with respect to air pollution was published by Le Blanc and Rao in 1971. It states that within last century the Belgium bryoflora has lost 20 species of liverworts and 94 species of mosses. The Dutch bryoflora was depleted by 15% of terrestrial and 13% of epiphytics. In Amsterdam 23 species of bryophytes are now extinct from the city.

It has been reported that air pollutants affect the habitat and growth form of bryophytes. The sensitivity of bryophytes towards air pollution increases from terricolous to saxicolous and corticolous species. The moss protonema is more sensitive than its mature gametophores (Gilbert, 1969).

Daly (1970) reported some bryophytes which are able to tolerate levels of pollution on stone walls than on tree tranks. Some species are *Tortula princeps, Bryum rubrum, Ceratodon purpureus* and *Pohila cruda*

Gilbert (1970) observed that the growth form of bryophytes in respect to tolerance of pollution gradually increases from tall turf, large cushion or leafy liverworts to smooth and small cushion and fianlly most resistant are sort turf and thalloid liverworts.

De Sloover and LeBlanc (1970) have also reported that fertility of bryophytes decreases as pollution level increases.

Bryophyte species sensitive to air pollution are :—

(*i*) *Ulota crispa* (*ii*) *Platydictya subtile*

(*iii*) *Paraleucobryum longifolium* (*iv*) *Frullania muscicola*

(*v*) *Trocholejeunea sandvicensis* (*vi*) *Lophocolea minor.*

13. VEGETATIVE REPRODUCTION (PROPAGATION) IN BRYOPHYTES

Reproduction by vegetative methods is the common mode of reproduction and propagation in bryophytes. This mode of reproduction does not involve fusion and meiosis and is a characteristic feature of this group of plants. In most of the dioceious byrophytes, the propagation of the species takes place by vegetative means. It was Correns (1899) who was the first to collect and summarise the vegetative methods of reproduction in bryopsida or mosses. Later Cavers (1903) did this in

Hepaticopsida or liverworts. A brief account of various methods of propagation through vegetative means has been presented below:

(i) By death and decay of older parts. In many liverworts like *Riccia, Marchantia, Anthoceros, Notothylas* etc. this is the most common mode of propagation. This process involves progressive death and decay of the older parts of the thallus and separation of young parts at the dichotomy of the thallus. These separated parts develop to form adult mature thalli.

(ii) By formation of adventitious branches. This means of vegetative reproduction takes place in *Riccia fluitans*, archegoniophore of *Marchantia, Metzgeria, Targionia, Reboulia, Asterella, Sphaerocarpos* etc. Adventitious branches develop usually from the underside of the midrib of the thallus. These branches on detachment develop into mature thalli.

(iii) By branch tips. During prolonged drought, all parts of a gametophyte except the branch tips weather away and are killed. Each such branch tip is capable of developing to a new plant as the favourable conditions return back. This method of vegetative reproduction is quite common in species of *Riccia.*

(iv) By formation of innovations and their separation is the method of vegetative propagation in acrogynous Jungermanniales and *Sphagnum.*

(v) By Cladia. Cladia are small detachable branches or brood branches which help in vegetative reproduction. These may develop on : (*i*) leaves and known as *Leaf cladia* which originate from individual cells of the leaf as in *Bryopteris fruticulosa, Plagiochila* and *Frullania fragilifolia;* and (*ii*) stems and known as *Stemcladia* which originate on the stems as the sexual branches as in *Bryopteris fruticulosa Leptolejeunea etc.*

(vi) By tubers. Vegetative reproduction by tubers takes place in many bryophytes. The tubers are round structures formed on the thalli under unfavourable conditions. On the approach of favourable conditions the tubers germinate into new thalli. In *Riccia discolor, Riccia billardieri, Anthoceros thallii* and *A. pearsoni* tubers are produced on the margins of the thalli while in *A. himalayensis* tubers are borne upon stalks on the ventral surface of the thallus. Tubers are also produced in species of *Fossombronia, Sewardiella tuberifera, Exormotheca tuberifera, Asterella angusta, Stephensonella tuberifera,* and *Aitchisoniella himalayensis.*

(vii) By gemmae. Gemmae are organs of propagation with definite form but different from the parent plant from which they arise. Gemmae are commonly formed in the genera of Hepaticopsida, less common in Anthocerotopsida but to somewhat lesser extent in Bryopsida. However, they are altogether absent in the subclass Sphagnidae.

Gemmae are of different shapes, may be stalked or sessile and may develop on different parts of the parent plant. A brief account of Gemmae in Hepaticopsida, Anthocerotopsida and Bryopsida is given below :

Class *Hepaticopsida.* (*a*) In *Marchantia, Lunularia, Marchasta* and *Cavicularia* gemmae are multicellular, stalked, green, discoid produced in gemma cups on the dorsal surface of the thallus.

(*b*) In *Blasia* gemmae are subspherical in form and are produced in abundance in flask shaped gemma receptacles.

(*c*) Gemmae are two celled endogenous structures produced within any external cell of thallus as in *Riccardia sinuata, R. pinguis* and *R. palmata.*

(*d*) Gemmae are one to three celled and produced on leaves in *Marsupella emarginata, Diplophyllum albicans.*

(*e*) Discoid multicelluar gemmae are produced on leaves in many species of *Radula* like *R. complanata, R. germana.*

(*f*) In *Lophozia heterocolpa, Cephalozia bicuspida, Cephaloziella byssacea* etc. one to three celled gemmae are produced on stem apex.

(*g*) In *Metzgeria uncigera* gemmae are discoid and produced on gemmiferous branches.

(*h*) Three to four celled gemmae are produced in the axil of the leaves in *Treubia.*

(*i*) *In Blasia* star shaped gemmae are produced on the dorsal surface of the thallus.

Class *Anthocerotopsida*. In this class gemmae are produced in the species of *Anthoceros* like *A. glandulosus, A. propaguliferous* and *A. formosae*. In these the gemmae are borne along the margin and dorsal surface of the thallus.

Class. *Bryopsida*. In the members of this class, gemmae are produced in a few genera only but are absent in the subclass Sphagnidae. In the genera of subclass Bryidae the gemmae are of different shapes and produced at different positions.

(*a*) Gemmae are stalked, multicellular, green, lenticular and are produced at the tip of the shoot surrounded by a cup-like structure formed by widened leaves, example *Tetraphis pellucida*.

(*b*) In *Aulocomnium androgynum* stalked fusiform gemmae are produced at the end of distinct leafless terminal stalks.

(*c*) Globular multicellular gemmae are produced at the base of stem in *Bryum rubens* and *B. erythrocarpum*.

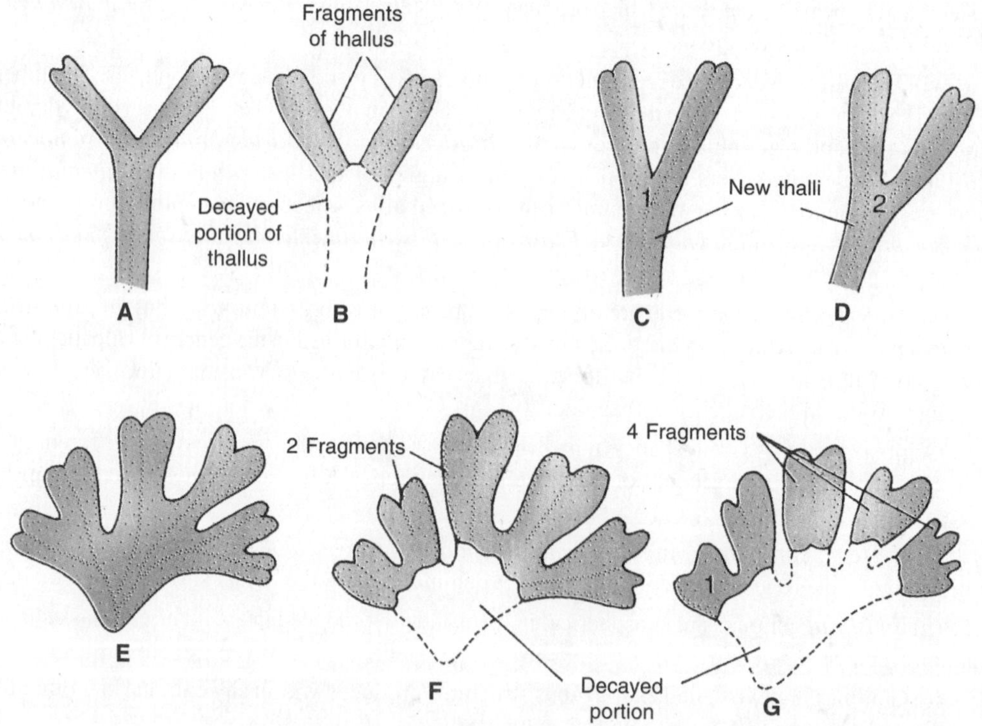

Fig. 21.12. Vegetative reproduction by death and decay; A—D, *Riccia*; E—G, *Marchantia*.

(*d*) In *Tortula papillosa Zygodon, Ulota phyllantha*, multicellular articulate gemmae are produced on the leaves.

(*e*) Multicellular gemmae are produced on the rhizoids of leaf shoots in *Ceratodon purpureum, Bryum erythrocarpum, Tortula stanfordensis etc.*

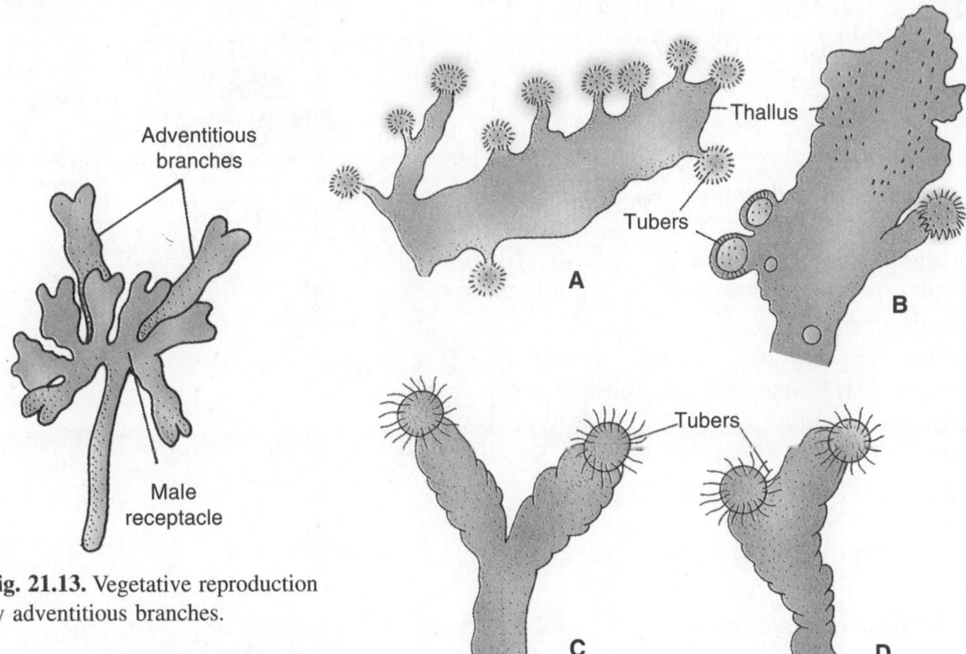

Fig. 21.13. Vegetative reproduction by adventitious branches.

Fig. 21.14. Vegetative reproduction by tubers.

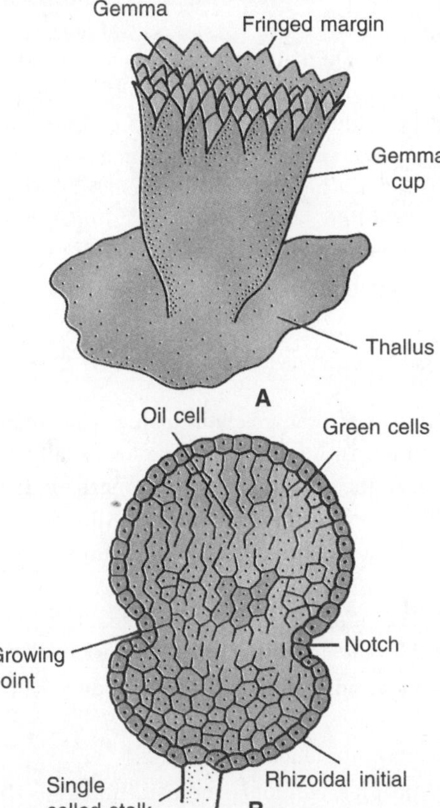

Fig. 21.15. *Marchantia.* Vegetative reproduction by gemmae.

(*f*) In *Pterygynandrum fileforme* stalked, ovoid, smooth, golden brown gemmae consisting of two cells borne on a hyaline stalk of three cells are produced on the stem.

(viii) By primary protonema. In *Funaria* the spores germinate to form flamentous structure, the primary protonema. The primary protonema may break into small pieces, each of these is capable of forming a new protonema. The protonema bears buds. Each bud develops into a new plant.

(ix) By secondary protonema. Secondary protonema are not produced by the germination of spores but these are formed by other methods. Morphologically secondary protonema is similar to primary protonema. On secondary protonema also, buds are produced, each bud develops to form the adult plant *e.g. Funaria hygrometrica.*

Secondary protonema may also develop from the marginal cell of primary protonema in *Sphagnum.*

(x) By rhizoids. In *Leucobryum glaucum,* vegetative reproduction takes place by rhizoids. In the centre of a terminal rosette of leaves is present a tuft of rhizoids. From the rhizoids new plants arise.

14. ECONOMIC IMPORTANCE OF BRYOPHYTA

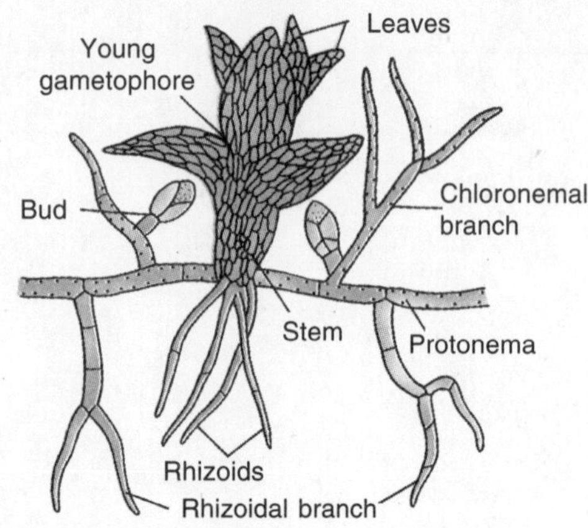

Fig. 21.16. ***Funaria hygrometnea.*** Vegetative reproduction by protonema.

The bryophytes, also called as liliputians amongst land plants, have shown their economic importance since stone age when pre historic man had made uses of feather moss (*Neckera crispa*). In modern age, these liliputians have attracted environmentalists, botanists, industrialists, horticulturists and pharmacists only because of their economic values.

The bryophytes include liverworts (Hepaticopsida) having over 300 genera and 6000-10,000 species, hornworts (Anthocerotopsida) having half a dozen genera and about fifty species and mosses (Bryopsida) having over 680 genera and about 15,000 species.

Economically the bryophytes can be grouped in two main catagories:

A. Direct use of bryophytes

B. Indirect use of bryophytes.

A. Direct use of Bryophytes

1. Sphagnum and the Peat,. The pieces of dead vegetable matter partially decomposed by water in the bog and gradually compressed and carbonized under pressure of the overlapping late deposits and water is called the *peat*. It is a brown or dark coloured spongy substance. *Sphagnum* and other mosses are the chief constituents of peat. Besides these peat contains remains of other plants growing in the bog such as the reeds, sedges, grasses, ferns and shrubs. Some peats however, consist mainly of the remains of *Sphagnum*. For this reason this moss is often called *peat moss*. These bog plants grow luxuriantly and in dense stands. Their basal older portions die. Thus large amounts of dead vegetable matter accumulate each year gradually filling the pond or lake. These deposits compressed and hardened by the weight of fresh deposits from above, in the course of time, attain considerable thickness. The compacted, partially decomposed and carbonized dead plant deposits are called the **peat**.

Uses of peat. (*i*) Peat is used as a **fuel**. The thick deposits of peat are cut into blocks and dried. Being rich in carbon the dried peat blocks are used as fuel. In Northern Europe, especially the Netherlands peat fuel is still used on a commercial scale. In the recent past the Europeans burned peat in the generation of power and there existed many factories in France for making illuminating gas from peat which has now been replaced by coal. Besides fuel, the following other uses of peat have been reported :

(*ii*) *Preparation of ethyl alcohol*. Odell and Hood (1926) reported that by chemical treatment cellulose in peat is broken down into sugar which through fermentation is converted into alcohol.

(*iii*) The Germans evolved a method to obtain ammonium sulphate as by-product in the production of gas from peat.

(*iv*) Nitrates, brown dye and tanning materials have been produced from peat.

(*v*) The other products of industrial use of peat are peat tar, ammonia and paraffin.

(*vi*) Davis (1911) reported that peat has been manufactured into paper, woven fabrics and artificial wood and employed as a mattress filler and as a bedding material for domesticated animals after cleaning the sticks and other coarse materials.

(*vii*) *Use in horticulture. Sphagnum* and peat are also of great use in horticulture. Peat is added to heavy (clayey) soils to improve their texture as it keeps them porous and prevents caking. When added to dry, sandy soils or other humus poor soils, it improves their water holding capacity and serves as a source of organic matter. Duffey (1954) observed that peat is the most important source of humus in the world. Dried sphagna are also used as garden mulch which helps to retain high soil acidity required by certain decorative and economically important plants. Cleansed peat and *Sphagnum* are extensively employed by horticulturists and florists as a substratum for seed germination, to start cuttings and to grow other plants and to propagate orchids. *Sphagnum* is also used as a packing for grafting scions to protect them against drying influence of the surrounding air.

(*viii*) Dried *Sphagnum* and moss peat for their ability to hold water tenaciously are remoistened and used as packing material for shipment of live plants, cut flowers, vegetables, perishable fruits, bulbs and tubers. Stokes (1931) observed that it (the packing material) retains enough moisture for a ling time and it protects against heat and cold. Peat is as well used as a packing material for fruits, fish, eggs and meat for cold storage.

(*ix*) Davis (1910) suggested that peat has a certain food value and thus has been used as a stock food in mixture with molasses.

(*x*) Davis (1946) reported that the various products of industrial use such as acetic acid, methyl alcohol, humic and allied acids, carbonic acid, paraffin, naphtha, montan wax and lignins used in making plastics have been obtained from peat by different methods.

(*xi*) Dacknowski-Stokes (1942) recommended peat moss as a suitable material for use in surgical dressings. Because of its great absorbent power and slight antiseptic properties carefully dried, cleansed and sterilized *Sphagnum* has long been employed for guaze to dress wounds and for making absorbent bandages in the treatment of boils and discharging wounds. Porter (1917) observed that the sphagnum dressings are cooler, softer and less irritating than those made with cotton.

2. Medicinal use of Bryophytes. Information on medicinal use of bryophytes is scanty. Watt (1891) had reported to the medicinal use of *Marchantia polymorpha, Fagetella conica* and a few species of *Jungermannia, Anthoceros* and *Riccia*. Wren (1956) mentioned only *Polytrichum juniperinum* in this connection. Roig Y. Mesa (1945) mentioned that among liverworts *Marchantia polymorpha* has been used to cure pulmonary tuberculosis and afflictions of the liver. Hartwell (1971) reported that extracts of *M. polymorpha, M. stellata* and *Polytrichum commune* possess antitumour properties. However, the use of mosses in the treatment of ailments is more pronounced. Shiu-ying (1945) reported that dried *Sphagnum* is boiled in water. The decoction is used in the treatment of acute haemorrhage and diseases of the eye. According to Roque (1941) tea made of *Polytrichum commune* helps to dissolve stones of kidney and gall bladder. Peat tar, one of the by-products of peat, has antiseptic properties and is used as a preservative. According to Grieve (1931), a distillate of peat tar known as *sphagnol* has been effectively used in the treatment of skin diseases. Hotson (1918 a) reported that Alaskan Indians prepared a healing ointment by mixing sphagnum leaves with grease or tallow. It was used in the treatment of wounds and cuts. The use of *Sphagnum* for making absorbent bandages in the treatment of boils and discharging wounds has been described above.

3. Antibiotic activities of Bryophyta. There is scanty information about the occurrence of antibiotical substances in the bryophytes. However in recent years the antibiotical activities of bryophytes have drawn the attention of several workers. Hayes (1947) reported that aqueous extract of *Conocephalum conicum* is antibiotically active. Madsen and Pates (1952) and Pates and Madsen (1955) tested the antibiotic activities of four species namely *C. conicum, Dumortiera hirsuta, Sphagnum portoricense* and *S. strictum*. They found the first two to be active against *Candida albicans*. The two species of *Sphagnum* inhibited the growth of *Staphylococcus aureus* and *Pseudomonas aeruginosa*. Ramaut (1959) observed that the extracts of a species of *Sphagnum* inhibited the growth of *Sarcina lutea*. McCleary *et al* (1960) reported *Anomodon rostratus* and

Orthotrichum rupestre to be antibiotically active against *Micrococcus flavus, M. rubens, Streptococcus pyogenes* and *Candida albicans*. Later McCleary and Walkington (1966) tested the antibiotical activities of 50 species of mosses against two bacteria, *Gaffkeya tetragena* and *Staphylococcus aureus*. *Atrichium, Mnium, Polytrichum* and *Sphagnum* showed pronounced antibiotic activity, 18 species were moderate to strongly active against one or both bacteria. The remainder showed slight but positive activity. Gupta and Singh (1971) reported that the petroleum ether extracts of two species of mosses namely *Barbula* and *Timella* are antibiotically active against 33 bacterial species which include gram negative, gram positive and acid fast bacteria. Later Bannerjee and Sen (1979) tested antibiotic activity of 52 species of bryophytes belonging to 40 genera against 12 micro organisms which included 3 gram positive (*Staphylococcus aureus, Sarcina lutea,* and *Bacillus subtills*), 5 gram negative (*Escherichia coli, Salmonella typhi, Vibrio Cholerae, Klebsiella pneumoniae* and *Pseudomonas aeruginosa*), one acid-fast bacterium (*Mycobacterium phlei*) and 3 fungi (*Curvularia lunata, Aspergillus niger* and *Heminthosporium oryzae*). They came to the conclusion that a variety of antibiotic substances occur among bryophytes.

4. During the last decade several unsaturated lipids, fatty acid esters, flavonoids, triterpenoids, phenolics and other chemical substances have been reported to be present in the bryophytes.

5. Use of bryophytes in experimental Botany. The liverworts and mosses have palyed an important role as research tools in the various phases of botany such as genetics, experimental morphology and physiology. The mechanism of sex determination in plants was discovered for the first time in a liverwort *Sphaerocarpos*. Allen's studies (1935, 1945) on the genetics of bryophytes and Wettstein's investigations (1932) on hetroploid bryophytes are classics. Berie (1964) made experimental studies on polyploidy in liverworts. Important contributions on desiccation and regeneration, which are their chief attributes, have been made in the recent past by various investigators. Giminghan and Birse (1957) studied correlation between growth form and habitat in bryophytes and Birse (1957) made experimental studies on growth forms in mosses.

6. Bryophytes as a source of food. Bryophytes are not directly used as human food. However, Landley (1856) made mention of *Sphagnum* as a wretched food in barbarous countries. Read (1946) listed peat moss as a famine food in China. Haines (1877) recorded Laplanders having made use of *Sphagnum* as an ingredient in the preparation of bread. There are, however, examples of animals useful to man which use bryophytes as a food source. Lid and Miedell (1933) reported that moss capsules such as that of *Bryum* and *Polytrichum* constitute the chief diet of the Norwegian grouse chicks. The capsules of moor-inhabiting mosses are the favourite food of the red grouse chicks. Collinge (1927) recorded that some English birds such as the field fare, song thrush and black bird include some mosses as a small part of their regular diet. Hone (1934), Hawden and Palmer (1922) observed that Alaskan reindeer grazes upon *Polytrichum* sp., *Aulacominum turgidum*, and *Hylocomium alaskanum* besides lichens and grasses in summer. In winter they include *Sphagnum fimbriatum* and *Dicranum* spp. in addition to the above.

7. Bryophytes as pollution indicators. Rubling and Tyler (1979) and Ferguson *et al* (1978) showed that both alive and air dried mosses particularly *Sphagnum* can absorb metals. The accumulation of heavy metal cations in mosses enables them to be used as atmospheric and aquatic pollution indicators and in minrological surveys.

8. Miscellaneous uses of bryophytes. *Dicranum elongate* was used by Cree Indians for lampwicks (Chamberlain, 1901) and the Eskimos of N.E. Labrador used *Rhacomitrium lanuginosum* for the same purpose (Hantzsch, 1931). Evans and Nichlos (1908) reported that foliose liverworts have been employed as a packing material for living plants in the tropics and some masses for vegetables. Mosses have been as well used as a decorative material for pillows. Brail and Moyle (1976) reported that birds employ fragments of gametophores of mosses and liverworts in the construction of their nests.

B. Indirect use of Bryophytes

1. As aids in soil conservation. The mosses prevent sheet erosion of soil. They grow in dense stands forming a mat or carpet-like structure. This thick moss carpet serves a twofold function. Firstly it bears the impact of the falling rain drops and secondly it holds much of the water that falls. Consequently the amount of run-off is considerably reduced. Besides there is no or little turbidity in the run-off. Conard (1935) demonstrated that the turbid water flowing through the moss mat is shorn much of its sediment. The inter-twined moss stems and the underground rhizoids bind the soil particles together to a considerable depth (6-8 inches) so firmly that there is no or little erosion even on a steepy hill side. Grout (1912) held that even the moss protonema mat checks soil erosion.

2. Formation of soil and development of vegetation cover. The lichens and mosses play an important role in soil formation. Both are slow but efficient soil formers. The lichens, however, are the pioneers to colonise barren, bare rocky surfaces where no other plants can grow. The lichen thalli secrete organic acids which gradually dissolve and disintegrate the rocks to which they cling. The rock particle together with the dead and decaying older parts of the lichen thalli form fertile soil. Mosses make their appearance when sufficient amount of this fertile soil gathers in the crevices of the rock surface. The progressive growth and death of the older parts of the mosses adds to the substratum begun by the lichens. Dust and debris blown by the wind rapidly accumulate between the erect moss stems. Weaver and Clements (1938) reported that in the course of time, the depth of soil under the moss mats may be more than one inch. The moss mat collects sufficient moisture and contains humus to form a suitable substratum for the growth of many rock loving herbaceous plants. In fact Schroeter (1926) recorded that *Saxifraga cotyledon* germinates only among the mosses. The other rock loving species which usually appear in the moss mats are *Sedum, Thymus, Saxifraga aizoon* and others. To sum up in the development of vegetation cover over rocky surfaces, the mosses play a vital role. The moss stage follows the lichen stage and precedes the herbs. The latter, in turn, may be succeeded by shrubs and trees.

3. Bog succession. Weaver and Clements (1938) remarked that mosses play an important role in bog succession from open water to climax forest. The mosses especially the peat mosses established on the banks of lakes and other shallow bodies of water extend inwards and grow over the surface of water with their stems intertwined to form thick mats. These surface mats over bodies of water give the appearance of solid soil. Such areas are called *quacking bogs*. The thick moss mat because of the moisture and humus forms a suitable substratum for the germination of seeds of various species of hydrophytic plants. The older parts of these plants gradually die and settle to the bottom. In the course of time, these lakes and shallow bodies of water become filled up with partially decomposed old parts of mosses and other hydrophytic plants. Thus the areas which originally were sterile sheets of water, become converted into solid soil supporting vegetation. The mosses and hydrophytic angiosperms eventually disappear. They are replaced by forest growth of mesophytic type. The mosses thus play a vital role in changing the landscape.

4. Role as rock builders. Certain mosses (*Bryum, Hypnum, Fissidens* and others) growing in association with other aquatic plants (such as *Chara* and many other algae) play a remarkable role as rock builders. These plants grow in shallow waters of lakes, streams and springs which contain a large amount of calcium bicarbonate. The plants bring about decomposition of bicarbonic ions by abstracting free carbon dioxide. The insoluble calcium carbonate precipitates. This insoluble mineral, on exposure, hardens forming calcareous (lime) rock-like deposits around these plants. These travertine deposits continue to grow by the aid of mosses and algae growing in the water extending over areas of several hundreds square feet. The travertine rock deposits are extensively used as a building stone.

Table I

COMPARISON BETWEEN THE GAMETOPHYTES OF

1. *Riccia*	2. *Marchantia*	3. *Pellia*	4. *Porella* or *Madotheca*	5. *Anthoceros*	6. *Sphagnum*	7. *Funaria*
Habitat Most of the species are terrestrial. They grow on moist soil. A few are aquatic. The latter grow floating or submerged in the water of quiet ponds and lakes.	It is more terrestrial in habit than *Riccia*. It grows in moist situation such as damp earth, walls of wells, along streams and wet rocks. No aquatic species has so far been reported.	It occurs commonly on damp soil by the sides of streams, springs, wells, sometimes actually under water and rarely on moist rocks.	It grows in damp, shady places on logs, tree trunks, branches, wet rocks etc. It often occurs in large mats in the tropics.	It is terrestrial and grows on soil generally in very moist, shady places on the sides of slopes, ditches and in moist hollows among rocks. The plants grow in dense clusters.	All species of *Sphagnum* grow in very wet places as semi-aquatics and also submerged confined to acidic water-logged habitats. They thrive best in cold bogs and marshes at higher altitudes and often form an important constituent of peat bog vegetation.	It grows in dense patches in moist situations such as damp soil, on the wall, on moist rocks and on lands burnt by fires.
Thallus (*a*) *External Features* The plant body is a small green thallus. It is dorsiventral and grows prostrate on the ground. It branches freely by dichotomy and frequently takes on a circular form. Each thallus lobe has a distinct **midrib**, a dorsal median **groove** or **furrow** and ends in a **termi-**	The plant body as in *Riccia*, is a green, prostrate, dichotomously branched thallus, fleshy in texture. Each thallus lobe has a distict **midrib** but no dorsal furrow. It ends in a **terminal notch**. The thallus of *Marchantia* is however, more terrestrial in habit. It has a definitely large size, broader and thicker	The plant body as in *Riccia*, and *Marchantia* is a simple, dorsiventral thallus. It is thin, flat, green and lobed. The upper surface is smooth. The margin is sinuous and irregularly lobed. The lobes often overlap one another. The branching is dichotomous. Each lobe has a slightly thickened *midrib* and *terminal notch*. The	The plant body is generally epiphytic in habit. The thallus is prostrate and dorsiventral. In external appearance it is, however, more elaborate than *Riccia, Pellia* and *Marchantia* being leafy. It consists of a more or less branched central axis with leaves arranged in three rows. There are two rows of lateral and symmetric leaves on the upper	The plant body is a simple somewhat flesy dorsiventral, green, non-leafy thallus as in *Riccia*, *Marchantia* and *Pellia*. The thalli are deeply lobed. The lobes overlap. Branching is dichotomous but due to unequal growth of the two parts of dichotomy the thallus usually becomes irregular in outline. The margin of the lobes is	The leafy gametophyte is a perennial plant. It has an upright stem. Individually the erect stem is weak and fragile. It gets support to grow upright from the neighbouring clumps of stems. The stem often grows to a considerable length a foot or more. It branches freely. The branching is lateral and the branches arise in tufts of 3—8 usually in the	The plant body is leafy, green upright and radial in symmertry. It consists of an erect, sparingly branched central axis 12—20 mm. in height bearing green leaf-like expansions. The leaves are spirally arranged. They are sessile, oblong-ovate with a smooth margin, pointed apex and distinct midrib. The branching is **monopodial.** The branches are

1. *Riccia*	2. *Marchantia*	3. *Pellia*	4. *Porella* or *Madotheca*	5. *Anthoceros*	6. *Sphagnum*	7. *Funaria*
nal notch the areolae and the gemma cups are absent.	lobes, more prominent, expanded midrib and upper surface marked by rhomboidal areas (**areolae**) each with a distinct central *pore*. Presence of **gemma cups** is another distinguishing feature.	median dorsal groove characteristic of the thallus of *Riccia* and the rhomboidal areas (areolae) characteristic of the thallus of *Marchantia* are absent.	surface of the axis. The third row of reduced leaves is on the lower side of the axis. The dorsal leaves are **bilobed** and **incubously** arranged. They are without a midrib. The branching of the axis is **monopodial**. Dichotomous branching is absent.	variable. It may be entire,toothed, folded or fringed. There is neither any **midrib** nor a dorsal **furrow**. The upper surface is smooth there being no rhombodial areas characteristic of the thallus of *Marchantia*. The thallus is usually inhabited by *Nostoc* colonies seen as small, dark, blue green specks or sports in surface view.	axil of every 4th leaf on the stem. At the apex of the stem is cluster of short, stout branches of limited growth. This terminal cluster of close set branches protects the apical bud and forms a conspicuous compact head called the **comal tuft**. The stem and branches bear small leaves.	never axillary. They arise from below the leaves. In its external appearance the moss gametophyte is the most highly developed of all the bryophytes.
From the ventral surface of the thallus arise the **scales** and the **rhizoids**. The scales arise along the margin and project beyond it. In some species they are absent and in still others rudimentary. The rhizoids are unicellular and unbranched. They anchor the thallus to the substratum and are usually of two types, **smooth-**	From the ventral surface of the thallus arise both the **scales** and the **rhizoids**. The scales are arranged in two or three rows, on either side of midrib. They are not marginal. The rhizoids as in *Riccia* serve to attach the thallus to the substratum and are of the two usual kinds **smooth-walled** and tuberculate. The ventral scales	From the under surface of the thallus arise only the rhizoids. The **Scales** are absent in *Pellia*. The rhizoids are also of **smooth-walled** type. The tuberculate rhizoids are lacking. The unicellular, unbranched smooth walled rhizoids secure the thallus to the substratum.	The **scales** are absent in *Porella*. The unicellular rhizoids are also of one kind only. They are **smooth-walled** and unbranched. They arise from the lower surface of the stem from the basal portions of the ventral leaves. They serve to attach the thallus to the substratum. The tuberculate rhizoids are lacking.	As in *Pellia* and *Porella* the scales and the tuberculate rhizoids are absent on the ventral surface of the thallus. It is fixed to the substratum by unbranched **smooth walled** rhizoids only.	The plant is erect and radial in organisation. There is thus no distinction into upper and lower surfaces. The mature gametophytes lack rhizoids.	The plant being upright there is no distinction into the upper and the lower surface. The rhizoids, which are the attaching organs, arise from the brown, naked, basal part of the stem. They are multicellular and branched. The septa between the cells are oblique and at long intervals. There are no scales. Nor is there any distinction

1. *Riccia*	2. *Marchantia*	3. *Pellia*	4. *Porella* or *Madotheca*	5. *Anthoceros*	6. *Sphagnum*	7. *Funaria*
walled and **tuberculate**.	help to retain moisture below the thallus which can be absorbed by the rhizoids. This enables *Marchantia* to grow in drier habitats as compared with *Riccia*.					into smooth-walled and tuberculate rhizoids.
(*b*) *Anatomy* Internally the thallus is several cell layers thick. The cells are differentiated and arranged in two distinct regions, the upper, green **photosynthetic regions** and the lower **storage region**.	As in *Riccia* internally the thallus is several cells thick. These cells are better differentiated and arranged in three distinct regions instead of two as in *Riccia*. These are :—	Internally the thallus is simple as compared to that of *Riccia* or *Marchantia*. It is several layers of cells thick in the median portion but there is no or little tissue differentiation. The cells are not arranged in any distinct regions such as the upper photosynthetic and the lower storage region.	Internally the young central axis is very simple in structure. It is made up of perfectly uniform, green parenchyma cells. It shows no differentiation of tissues.	Internally the thallus is very simple in structure. It is several cells thick in the median portion. The cells however, show no or little tissue differentiation. Nor are they arranged in photosynthetic and storage regions. All the cells are uniform, compactly arranged and parenchymatous except the surface layer.	Internally the stem shows well marked differentiation of tissues into 3 regions namely, the outer cortex or the hyalo dermis, the middle hadrom (prosenchymatous region) and the central **medulla** or the **axial cylinder**	Internally as well the so called moss stem shows certain amount of tissue differentiation. The cells are arranged in three distinct regions: epidermis, cortex and central cylinder.
(*i*) There is no well-defined epidermal layer. It is represented by the terminal, colourless cells of	(*i*) *Epidermal region*. It consists of a well-defined upper epidermis with true, barrel-shaped pores.	(*i*) There is no well developed and well defined upper epidermis. Of course the surface layer is	(*i*) The epidermal layer is not well defined. Nor is there any trace of a central strand.	(*i*) The cells of the surface layer are smaller but not cuticularized or otherwise modified as epi-	(*i*) Epidermis is not differentiated in *Sphagnum*.	(*i*) *Epidermis*. It is the surface layer. In the mature portions of the stem the epidermal cells are thick-

1. *Riccia*	2. *Marchantia*	3. *Pellia*	4. *Porella* or *Madotheca*	5. *Anthoceros*	6. *Sphagnum*	7. *Funaria*
the vertical rows of green cells. Together the hyaline cells of the neighbouring green filaments form an ill defined discontinuous **upper epidermis,** one cell in thickness.	The epidermal cells have slightly thickened walls. They are protective in furnction and tend to check evaporation from the underlying tissue over which the epidermis forms a single layered roof.	often referred to as epidermis but the epidermal cells are not in any way different from the other cells of the thallus.		dermal cells. Hence there is no organised epidermis.		walled and lack chloroplasts. There are neither any air pores nor stomata.
(*ii*) The photosynthetic region consists of a loose, green tissue. The green cells rich in chloroplasts are arranged in vertical rows usually with **narrow slits** between them. The empty air chambers open to the exterior through airpores which are simply intercellular spaces bounded by 4—8 epidermal cells. The photosynthetic of *Marchantia* are absent in *Riccia*.	(*ii*) *Photosynthetic region*. It lies beneath the upper epidermis and consists of a chlorophyll bearing tissue with air chambers. The chambers are arranged in a single horizontal layer and are of fairly regular size. Each chamber is separated from its neighbours by partitions of green cells 3 or 4 cells in height. It opens to the exterior through a centrally placed barrel-shaped, epidermal **air pore**. From the floor of each chamber arise short, simple, or branched	(*ii*) The air pores and air chambers characteristic of Marchantia are absent. The entire thallus consists of uniform tissue of chlorophyll bearing polyhedral, parenchyma cells arranged compactly. The cells of the upper layers contain abundant chloroplasts. Starch grains occur in all the cells.	(*ii*) In older portions of the stem, however, there is differentiation into the outer cortical and inner medullary regions. The cortex consists of small cells with slightly thickened walls. The medulla is composed of comparatively larger cells with thinner walls.	(*ii*) There are no chambers, and air pores. In fact in its structure the *Anthoceros* thallus approaches that of *Pellia* as it does in the absence of scales and tuberculate rhizoids. There are, however, differences in detail.	(*ii*) The cortex varies in thickness. In young stems and branches it may be only one cell in thickness but in older stems it is 3-6 layers of cells in thickness. The cells are dead, empty and colourless. In some species the cortical cells develop pores and spiral thickenings on their walls. The prosenchymatous region which lies next to the cortex consists of elongated thickwalled prosenchymatous cells. It functions as a supporting tissue.	(*ii*) *Cortex*. It is several cell layers thick and consists of large, thin-walled cells. They are compactly arranged and in young stems contain chloroplasts. The mature portions of the stem have the cortex differentiated into an outer **thick-walled cortex** and an inner **thin-walled cortex**. There are no air spaces.

1. *Riccia*	2. *Marchantia*	3. *Pellia*	4. *Porella* or *Madotheca*	5. *Anthoceros*	6. *Sphagnum*	7. *Funaria*
	filaments of cells rich in chloroplasts.					
(*iii*) The lower storage region is colourless and several layers thick. It consists of closely packed, undifferentiated, parenchymatous cells which may contain starch. A few cells contain oil. These cells thus serve for food and water storage. There are no mucilage cells.	(*iii*) *Storage region*: It is the lowermost region of the thallus where food and water are stored. It is more extensive and many layers thick. It is compact and colourless. The cells of the upper layers of this region may contain few or no chloroplasts. It consists of relatively large, thin walled, colourless, parenchyma cells. Most of them contain starch. Isolated cells in this region may contain a single oil body or be filled with mucilage. The former are called oil body cells and the latter **mucilage cells**.	(*iii*) There is no distinct storage region.	(*iii*) The leaf consists of a plate of one cell layer thick. Cells are rich in chloroplasts and are polygonal in form. There is no midrib. The axis is cylindrical in outline.	(*iii*) All the cells have a single large chloroplast each with a pyrenoid in the centre—an unusal feature. Some cells contain mucilage. The distinction of the thallus into the ventral storage and the dorsal photosynthetic region as is characteristic of the Marchantiaceae is lacking. In some species of *Anthoceros* the superficial cells on the lower surface of the thallus separate from each other to form intercellular spaces which are filled with mucilage. These mucilage pits often deepen and broaden to form large, rounded cavities. They are filled with soft, mucilage and open on the ventral surface by stoma like clefts. Very often	(*iii*) Central conducting strand is absent in *Sphagnum*. Its place is taken up by the medulla or axial cylinder which consists of colourless, collenchymatous cells with thin walls. The medulla than forms a tissue corresponding somewhat to the pith of higher plants and functions as a storage and not conducting region. **The leaves are small sessile, thin** scale like and without a midrib. They are arranged spirally on the stem with a divergence of 2/5. The leaf consists of a single layer of cells in thickness but is unique in the fact that it is composed of two types of cells (*i*) narrow elongate green	(*iii*) *Central Cylinder*. It occupies the core or the stem and consists of vertically elongated thin-walled cells. Theya re narow and compactly arranged. It provides mechanical support to a certain extent and functions in conduction. The so-called leaf consists of a single layer of cells rich in chloroplasts. The midrib is several cells thick. It constains a narrow strand of thin-walled, elongated cells.

1. *Riccia*	2. *Marchantia*	3. *Pellia*	4. *Porella* or *Madotheca*	5. *Anthoceros*	6. *Sphagnum*	7. *Funaria*
				Nostoc finds its way into these intercellular spaces through the slit like or circular openings of the mucilage clefts. Once lodged within, the alga multiplies extensively in the intercellular spaces. The latter by the disorganisation of the neighbouring cells broaden into conspicuous cavities inhabited by the alga.	assimilatory cells forming the network and (ii) the large hyaline capillary cells which occupy the meshes.	
(*iv*) The lowermost cells of this region are smaller in size and more regularly arranged to form the lower epidermis.	(*iv*) The lower epidermis is distinct and well developed. It is continuous.	(*iv*) A single layer of regularly arranged cells on the lower surface of the thallus is referred to as the lower epidermis.		(*iv*) There is no distinct lower epidermis.		
Apical growth						
Growth in length of the thallus takes place by means of a group of apical initials constituting the growing point. It lies in the deeply emarginate apex of each lobe.	As in *Riccia* the growing point lies at the bottom of a terminal notch of each thallus lobe. It consists of a group of apical initials. By the activity of these the thallus grows in length.	Growth takes place by the activity of a single large **apical cell**. It lies in a notch at the forward end of each thallus lobe.	The thallus grows by means of a single pyramidal **apical cell** with three cutting faces. It lies at the tip of the main axis and each of the branches.	Campbell, Bower and others report the occurrence of a single four sided pyramidal **apical cell** at the growing point which lies in a shallow depression at the anterior end of each thal-	The main stem and the branches grow by means of a single tetrahedral apical cell with three cutting faces.	It takes place by means of a single pyramidal **apical cell** at the stem tip. It has three cutting faces.

1. *Riccia*	2. *Marchantia*	3. *Pellia*	4. *Porella* or *Madotheca*	5. *Anthoceros*	6. *Sphagnum*	7. *Funaria*
				lus lobe. Leitgeb recognized several marginal cells of equal rank. Mehra and Handoo confirm Leitgeb's observation. They hold that in *A. erectus* and *A. himalayensis* there is a group of cells which initiate growth. They are protected by mucilage.		
Juvenile State						
There is no juvenile stage or protonema. The thalloid gametophyte is formed directly from the germinating spore.	The same as in *Riccia*.	The same as in *Riccia* and *Marchantia*.	The adult leafy thallus proceeded by a **juvenile stage** or **protonema** which is of a simple type. It is multicellular and develops one or more rhizoids prior to the differentiation of the leafy thallus (gametophyte).	There is no juvenile stage as in *Riccia, Marchantia* and *Pellia*.	The leafy gametophyte is preceded by the **juvenile** or **protonema** stage as in other mosses. The adult protonema is a green irregularly lobed thallus-like structure fixed to the substratum by multicellular rhizoids. The septa between the cells are oblique. The leafy gametophyte arises from the margin of the thallose protonema.	The upright, leafy gametophyt eis preceeded by the **juvenile** or **protonema** stage which is a green branched system of filaments

Table II

COMPARISON BETWEEN THE SEX ORGANS OF

1. *Riccia*	2. *Marchantia*	3. *Pellia*	4. *Porella* or *Madotheca*	5. *Anthoceros*	6. *Sphagnum*	7. *Funaria*
Sex Organs						
(*i*) Many species are monoecious but a few are dioecious.	(*i*) Without exception all species of *Marchantia* are dioecious.	(*i*) Some species are monoecious, others dioecious. The monoecious species are distinctly protandrous.	(*i*) All species are reported to be dioecious.	(*i*) Some species are **monoecious** and other dioecious. The monoecious species are reported to be **protandrous**.	(*i*) Some species of *Sphagnum* armonoecious and some dioecious. Even in the monoecious the two kinds of sex organs do not occur on the same branch.	(*i*) *Funaria hygrometrica* is **monoecious** and **autoecious**. Some mosses are monoecious and paraoicous, others monoecious and synoicous. Dioecious mosses are also common.
(*ii*) In the dioecious species the two kinds of thalli are similar but in *R. himalayensis* the male plants are smaller than the females.	(*ii*) The male and the female thalli are similar.	(*ii*) The male and the female thalli in the dioecious species are similar.	(*ii*) The male and female plants are **dimorphic**, the former being decidedly smaller than the latter.	(*ii*) In the dioecious species the male and the female thalli are similar.	(*ii*) The male branches are spindle-shaped, resemble small catkins and are usually shorter but stouter than the vegetative branches. They are densely clothed with strongly pigmented leaves. The female branches are, short bud-like aggregates of bracts and archegonia.	(*ii*) The male and the female branches do not exhibit dimorphism.
(*iii*) The sex organs lie in the dorsal furrow on the upper	(*iii*) They are borne on special sexual upright	(*iii*) The sex organs are developed on the thallus and not on	(*iii*) The sex organs are borne on specialised sexual	(*iii*) The sex organs are not borne on any specialised sexual	(*iii*) The sex organs are thus borne on specialized sexual	(*iii*) The sex organs occur at the tips of branches which are

1. *Riccia*	2. *Marchantia*	3. *Pellia*	4. *Porella* or *Madotheca*	5. *Anthoceros*	6. *Sphagnum*	7. *Funaria*
surface of the thallus and not on any special sexual branches.	branches of the thallus called the gametophores, which are terminal in positionon the thallus lobes.	any special sexual branches.	branches.	branches.	branches.	not in any way specialised.
(*iv*) The sex organs are developed in lines back from the apex, in acropetal order.	(*iv*) In contrast to the scattered arrangement in *Riccia*, the sex organs are developed in localized areas called the receptacles which are elevated, later on, on long stalks.	(*iv*) The antheridia occur irregularly scattered in two or more rows in the broad midrib region.	(*iv*) The antheridia occur singly in the axils of closely imbricated, light green bracts on the antheridial branches which stand at right angles to the main axis.	(*iv*) The antheridia occur scattered singly or in groups immersed beneath the upper surface of the thallus.	(*iv*) The antheridia occur singly in the axils of leaves towards the tip on the antheridial branch. The paraphyses are absent.	(*iv*) The antheridia occur in a cluster at the apex of the male branch whcih is the main shoot. Intermingled with the antheridia are found the paraphyses.
		(*v*) The archegonia occur in a cluster close to the growing apex on a ridge of tissue called the receptacle remains sessile.	(*v*) The archegonia occur in a terminal cluster on the female brnaches which are very short and bear 2 or 3 leaves only.	(*v*) The archegonia occur singly and not in clusters embedded in the upper surface of the thallus.	(*v*) The archegonia occur in a small terminal group of 2 to 5 on the specialized archegonial branches which are very short and more less globular in form.	(*v*) The archegonia are borne in a cluster at the apex of the female branch which arises as a lateral out-growth from the base of the male shoot. Intermingled with the archegonia are found the paraphyses.
Position and origin of sex organs						
(*i*) Both (antheridia and archegonia) lie immersed, each	(*i*) The antheridia lie embedded on the upper surface of	(*i*) The antheridia lie embedded on the upper surface of	(*i*) The antheridia occur singly projecting in the axils of	(*i*) The antheridia occur singly or in groups inside closed	(*i*) The antheridia occur singly and projecting in the axil	(*i*) The antheridia occur in a cluster projecting at the tip of

1. *Riccia*	2. *Marchantia*	3. *Pellia*	4. *Porella* or *Madotheca*	5. *Anthoceros*	6. *Sphagnum*	7. *Funaria*
in a separate cavity or chamber on the dorsal surface of the thallus.	the male receptacle, each in a pit which opens by a pore on the surface of the disc.	the thallus; each in its own pit which opens by a pore on the upper surface of the thallus.	small bracts on the antheridial branches.	antheridial chambers on the upper surface of the thallus.	of perigonial bracts on the male branches.	the male shoot.
	(*ii*) The archegonia are projecting. In the young receptacle they are borne on the upper surface with their necks directed up wards. They are not sunk in separate pits. In the mature receptacle they hang downwards from the undersurface of the disc with their necks directed dowanwards.	(*ii*) The archegonia occur in a cluster projecting on the upper surface of the thallus.	(*ii*) The archegonia occur projecting in the cluster at the apex of the female branch.	(*ii*) The archegonia occur singly sunk deep in the fleshy thallus on its upper surface with tip projecting out.	(*ii*) The archegonia occur projecting in a small cluster at apex of a specialized female branch.	(*ii*) The archegonia occur projecting in a cluster at the apex of the female branch.
(*iii*) The sex organs are **exogenous** in origin.	(*iii*) The sex **exogenous** in origin.	(*iii*) The sex organs are **exogenous** in origin.	(*iii*) The sex organs are **exogenous** in origin.	(*iii*) The antheridia are **endogenous** in origin whereas archegonia are **exogenous**.	(*iii*) Both the antheridia and **archegonia** are exogenous in origin and are protected by subtending bracts.	(*iii*) Both the sex organs are **exogenous** in origin.
(*a*) **Antheridia**						
(*i*) the mature antheridium	(*i*) The mature antheridium is essen-	(*i*) The mature antheridium as in	(*i*) The mature antheridium of	(*i*) The mature antheridium is orange	(*i*) The orange coloured antheridium	(*i*) The mature antheridium is club-

1. *Riccia*	2. *Marchantia*	3. *Pellia*	4. *Porella* or *Madotheca*	5. *Anthoceros*	6. *Sphagnum*	7. *Funaria*
consistsof an ovoid or pearshaped body attached at its broader end to the bottom of the antheridial chamber by a short, multicellular stalk.	tially similar to that of *Riccia*. It has an ovoid body supported on a short, multicellular stalk. The latter arises from the bottom of the antheridial chamber.	*Riccia* and *Marchantia* consists of a body and a stalk. The stalk is short but multicellular. It ariss from the bottom of a round flask-shaped antheridial chamber.	*Porella* has a globose or globular body elevated stalk. The stalk consists of two rows of cells.	coloured. The club-shaped or pouch-like body is raised on a long multicellular, four rowed stalk arising form the floor of a roofed over chamber.	has a globular body elevated on a long slender stalk consisting of cells arranged in two or four vertical rows.	shaped and orange coloured. It is shortly stalked. The stalk is multicellular.
(*ii*) The body of the antheridium is made up of a central mass of numerous small internal cells protected and covered by a layer of larger; sterile cells forming the **jacket** or **antheridial wall**. The internal cells of the last cell generation produce the biflagellate **sperms**.	(*ii*) The body of the antheridium has a jacket layer one cell in thickness. It encloses a mass of **androcytes**. Each androcyte gives rise to a biflagellate sperm.	(*ii*) The globular or globose body of the antheridium has a jacket one cell-layer in thickness. The cells contain chloroplasts. The jacket layer encloses a mass of androcytes. Each androcyte metamorphoses into a biflagellate sperm.	(*ii*) The body has a jacket layer 2-3 cells thick towards the base. It encloses a mass of colourless internal cells which produce the sperms. The ripe antheridium is reported to the almost pure white. The antheridium thus difers from those of *Riccia*, *Marchantia* and *Pellia* in its large size, long stalk, jacket 2-3 cells thick at the base and no antheridial chamber.	(*ii*) The body of the antheridium has a single layered jacket forming the wall. The jacket cells in some species are rectangular and arranged in four tiers. The cells of the upper tier constitute the dehiscence cap. Within the wall is a mass of androcytes which produce the sperms. The roof of the antheridial chambers bursts open when the sperms are ripe.	(*ii*) The body of the antheridium consists of a jacket layer of sterile cells constituting the antheridial wall which encloses a mass of sperm producting cells.	(*ii*) The body of the antheridium consists of a jacket layer one cell in thickness. The cells contain chloroplasts. The jacket has a cap of one or two large cells at its distal end. Within the jacket is a mass of sperm producing cells.
(*iii*) Each sperm is a minute, slender curved structure furnished with a pair of flagella at its	(*iii*) The sperm has a narrowly curved or rod-like body furnished with two apical flagella.	(*iii*) The sperm has a spirally coiled body with two flageila attached at its forward narrow end. The	(*iii*) The sperm is a slender structure. It has a body consisting of about 2 complete coils. A small	(*iii*) The liberated sperm has a small, slender linear or slightly curved body furnished with two	(*iii*) The sperm is a small, biflagellate, spirally coiled structure. The number of coils is 2-3.	(*iii*) The liberated sperms are minute, biflagellate, spirally coiled structures.

1. *Riccia*	2. *Marchantia*	3. *Pellia*	4. *Porella* or *Madotheca*	5. *Anthoceros*	6. *Sphagnum*	7. *Funaria*
anterior end.		sperms of *Pellia* are larger than those of *Riccia* and *Marchantia* and have more coils.	vesicle is attached at its posterior end. The two flagella are somewhat longer than the body and are inserted at the pointed anterior end.	flagella at its forward end. The flagella are almost equal in length.		
(*b*) **Archegonia** The somewhat flask-shaped archegonium consists of an enlarged, basal venter and a long slender neck the venter is usually directly attached to the thallus there being no visible stalk. The neck consists of a narrow, vertical neck canal filled by a row of four neck canal cells surrounded by a layer of neck cells arranged in six longitudinal rows. The tip of the neck is make up of four large **cap or lid cells**. The distal portion of the neck projects above the surface of the thallus	In form and structure the archegonia of *Marchantia* are similar to those of *Riccia*. The only differences are :— 1. Presence of a short but distinct stalk which attaches the venter to the receptacle. 2. Slightly longer neck. 3. Greater number of neck canal cells. 4. Hang downwards from the undersurface of the receptacle.	The archegonium of *Pellia* is typically flask-shaped and essentially similar to that of *Riccia* and *Marchantia* except : 1. It is borne on a short but stout, massive stalk. 2. The neck consists of 5 longitudinal rows of neck cells instead of 6 characteristics of Marchantiales. 3. The number of neck canal cells varies from 6 to 8. 4. The neck is not sharply marked off from the venter.	The mature archegonium is more or less a cylindrical object. It is seated on a stalk. The neck consists of 5 vertical rows of cells as in *Pellia*. They enclose the neck canal. The neck canal is filled with usually 8 broad neck canal cells. The venter is but little enlarged.	In structure the archegonium of *Anthoceros* differs from that of the bryophytes and resembles that of certain Pteridophytes:— It has no stalk and is embedded int he tissue of the thallus. There is a central row of 4-5 neck canal cells but there is no jacket of sterile neck cells around it except the uppermost tier of neck cells which form the tip and project above the surface of the thallus.	The archegonium is a flask-shaped stalked structure. The stalk is fairly long. The archegonial neck is long and twisted. It consists of six vertical rows of neck cells. The neck canal contains 8 or 9 neck canal cells.	The archegonium is typically flaskshaped. It is supported on a long, stoutly developed stalk which attaches it to the tip of the female branch. It projects above the adjacent vegetative tissue. The neck is long and twisted. There are numerous (8 to 10) neck canal cells.

1. *Riccia*	2. *Marchantia*	3. *Pellia*	4. *Porella* or *Madotheca*	5. *Anthoceros*	6. *Sphagnum*	7. *Funaria*
into the dorsal furrow.						
5. The venter consists of a layer of jacket cells enclosing the lower larger egg cell and an upper smaller ventral canal cell.	5. The same as in *Riccia*.	5. The venter wall consists of two layers of cells instead of one characteristic of *Riccia* and *Marchantia* It encloses the egg and the ventral canal cells. Sometimes the lower portion of the neck also becomes two cell layers thick.	5. As in **Pellia** the venter wall consists of two layers of cells in thickness. The venter cavity contains the egg and the ventral canal cell above it.	5. The venter contains the egg and the ventral canal cell but there is no venter wall of sterile cells around them.	5. The venter and the lower portion of the neck is 2 or 3 layers of cells in thickness. The venter cavity contains the small ovoid egg and the ventral canal cell above it.	5. The venter wall is two cell layers thick. The venter cavity contains the egg and the ventral canal cell above it.
6. It is protected by the surrounding archegonial chamber. The protective sheaths like the perigonium and perichaetium are absent.	6. There is a collar-like structure at the base of the venter of each archegonium. It is the **perigynium**. In addition there is a two lipped curtain-like **perichaetium** with fimbriated margins around each series of archegonia.	6. The perigynium absent. The **involucre** which is homologous to the erichaetium of *Marchantia* surrounds and protects the archegonial cluster.	6. They are protected by the surrounding perichaetial bracts, the upper ones forming the **perianth** and the lower ones constituting the involucre.	6. The protection to the axial row of cells is afforded by the adjacent thallus tissue. The protective investments such as the perigynium and the perichaetium are lacking.	6. Protection is afforded by the subtending perigonial bracts in the case of antheridia and the surrounding perichaetial leaves in the case of archegonia.	6. The protective sheaths in the form of perigynium and perichaetium are absent. Protection is afforded by the surrounding perigonial and perichaetial brackets as in *Sphagnum*.

Table III

COMPARISON BETWEEN THE SPOROPHYTES OF

1. *Riccia*	2. *Marchantia*	3. *Pellia*	4. *Anthoceros*	5. *Sphagnum*	6. *Funaria*
SPOROPHYTE					
(*i*) The sporophyte of *Riccia* is the simplest known among the bryophytes.	(*i*) It is larger than and more than that of *Riccia*.	(*i*) It is more elaborate than those of *Riccia*, and *Marchantia*.	(*i*) It is larger and more complex than those of *Riccia*, *Marchantia* and *Pellia*. The elaboration is internal.	(*i*) It is much simpler than that of the other mosses. In certain features it resembles that of *Anthoceros* and in a few others that of *Funaria*.	(*i*) It is far more elaborate both externally as well as internally than that of any other bryophyte.
(*ii*) It consists of a spore sac or capsule only. There is no foot and no seta.	(*ii*) It is differentiated into **foot**, short **seta** and **capsule**.	(*ii*) It consists of a **foot**, a long **seta** and a capsule.	(*ii*) It is differentiated into a foot, a constriction-like **intermediate zone** and a **capsule**. There is no seta.	(*ii*) It consists of a **foot** and a **capsule**. Between the two is a constriction-like structure apparently resembling that of *Anthoceros*. The seta is absent.	(*ii*) The sporophyte consists of a **foot**, a long slender **seta** and a **capsule**.
(*iii*) It lies completely sunk in the tissue of the thallus and has no protective sheaths around it except the calytra.	(*iii*) It hangs freely from the undersurface of the female receptacle surrounded by the **perigynium** and the perichaetium.	(*iii*) It arises from the dorsal surface of the thallus surrounded byt he **involucre** at the base. There is no **perigynium**.	(*iii*) Arises in clusters from the dorsal surface of the thallus each surrounded at the base by a tubular **involucre** only.	(*iii*) Arises from the apex of the fmale branch and is elevated on a leafless, stalk-like **pseudopodium**. The protective sheaths are absent.	(*iii*) It is situated at the distal end of the female branch. There is no pseudopodium. The protective sheaths are lacking.
(*iv*) The foot is lacking.	(*iv*) The foot is well developed and broad. It functions as an attaching and absorbing organ.	(*iv*) It is conical with its edges proforming a collar-like structure at the base of the seta. Functions both inabsorption	(*iv*) It is a rounded, bulbous structure keeping the long capsule well anchored upon and attached to the	(*iv*) The foot is well-developed and massive as in *Anthoceros* but develops no rhizoid-like outgrowths. Functions	(*iv*) It is a small, poorly developed dagger-like conical object which functions both as an attaching and absorbing or-

1. *Riccia*	2. *Marchantia*	3. *Pellia*	4. *Anthoceros*	5. *Sphagnum*	6. *Funaria*
		and attachment.	thallus, often develops rhizoid-like outgrowths increasing its absorptive surface.	both in absorption and attachment.	gan.
(*v*) The seta is absent.	(*v*) The short seta elongates rapidly but slightly; simply, to push the mature capsule through and beyond the surrounding protective sheaths.	(*v*) The seta is long, or pure white colour, almost transparent. It elongates rapidly after the ripening of the spores to elevate the capsule far above the surrounding protective sheath and thus helps in the dispersal of spores.	(*v*) The seta is absent. Its place is taken up by the constriction-like intermediate zone which is meristematic. This intercalary meristem constantly adds new cells at the base of capsule which progressively become differntiated into the various tissues of the capsule.	(*v*) The setas is absent. The constriction-like intermediate zone which apparently resembles that of *Anthoceros* lacks the meristem. The absence of seta is compensated by the presence of **pseudopodium**. The latter helps in the dispersal of of spores by elevating the capsule.	(*v*) The long, slender seta elevates the capsule far above the surrounding perichaetial leaves and helps in the dispersal of spores. It is hygroscopic.
(*vi*) The capsule is a spherical spore sac. Its chief function is the production of spores. It has no distributing function.	(*vi*) At maturity the capsule is an oval yellow body concerned both in the production and distribution of spores.	(*vi*) The ripe, black capsule is spherical and specialised both as a spore producing and spore distributing organ.	(*vi*) It is a long, slender, cylindrical, upright object of fairly uniform thickness throughout its length. Its unusual length compensates for the absence of the seta. Functions both in the production and dispersal of spores.	(*vi*) The spherical capsule is externally more elaborate than that of the liverworts. It is differentiated into the theca portion concerned with spore production and lid-portion concerned with dehiscence.	(*vi*) The pear-shaped usually nodding capsule is far more elaborate both internally as well as externally than that of any other bryophyte. Externally it is differentiated into three regions, the basal **apophysis** for photosynthesis, middle theca for production of spores and the apical opercular or lid portion concerned with dehiscence.

1. *Riccia*	2. *Marchantia*	3. *Pellia*	4. *Anthoceros*	5. *Sphagnum*	6. *Funaria*
Structurally the capsule or *Riccia* is the simplest among the bryophytes. The capsule wall consists of a single layer of cells.	It is slightly more elaborate in structure than that of *Riccia*. The capsule wall is single-layered in thickness. The wall-cells towards maturity develop ring-like thickenings on their walls.	It is still more complex than that of *Riccia* and *Marchantia*. The capsule wall is 2 or more cell layers thick. The walls of these cells are strengthened by bands of thickenign material. In addition the capsule wall at maturity has on its surface 4 vertical strips of thin-walled cells. These are the **lines of dehiscence**. They are absent in *Riccia* and *Marchantia*.	The capsule of *Anthoceras* displays striking compexity in its internal structure. The capsule wall is several layers of cells (4-6) in thicknes. The outermost layer is called the **epidermis**. It is punctured here and there by the presence of the true **stomata**. Within the epidermis is the typically ventilated **photosynthetic tissue** consisting of chlorenchymatous cells with intercellular spaces between them. It is absent in *Riccia, Marchantia* and *Pellia*. The capsule wall has on its surface generally two vertical **lines of dehiscence** on the opposite sides of the capsule each in a shallow depression.	The capsule wall as in Anthoceros is 4 to 6 layers in thickness. The outermost layer is the **epidermis**. It bears rudimentary stomata which lack the stomatal aperture. Within the epidermis is the non-ventilated photosynthetic tissue consisting of chlorenchymatous cells with no intercellular spaces between them.	The capsule wall is several alyers thick and is highly differentiated. The outermost layer is the epidermis. It contains numerous stomata int he apophysis region, fewer in the theca region and none in the opercular region. The epidermal cells in the operculum have greatly thickened walls excepting the **annulas**. Within the epidermis and restricted to theca region only are the colourless, compactly arranged two layers of cells constituting the **hypodermis**. Within the hypodermis in this region is the narrow **spongy layer** which is continuous below with that of the apophysis where it becomes broader. Inside the spongy layer is the wide **air space** teaversed by the trabeculae and the outer **spore sac** are absent in the apophysis and operculum regions. Within the epidermis in the apophysis region is the broad spongy zone

1. *Riccia*	2. *Marchantia*	3. *Pellia*	4. *Anthoceros*	5. *Sphagnum*	6. *Funaria*
					and in the operculum 3-4 layers of small parenchyma cells and then a double ring of peristome teeth.
The capsule wall is formed from the entire amphithecium.	The capsule wall is formed from the entire amphithecium.	The capsule wall is formed from the entireamphithecium.	The capsule wall is differentiated from the outer layer of the amphithecium.	As in *Anthoceros* the capsule wall is formed from the outer layer of the amphithecium.	The capsule wall is derived from the **amphithecium**.
Prior to maturity the capsule wall disorganises and disapperars.	The capsule wall is persistent.	The capsule wall is persistent.	The capsule wall is persistent.	The capsule wall is persistent.	The capsule wall is persistent.
The **archesporium** is formed from the entire **endothecium**.	The entire **endothecium** forms the **archesporium** as in *Riccia*.	The entire **endothecium** functions as the **archesporium** as in *Riccia* and *Marchantia*.	The **archesporium** formed from the **inner layer** of the **amphithecium**.	The **archesporium** develops from the **inner layer** of the **amphithecium** as tin *Anthoceros*.	The **archesporium** and inner spore sac originate from the **outer layers** of the **endothecium**.
The columella is absent.	The **columella** is absent.	The **columella** is absent. Some scientists consider **elaterophore** as the **forerunner** of the columella.	The **columella** forms the central core of the capsule. It is formed from the entire endothecium which in *Riccia*, *Marchantia* and *Pellia* forms the archesporium.	As in *Anthoceros* the entire endothecium forms the **columella** which forms the central bulky mass of sterile tissue.	The major central portion of the endothecium forms the **columella** continuous below with the conducting strand of the apophysis.
The primary archesorium divides to form the **sporogenous**	The same as in *Riccia*.	The same as in *Riccia* and *Marchantia*.	The archesporium divides to form the **sporogenous tissue** one	The archesporium divides to form the sporogenous tissue 2-4	The archesporium may undergo division to form two layers thick

1. *Riccia*	2. *Marchantia*	3. *Pellia*	4. *Anthoceros*	5. *Sphagnum*	6. *Funaria*
tissue which fills the entire space within the capsule wall.			to 4 layers in thickness. It is narow and overarches the rounded apex of the columella like a dome and surrounds it.	layers in thickness. It overarches the rounded apex of the massive columella and forms a dome-shaped zone in the upper part of the capsule only.	**sporogenous tissue**. It is thus extremely reduced forming but a small and narrow part of the theca region of the capsule. It neither extends to the base nor apex of the capsule. It simply surrounds the columella and does not overarch it.
Major protion of the sporogenous tissue is differentiated into the **spore mother cells**. Only a few peripheral cells remain abortive and function as **nurse cells**. By some scientists, the nurse cells are considered as forerunners of the elaters of *Marchantia*.	Half the sporogenous tissue differentiates into the **spore mother cells** and the rest into the **spore mother cells**. The latter give rise to the sterile, hygroscopic **elaters** which help in scattering thespores differentiated from the spore mother cells.	A central mass of **sporogenous cells** at the base of the capsule becomes differentiated into the **elaterophore** whereas the remaining sporogenous cells surrounding the elaterophore form the **spore mother cells** and the **elaters**.	The sporogenous tissue differentiates into fertile **spore mother cells** and the sterile **pseudoelater** mother cells. The former give rise to the spores and the latter to the **pseudoelaters**.	The entire sporogenous tissue gives rise to the **sporo mother cells**. The **elaters** are absent.	The entire sporogenous tissue as in *Sphagnum* differentiates into the **spore mother cells**. The elaters are absent.
There is no regular method of dehiscence to allow the spores to escape. The surviving outer layer of the calyptra and the adjacent thallus tissue undergo decay. The spores are simply left behind in the soil to be dispersed by the wind.	The capsule of *Marchantia* dehisces to allow the spores to escape. The capsule wall splits open into several usually 4-6 irregular teeth-like structures from the apex to about the middle of the capsule exposing the mass of spores and elaters.	The capsule dehisces in a more regular manner as compared with *Marchantia*. It dehisces by crossed cleavages along the four lines of dehiscence into four valves which get reflexed.	Dehiscence is very regular. The mature capsule splits along 1-4 lines of dehiscence. The splits extend downwards separating into valves which remain united at the tip. Pseudoelaters help in spore dispersal.	Dehiscence is by the separation of a lid and is explosive. The spores are forcibly blown out.	The annulus cells perish and the operculum falls off excepting the peristome teeth. The latter by their peculiar disposition and hygroscopic movement release a few spores at a time during dry weather.

1. *Riccia*	2. *Marchantia*	3. *Pellia*	4. *Anthoceros*	5. *Sphagnum*	6. *Funaria*
The sporophyte is **totally parasitic** for its nutrition on the parent thallus (gametophyte).	As in *Riccia* the sporophyte is **totally parasitic** for its nutrition on the parent thallus (gametophyte).	As in *Riccia* and *Marchantia* the photosynthetic tissue is absent in the capsule wall. So the sporophyte is **parasitic** for its nutrition on the parent thallus (gametophyte).	Unlike *Riccia*, *Marchantia* and *Pellia* there is a well developed ventilated photosynthetic tissue in the capsule wall. The sporophyte is thus able to prepare its carbohydrate food. For water and minerals in solution it still depends on the parent gametophyte. It is therefore a **semiparasite**.	The photosynthetic tissue in the capsule wall is poorly developed and non-ventilated. It cannot fully meet the carbohydrate requirements of the sporophyte which is thus **mainly dependent** for its nutrition on the gametophyte.	There is a well developed and well ventilated photosynthetic tissue in the apophysis region. The sporophyte thus depends on the parent gametophore only for its supply of water and mineral salts. It is a **semiparasite**.
The sporophyte is a short-liveed structure. The whole sporophyte tissue perishes by the time the spores reach maturity. 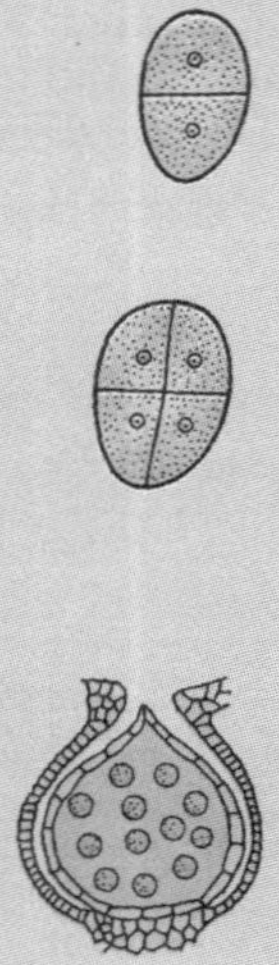	The sporophyte is a short-lived structure. It dies as soon as the spores are shed. 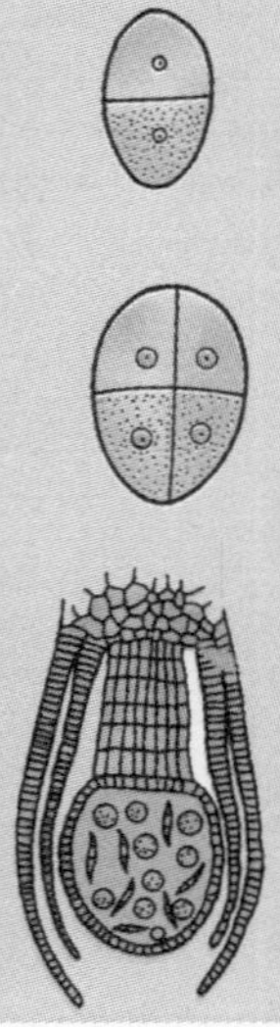	The sporophyte dies as soon as the spores are shed. 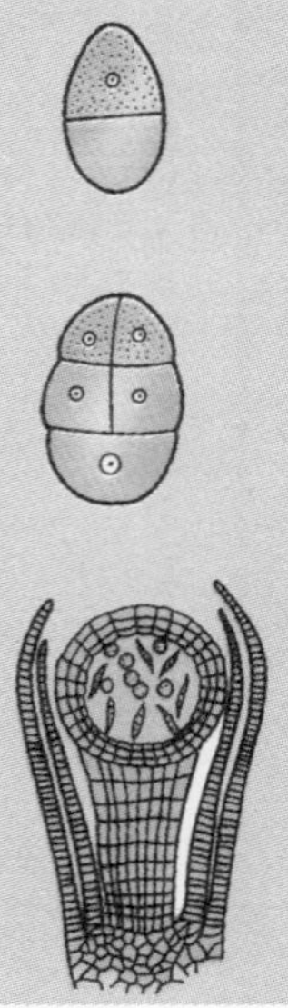	The sporophyte is comparatively a long-lived structure. Within the help of its intercalary meritem it continues to live and produce spores as long as the thallus lives. 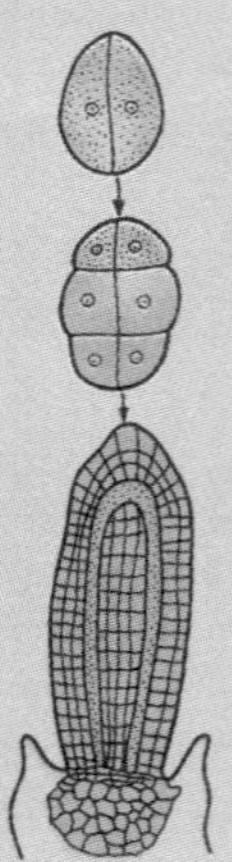	The sporophyte perishes as soon as the spores are shed. 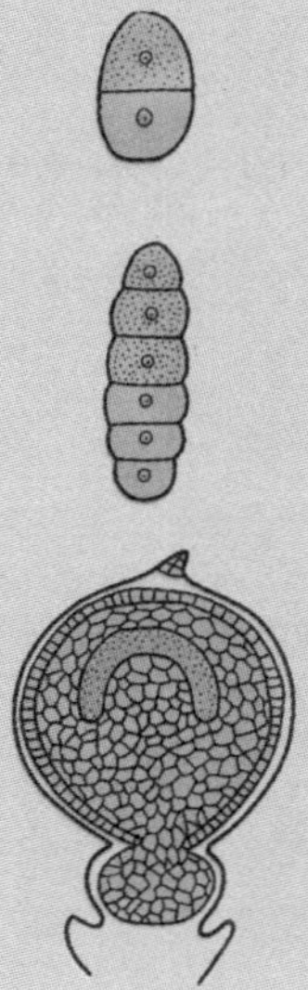	With the complete shedding of spores, which are released in successive showers and not all simultaneously, the sporophyte, dies. 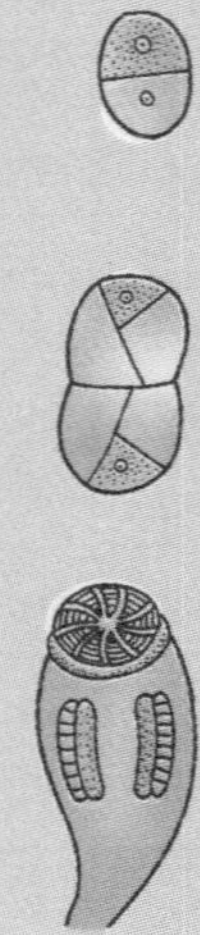

QUESTIONS

ESSAY TYPE

1. (*a*) Give an account of the vegetative propagation and modes of perennation in Bryophyta.
(Rohilkhand M.Sc., 1992; Kanpur MSc., 1995, 2002)

(*b*) Give an illustrated account of two chief methods of vegetative propagation
(Kanpur M.Sc., 1995, 2002)

2. Discuss the evolutionary tendencies in the gametophytic generations of Bryophytes.
(Rohilkhand M.Sc., 1993).

3. Discuss the evolutionary tendencies in the sporophytic generation of Bryophytes.
(Rohilkhand M.Sc., 1994)

4. (A). Write a critical note on the evolution of sporophytes in Liverworts/Bryophytes.
(Rohilkhand M.Sc., 1998, 2003; Bundelkhand, 1996)

(B). Write an essay on progressive evolution of sporophytes in bryophytes.
(Kanpur, 2002; Poorvanchal, M.Sc. 2002)

(C). Trace the gradual advancement in the sporophytes of bryophytes you have studied.
(Rohilkhand, 2004; Calicut, 2004)

5. With the help of labelled diagrams and suitable examples describe the range of sporophytes in Bryophytes
(Rhohilkhand M.Sc., 2000)

6. Give an account of fossil histories of some three bryophytes studied by you.
(Awadh M.Sc., 1999)

7. Write a brief account of Ecological nature of Bryophytes
(Kanpur M.Sc., 1990, 2005).

8. Giving examples from fossil bryophytes write a short account on the origin of Bryophytes. *(Kanpur M.Sc., 1990)*

9. Give in detail the evolutionary tendencies of sporophytes in Bryophytes.
(Kanpur M.Sc., 1991, 1994, 2005)

10. Discuss (Describe) various method of vegetative reproduction in Bryophytes.
(Kanpur M.Sc., 1995, 1999; Lucknow, 1994, 1996, 1997, 1999, 2005; Allahabad, 1995, 2003; Kumaon, 1995; Meerut, 1997; Gorakhpur, 1990; Bundelkhand, 1993; Madras, 1995; Trichy, 1995; Magadh, 1993; Kanpur, 2003, Rohilkhand, 2004, Himachal Pradesh, 2000)

11. Describe and discuss the evolution of sporophytes in Bryophytes.
(Kanpur MSc., 1996, 1998, 2005; Meerut, 1997; Rohilkhand, 1997; Awadh, 1995; Vinoba Bhave, 1998; Kerala, 1998; Rohilkhand M.Sc., 2003)

12. (a) Are the bryophytes derived from Pteridophytes or are they ancestral to them? Discuss briefly
(Kanpur' M.Sc., 1996)

(b) Discuss different views regardingorigin of Bryophytes. *(Kanpur' M.Sc., 2009)*

13. Write an illustrated account of the modes of vegetative reproduction and perennation in Indian Hepatics.
(Kanpur, M.Sc. 1998)

14. Taking examples from different groups justify the following statement "The regenerative potention of gametophyte in Bryophyte is enormous".
(Kanpur, M.Sc. 1999, 2004)

15. Discuss Bryophytes as indicators of Environmental pollution. *(Lucknow, 1998)*

16. What is an archesporium? How does it originate? What is its ultimate fate in the bryophytes studied by you?
(Lucknow, 2000, Allahabad, 2000; 2006 Agra, 1993)

17. Justify the statement that complex sporophytes in Bryophytes have been evolved from simple sporophytes of *Riccia* by progressive sterilization of sporogenous tissues. *(Agra, 1991)*

18. With the help of labelled diagrams describe methods of vegetative reproduction in Bryophytes. *(Meerut, 1997, 1999; Bhagalpur, 1991; Himachal Pradesh, 1992)*
19. Write an essay on vegetative reproduction in Bryophytes. *(Rohilkhand, 2000, 2002)*
20. Define vegetative reproduction and discuss the methods of vegetative reproduction in Bryophyte s. *(Kanpur, 2000; Vinoba Bhave, 1999)*
21. Describe/Discuss economic importance of bryophytes. *(Kanpur, M.Sc., 2006; Poorvanchal, M.Sc. 2002; Kanpur, 2001)*
22. Write an essay on vegetative reproduction in Bryophytes. *(U.P. College, 1996)*
23. Trace the progressive sterilizations of sporogenous tissue in Bryophytes studied by you. *(Poorvanchal, 1998; Bhagalpur, 1991)*
24. Describe asexual reproduction in Bryophyta with diagrams. *(Poorvanchal, 1999)*
25. Give an account of the range of the structure of gametophytes of bryophytes studied by you. *(Gorakhpur, 1993)*
26. Describe the economic importance and distribution of bryophytes studied by you. *(Awadh, 1999)*
27. Give an account of photosynthetic tissues in bryophytes studied by you. *(Awadh, 2000)*
28. Give a general account of various methods of spore dispersal in bryophytes. *(Bundelkhand, 1995, 1997)*
29. There is a progressive sterilization of the potential sporogenous tissues in Bryophytes. Discuss. *(Madras, 1997)*
30. Give a short account of classification of Bryophytes. Among the sporophytes of Bryophytes you have studied which genus is most primitive and which genus is most advanced. Explain with suitable evidences. *(Manomaniam Sundarnar, 1995; Trichy, 1995)*
31. Compare the evolutionary trends in the sporogonium of Bryophyta studied by you *(Bihar, 1991)*
32. Describe modes of perennation in Bryophytes studied by you giving specific examples. *(Punjab, 1991, 1993)*
33. Write a brief essay on Bryophytes and pollution.
34. Give a brief account of morphogenesis in bryophytes.
35. Describe the fate of archesporium in the bryophytes.
36. Write a brief account of origin of bryophytes.
37. Write a short essay on Fossil bryophytes. *(Kanpur, M.Sc., 2005)*
38. Discuss the evolution of sporophytes in Bryophytes specially with reference to sterilisation of sporogenous tissues. *(Rohilkhand, 2001)*
39. (a) Give an account of the progressive sterilisation of sporogenous tissue in bryophyte studied by you. Among the sporogonia of *Riccia* and *Anthoceros* which is more primitive and why? *(Poorvanchal, 2003)*

    (b) What do you know of progressive sterilisation of sporogenous tissue in bryophyte? Describe with suitable examples. *(Poorvanchal, 2004)*
40. Write the evolutionary trends in the structural organisation in Bryophytea gametophytes. Mention the line of evolution within the group. *(Gauhati M.Sc. 2002)*
41. Give an account of origin and evolution of first land plants. *(Kerala, 2001)*
42. Give a comparative account of the thallus structure in the major classes of Bryophyta. Mention their taxonomic value. *(Gauhati, 2002)*
43. Explain condensation theory of the evolution of gametophytes in Bryophyta. *(Poorvanchal, M.Sc. 2002)*
44. From primitive sporophyte the more complex sporophytes of Bryophytes have been evolved by progressive sterilisation of potentially sporogenous tissue. Disscuss with suitable examples and figures. *(Poorvanchal, M.Sc. 2003)*

45. (*a*) Describe geographical distribution of bryophytes with special reference to India. *(Poorvanchal, M.Sc. 2003)*
(*b*) Discuss distribution of Bryophytes in India. *(Kanpur, M.Sc. 2006)*

46. The entire range of Himalayas are rich with different kinds of Bryophytes- Make a comprehensive account of them with special reference to their habitat and altitudes. *(Poorvanchal, M.Sc. 2001)*

47. Having the origin of land habits among plants, justify the Bryophytes as amphibians in plant kingdom. *(Poorvanchal M.Sc. 2001)*

48. Give an account of general habitat and geographical distribution of Bryophytes with special reference to India. *(Awadh M.Sc. 2001)*

49. Discuss the evolution and affinites of Bryophytes. *(Rohilkhand, M.Sc. 2003)*

50. Write in detail the various modes of spore dispersal in Bryophytes. *(Kanpur, M.Sc. 2003)*

51. Give an account of probable ancestors of Bryophytes. *(Lucknow,, M.Sc. 2006)*

52. Write an explanatory note on distribution of Bryophytes in Himalayas. Mention the evidence given of the Hepaticae in western Himalayas. *(Lucknow, M.Sc. 2006)*

53. Give reasons for the following :
(a) Moss capsule is partially dependent on gametophyte.
(b) Bryophytes always grow in moist soul *(Kanpur, M.Sc. 2008)*

54. Answer the following very briefly:
(*a*) Who described Hepaticites devoricus. How can you distinguish Hepaticites from Thallites ? *(Lucknow, M.Sc. 2007)*
(*b*) Distinguish between Thallites, Hapaticites and Muscites *(Lucknow, M.Sc. 2006)*

55. Write an account of the following :
(*i*) Pteridophytic ancestry of Bryophytes. *(Lucknow, M.Sc. 2007)*
(*ii*) Affinities and structural peculiarities of *Naiadita* *(Lucknow, M.Sc. 2007, 2004)*
(*iii*) Role of Bryophytes in pollution *(Lucknow, M.Sc. 2007)*
(*iv*) Conducting strand in Bryophytes *(Lucknow, M.Sc. 2007)*
(*v*) Probable ansestor of Bryophytes *(Lucknow, M.Sc. 2006)*
(*vi*) Ecological importance of Bryophytes *(Lucknow, M.Sc. 2004)*

SHORT ANSWER TYPE

56. **Write short notes on :**
(*i*) Fossil Bryophytes *(Rohilkhand M.Sc, 1990, 1994, 1995, 1997, 1998, 2002, 2003; Awadh M.Sc., 2003, 2002; Kanpur, MSc,. 1994, 1996, 1999, 2000, 2002, 2006, 2009)*
(*ii*) (*a*) Spore discharge / dispersal in liverworts/bryophytes *(Kanpur, M.Sc., 1992, 1999; 2005, Lucknow 1994, 1996; Meerut, 2000; Awadh, 1996)*
(*b*) Mechanism of spore diseharge in Bryophytes *(Kanpur, M.Sc., 2007)*
(*iii*) Bryophytes as ecological (biological) indicators *(Kanpur, M.Sc., 2000), 2006, 2007)*
(*iv*) Spore dispersal in Mosses *(Rohilkhand M.Sc., 1990, 1999; Kumaon, 1997)*
(*v*) *Naidita* *(Allahabad, M.Sc. 2000; Rohilkhand M.Sc., 1991, 1996; Awadh M.Sc, 2000; Kanpur MSc., 1997)*
(*vi*) Evolution of Sporophytes in Bryophytes *(Rohilkhand M.Sc., 1993; Kumaon, 1999; Andhra Pradesh, 2002)*
(*vii*) Perennation of Bryophytes in Hills *(Rohilkhand M.Sc., 1996; Awadh M.Sc., 1998; Awadh, 1993)*
(*viii*) Rhizoids in Bryophytes *(Rohilkhand M.Sc., 1996; Awadh M.Sc., 1998; Awadh, 1993; Poorvanchal, M.Sc. 2003)*

(*ix*) Protonema *(Rohilkhand M.Sc., 1998; Kumaon, 1996; Kanpur, 1994, 1997; Gorakhpur, 1993, 1995; Himachal Pradesh, 1996; Poorvanchal, 2003, M.Sc. 2003 Lucknow, 2008)*

(*x*) Alternation of generation in bryophytes. *(Kanpur, 2006; Garhwal, 2000)*

(*xi*) Vegetative reproduction (propagation) in Bryophytes *(Rohilkhand MSc., 1999; Awadh MSc., 2001; Kanpur MSc., 1994, 1996; 2006; Lucknow, 1995, 2006; Agra, 1994, 1996; Kumaon 1999; Meerut 1998; Gorakhpur, 1994, 1976; Awadh, 1992, 1993, 1997; Bundelkhand, 1998; Bihar, 1990; Allahabad, 2002, 2004, 2005; Poorvanchal, 2003; 2004 Poorvanchal, M.Sc. 2003)*

(*xii*) Ventral scales *(Rohilkhand M.Sc., 1999)*

(*xiii*) Range of photosynthetic tissues in Bryophytes *(Rohilkhand M.Sc., 2000)*

(*xiv*) Scales and Rhizoids of Bryophytes *(Rohilkhand M.Sc., 2000; Kanpur, 1994; Meerut, 1996; Rohilkhand, 1999; Kanpur, 2001)*

(*xv*) Pteridophytic ancestry of Bryophytes *(Awadh M.Sc., 2000)*

(*xvi*) Conducting strand in Bryophytes. *(Awadh M.Sc., 2000; Kanpur M.Sc., 1991, 1994, 1996, 1999; Vinoba Bhave, 1997)*

(*xvii*) Economic importance of Bryophytes. *(Awadh M.Sc., 2001; Lucknow 1995, 1996, 1997, 2009, 1999, 2006, 2008; Allahabad, 1995, 1999, 2000, 2004; Agra, 1994; Kumaon, 1996; Kanpur, 1995, 1996, 1997, 1998, 2005, 2006; Poorvanchal, 1997, 2004, 2006; Gorakhpur, 1996; Awadh, 1997, 1994; Bundelkhand, 1995, 1998, 1999; Nagpur, 1995; Rohilkhand M.Sc. 2003; Gharwal, 2000, 2003; Poorvanchal, M.Sc. 2003; Kanpur M.Sc. 2003)*

(*xviii*) Perennating structures in Bryophytes *(Kanpur M.Sc., 1991)*

(*xix*) Ecology of Bryophytes *(Kanpur M.Sc., 1993; Kumaon, 1996)*

(*xx*) Peristome teeth *(Kanpur M.Sc., 1994, 2006; Kumaon, 1996; Rohilkhand, 1995; Kanpur 2001; Allahabad, 1991, 2005; Gorakhpur, 1991, 1995, 1999; Kerala, 1998; Nagpur, 1995; Bhagalpur, 1991; Poorvanchal, M.Sc. 2003)*

(*xxi*) Importance of Bryophytes in relation to environmental pollution *(Lucknow, 1993, 1997, 1999, 2001)*

(*xxii*) Sensitive Bryophytes *(Lucknow, 1994)*

(*xxiii*) Sporogenous tissue in Bryophytes studied by you *(Lucknow, 1994; Allahabad, 1994)*

(*xxiv*) Distribution of Bryophytes in India and their economic importance *(Agra, 1991; Kumaon, 1996)*

(*xxv*) Methods of vegetative propagation in Bryophytes studied by you *(Agra, 1991; Kanpur, 1995, 1998; Rohilkhand, 1996; Awadh, 1998; Bundelkhand, 1999)*

(*xxvi*) Physiology of Bryophytes *(Kumaon, 1998)*

(*xxvii*) Asexual reproduction in Bryophytes *(Gorakhpur, 1993; Awadh, 2000)*

(*xxviii*) Structure and position of archegonia in bryophytes studied by you *(Gorakhpur, 1996)*

(*xxix*) Bryophyte are Amphibians of plant Kingdom *(Awadh, 1992, 1995)*

(*xxx*) Apospory in bryophytes.

(*xxxi*) Apogamy in bryophytes

(*xxxii*) Morphogenesis

(*xxxiii*) Chemotaxonomy in bryophytes

(*xxxiv*) Oil bodies

(*xxxv*) Bryophytes and Water pollution

(*xxxvi*) Ecology of bryophytes

(*xxxvii*) Reduction theory

(*xxxviii*) Role of bryophytes in relation to environmental pollution. *(Lucknow, 2002)* (*xxxix*) Methods of reproduction in bryophytes *(Poorvanchal, 2005)*

(*xl*) Economic value of Bryophytes. *(Garhwal, 2001)*

(*xli*) Scales in Bryophytes *(Allahabad, 2005)*

(*xlii*) Ecological importance of bryophytes *(Lucknow, 2004)*

(*xliii*) Endothecium *(Lucknow, 2008)*

(*xliv*) Bryophytes as biological indicator *(Kanpur M.Sc., 2009)*

(*xlv*) Sterilisation of sporogenous tissues in Bryophytes *(Kanpur M.Sc., 2006)*

(*xlvi*) Progressive theory of evolution of Bryophyte *(Kanpur M.Sc., 2006)*

57. How are spores discharged in Bryophytes? *(Kanpur M.Sc., 1997)*

58. In what different ways bryophytes reflect the ancestry of pteridophytes? *(Kanpur M.Sc., 1997, 2000)*

59. Which bryophyte may increase soil fertility? *(Rohilkhand, 1995)*

60. The sporogonium of Bryophytes sometimes do not possess foot or seta. Explain. *(U.P. College, 1996)*

61. Which group of plants has free living gametophyte? Also mention its habitat. *(U.P. College, 1997)*

62. Name a bryophyte in which the study of sex chromosomes has been made. *(U.P. College, 2000)*

63. Write two economic importance of Bryophyta. *(Poorvanchal, 1999)*

64. Discuss the significance of apogamy and apospory in Bryophytes. *(Madras, 1997)*

65. Give a brief account of distribution of Bryophytes in west Himalayas. *(Kanpur, M.Sc., 2002)*

66. How the *Equisetum* elaters differ from Bryophyte elaters. *(M.G. Uni., 2004)*

67. Distinguish between exocopic and endoscopic polarity of embryo germination. Mention which one of the two is found in bryophytes. *(Kanpur, 2004)*

68. Write in brief the distribution of bryophytes in India. Also name any one bryophytes found in Kanpur and its adjoining areas. *(Kanpur M.Sc. 2004; Poorvancal M.Sc. 2002)*

69. (*a*) Describe different types of rhizoids and scales in the bryophytes studied by you. *(Himanchal Pradesh, 2000)*

70. Give examples of smallest bryophytes. *(Poorvanchal, M.Sc., 1998)*

71. Mention the name of the liverwort in which mechanism of sex determination in plants was discovered. *(Poorvanchal, M.Sc. 1998)*

72. Mention briefly the role of bryophytes as pollution indicator. *(Poorvanchal, M.Sc. 2002)*

73. Differentiate between :

(*i*) Succubous and Incubous arrangement of leaves.

(*ii*) Paroicos and synoicus mosses.

(*iii*) Acrogynous liverworts and Abacrogynous liverworts.

(*iv*) Elaters and Pseudoelaters.

(*v*) Nematodontous and orthodontous Peristomes.

(Poorvanchal, M.Sc. 2002)

74. Comment upon

(*a*) The peat and its importance. *(Poorvanchal, M.Sc. 2001)*

(*b*) Algal hypothesis of the origin of Bryophytes. *(Poorvanchal, M.Sc. 2001)*

(*c*) Origin of archesporum is proyphytes *(Luckonw M.Sc. 2006)*

75. Progressive sterilisation of the potentially sporogenous tissues resulted in the evolution of sporophytes of Bryophytes. Discuss *(Kanpur, M.Sc. 2009)*

OBJECTIVE TYPE

76. Select the correct answer :

(*i*) Which of the following is a fossil bryophyte?
(*a*) *Riccia gangetica*
(*b*) *Naiadita*
(*c*) *Marchantia*
(*d*) *Funaria.*

(*ii*) According to the reduction theory, the advanced sporophyte is present in
(*a*) *Anthoceros*
(*b*) *Riccia*
(*c*) *Jungermannia*
(*d*) *Pogonatum.*

(*iii*) Which of the following plants has a close resemblance with a fossil pteridophyte?
(*a*) *Anthoceros*
(*b*) *Riccia*
(*c*) *Jungermannia*
(*d*) *Pogonatum.*

(*iv*) The bryophyte which is marine is
(*a*) *Riccia gangetica*
(*b*) *Funaria hygrometrica*
(*c*) *Riccia flutans*
(*d*) *Scapania undulata.*

(*v*) Enzymes of *Riccia* were first studied by
(*a*) S.K. Pande
(*b*) R.N. Chopra
(*c*) Ram Udar and Satish Chandra
(*d*) D.C. Bhardwaj.

(*vi*) The bryophyte used as surgical pad is
(*a*) *Funaria*
(*b*) *Sphagnum*
(*c*) *Polytrichum*
(*d*) *Pogonatum.*

(*vii*) The group of plants which act as rock builders are
(*a*) Algae
(*b*) Fungi
(*c*) Bryophytes
(*d*) Pteridophytes.

(*viii*) Some bryophytes also produce antibiotics. Which of the following is reported to produce an antibiotic.
(*a*) *Barbula*
(*b*) *Riccia*
(*c*) *Marchantia*
(*d*) *Anthoceros.*

(*ix*) Most economically important bryophyte is
(*a*) Funaria
(*b*) Marchantia
(*c*) *Riccia*
(*d*) Sphagnum.

(*x*) Which one of the following is the richest liverwort territory in India ?
(*a*) Eastern Himalayas
(*b*) Western Himalayas
(*c*) Eastern Ghat
(*d*) Western Ghat.

77. Fill in the blanks :

(*i*)____________is an example of best preserved fossil bryophyte.

(*ii*) Bryophytes are best indicators of____________pollution.

(*iii*) Reduction theory was proposed by____________.

(*iv*) Progressive evolution of____________is observed in bryophytes.

(*v*) Mosses and liverworts are the two main groups of____________.

(*vi*) Chemotaxonomy of bryophytes was suggested by____________.

(*vii*) ____________is a fossil bryophyte

(*viii*) Fossil history of bryophytes is little known because the plant body is ____________ and____________.

(*ix*) ____________was the first to collect and summarise the vegetative methods of propagation in bryophytes.

SELECTED BIBLIOGRAPHY

1. Abeywickrama, B.A. 1945. The structure and life history of *Riccia crispatula* Mill., *Ceylon Jour. Sci. A. Bot.,* **12** : 145-153.
2. Ahmad, S. 1912. Three new species of *Riccia* from India. *Curr, Sci.,* **11** : 433-434.
3. Allen, C.E. 1917, Spermatogenesis of *Polytrichum juniperinum. Ann. Bot.* **31** : 269-291.
4. ________1945. The Genetics of Bryophytes. II *Botan, Rev.,* **11** : 260-287.
5. _________1912. Cell structure, growth and division in the antheridia of *Polytrichum juniperinum Willed Arch. Zellforch* **8** : 121-188.
6. Allsopp, A. and Mitra, G.C. 1958. The morphology of protonema and bud formation in the Bryales, *Ann. Bot.* N.S. **22** : 95-115.
7. Anderson, F.N. 1929. Morphology of sporophyte of *Marchantia domingensis. Bot. Gaz.,* **88** : 150-166.
8. Anderson, F.N. 1931. Discharge of sperms in *Marchantia domingensis. Bot. Gaz.,* **65** : 66-84.
9. Anderson L.S., and M.R. Croosby. 1965. The protonema of *Sphagnum meridense. The Bryologist* **68** : 47-54.
10. Asakawa, Y. 1980, Chemosystematics of bryophytes IV. The distribution of terpenoids and aromatic compounds in hepatics and anthocerotae. *Journ. Hattori Bot. Lab.* **47** : 153-164.
11. _______1980 a. Chemosystematics of bryophytes V. The distribution of terpenoids and aromatic compound in European and Japanese hepatics. *Journ. Hattori Bot. Lab.* **48** : 285-303.
12. Bagchee, K.D. 1924. The spermatogenesis of *Anthoceros laevis. Ann. Bot.,* **38** : 105-111.
13. Bapna, K.R. and P. Kachroo. 1975. Further Studies in the genus *Riccia* in India. *J. Indian Bot. Soc.* **54** : 219-224.
14. ______________ & __________ 2000. Hepaticology in India. Vol. I & II. Himanshu Publications. India
15. Barnes, C.R., and W.J. Land. 1907. The origin of air chambers. *Bot. Gaz.* **44** : 197-213.
16. ______1908. The origin of the capsule of *Marchantia. Bot. Gaz.* **46** : 401-409.
17. Bartlett. E.H. 1928. A comparative study of the development of the sporophyte of Anthocerotaceae with special reference to the genus *Anthoceros. Ann. Bot.* **42** : 409-430.
18. Bassi, M., and M.A. Favoli. 1975. Seta ultrastructure in *Mnium orthorhycum. Nova Hedwigia,* **24** : 337-346.
19. Bauer, L. 1963. On the physiology of sporogonium differentiation in mosses. *Jour. Linn. Soc.* (Bot) **58** : 337-342.
20. Beer, R. 1906. On the development of spores of *Riccia glauca. And Bot.,* **20** : 271-291.
21. Benson, E.K. 1964. Physiology of the reproduction of Bryophytes. *The Bryologist,* **67** : 431-445.

22. Berry, G.K. 1960. Chromosome numbers of liverworts (Hepaticae and Anthocerotae). *Trans. Br. bryol. Soc.,* **3** : 668-705.

23. Berkley, E.E. 1941. Gemmae of *Funaria hygrometrica. Trans. Illinois State Acad. Sci.,* **24** : 102-104.

24. Berrie, G.K. 1963. Cytology and phylogeny of liverworts. *Evolution,* **17** : 347-357.

25. Bhardwaj, D.C. 1948. Studies in Indian hepaticae. V. On a new species of *Aspiromitus* from Kandy, Ceylon, *Aspiromitus mamilospora* Bhardwaj. *Jour. Indian Bot. Soc.* **27** : 200-205.

26. _______1950. Studies in Indian Anthocerotaceae. I. On the morphology of *Anthoceros crispulus.* Jour. Ind. *Bot. Soc.,* **29** : 145-163.

27. Bhardwaj, D.C. 1958. Studies in Indian Anthocerotaceae. II. The morphology of *Anthoceros gemmulosus* (Hattori) Pande. Jour. Ind. *Bot. Soc.*, **37** : 75-92.

28. Black, C.A. 1913. The morphology of *Riccia frostii. Ann. Bot.,* **27** : 511-532.

29. Blaikley, N.M. 1932. Absorption and conduction of water and transpiration in *Polytrichum commune. Ann. Bot.* **46** : 289-300.

30. _______ 1933. The structure of the foot in certain mosses and in *Anthoceros laevis. Trans. Roy, Soc. Edinburgh,* **57** : 699-709.

31. Boatman, D.J., and P.M. Lark. 1971. Inorganic nutrition of protonemata of *Sphagnum pappilosum.*—Lindb., *S. magellanicum* Bird, and *S. cuspidatum* ENRH *New Phytol.* **70** : 1053-1059.

32. Bold, H.C. 1938. The nutrition of the sporophyte in the Hepaticae, *Am. Jour. Bot.,* **25** : 551-557.

33. _______1948. The prothallium of *Sphagnum palustre. Bryologist,* **51** : 55-63.

34. _______1940. The nutrition of the sporophyte in mosses. *Am. J. Bot.* **27** : 318-322.

35. Bopp, M.E. 1963. Development of the protonema and bud formation in mosses. *Jour. Linn. Sac. (Bot.),* **58** : 305-309.

36. Bowen, E.J. 1931. Water conduction in *Polytrichum commune. Ann. Bot.* **45** : 175-200.

37. ______1933. The mechanism of water conduction in the Musci considered in relation to habitats. *Ann. Bot.,* **47** : 401-422.

36. Bower, F.O. 1935 P(B) in *Land Plant.* Macmillan and Co. London.

39. Brodie, H.J. 1951. The splash cup mechanism in plants. *Can. J. Bot.* **29** : 524-234.

40. Brown, M.M. 1919. The development of the gametophyte and the distribution of sexual characters *Funaria hygrometrica. Am. Jr. Bot.* **6** : 387-400.

41. Brown, R.C., Betty, E. Lemmon and Zane B. Carothers, 1982. Spore wall differentiation in *Sphagnum leseuris. Can. J. Bot.* **60** (11) : 2394-2409.

42. Brown, R.C., and B.E. Lemmon, 1984. Spore wall development in *Andreaea. Am. J. Bot.* **71** (3) : 412-420.

43. Browning, A.J. B.E.S. Gunning (1977). Wall labyrinth in *Funaria* sporophytes. *Protoplasma* **93** : 7-28.

44. _______1979 a. Structure and function of transfer cells in the sporophyte haustorium of *F. hygrometrica* **I.** The development and ultrastructure of haustorium *J. Exp. Bot.* **30** (119) 1233-1246.

45. _______1976 b. **II** Kinetics of uptake of labelled sugars and localization of absorbed products by freeze substitution and autoradiography *J. Exp. Bot.* **30** (119) 1247-1264.

46. _______1979 c. **III.** Translocation of assimilate into the attached sporophyte and along the seta of attached and exised sporophytes. *J. Exp. Bot.* **30** (119) : 1265-1273.

47. Bruhl, P. 1931. A census of Indian mosses. *Records of Botanical Survey of India.* **Vol. 13,** No. 1-2.

48. Bryan, G.S. 1915. Archegonium of *Sphagnum. Bot. Gaz.,* **59** : 40-56.

49. _______1920, Early stages in the development of the sporophyte of *Sphagnum subsecundum. Am. Jr. Bot.,* **7** : 269-303.

50. Bryan, V.S. 1955. Chromosome studies in the genus *Sphagnum. The Bryologist.* **58** : 16-39.

51. Buck and Graffinet. 2000. Bryophyte Biology Cambridge University Press, Cambridge.

52. Burr, F.A. 1970. Phylogenetic transitions in the chloroplasts of the Anthocerotales I. The number and ultrastructure of the mature plastids. *Am. J. Botany.* **57** (1) : 97-110.

53. Burr, R.J., B.G. Butterfield and C. Hebant. 1974. A correlated scanning and transmission electron microscope study of the water conductive elements in the gametophytes of *Haplomitrium gibbsiae and Hymenophyton flabellatum. The Bryologist* **77** : 612-617.

54. Campbell, D.H. 1918. The structure and development of mosses and ferns, New York.

55. _______1924. A remarkable development of the sporophyte in *Anthoceros fusiformis Ann. Bot.,* **38** : 473-483.

56. Campbell, D.H. 1925. The relationship of the Anthocerotaceae. *Flora,* 118-119 : 62-74.

57. _______1936. The relationships of the Hepaticae. *Bot. Rec.,* **2** : 53-66.

58. _______1940. The evolution of land plants (Embryophyta). Stanford University Press, California.

59. Campbell, E.O. 1954. The structure and development of *Monoclea forsteri. Trans. Roy. Soc. Newzealand,* **82** : 237-248.

60. _______1961. Problems in the origin and classification of bryophytes with particular reference to liverworts. *Newzealand Jour. Bot.,* **9**(4) : 678-688.

61. Carothers, Z.B., J.W. Moser and J.G. Duckett. 1977. Ultrastructural studies of spermatogenesis in Anthocerotales II. The blepharoplast and the anterior mitochondrion in *Phaeoceros laevis* later development, *Am. J. Bot.* **64** : 1107-1116.

62. Carothers, Z.B., and G.L. Kreitner, 1967. Studies of spermatogenesis in the Hepaticae I. Ultrastructure of Vierergruppe in *M archantia. J. cell Biol.* **33** : 43-51.

63. Carothers, Z.B. and G.L. Kreitner. 1968. Studies of spermatogenesis in the Hepaticae II. Blepharoplast structure in the spermatid of *Marchantia J. Cell biol.,* **36** : 603-616.

64. _______and_______1975. Comparative studies on spermatogenesis in the bryophytes P. 71-84. In J.G. Duckett and P.A. Racey, [ed.], Biology of the male gamete. Academic Press, New York.

65. Carothers, Z.B., and J.G. Duckett. 1980. The bryophyte spermatozoid. a source of new phylogenetic information. *Bull. Torrey Bot. Club.* **187** (3) : 281-297.

66. Carr, D.J. 1956. Contributions to Australian Biology, I. The structure, development and systematic affinities of *Monocarpus sphaerocarpus. Australian Jour. Bot.* **4** : 175-191.

67. Caussin, C., P.F. Fleurat Lessard and J.L. Bonnemain, 1983. Absorption of some aminoacids by sporophytes of *Polytrichum formosum* and ultrastructure of the haustorium transfer cells, *Ann. Bot.* **51** (2) : 167-173.

68. Cavers, F. 1903. On sexual reproduction and regeneration in Hepaticae. *New Phytol.,* **2** : 121-133; 155-165.

69. ______1910. The inter-relationships of the Bryophyta. *New Phytol.,* **9** : 81-112, 157-186, 193-234, 269-304, 341-353.

70. ______1911. The inter-relationships of the Bryophyta. VII-X, *New Phytol.,* **10** : 1-46, 84-86.

71. ______ 1911. The inter-relationships of the Bryophyta. *New Phytol.,* Reprint no. **4** : 1-203.

72. ______1910. The life history of Peat moss. *Knowledge,* **33** : 263-268.

73. Chopra, R.N. and Ram Udar. 1957. Cyto-taxonomic studies in the genus *Riccia I.R. billardieri and R. gangetica. Jour. Indian Bot. Soc.,* **36** : 191-195.

74. ______1957. Cyto-taxonomic studies in the genus *Riccia II. R. crystallina and R. cruciata. Jour. Indian Bot. Soc.,* **36** : 535-538.

75. Chopra, R.N. and Gupta, Urmila, 1967. Dark induction of Buds in *Funaria hygrometrica* Hedw. *Bryologist,* **70** : 102-104.

76. Chopra, R.N. and Rashid. 1967. Apogamy in *Funaria hygrometrica* Hedw. *Bryologist,* **70** : 206-208.

77. ______and Sneh Sood. 1973. In vitrio studies on the Reproductive Biology of *Riccia crystallina. The Bryologist,* **76** (2) : 278-285.

78. ______and M.S. Rawat. 1977. Studies on production and behaviour of protonemal gemmae in some Bryaceae. *The Bryologist,* **80** (4) 655-661.

79. Chopra, R.S. 1983. Status and position of Hornworts. *The Paleobotanist.* **31** (1) 82-99.

80. ______1981. Origin of the Bryophyta. *Miscellanea Bryologica et Lichenologiea,* **9**(1) : 1-7.

81. Chopra, R.S. 1943. A census of Indian Hepatics. *Jour. Ind. Bot. Soc.,* **22** : 237-259.

82. ______1967. Relationships between Liverworts and Mosses. *Phytomorphology,* **17** : 70-71.

83. Chopra, R.S. and N.N. Bhandari 1960. Cytomorphological studies of genus *Atrichium. Res. Bull Punjab Univ. N. Ser.,* **10** : 221-231.

84. ______ 1967. Relationship between liverworts and mosses. *Phytomorphology* **17** : 70-78.

85. ______and P.D. Sharma 1958. Cytomorphology of genus *Pogonatum. Phytomorphology,* **8** : 41-50.

86. ______1958. Cytomorphological studies of *Oligotrichum. Jour. Ind. Bot. Soc.,* **38** : 400-414.

87. Christensen, T. 1954. Some. considerations on the phylogeny of the Bryophyta. *Bot. Tidsskr.,* **51** : 53-58.

88. Clapp, G.L. 1912. The life history of *Aneura pinguis. Bot. Gaz.,* **54** : 177-193.

89. Clayton-Green, K.A., and B. Stapples. 1977. Studies of *Dawsonia superba* Grev, I Antherozoid dispersal. *The Bryologist* **80** (3) : 439-444.

90. Clayton-Green, K.A., N.J. Collins, T.G.A. Green, and M.C.F. Proctor, 1985. Surface wax, structure and function in-leaves of Polytrichaceae. *J. Bryol.* **13** : 549-561.

91. Clee, D.A. 1939. The morphology and anatomy of *Pellia epiphylla* considered in relation to the mechanism of absorption and conduction of water. *Ann. Bot.,* 3 N.S. : 106-111.

92. Crandall-stotler, B., R.E. Stotler and D. G.L. Long. (2008) 2009. Morphology and classification of the Marchantiophyta : 1-54, in B. Goffinet and A.J. Shaw (eds.) Bryophyte Biology, 2nd Ed., Cambridge University Press, Cambridge.

93. Dalton, D.A. and J.M. Chatfield, 1985. A new nitrogen fixing cyanophyto-hepatic association. *Nostoc* and *Porella. Am. J. Bot.* **72** (3) : 781-784.

94. Davis, B.M. 1899. The spore mother cells of *Anthoceros Bot. Gaz.* **28** : 89-108.

95. ______1903. The origin of archegonium. *Ann. Bot.* **17** : 477-492.

96. Dietert, M.F. 1979. Studies on the gametophyte nutrition of the cosmopolitan species *Funaria hygrometrica* and *Weissia controversa* Bryologist **82** (3) : 417-431.

97. Dixon, H.N. 1924. The students handbook of British mosses. London.

98. ______1932. Classification of mosses. In Verdoorn's Manual of Bryology P 391-412.

99. Dorothy, J.G., Stephen J. Dufresue and N.G. Maravolo, 1982. Transport of 14_C indole-acetic acid in the hepatic *Marchantia polymorpha. The Bryologist* **85** (4) : 410-418.

100. Doyle, William T. 1964. *Nonvascular Plants. Form and Function,* Belmont; Calif. Wadsworth.

101. ______1970. *The Biology of Higher Cryptogams.* The Macmillan Company, London.

102. ______1975. Spores of *Sphaerocarpus donnellii. The Bryologist,* **78** : 80.

103. Duckett, J.G. 1973. Wall ingrowths in the jacket cells of the antheridium of *Anthoceros laevis L.J. Bryology* **7** : 405-412.

104. ____________, S.K. Prasad, D.A. Davies and S. Walker. 1977. A cytological analysis of the Nostoc-Bryophyte relationship. *New Phytol,* **79** : 349-362.

105. Duncan, D. and P.S. Dalton, 1982. Recolonisation by bryophytes following fire. *J. Bryol.* **12** : 53-63.

106. Durand, E.J. 1908. The development of the sexual organs and sporogonium of *Marchantia polymoprha. Bull. Torrey Bot. Club,* **35** : 321-335.

107. Egunyomi, A. 1980. Observations on the taxonomy and propagules of *Bryum nitens. J. Bryol.* **11** (I) : 129-131.

108. Erichsen, J., B. Knoop and M. Bopp. 1977. On the action mechanism of cytokinin in mosses : caulonema specific proteins. *Planta* **135** (2) : 161-168.

109. Eschrich, W., and M. Steiner. 1968. The structure of the conducting system of *Polytrichum commune. Planta* **82** : 33-49.

110. ______and______1967. Autoradiographic investigation on the transport of organic material in *Polytrichum commune. Planta* (Berl.) **74** : 330-349.

111. Evans, A.W., 1912. Branching in the leafy Hepaticae. *Ann. Bot.* **26** : 1-37.

112. ______1939. The classification of Hepaticae. *Bot. Rev.* **5** : 49-96.

113. Farmer, J.B. 1895. On spore formation and nuclear division in the Hepaticae. *Ann. Bot.* **9** : 469-523.

114. Favoli, M.A., and M. Bassi, 1973. Seta ultrastructure in *Polytrichum commune. Nova Hedgwigia.*

115. Ferguson, F.R., R.N. Robinson, M.C. Press and J.A. Lec. 1984. Element concentration in five species of *Sphagnum* in relation to atmospheric pollution. *J. Bryology.* **13** : 197-114.

116. French, J.C., and D.J. Paolillo, Jr. 1975. Intercalary meristematic activity in sporophyte of *Funaria. Am. Jour. Bot.,* **62** : 86-96.

117. ______and______1975. On the role of calyptra in permitting expansion of capsule in the moss *Funaria. The Bryologist* **78** : 438-446.

118. ______and______1976. Effect of calyptra on intercalary meristematic activity in the sporophyte of *Funaria. Am. J. Botany* **63** : 492-498.

119. ______and______1976. Effect of light and other factors on the capsule expansion in *Funaria hygrometrica. The Bryologist* **97** (4) : 457-465.

120. Fulford, M. 1944. Vegetative reproduction in *Porella pinnata. Bryologist,* **47** : 78-81.

121. Fulford, M. 1948. Recent interpretations of the relationships of the Hepaticae. *Bot. Rev.,* **14** : 127-173.

122. ______1956. The young stages of leafy Hepaticae. A resume, *Phytomorphology* **6** : 199-235.

123. ______1965. Evolutionary Trends and covergence in the Hepaticae. *The Bryologist,* **69** : 1-30.

124. ______1975. Young stages of some thalloid Hepaticae. A resume of Anacrogynae. *Phytomorphology,* **25** (2) : 176-193.

125. Fulford, M. 1976. Recent advances and trends in Hepaticae. In : P. Kachroo (ed) *Recent advances in Botany.*

126. Galatis, B., and P. Apostolakos. 1977. Association between microbodies and a system of cytoplasmic tubules in oil body cells of *Marchantia. Planta* (Berlin) **131** (3) : 217-222.

127. Galatis, B., and P. Apostokalos. 1977. On the fine structure of differentiating mucilage papillae of *Marchantia. Can. J. Bot.* **55** : 772-795.

128. Garber, J.P. 1904. The life history of *Ricciocarpus natans. Bot. Gaz.,* **37** : 161-177.

129. Garner, D., and D.J. Paolillo, Jr. 1973. A time course of sporophyte development in *Funaria hygrometrica* Hedw. *The Bryologist* **76** : 356-360.

130. ______, and______ 1973. On the functioning of stomates in *Funaria. The bryologist* **76** : 423-427.

131. Gerald, L.K., and Z.B. Carothers, 1976. Studies of spermatogenesis in the Hepaticae V. Blepharoplast development in *Marchantia polymorpha. Am. J. Bot.* **63** : 545-557.

132. Gibs, K.L. (1971-72). Differentiation and regeneration in bryophtes. A selective review. *New Zealand Jour. Bol.*, **9** : 689-694.

133. Goebel, K. 1930, *Organographie der Pflanzen.* Jena.

134. Greenwood, H. 1911. Development of *Pellia epiphylla. The Bryologist,* **14** : 59-70, 77-83, 93, 100.

135. Griffith, W. 1842. Muscologia Itineris Assamici. Calcutta. *J. Nat. Hist.* **2** : 474-512.

136. ______1849. Notulae-ad Plantae Asiaticae Calcutta.

137. ______1849a. Icones Plantarum Asiaticarum II. Calcutta.

138. Grolle, R. 1963. *Takakia* in the Himalayas. *Ost, Bot, Zeitchr.* **110** : 444-447.

139. Grubb, P.J. 1970. Observations on the structure and biology of *Haplomitrium* and *Takakia,* Hepatics with roots, *New Phytol.* **69** : 303-326.

140. Gunning, B.E.S., and J.S. Pate, 1969. "Transfer cells". *Protoplasma* **68** : 230-240.

141. haberlein, E.A. 1929. Morphological notes on a new species of *Marchantia. Bot. Gaz.* **88** : 427.

142. Hart, P.F.W., and H.L.K. Whitehouse, 1978. The tubers of *Pohlia lutescens* as seen on scanning electron micrographs. *J. Bryol.* **10** : 143-144.

143. Harvey-Gibson, R.J., and D. Miller Brow. 1927. Fertilisation of Bryophyta. *Polytrichum commune* (Preliminary note). *Ann. Bot.* **41** : 190-191.

144. Haskeil, G. 1949. Some evolutionary problems concerning the *Bryophyta. The Bryologist,* **52** : 49-57.

145. Hattori, S., and Inoue, 1958. Preliminary report on *Takakia lepidozioides, J. Hottari Bot. Lab.,* **19** : 133-137.

146. ______and M. Mizutani. 1958. What is *Takakia lepidozioides ? J. Hattori Bot. Lab.,* **20** : 295-303.

147. ______and H. Inoue, 1958. On the archegonia of *Takakia lepidozioides. Jour. Jap., Bot.* **38** : 321-322.

148. Hattori, S., Z. Iwatsuki, M. Mizutanc and K. Yamacha. 1973. The genus *Takakia in East Nepal. Jour. Jap. Ot.,* **48** : 1-9.

149. Haupt, A.W. 1918. A morphological study of *Pallavicinia lyellii. Bot. Gaz.,* **66** : 524-533.

150. Haupt, A.W. 1920. Life history of *Fossombronia cristula. Bot. Gaz.,* **67** : 318.

151. ______1926. Morphology of *Preissia quadrata. Bot. Gaz.,* **82** : 30-54.

152. Hausmann, M.K., and D.J. Paolillo Jr. 1977. On the development and maturation of antheridia in *Polytrichum. The Bryologist* **80** (1) : 143-148.

153. Hausmann, M.K., and D.J. Paolillo Jr. 1978. The ultrastructure of the stalk and base of the antheridium of *Polytrichum. A.m. J. Bot.* **65** (6) : 646-653.

154. Hebant, C. 1964, "Signification et evolution de Tissue Conducteurs chezles Bryophytes" *Nat. Monspeliensia.*

155. Hebant, C. 1967. "Structure et differentiation des Tissue Conducteurs dans be Gametophyte des Polytrichum". *Nat Monspeliensia (Botany),* **18** : 293-297.

156. ______1970. A new look at the conducting tissues of mosses; their structures, distribution and significance. *Phytomorphology,* **20** : 390-410.

157. 1975. Organisation of the conducting tissue system in the sporophytes of *Dawsoma* and *Dendroligotrichum. J. Hattori Bot. Lab.* **39** : 235-254.

158. ______ 1977. The conducting tissues of Bryophytes, **157** pp. Cramer, J. Vanduz.

159. ______, and R.P.C. Johnson, 1976. Ultrastructural features of freeze-etched water-conducting cells in *Polytrichum. Cytobiologie* **13** : 354-363.

160. 1975. On the occurrence of lysomal acid phosphate activity in the differentiating water conducting strand of *Takakia* and its evolutionary significance. *Phytomorphology* **75** (3) : 279-282.

161. 1973. Diversity of structure of the water conducting elements in liverworts and mosses. *Jour. Hottari Bot. Lab.,* **37** : 229-234.

162. ______1974. Studies on the development of the conducting tissue system in the gametophores of some Polytrichaceae. II. Development and structure at maturity of the hydroids of the central strand. *Jour. Hottari Bot. Lab.,* **38** : 565-607.

163. ______and F. Marty. 1972. Fine structural identification of peroxisomes in the cells of the photosynthetic lamellae of the leaf of *Polytrichum commune* gametophytes. *Jour. Bryology* **7,** Part **II.**

164. Hicks, M.L. 1974. Marginal gemmae in *Frullania eboracensis. The Bryologist* **77** : 460-463.

165. Higuchi, M. & Zhang, D. 1998 sporophytes of *Takakia ceratophyllo found* in China. *J. Hattori* Bot. Lab. 84; 57-69.

166. Hirsch, P.E. 1910. The development of air chambers in *Ricciaceae. Bull. Torrey Bot. club,* **37** : 73-77.

167. Holferty, G.M. 1904. Development of the archegonium of *Mnium cuspidatum. Bot. Gaz.,* **37** : 106-126.

168. Hoffman, G.R. 1964. The effects of certain sugars on spore germination in *Funaria hygrometrica* Hedw. *Bryologist,* **67** : 321-329.

169. ______1966. Observations on the mineral nutrition of *Funaria hygrometrica. The Bryologist* **69** : 182-192.

170. Holmen, K. 1955. Chromosome numbers of some species of *Sphagnum. Bot. Tidsskr,* **52** : 37-42.

171. Hooker, W.J. 1818. *Musci Exotici.* **I.** London.

172. ______ 1820 *Musci Exotici* **II.** London.

173. Horner, H.T., N.R. Lerston and C.C. Brown. 1966. Spore development in the liverwort *Riccardia Pinguis, Am. J. Bot,* **53** : 1048-1064.

174. Horne, A.S. 1909. Discharge of antherozoids in *Fossombronia, Ann. Bot.* XXIII : 159-160.

175. Humphrey, H.B. 1906. The development of *Fossombronia longiseta Aust. Ann. Bot.* **20** : 83-109.

176. Hutchinson, A.H. 1915. Gametophyte of *Pellia epiphylla. Bot. Gaz.,* **60** : 134-143.

177. Ingold, C.T. 1939. Spore discharge in land plants. Oxford.—1965. "Spore liberation". Oxford, Clarendon Press.

178. Ikeno, S. 1903. Die spermatogenese von *Marchantia polymorpha. Beihefiz Z. Bot. Centrabl,* XV : 65-68.

179. Inoue, H. 1960. Studies in the spore germination and earlier stages of gametophyte development in the Marchantiales. *Jour. Hattori Bot. Lab.* **23** : 148-191.

180. Inoue, H. 1973. Karyological studies on *Takakia ceratophylla* and *T. lepidozioides. Jour. Hattori Bot. Lab.,* **37** : 275-286.

181. ______1974. The origin of *Bryophyta. Misc. Bryol. Lichenol.* **6** : 145 (Japanese).

182. Isaac, J. 1941. The structure of *Anthoceros laevis* in relation to its water supply. *Ann. Bot.* N.S. **5** : 339-351.

183. Iwastuki, Z. 1986. A peculiar Calcdonian Sphagnum with rhizoids. *The Bryologist* **89** (1) : 20-22.

184. Jaffe, L., and H. Etzold. 1965. Tropic responses of *Funaria* spores to light. *Biophys J.* **5** : 715-742.

185. Jensen, K.G., and R.L. Hulbary, 1978. Chloroplast development during sporogenesis in six species of mosses. *Am. J. Bot.* **65** (8) : 823-833.

186. Kachroo, P. 1950. A note on the morphology of some species of *Riccia. Bryologist.* **58** : 134-136.

187. Kachroo, P. 1969. Hepaticae of India—A taxonomic survey and census. I. Floristic and taxonomic considerations. *Kashmir J. Sci.* **6** : 39-55.

188. ______Kachroo, P., Bapna, K.R. and Dhar, G.L. 1977. Hepaticae of India : Taxonomic survey and census V. Fossombroniaceae through the Anthocerotaceae, *J. Indian Bot. Soc.* **56** : 62-86.

189. Kamimura, M. 1961. A monograph of Japanese Frullaniaceae *Jour. Hottari Bot. Lab.,* **24** 1-190.

190. ______1971. Studies on the fine structure of spore walls in Frullaniaceae (Hepaticae) II. Scanning electron microscope studies on the fine structure of spore walls of *Frullania takayiensis* and *F. mayebarae. Misc. Bryol. Lichenol.,* **5** (10-12) : 187-190.

191. Karl, A., and R. Kaul, 1974. Response of Marchantia nepalensis gemmae toward certain factors during germination and early stages of growth. *Jour. Hattori. Bot. Lab.* **38** : 435-441.

192. Karunen, P., and A. Ihantola, 1977. Studies on the moss spores V. Carotenoids of *Polytrichum commune. The Bryologist* **80** (1) : 88-91.

193. ______, and ______ 1977 ______ VI. Production of caroteinoids in germinating *Polytrichum* spores. *The Bryologist* **80** (2) : 313-316.

194. Kashyap, S.R. 1915. Morphological and biological notes, on new and little known West Himalayan liverworts, *New Phytol.* **14** : 1-18.

195. ______1916. Liverworts of the Western Himalayas and the Punjab with notes on known species and descriptions of new species. *Jour. Bombay Nat., Hist. Soc.,* **24** : 343-352.

196. ______1919. The relationships of liverworts in the light of some recently discovered Himalayan forms. *Proc. Asiatic Soc. Bengal,* N. Ser. **15** clii-clxvi.

197. 1929. Liverworts of the Western Himalayas and the Punajb Plain. Part I. University of the Punjab, Lahore.

198. ______1932______Part II. Uni. Punjab, Lahore.

199. Kashyap, S.R. and N.L. Datt. 1925. Two Indian species of genus *Notothylas. Proc. Lahore Phil, Soc.,* **4** : 49-56.

200. ______and S.K. Pande, 1922-23. A contribution to the life history of *Aneura indica. Jour. Indian Bot. Soc.,* **3** : 79-89.

201. Kelley Carole B., and W.T. Doyle. 1975. Differentiation of intercapsular cells in the sporophyte of *Sphaerocarpus donnellii. Am. Jour. Bot.,* **62** (6) : 560.

202. Khanna, L.P. 1930. An abnormality in the female receptacle of *Marchantia palmata Nees. Annls. bryol* **3** : 150.

203. Koch, L.F. 1956. Note on Bryological terminology. *Bryologist,* **59** : 23-25.

204. Kranjina, V., and T.M. Brayshaw. 1951. A new species of *Pellia. The Bryologist* **54** : 59-67.

205. Kreitner, G.L., and Z.B. Carothers. 1976. Studies of spermatogenesis in the Hepaticae. V. Blepharoplast development in *Marchantia polymorpha. Am. J. Bot.,* **63** (5) : 545-557.

206. Kreitner, G.L. 1977. Influence of multiplayered structure on the morphogenesis of *Marchantia spermatids. Am. J. Bot.* **64** (1) : 57-64.

207. ______1977 Transformation of nucleus in *Marchantia spermatids. Morphogenesis. Am. J. Bot.* **64** (4) : 464-475.

208. Krisko, M.E.P., and D.J. Paolillo, Jr. 1972. Capsule expansion in the hairy cap moss *Polytrichum, The Bryologist* **75** : 509-515.

209. Krupa, I. 1969. Photosynthetic activity and productivity of the sporophyte of *Funaria hygrometrica* during ontogenesis. *Acta. Soc. Bot. Poloneae* **38** : 207-215.

210. Kumar, A. and A.K. Sinha. 1989. Bryophytes and water pollution. Water pollution. Gyanodaya Prakashan, Nainital.

211. Kumar, A., A.K. Sinha and D.C. Pandey. 1987. SEM studies on the spore of *Riccia frostii Curr. Sci.* **56** : 543-544.

212. ______________, ______________ and Meenakshi Shukla, 2003, Morphology and ecology of bryophytes in relation to river pollution in 'River Pollution and its Management, pp. 81-96. APH Publishing Corp. New Delhi

213. Kumar, D.S., and Udar R. 1976, *Calobryum denundatum* Kumar et Udar. Sp. nov. : a new species of *Calobryum* from India *J. Indian Bot. Soc.* **55** : 23-30.

214. Kuwahara, Y. 1978. Elaterophore observed in two species of *Metzgeria* from Peru and consideration of the elaterophore in the Hepaticae. *The Bryologist* **81** (3) : 404-410.

215. Lander, C.A. (1935) The relation of the plastids to nuclear division in *Anthoceros laevis. Am. Jour. Bot.,* **22** : 42-51.

216. Lang, W.H. 1901. On apospory in *Anthoceros laevis. Ann. Bot.,* **15** : 503-510.

217. ______1907. On the sporogonium of *Notothylas. Ann. Bot.,* **21** : 201-210.

218. ______1909. A theory of alternation of generations in Archegoniatae based upon the ontogeny. *New Phytol.* **8** : 1-12.

219. Lewis, C.E. 1906. The embryology and development of *Riccia lutescence* and R. *crystallina. Bot. Gaz.,* **41** : 109-138.

220. Lewis, K.R. 1961. The genetics of bryophytes. *Trans. Brit. Bryol. Soc.* **4** : 111-130.

221. Mac Vicar, S.M. 1926. *The students handbook of British Hepatics,* 2nd ed. London.

222. Mahabale, T.S. 1941. On a long lost liverwort from South India, *Aspiromitus*, a rare member of Anthocerote, *Curr. Sci.* **10** : 530-533.

223. ______and Gorji, G.H. 1941. Chromosomes of *Riccia himalayensis. Gurr. Sci.,* **10** : 28.

224. ______1947. On the chromosomal complex of two species of *Riccia, Jour, Uni. Bombay,* **16** : 1-16.

225. Maier, K. 1967. Wall labyrinths in sporophyte of *Polytrichum. Planta* (Berl.) **77** : 108-126.

226. ______and Maier, U. 1972. Sporophyte transfer cells in *Polytrichum. Protoplasma* **75** : 91-112.

227. Manning, F.L. 1914. Life history of *Porella platyphylla Bot. Gaz.* **57** : 320-323.

228. Manton, I. 1961. Observations on phragmosomes, *J. Exp.,* **12** : 108-113.

229. ______1957. Observations with electron microscope on the cell structure of antheridium and spermatozoid of *Sphagnum, J. Exp. Bot.* **8** : 382-400.

230. ______and Clarke, B. 1952. An electron microscope study of the spermatozoid of *Sphagnum. J. Exp. Bot.* **3** : 265-275.

231. Maravolo, N.C. 1976. Polarity and localization of auxin movement in the hepatic *Marchantia polymorpha. Ame. J. Bot.,* **63** (5) : 526-531.

232. MatzKe, F.B. and L. Raudzens, 1969. Apospory in Hepaticae. *Current Topics in Plant Science.* Page 117-119.

233. McAllister, F. 1914. The pyrenoids of *Anthoceros. Am. Jour. Bot.* **1** : 79-95.

234. ______1916. The morphology of *Thallocarpus curtissi. (Riccia curtisii) Bull Torry Bot. club,* **43** : 126-127.

235. McAllister, F. 1927. The pyrenoids of *Anthoceros* and *Notothylas* with special reference to their presence in the spore mother cells. *Amer, Jour. Bot.* **14** : 246-257.

236. ______1928. Sex ratio and chromosomes in *Riccia curtisii. Bull. Torrey Bot. club,* **55** : 1-10.

237. McClymont, J.W. and D.A. Larson. 1964. An electron microscopic study of spore wall structure in the Musci. *Am. J. Bot.* **51** (2) : 195-200.

238. McClymont, J.W. 1955. Spore studies in the Musci with special reference to the genus *Bruchia. Bryologist* **58** : 257-306.

239. McConaha, M. 1941. Ventral structures affecting capillarity in the Marchantiales. *Amer. Jour. Bot.* **28** : 301-306.

240. McNaught, H.L. 1929. Development of sporophyte of *Marchantia chenopoda. Bot. Gaz.* **88** : 400-416.

241. Mehra, P.N. and B.R. Vasisht. 1950. Embryology of *Petalophyllum indicum* kash. and a new suggestion of the evolution of thalloid habit from foliose forms. *The Bryologist,* **53** : 89-114.

242. ______and O.N. Handoo 1953. Morphology of *Anthoceros erectus* and *A. himalayensis* and the phylogeny of Anthocerotales. *Bot. Gaz.* **114** : 371-382.

243. ______and P. Kachroo. 1951. Sporeling germination studies in Marchantiales. I. Rebouliaceae. *The Bryologist.* **54** : 1-16.

244. ______and______1952. Sporeling germination studies in Marchantiales. II. *Stephensoniella brevipedunculata. Bryologist.* **55** : 59-64.

245. ______and______1962. Sporeling germination studies in Anthocerotales. *J. Hattori Bot. Lab.,* **25** : 145-153.

246. Mehra, P.N. and R.S. Pathania. 1959. Chromosome number in some western Himalayan acrogynous Jungermanniales. *Bryologist.* **62** : 242-247.

247. ______and Sood, S. 1969. Studies on the spore morphology of some Western Himalayan Hepatics and Anthocerotes. *Bull. Res. Punjab Univ.,* **20** : 71-73.

248. Mehra, P.N. 1967. Phyletic evolution in the Hepaticae. *Phytomorphology,* **17** : 47-58.

249. ______(1969-70). Evolutionary trends in the Hepaticae with particular reference to Marchantiales. *Phytomorphology,* **19** (3) : 203-218.

250. ______1968. Palynology of Archegoniatae—an evolutionary approach *Jour. Palynology,* **4** : 56-72.

251. Mehra, P.N. 1957 a. A new suggestion on the origin of thallus in the Marchantiales. I. The thallus structure. *Am. J. Bot.* **44** : 505-513.

252. Mehra, P.N. 1958 b. A New suggestion on the origin of thallus in the Marchantiales. II. The theory. *Am. J. Bot.,* **44** : 573-581.

253. ______1958. Fossil evidence on the condensation theory of the origin of Marchantiaceous thallus. *J. palaeont. Soc. India.* **3** : 130-34.

254. Mitra, G.C., A. Allsopp and P.F. Wareing. 1959. I. Effects of light of various qualities on the development of the protonema and bud formation in *Pohlia nutans* (Hedw) *Lindb. Phytomorphology.* **9** : 47-55.

255. Monroe, J.H. 1968. Light and electron microscopic observations on spore germination in *Funaria hygrometrica. Bot. Gaz.* **129** : 247-258.

256. Monroe, J.H. 1965. Some factors invoking formation of sex organs in *Funaria. The Bryologist* **68** : 337-339.

257. Moser, J.W., and G.L. Kreitner. 1970. Centrosome structure in *Anthoceros laevis* and *Marchantia polymorpha. J. cell. Biol.* **44** : 454-458.

258. ______, Duckett, J.G., and Z.B. Carothers. 1977. Ultrastructure studies of spermatogenesis in the Anthocerotales. I. Early development. *Am. J. Bot.* **64** : 1097-1106, 1107-1116.

259. Mottier, D.M. 1904. Contributions to the life history of *Notothyllas. Ann. Bot.* **8** : 391.

260. Muggoch, H., and J., Walton, 1942. On the dehiscence of the antheridium and part played by surface tension in the dispersal of spermatocytes in *Bryophyta. Proc. Roy. Soc. B.,* **130** : 440-461.

261. Naidu, T.R. 1973. Occurrence of androgynous receptacles in *Marchantia polymorpha. The Bryologist,* **76** : 428-430.

262. Nakosteen, P.C. and K.W. Hughes. 1978, Sexual life cycle of three species of Funariaceae in culture. *The Bryologist* **81** (2) : 307-314.

263. Nehira, K. 1971. Evolution of sporeling type in Hepaticae. *Hikobia* **6** ($^1/_2$) : 76-84.

264. ______1974. Phylogenetic significance of the sporeling pattern in Jungermanniales. *Jour. Hattori, Bot. Lab.* **38** : 151-60.

265. Nirula, R.L. 1949. Embryogeny of *Notothyllas chaudhurii* and its theoretical significance. *Proc. Indian Sci. Congress,* **36** (4) : 4-5.

266. Nishida, Y. 1971. Studies on the formation of the protonema and the leafy shoot in *Andreaea rupestris* var. fauriei. *Bot. Mag.* **84** : (Tokyo) 187-192.

267. Noguchis, A. 1958. Germination of spores in two species of *Sphagnum. J. Hattori Bot. Lab.* **19** : 71.

268. O'Hanlon, S.M.E. 1926 Germination of spores and early stages in the development of gametophyte of *Marchantia polymorpha. Bo. Gaz.* **82** : 215-222.

269. Odu, E.A. 1978. The adaptive importance of moss rhizoids for attachment to substratum. *J'Bryol.* **10** : 163-181.

270. Olesen, P., and G.S. Magensen. 1978. Ultrastructure, histochemistry and notes on germination stages of spores in selected mosses. *The Bryologist* **81** (4) : 493-516.

271. Pagen, F.M. 1932. Morphology of the sporophyte of *Riccia crystallina. Bot. Gaz.,* **93** : 71-84.

272. Pandey, D.C. A.Kumar and A.K. Sinha. 2001. Bryophytes from river Ganga Banks—A study on concentration of Heavy Metals. Perspective in Indian Bryology. BSMPS. Dehradun.

273. Pande, S.K. 1924. Notes on the morphology and biology of *Riccia sanguinea, Jour. Ind. Bot. Soc.,* **4** : 117-128.

274. ______1932. On the morphology of *Notothyllas indica. Jour. Ind. Bot. Soc.,* **11** : 169-177.

275. ______1933. On the morphology of *Riccia robusta. Jour. Ind. Bot. Soc.* **12** : 110-121.

276. ______1934. On the morphology of *Notothylas levieri. Proc. Ind. Acad. Sci. B.* **5** : 205-217.

277. Pande, S.K. 1936, Studies in Indian liverworts : A review. *J. Indian Bot. Soc.* **15** : 221-233.

278. Pande, S.K. and S. Ahmad. 1944. *Riccia discolor :* its allies and synonyms. *Proc. 31st Ind. Sci. Congress : 80*

279. ______and D.C. Bhardwaj, 1949. On the morphology of *Anthoceros jackii. Proc. 36th ind. Sci. Congress.*

280. ______and ______D.C. Bhardwaj. 1952. The Present position of Indian Hepaticology, *Palaeobotanist* **I** : 368-381.

281. ______, T.S. Mahabale, Y.B. Raje and K.P. Srivastava. 1954. Studies in Indian Metzgerineae. *Fossombronia himalayensis.* Kash. *Phytomorphology* **4** : 365-378.

282. Pande, S.K., K.C. Misra and K.P. Srivastava. 1954. A species of *Riella* Mont. *R. vishwanathai* sp. nov-from India. *Rev. Bryol. Lichen* **23** : 25-35.

283. ______ Pande, S.K., and N. Chopra. 1957. Sporeling germination in *Notothylas indica. Proc. 44th Indian Sci. Congress* P. 230.

284. ______ and R. Udar. 1956. Studies in Indian Metzgerineae. III. *Calycularia crispula. Phytomorphology,* **6** : 331-345.

285. ______and R. Udar. 1957. Genus *Riccia in* India. I. A reinvestigation of taxonomic status of Indian species of *Riccia. Jour. Ind. Bot. Soc.,* **36** : 564-579.

286. ______and R. Udar 1958. Genus *Riccia* in India II. Species of *Riccia* from India with a description of new species and notes on synonyms of some recently described ones. *Proc. Nat. Insti. Sci. India,* **24** : 79-88.

287. ______and K.P. Srivastava. 1957. The genus *Riccardia Gray* in India. *Jour. Ind. Bot. Sec.,* **37** : 417-421.

288. Pande, S.K. 1960. The Anthocerotales, some aspects of their systematics and morphology. *Presidential address, Botany Section, 47th Indian Science Congress.*

289. Paolillo, D.J. Jr. (1968 a). Spermatogenesis in *Polytrichum juniperinium* I. The origin of the apical body and the elongation of the nucleus. *Planta* **78** : 226-247.

290. Paolillo, D.J. Jr. G.L. Krietner and J.A. Reighard. 1968 (b). Spermatogenesis in *Polytrichum juniperinium* II. *Planta,* **78** : 248-261.

291. Paolillo, D.J., and Reighard, J.A. 1967. Ultrastructural features of some polytrichaceous moss leaves. *Bryologist,* **70** : 61-69.

292. Paolillo, D.J. Jr. 1977. Release of sperms in *Funaria hygrometrica. The Bryologist* **80** : 619-624.

293. ______1977. On the release of sperms in *Atrichium. Am. J. Bot.* **64** (I) : 81-85.

294. ______1975. The release of sperms from the antheridium of *Polytrichum juniperinium.* Hedw. *New Phytologist* **74** : 287-293.

295. ______1969. The plastids of *Polytrichum* II. The sporogenous cells. *Cytologia* **34** : 133-144.

296. ______, ______and M. Cukierski. 1976. Wall development and coordinated cytoplasmic changes in the spermatogenous cells of *Polytrichum* (Musci). *The Bryologist* **79** (4) : 466-479.

297. ______and Bazar, F.A. 1968. Photosynthesis in the sporophytes of *Polytrichum* and *Funaria The Bryologist* **71** : 335-343.

298. Paolillo, D.J. Jr. 1974. Motilc male gametes of plants. pp. 504-53 in A.W. Robard's Dynamic aspects of plant ultrastructure. McGraw Hill Co., England.

299. ______and L.B. Kassa, 1977. The relationship between cell size and chloroplast number in spores of a moss, *Polytrichum Jour Exp. Bot.* **28** : 457-467.

300. Paolillo, D.J. Jr. 1965. The androcyte of *Polytrichum* with special reference to the Dreiergruppe and the limosphere (Neberkern). *Can. J. Bot.* **43** : 669-676.

301. Paolillo, D.J. Jr. 1968. The effect of calyptra on capsule symmetry in *Polytrichum juniperinum* Hedw. *The Bryologist* **71** : 323-334.

302. Parihar, N.S. 1967. *An Introduction to Embryophyta.* Vol. I. Central Book Depot. Allahabad.

303. Parihar, N.S., and Jagdish Lal. 1972. Anomalous carpocephala in *Marchantia* and their phyletic significance. *The Bryologist,* **75** : (1).

304. Paton, J.A. and J.V. Pearce. 1957. The occurrence, structure and function of stomata in British Bryophytes. *Trans. British Bryal. Soc.,* **3** : 228-259.

305. Peirce, G.J. 1906. *Anthoceros* and its *Nostac* colonies, *Bot. Gaz.,* **42** : 55-59.

306. Persson, H. 1958 The genus *Takakia* found in North America, *Bryologist,* **61** : 359-61.

307. Proskaeur, J. 1948. Studics on the morphology of *Anthoceros.* I. *Ann. Bot.* (Lond.) N.S. **12** : 237-265.

308. ______1948. Studies on the morphology of *Anihoceros,* II. *Ann. Bot.* (Lond.), N.S. **12** : 427-440.

309. ______1950. Notes on the Hepaticae. I. *The Bryologist,* **53** : 165-172.

310. ______1951. Studies on the Anthocerotales, III. *Bull : Torrey Bot. Club.* **78** : 331-349.

311. ______1953. Studies on the Anthocerotales, IV. *Bull. Torrey Bot. Club.* **80** : 65-75.

312. ______1954. On *Sphaerocarpus stipulatus* and the genus *Sphaerocarpus. Jour. Linn. Bot. Soc.,* **LV** : 143-157.

313. ______1955. Notes on Hepaticae, III. *The Bryologist.* **58** : 192-200.

314. ______1957. Studies on the Anthocerotales, V. *Phytomorphology,* **7** : 113-135.

315. ______1958. On the peristome of *Funaria hygrometrica. Ame. J. Bot.* **45** : 560-563.

316. ______1960. Studies on the Anthocerotales. VI. On spiral thickening in the columella and its bearing on phylogeny, *Phytomorphology,* **10** : 1-19.

317. Proskaeur, J. 1961. Our *Corus* and *Carrpos. Taxon,* **10** : 155-156.

318. ______1961. On *Carrpos* I. *Phytomorphology,* **11** : 359-378.

319. ______1962. On *Takakia,* especially its mucilage hairs. *Jour. Hattori Bot. Club,* **25** : 217-223.

320. ______1962. Notes on the Hepaticae. IV. *The Bryologist,* **65** : 213-233.

321. ______1967. Studies on the Anthocerotales. VII. On day length and Western Himalayan Hornwort Flora and on some problems in cytology. *Phytomorphology.* **17** : 61-70.

322. Proctor, M.C.F. 1977. Sporophyte-gametophyte assimilate transport in bryophytes *J. Bryol.* **9** : 375-386.

323. Redhead, S.A. 1973. Observations on the rhizoids of *Andreaea. The Bryologist* **76** : 185.

324. Richards, P.W. 1958. Famous plants, 9. The liverworts. *Marchantia,* New Biology, **27** : 87-108.

325. Ricket, H.W. 1920. The development of thallus of *Sphaerocarpus donnellii. Amer. Jour. Bot.,* **7** : 182-195.

326. Ridgway, J.E. 1967. Factors initiating antheridial formation in six Anthocerotales. *Bryologist,* **70** : 203-205.

327. Ridgway, J.E. 1968. Ultrastructural features of the sporophytic gametophytic interphase in bryophytes. Page 86-87 in C.J. Arceneaux ed. Proceedings of the 26th Annual meeting of the Electron microscope society of America, claitor Pub. Dev., Baton Rouge, La.

328. Robert J. Thomas, Edwin M. Schiele and Daniel C. Scheirer. 1988 Translocation in *Polytrichum communis* and allocation of photoassimilates. *Amer. J. Bot.* **75** (2) : 275-281.

329. Rodgers, G.A., and D.P. Stewart. 1977. The Cyanophyte. Hepatic symbiosis I. Morphology and physiology. *New Phytologist.* **78** : 441-459.

330. Sack, F.D., and D.J. Paolillo Jr. 1985. Incomplete Cytokinesis in *Funaria* stomata. *Am. J. Bot.* **71** (9) : 1325-1333.

331. Sato, sy. 1950-1951. Electron microscopical studies on the reproductive cells of plants. II. Structure of spermatozoids of *Marchantia polymorpha. Cytologia.* **16** : 153-163.

332. Scheirer, D.C. 1972. Anatomical studies in the Polytrichaceae. I. *The Bryologist,* **74** : 458-463.

333. ______1973. Hydrolysed walls in the water conducting cells of *Dendroligotrichum :* histochemistry and ultrastucture. *Planta.* **115** : 37-46.

334. ______1975. Anatomical studies in the Polytrichaceae. II. Histochemical observations on thickened lateral walls of hydroids of *Dendroligotrichum. The Bryologist* **78** : 113-123.

335. ______1977. The thickened leptoid (sieve element) wall of *Dendroligotrichum* (Bryopsida). *Am. J. Botany* **64** (3) : 369-376.

336. ______and Ira. J. Goldklang, 1977. Pathway of water movement in the hydroids of *Polytrichum commune* Hedw (Bryopsida) *Am. J. Bot.* **64** (8) : 1046-1047.

337. Scheirer, D.C. 1980. Differentiation of bryophyte conducting tissues : Structure and histochemistry, *Bull. Torrey Bot. club.* **107** (3) 298-307.

338. ______and H.A. Dolan, 1983. Bryophyte leaf epiflora. An. *SEM* and *TEN* study of *Polytrichum commune. Am. J. Bot.* **70** (5) 712-718.

339. Schmiedal, G. and E. Schnepf. 1979. Side branch formation and orientation in the caulonema of the moss, *Funaria hygrometrica.* Normal development and fine structure. *Protoplasma* **100** : 367-383.

340. Schofield, W.B. 1972. Takakia lepidoziods in Hokkaido, Japan. *Misc. Bryol. Lichenol.,* **6** : 17-18.

341. Schuster, R.M. 1967. Studies on Hepaticae XV Calobryales. *Nova Hedgwigia* **13** : 1-63.

342. Schuster, R.M. 1966. *The Hepaticae and Anthocerotae of North America.* **I.** New York and London.

343. __________ 1997. On *Takakia* and the phylogenetic relationship the Takakiales. *Novo Hedwigia.* 64 (3-4) : 281-310.

344. Sharma, A.K. 1949. Indian Sphagnums. *Bull. Bot. Soc. Bengal,* **3** : 99-111.

345. Sharma., P.D. 1963. Cytology of some Himalayan Polytrichaceae. *Caryologia,* **16** : 111-120

346. ______1971. Abnormal sex organs in *Pogonatum microstomum* and the origin of gametangia. *The Bryologist,* **74** : 458-463.

347. ______and R.S. Chopra. 1964. The life history of *Lyellia crispa*. *The Bryologist,* **67** : 329-343.

348. Sheldrake, A.R. 1971. The occurrence and significance of auxin in the substrata of bryophytes. *New Phytl.* **70** : 519-526.

349. Sherrin, A.S. 1918. The lamellae of *Polytrichum*. *J. Bot.,* London, **56** : 105-107.

350. Showalter, A.M. 1923. Studies in the morphology of *Riccardia pinguis*. *Amer. J. Bot.,* **10** : 148-166.

351. ______1925. Germination of the spore of *Riccardia pinguis* and *Pellia fabbroniana*. *Bull. Torrey Bot. Club.* **52** : 157-166.

352. ______1927. Fertilisation in *Fossombronia*. *Ibid* **41** : 37-46.

353. Siegel, S.M. 1969, "Evidence for the presence of Lignin in moss Gametophytes". *Amer. J. Bot.,* **56** : 603-607.

354. Siler, M.B. 1934. Chromosome numbers in certain *Ricciaceae*. *Proc. Nat. Acad. Sci. U.S.A.,* **20** : 603-607.

355. Sinha, A.K., D.C. Pandey and A. Kumar. 1987. SEM studies on spores of *Riccia gangetica* collected from Ganga bank. *Geophytology.* **17** : 116-117.

356. Smith, D.K. and Paul G. Davision. 1993. Antheridia and sporophytes in *Takakia* Ceratophylla (Mitt). Grolle : Evidence for reclassification among mosses. J. Hattori Bot. Lab73 : 263-271.

357. Smith, G.M. 1955. Cryptogamic Botany. Vol. II. *Bryophytes and Pteriodophotes.* Edi. 2, New York.

358. Smith, J.L. 1966. The liverworts *Pallavicinia* and *Shymphyogyna* and their conducting system, *Uni. Calif. Publ. Botany.* **39** : 1-83.

359. Southorn, A. L.D. 1976. Bryophyte recolonisation of burnt ground with particular reference to *Funaria hygrometrica*. I *Jour. Bryology.* V. **9.** Part I : 63-80.

360. ______1977 II. The nutrient requirement of *Funaria hygrometrica.* Jour. Bryology **9** (3) : 361-373.

361. Srinivasan, K.N. 1939. The developmental morphology of Androgynous receptacles in *Marchantia palmata. Proc, Ind. Acad. Sci.* **10B** : 88.

362. Srinivasan, K.N. 1940. On the morphology, life-history and cytology of *Riccia himalayensis. Jour. Madras Univ.,* **5** : 59-80.

363. ______1944. The developmental morphology and cytology of *M. palmata. Jour. Madras Univ.,* **12** : 101-133.

364. Srivastava, K.P. 1957. Spermatogenesis in *Notothylas levieri. Jour. Ind. Bot. Soc.,* **36** : 537-547.

365. ______1960. Studies in Indian Metzgerineae. IV. *Riccardia levieri. Jour. Ind. Bot. Soc.* **39** : 537-547.

366. ______1964. Bryophytes of India. I. *Ricciaceae. Bull. Nat. Bot. Gardens. Lucknow.*

367. Stange, L. 1964. "Regeneration in Lower Plants". In *Advances in Morphogenesis* V. IV, New York Academic Press. PP. 111-153.

368. Steinkamp, M.P., and W.T. Doyle. 1979. Spore wall ultrastructure in four species of *Riccia. Am. J. Bot.* **66**(5) : 546-556.

369. Steere, W.C. 1969. A New look at phylogeny of and evolution in Bryophyta, *Current topics in Plant Science,* P. 135-143.

370. Stephani, F. 1900-1912. *Species Hepaticarum* **1-6** Geneve.

371. Stewart, W.D.P., and G.A. Rodgers. 1977. The Cyanophyte-Hepatic symbiosis II. Nitrogen fixation and interchange of nitrogen and carbon. *New Phytologist* **78** : 459-471.

372. Stotler, R.E. 1970. The genus *Frullania* sub-genus *Frullania* in Latin America. *Nova Hedgewigia* Bd. **XVIII.**

373. Stotler, R.E. and B. Crand - Stotler. 2005. A revised classification of the Anthocerotophyta and a checklist of the hornworts of North America, north of Mexico Bryologst,108 16-26.

374. Tallis, J.H. 1962. The identification of *Sphagnum* spores. *Trans. Brit. Biol. Soc.,* **4** : 209-213.

375. Tansely, A.G. and E. Chick. 1901. Notes on the conducting tissue system in Bryophyta. *Ann. Bot.,* **15** : 1-38.

376. Taylor, J., P.J. Hollinsgrowth, and W.C. Biglow. 1977. Scanning electron microscopy of liverwort spores and elaters. *The Bryologist* **77** : 281-327.

377. Tersamae, J. 1955. On the spore morphology of some *Sphagnum* species. *The Bryologist,* **58** : 306-311.

378. Thomas, R.J., D.S. Santon, D.G. Longendorfer and M.E. Farr. 1978. Physiological evaluation of the nutritional autonomy of a hornwort sporophyte. *Bot. Gaz.* **139** (3) : 306-311.

379. Tolbert, N.E. 1971. Microbodies-Peroxiosomes and glyoxysomes. *A Rev. Pl. Physiol,* **22** : 45-74.

380. Trachtenberg, S. and E. Zamski, 1978. Conduction of ionic solutes and assimilates in leptom of *Polytrichum juniperinum.* Willed *J. Exp. Bot.* **29** (110) : 719-727.

381. Udar, R. 1950. Studies in Indian Ricciaceae. I. *Proc. 37th, Ind. Sci. Congress,* 40.

382. ______1956. On two species of *Riccia* new to Indian flora, *Curr. Sci.* **25** : 232-233.

383. ______1957. On the synonymy of some Indian species of *Riccia. Curr. Sci.,* **26** : 20-22.

384. ______1957. Cultural studies in the genus *Riccia* I. Sporeling germination in *R. billardieri, Jour. Ind. Bot. Soc.,* **36** : 46-50.

385. ______1957. Cultural studies in the genus *Riccia* II. Sporeling germination and regeneration in *R. Crystallina. Jour. Ind. Bot. Soc.,* **36** : 580-586.

386. ______1958. Cultural studies in the genus *Riccia* III. Sporeling germination in *R. trichocarpa*—A reinvestigation. *Jour. Ind. Bot. Soc.,* **37** : 70-74.

387. __________. 1976. *Bryology in India.* New Delhi.

388. Udar, R., ______1961. Genus *Riccia* in India V. A new *Riccia, R. reticulata.* Udar from Pillani with a note on the species of Riccia from the Central Indian Zone, Gangetic plains, Punjab and Rajasthan. *Bull. Bot. Soc. Univ. of Saugor,* **13** : 46-55.

389. Udar, R., and N. Chopra 1957. Cytotaxonomic studies in the genus *Riccia.* I. *R. billardierii* and *R. gangetica, Jour. Ind. Bot. Soc.,* **36** : 191-195.

390. Udar, R., and N. Chopra 1957. *Riccia crozalsii* and *R. warnstorfi* from India. *Curr. Sci.*, **26** : 282-287.

391. ______and V. Chandra. 1964. On the occurrence of branched female receptacles in *Marchantia grisea* Burgeff. *Current Science* **33** : 251-255.

392. Udar, R. 1665 a. On a new species of *Calobryum. C. indicum* Udar et Chandra from Darjeeling, India. *Rev. Bryol. et. Lichenol* (Paris) **33** : 555-559.

393. ______and S. Chandra. 1968. *Calobryum brumii* Nees. A taxon new to Indian flora. *Ibid.* **37** : 265.

394. ______and 1976. Bryology in India. Chronica Botanica Co. New Delhi.

395. Udar, R. and D.K. Singh. 1976. A new *Cyathodium* from India. *The Bryologist.* **79** : 234-238.

396. ______and 1977. *Haplomitrium hookeri* in Western Himalayas, India. *The Bryologist* **80** : 340-342.

397. ______and ______1978. Thickened bands in the capsule wall of *Notothylas levieri. The Bryologist* **81** : 575-577.

398. Udar, R. and D. Kumar. 1980. Further observations on *Calobryum dentatum. J. Indian Bot. Soc.* **59** : 187-189.

399. Udar, R. and A. Gupta. 1983. Differentiation of the genus *Targionia* L. in India-II. The east himalayan and south Indian complex and description of a new species of *Targionia. Geophytology.* **13** (i) : 83-87.

400. Udar, R. and S.C. Srivastava. 1973. On a species of *Riccardia : R. Santapaui* from Chhindwara (M.P.) India. *Rev. Bryol. et. Lichenol.* **39** : 155-161.

401. Udar, R. and V. Nath. 1976. Oil-bodies in west himalayan liverworts. *J. Indian Bot. Soc.* **55** : 80-83.

402. Udar, R. and A. Kumar. 1982. A new *Chonecolea* from India. *The Bryologist.* **85** (3) : 315-318.

403. Udar, R. and F. Shaheen 1983. Fertile plants of *Porello plumosa* from India and their affinities with *P. hattorii. Misc. Bryol. et. Lichenol.* **9** : 196-198.

404. ______and V. Chandra, 1965 b. Discovery of *Haplomitrium hookeri* (Smith) Nees in Asiatic flora. *Cur. Sci.* **34** : 618.

405. Underwood, L.M. 1894. The evolution of the Hepaticae. *Bot. Gaz.,* **19** : 347-361.

406. Vaisay, J.R. 1888. On the anatomy and development of the sporogonium of the mosses. *J. Linn. Soc. Bot.,* **24** : 262-285.

407. Valanne, N. 1966. The germination phases of moss spores and their contol by light. *Ann. Botani Fennici,* **3** : 1-60.

408. Van Andel, O.M. 1952. Germination of the spores and development of primary protonema and secondary protonema of *Funaria hygrometrica. Trans. Brit. Bryol Soc.* **20** : 74-81.

409. Verdoorn, Fr. 1932. Classification of Hepatics. In Manual of Bryology, Chapter **15** : 413-422. The Hague.

410. Voth, P.D. 1937. Spore germination and thallus development in *Porella* (Abstract). *Trans. Ill. Acad. Sci.* **30** : 158-159.

411. ______and K.C. Hammer 1940. Response of *Marchantia polymorpha* to nutrient supply and photoperiod. *Bot. Gaz.* **102** : 169-205.

412. Wallis, T.E. 1910. Note on *Pellia epiphylla. New Phytol* **10** : 347-348.

413. Walton, J. 1643. How the sperm reaches the archegonium in *Pellia epiphylla. Nature* (Lond.), **152** : 51.

414. Wann, F.B. 1925. Some of the factors involved in the sexual reproduction of *Marchantia polymorpha. Amer. J. Bot.,* **12** : 307-318.

415. Ward, M. 1960. Vegetative propagation from intact leaves of *Polytrichum commune. Phytomorphology,* **10** : 325-329.

416. Watson, E.V. 1955. *British mosses and liverworts.* Cambridge, 419 pp.

417. ______1957. Famous plants. 6. *Funaria.* New Biology **22** : 104-124.

418. ______1971. *The structure and life history of bryophytes.* Third Edition. Hutchinson and Co., London.

419. Watson, W, 1918. Sphagna, their habitats, adaptations and associates. *Ann. Bot.* **32** : 35-55.

420. Whitehouse, H.L.K. 1978, *Bryum cruegeri* Hampe : a tuber bearing moss new to Africa. *J. Bryol.* **10** : 113-115.

421. Wigglesworth. G. 1947. Reproduction in *Polytrichum commune* and the significance of rhizoid system. *Trans. Brit. Bryol. Soc,* **1** : 4-13.

422. Willston, Ruth, 1912. Discoid gemae in *Radula. Bull. Torrey Bot. club,* **39** : 329-339.

423. Wilmont-Dear, C.M. 1980. A study of regeneration from leaves in some species of *Pogonatum* and *Polytrichum. J. Bryol.* **11** : (1) : 145-160.

424. Wilson, M. 1911. Spermatogenesis in Bryophyta. *Ann. Bot.,* **25** : 415-459.

425. Wolf, F.T. 1958. Comparative chlorophyll content of the two generations of the bryophytes. *Nature* **181** : 579-580.

426. Wolfson, A.M. 1928. Germination of the spores of *Pellia epiphylla* and *F. neesiana Amer. Jour. Bot.,* **15** : 179-184.

427. Wyatt. R. 1977. Spatial pattern and gamete dispersal distances in *Atrichium angustatum,* a dioecious moss. *The Bryologist* **80** : 284-291.

428. Zamski, E., and Trachtenberg, S 1976. Spore development in liverwort *Riccardia pinguis. Isr. J. Bot.* **25** : 168-173.

429. Zerov, D.K. 1966. The problem of phylogeny of liverworts (Hepaticopsida). *Bot. Zhurn Acad. Nauk. U.S.S.R.* **51** : 3-14.

430. Zimmeister, D.D., and Z.B. Carothers. 1974. The fine structure of oogenesis in *Marchantia polymorpha. Am. J. Bot.* **61** : 499-512.

INDEX

B

C

D

E

F

G

H

I

J

K

L

M

N

Q

R

S

T